Basic
Electronic Instrument
Handbook

Other McGraw-Hill Handbooks of Interest

Basic Electronic Instrument Handbook

CLYDE F. COOMBS, JR. *editor-in-chief*

Hewlett-Packard Singapore Ltd.

McGRAW-HILL BOOK COMPANY

New York St. Louis San Francisco Düsseldorf Johannesburg
Kuala Lumpur London Mexico Montreal New Delhi
Panama Rio de Janeiro Singapore Sydney Toronto

Library of Congress Cataloging in Publication Data
Main entry under title:

Basic electronic instrument handbook.

Includes bibliographical references.
1. Electronic instruments. I. Coombs, Clyde F., ed.
TK7878.4.B37 621.381'028 72-1394
ISBN 0-07-012615-1

567890 KPKP 7987

The editors for this book were Harold B. Crawford and Lila M. Gardner, the designer was Naomi Auerbach, and its production was supervised by Stephen J. Boldish. It was set in Caledonia by The Maple Press Company.

It was printed and bound by The Kingsport Press.

For Ann

Contents

Section Four. Using Electronic Instruments

Section Five. Instrumentation Systems

Section Six. Current- and Voltage-measurement Devices

Section Seven. Circuit-element Measuring Instruments

Section Eight. Signal-generation Instruments

Section Nine. Frequency- and Time-measurement Instruments

Section Ten. Recording Instruments

Section Eleven. Special-function Instruments

Section Twelve. Microwave Passive Devices

Instrument Chapters Listed Alphabetically

Contributors

KAY D. BAKER, Ph.D. *Director, Space Science Laboratory and Professor of Electrical Engineering and Physics at Utah State University. From 1955 to 1970 Dr. Baker was a member, and then director, of the Upper Air Research Laboratory, University of Utah.*

DAVID BURT *Chief Engineer for the Space Science Laboratory, Utah State University. Mr. Burt received his B.S. and M.S. degrees in electrical engineering from the University of Utah, where he was a member of the Upper Air Research Laboratory.*

LARRY L. CARLSON *Loveland Division, Hewlett-Packard Company. Mr. Carlson received his B.S.E.E. and M.S.E.E. degrees from Colorado State University. He has been associated with the design and manufacture of dc standard voltmeters and calibrators since 1962.*

ARTHUR DARBIE *New Jersey Division, Hewlett-Packard Company. Mr. Darbie received his B.S.E.E. and M.S.E.E. degrees from the Newark College of Engineering. He has worked in the field of power supplies since 1955. He is now responsible for the engineering, marketing, and manufacturing of power supplies at the Hewlett-Packard Company.*

JACK E. DAY *Development Officer, Oregon Museum of Science and Industry. Mr. Day was formerly Patent and License Administrator for Tektronix, Inc. He holds degrees in both electrical engineering and law.*

EDWARD W. ERNST, Ph.D. *Professor and Associate Head, Department of Electrical Engineering, University of Illinois. Dr. Ernst has had industrial experience with General Electric Company and Stewart Warner Electronics. He has published work on digital techniques for radio direction finding and laboratory-oriented studies for engineering students. He is past-president of the Board of National Electronics Conference.*

HENRY P. HALL *Engineering Staff Consultant, General Radio Company. Mr. Hall received a B.A. from Williams College prior to receiving his B.S.E.E. and M.S.E.E. degrees from the Massachusetts Institute of Technology. He has been with the General Radio Company as a development engineer and group leader since 1952. His primary design area has been impedance bridges and standards.*

HARLEY L. HALVERSON *Microwave Division, Hewlett-Packard Company. Mr. Halverson holds a B.S.E.E. degree from South Dakota State College, and an M.S.E.E. degree from Stanford University. He has been with the Hewlett-Packard Company since 1957, specializing in spectrum analysis and signal generation. He is presently Manager of Microwave Communications Systems.*

DEXTER HARTKE *Engineering Manager, Santa Clara Division, Hewlett-Packard Company. Mr. Hartke received his B.S.E.E. degree from the University of California. He has worked with the Hewlett-Packard Company since 1950 in the fields of digital instrumentation, time and frequency standards, and other related areas.*

CHARLES HOUSE *Research Engineer, Colorado Springs Division, Hewlett-Packard Company. Mr. House holds degrees in solid-state physics, electronics, and history. He has taught, and coordinated, college electronics education programs since 1966. He is a member of the Colorado Air Pollution Control Commission.*

EDWIN C. JONES, Ph.D. *Associate Professor of Electrical Engineering, Iowa State University. He has a B.S.E.E. degree from the University of West Virginia, a D.I.C. degree from the University of London, and a Ph.D. from the University of Illinois. His industrial experience includes work with General Electric Company, Westinghouse Electric Company, and the U.S. Army.*

EUGENE L. MLECZKO *Engineering Manager, Automatic Measurement Division, Hewlett-Packard Company. Mr. Mleczko is a registered professional engineer, and an Associate Fellow of the American Association of University Professors, the Institute of Electrical and Electronics Engineers, and the Instrument Society of America.*

FRANCIS L. MOSELEY *President, Servo Products Company. Mr. Moseley holds approximately 60 patents in servo systems, radio navigation, and graphic recording. He is the recipient of several awards for the development of radio direction finding. He pioneered in graphic recording development and started the F. L. Moseley Company. This company subsequently merged with the Hewlett-Packard Company for which he is now a member of the Board of Directors.*

ATHERTON NOYES, JR., A.B., A.M., S.M., SC.D. *Ath Noyes and Associates. Dr. Noyes was the prime mover in the General Radio Company frequency synthesizer program prior to 1971 when he left to do private consulting. Before 1960 he spent many years with Aircraft Radio Corporation (now a subsidiary of Cessna Aircraft) in engineering of communication and navigation equipment. He was on the instructional staff at Cruft Laboratory, Harvard College, in association with Professor C. W. Pierce.*

DONALD H. SCHUSTER, Ph.D. *Professor in both the Psychology and Computer Science Departments, Iowa State University. Dr. Schuster has taught educational engineering psychology, psychological measurement, and research on artificial intelligence. He is the author of "Logical Electronic Troubleshooting" and "Basic Electronic Test Equipment: A Programmed Introduction."*

JEROME L. SHANNON *Manager, general-purpose oscilloscope development, Tektronix, Inc. Mr. Shannon has been associated with oscilloscope and pulse generator development and new product evaluation for over ten years.*

W. F. SNYDER *Staff Member, National Bureau of Standards. Mr. Snyder has been with NBS for over 40 years in Washington, D.C., and Boulder, Colorado. He has specialized in research and administration in sound and acoustics, radar countermeasures, development of electromagnetic standards, and calibration services.*

FREDERICK E. TERMAN, Ph.D. *Provost Emeritus, Stanford University.*

LEE THOMPSON *Circuit Designer, Loveland Division, Hewlett-Packard Company. Mr. Thompson has received B.S.E.E. and M.S.E.E. degrees. He has worked in the field of ac/dc converter design since 1966.*

JAMES D. WAGNER, Ph.D. *Tektronix, Inc. Dr. Wagner has degrees in physics and electrical engineering. His industrial experience includes work as a design engineer for Exact Electronics and Tektronix, Inc. He is a registered professional engineer.*

GERSHON WHEELER *Consultant, author, and editor in the field of microwave electronics. Mr. Wheeler has had over 25 years of experience in various industrial organizations in this field.*

MARVIN J. WILLRODT *Santa Clara Division, Hewlett-Packard Company. Mr. Willrodt holds a Bachelor's degree and has done graduate work in electrical engineering. He has been associated with the Hewlett-Packard Company since 1951 during which time he has worked primarily in the fields of high-speed electronic counters, printers, frequency standards, and related equipment.*

THOMAS L. ZAPF *Physicist, National Bureau of Standards. Mr. Zapf has specialized in developing accurate standards, instrumentation, and measurement techniques in the audio and radio-frequency region. Formerly with the Electricity Division of NBS in Washington, D.C., he has been with NBS in Boulder, Colorado since 1957, currently he is in the Electromagnetics Division.*

Preface

This is a book about electronic instruments. In it we have described and discussed the equipment and devices themselves: what they do, how they do it, how to select the best one for your use, and how to get the most out of the instruments in actual use. The information available here ranges from very basic to highly sophisticated, and from the general nature of types of instruments to the specific definition of an individual device.

Although the act of measurement itself is the result of using instruments, this is not a "measurements" book. There are so many types of measurements possible with the instruments described that to include them all would be impossible and any attempt would be confusing. As a result, specific measurements are discussed only as examples of applications of the instruments. It is felt that with a clear understanding of the instruments themselves and how they work together, the reader is in the best position to define his own solution to a measurement problem.

The title, therefore, states exactly what the book contains: handbook information on basic electronic instruments.

The fundamental nature of commercial electronic instrumentation has not changed significantly since its beginning. The process by which an electronic quantity is detected and measured is still essentially the same, but the equipment used has undergone great changes in accuracy, ease of operation, reliability, and range of capabilities. To understand this, it must be kept in mind that there are only certain physical properties that can be detected electronically. All other phenomena must be changed into analogous electrical units before they can be measured. After the physical property is represented as an electronic quantity, it must proceed through the same series of processing steps used from the beginning of the art of electronic measurement that allow it finally to be presented to the human senses for interpretation, or to another machine, such as a computer, for further processing. These steps are all basic to the measurement process and will continue to be in the foreseeable future.

In the first half of the book (Chapters 1 to 19) we discuss the general steps, in both measurement and signal generation, as they apply to all instruments in these categories. We also review the problems in guaranteeing accuracy, the problems associated with the use of any electronic device, and the general problems involved in putting instruments into systems. These chapters approach the instrument usage situation from the common denominators associated with each class of electronic device, signal measurement, or signal generation.

In the second half of the book (Chapters 20 to 40) individual instruments are described in detail and their unique applications and usage are considered. This is to give the reader all the specific information he needs about a particular device so that he will have an intuitive feeling for the instrument as well as a theoretical understanding of its operation. He should feel comfortable with the tools he is using.

This book should give those who use electronic instruments, for any reason, a source of better understanding of what they are using, and provide a ready reference to refresh the backgrounds of professional engineers and scientists.

The early encouragement of Ralph Lee, Jack Melchoir, Bill Abbott, and Bob Brunner is gratefully acknowledged. I also thank the international team of typists who made this book possible: Virginia DeBoer in Colorado, Sally Wells and Carol Board in California, and Linda Ng in Singapore.

Clyde F. Coombs, Jr.

Basic Electronic Instrument Handbook

Section One

Introduction to Instrumentation

The most important aspect of the information one receives from a measuring device is the confidence the user has in the accuracy of that information. As the ability to measure electrical quantities has been refined over the years the need to ensure a greater and greater degree of accuracy has increased. Or, to express it another way, the limits of uncertainty have had to be narrowed and those limits themselves have had to be defined more precisely.

To provide a common source of information on the relationship of the absolute magnitude of a measurable quantity to that actually measured by a particular device, the governments of most countries maintain a set of "standards." These standards are used for comparison with the local "quantity," which defines the amount of uncertainty involved in the measurement. In the United States this service is provided by the National Bureau of Standards. The need for this service and how it operates for each electrical unit are described in this section.

There are some statistical aspects of understanding the degree of uncertainty involved in a measurement, and these are discussed in this section. Also considered are the differences between "precision" and "accuracy" as well as the types and sources of error involved in electrical measurements.

A basic understanding of the use of standards and the sources and risks of error in electrical measurement is therefore fundamental to the confidence one has in the information his equipment is providing.

Chapter 1

Measurement and the Growth of Knowledge

FREDERICK E. TERMAN

Stanford University, Stanford, California

The advancement of science and technology is matched by a parallel progress in the art of measurement. It can, in fact, be said that the quickest way to assess the state of a nation's science and technology is to examine the measurements that are being made and the way in which the data accumulated by measurements are utilized.

The reasons for this are simple. As science and technology move ahead, phenomena and relations are discovered that make new types of measurements desirable. Concurrently, advances in science and technology provide means of making new kinds of measurements that add to understanding. This in turn leads to discoveries that make still more measurements both possible and desirable.

It is thus axiomatic that sophisticated science and technology are associated with sophisticated measurements, while simple-minded science is associated with only elementary measuring techniques.

As the art of measurement has advanced, the technology of making measurements has increasingly relied on electrical and electronic methods. This comes about for two reasons. First, once information is transformed into electrical form, it can be readily processed in ways that will meet the needs of a great variety of individual situations. Second, most phenomena, such as temperature, speed, distance, light, sound, and pressure, can be readily transformed into electrical indications for processing and interpretation.

The result has been that during the last 30 years, there has developed a remarkable world of instruments based on electronics, which both supports and feeds on the ever-advancing frontiers of knowledge, and concurrently makes it possible to carry on the old tasks more easily and with greater accuracy.

Modern electronic instruments are typically direct-reading, making it unnecessary to resort to calibration curves. Increasingly, their outputs are available in digital form, which eliminates the necessity of even reading the indication of a needle or the scale of a cathode-ray tube. Moreover, data in digital form can be processed through a computer that can instantly perform necessary ancillary calculations; this eliminates possibilities of error and saves time of high-priced personnel. Through the use of recorders and cathode-ray oscilloscopes, it is now even possible to draw the final results in the form of plotted curves, thereby further speeding up the entire process of gathering and analyzing data.

A third of a century ago, most electronic measurements were made with instruments which the experimenter had constructed with his own hands. More often than not these early instruments were not only inconvenient but also useless unless operated by highly skilled personnel, preferably the men who had built them.

This situation has now changed completely. Today one can usually buy a much better instrument than he can build, and one does not have to possess expert knowledge about a particular instrument in order to keep it in adjustment and functioning properly.

At the same time, even with the marvelous array of professionally made instruments that are listed in catalogs today, the user must provide an input of his own in order to take full advantage of the opportunities available to him. He must know what the instruments he uses, or is considering purchasing, will and will not measure; types of difficulties that can arise in making measurements under special or unusual conditions; possibilities and limitations; and the errors that can be introduced by distortions in waveform, by noise, by stray electric currents, etc. Today's user of instruments must also consider the characteristics of what he wishes to measure, and then relate these characteristics to the properties, possibilities, and limitations of the measuring instrument he plans to use.

It is the purpose of this book to help a worker in some field of science and technology match his needs with those of the world of instruments, in situations in which he is a nonexpert "consumer" of the fruits of instrumentation technology.

Chapter 2

Standards*

WILBERT F. SNYDER

National Bureau of Standards, Boulder, Colorado

1. Measurement Standards of the Past Lost in the artifacts of antiquity are man's first attempts that gave him the concept of size in shaping his weapons and tools. As he began to construct dwellings, places of worship, and burial places for the exalted, man found need to "scale" his constructions. Thus the Egyptians developed the Royal Cubit, the first known useful standard of length. Today we see it on display in museums as a piece of granite about 20.5 in. long and inscribed with many increments of smaller lengths. Such length standards were passed on to the Greeks and Romans.

During medieval times, and particularly in England, various standards of measurement evolved, with little thought given to their relationship. Much from these systems was inherited by the United States, with the result of a conglomerate of measurement systems. However, there was a relatively simple relationship in the English length standards, 12 inches being equivalent to 1 foot, and 3 feet

* Contribution of the National Bureau of Standards, not subject to copyright.

equivalent to 1 yard. But each unit had an independent origin: Three barley corns (grains of barley) laid end to end made an inch, and the length of the actual foot of the ruling monarch was a unit of length (the foot) during his reign. Possibly the yard had its origin in the distance from the tip of the nose to the end of the outstretched thumb of an early English king. More certainly the yard has been the various lengths of a series of metal bars. In contrast to these units of length, the pound has been defined by many relationships to other units of weight.

2. Development of the Metric System The French had proposed the metric system in 1670 and adopted it in 1791. In 1875, an international treaty (known as the Treaty of the Meter) was signed by 17 nations, including the United States. It established the International Bureau of Weights and Measures. The units of the metric system form decimal systems of weights and measures based upon the kilogram and the meter. Scientists the world over were quick to grasp the simplicity and unity of such a measurement system. Others, especially in the English-speaking countries, were more reluctant to adapt themselves to the metric system.

Japan, after a 40-year period of education and publicity programs, converted to the metric system in 1966. England has taken active steps to adopt the metric system by 1975. In 1866, Congress legalized the use of the metric system in the United States (along with the English system), and it has enjoyed widespread use in scientific work. There has been an increasing interest in the United States in the metric system, probably primarily because of concern over world markets for manufactured goods. In August, 1968, Congress passed legislation for a 3-year study to be made by the National Bureau of Standards of the feasibility and costs of converting industry and everyday practice to the use of the metric system. Today all but a few nations use this simplified system of measurements.

3. Genealogy of Measurement Quantities This section follows today's concepts and practices in the use of measurement systems. It is based upon the Système International (SI), or International System of Units, and more specifically, upon the meter-kilogram-second-ampere system (mksa) of relationships of units of electrical quantities (see Sec. 4).

In a genealogy of measurement quantities we picture a lineage of derived quantities that are related to the base quantities. This is shown in Fig. 1. In this delineation the derived quantities are limited to those associated with the electrical measurement system, plus several others that are of general interest. About thirty such derived quantities are recognized today (see Sec. 5).

Although various physical quantities could be considered as basic in a measurement system, at least academically, the SI is based upon those of length, mass, time, electric current, temperature, and luminous intensity. The quantities of length, mass, and time, and their corresponding units (in any measurement system) have come to be called mechanical quantities and units by common usage. Some systems, such as the centimeter-gram-second system (cgs) or the meter-kilogram-second system (mks) for electromagnetic quantities, recognize only three base units. Both these systems are coupled to the metric system of units. In the older cgs system (actually two, the electrostatic and the electromagnetic) the base units are the centimeter, gram, and second. In the mks system the base units are the meter, kilogram, and second. It is this latter system that is the foundation of the now universally accepted International System of Units* (see Sec. 4). The base units in their present status are listed on page 2-4.†

* The National Bureau of Standards adopted the International System of Units in 1964. See *NBS Tech. News Bull.*, vol. 48, pp. 61–62, April, 1964. S. A. Mechtly, "The International System of Units—Physical Constants and Conversion Factors," NASA SP-7012, National Aeronautics and Space Administration, Washington, D.C., 1964.

† Definitions of the Base Units of SI (a translation from the French of Définitions des unités de base du SI, reported by CGPM: Conférence Générale des Poids et Mesures, General Conference of Weights and Measures), *IEEE Spectrum*, vol. 6, no. 2, p. 8, February, 1969.

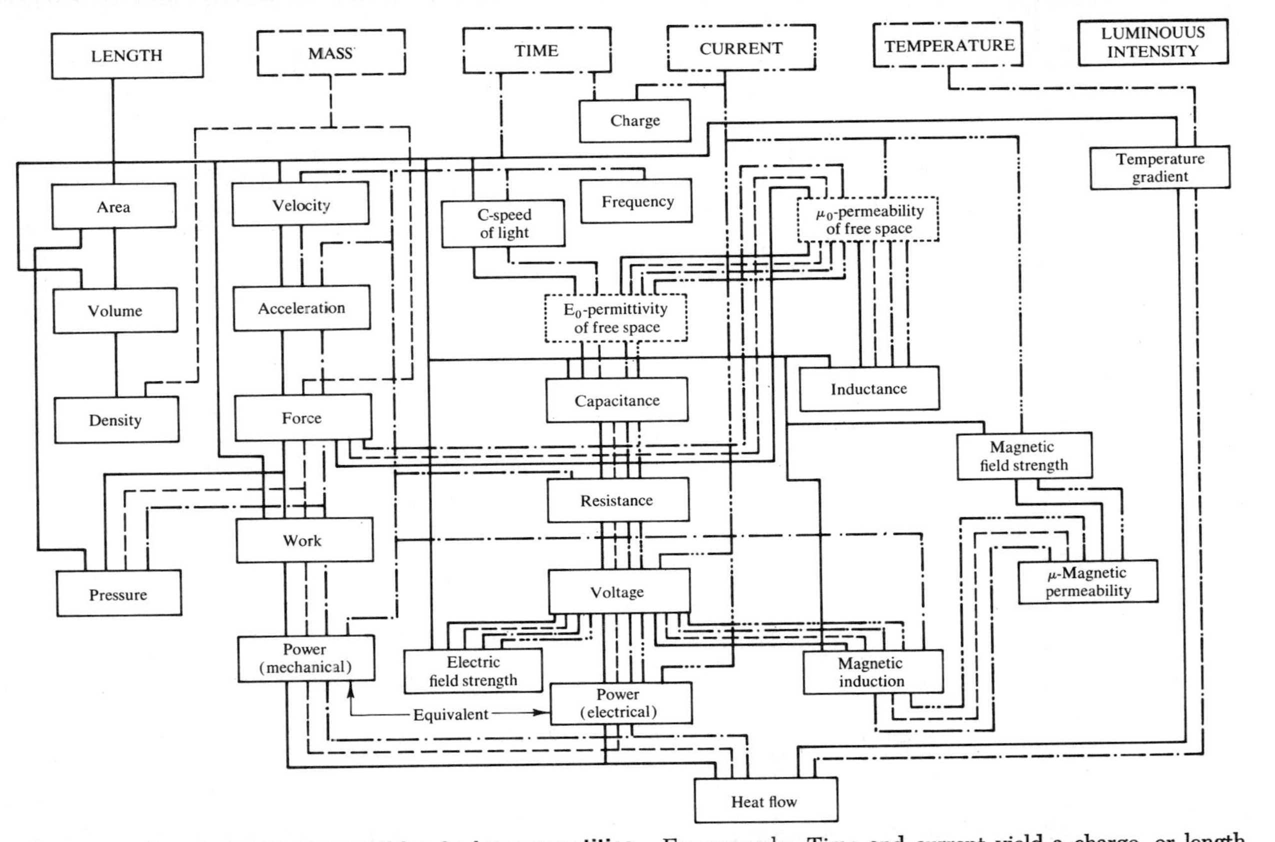

Fig. 1. Relation of derived quantities to base quantities. For example: Time and current yield a charge, or length and temperature yield temperature gradient, or current and resistance yield voltage.

1. Metre (m), or meter—length: The meter is the length equal to 1,650,763.73 wavelengths in vacuum of radiation corresponding to the transition between the levels $2_{p_{10}}$ and 5_{d_5} (orange-red line) of the krypton 86 atom (excited at the triple point* of nitrogen, 63.15 kelvins).

2. Kilogram (kg)—mass: The kilogram is the unit of mass; it is equal to the mass of the international prototype of the kilogram.

3. Second (s)—time: The second† is the duration of 9,192,631,770 periods of the radiation corresponding to the transition between the two hyperfine levels of the ground state of the cesium 133 atom.

4. Ampere (A)—electric current: The ampere is that constant current which, if maintained in two straight parallel conductors of infinite length, of negligible circular cross section, and placed 1 meter apart in vacuum, would produce between these conductors a force equal to 2×10^{-7} newton per meter of length.

5. Kelvin (K)—temperature: The kelvin,‡ unit of thermodynamic temperature, is the fraction 1/273.16 of the thermodynamic temperature of the triple point of water. [The International Practical Temperature Scale of 1968 (IPTS 68)§ and the International Practical Celsius Temperature Scale are referenced to the triple point of water and at least five other reference points.]

6. Candela (cd)—luminous intensity: The candela is the luminous intensity, in the perpendicular direction, of a surface of 1/600,000 square meter of a blackbody at the temperature of freezing platinum under a pressure of 101,325 newtons per square meter. (In the SI the candela is considered to be a base unit of luminous intensity, although it is not completely a physical unit, as it involves the wavelength sensitivity of the average human eye.)

To the six SI base units have been added two supplemental units, the radian for plane angles and the steradian for solid angles.

7. Radian (rad): Plane angle subtended by an arc of a circle equal in length to the radius of the circle.

8. Steradian (sr): Solid angle subtended at the center of a sphere by a portion of the surface whose area is equal to the square of the radius of the sphere.

Of interest to physicists, and particularly to electrical engineers, are the derived units that express the magnitude of the various electrical and magnetic quantities. Approximately thirty of these are considered as SI units, including the units of the rather simple quantities of area, volume, and frequency (see Sec. 5). The subject of derived quantities and the associated units is an extensive one in physics. It is a field in which many ideas have been expressed, with the unfortunate result that much confusion exists in the understanding of the various systems that have evolved. This has been particularly true in the area of electricity. In each of the various electrical systems one starts by expressing electrical quantities with fundamental and relatively simple equations, which relate the electrical quantities to mechanical quantities, such as force, work (energy), and power. The latter, in turn, are expressible in terms of length, mass, and time. The mathematical process known as dimensional analysis is used as an aid to keep the physical and mathematical steps logical in using the equations. There is also the process known as "rationalization" (also "subrationalization") that is applied to the equations of some of the electrical measurement systems. The process treats the factor 4π (associated with spherical symmetry and commonly found in many equations) in

* Triple point is the temperature of equilibrium between the solid, liquid, and vapor states.

† Atomic Second Adopted as International Unit of Time, *NBS Tech. News Bull.*, vol. 52, no. 1, pp. 10–12, January, 1968.

‡ The name *kelvin* (*symbol:* °K) of the unit of thermodynamic temperature was changed from *degree kelvin* (symbol: K) by action of the 13th General Conference on Weights and Measures, Paris, October, 1967. See *NBS Tech. News Bull.*, vol. 52, p. 12, January, 1968.

§ New Definitions Authorized for SI Base Units, *NBS Tech. News Bull.*, vol. 53, pp. 12–13, January, 1969.

various ways. This too has caused considerable confusion in its application. A detailed listing of the derived quantities is given in Sec. 5.*

Figure 1 shows the relationships of the derived quantities to the basic quantities. A more detailed chart could show this relationship in dimensional terminology. Even greater detailing could show the relationships by definition and physical equations.

Lineage of the derived quantities is indicated by hatched lines representing the several fundamental quantities. Each derived quantity (outlined in a block) is related to one or more base quantities and in some cases, such as electric power, through a chain of derived quantities. These relationships are expressed by physical equations and can be verified by expressing the relationships in dimensional terminology. Two of these chains, namely, mechanical and electrical quantities, have a common equivalency in the quantity of power. In turn, they have a common "sink," depicted by heat flow, mechanical power as the mechanical equivalent of heat, and electrical power as completely dissipated into heat.

Of interest in this genealogy of the International System is the role played by the permeability of free space.† Also of interest is the role played by the permittivity of free space.‡ By definition, current is considered to be a base quantity, although it is not independent of length, mass, and time. It is related, by definition, to these "mechanical" quantities by assigning a value of 4×10^{-7} henry/meter to the permeability of free space.§ Experimentally, the relationship of current to the mechanical quantities is established by means of the current balance or the Pellat-type dynamometer (see Sec. 4). Voltage is derived from current and resistance through the relationship of Ohm's law. In early work the unit of resistance was established from the reactance of a self-inductor or mutual inductor. More recently, greater accuracy has been attained by using a computable capacitor.‖

The value of permittivity of free space ϵ_0 is derived from the defined value of the permeability of free space μ_0 and the best value of the observed speed of light c, the relationship being $\epsilon_0 = 1/\mu_0 c^2$. A presently used value of the permittivity of free space is 8.8542×10^{-12} farad/meter.¶ Derivation of resistance by the capacitor method is indicated in the genealogy diagram.

4. Development of the Electrical Systems of Units The development of electrical systems of units has progressed over a period of nearly one and a half centuries. During this time no fewer than eight recognized systems have evolved.** In consequence

* The International System of Derived Units tabulated for electrical and magnetic quantities in Sec. 5 is applicable only to quantities appearing in rationalized equations.

† Permeability of free space μ_0 is a derived quantity and is expressed as the ratio of magnetic flux density (induction) B_0 to magnetic field intensity H_0 in free space. In the mksa system it is assigned the value of $4\pi \times 10^{-7}$ henry/meter. The quantity can also be expressed in terms of Maxwell's equations.

‡ Permittivity of free space ϵ_0 is a derived quantity and is expressed as the ratio of electric flux density (displacement) D_0 to electric field strength E_0 in free space. In the mksa system ϵ_0 has a value of 8.8542×10^{-12} farad/meter. The quantity can also be expressed in terms of Maxwell's equations.

§ This rather confusing subject of the definition of the electrical units in the mksa system and the relation of the electrical units to the mechanical units is discussed and clarified by Page. See C. H. Page, Definition of "Ampere" and "Magnetic Constant," *Proc. IEEE*, vol. 53, no. 1, pp. 100–101, January, 1965. Also, refer to Secs. 4 and 5.

‖ W. K. Clothier, A Calculable Standard of Capacitance, *Metrologia*, vol. 1, pp. 36–55, 1965. A capacitor designed upon a theorem that permits a small capacitance (approximately 1 picofarad) to be calculated directly in terms of unit lengths of cylindrical solid rods placed in various geometrical configurations, with an uncertainty of about 1 part in 10^7.

¶ Electric Engineering Units and Constants, *NBS Tech. News Bull.*, vol. 49, no. 5, p. 75, May, 1965.

** W. R. Varner, "The Fourteen Systems of Units," Vantage Press, Inc., New York, 1961. F. B. Silsbee, Systems of Electrical Units, NBS Monograph 56, September, 1962.

quence, much confusion has existed because of varied terminology, multiplicity of concepts and methods of approach, complexity of the subject, lack of standardization, and lack of understanding of various viewpoints. The electrical system of units as we know them today had its origin with the expression of Ohm's law, $E = IR$, in 1827. In 1833, Gauss first related magnetic quantities to mechanical units by experimental methods.* At later dates, Weber developed methods of measuring electric current and resistance in terms of the mechanical units of length, mass, and time. Such methods of relating the electrical quantities (or heat, light, etc.) to the so-called mechanical units of length, mass, and time are known as "absolute" methods,† with no special reason except that early workers in the field chose this terminology.

Formed in 1861, and continuing its influence for many years, was the Committee on Electrical Standards‡ appointed by the British Association for the Advancement of Science. This committee, under the chairmanship of Clerk Maxwell in its early years, established the centimeter-gram-second (cgs) system of electrical units in both the electrostatic and electromagnetic relationship of units, and also the practical units, all expressed in terms of the metric system. The cgs system of electrical units, by its very name, was directly related to the mechanical units and thus was an "absolute" system. The magnitudes of the practical units were selected to be of greater convenience to engineering applications than some of the more extreme values of the electrostatic and electromagnetic units.

During a period of many years, after the establishment of the cgs system, the basic units of the volt, ohm, and ampere became embodied in such standards as the standard cell§ (culminating in the Weston saturated cell), the mercury ohm,‖ and the silver voltameter¶ (also known as the coulometer). The electrical

* A paper entitled On the Intensity of the Earth's Magnetic Field Expressed in Absolute Measure, written by Gauss in 1833, gave the first example of determining magnetic and electrical quantities by measurements in terms of length, mass, and time. Gauss measured the horizontal component of the earth's magnetic field by using a deflection magnetometer and a vibration magnetometer in combination.

† The word "absolute" can be confusing. Its long-time usage in electrical measurements has been that of relating electrical units to the mechanical units of length, mass, and time. However, sometimes it is given the connotation of a state of perfection; that is, no errors, deviations, or residuals exist in the system of measurement units.

Other connotations have been given to the expression "absolute" method of measurement, for example, "bootstrap" techniques that are employed for the calibration of devices used to determine the magnitude of dimensionless quantities such as attenuation. In this usage the measurement is not dependent upon any other device or upon measured characteristics of the device itself. Another example of an "absolute" method of measurement is the calibration of an "ideal" rotary-vane attenuator by measuring the angles of rotation of various settings of the revolving section of the attenuator.

‡ Reports of the Committee on Electrical Standards of the British Association for Advancement of Science, Cambridge University Press, 1913.

§ The early Clark cell, developed in 1873, was followed by the Weston cell as a standard of voltage. The Weston standard cell has a positive electrode of mercury, a negative electrode of a cadmium amalgam (mercury alloy), and a solution of cadmium sulfate as the electrolyte. Two forms of the cell are used, the unsaturated (electrolyte) and the saturated (electrolyte). The saturated cell is more stable but has a higher temperature coefficient than the unsaturated cell and thus must be carefully temperature-controlled. These standard cells operate at approximately 1.02 V. In recent years specially selected zener diodes have come into common use as voltage standards.

‖ The mercury ohm, which had its origin in Germany, became a considerably less than satisfactory international unit of resistance. In its final development it was defined as the resistance of a column of pure mercury 106.3 cm long and having a mass of 14.4521 g (approximately 1 mm^2 in cross section). It went into general disuse during the early 1900's, although used for occasional reference as late as the 1930's

¶ The silver voltameter served for many years as the standard for electric current. The international ampere was defined as the current which when passed through a

units in terms of these standards became known as the International Units and existed as such until 1948. In some countries, including the United States, these units were also known as the "legal" units.

During the long period of use of the cgs system highly precise methods of determining the volt, ohm, and ampere in terms of the mechanical units were carried out by the national laboratories of England, Germany, and the United States. Eventually, unit values of the ohm and volt became embodied in the standard 1-ohm resistor of the Thomas or similar type and in the Weston saturated cell (very nearly 1 volt), and they remain such today. As a result of these measurements (using the current balance and the self- or mutual-inductance method of measuring resistance), beginning Jan. 1, 1948, a new set of values known as the absolute volt and absolute ohm were assigned to national standards of voltage and resistance.* During the transition period it was necessary to state their relationship to the International Units that had been used for over a half century. Although these values remain essentially the same today as in 1948, they are subject to slight changes with more accurate methods of determination. Such a change brought a change to the legal U.S. volt† on Jan. 1, 1969, because of the development of the computable-capacitor method of determining the ohm,‡ and a more precise current balance§ and the Pellat-type dynamometer methods‖ of determining the ampere.

In 1954, the 10th General Conference on Weights and Measures established the "Système International" (SI), or International System of Units, based upon the meter, kilogram, second, ampere, degree Kelvin (now kelvin), and candela.

The electrical units of the International System of Units are based on the mksa system adopted by the International Electrotechnical Commission (IEC) as a development of Giorgi's¶ 1901 proposal for a four-dimensional mks system.** The system includes the ampere and is therefore known as the meter-kilogram-second-ampere system (see Secs. 3 and 5).

5. The International System of Derived Units Table 1 lists the derived units of the International System of Units, a portion of which is shown in Fig. 1, A Genealogy of the International System of Units (by Quantities).

6. Internationalization of Electrical Units and Standards The almost universal use of the metric system has probably been a determining force to engender interna-

---

solution of silver nitrate deposits silver on a platinum cup (cathode) at the rate of 0.001118 g/s under specified conditions. Because of lack of agreement between different forms of the voltameter and of the more fundamental approach in determining the ampere by the current balance (see the following paragraph in the text), the silver voltameter has fallen into disuse.

* Announcement of Changes in Electrical and Photometric Units, *NBS Circ.* 459, May, 1947.

† Reference Base of the Volt to Be Changed, *NBS Tech. News Bull.*, vol. 52, pp. 204–206, September, 1968. Also, 1968 Actions, International Committee of Weights and Measures, *NBS Tech. News Bull.*, vol. 53, pp. 12–13, January, 1969.

‡ R. D. Cutkosky, Evaluation of the NBS Unit of Resistance Based on a Computable Capacitor, *J. Res. NBS*, vol. 65A, pp. 147–158, June, 1961.

§ R. L. Driscoll and R. D. Cutkosky, Measurement of Current with the National Bureau of Standards Current Balance, *J. Res. NBS*, vol. 60, pp. 297–305, April, 1958.

‖ R. L. Driscoll, Measurement of Current with the Pellat Electrodynamometer, *J. Res. NBS*, vol. 60, pp. 287–296, April, 1958.

¶ G. Giorgi, Rational Units of Electromagnetism, *Atti dell' Associoz Elettr Italiene,* 1901, p. 201.

** L. H. A. Carr, the M.K.S. or Giorgi system of units, *Proc. Inst. Elec. Engrs. (London)*, vol. 97, part 1, pp. 235–240, 1950. This paper was one of four papers of a symposium on the mks system of units. The four papers and an extensive discussion are found in this referenced publication. A. E. Kennelly, The M.K.S. System of Units, *J. Inst. Elec. Engrs. (London)*, vol. 78, pp. 235–244, 1936. A. E. Kennelly, I.E.C. Adopts M.K.S. System of Units, *Trans. Am. Inst. Elec. Engrs.*, vol. 54, pp. 1373–1384, December, 1935. The last two references are papers that are quite similar and contain a very extensive list of references on systems of electrical units.

tional agreements on electrical units and standards. The agreement process is rather involved. It begins with the International Advisory Committee on Electricity that passes its recommendations on to the International Committee on Weights and Measures. Final action is taken by the (International) General Conference on Weights and Measures. The latter is a meeting of delegates from countries that hold to the Treaty of the Meter. The General Conference convenes every few years.

The International Bureau of Weights and Measures serves as the laboratory facility for this international system that has evolved over nearly a 100-year period.

TABLE 1 The International System of Derived Units

Physical quantity	SI unit	Symbol
Area	square meter	m^2
Volume	cubic meter	m^3
Frequency	hertz	Hz
Density	kilogram per cubic meter	kg/m^3
Velocity	meter per second	m/s
Acceleration	meter per second per second	m/s^2
Force	newton	N ($kg\ m/s^2$)
Pressure	newton per square meter	N/m^2
Work (energy), quantity of heat	joule	J
Power (mechanical, electrical)	watt	W (J/s)
Electrical charge	coulomb	C
Permeability	henry per meter	H/m
Permittivity	farad per meter	F/m
Voltage, potential difference, electromotive force	volt	V
Electric flux density, displacement	coulomb per square meter	C/m^2
Electric field strength	volt per meter	V/m
Resistance	ohm	Ω
Capacitance	farad	F
Inductance	henry	H
Magnetic flux	weber	Wb
Magnetic flux density (magnetic induction)	tesla	T (Wb/m^2)
Magnetic field strength (magnetic intensity)	ampere per meter	A/m
Magnetomotive force	ampere	A
Magnetic permeability	henry per meter	H/m
Luminous flux	lumen	lm (cd sr)
Luminance	candela per square meter	cd/m^2
Illumination	lux	lx (lm/m^2)

For base units, see Sec. 3.

The common usage of the cgs system in the past will associate electric current, in amperes, with the electrical quantities in the above tabulations. In the International System electric current is considered to be a base quantity (unit) rather than a derived quantity.

It is located at Sevres, France, in suburban Paris. Cooperating in the international program are a number of national standardizing laboratories such as the National Bureau of Standards (U.S.A.); the National Physical Laboratory (England); and the Physikalisch-Technische Bundesanstalt (West Germany), formerly the Physikalisch-Technische Reichsanstalt (Germany).

7. National Bureau of Standards The National Bureau of Standards, founded in 1901, is the national standardizing laboratory of the United States. Responsibility for a national system of electromagnetic measurements in the frequency range of zero (direct current) to above 300 GHz is with the Electricity Division (Electromagnetics Division, Quantum Electronics Division), and the Time and Frequency Division. See Fig. 2 for an organizational plan of the National Bureau of Standards. These four divisions and a number of others form the Institute of Basic Standards as one of three technical institutes within the National Bureau

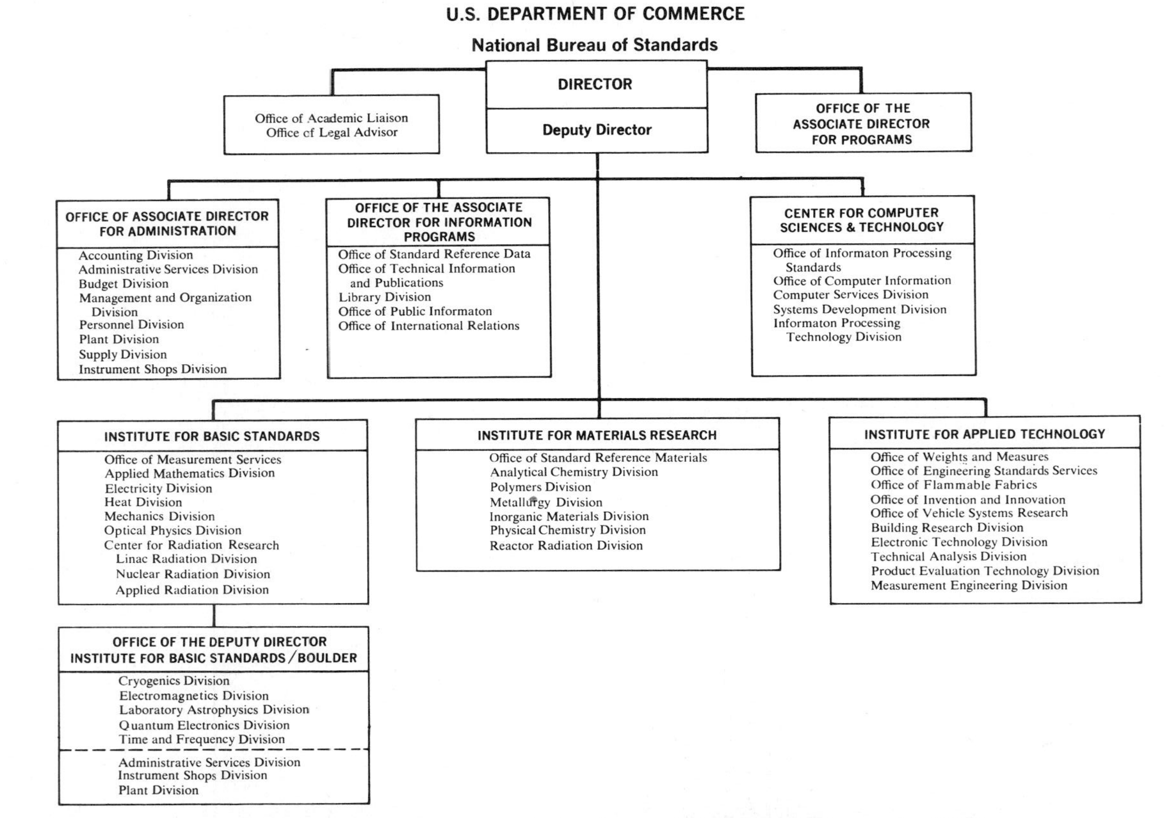

Fig. 2. Organizational plan of the National Bureau of Standards (NBS).

of Standards. The Institute's mission is to develop and maintain the national standards of measurements and furnish essential services that lead to accurate and uniform physical measurements throughout the nation. The mission provides the central basis for a complete and consistent system of physical measurements that is coordinated with those of other nations.

The NBS Reference Standards and the NBS Working Standards maintained by the Institute for Basic Standards for electrical and radio-frequency quantities are listed in Chap. 3 within the Echelon I notation. Methods of measurements are listed by name to indicate techniques used to compare one level of standards with another level, including the method of comparing a customer's interlaboratory standard with NBS standards.*

8. An Echelon of Standards It is natural that an echelon or hierarchy of standards will evolve if a measurement system is to show lineage or traceability to a common source. Conversely, this common source provides the point from which a chain of measurement leads to the ultimate user of a system. The term base is used to designate the standards at the source of a measurement system. However, the term "prototype" standard† is frequently used, particularly if it is of an arbitrary type such as the International 1-kilogram mass. National standardizing laboratories have replicas of the International kilogram; in the United States the National Bureau of Standards has Prototype Kilogram No. 20. Today, atomic standards of length have supplanted the former meter bar, and in the SI system atomic standards of time (interval as differentiated from epic) have supplanted the second as determined from the rotation of the earth on its axis or around the sun. Probably the ultimate of all basic standards is atomic‡ in nature rather than macroscopic.

An echelon of standards of a measurement system is shown in Fig. 3. Such an echelon is fairly common in practice, although it is somewhat idealized as shown in this format. The numbering of the echelons is based upon a standardizing program for electronic measurements prepared by an IEEE committee§ on basic standards and calibration methods. The general concept of this format comes from the work of a committee within the Interservice (Army, Navy, Air Force) Calibration Conference of 1960, with the purpose of attaining a more uniform nomenclature for classes or echelons of laboratory standards.

In brief, the echelon structure as shown by Echelon I in Fig. 3 is typical of chains of standards as they exist within the National Bureau of Standards. Much of the terminology used in this presentation is after McNish.‖ The system of

* For detailed information on many of these comparison-measurement techniques the reader is referred to the new *NBS Special Publication* 300 entitled Precision Measurement and Calibration. This publication in 12 volumes and an index is a compilation of a large number of selected papers previously published by the staff of the National Bureau of Standards on precision measurement, calibration, and related subjects. It supersedes NBS Handbook 77 of three volumes. To those concerned with basic electronic instrumentation, vol. 3, "Electricity—Low Frequency," and vol. 4, "Electricity—Radio Frequency," are of particular interest. The publication may be obtained in single volumes or as a set from:

Superintendent of Documents
U.S. Government Printing Office
Washington, D.C. 20402

† A. G. McNish, Classification and Nomenclature for Standards of Measurements, *IRE Trans. Instr.*, vol. I-7, pp. 371–378, December, 1958.

‡ R. D. Huntoon and U. Fano, Atomic Definition of Primary Standards, *Nature*, vol. 116, pp. 167–168, July 29, 1950.

§ A Program to Provide Information on the Accuracy of Electromagnetic Measurements, *Report* 62 IRE 20, TR2; also *Proc. IEEE*, vol. 51, no. 4, pp. 569–574, April, 1963; also, see any subsequent IEEE Standards Report on State of the Art of Measuring (specific electromagnetic quantity) prepared by the various subcommittees of the Electromagnetic Measurement State-of-the-Art Committee of the IEEE Instrumentation and Measurement Group.

‖ A. G. McNish, Classification and Nomenclature for Standards of Measurements, *IRE Trans. Instr.*, vol. I-7, pp. 371–378, December, 1958.

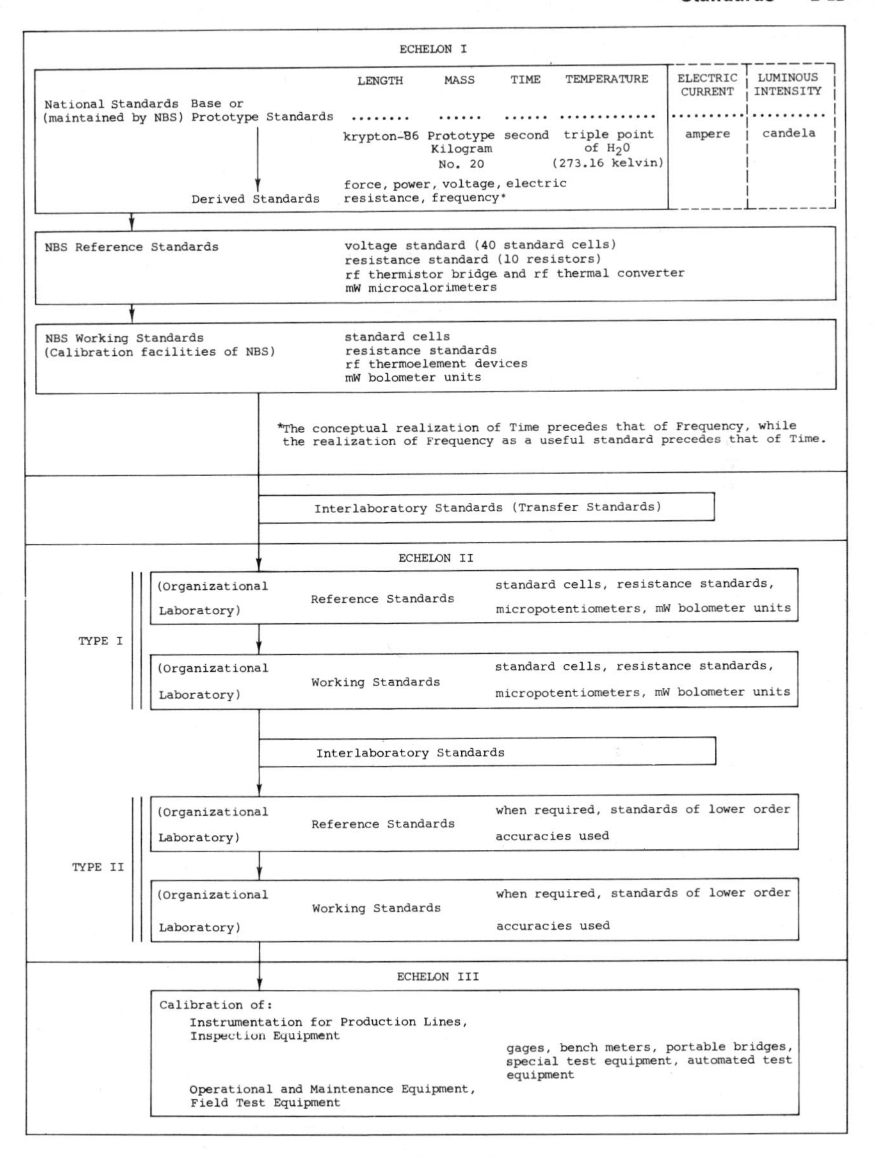

Fig. 3. An Echelon of standards of a measurement system.

measurement quantities shown in Echelon I has already been indicated in Sec. 3. It consists of the base units that are embodied in prototype standards such as standards of length and mass, and of the many derived units that are expressed by their mathematical relationships to the base units. Many of these derived units can be embodied in standards; for example, the saturated Weston-type cell serves as the standard for the volt. Whether standards exist singly, such as Prototype Kilogram No. 20, or uniquely as the group of 40 saturated standard cells, they are classed as the national standards. The national standards serve to establish and stabilize the units of measurement for the United States.

Within Echelon I there usually exist two additional levels of standards, and usually at a lower level of accuracy than the national standards. The first, or higher-accuracy standards, known as NBS reference standards, are often the same as the national standards. In any case the reference standards serve as highly stable standards to be used infrequently (probably once or twice a year) to calibrate NBS working standards. The working standards are used on a day-to-day basis to calibrate customer's standards. The customer's standards, known as interlaboratory standards, are usually shipped or brought to NBS on a time schedule ranging from 6 months to several years, depending upon the nature of the standard.

The structure of Echelon II is of particular interest to those engaged in the art of making precision measurements. It depicts the calibration steps through which a measured physical quantity (embodied in standards and expressed in units) is passed from level to level and invariably with a degradation of accuracy of measurement.*

To a considerable extent the structure within Echelon II resembles that of Echelon I, there being reference standards and working standards associated with most measurement laboratories. The number of levels involved will depend upon the complexity of the measurement system used by an organization, upon the complexity (or simplicity) of measurements and standards involved, and upon various other factors. There may not, and in the interest of minimizing accuracy degradation and calibration costs, there probably should not be as many levels of standards as indicated in Echelon II. In many cases the reference standard, which is used infrequently for calibration of a working standard, also serves as an interlaboratory standard, say once a year. In many organizations there need be but one laboratory typical of a Type I laboratory, using but one set of interlaboratory, reference, and working standards. Conceivably, in some cases the three standards could coalesce into one standard, and there would be a lesser degradation in accuracy. However, most measurement systems do not offer this simplicity because of the organizational structure or logistic requirements involved in the calibration facilities of an industrial firm or a government agency.

As an example of how the calibration of an Echelon III instrument is related to the total echelon structure, we might select the dc voltage scale of a bench-type multimeter. Such an instrument is usually rated at about ± 3 percent (3 parts in 10^2) accuracy (more correctly, inaccuracy) of full-scale reading. It would be calibrated by comparison with a precision-type dc voltmeter or with an accurately known dc voltage source combined with a ratio-measurement system. Such instrumentation would be in a laboratory classified at the Echelon II level. Within this same laboratory or possibly within a Type I laboratory of Echelon II, this instrumentation would be calibrated by means of a standard cell in combination with a dc potentiometer and voltage divider. This cell, which serves as the laboratory's working standard, is compared with a cell used as the laboratory's reference standard. The reference standard usually serves as the laboratory's interlaboratory standard and would be calibrated by the National Bureau of Standards if the standard cell is of the saturated type. In some instances the interlaboratory standard may be a standard cell that is used as an interlaboratory or transfer standard only, in which case the laboratory's reference standard would be calibrated by comparison with the interlaboratory standard. At the Echelon I level, within the National Bureau of Standards, the interlaboratory standard is calibrated by compari-

* Degradation of accuracy in a measurement system has been a matter of considerable discussion in recent years, particularly in meetings of the National Conference of Standards Laboratories and the Instrument Society of America. Treatment of the subject has appeared in papers in various technical journals. A listing of references would be rather extensive and is not given here. In magnitude it ranges from practically zero (or 1:1, expressed as an accuracy ratio) to as much as 10 times (or 10:1, expressed as an accuracy ratio). The techniques and the costs involved in making measurements have a bearing on the magnitude of degradation. The subject of accuracy of measurement, in general, is discussed in Chap. 4.

son with a cell (or cells) of the group of 40 standard cells that form the national reference standard of voltage. However, at times, an interlaboratory standard cell will be calibrated by comparison with a cell (or cells) that serves as part of a working group of cells, and is essentially a working standard within Echelon I. Thus many calibration levels can or do exist between the dc voltage scale of a bench-type multimeter and the national standard of voltage.

9. Standards Laboratories and the Calibration of Standards In recent years there has been a rapid increase in the number of standards and calibration laboratories as a part of industry, in the military establishment, as well as laboratories set up as self-supporting firms engaged in the repair and calibration of instruments. The majority of these laboratories support quality-assurance and inspection programs within the organizational structure of the parent firm. In the military these laboratories support maintenance programs, especially for the complex and sophisticated weaponry and maintenance equipment that has been developed in recent years. All these laboratories engage in calibration activities, some limited in their scope of capabilities, others being engaged in many kinds of measurements. Many of the industry-related laboratories offer calibration services to others beyond the limits of their own organization.

Out of this proliferation of standards laboratories has come an organization known as the National Conference of Standards Laboratories (NCSL), representing approximately 250 laboratories. Many of these laboratories offer calibration services to others. The NCSL publishes a Directory of Standards Laboratories which lists the types of calibration services available from the various laboratories. The Directory may be obtained from:

National Conference of Standards Laboratories
c/o National Bureau of Standards
Washington, D.C. 20234

If calibration services are to be obtained from the National Bureau of Standards, such services are listed in *NBS Special Publication* 250, entitled Calibration and Test Services of the National Bureau of Standards. This publication may be obtained at a nominal cost from:

Superintendent of Documents
U.S. Government Printing Office
Washington, D.C. 20402

In addition to describing the nature of specific standards and instruments suitable for calibration by NBS, this publication states the magnitude and frequency range over which the device can be calibrated and also the measurement accuracy that can be obtained. Detailed information is given on fees, request procedure, and shipping of standards.

Announcements of new services and discontinued services also appear in issues of the *NBS Technical News Bulletin*. This monthly publication is available on a subscription basis at a nominal cost from the Superintendent of Documents listed above. The publication consists largely of information on the Bureau's research, development, cooperative, and publications programs.

10. Environments for Standards and for Standards Laboratories Measurement standards and measurement equipment are susceptible to the vagaries of their environment. In general, the greater the accuracy of measurement sought for, the greater is the need for control of environment to within narrow ranges of operation or maximum limits of disturbances. Because of susceptibility to ambient temperature, all electrical measurement equipment must be kept within reasonable bounds of proper operating temperatures. This is due to changes in dimensions of materials, in the electrical resistance of conductors, and in the dielectric constant of dielectrics, and other changes in the characteristics of materials with temperature. It is quite natural to expect that the greater the precision of measurement the better must be the temperature control.

Some of the criteria of environments for measurement laboratories have come from European practices. This is the case of the "standard" temperature of 20°C used as a reference temperature, particularly for dimensional measurements. The early laboratory workers had little means of controlling room temperature, but they could reduce their observations to a common temperature. With the availability of modern air-conditioning equipment it is possible to control the temperature as well as the relative humidity of large working areas within narrow operating limits. In general, temperature control is considered to be the most important control for measurement laboratories.

Beginning in 1942, with the American Society for Testing Materials, several technical groups have been active in evaluating temperature criteria for measurement and testing operations in laboratories. Other groups have included the Federal Specification Board of the U.S. Treasury Department, National Bureau of Standards, American Ordnance Association, and the Instrument Society of America. With the exception of laboratories performing dimensional measurements (operating temperature of 20°C, or 68°F), recommendations by all these groups have been toward an operating temperature of 23°C (73.4°F). Quite naturally, the comfort* of the operating personnel is of prime importance. American laboratory personnel prefer such a temperature.

Most electrical standards and measurement equipment can be used satisfactorily within a range of several degrees Celsius of normal room temperatures. Precision dimensional metrology requires that the temperature in the immediate vicinity of the standards and associated equipment be held within ±0.05°C of a known temperature during the course of a measurement. In contrast, special types of liquid baths are used in order to obtain the temperature control required for several kinds of high-precision electrical measurements. Resistance measurements at the Echelon I level require control to about 0.01°C of a known temperature, saturated standard cells within two or three thousandths of a degree Celsius. One bath,† now available, will operate at stable temperatures to better than one ten-thousandth of a degree Celsius. Such a bath is a requirement for measurements with a high-precision microwave microcalorimeter at the National Bureau of Standards.

Although control of moisture content in the laboratory atmosphere is not as important as temperature control, it is desirable to keep it within certain limits. Corrosion of steel and other ferric materials can occur rapidly above 60 percent relative humidity. Below 30 percent relative humidity nuisance can occur from the development of static charges. Consideration should also be given to the condition of human comfort by the control of relative humidity within certain limits. However, control of relative humidity for maximum comfort is not as clearly defined‡ as is the control of temperature.

For nearly a decade the Instrument Society of America has had an interest in recommended environmental conditions for laboratories and particularly standards laboratories. A committee report was published in the *ISA Transactions* in 1964.§ A summary of these recommendations is presented here; however, the reader is referred to the complete committee report for detailed explanatory material and an extensive list of literature references. The alphabetical order of the recommendations has no relation to the order of their importance. Only generalizations are given here for the many types of laboratory areas that the report considers. Some of these recommendations are being reconsidered for revision by the ISA committee.

Acoustic Noise. Noise level no greater than a noise criterion (NC) of 35 between 20 and 9,600 Hz. Expressed by a less sophisticated method of measurement, the

* See chapter, Physiological Principles, Human Reactions, "ASHRAE Guide and Data Book" (late edition), published by American Society of Heating, Refrigerating and Air-Conditioning Engineers, Inc.

† M. E. Harvey, Precision Temperature-controlled Water Bath, *Rev. Sci. Instr.*, vol. 39, no. 1, pp. 13–18, January, 1968.

‡ See the chapter in the "ASHRAE Guide and Data Book" referred to above.

§ Recommended Environments for Standards Laboratories, *ISA Trans.*, vol. 3, pp. 366–377, October, 1964.

noise level would be no greater than between 40 and 45 dB as measured on a sound-level meter using the A, or 40-dB, weighting network.

Dust-particle Count. In some areas there is the need for a "clean room" environment in a standards area. As a generalization, dust particles of 1 micron (1 μm) size and greater should not exceed 10^4 to 10^5 in number per cubic foot of room volume, with no particles greater than 50 microns (50 μm). Particles of 0.5 micron (0.5 μm) size and greater should not exceed 10^5 to 10^6 in number. The degree of freshness of air should be a matter of concern in the control of laboratory environment.

Electrical and Magnetic Fields. Extraneous electrical disturbance is usually of concern only when electrical measurements are made, but often of importance throughout a wide frequency range of measurement. A radiation field strength of radio interference no greater than 10 μV/m in the vicinity of the measurement area is recommended. Reduction to this level of field strength within a laboratory area sometimes must be obtained by attenuation shielding to the extent of 80 to 100 or more decibels.

Laboratory Air Pressure. Maintenance of a positive air pressure within a laboratory area is for the purpose of minimizing the infiltration of dust into the room. A positive air pressure of 0.1 to 0.2 mbar (0.04 to 0.08 in. of water) is considered sufficient for this purpose (10 to 20 N/m^2, SI).

Lighting. An illumination of 100 footcandles (1,076 lm/m^2) at bench or desk level is recommended. Other factors, such as maximum ratios of brightness between the task area and surrounding areas, and between different room surfaces, are also important.

Relative Humidity. A relative humidity in the range of 35 to 55 percent appears to be acceptable for most laboratory environments. Relative humidities less than 45 percent are more economical to obtain in drier climates. Fairly close regulation around a design value of the humidity is quite easy to obtain with some types of air-conditioning systems if the temperature is held reasonably constant.

Temperature. Two operating temperatures are recognized and recommended for standards laboratories, with recommended limits of variation around a specific operating temperature. For dimensional metrology and optical laboratories, the temperature is 20°C (68°F) with a ±0.1°C limit of variation at the measuring point and ±0.3°C for the room. For other laboratories it is 23°C (73.4°F) with a ±1 to 1.5°C limit of variation for the room.

Rate of Change of Temperature. The rate at which changes of temperature occur during a measurement period is important. Changes in temperature are usually due to cyclic operation of an air-conditioning system. Recommendations for rate of change of temperature range from 0.5 to 1.5°C/h.

Vibration. Vibration can be a serious problem in some laboratory environments. The extent to which it can be tolerated depends upon the nature of the measurement system. In general, the recommendation is a maximum acceleration of 0.001 *g* or maximum displacement of 1 μin. (25.4 nm) at the instrument base for vibration frequencies below 200 Hz.

Voltage Regulation. Although not always associated with the usual concepts of environmental control of standards and calibration laboratories, voltage regulation (voltage stabilization) of the electrical power source plays an important role in the efficient use of many measurement systems. Voltage regulators are available in a variety of power-handling capacities with the output voltage stabilized to about 0.01 percent for constant-load conditions if line-voltage variations are within reasonable limits, say 2 percent. Such devices are a boon to the laboratory worker who, otherwise, must spend much extra time in making measurements when combating poorly regulated line voltage. Other considerations in voltage regulation are rate of recovery from transients, magnitude of harmonics, and power efficiency of the regulator.

11. The National Measurement System With the very rapid growth of industrial processes and of factual technical knowledge in this country, there has recently come the concept of a National Measurement System (NMS). Dr. Robert Huntoon, former Director of the NBS Institute of Basic Standards, has brought attention to the fact that such a measurement system has developed in the United States over a period of a number of years.* The NMS is taken to be the sum total of all the standards, equipment, practices, and people that relate to the measurement system in the nation. Use of the NMS concept provides a perspective of the vast complex of measurement activities that is associated with the national scientific and technological growth. In its earliest form, one might say that NMS goes back to the time of the American Revolution when the founding fathers wrote into the Articles of Confederation that the Congress have sole and exclusive right of fixing the standard of weights and measures throughout the United States. Such power was later transferred to Congress by the Constitution.

Today the NMS provides the basis for the interchange of goods and services in commerce and for a quantitative approach to the making of myriads of daily measurement decisions throughout the country. From the housewife measuring ingredients for cooking to the scientist making the most precise of measurements, all people become involved in the National Measurement System. The electronic industry plays a significant role in the total system. The National Bureau of Standards provides the central core of the system in support of uniformity and compatibility. Further changes in the present systems are possible as evidenced by such developments as a pilot program for mass calibration,† self-calibration methods, calibration by comparison with natural standards (atomic standards), and the calibration of complete systems rather than of single standards as components of a system.

BIBLIOGRAPHY

"ASTM Metric Practice Guide," National Bureau of Standards Handbook 102, Mar. 10, 1967.

Chertov, A. G.: "Units of Measures of Physical Quantities," Hayden Book Company, Inc., New York, 1964.

Harris, F. K.: Units and Standards of Electrical Measure, *Electron. World,* vol. 72, pp. 29–32, 55, August, 1964.

Harris, F. K.: Electrical Units, *19th Ann. ISA Conf. Proc.,* vol. 19, part 1, Paper no. 12.1-1-64.

McNish, A. G.: Dimensions, Units and Standards, *Physics Today,* vol. 10, pp. 19–25, April, 1957.

McNish, A. G.: The International System of Units (SI), *Materials Research and Standards,* vol. 5, pp. 528–532, October, 1965.

NBS Interprets Policy on SI Units, *NBS Tech. News Bull.,* vol. 52, pp. 121–124, June, 1968.

Silsbee, F. B.: Establishment and Maintenance of the Electrical Units, *NBS Circ.* 475, June, 1949.

Silsbee, F. B.: Extension and Dissemination of the Electric and Magnetic Units, *NBS Circ.* 531, July, 1952.

Silsbee, F. B.: Systems of Electrical Units, *J. Res. NBS,* vol. 66C, pp. 137–178, April–June, 1962; reprinted in NBS Monograph 56, September, 1962.

Varner, W. R.: "The Fourteen Systems of Units," Vantage Press, Inc., New York, 1961.

Young, L.: "Systems of Units in Electricity and Magnetism," Oliver & Boyd Ltd., Edinburgh, 1967.

* R. D. Huntoon, The Measurement System of the United States, *NBS Misc. Publ.* 291, pp. 89–98, July, 1967. R. D. Huntoon, Concept of a National Measurement System, *Science,* vol. 158, no. 3797, pp. 67–71, Oct. 6, 1967.

† P. E. Pontius, Measurement Philosophy of the Pilot Program for Mass Calibration, *NBS Tech. Note* 288, May 6, 1966. P. E. Pontius and J. M. Cameron, Realistic Uncertainties and the Mass Measurement Process, an Illustrated Review, NBS Monograph 103, Aug. 15, 1967.

Chapter **3**

Basic Electronic Standards*

WILBERT F. SNYDER

National Bureau of Standards, Boulder, Colorado

* Contribution of the National Bureau of Standards, not subject to copyright.

CLASSIFICATION KEY TO STANDARDS

A Classification Key to *Literature Sources* on Basic Electronic Standards by Selection of Frequency Range, Electrical Quantity, and an Echelon of Standards

1. Introduction It is the primary purpose of this chapter to direct the reader to selected subjects in the extensive literature relating to electronic standards by means of the echelon relation discussed in Chap. 2, Sec. 8. The 20 charts found in this chapter show the echelon relations of many standards, instruments, and measurement techniques. The charts are grouped by frequency ranges, and are individually separated into various electrical quantities. Accompanying each chart is a reference list of literature sources of information that relates to the subjects delineated on the chart. The format of the Classification Key not only gives a relatively simple method of "keying out" the literature sources of information on electronic standards but also displays the echelon relations of standards, instruments, and measurement techniques in much greater detail than was possible in Chap. 2. The classification is divided further into three frequency ranges and by a number of electrical quantities.

By using this Classification Key, the reader can, with little effort, find the literature references on specific subjects that he is seeking in a broad field of technical literature. Although the literature on modern subjects in electricity spreads over much of the nineteenth century and has accelerated rapidly in the twentieth century, the subjects referred to in this chapter cover only the past several decades. It is the intention not to cover the historical development of electronic standards but to refer the reader to the description and use of standards and to measurement techniques that can be considered contemporary.

2. The Classification Key To use the Classification Key to the literature references, three selections are made in the areas of frequency range, electrical quantity,* and the echelon of the standard or instrument of interest, as follows:

* Sometimes, in the usage associated with the term "electrical quantity," there is divergence from the usual concept of this term in order to achieve a more

Step 1. Selection by frequency range.

Step 2. Selection by electrical quantity. These are grouped in three frequency ranges indicated in outline form below:

1. Dc and low-frequency standards (0 to 30 kHz)
   a. Resistance
   b. Voltage (dc)
   c. Dc ratio
   d. Ac-dc transfer, low-frequency voltage or current
   e. Ac ratio
   f. Capacitance and inductance
   g. Power and energy
2. Approximately 30 kHz to 1 GHz and higher (standards and instruments usually fitted with coaxial connectors)*
   a. Voltage, cw and pulse (baseband)†
   b. Current
   c. Power, cw and pulse
   d. Impedance (immittance)
   e. Phase shift
   f. Attenuation
   g. Noise
3. Approximately 1 to 40 GHz and higher (standards and instruments usually constructed of rectangular waveguide, interconnected with waveguide connectors; also, at lower frequencies of this region, standards and instruments constructed of coaxial lines, with precision coaxial connectors)*
   a. Power
   b. Impedance
   c. Phase shift
   d. Attenuation
   e. Noise

---

generic approach in describing a group of standards or measurement techniques. A case in point is the term "ac-dc transfer," as expressed as a subdivision under dc and low-frequency standards in the frequency range of 0 to 30 kHz. This term has a functional meaning rather than that of being an electrical quantity, which would be that of "voltage" or "current." To a lesser extent this is also true of the terms "dc ratio" and "ac ratio."

In a somewhat different sense, the term frequency is also being considered as an "electrical quantity" in this Classification Key to literature references. However, because the term encompasses all frequency ranges being considered, it is treated as an electrical quantity without association with any particular frequency range.

* The matter of designation, definition, and nomenclature for various regions of the radio-frequency spectrum has plagued the engineering community for years. Unanimity has been rarely achieved in this matter, even within small groups. The treatment given here is but one of several methods that can be used in naming and setting the boundaries of several regions within the radio-frequency region of the electromagnetic spectrum.

The range from 30 kHz to 1 GHz is sometimes referred to as the High-Frequency Region. Today, in this frequency range, interconnection of measurement equipment usually is made with precision coaxial connectors. The microwave region sometimes is considered to extend from 1 GHz upward to 300 GHz (however, the range from 30 to 300 GHz is often called the Millimeter-Wave Region). Above 1 GHz precision measurement equipment is constructed largely of waveguide (usually of rectangular cross section), although there is an increasing trend toward the use of precision coaxial lines.

Except for resonant frequency standards (cavity-type frequency meters), the upper frequency limit of standards and calibration services at the National Bureau of Standards (Echelon I) is about 40 GHz at present.

† A pulse whose frequency spectrum extends from zero frequency or near zero frequency upward without limit.

Step 3. Selection by echelon of standards* (defined in terms of use)

Echelon I: Standards and measurement techniques used by the U.S. National Bureau of Standards, or a comparable national laboratory

Interlaboratory (transfer standards)

Echelon II: Standards and measurement techniques used by industrial and government standards laboratories

Echelon III: Instruments used for production work and quality control in manufacturing, for maintenance, and for general measurement purposes

The device used as a standard that embodies a known magnitude† (numerical expression of the measurement units involved) of the electrical quantity being transferred from one standard to another is labeled in the charts with capital letters. This labeling with capital letters is carried down through the echelon structure from the NBS Reference Standards (or comparable levels of instrumentation) to various instruments used by the ultimate user at Echelon III. The name of the measurement technique or the measurement instrumentation involved is outlined with a rectangular box. The progression of transferring the known magnitude of an electrical quantity from one standard to another is delineated by arrows.

* The association of each reference in the literature references with that of each of the several levels of the echelon structure is indicated by symbols, as follows:

Echelon I	I
Interlaboratory standards	IS
Echelon II	II
Echelon III	III

† A comment should be made on the interpretation of measurement magnitudes for the electrical quantities delineated in this chapter. In most cases the quantities are dimensional in nature, the base quantities of length, mass, and time being transferred through derived quantities to the reference and working standards embodying various units of measurement. Throughout a measurement chain the electrical quantities are usually expressed as dimensional quantities (see Chap. 2, Sec. 3). However, there are cases where dimensionless quantities are involved, as defined in terms of a ratio of two magnitudes of a dimensional quantity. Such "electrical quantities" are useful expressions in electrical terminology, but these expressions are not a "purist's" treatment of physical terminology.

Among the more common terms for dimensionless electrical quantities are attenuation, reflection coefficient, and voltage ratio. More specifically:

Attenuation, expressed in decibels (dB), is not a dimensional quantity expressed by a physical unit in the accepted sense, but by common usage attenuation is usually considered to be one of the electrical quantities, with the decibel as the "unit."

By definition,

$$\text{Decibel(s)} = 10 \log_{10} \frac{W_1}{W_2}$$

where W_1 and W_2 are power levels of electrical or acoustical energy, expressed in watts.

Reflection-coefficient magnitude, expressed as $|\Gamma|$ at radio frequencies, where

$$|\Gamma| = \frac{\dfrac{|V|_{max}}{|V|_{min}} - 1}{\dfrac{|V|_{max}}{|V|_{min}} + 1}$$

$|V|$ being the modal-voltage magnitude at a probe used to indicate the magnitude of standing waves. (See Definitions of v, i, Z, Y, a, b, Γ, and S in D. M. Kerns, *Proc. IEEE*, vol. 55, no. 6, pp. 892–900, June, 1967.)

Thus reflection-coefficient magnitude is a dimensionless quantity, derived from a ratio of ratios of voltages, voltage being a dimensional quantity.

Voltage ratio is a useful expression to indicate a numerical ratio of voltages, or the quotient itself, of readouts on inductive voltage dividers and universal ratio sets. Voltage ratio is dimensionless.

Normally, a transfer requires the medium of measurement instrumentation. The precision of the instrumentation and measurement process usually is compatible with the degree of accuracy required in the transfer process. If the precision is lower, accuracy of measurement will be lost in the transfer process; if it is much higher, the cost of the measurement process will be excessive.

Occasionally, a standard or measurement technique is designated in the chart by a specific name (name of person originating the device, or descriptive name of device). Wherever applicable and feasible, the literature reference (coded by numerals) in the Classification Key is placed in close to the left side of the name of the standard or measurement technique, thereby giving the reference specific significance.

The literature references associated with each diagram are keyed by numerals to the standards or measurement techniques indicated on the diagram. As much as possible, the keying of specific subjects covered in the referenced literature is matched with that of compatible levels of standards or measurement instrumentation in the echelon structure. Some referenced literature is keyed to Echelon I (NBS) only; others of a more general nature may be keyed to several echelons as well as to the interlaboratory standards.

3. Use of the Classification Key, Examples The following is an example of how the Classification Key is used to seek out specific information from the literature. Say the information being sought is that on the design and characteristics of standards (Interlaboratory Standards) suitable for accurately transferring the values of low-frequency (below 30 kHz) voltages from the National Bureau of Standards to an Echelon II laboratory by means of the ac-dc transfer method. (It is fairly well known that the ac-dc transfer method, using thermal-voltage converters, is the presently accepted method of accurately transferring ac voltages in the range of one to several hundred volts.) As Step 1, we select by frequency range the charts titled "DC and/or Low-frequency Standards (0 to 30 kHz)," and as Step 2, we find the chart titled with the electrical quantity* of "Low-frequency VOLTAGE" by the AC-DC TRANSFER method of measurement, and then, as Step 3, we find the code numerals "91, 92, 94, . . ." entered with "Interlaboratory Standards." These code numerals lead us to the several sources of information found in the literature references accompanying the chart. In this case, the code numerals refer us to the design and characteristics of thermal-voltage converters that are suitable as standards in the transfer of low-frequency ac voltages by the ac-dc transfer method.

As another example, say the information being sought is that on attenuation-measurement techniques in waveguide (microwave frequencies) that are suitable for Echelon II laboratories (industrial laboratories). As Step 1, we select by frequency range the charts titled "Approximately 1 GHz to 40 GHz and higher," and as Step 2, we find the chart titled with the electrical quantity* of "ATTENUATION," and then, as Step 3, we find the code numerals "751, 752, 753, . . ." entered with Echelon II. These code numerals lead us to the several sources of information on attenuation measurements in waveguide found in the literature references accompanying the chart.

4. Literature Sources Because the National Bureau of Standards (NBS) is the fountainhead for development of standards of measurement in the United States,† it is natural that many literature references in the Classification Key will be to publications of this technical organization, particularly as found in Echelon I (NBS). However, many of the standards and measurement techniques developed and described in publications by NBS have application as transfer standards and as measurement techniques at lower echelons. The Bureau is also responsible for the dissemination of measurement quantities to the lower echelons through the medium of interlaboratory standards calibrated by NBS. A considerable portion of the Bureau's literature has been collected into *NBS Special Publication* 300,

* See the footnote on page 3-2.

† See Chap. 2, Sec. 7, The National Bureau of Standards.

Precision Measurement and Calibration (NBS SP 300). It is available in 12 volumes (or can be obtained as single volumes on specific subjects) from:

Superintendent of Documents
U.S. Government Printing Office
Washington, D.C. 20402

Of interest in the area of electronic standards are:

Vol. 3, Electricity—Low Frequency
Vol. 4, Electricity—Radio Frequency
Vol. 5, Frequency and Time

Also of interest in the area of measurements is:

Vol. 1, Statistical Concepts and Procedures. NBS SP 300 includes many of the papers, reprinted in full text, that are listed in the literature references. The papers so listed are designated with an asterisk (*).

An earlier edition of NBS SP 300 was published in 1961 as NBS Handbook 77, "Precision Measurement and Calibration." It was published in three volumes, of which vol. 1, entitled "Electricity and Electronics," is of particular interest. Some papers were reprinted in full text in this volume that are not reprinted in the later edition, NBS SP 300. The papers so listed in the literature references are designated with a double asterisk (**).

Manufacturers of electronic standards and associated precision measurement equipment usually have available, upon request, a variety of technical information on their products. Some manufacturers publish technical information on a periodic basis that give detailed accounts of the development, descriptions, operation, and uses of their measurement instruments. Information on specific instruments can be quite valuable and usually will not be found elsewhere. This information in the format of handbooks, manuals, and "notes" is particularly applicable to instrumentation in Echelon II and Echelon III.*

Other areas of information are textbooks and treatises of a tutorial nature that treat broad subjects in electricity and electronics with considerable detail. Such books usually draw their material from many literature sources, including an author's own or his colleagues' research.

A large and diversified source of information in the literature references comes from the periodical literature. In recent years an abundance of material has come from the *IEEE Transactions on Instrumentation and Measurement* (formerly the *IRE Transactions on Instrumentation*) as the record of the biennial conferences on Precision Electromagnetic Measurements sponsored by the National Bureau of Standards and several scientific societies.

* Several publications have special issues, usually on a yearly schedule, that give extensive information in the following areas:

1. Guide to applications literature on electronic instrumentation—handbooks, manuals, bulletins, "notes," catalogs, etc.

Electronic Instrument Digest
222 West Adams Street
Chicago, Illinois 60606

2. Survey information on measurement instruments and measurement techniques.

EDN
270 St. Paul Street
Denver, Colorado 80206

Other periodicals, such as *Measurement and Data News* and the more extensive *Measurements and Data* (*Journal of the Measurements and Data Society of America*), contain such information related to electronic instruments. These two mentioned periodicals are published by

Measurements and Data Corporation
1687 Washington Road
Pittsburgh, Pennsylvania 15228

RESISTANCE (DC AND LOW FREQUENCY)

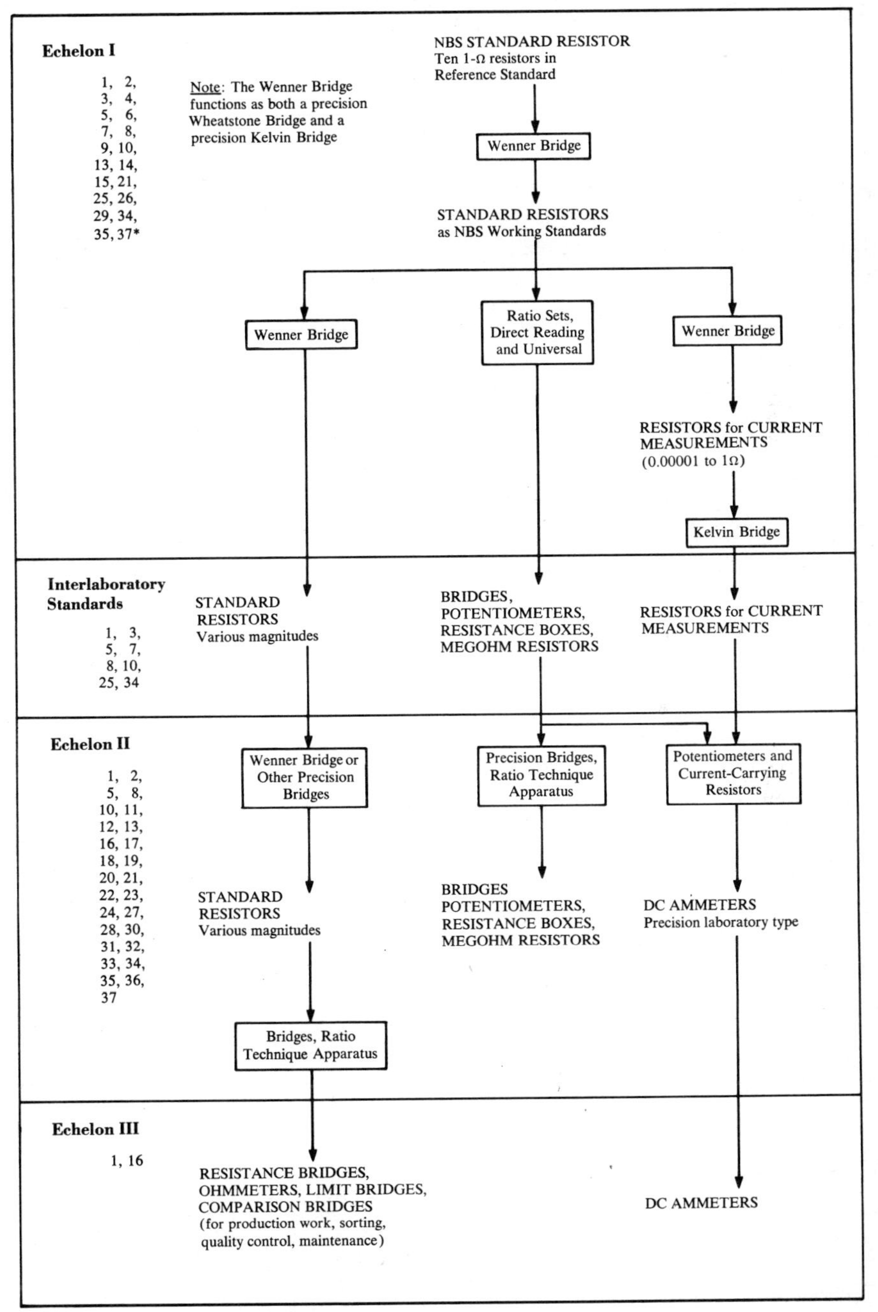

*These numbers refer to the list of references.

CHARTS OF BASIC ELECTRONIC STANDARDS AND TRACEABILITY (DC and Low-frequency)

5. Resistance (DC and Low-frequency)

1 Manufacturers of precision resistors and resistance-measurement equipment
I usually have available, upon request, a variety of technical information
I S on their products, as well as valuable and informative literature on general-
II ized and specialized topics of resistance standards and measurements.
III

2 Listed in *NBS Special Publication* 300, vol. 3, "Electricity—Low Fre-
I quency," are some laboratory notes, copies of which are available from
II the

Electricity Division
Institute of Basic Standards
National Bureau of Standards
Washington, D.C. 20234

By title, these are listed in vol. 3, as follows:

1. Notes on the calibration of the direct-reading ratio set
2. Calibration of the Wenner low-range potentiometer
3. Calibration of the Mueller thermometer bridge
4. Calibration of the universal ratio set
5. The six-dial thermofree potentiometer

3 A New Design of Precision Resistance Standard, J. L. Thomas, *J. Res.*
I *NBS*, vol. 5, no. 2, pp. 295–304, August, 1930.
I S

4 A Determination of the Absolute Ohm, Using an Improved Self Inductor,
I H. L. Curtis, C. Moon, and C. M. Sparks, *J. Res. NBS*, vol. 21, no. 4, pp. 375–423, October, 1938.

***5* Methods, Apparatus, and Procedures for the Comparison of Precision Stan-
I dard Resistors, F. Wenner, *J. Res. NBS*, vol. 25, no. 2, pp. 229–293,
I S August, 1940.
II This paper has an extensive list of references on resistance measurements.

6 Review of Recent Absolute Determinations of the Ohm and the Ampere,
I H. L. Curtis, *J. Res. NBS*, vol. 33, no. 4, pp. 235–254, October, 1944.

**7* Stability of Double-walled Manganin Resistors, J. L. Thomas, *J. Res. NBS*,
I vol. 36, no. 1, pp. 107–110, January, 1946.
I S

***8* Precision Resistors and Their Measurement, J. L. Thomas, *NBS Circ.* 470,
*I October, 1948.
I S
II

9 An Absolute Measurement of Resistance by the Wenner Method, J. L.
I Thomas, C. Peterson, I. L. Cooter, and F. R. Kotter, *J. Res. NBS*, vol. 43, no. 4, pp. 291–353, October, 1949.

***10* Measurement of Multimegohm Resistors, A. H. Scott, *J. Res. NBS*, vol.
I 50, no. 3, pp. 147–152, March, 1953.
I S
II

11 Lindeck Potentiometer, D. W. Oliver, *Rev. Sci. Instr.*, vol. 26, no. 11,
II pp. 1078–1079, November, 1955.

12 A Low-cost Microvolt Potentiometer, W. H. Wood, *Rev. Sci. Instr.*, vol.
II 28, no. 3, pp. 202–203, March, 1957.

**13* A Method of Controlling the Effect of Resistance in the Link Circuit
I of the Thompson or Kelvin Double Bridge, D. Ramaley, *J. Res. NBS*,
II vol. 64C, no. 4, pp. 267–270, October–December, 1960.

14 Evaluation of the NBS Unit of Resistance Based on a Computable Capaci-
I tor, R. D. Cutkosky, *J. Res. NBS*, vol. 65A, no. 2, pp. 147–158, March–April, 1961.

15 Redetermination of NBS Unit of Resistance by New Method, *NBS Tech.*
I *News Bull.*, vol. 45, no. 10, pp. 164–165, October, 1961.

16 Calibration Procedures for Direct Current Resistance Apparatus, P. P. B.
II Brooks, NBS Monograph 39, March, 1962.
III

17 II Practical Methods for Calibration of Potentiometers, D. Ramaley, *NBS Tech. Note* 172, Mar. 25, 1963.

**18* II Calibration of Potentiometers by Resistance Bridge Methods, D. Ramaley, *Instruments and Control Systems,* vol. 37, no. 1, pp. 106–108, January, 1964.

19 II Some Modifications in Methods of Calibration of Universal Ratio Sets, D. Ramaley, *NBS Tech. Note* 220, Aug. 30, 1964.

20 II The Calibration of DC Resistance Standards by an AC Method, J. J. Hill, *IEEE Trans. Instr. Meas.,* vol. IM-13, no. 4, pp. 239–243, December, 1964.

**21* I II Errors in the Series-Parallel Buildup of Four-terminal Resistors, C. H. Page, *J. Res. NBS,* vol. 69C, no. 3, pp. 181–189, July–September, 1965.

22 II Comparison of Standard Resistors by the DC Current Comparator, S. K. Basu and N. L. Kusters, *IEEE Trans. Instr. Meas.,* vol. IM-14, no. 3, pp. 149–156, September, 1965.

23 II A Versatile Ratio Instrument for the High Ratio Comparison of Voltage or Resistance, A. E. Hess, *J. Res. NBS,* vol. 70C, no. 3, pp. 169–172, July–September, 1966.

**24* II Direct Ratio Readings from a URS (Universal Ratio Set), D. Ramaley and J. F. Shafer, *Instruments and Control Systems,* vol. 39, no. 1, pp. 73–74, January, 1966.

25 I I S Increased Accuracy for Resistance Measurements, A. F. Dunn, *IEEE Trans. Instr. Meas.,* vol. IM-15, no. 4, pp. 220–226, December, 1966.

26 I An Absolute Determination of Resistance by Campbell's Method, G. H. Rayer, *Metrologia,* vol. 3, no. 1, pp. 12–18, 1967.

27 II A Universal Potentiometer for the Range from One Nanovolt to 10 Volts, L. Julie, *IEEE Trans. Instr. Meas.,* vol. IM-16, no. 3, pp. 187–191, September, 1967.

28 II The Accuracy of Series and Parallel Connections of Four-terminal Resistors, J. C. Riley, *IEEE Trans. Instr. Meas.,* vol. IM-16, no. 3, pp. 258–268, September, 1967.

29 I An Absolute Determination of Resistance Based on a Calculable Standard of Capacitance, A. M. Thompson, *Metrologia,* vol. 4, no. 1, pp. 1–7, 1968.

30 II Precision Comparison of Resistors by Ordinary Wheatstone Bridge, M. B. Stout, *ISA J.,* vol. 12, no. 5, pp. 76–78, May, 1965.

31 II A Direct-current-comparator Ratio Bridge for Four-terminal Resistance Measurements, M. P. MacMartin and N. L. Kusters, *IEEE Trans. Instr. Meas.,* vol. IM-15, no. 4, pp. 212–220, December, 1966.

32 II An Application of the Potentiometer Method for Measurement of Small Electrical Resistances, L. J. Verheyden and G. W. A. Akkermans, *IEEE Trans. Instr. Meas.,* vol. IM-17, no. 1, pp. 47–48, March, 1968.

33 II The Application of the Direct Current Comparator to a Seven-decade Potentiometer, M. P. MacMartin and N. L. Kusters, *IEEE Trans. Instr. Meas.,* vol. IM-17, no. 4, pp. 263–268, December, 1968.

34 I I S II NPL Precision Resistance Standards Covering the Range 10^{-4} to 10 Ohms, F. J. Wilkins and M. J. Swan, *Proc. IEE* (*London*), vol. 116, no. 2, pp. 303–314, February, 1969.

35 I II Measurements of Low- and High-value Resistance Standards at NPL, F. J. Wilkins and M. J. Swan, *Proc IEE* (*London*), vol. 116, no. 2, pp. 315–317, February, 1969.

36 II Contact Resistance of NBS-type Standard Resistors, R. M. Shaw, *Meas. and Data,* vol. 3, no. 5, pp. 80–81, September–October, 1969.

37 I II Taking a Giant Step, Current-comparator Bridges and Potentiometers (the DC current comparator), J. Sutcliffe, *Electronic Instrument Digest,* vol. 5, no. 10, pp. 10–18, October, 1969.

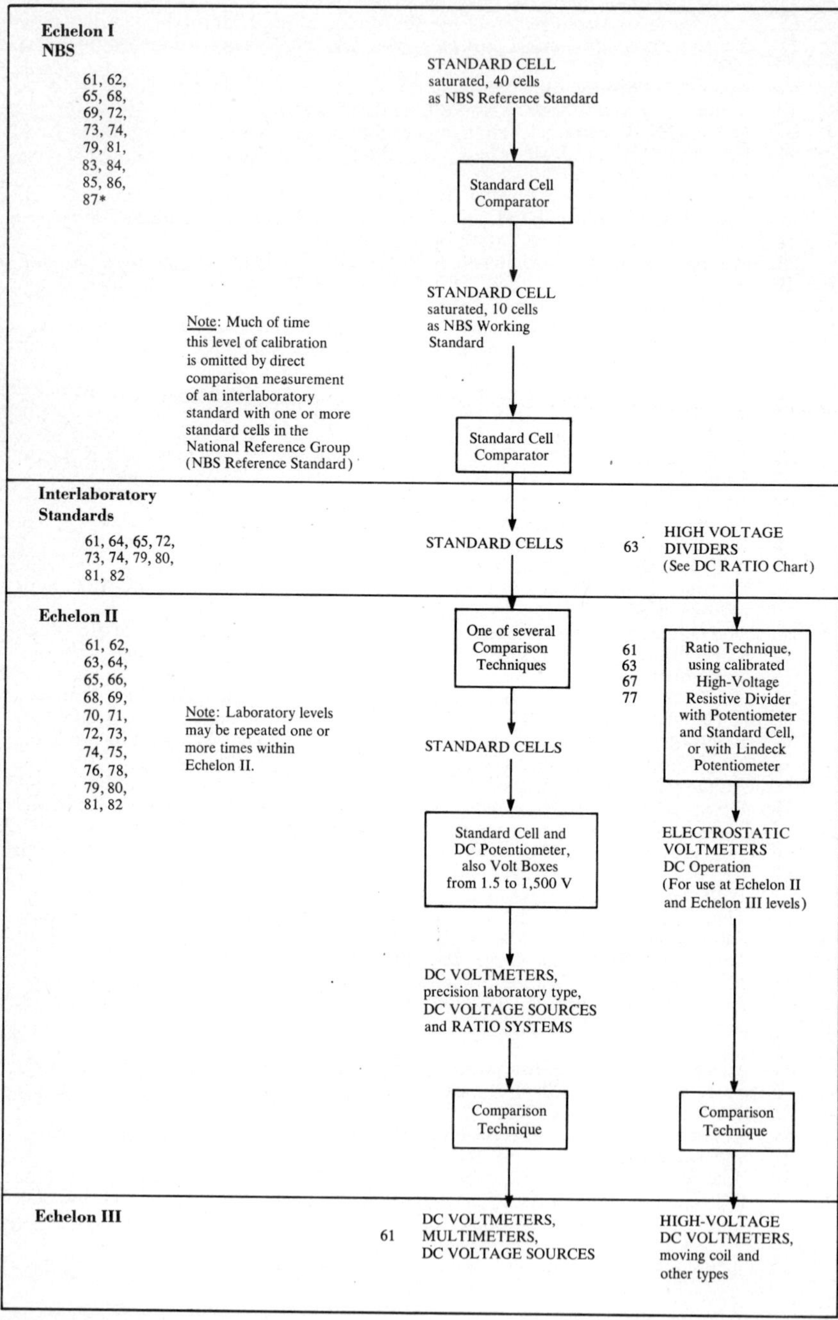

*These numbers refer to the list of references.

6. Voltage (DC)

61 I, I S, II, III — Manufacturers of standard cells, zener diodes, voltage comparators, high-voltage voltmeters, and related equipment usually have available, upon request, a variety of technical information on their products, as well as valuable and informative literature on generalized and specialized topics of voltage standards and voltage calibration equipment.

62 I, II — The Standard-cell Comparator, a Specialized Potentiometer, H. B. Brooks, *J. Res. NBS*, vol. 11, no. 2, pp. 211–231, August, 1933.

****63** I S, II — The Measurement of High Voltage, F. M. Defandorf, *J. Washington Academy of Science*, vol. 38, no. 2, pp. 33–60, February, 1948. This paper has an extensive list of references on high-voltage measurements.

64 I S, II — Portable Potentiometer and Thermostatted Container for Standard Cells, A. W. Spinks and F. L. Hermach, *Rev. Sci. Instr.*, vol. 26, no. 8, pp. 770–772, August, 1955.

65 I, I S, II — The Construction and Characteristics of Standard Cells, G. D. Vincent, *IRE Trans. Instr.*, vol. I-7, nos. 3, 4, pp. 221–234, December, 1958. This paper has an extensive list of references on standard cells.

66 II — A Simple Comparator for the Intercomparison of Unsaturated Standard Cells, R. C. Bean, *IRE Trans. Instr.*, vol. I-9, no. 3, pp. 313–314, December, 1960.

***67** II — Special Shielded Resistor for High-voltage D-c Measurements, J. H. Park, *J. Res. NBS*, vol. 66C, no. 1, pp. 19–24, January–March, 1962.

***68** I, II — Controlled Temperature Oil Baths for Saturated Standard Cells, P. H. Lowrie, *NBS Tech. Note* 141, August, 1962.

69 I, II — Oil Baths for Saturated Standard Cells, P. H. Lowrie, *ISA J.*, vol. 9, no. 12, pp. 47–50, December, 1962.

70 II — A Direct Reading Voltage Divider with Standard Cell Reference, R. P. McKnight, *IRE Trans. Instr.*, vol. I-11, nos. 3, 4, pp. 128–132, December, 1962.

71 II — A Method of Comparing Two Nearly Equal Potentials Directly in Parts per Million, C. J. Saunders, *Rev. Sci. Instr.*, vol. 34, no. 12, pp. 1452–1453, December, 1963.

***72** I, I S, II — The Operating Characteristics of Zener Reference Diodes and Their Measurements, W. G. Eicke, *ISA Trans.*, vol. 3, no. 2, pp. 93–99, April, 1964.

***73** I, I S, II — Making Precision Measurements of Zener Diode Voltages, W. G. Eicke, *IEEE Communication and Electronics*, vol. 83, no. 74, pp. 433–438, September, 1964.

***74** I, I S, II — Standard Cells, Their Construction, Maintenance, and Characteristics, W. J. Hamer, NBS Monograph 84, January, 1965.

***75** II — A System for Accurate Direct and Alternating Voltage Measurements, F. L. Hermach, J. E. Griffin, and E. S. Williams, *IEEE Trans. Instr. Meas.*, vol. IM-14, no. 4, pp. 215–224, December, 1965.

76 II — Control Chart for Saturated Standard Cells, R. B. F. Schumacher, *IEEE Trans. Instr. Meas.*, vol. IM-15, nos. 1, 2, pp. 6–8, March–June, 1966.

77 II — The Design and Operation of a High Voltage Calibration Facility, W. W. Scott, *NBS Tech. Note* 349, Nov. 10, 1966.

78 II — The Zener Diode, a Working D-C Voltage Standard, W. G. Eicke, *IEEE International Convention Digest*, March, 1968, p. 71.

79 I, I S, II — Reappraising the Zener Diode as a Reference and Transport Standard, W. G. Eicke, *Electronic Instrument Digest*, vol. 6, no 5, pp. 50–59, May, 1970.

80 I S, II — Truly Transportable Standard-cell Air Bath, D. W. Braudaway, *IEEE Trans. Instr. Meas.*, vol. IM-19, no. 4, pp. 263–266, November, 1970.

II
81 Dual Highly Stable 150-kV Divider, N. F. Ziegler, *IEEE Trans. Instr.*
I *Meas.*, vol. IM-19, no. 4, pp. 281–285, November, 1970.
I S
II
82 Solid State Voltage References, E. Hineman and J. Roberson, *Instruments*
I S *and Control Systems,* vol. 44, no. 3, pp. 133–135, March, 1971.
II
83 Possible New Effects in Superconductive Tunnelling, B. D. Josephson,
I *Physics Letters,* vol. 1, no. 7, pp. 251–253, July 1, 1962.
84 Determination of *e/h,* Using Microscopic Quantum Phase Coherence in
I Superconductors. I. Experiment, W. H. Parker, D. N. Langenberg, A. Denenstein, B. N. Taylor, *Physical Review,* vol. 177, no. 2, pp. 639–664, January, 1969.
85 A Measurement of 2 *e/h* by the AC Josephson Effect, B. W. Petley and
I K. Morris, *Metrologia,* vol. 6, no. 2, pp. 46–51, April, 1970.
86 Accurate Hamon-pair Potentiometer for Josephson Frequency-to-Voltage
I Measurements, F. K. Harris, H. A. Fowler, P. T. Olsen, *Metrologia,* vol. 6, no. 4, pp. 134–142, October, 1970.
87 Accurate Measurements of Josephson Junction Voltage, *NBS Tech. News*
I *Bull.* vol. 55, no. 1, p. 3, January, 1971.

DC RATIO

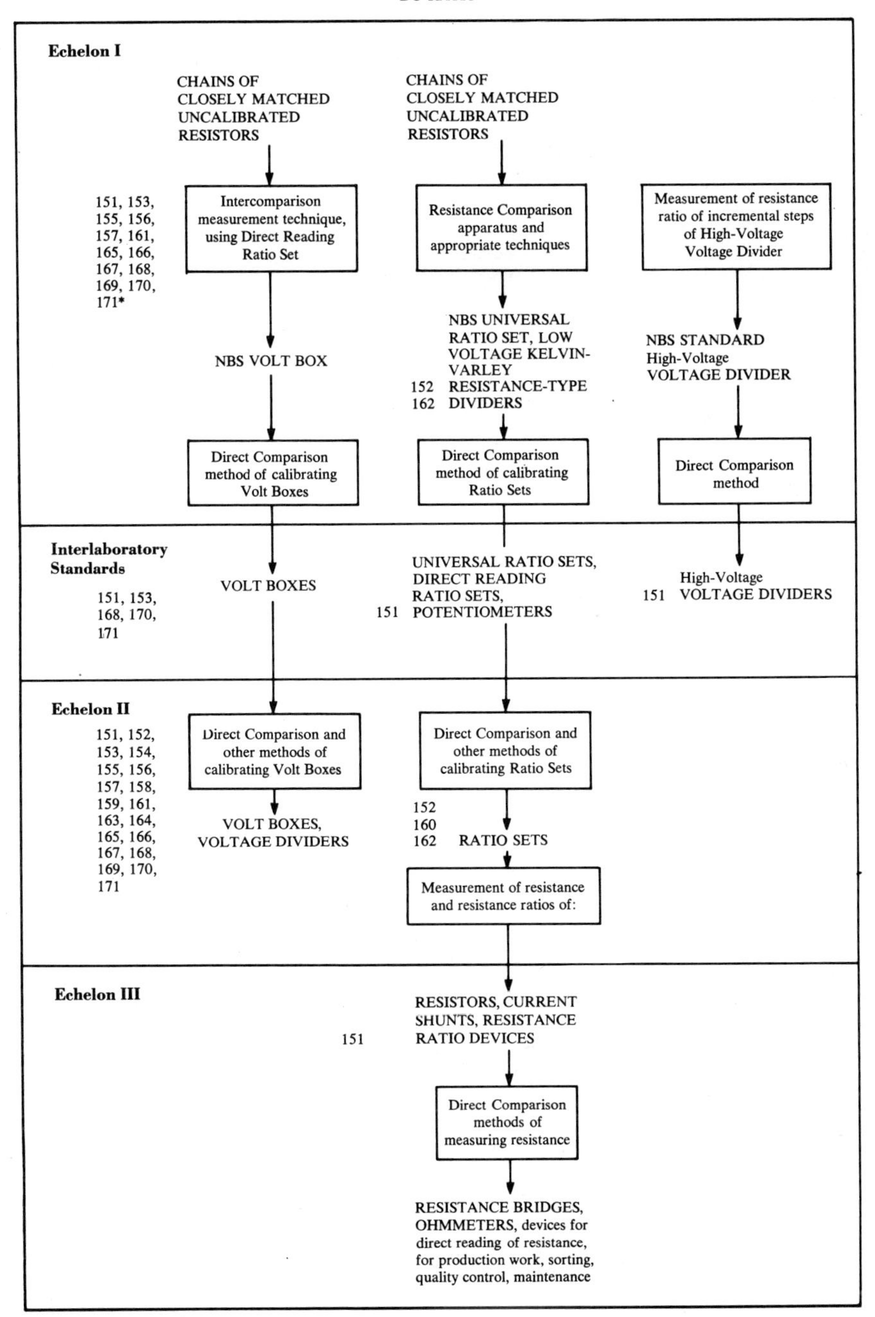

*These numbers refer to the list of references.

7. DC Ratio

151 I I S II III
Manufacturers of precision ratio sets, voltage dividers, and volt boxes usually have available, upon request, a variety of technical information on their products, as well as valuable informative literature on generalized and specialized topics of dc ratio equipment.

152 I II
Listed in *NBS Special Publication* 300, vol. 3, "Electricity—Low Frequency," are some laboratory notes, copies of which are available from the

Electricity Division
Institute of Basic Standards
National Bureau of Standards
Washington, D.C. 20234

By title, these are listed in *NBS Special Publication* 300, vol. 3, as follows:
1. Notes on the calibration of the direct-reading ratio set
2. Calibration of the universal ratio set

*****153*** I I S II
Testing and Performance of Volt Boxes, F. B. Silsbee and F. J. Gross, *J. Res. NBS,* vol. 27, no. 3, pp. 269–287, September, 1941.

154 II
Calibration of a Kelvin-Varley Standard Divider, M. L. Morgan and J. C. Riley, *IRE Trans. Instr.,* vol. I-9, no. 2, pp. 237–243, September, 1960.

****155*** I II
A Method of Controlling the Effect of Resistance in the Link Circuit of the Thomson or Kelvin Double Bridge, D. Ramaley, *J. Res. NBS,* vol. 64C, no. 4, pp. 267–270, October–December, 1960.

****156*** I II
Method for Calibrating a Standard Volt Box, B. L. Dunfee, *J. Res. NBS,* vol. 67C, no. 1, pp. 1–13, January–March, 1963.

****157*** I II
Calibration of Potentiometers by Resistance Bridge Methods, D. Ramaley, *Instruments and Control Systems,* vol. 37, no. 1, pp. 106–108, January, 1964.

158 II
Calibration of a Kelvin-Varley Voltage Divider, A. F. Dunn, *IEEE Trans. Instr. Meas.,* vol. IM-13, nos. 2, 3, pp. 129–139, June–September, 1964.

159 II
Design and Error Analysis of High-accuracy DC Voltage-measuring Systems, W. J. Karplus, *IEEE Trans. Instr. Meas.,* vol. IM-13, nos. 2, 3, pp. 139–145, June–September, 1964.

160 II
Some Modifications in Methods of Calibration of Universal Ratio Sets, D. Ramaley, *NBS Tech. Note* 220, Aug. 30, 1964.

****161*** I II
Human Engineering a Console for the Comparison of Volt Boxes, P. H. Lowrie, Jr., *ISA J.,* vol. 12, no. 7, pp. 67–71, July, 1965.

****162*** I II
Direct Ratio Readings from a URS (Universal Ratio Set), D. Ramaley and J. E. Shafer, *Instruments and Control Systems,* vol. 39, no. 1, pp. 73–74, January, 1966.

163 II
Ratiometric DC Calibration Technique, L. Julie, *Instruments and Control Systems,* vol. 39, no. 1, pp. 67–71, January, 1966.

****164*** II
A Method of Calibrating Volt Boxes, with an Analysis of Volt-box Self-heating Characteristics, R. F. Dziuba and T. M. Souders, *IEEE Convention Record,* March, 1966.

165 I II
Console for the Rapid Comparison of Volt Boxes, P. H. Lowrie, Jr., *J. Res. NBS,* vol. 70C, no. 3, pp. 173–185, July–September, 1966.

166 I II
A Versatile Ratio Instrument for the High Ratio Comparison of Voltage and Resistance, A. E. Hess, *J. Res. NBS,* vol. 70C, no. 3, pp. 169–172, July–September, 1966.

167 I II
Principles, Current Practice and Application of Potentiometers Based on Poggendorff's Second Method, A. Abramovitz, *Rev. Sci. Instr.,* vol. 38, no. 7, pp. 898–904, July, 1967.

168 I I S II
A New Type of Volt Box, R. Ohlon, *Metrologia,* vol. 5, no. 1, pp. 21–25, January, 1969.

169 I II Taking a Giant Step, Current-comparator Bridges and Potentiometers (the DC Current Comparator), J. Sutcliffe, *Electronic Instrument Digest,* vol. 5, no. 10, pp. 10–18, October, 1969.

170 I I S II The Julie-Dean Double Potentiometer, L. W. Dean and D. R. Ludwig, *Meas. and Data,* vol. 4, no. 1, pp. 74–80, January–February, 1970.

171 I I S II Resistive Voltage-Ratio Standard and Measuring Circuit, R. F. Dziuba and B. L. Dunfee, *IEEE Trans. Instr. Meas.,* vol. IM-19, no. 4, pp. 266–277, November, 1970.

AC-DC TRANSFER (LOW FREQUENCY VOLTAGE, OR CURRENT)

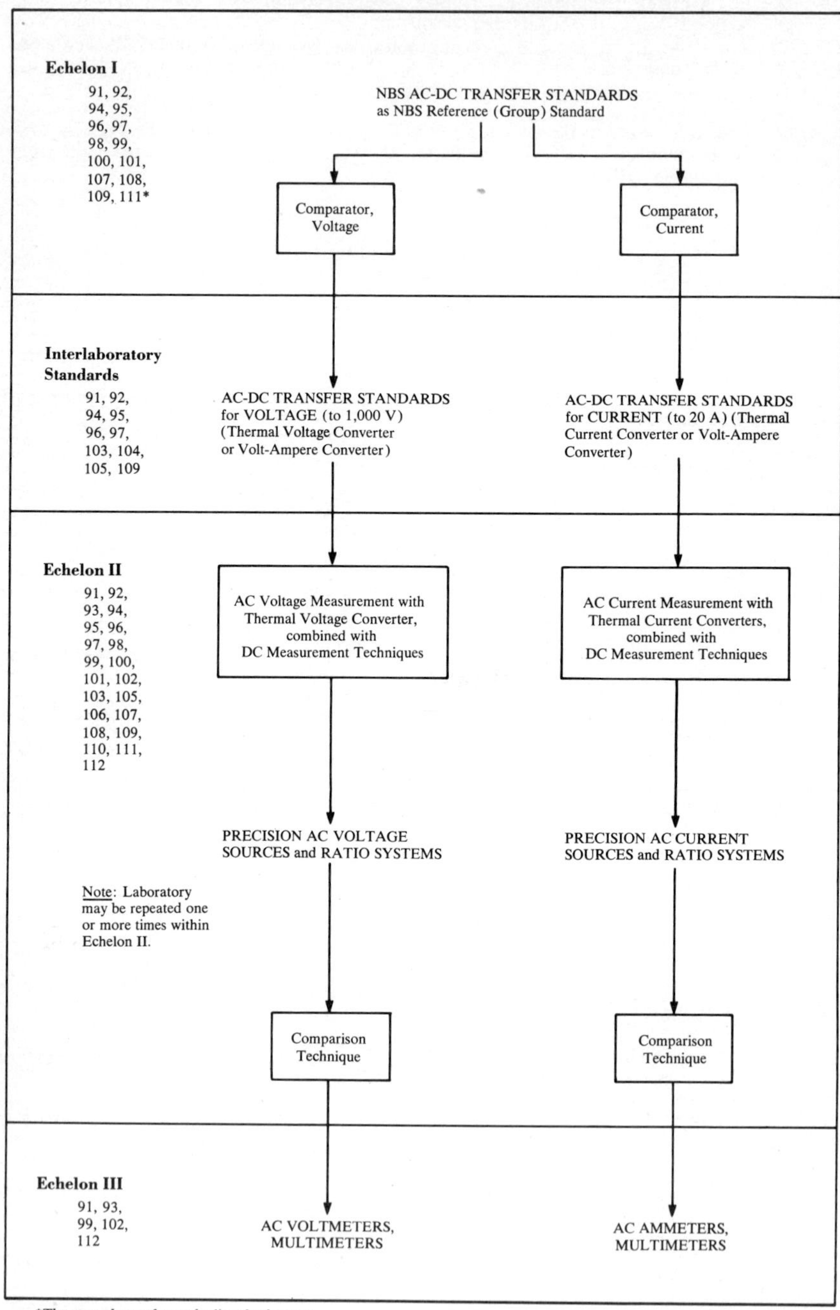

*These numbers refer to the list of references.

8. AC-DC Transfer (Low-frequency Voltage or Current)

91 I I S II III Manufacturers of thermal-voltage converters, thermal-current converters, and related equipment usually have available, upon request, a variety of technical information on their products as well as valuable and informative literature on generalized and specialized topics of ac-dc transfer standards and measurements.

**92 I I S II Thermal Converters as AC-DC Transfer Standards for Current and Voltage Measurements at Audio Frequencies, F. L. Hermach, *J. Res. NBS,* vol. 48, no. 2, pp. 121–138, February, 1952.

93 II III AC Measurements to 10,000 cps, F. D. Weaver, *Instruments,* vol. 25, no. 6, pp. 757, 798, 800, June, 1952.

94 I I S II Multirange Audio Frequency Thermocouple Instruments of High Accuracy, F. L. Hermach and E. S. Williams, *J. Res. NBS,* vol. 52, no. 5, pp. 227–234, May, 1954.

95 I I S II The Definition and Measurement of the Time Constant and Response Time of Thermal Converters, F. L. Hermach, *AIEE Trans.* (*Communication and Electronics*), vol. 77, pp. 277–283, July, 1958.

**96 *I I S II AC-DC Transfer Instruments for Current and Voltage Measurements, F. L. Hermach, *IRE Trans. Instr.,* vol. I-7, nos. 3, 4, pp. 235–240, December, 1958.

**97 I I S II A Wide-range Volt-ampere Converter for Current and Voltage Measurements, F. L. Hermach and E. S. Williams, *AIEE Trans.* (*Communication and Electronics*), vol. 78, pp. 384–388, September, 1959.

98 I II Thermal Voltage Converters for Accurate Voltage Measurements to 30 Megacycles per Second, F. L. Hermach and E. S. Williams, *AIEE Trans.* (*Communication and Electronics*), vol. 79, pp. 200–206, July, 1960.

99 I II III An Analysis of Errors in the Calibration of Electrical Instruments, F. L. Hermach, *AIEE Trans.* (*Communication and Electronics*), vol. 80, pp. 90–95, May, 1961.

**100* I II A Differential Thermocouple Voltmeter, J. E. Griffin and F. L. Hermach, *AIEE Trans.* (*Communication and Electronics*), vol. 81, pp. 339–344, November, 1962.

101 I II Calibration of Volt-ampere Converters, E. S. Williams, *NBS Tech. Note* 188, Apr. 25, 1963.

102 II III Modern AC Voltage Calibration for Audio and Sub-audio Frequencies, P. Richman, *ISA Conference Proc.,* vol. 19, part 1, preprint 21.4-2-64, 1964.

103 I S II Practical Aspects of the Use of AC-DC Transfer Instruments, E. S. Williams, *NBS Tech. Note* 257, Mar. 9, 1965.

104 I S Multijunction Thermal Converter, an Accurate d.c./a.c. Transfer Instrument, F. J. Wilkins, T. A. Deacon, and R. S. Becker, *Proc. IEE* (*London*), vol. 112, no. 4, pp. 794–805, April, 1965.

**105* I S II Calibration of Peak A-C to D-C Comparators, D. Flach and L. A. Marzetta, *ISA Conference Proc.,* vol. 20, part 1, preprint 14.2-3-65, 1965.

**106* II A System for Accurate Direct and Alternating Voltage Measurements, F. L. Hermach, J. E. Griffin, and E. S. Williams, *IEEE Trans. Instr. Meas.,* vol. IM-14, no. 4, pp. 215–224, December, 1965.

107 I II A Peak AC-DC Voltage Comparator for Use in a Standards Laboratory, L. A. Marzetta, *NBS Tech. Note* 280, Jan. 17, 1966.

**108* I II A Comparator for Thermal AC-DC Transfer Standards, R. S. Turgel, *ISA Conference Proc.,* vol. 21, part 1, preprint 12.3-1-66, 1966.

**109* Thermal Converters for Audio Frequency Voltage Measurements of High
I Accuracy, F. L. Hermach and E. S. Williams, *IEEE Trans. Instr. Meas.*,
I S vol. IM-15, no. 4, pp. 260–268, December, 1966.
II

110 A New Wideband True RMS-to-DC Converter, P. L. Richman, *IEEE*
II *Trans. Instr. Meas.*, vol. IM-16, no. 2, pp. 129–134, June, 1967.

111 Design Features of a Precision AC-DC Converter, L. A. Marzetta and
I D. R. Flach, *J. Res. NBS*, vol. 73C, nos. 3, 4, pp. 47–55, July–December,
II 1969.

112 How to Measure Low Frequency Current, C. Andren, *EEE*, vol. 18, no.
II 2, pp. 60–61, February, 1970.
III

AC RATIO (LOW FREQUENCY)

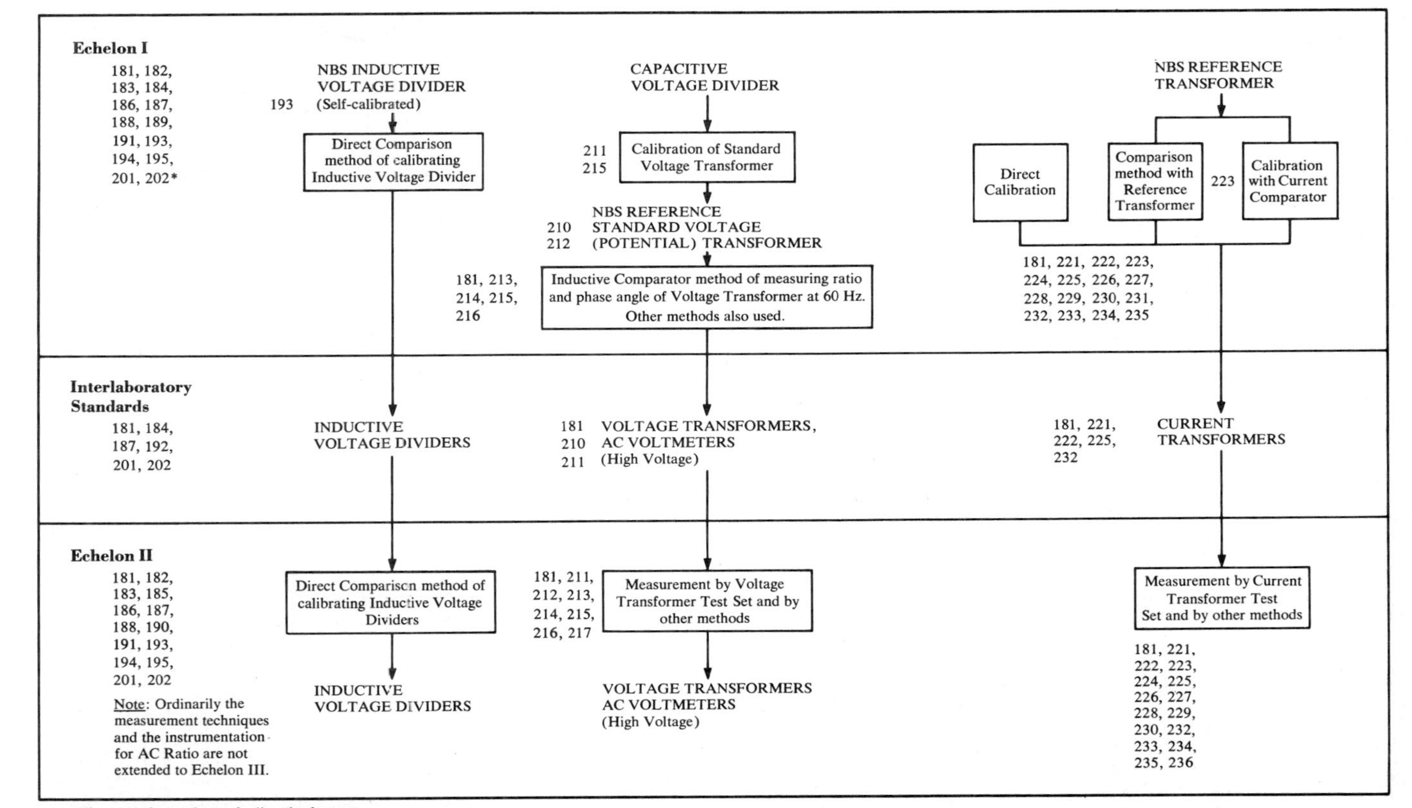

*These numbers refer to the list of references.

9. AC Ratio (Low-frequency)

181 I I S II — Manufacturers of inductive voltage dividers, voltage transformers, current transformers, and kilovoltmeters usually have available, upon request, a variety of technical information on their products, as well as valuable and informative literature on generalized and specialized topics of ac ratio devices suitable for standards and of measurement methods.

Inductive Voltage Dividers

182 I II — Calibration of Inductive Voltage Dividers, *NBS Tech. News Bull.*, vol. 45, no. 5, pp. 73–74, May, 1961.

183 I II — Voltage Ratio Measurements with a Transformer Capacitance Bridge, T. L. Zapf, *J. Res. NBS,* vol. 66C, no. 1, pp. 25–32, January–March, 1962.

184 I I S — A Seven-decade Adjustable-ratio Inductively-coupled Voltage Divider with 0.1 Part per Million Accuracy, J. J. Hill and A. P. Miller, *Proc. IEE* (*London*), vol. 109, part B (*Electronic and Communication Engineering*), pp. 157–164, March, 1962.

185 II — DC and Low Frequency AC Ratio Measurements, M. L. Morgan, *ESI Engineering Bull.* 29, September, 1962. Obtainable from Electro Scientific Industries, Portland, Ore.

186 I II — The Calibration of Inductive Voltage Dividers and Analysis of Their Operational Characteristics, T. L. Zapf, *ISA Trans.*, vol. 2, no. 3, pp. 195–201, July, 1963.

187 I I S II — Inductive Voltage Dividers with Calculable Relative Corrections, T. L. Zapf, C. H. Chinburg, H. K. Wolf, *IEEE Trans. Instr. Meas.*, vol. IM-12, no. 2, pp. 80–85, September, 1963.

188 I II — Comparison Calibration of Inductive Voltage Dividers, R. V. Lisle and T. L. Zapf, *ISA Trans.*, vol. 3, no. 3, pp. 238–242, July, 1964.

**189* I — An International Comparison of Inductive Voltage Divider Calibrations at 400 to 1000 Hz, W. C. Sze, A. F. Dunn, and T. L. Zapf, *IEEE Trans. Instr. Meas.*, vol. IM-14, no. 3, pp. 124–131, September, 1965.

190 II — Precise Voltage-ratio Measurement, T. L. Zapf, *Electro-Technology,* vol. 76, no. 4, pp. 95–102, October, 1965.

**191* I II — Comparator for Calibration of Inductive Voltage Dividers from 1 to 10 kHz, W. C. Sze, *ISA Conference Proc.*, vol. 21, part 1, preprint 12.3-2-66, 1966.

192 I S — Leakage Inductance and Interwinding Capacitance in Torroidal Ratio Transformers, A. J. Binnie and T. R. Foord, *IEEE Trans. Instr. Meas.*, vol. IM-16, no. 4, pp. 307–314, December, 1967.

193 I II — An Injection Method for Self-calibration of Inductive Voltage Dividers, W. C. Sze, *J. Res. NBS,* vol. 72C, no. 1, pp. 49–59, January–March, 1968.

194 I II — Voltage-ratio Measurement with a Precision of Parts in 10^9 and Performance of Inductive Voltage Dividers, J. J. Hill and T. A. Deacon, *IEEE Trans. Instr. Meas.*, vol. IM-17, no. 4, pp. 269–278, December, 1968.

195 I II — Isolated-section Inductive Divider and Its Self-calibration, T. Nakase, *IEEE Trans. Instr. Meas.*, vol. IM-19, no. 4, pp. 312–317, November, 1970.

Within the past several years NBS Boulder has had considerable success in the development of inductive voltage dividers up to a frequency of 1 MHz. Although these voltage dividers are operating much above 30 kHz, the upper limit of the range of low-frequency standards, they have been included with references on low-frequency standards and measurements.

**201* I I S II — A 2-1 Ratio Inductive Voltage Divider with Less than 0.1 ppm Error to 1 MHz, C. A. Hoer and W. L. Smith, *J. Res. NBS,* vol. 71C, no. 2, pp. 101–109, April–June, 1967.

202 I — A 1-MHz Binary Inductive Voltage Divider with Ratios of 2 n to 1 or 6 ndB, C. A. Hoer and W. L. Smith, *IEEE Trans. Instr. Meas.*, vol.

I S II IM-17, no. 4, pp. 278–284, December, 1968.

Voltage Transformers

**210 I I S — The Measurement of High Voltage, F. M. Defandorf, *J. Washington Academy of Science,* vol. 38, no. 2, pp. 33–60, February, 1948. This paper has an extensive list of references.

211 I I S II — "Electrical Measurements," pp. 564–576, 599–615, F. K. Harris, John Wiley & Sons, Inc., New York, 1951.

212 I II — The Absolute Calibration of Voltage Transformers, W. K. Clothier and L. Medina, *Proc. IEE (London),* vol. 104A, pp. 204–214, 1957.

*213 I II — The Precision Measurement of Transformer Ratios, R. D. Cutkosky and J. Q. Shields, *IRE Trans. Instr.,* vol. I-9, no. 2, pp. 243–250, September, 1960.

214 I II — Adjustable Complex-ratio Transformer, P. N. Miljanic, *IEEE Trans. Instr. Meas.,* vol. IM-14, no. 3, pp. 135–141, September, 1965.

*215 I II — Comparators for Voltage Transformer Calibrations at NBS, W. C. Sze, *J. Res. NBS,* vol. 69C, no. 4, pp. 257–263, October–December, 1965.

216 I II — The Design and Operation of a High Voltage Calibration Facility, W. W. Scott, Jr., *NBS Tech. Note* 349, November, 1966.

217 II — Four-Terminal Equal-power Transformer-ratio-arm Bridge, H. P. Hall, *IEEE Trans. Instr. Meas.,* vol. IM-19, no. 4, pp. 308–311, November, 1970.

Current Transformers

221 I I S II — "Electrical Measurements," pp. 542–564, 576–599, F. K. Harris, John Wiley & Sons, Inc., New York, 1951.

222 I I S II — A Standard Current Transformer and Comparison Method—A Basis for Establishing Ratios of Currents at Audio Frequencies, B. L. Dunfee, *IRE Trans. Instr.,* vol. I-9, no. 2, pp. 231–236, September, 1960.

223 I II — The Current Comparator and Its Application to the Absolute Calibration of Current Transformers, N. L. Kusters and W. J. M. Moore, *AIEE Trans.* (Power Apparatus and System), vol. 80, pp. 94–104, April, 1961.

224 I II — The Development of the Current Comparator, a High-accuracy AC Ratio Measuring Device, P. N. Miljanic, N. L. Kusters, and W. J. M. Moore, *AIEE Trans.* (*Communication and Electronics*), vol. 81, pp. 359–368, November, 1962.

225 I I S II — The Design and Performance of High Precision Audio-frequency Current Transformers, J. J. Hill, *IRE Trans. Instr.,* vol. I-11, nos. 3, 4, pp. 109–114, December, 1962.

226 I II — The Precise Measurement of Current Ratios, N. L. Kusters, *IEEE Trans. Inst. Meas.,* vol. IM-13, no. 4, pp. 197–209, December, 1964.

227 I II — Capacitive Error in Current Comparators, P. N. Miljanic, *IEEE Trans. Instr. Meas.,* vol. IM-13, no. 4, pp. 210–216, December, 1964.

228 I II — Audio Frequency Current Comparator for Instrument Transformer Calibration, J. H. Park, *IEEE Trans. Instr. Meas.,* vol. IM-13, no. 4, pp. 251–258, December, 1964.

229 I II — Adjustable Complex-ratio Transformer, P. N. Miljanic, *IEEE Trans. Instr. Meas.,* vol. IM-14, no. 3, pp. 135–141, September, 1965.

230 I II — The Development and Performance of Current Comparators for Audio Frequencies, N. L. Kusters and W. J. M. Moore, *IEEE Trans. Instr. Meas.,* vol. IM-14, no. 4, pp. 178–190, December, 1965.

*231 — An International Comparison of Current-ratio Standards at Audio Frequen-

I cies, B. L. Dunfee and W. J. M. Moore, *IEEE Trans. Instr. Meas.*, vol. IM-14, no. 4, pp. 172–177, December, 1965.

232 I I S II The Design and Performance of Multirange Current Transformer Standards for Audio Frequencies, B. L. Dunfee, *IEEE Trans. Instr. Meas.*, vol. IM-14, no. 4, pp. 190–204, December, 1965.

*233 I II Electrical Standards and Measurements, I. L. Cooter, B. L. Dunfee, F. K. Harris, W. P. Harris, F. L. Hermach, and C. Peterson, *Electro-Technology,* vol. 79, no. 1, pp. 53–70, January, 1967.

234 I II The Application of Current Comparators to the Calibration of Current Transformers at Ratios up to 36,000/5 Amperes, P. N. Miljanic, N. L. Kusters, and W. J. M. Moore, *IEEE Trans. Instr. Meas.*, vol. IM-17, no. 3, pp. 196–203, September, 1968.

235 I II The Application of the Compensated Current Comparator to the Calibration of Current Transformers at Ratios Less than Unity, M. L. Kusters and W. J. M. Moore, *IEEE Trans. Instr. Meas.*, vol. IM-18, no. 4, pp. 261–265, December, 1969.

236 II Four-terminal Equal-power Transformer-ratio-arm Bridge, H. P. Hall, *IEEE Trans. Instr. Meas.*, vol. IM-19, no. 4, pp. 308–311, November, 1970.

CAPACITANCE AND INDUCTANCE (LOW FREQUENCY)

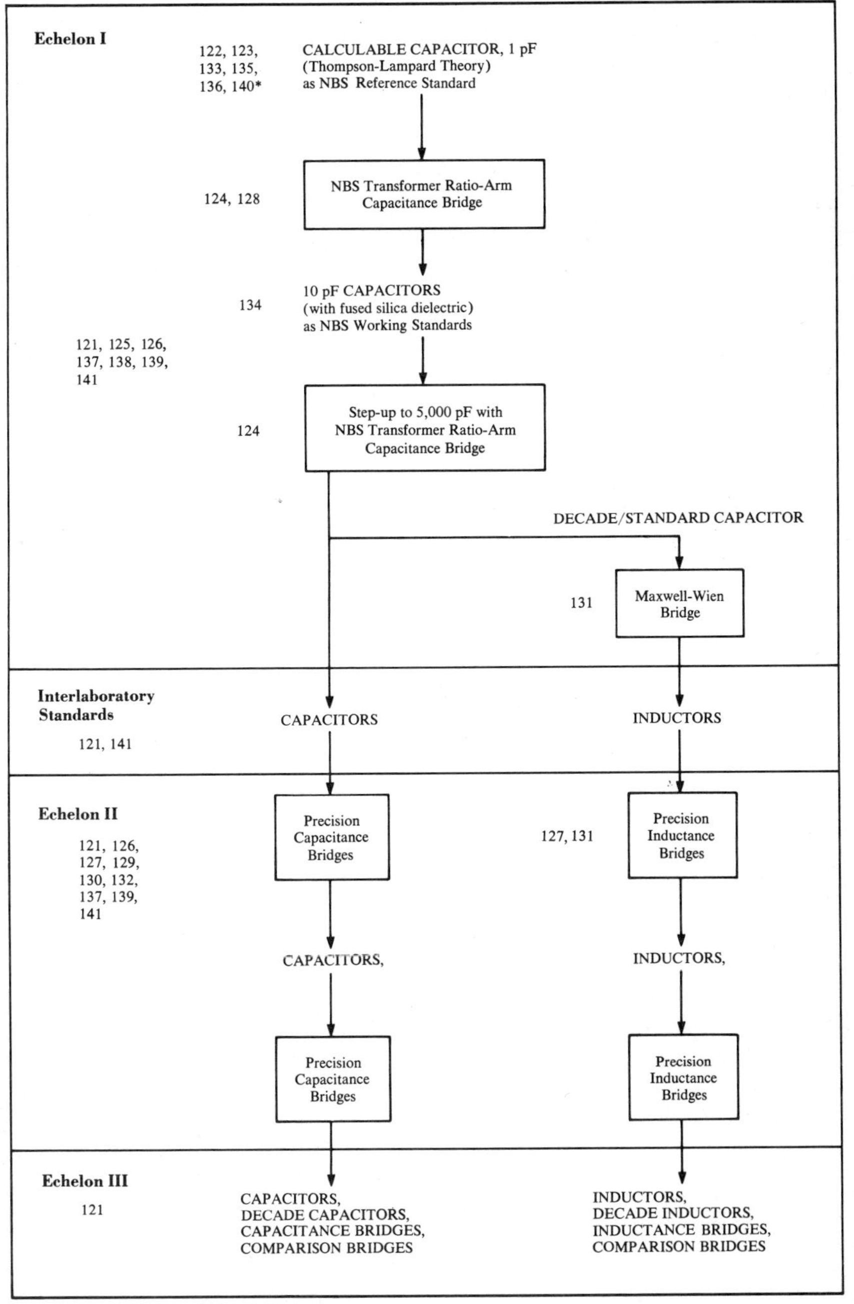

*These numbers refer to the list of references.

10. Capacitance and Inductance (Low-frequency)

121 I I S II III Manufacturers of precision capacitors and inductors and related measurement equipment usually have available, upon request, a variety of technical information on their products as well as valuable informative literature on generalized and specialized topics of capacitance and inductance standards and measurements.

122 I A New Theorem in Electrostatics and Its Application to Calculable Standards of Capacitance, A. M. Thompson and D. G. Lampard, *Nature,* vol. 177, no. 4515, p. 888, May, 1956.

123 I A New Theorem in Electrostatics and Its Application to Calculable Standards of Capacitance, D. G. Lampard, *Proc. IEE (London)*, vol. 104, part C, no. 6, pp. 271–280, September, 1957.

124 I New Apparatus at the National Bureau of Standards for Absolute Capacitance Measurement, M. C. McGregor, J. F. Hersh, R. D. Cutkosky, F. K. Harris, and F. R. Kotter, *IRE Trans. Instr.,* vol. I-7, nos. 3, 4, pp. 253–261, December, 1958.

125 I The Derivation of Resistance, Inductance, and Capacitance from the NPL Primary Standard of Mutual Inductance, G. H. Rayner, *IRE Trans. Instr.,* vol. I-7, nos. 3, 4, pp. 212–220, December, 1958.

126 I II The Precise Measurement of Small Capacitances, A. M. Thompson, *IRE Trans. Instr.,* vol. I-7, nos. 3, 4, pp. 245–253, December, 1958.

127 II A Bridge for the Precision Measurement of Inductance, J. F. Hersh, *General Radio Experimenter,* vol. 33, no. 11, pp. 3–9, November, 1959.

128 I The Precision Measurement of Transformer Ratios, R. D. Cutkosky and J. Q. Shields, *IRE Trans. Instr.,* vol. I-9, no. 2, pp. 243–250, September, 1960.

**129* II Capacitor Calibration by Step-up Methods, T. L. Zapf, *J. Res. NBS,* vol. 64C, no. 1, pp. 75–79, January–March, 1960.

130 II Variable Capacitor Calibration with an Inductive Voltage Divider Bridge, T. L. Zapf, *NBS Tech. Note* 57, May, 1960.

**131* I II Calibration of Inductance Standards in the Maxwell-Wien Bridge Circuit, T. L. Zapf, *J. Res. NBS,* vol. 65C, no. 3, pp. 183–188, July–September, 1961.

132 II Accuracy, Precision, and Convenience for Capacitance Measurements, J. F. Hersh, *General Radio Experimenter,* vol. 36, nos. 8, 9, pp. 3–14, August–September, 1962.

133 I A Calculable Standard of Capacitance, W. K. Clothier, *Metrologia,* vol. 1, no. 2, pp. 36–55, 1965.

**134* I Improved Ten-picofarad Fused Silica Dielectric Capacitor, R. D. Cutkosky and L. H. Lee, *J. Res. NBS,* vol. 69C, no. 3, pp. 173–179, July–September, 1965.

**135* I Voltage Dependence of Precision Air Capacitors, J. Q. Shields, *J. Res. NBS,* vol. 69C, no. 4, pp. 265–274, October–December, 1965.

136 I Determination of an Absolute Capacitance by a Horizontal Cross Capacitor, T. Igarashi, Y. Koizumi, and M. Kanno, *IEEE Trans. Instr. Meas.,* vol. IM-17, no. 4, pp. 226–231, December, 1968.

137 I II A Varactor Null Detector for Audio Frequency Capacitance Bridges, R. D. Cutkosky, *IEEE Trans. Instr. Meas.,* vol. IM-17, no. 4, pp. 232–238, December, 1968.

138 I A New Computable Capacitor, D. Makow, *Metrologia,* vol. 5, no. 4, pp. 126–128, October, 1969.

139 I II Ratio Comparisons of Impedance Standards, A. F. Dunn and S. H. Tsao, *IEEE Trans. Instr. Meas.,* vol. IM-18, no. 4, pp. 276–283, December, 1969.

140 I Improved Horizontal Cross Capacitor, T. Igarashi, M. Kanno, Y. Koizumi, and K. Handea, *IEEE Trans. Instr. Meas.,* vol. IM-19, no. 4, pp. 297–302, November, 1970.

141 I I S II New Fused-silica-dielectric 10- and 100-pF Capacitors and a System for Their Measurement, D. Abenaim and J. H. Hersh, *IEEE Trans. Instr. Meas.,* vol. IM-19, no. 4, pp. 302–307, November, 1970.

POWER AND ENERGY (DC AND LOW FREQUENCY)

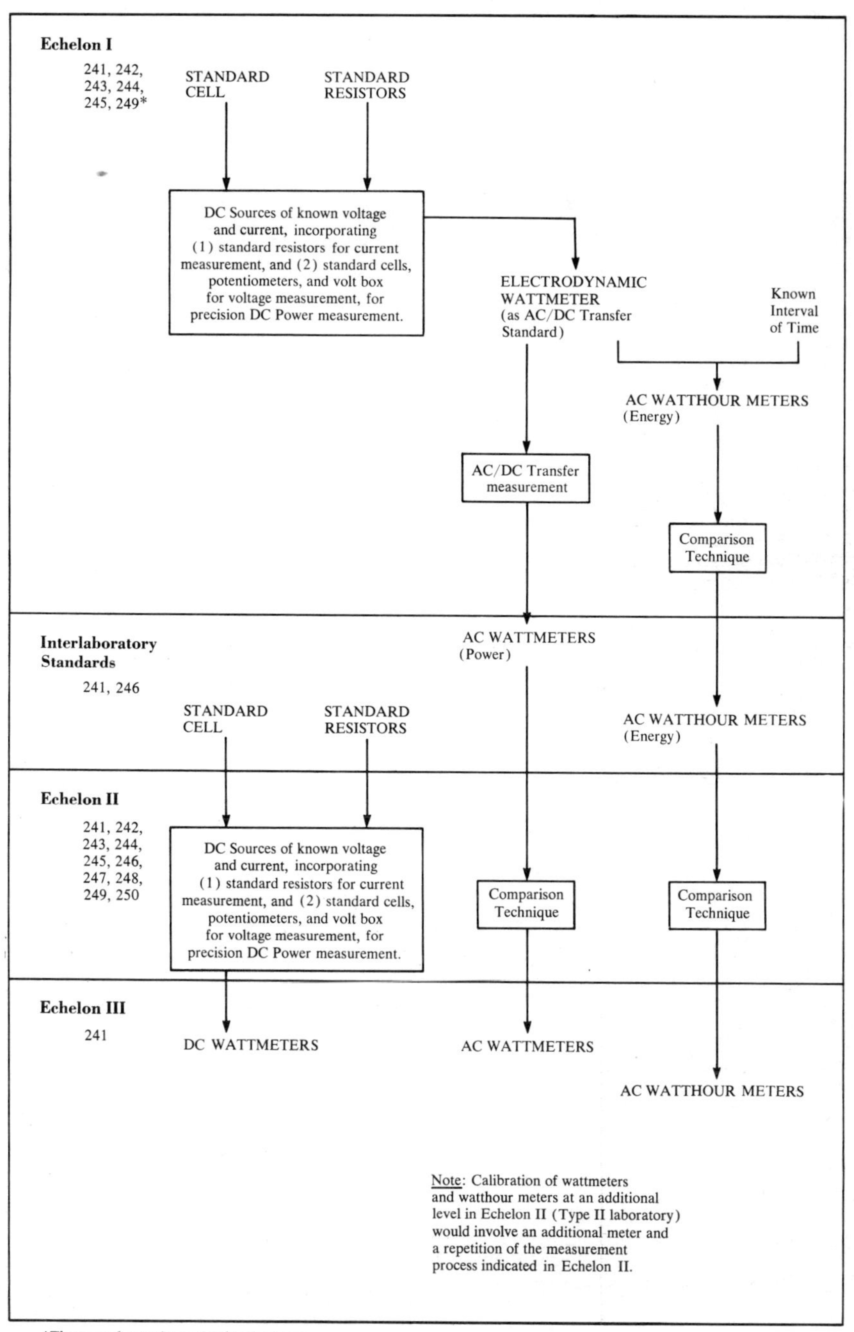

*These numbers refer to the list of references.

11. Power and Energy (DC and Low-frequency)

241 I, I S, II, III — Manufacturers of wattmeters and watthour meters usually have available, upon request, a variety of technical information on their products as well as valuable informative literature on generalized and specialized topics of power measurements and precision power-measurement equipment.

**242 I, II — Standard Electrodynamic Wattmeter and AC-DC Transfer Instrument, J. H. Park and A. B. Lewis, *J. Res. NBS,* vol. 25, no. 5, pp. 545–579, November, 1940.

243 I, II — A Precision Electrodynamometer Standard and A.C./D.C. Transfer Instrument, J. W. Whittaker, *Proc. IEE (London),* vol. 101, part II, pp. 11–20, February, 1954.

244 I, II — Lead Resistance Errors in Watthour Meter Tests, F. L. Hermach and T. L. Zapf, *Electrical World,* vol. 141, no. 16, pp. 113–114, April, 1954.

**245 I, II — Precision Comparison Method of Testing Alternating-current Watthour Meters, A. W. Spinks and T. L. Zapf, *J. Res. NBS,* vol. 53, no. 2, pp. 95–105, August, 1954.

246 I S, II — A Precision Thermo-electric Wattmeter for Power and Audio Frequencies, J. J. Hill, *Proc. IEE (London),* vol. 105, no. 19 (part B, *Radio and Electronic Engineering*), pp. 61–68, January, 1958.

247 II — An Interim Report on the Inductronic Electrodynamometer for the Precise Measurement of Voltage, Current, and Energy, R. F. Estoppey, *IRE Trans. Instr.,* vol. I-7, nos. 3, 4, pp. 241–245, December, 1958.

248 II — Watthour Calibrator Refers Directly to DC Volt and Amps., R. F. Estoppey, *Electrical World,* vol. 160, no. 25, pp. 101, 103, Dec. 16, 1963.

249 I, II — Precision Measuring Equipment for Electrical Power in the Range of Audio Frequencies, R. Friedl and G. Wolf, *IEEE Trans. Instr. Meas.,* vol. IM-15, no. 4, pp. 227–233, December, 1966.
See reference list on p. 233 of this paper for additional references on power measurements.

250 II — A New DC-AC Digital Power and Energy Meter, F. Bombi and D. Ciscato, *IEEE Trans. Instr. Meas.,* vol. IM-19, no. 1, pp. 57–61, February, 1970.

DC and Low-Frequency

GENERAL REFERENCES

261 Basis of Standardization of Electrical Instruments and Meters, F. B. Silsbee, *Electrical World,* vol. 130, no. 21, pp. 90–93, Nov. 20, 1948.

**262 Notes on the Care and Use of Electrical Instruments, F. D. Weaver, *Instruments,* vol. 23, no. 12, pp. 1236–1239, December, 1950.

263 A-C Measurements to 10,000 cps, F. D. Weaver, *Instruments,* vol. 25, no. 6, pp. 757, 798, 800, June, 1952.

264 "Electrical Measurements," F. K. Harris, John Wiley & Sons, Inc., New York, 1952.

265 "Electronic Measurements," F. E. Terman and J. M. Pettit, McGraw-Hill Book Company, New York, 1952.

**266 Testing Electrical Instruments, F. D. Weaver, *Instruments,* vol. 26, no. 9, pp. 1362–1363, 1408–1410, 1412, September, 1953.

**267 Scale and Reading Errors of Electrical Indicators, F. D. Weaver, *Instruments and Automation,* vol. 27, no. 11, pp. 1812–1814, November, 1954.

***268 Suggested Practices for Electrical Standardizing Laboratories, F. B. Silsbee, *NBS Circ.* 578, Aug. 30, 1956.

269 "Applied Electrical Measurements," I. F. Kinnard, John Wiley & Sons, Inc., New York, 1956.

270 "Principles of Electronic Instruments," G. R. Partridge, Prentice-Hall, Inc., Englewood Cliffs, N.J., 1958.

271 How to Make Basic D-C Measurements—1, J. B. Kelley, *Electrical Manufacturing,* vol. 65, no. 5, pp. 224–237, May, 1960.

272 "Electrical Measurements and Their Application," E. Frank, McGraw-Hill Book Company, New York, 1959.

273 "Handbook of Electrical Measurements," edited by M. H. Aronson, published by Instrument Publishing Co., Inc., 845 Ridge Ave., Pittsburgh, Pa., 1960.

274 "Basic Electrical Measurements," M. B. Stout, Prentice-Hall, Inc., Englewood Cliffs, N.J., 1960.

275 How to Make Basic D-C Measurements—2, J. B. Kelley, *Electro-Technology,* vol. 67, no. 4, pp. 138–147, April, 1961.

276 An Analysis of Errors in the Calibration of Electric Instruments, F. L. Hermach, *AIEE Trans.* (*Communication and Electronics*), vol. 80, pp. 90–95, May, 1961.

277 Basic Low-frequency A-C Measurements—1, J. B. Kelley, *Electro-Technology,* vol. 71, no. 5, pp. 129–139, May, 1963.

278 Basic Low-frequency A-C Measurements—2, J. B. Kelley, *Electro-Technology,* vol. 71, no. 6, pp. 103–108, June, 1963.

**279* Achievement of Measurement Agreement among Electrical Standards Laboratories, F. D. Weaver, *Instruments and Control Systems,* vol. 36, no. 7, pp. 128–131, July, 1963.

280 Low-frequency Electrical Calibrations at the National Bureau of Standards, F. L. Hermach, *NBS Misc. Publ.* 248, pp. 31–36, Aug. 16, 1963. (Paper 1.5, *Proceedings of the 1962 Standards Laboratory Conference.*)

281 "Electrical Measurements and Instrumentation," D. Bartholomew, Allyn and Bacon, Inc. Boston, 1963.

282 AC Measurements Using Ratio Techniques, J. C. Riley, *ISA Conference Proc.,* vol. 19, part I, preprint 21.5-2-64, 1964.

283 Accuracy in Measurements and Calibrations, *NBS Tech. Note* 262 edited, by W. A. Wildhack, R. C. Powell, and H. L. Mason, June 15, 1965.

284 Electrical Measurement Standards (a Review of the Test and Calibration Services of NBS in the Area of Electrical Measurements), *Instruments and Control Systems,* vol. 39, no. 1, pp. 59–65, January, 1966.

**285* Electrical Standards and Measurements, I. L. Cooter, B. L. Dunfee, F. R. Harris, W. P. Harris, F. L. Hermach, and C. Peterson, *Electro-Technology,* vol. 79, no. 1, pp. 55–70, January, 1967.

286 A variety of short papers on instruments, measurements, and related subjects, including electrical measurements, appears in the periodical *Measurements and Data, the Journal of the Precision Measurements Association.* It is published bimonthly by the Measurements and Data Corporation, 1687 Washington Road, Pittsburgh, Pa., 15228. Vol. 1 began with the January–February, 1967, issue.

**287* Electrical Calibration Accuracies at NBS, F. L. Hermach, *Instrumentation Technology,* vol. 14, no. 11, pp. 63–66, November, 1967.

288 Low-frequency Electrical Calibrations at the National Bureau of Standards, F. L. Hermach, *ISA Conference Proc.,* vol. 22, part I, preprint M5-1-MESTIND-67, 1967.

289 "Grounding and Shielding Techniques in Instrumentation," R. Morrison, John Wiley & Sons, Inc., New York, 1967.

290 "Handbook of Electronic Instruments and Measurement Techniques," H. E. Thomas and C. A. Clarke, Prentice-Hall, Inc., Englewood Cliffs, N.J., 1967.

291 "Experimental Backgrounds for Electronic Instrumentation," W. L. Erickson and C. V. Wells, Laboratory Systems Research, Inc., Boulder, Colo., 1968. This book has many lists of references relating to direct-current and low-frequency measurements.

292 "Precision DC Measurements and Standards," D. S. Luppold, Addison-Wesley Publishing Company, Inc., Reading, Mass., 1969.

293 "Electronic Instrumentation and Measurement Techniques," W. D. Cooper, Prentice-Hall, Inc., Englewood Cliffs, N.J., 1970.
Although some radio-frequency instruments are described, most of the measurement techniques relate to dc and low frequency.

294 Recent Developments in AC Metrology, I. Malcolm, *Electronic Instrument Digest,* vol. 6, no. 4, pp. 51–57, April, 1970.

295 "A. C. Bridge Methods," 6th edition, B. Hague, revised by T. R. Foord, Sir Isaac Pitman & Sons, Ltd., London, 1971.

296 A New Universal Automated Electronic Testing System, L. Julie, paper
II 716–70, *Proc. 25th Ann. ISA Conf.,* vol. 25, part 3, October, 1970.
III

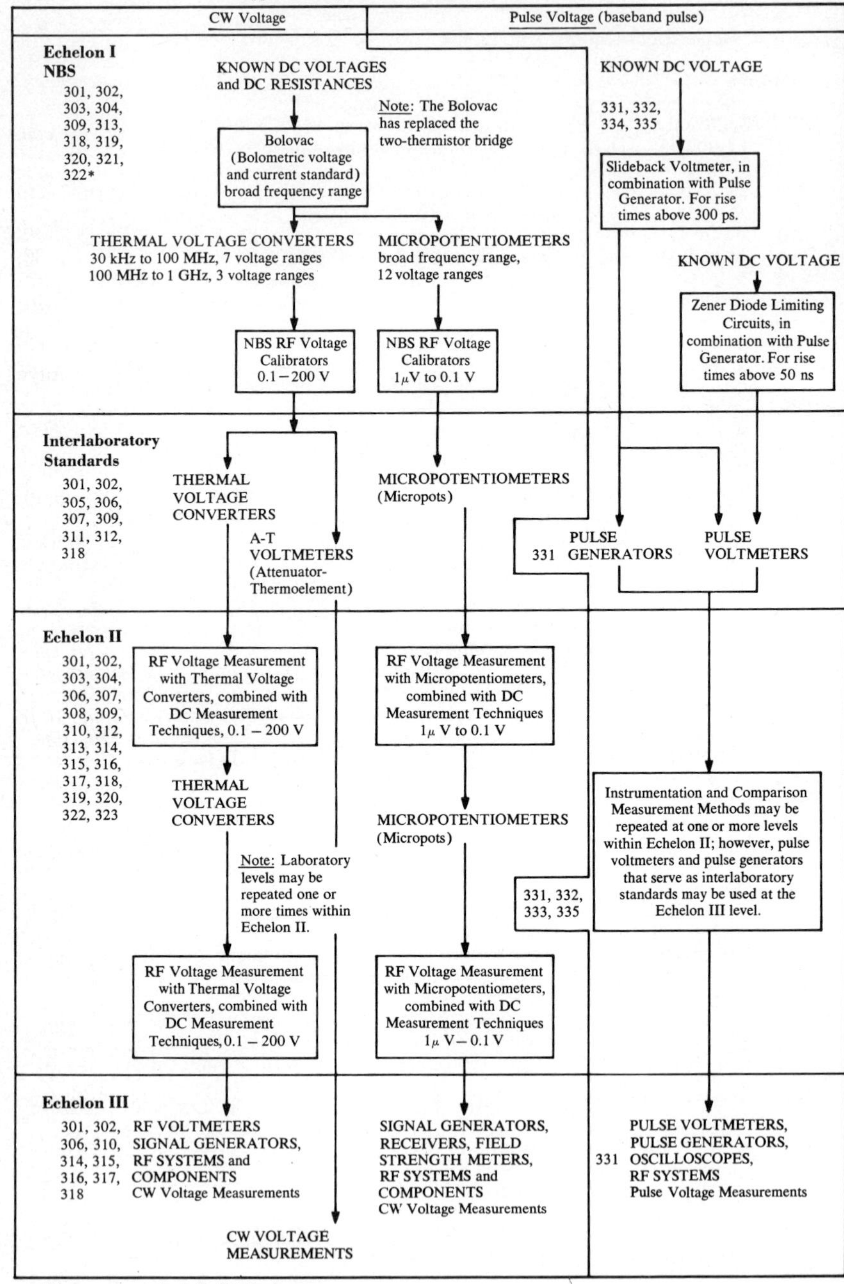

*These numbers refer to the list of references.

CHARTS OF BASIC ELECTRONIC STANDARDS AND TRACEABILITY (APPROXIMATELY 30 kHz TO 1 GHz, COAXIAL CONNECTORS)

12. Voltage

CW Voltage

301 I, I S, II, III — Manufacturers of laboratory-type radio-frequency equipment usually have available, upon request, a variety of technical information on their products, as well as informative literature on specialized topics of apparatus (with coaxial connectors) suitable for cw voltage standards and measurements.

302 I, I S, II, III — High-frequency Voltage Measurement, M. C. Selby, *NBS Circ.* 481, Sept. 1, 1949.

303 I, II — A Bolometer Bridge for Standardizing Radio-frequency Voltmeters, M. C. Selby and L. F. Behrent, *J. Res. NBS*, vol. 44, no. 1, pp. 15–30, January, 1950.

304 I, II — Accurate Radio-frequency Microvoltages, M. C. Selby, *AIEE (Communication and Electronics)*, vol. 72, pp. 158–164, May, 1953.

305 I S — Fabrication of Radio-frequency Micropotentiometer Resistance Elements, L. F. Behrent, *J. Res. NBS*, vol. 51, no. 1, pp. 1–9, July, 1953.

306 I S, II, III — R. F. Potentiometers, M. C. Selby, *Radio and Television News*, vol. 50, no. 4, pp. 5–7, October, 1953.

307 I S, II — Stable Radio-frequency Voltmeters, *NBS Tech. News Bull.*, vol. 40, no. 2, pp. 29–30, February, 1956.

308 II — Measurement of Voltage and Current, B. Rudner, chap. I, 2.1–2.52 of "Handbook of Electronic Measurements," vol. 1 (M. Wind, editor), Polytechnic Press, Polytechnic Institute of Brooklyn, Brooklyn, N.Y., 1956.

309 I, I S, II — RF Voltmeter Calibrating Consoles, M. C. Selby, L. F. Behrent, and F. X. Ries, *IRE National Convention Record*, vol. VI, part 5, pp. 251–257, 1958.

310 II, III — Application of RF Potentiometers for Calibration of Signal Generators to 1000 MC, L. F. Behrent, *NBS Tech. Note* 37, January, 1960.

311 I S — Thermal Voltage Converters for Accurate Voltage Measurements to 30 Megacycles per Second, F. L. Hermach and E. S. Williams, *AIEE Trans. (Communication and Electronics)*, vol. 79, pp. 200–206, July, 1960.

312 I S, II — Techniques and Errors in High-frequency Voltage Calibration, E. Uiga and W. F. White, *IRE Trans. Instr.*, vol. I-9, no. 2, pp. 274–279, September, 1960.

313 I, II — Functional and Design Problems of the NBS RF Voltage Bridge, L. F. Behrent, *NBS Tech. Note* 123, January, 1961.

314 II, III — An RF Voltage Standard for Receiver Calibration, G. U. Sorger, B. O. Weinschel, and A. L. Hedrich, *IRE Trans. Instr.*, vol. I-10, no. 1, pp. 9–17, June, 1961.

315 II, III — Precision Calibration of RF Vacuum Tube Voltmeters, L. F. Behrent, *NBS Tech. Note* 121, December, 1961.

316 II, III — Improving the Accuracy of RF Voltage Measurements, R. E. Lafferty, *Electronic Ind.*, vol. 22, no. 7, pp. 87–91, July, 1963.

317 II, III — Radio-frequency Voltage Measurement, B. P. Hand, *Electro-Technology*, vol. 72, no. 4, pp. 109–116, October, 1963.

318 Voltmeter Calibration to 1 GHz, M. C. Selby, W. J. Blank, and R. P.
I Chariton, Paper 8.8, *IEEE WESCON Tech. Papers,* vol. 9, part 6, *Instr.*
I S *Meas.,* pp. 1–12, August, 1965.
II
III

**319* Voltage Measurement at High and Microwave Frequencies in Coaxial Sys-
I tems, M. C. Selby, *Proc. IEEE,* vol. 55, no. 6, pp. 877–882, June, 1967.
II This paper has a fairly extensive list of references on voltage standards and measurements at the lower radio-frequency range.

320 Calibration of Thermal Transfer Standards of RF Voltage, R. F. Clark
I and A. P. Jurkus, *IEEE Trans. Instr. Meas.,* vol. IM-16, no. 3, pp. 232–237,
II September, 1967.

321 The Bolovac, Voltage and Current Measurements to 10 GHz, *NBS Tech.*
I *News Bull.,* vol. 51, no. 12, pp. 270–271, December, 1967.

322 Bolometric Voltage and Current (Bolovac) Standard for High and Micro-
I wave Frequencies, M. C. Selby, *J. Res. NBS,* vol. 72C, no. 1, pp. 61–79,
II January–March, 1968.

323 A Wideband RF Voltmeter-comparator, L. D. Driver and M. G. Arthur,
II *IEEE Trans. Instr. Meas.,* vol. IM-17, no. 2, pp. 146–150, June, 1968.

Pulse Voltage (baseband pulse)*

Accurate standards and accurate measurements of pulse voltage are dependent upon precise pulse terminology, an area that is in need of updating. For available information on terminology the reader is referred to the following sources:

1. Standards on Pulses—Definitions of Terms, part I, 1951, *Proc. IRE,* vol. 39, no. 6, pp. 624–626, June, 1951.
2. Standards on Pulses—Definitions of Terms, part II, 1952, *Proc. IRE,* vol. 40, no. 5, pp. 552–554, May, 1952.
3. IRE Standards on Pulses, Methods of Measurement of Pulse Quantities, 1955, *Proc. IRE,* vol. 43, no. 11, part 1, pp. 1610–1616, November, 1955.
4. The New Pulse—A Glossary of Proposed Standard Pulse Definitions, J. C. Hubbs, E-H Research Laboratories, Inc., Oakland, Calif., Sept. 1, 1965, revised Jan. 15, 1966.

331 Manufacturers of laboratory-type radio-frequency equipment usually have
I available, upon request, a variety of technical information on their products.
I S Some manufacturers have informative literature on specialized types of
II apparatus (with coaxial connectors) suitable for pulse voltage standards
III and measurements.

332 Measurement Standards for Low and Medium Peak Voltages, A. R.
I Ondrejka and P. A. Hudson, *J. Res. NBS,* vol. 70C, no. 1, pp. 13–18,
II January–March, 1966.

333 A Sensitive New 1-GHz Sampling Voltmeter with Unusual Capabilities,
II F. W. Wenninger, Jr., *Hewlett-Packard J.,* vol. 17, no. 11, pp. 2–8, July, 1966.

334 Pulse Voltage Calibration Service, *NBS Tech. News Bull.,* vol. 51, no.
I 3, pp. 48–49, March, 1967.

335 Peak Pulse Voltage Measurement (Baseband Pulse), A. R. Ondrejka, *Proc.*
I *IEEE,* vol. 55, no. 6, pp. 882–885, June, 1967.
II

* Baseband pulse: a pulse whose frequency spectrum extends from zero frequency or near zero frequency upward without limit.

CURRENT

Approximately 30 kHz to 1 GHz (coaxial connectors).

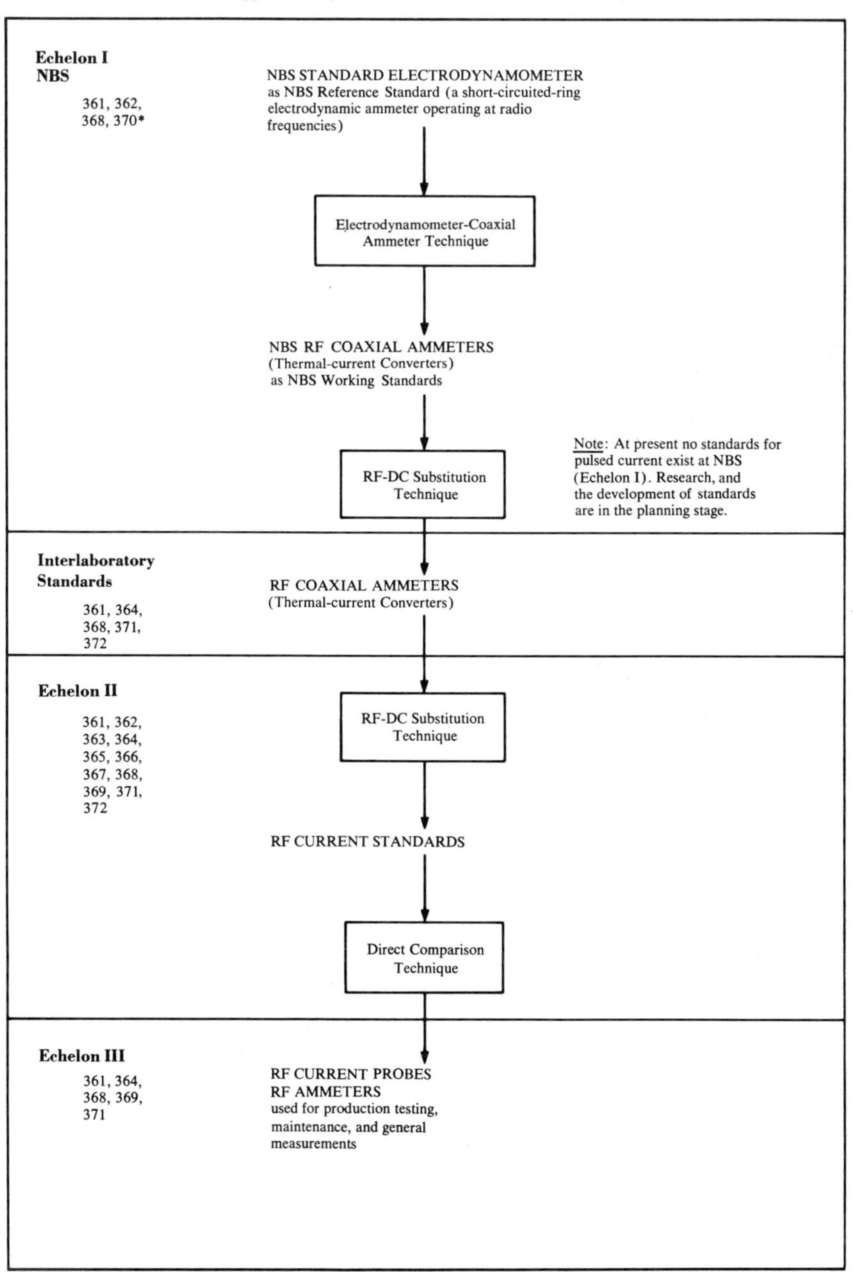

*These numbers refer to the list of references.

Approximately 30 kHz to 1 GHz, Coaxial Connectors

13. Current

The rf ammeter was the earliest instrument developed to measure the performance of electronic equipment operating at radio frequencies (radio-communication transmitters). However, use has decreased with the development of accurate power meters and with the measurement of voltage across known impedances. In recent years several methods of measuring current at radio frequencies have been developed or improved upon, including a current standard developed by the National Bureau of Standards that has an accuracy of approximately 0.5 percent—see Ref. 370.

The reader is referred to Ref. 368 for literature on rf current measurements that is earlier than the literature references cited below.

361 I, I S, II, III — The precision measurement of current at radio frequencies is relatively new, and very little laboratory-type equipment or informative literature is available from manufacturers.

362 I, II — Electrodynamic Ammeter for Very High Frequencies, *NBS Tech. News Bull.*, vol. 34, no. 7, pp. 103–104, July, 1950.

363 II — Calibrating Ammeters above 100 MC, H. R. Meahl, *Proc. IRE,* vol. 41, no. 1, pp. 152–159, January, 1953.

364 I S, II, III — Thermocouple-type Ammeters for Use at Very High Frequencies, O. G. McAnich, *Electrical Eng.,* vol. 73, no. 5, pp. 431–435, May, 1954.

365 II — Measurement of Voltage and Current, B. Rudner, chap. I, 2.1–2.52 of "Handbook of Electronic Measurements," vol. 1 (M. Wind, editor), Polytechnic Press, Polytechnic Institute of Brooklyn, Brooklyn, N.Y., 1956.

366 II — Electrodynamic Ammeter for Measuring High-frequency Currents, V. L. Lopan, *Meas. Techniques* (translated from the Soviet journal *Izmeritel'naia Tekhnika*), no. 1, pp. 85–90, January–February, 1958.

367 II — A New Clip-on Oscilloscope/Voltmeter Probe for 25 cps–20 Mc Current Measurements, C. O. Forge, *Hewlett-Packard J.*, vol. 11, nos. 11, 12, pp. 1–6, July–August, 1960.

**368* I, I S, II, III — The Measurement of Current at Radio Frequencies, W. W. Scott and N. V. Frederick, *Proc. IEEE,* vol. 55, no. 6, pp. 886–891, June, 1967. This paper has an extensive list of references on rf current standards and measurements. Included in this paper is a survey of various types of rf ammeters.

**369* II, III — A Precision Current Comparator, C. M. Allred and R. A. Lawton, *IEEE Trans. Instr. Meas.,* vol. IM-16, no. 2, pp. 142–145, June, 1967.

370 I — A New High-frequency Current Standard, N. V. Frederick, *IEEE Trans. Instr. Meas.,* vol. IM-17, no. 4, pp. 285–290, December, 1968.

371 I S, II, III — New R-F Ammeter Developed, *NBS Tech. News Bull.,* vol. 53, no. 12, pp. 276–277, December, 1969.

372 I S, II — New Coaxial RF-DC Ammeter, W. W. Scott, Jr., *IEEE Trans. Instr. Meas.,* vol. IM-19, no. 4, pp. 318–323, November, 1970.

POWER, CW AND PULSE

Approximately 30 kHz to 17 GHz (coaxial connectors).

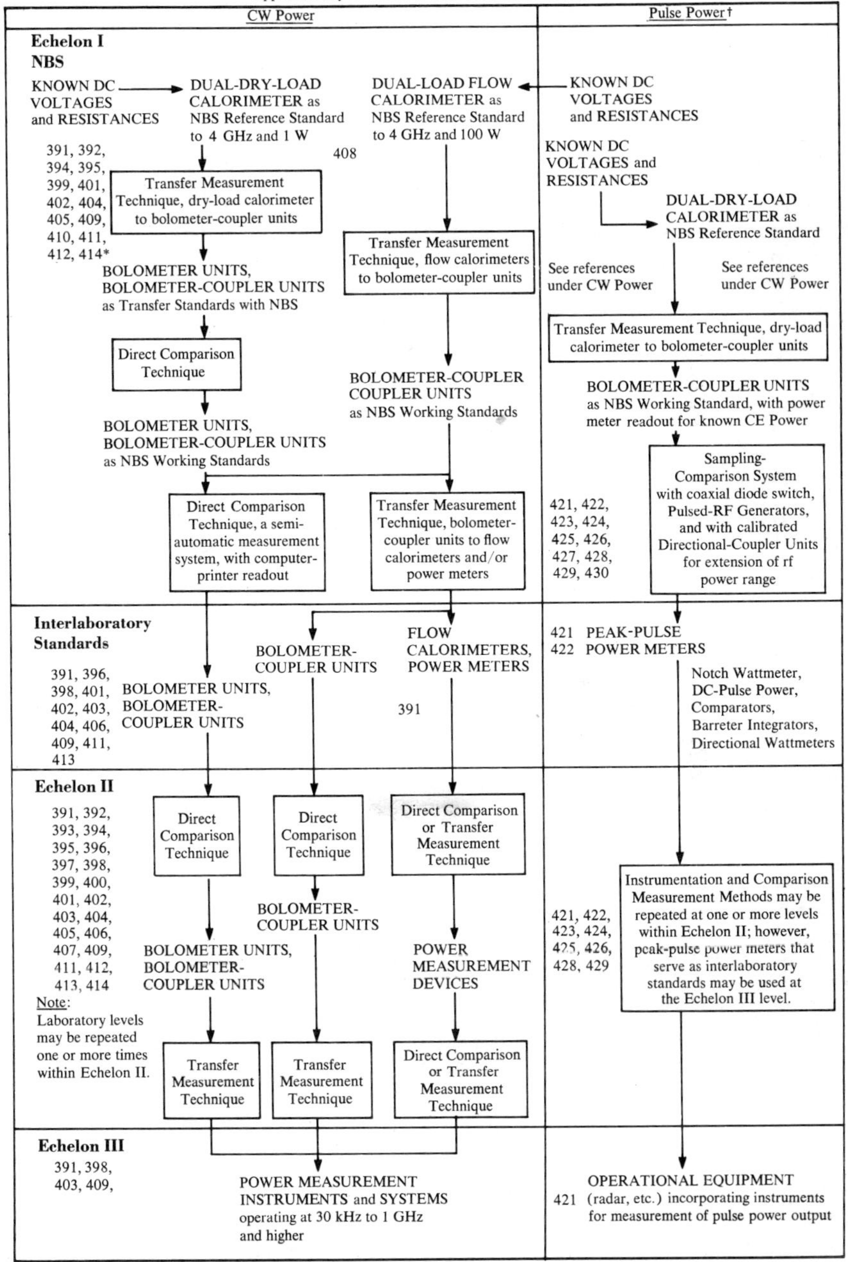

*These numbers refer to the list of references.

†Although PULSE POWER is listed under Coaxial Standards (or High Frequency) due to the order of development at NBS, the standards and measurement techniques are applicable, with some modifications, in waveguide at microwave frequencies (above 1 GHz).

Approximately 30 kHz to 17 GHz, Coaxial Connectors

14. Power, CW, and Pulse

CW Power

391 I, I S, II, III — Manufacturers of laboratory-type radio-frequency equipment usually have available, upon request, a variety of technical information on their products, as well as informative literature on specialized topics of apparatus (with coaxial connectors) suitable for cw power standards and measurements.

392 I, II — An Improved Method of Measuring Efficiencies of Ultra-high-frequency and Microwave Bolometer Mounts, R. W. Beatty and F. Reggia, *J. Res. NBS*, vol. 54, no. 6, pp. 321–327, June, 1955.

393 II — Measurement of Power, M. Sucher, chap. III, 3.1–3.114, of "Handbook of Electronic Measurements," vol. 1 (M. Wind, editor), Polytechnic Press, Polytechnic Institute of Brooklyn, Brooklyn, N.Y., 1956.

394 I, II — A Self-balancing DC Bridge for Accurate Bolometric Power Measurements, G. F. Engen, *J. Res. NBS,* vol. 59, no. 2, pp. 101–105, August, 1957.

395 I, II — A Dry Static Calorimeter for RF Power Measurement, P. A. Hudson and C. M. Allred, *IRE Trans. Instr.,* vol. I-7, nos. 3, 4, pp. 292–296, December, 1958.

396 I S, II — A Precision RF Power Transfer Standard, P. A. Hudson, *IRE Trans. Instr.,* vol. I-9, no. 2, pp. 280–283, September, 1960.

397 II — A Subtle Error in RF Power Measurements, S. J. Raff and G. U. Sorger, *IRE Trans. Instr.,* vol. I-9, no. 2, pp. 284–291, September, 1960.

398 I S, II — Temperature-compensated Microwatt Power Meter, E. E. Aslan, *IRE Trans. Instr.,* vol. I-9, no. 2, pp. 291–297, September, 1960.

**399* I, II — A Bolometer Mount Efficiency Measurement Technique, G. F. Engen, *J. Res. NBS,* vol. 65C, no. 2, pp. 113–124, April–June, 1961.

400 II — A Variable Impedance Power Meter, and Adjustable Reflection Coefficient Standard, G. F. Engen, *J. Res. NBS,* vol. 68C, no. 1, pp. 7–24, January–March, 1964.

**401* I, I S, II — A DC-RF Substitution Error in Dual-element Bolometer Mounts, G. F. Engen, *IEEE Trans. Instr. Meas.,* vol. IM-13, nos. 2, 3, pp. 58–64, June–September, 1964.

402 I, I S, II — A Coaxial Calorimeter for Use as a Microwave Power Standard, R. F. Clark, *IEEE Trans. Instr. Meas.,* vol. IM-14, nos. 1, 2, pp. 59–63, March–June, 1965.

403 I S, II, III — Microwave Power Meters: A User's Guide, J. Macrie, *Microwaves,* vol. 4, no. 1, pp. 24–35, January, 1965.
The power meters discussed in this paper are applicable at radio frequencies below 1 GHz as well as at microwave frequencies.

**404* I, I S, II — Coaxial Power Meter Calibration Using a Waveguide Standard, G. F. Engen, *J. Res. NBS,* vol. 70C, no. 2, pp. 127–138, April–June, 1966.

405 I, II — A High Directivity, Broadband Coaxial Coupler, P. A. Hudson, *IEEE Trans. Microwave Theory and Techniques,* vol. MTT-14, no. 6, pp. 293–294, June, 1966.

406 I S, II — A Coaxial Radio-frequency Power Standard, A. Jurkus, *IEEE Trans. Instr. Meas.,* vol. IM-15, no. 4, pp. 338–342, December, 1966.

407 II — System for the Transfer of Calibration Factor for Coaxial Bolometer Mounts with One Percent Transfer Inaccuracy, G. U. Sorger and B. O. Weinschel, *IEEE Trans. Instr. Meas.,* vol. IM-15, no. 4, pp. 343–358, December, 1966.

**408* — A Dual-load Flow Calorimeter for RF Power Measurement to 4 GHz,

I M. L. Crawford and P. A. Hudson, *J. Res. NBS*, vol. 71C, no. 2, pp. 111–117, April–June, 1967.

409 I; I S; II; III — Radio Frequency Power Measurements, A. Rumfelt and L. B. Elwell, *Proc. IEEE*, vol. 55, no. 6, pp. 837–850, June, 1967.
This paper has an extensive list of references on cw power standards and measurements at radio frequencies. Included in this paper is a short survey of various types of rf power-measurement devices.

410 I — Coaxial Power, Impedance and Attenuation Calibration Methods at NBS, R. W. Beatty, *Microwave J.*, vol. 11, no. 5, pp. 65–75, May, 1968.
A fairly extensive list of references on measurement of power in coaxial equipment accompanies this paper.

411 I; I S; II — A New RD-DC Substitution Calorimeter with Automatically Controlled Reference Power, M. L. Crawford, *IEEE Trans. Instr. Meas.*, vol. IM-17, no. 4, pp. 378–384, December, 1968.

412 I; II — A Wide-range CW Power Measurement Technique, R. A. Lawton, C. M. Allred, and P. A. Hudson, *IEEE Trans. Instr. Meas.*, vol. IM-19, no. 1, pp. 28–34, February, 1970.

413 I S; II — New Coaxial Thermistor Mounts for Use as Precision Transfer Standards, M. L. Crawford and G. R. Smart, paper 708–70, *Proc. 25th Ann. ISA Conf.*, vol. 25, part 3, October, 1970.

414 I; II — The Bolovac and Its Applications, M. C. Selby, *IEEE Trans. Instr. Meas.*, vol. IM-19, no. 4, pp. 324–331, November, 1970.

Pulse Power

421 I; I S; II; III — Manufacturers of laboratory-type radio-frequency equipment usually have available, upon request, a variety of technical information on their products, as well as informative literature on specialized types of apparatus (with coaxial connectors) suitable for pulse power standards and measurements.

422 I; I S; II — The Notch Wattmeter for Low-level Power Measurement of Microwave Pulses, D. F. Bowman, *Proc. National Electronics Conference, Chicago*, vol. II, pp. 361–371, October, 1946.

423 I; II — Measurement of RF Peak-pulse Power by a Sampling Comparison Method, P. A. Hudson, W. L. Ecklund, and A. R. Ondrejka, *IRE Trans. Instr.*, vol. I-11, nos. 3, 4, pp. 280–284, December, 1962.

424 I; II — Microwave Pulse-power Measurements, C. A. Denney, C. L. Mavis, and C. J. Still, *IRE Trans. Instr.*, vol. I-11, nos. 3, 4, pp. 276–280, December, 1962.

425 I; II — Peak Power Measurements, H. J. Carlin, chap. III, vol. I, pp. 212–216 of "Handbook of Microwave Measurements" (M. Sucher, editor), Polytechnic Press, Polytechnic Institute of Brooklyn, Brooklyn, N.Y., 1963.

426 I; II — Microwave Peak Power Measurements, S. Evendorf, *ISA J.*, vol. 12, no. 5, pp. 71–75, May, 1965.

427 I — Peak-pulse Power Calibrations Initiated, *NBS Tech. News Bull.*, vol. 49, no. 12, pp. 212–213, December, 1965.

428 I; II — Measurement of RF Peak Pulse Power, P. A. Hudson, *Proc. IEEE*, vol. 55, no. 6, pp. 851–855, June, 1967.

429 I; II — Peak-pulse Power Switch, *NBS Tech. News Bull.*, vol. 52, no. 11, pp. 240–241, November, 1968.

430 I — Improvements to the NBS RF Peak-pulse Power Standard, P. A. Simpson, and A. R. Ondrejka, paper 709–70, *Proc. 25th Ann. ISA Conf.*, vol. 25, part 3, October, 1970.

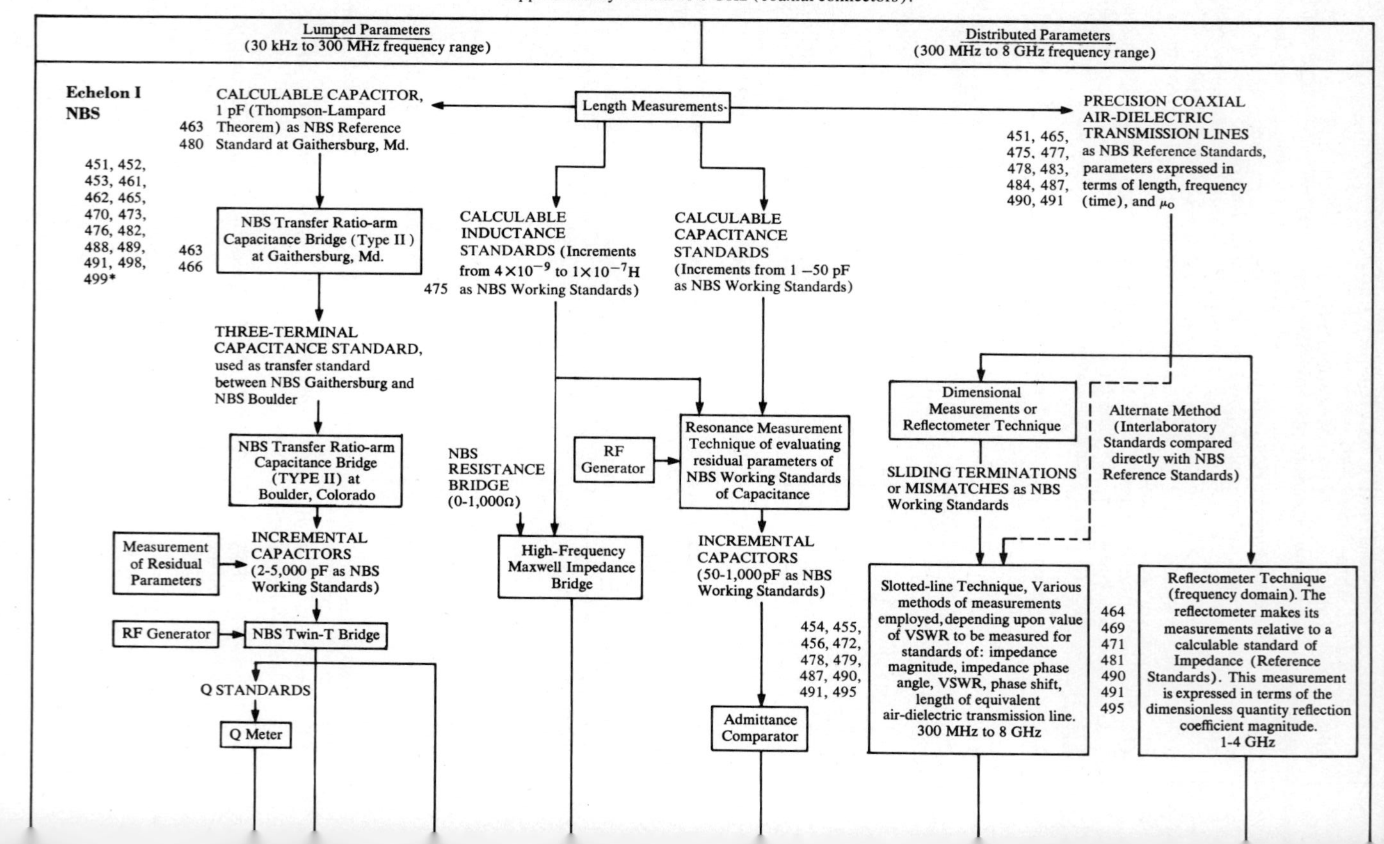

IMPEDANCE (IMMITTANCE)
Approximately 30 kHz to 8 GHz (coaxial connectors).
Lumped Parameters
(30 kHz to 300 MHz frequency range)
Distributed Parameters
(300 MHz to 8 GHz frequency range)
Echelon I
NBS
451, 452, 453, 461, 462, 465, 470, 473, 476, 482, 488, 489, 491, 498, 499*
CALCULABLE CAPACITOR, 1 pF (Thompson-Lampard Theorem) as NBS Reference Standard at Gaithersburg, Md.
463
480
Length Measurements
PRECISION COAXIAL AIR-DIELECTRIC TRANSMISSION LINES as NBS Reference Standards, parameters expressed in terms of length, frequency (time), and μ_o
451, 465, 475, 477, 478, 483, 484, 487, 490, 491
NBS Transfer Ratio-arm Capacitance Bridge (Type II) at Gaithersburg, Md.
463
466
CALCULABLE INDUCTANCE STANDARDS (Increments from 4×10^{-9} to 1×10^{-7}H as NBS Working Standards)
475
CALCULABLE CAPACITANCE STANDARDS (Increments from 1 –50 pF as NBS Working Standards)
THREE-TERMINAL CAPACITANCE STANDARD, used as transfer standard between NBS Gaithersburg and NBS Boulder
Dimensional Measurements or Reflectometer Technique
Alternate Method (Interlaboratory Standards compared directly with NBS Reference Standards)
NBS Transfer Ratio-arm Capacitance Bridge (TYPE II) at Boulder, Colorado
NBS RESISTANCE BRIDGE (0-1,000Ω)
RF Generator
Resonance Measurement Technique of evaluating residual parameters of NBS Working Standards of Capacitance
SLIDING TERMINATIONS or MISMATCHES as NBS Working Standards
Measurement of Residual Parameters
INCREMENTAL CAPACITORS (2-5,000 pF as NBS Working Standards)
High-Frequency Maxwell Impedance Bridge
INCREMENTAL CAPACITORS (50-1,000pF as NBS Working Standards)
Slotted-line Technique, Various methods of measurements employed, depending upon value of VSWR to be measured for standards of: impedance magnitude, impedance phase angle, VSWR, phase shift, length of equivalent air-dielectric transmission line. 300 MHz to 8 GHz
464
469
471
481
490
491
495
Reflectometer Technique (frequency domain). The reflectometer makes its measurements relative to a calculable standard of Impedance (Reference Standards). This measurement is expressed in terms of the dimensionless quantity reflection coefficient magnitude. 1-4 GHz
RF Generator
NBS Twin-T Bridge
454, 455, 456, 472, 478, 479, 487, 490, 491, 495
Q STANDARDS
Q Meter
Admittance Comparator

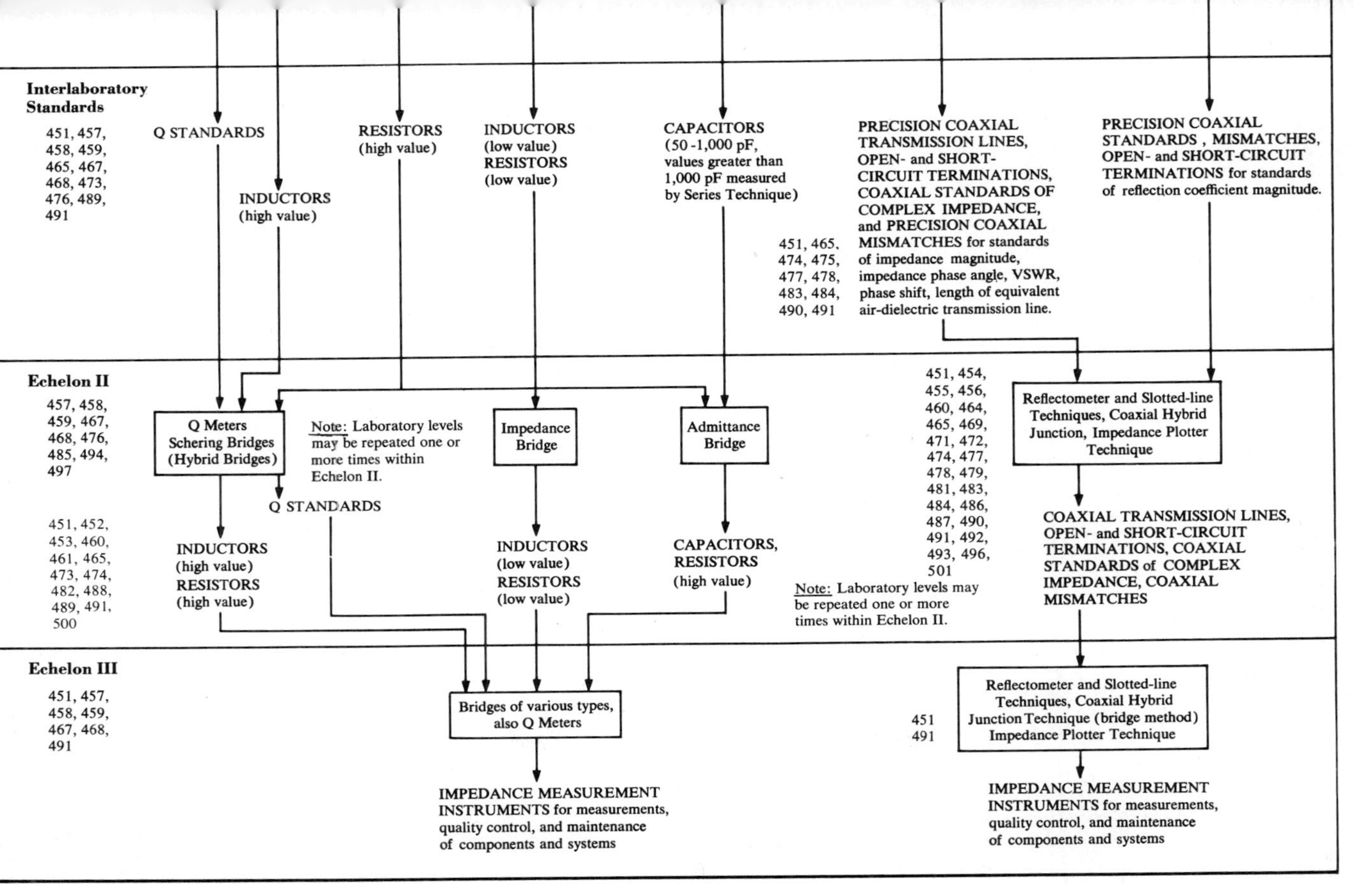

*These numbers refer to the list of references.

Approximately 30 kHz to 8 GHz, Coaxial Connectors

15. Impedance or Immittance

451 I, I S, II, III — Manufacturers of laboratory-type radio-frequency equipment usually have available, upon request, a variety of technical information on their products, as well as informative literature on specialized topics of apparatus (with coaxial connectors, also unshielded connectors at lower frequencies) suitable for impedance standards and measurements.

452 I, II — Bridged-T and Parallel-T Null Circuits for Measurements at Radio Frequency, W. N. Tuttle, *Proc. IRE,* vol. 28, no. 1, pp. 23–29, January, 1940.

453 I, II — The Twin-T, a New Type of Null Instrument for Measuring Impedance at Frequencies up to 30 Megacycles, D. B. Sinclair, *Proc. IRE,* vol. 28, no. 7, pp. 310–318, July, 1940.

454 I, II — Methods for Obtaining the Voltage Standing-wave Ratio on Transmission Lines Independently of the Detector Characteristics, A. M. Winzemer, *Proc. IRE,* vol. 38, no. 3, pp. 275–279, March, 1950.

455 I, II — Evaluation of Coaxial Slotted-line Impedance Measurements, H. E. Sorrows, W. E. Ryan, and R. C. Ellenwood, *Proc. IRE,* vol. 39, no. 2, pp. 162–168, February, 1951.

456 I, II — The Determination of Impedance with a Double-slug Transformer, R. C. Ellenwood and E. H. Hurlburt, *Proc. IRE,* vol. 40, no. 12, pp. 1690–1693, December, 1952.

457 I S, II, III — The Nature of Q, W. C. Moore, *BRC Notebook, Boonton Radio Corp.,* no. 1, pp. 1–4, spring, 1954.

458 I S, II, III — The Q-standard, C. L. Kang and J. E. Wachter, *BRC Notebook, Boonton Radio Corp.,* no. 1, pp. 4–5, spring, 1954.

459 I S, II, III — A Versatile Instrument—the Q Meter, L. Cook, *BRC Notebook, Boonton Radio Corp.,* no. 4, pp. 1–4, winter, 1955.

460 II — Measurement of Impedance and Circuit Elements, L. Eisenberg, chap. IV, 4.1–4.129, of "Handbook of Electronic Measurements," vol. 1 (M. Wind, editor), Polytechnic Press, Polytechnic Institute of Brooklyn, Brooklyn, N.Y., 1956.

461 I, II — A Precision Dual Bridge for the Standardization of Admittance at Very High Frequencies, D. Woods, *Proc. IEE (London),* vol. 104C, Monograph 244R, pp. 506–521, June, 1957.

462 I — High-frequency Impedance Standards at the National Bureau of Standards, R. C. Powell, R. M. Jickling, and A. E. Hess, *IRE Trans. Instr.,* vol. I-7, nos. 3, 4, pp. 270–274, December, 1958.

463 I — New Apparatus at the National Bureau of Standards for Absolute Capacitance Measurement, M. C. McGregor, J. F. Hersh, R. D. Cutkosky, F. K. Harris, and F. R. Cotter, *IRE Trans. Instr.,* vol. I-7, nos. 3, 4, pp. 253–261, December, 1958.

464 I, II — Microwave Reflectometer Techniques, G. F. Engen and R. W. Beatty, *IRE Trans. Microwave Theory and Techniques,* vol. MTT-7, no. 3, pp. 351–355, July, 1959.

465 I, I S, II — Admittance Standardization and Measurement in Relation to Coaxial Systems, D. Woods, *IRE Trans. Instr.,* vol. I-9, no. 2, pp. 258–268, September, 1960.

466 I — The Precision Measurement of Transformer Ratio, R. D. Cutkosky and J. Q. Shields, *IRE Trans. Instr.,* vol. I-9, no. 2, pp. 242–250, September, 1960.

467 I S, II, III — The BRC UHF Q Meter, a New and Versatile Tool for Industry, C. W. Quinn, *BRC Notebook, Boonton Radio Corp.,* no. 28, pp. 1–6, spring, 1961.

468 I S, II, III — Calibration of a UHF Q Meter, C. G. Gorss, *BRC Notebook, Boonton Radio Corp.*, no. 29, pp. 1–5, summer, 1961.

**469* I, II — A Guide to the Use of the Modified Reflectometer Technique of VSWR Measurement, W. J. Anson, *J. Res. NBS*, vol. 65C, no. 4, pp. 217–223, October–December, 1961.

470 I — The Role of Capacitance in the National Reference Standards for High Frequency Impedance, R. N. Jones and R. E. Nelson, *ISA Conference Proc.*, vol. 17, part I, paper 18.1.62, 1962.

471 I, II — Application of Reflectometer Techniques to Accurate Reflection Measurements in Coaxial Systems, R. W. Beatty and W. J. Anson, *Proc. IEE (London)*, vol. 109, part B, pp. 345–348, July, 1962.

472 I, II — Measurement of Standing-wave Ratio, A. B. Giordano, chap. II, pp. 73–133, of "Handbook of Microwave Measurements" 3d edition (M. Sucher and J. Fox, editors), Polytechnic Press, Polytechnic Institute of Brooklyn, N.Y., 1963.

473 I, I S, II — A Technique for Extrapolating the 1 kc Values of Secondary Capacitance Standards to Higher Frequencies, R. N. Jones, *NBS Tech. Note* 201, Nov. 5, 1963.

474 I S, II — Calibration Techniques for One- and Two-port Devices Using Coaxial Reference Air Lines as Absolute Impedance Standards, A. E. Sanderson, *Reprint* B21, *General Radio Company,* West Concord, Mass., 1964.

475 I, I S — Air-filled Coaxial Lines as Absolute Impedance Standards, B. O. Weinschel, *Microwave J.*, vol. VII, no. 4, pp. 47–50, April, 1964.

476 I, I S, II — Standards for the Calibration of Q-meters 50 kHz to 45 MHz, R. N. Jones, *J. Res. NBS,* vol. 68C, no. 4, pp. 243–248, October–December, 1964.

477 I, I S, II — The Realization of High-frequency Impedance Standards Using Air-spaced Coaxial Lines, I. A. Harris and R. E. Spinney, *IEEE Trans. Instr. Meas.,* vol. IM-13, no. 4, pp. 265–272, December, 1964.

478 I, I S, II — Precision Coaxial VSWR Measurements by Coupled Sliding-load Technique, B. O. Weinschel, G. U. Sorger, S. J. Raff, and J. E. Ebert, *IEEE Trans. Instr. Meas.*, vol. IM-13, no. 4, pp. 292–300, December, 1964. This paper has a fairly extensive list of references on VSWR measurements of coaxial lines.

479 I, II — A Slotted-line Recorder System, A. E. Sanderson, *General Radio Experimenter,* vol. 39, no. 1, pp. 3–10, January, 1965.

480 I — A Calculable Standard of Capacitance, W. K. Clothier, *Metrologia,* vol. I, no. 2, pp. 36–55, 1965.

481 I, II — Measurement of Precision Coaxial Connectors Using Reflectometer Techniques, W. E. Little and J. P. Wakefield, *IEEE International Convention Record,* part II, pp. 89–97, March, 1965.

482 I, II — A Self-calibrating Instrument for Measuring Conductance at Radio Frequencies, L. E. Huntley, *J. Res. NBS,* vol. 69C, no. 2, pp. 115–126, April–June, 1965.

483 I, I S, II — Some Fundamental Design Principles for the Development of Precision Coaxial Standards and Components, T. E. MacKenzie and A. E. Sanderson, *IEEE Trans. Microwave Theory and Techniques,* vol. MTT-14, no. 1, pp. 29–39, January, 1966.

484 I, I S, II — Electrical Parameters of Precision, Coaxial, Air-dielectric Transmission Lines, R. E. Nelson and M. R. Coryell, NBS Monograph 96, June 30, 1966.

485 II — Method for the Measurement of "Q", O. W. Dopheide, *IEEE Trans. Instr. Meas.*, vol. IM-15, no. 3, pp. 109–112, September, 1966.

486 II — Swept Frequency SWR Measurements in Coaxial Systems, S. F. Adams, *Hewlett-Packard J.*, vol. 18, no. 4, pp. 15–20, December, 1966.

487 — Some Techniques and Their Limitations as Related to the Measurement

I II of Small Reflections in Precision Coaxial Transmission Lines, T. E. MacKenzie, *IEEE Trans. Instr. Meas.*, vol. IM-15, no. 4, pp. 365–374, December, 1966.

488 I II Precision Coaxial Connectors in Lumped Parameter Immittance Measurement, R. N. Jones and L. E. Huntley, *IEEE Trans. Instr. Meas.*, vol. IM-15, no. 4, pp. 375–380, December, 1966.

**489* I IS II Lumped Parameter Impedance Measurements, L. E. Huntley and R. N. Jones, *Proc. IEEE*, vol. 55, no. 6, pp. 900–911, June, 1967.
This paper has an extensive list of references on lumped-parameter impedance standards and measurements.

**490* I IS II Impedance Measurements in Coaxial Waveguide Systems, R. L. Jesch and R. M. Jickling, *Proc. IEEE*, vol. 55, no. 6, pp. 912–923, June, 1967.
This paper has an extensive list of references on distributed-parameter impedance standards and measurements.

491 I IS II III Standardization of Precision Coaxial Connectors, B. O. Weinschel, *Proc. IEEE*, vol. 55, no. 6, pp. 923–932, June, 1967.
This paper has an extensive list of references on the design of and the measurement techniques to evaluate precision coaxial connectors. The development of precision coaxial connectors has played a major role in the increased accuracy of lumped-parameter and distributed-parameter impedance measurements. Also see IEEE Standard for Precision Coaxial Connectors, *IEEE Trans. Instr. Meas.*, vol. IM-17, no. 3, pp. 204–218, September, 1968.

492 II Swept-frequency Techniques, P. C. Ely, Jr., *Proc. IEEE*, vol. 55, no. 6, pp. 991–1002, June, 1967.
This paper describes swept-frequency techniques for measurement of network parameters, particularly by adaption of slotted-line and reflectometer methods. An extensive list of references accompanies the paper.

493 II A Technique for Measurement of Impedance through a Lossless Transition, T. J. Russell, *IEEE Trans. Instr. Meas.*, vol. IM-16, no. 3, pp. 269–276, September, 1967.

494 II A New Type of Q Meter Using Variable-width Pulse Excitation, G. H. Kramer, *IEEE Trans. Instr. Meas.*, vol. IM-16, no. 4, pp. 315–319, December, 1967.

495 I Coaxial Power, Impedance and Attenuation Calibration Methods at NBS, R. W. Beatty, *Microwave J.*, vol. 11, no. 5, pp. 65–75, May, 1968.

496 II Coaxial Swept-frequency VSWR Measurements Using Slotted Lines, G. U. Sorger, *IEEE Trans. Instr. Meas.*, vol. IM-17, no. 4, pp. 403–412, December, 1968.

497 II Measurement of High Q at High Frequencies, R. D. Ryan and J. E. Eberhardt, *IEEE Trans. Instr. Meas.*, vol. IM-18, no. 2, pp. 129–132, June, 1969.

498 I Two-terminal Capacitors with Precision Coaxial Connectors, *NBS Tech. News Bull.*, vol. 53, no. 12, p. 283, December, 1969.

499 I A Precision, High Frequency Calibration Facility for Coaxial Capacitance Standards, R. N. Jones and L. E. Huntley, *NBS Tech. Note* 386, March, 1970.

500 II Accurate Immittance Measurements at Frequencies up to 20 MHz, L. D. White, *IEEE Trans. Instr. Meas.*, vol. IM-19, no. 4, pp. 331–336, November, 1970.

501 II Precision Slotted-line Impedance Measurements Using Computer Simulation for Data Correction, B. J. Clifton, *IEEE Trans. Instr. Meas.*, vol. IM-19, no. 4, pp. 358–364, November, 1970.

PHASE SHIFT

Approximately 30 kHz to 12 GHz (coaxial connectors).

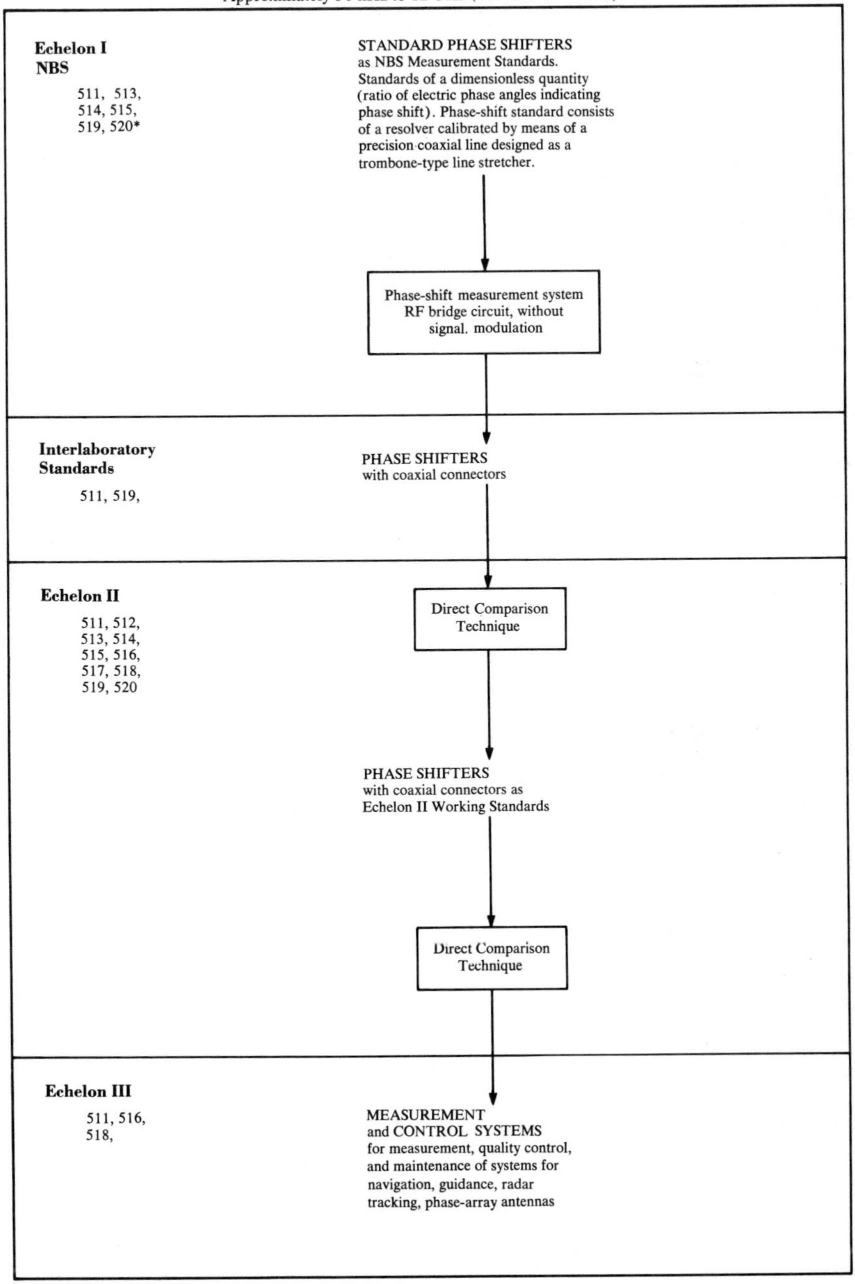

*These numbers refer to the list of references.

Approximately 30 kHz to 12 GHz, Coaxial Connectors

16. Phase Shift

511 (I; I S; II; III) Manufacturers of laboratory-type radio-frequency equipment usually have available, upon request, a variety of technical information on their products, as well as informative literature on specialized topics of apparatus (with coaxial connectors) suitable for phase-shift standards and measurements.

512 (II) Measurement of Phase, S. Rinkel, chap. VII, 7.1–7.48 of "Handbook of Electronic Measurements," vol. II (M. Wind, editor), Polytechnic Press, Polytechnic Institute of Brooklyn, Brooklyn, N.Y., 1956.

513 (I; II) Precision Microwave Phase Shift Measurements, M. Magid, *IRE Trans. Instr.*, vol. I-7, nos. 3, 4, pp. 321–331, December, 1958.

514 (I; II) Evaluation of a Microwave Phase Measurement System, D. A. Ellerbruch, *J. Res. NBS*, vol. 69C, no. 1, pp. 55–65, January–March, 1965.

515 (I; II) An Unmodulated Twin-channel Microwave Measurement System, D. H. Russell, *ISA Trans.*, vol. 4, no. 2, pp. 162–169, April, 1965.
This system is adaptable to measurement of phase shift.

516 (II; III) A Precision Phase Meter, R. H. Frater, *IEEE Trans. Instr. Meas.*, vol. IM-15, nos. 1, 2, pp. 9–19, March–June, 1966.

517 (II) The Measurement of Phase at UHF and Microwave Frequencies, J. D. Dyson, *IEEE Trans. Microwave Theory and Techniques,* vol. MTT-14, no. 9, pp. 410–423, September, 1966.

518 (II; III) A 5 to 50 MHz Direct-reading Phase Meter with Hundredth-degree Precision, D. E. Maxwell, *IEEE Trans. Instr. Meas.*, vol. IM-15, no. 4, pp. 304–310, December, 1966.

**519* (I; I S; II) UHF and Microwave Phase-shift Measurements, D. A. Ellerbruch, *Proc. IEEE*, vol. 55, no. 6, pp. 960–969, June, 1967.
This paper has an extensive list of references on phase-shift standards and measurements at the lower radio-frequency range. Included in this paper is a short survey of various types of phase shifters.

520 (I; II) Calibration of Phase Shifters at Radio Frequencies, *NBS Tech. News Bull.*, vol. 53, no. 6, pp. 130–131, June, 1969.

ATTENUATION

Approximately 30 kHz to 18 GHz (coaxial connectors).

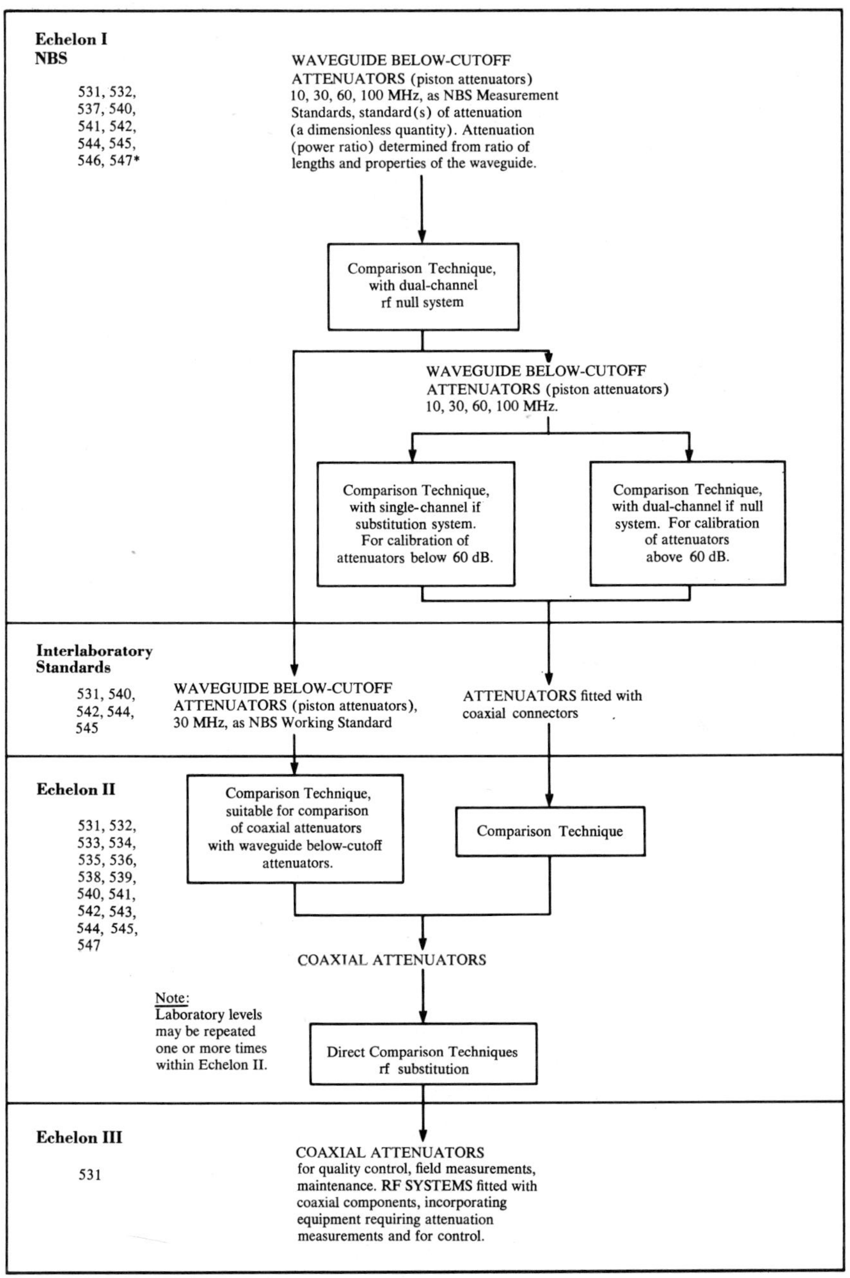

*These numbers refer to the list of references.

Approximately 30 kHz to 18 GHz, Coaxial Connectors

17. Attenuation

531 I I S II III Manufacturers of laboratory-type radio-frequency equipment usually have available, upon request, a variety of technical information on their products, as well as informative literature on specialized topics of apparatus (with coaxial connectors) suitable for attenuation standards and measurements.

532 I II Determination of Attenuation from Impedance Measurements, R. W. Beatty, *Proc. IRE,* vol. 38, no. 8, pp. 895–897, August, 1950.

533 II Cascade-connected Attenuators, R. W. Beatty, *J. Res. NBS,* vol. 45, no. 3, pp. 231–235, September, 1950.

534 II Mismatch Errors in the Measurements of Ultrahigh-frequency and Microwave Variable Attenuators, R. W. Beatty, *J. Res. NBS,* vol. 52, no. 1, pp. 7–9, January, 1954.

535 II Attenuation and Its Measurement, A. B. Giordane, chap. XVIII, 18.1–18.79 of "Handbook of Electronic Measurements," vol. II (M. Wind, editor), Polytechnic Press, Polytechnic Institute of Brooklyn, Brooklyn, N.Y., 1956.

536 II Self-calibrating Method of Measuring Insertion Ratio, *NBS Tech. News Bull.,* vol. 41, no. 9, pp. 132–133, September, 1957.

**537* I A Precision RF Attenuation Calibration System, C. M. Allred and C. C. Cook, *IRE Trans. Instr.,* vol. I-9, no. 2, pp. 268–274, September, 1960.

538 II A Method for the Self-calibration of Attenuation Measuring Systems, R. L. Peck, *J. Res. NBS,* vol. 66C, no. 1, pp. 13–18, January–March, 1962.

539 II Intrinsic Attenuation, R. W. Beatty, *IEEE Trans. Microwave Theory and Techniques,* vol. MTT-11, no. 3, pp. 179–182, May, 1963.

540 I I S II A Standard Attenuator and the Precise Measurement of Attenuation, D. L. Holloway and F. P. Kelly, *IEEE Trans. Instr. Meas.,* vol. IM-13, no. 1, pp. 33–44, March, 1964.

**541* I II Insertion Loss Concepts, R. W. Beatty, *Proc. IEEE,* vol. 52, no. 6, pp. 663–671, June, 1964.

**542* I I S II Effects of Connectors and Adapters on Accurate Attenuation Measurements at Microwave Frequencies, R. W. Beatty, *IEEE Trans. Instr. Meas.,* vol. IM-13, no. 4, pp. 272–284, December, 1964.

543 II A New Technique for Accurate RF Attenuation Measurements, H. L. Kaylie, *IEEE Trans. Instr. Meas.,* vol. IM-15, no. 4, pp. 325–332, December, 1966.

544 I I S II Microwave Attenuation Measurements and Standards, R. W. Beatty, NBS Monograph 97, Apr. 3, 1967.
Although this monograph is titled "Microwave," the subject matter treated is equally applicable to the lower ranges of the radio frequencies for equipment incorporating coaxial connectors. This paper has an extensive list of references on attenuation standards and measurements at the lower ranges of the radio frequencies.

**545* I I S II RF Attenuation, D. Russell and W. Larson, *Proc. IEEE,* vol. 55, no. 6, pp. 942–959, June, 1967.
This paper has an extensive list of references on attenuation standards and measurements at the lower radio-frequency range.

546 I Coaxial Power, Impedance and Attenuation Calibration Methods at NBS, R. W. Beatty, *Microwave J.,* vol. 11, no. 5, pp. 65–75, May, 1968.

547 I II VHF and UHF Attenuation Measurements to 140 dB, S. B. Pullman, *IEEE Trans. Instr. Meas.,* vol. IM-18, no. 1, pp. 7–15, March, 1969.

NOISE

Approximately 30 kHz to 1 GHz (coaxial connectors). Measurements at NBS limited to certain frequencies.

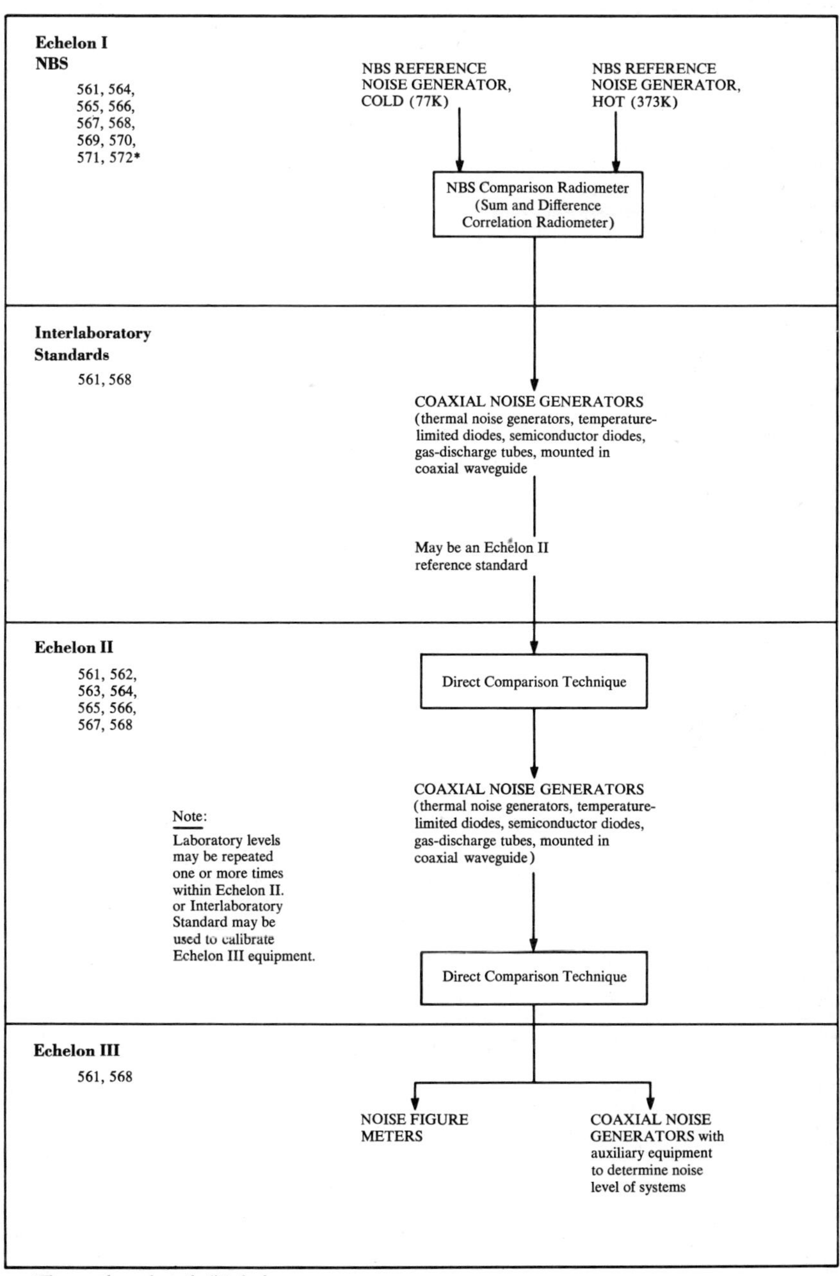

*These numbers refer to the list of references.

Approximately 30 kHz to 1 GHz, Coaxial Connectors (measurement at NBS limited to certain frequencies)

18. Noise

561 I, I S, II, III — Manufacturers of laboratory-type radio-frequency equipment usually have available, upon request, a variety of technical information on their products. Some manufacturers have informative literature on specialized topics of apparatus (with coaxial connectors) suitable for noise standards and measurements.

562 II — Absolute Measurement of Receiver Noise Figures at UHF, E. Maxwell and B. J. Leon, *IRE Trans. Microwave Theory and Techniques,* vol. MTT-4, no. 2, pp. 81–85, April, 1956.

563 II — Measurement of Noise Figures, M. Leberbaum, chap. XI, 11.1–11.51 of "Handbook of Electronic Measurements," vol. II (M. Wind, editor), Polytechnic Press, Polytechnic Institute of Brooklyn, Brooklyn, N.Y., 1956.

564 I, II — Design and Development of a Standard White Noise Generator and Noise Indicating Instrument, H. Zucker, Y. Baskin, S. I. Cohn, I. Lerner, and A. Rosenblum, *IRE Trans. Instr.,* vol. I-7, nos. 3, 4, pp. 279–291, December, 1958.

565 I, II — Electrical Noise, J. J. Freeman, *Electro-Technology,* vol. 66, no. 5, pp. 126–144, November, 1960.

**566* I, II — A Precision Noise Spectral Density Comparator, C. M. Allred, *J. Res. NBS,* vol. 66C, no. 4, pp. 323–330, October–December, 1962.

**567* I, II — A Precision Noise-power Comparator, M. G. Arthur, C. M. Allred, and M. K. Cannon, *IEEE Trans. Instr. Meas.,* vol. IM-13, no. 4, pp. 301–305, December, 1964.

**568* I, I S, II, III — Noise Standards, Measurements, and Receiver Noise Definitions, C. K. S. Miller, W. C. Daywitt, and M. G. Arthur, *Proc. IEEE,* vol. 55, no. 6, pp. 865–877, June, 1967. This paper has an extensive list of references on noise standards and measurements.

569 I — A Method of Calibrating Coaxial Noise Sources in Terms of a Waveguide Standard, G. F. Engen, *IEEE Trans. Microwave Theory and Techniques,* vol. MTT-16, no. 9, pp. 636–639, September, 1968.

570 I — Coaxial Noise Generators, *NBS Tech. News Bull.,* vol. 52, no. 11, pp. 251–252, November, 1968.

571 I — Calibration of Coaxial Noise Sources Fitted with 14mm Precision Connectors, *NBS Tech. News Bull.,* vol. 54, no. 3, pp. 62–63, March, 1970.

572 I — A Precision HF Noise Power Measurement System, M. G. Arthur, paper 714–70, *Proc. 25th Ann. ISA Conf.,* vol. 25, part 3, October, 1970.

Approximately 30 kHz to 1 GHz and Higher

GENERAL REFERENCES

581 "Radio-frequency Measurements by Bridge and Resonance Methods," L. Hartshorn, John Wiley & Sons, Inc., New York, 1940.

582 "Handbook of Electronic Measurements," M. Wind (editor), vols. I, II, Polytechnic Press, Polytechnic Institute of Brooklyn, Brooklyn, N.Y., 1956. This handbook is primarily a treatment of measurement techniques using electronic instrumentation over a frequency range extending from direct current into the microwave region (above 1 GHz).

583 "Handbook of Electronic Instruments and Measurement Techniques," H. E. Thomas and C. A. Clarke, Prentice-Hall, Inc., Englewood Cliffs, N.J., 1967.

584 Radio-frequency Measurements in the NBS Institute for Basic Standards, edited by R. S. Powers and W. F. Snyder, *NBS Tech. Note* 373, June, 1969.

585 "Electronic Instrumentation and Measurement Techniques," W. D. Cooper, Prentice-Hall, Inc., Englewood Cliffs, N.J., 1970. Although some radio-frequency instruments are described, most of the measurement techniques relate to dc and low frequency.

586 A valuable source of information on standards and precision measurement techniques at radio frequencies is being made available by the Technical Committee on Electromagnetic Measurement—State of the Art, IEEE Group on Instrumentation and Measurement. Information on reports by this committee may be obtained from:

The Institute of Electrical and Electronics Engineers, Inc.
345 East 47th Street
New York, N.Y. 10017

Books of the kind referenced above, which give extensive coverage to the field of measurements in the radio-frequency range below 1 GHz, are relatively rare. This is particularly true for instruments and measurement techniques involving circuitry with coaxial components.

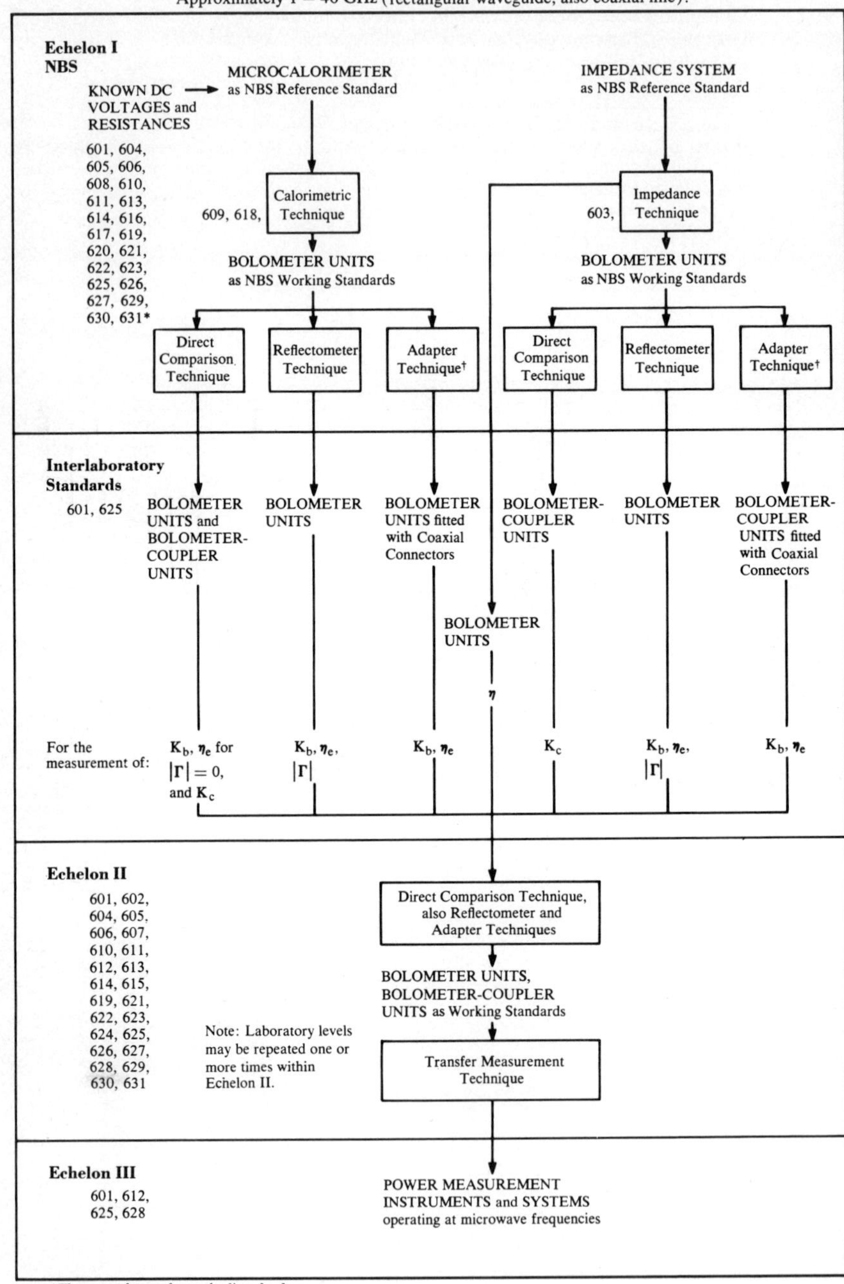

*These numbers refer to the list of references.
†Frequency range of 4 - 17 GHz.

CHARTS OF BASIC ELECTRICAL STANDARDS AND TRACEABILITY (APPROXIMATELY 1 TO 40 GHz, WAVEGUIDE OR COAXIAL LINE)

19. Power

601 I, I S, II, III — Manufacturers of laboratory-type microwave equipment usually have available, upon request, a variety of technical information on their products, as well as informative literature on specialized topics of waveguide apparatus suitable for power standards and measurements.

602 II — Microwave Power Measurements at Low and Medium Levels, R. M. Griesheimer, chap. 3, pp. 79–194, of "Technique of Microwave Measurements, Radiation Laboratory Series" (C. G. Montgomery, editor), McGraw-Hill Book Company, New York, 1947.

603 I — Determination of Efficiency of Microwave Bolometer Mounts from Impedance Data, D. M. Kerns, *J. Res. NBS,* vol. 42, no. 1, pp. 579–585, June, 1949

604 I, II — Accuracy of Laboratories' Power Measurements, H. V. Carlin and M. Sucher, *Proc. IRE,* vol. 40, no. 9, pp. 1042–1048, September, 1952.

605 I, II — Mismatch Errors in Microwave Power Measurements, R. W. Beatty and A. C. MacPherson, *Proc. IRE,* vol. 41, no. 9, pp. 1112–1119, September, 1953.

606 I, II — An Improved Method of Measuring Efficiencies of Ultra-high Frequency and Microwave Bolometer Mounts, R. W. Beatty and F. Reggia, *J. Res. NBS,* vol. 54, no. 6, pp. 321–327, June, 1955.

607 II — Measurement of Microwave Power, chap. 3, pp. 145–202, "Microwave Measurements," E. L. Ginzton, McGraw-Hill Book Company, New York, 1957.

608 I — Recent Developments in the Field of Microwave Power Measurements at the National Bureau of Standards, G. F. Engen, *IRE Trans. Instr.,* vol. I-7, nos. 3, 4, pp. 304–306, December, 1958.

609 I — A Refined X-band Microwave Microcalorimeter, G. F. Engen, *J. Res. NBS,* vol. 63C, no. 1, pp. 77–82, July–September, 1959.

610 I, II — A Transfer Instrument for the Intercomparison of Microwave Power Meters, G. F. Engen, *IRE Trans. Instr.,* vol. I-9, no. 2, pp. 202–208, September, 1960.

611 I, II — A Subtle Error in RF Power Measurements, S. J. Raff and G. U. Sorger, *IRE Trans. Instr.,* vol. I-9, no. 2, pp. 284–291, September, 1960.

612 II, III — Temperature-compensated Microwatt Power Meter, E. E. Aslan, *IRE Trans. Instr.,* vol. I-9, no. 2, pp. 291–297, September, 1960.

Definitions for Power Chart (1 to 40 GHz) on page 3-48.

η = efficiency of bolometer units: the ratio of the microwave power dissipated within the bolometer unit to the microwave power incident upon the bolometer unit

η_e = effective efficiency of bolometer units: the ratio of the substituted dc power in the bolometer unit to the microwave power dissipated within the bolometer unit

K_b = calibration factor of bolometer units: the ratio of the substituted dc power in the bolometer unit to the microwave power incident upon the bolometer unit

K_c = calibration factor of bolometer-coupler units: the ratio of the substituted dc power in the bolometer unit on the sidearm of the directional coupler to the microwave power incident upon a nonreflecting load attached to the output port of the main arm

$|\Gamma|$ = reflection-coefficient magnitude: for a single mode of propagation, the ratio of the magnitude (of the amplitude) of the incident to the reflected wave at a given terminal plane

*613 I II — A Bolometer Mount Efficiency Measurement Technique, G. F. Engen, *J. Res. NBS,* vol. 65C, no. 2, pp. 113–124, April–June, 1961.

614 I II — Microwave Power Measurement, A. L. Cullen, *Proc. IEE* (*London*), vol. 109, part B, supplement no. 23, pp. 724–733, May, 1962.

615 II — A New Precision Low-level Bolometer Bridge, W. C. Reisener and D. F. Birx, *Proc. IRE,* vol. 52, no. 1, pp. 39–42, January, 1962.

616 I — Microwave Measurements in the NBS Electronic Calibration Center, R. E. Larson, *Proc. IEE* (*London*), vol. 109, part B, supplement 23, pp. 644–650, May, 1962.

617 I — A Survey of Microwave Power Measurement Techniques Employed at the National Bureau of Standards, G. F. Engen, *Proc. IEE* (*London*), vol. 109, part B, supplement 23, pp. 734–739, May, 1962.

618 I — A Millimeter-wave Microcalorimeter, K. Sakurai and T. Maruyama, *IRE Trans. Instr.,* vol. I-11, nos. 3, 4, pp. 270–276, December, 1962.

619 I II — Microwave Power Measurements, H. M. Barlow, *IRE Trans. Instr.,* vol. I-11, nos. 3, 4, pp. 257–263, December, 1962.

620 I — Bolometric Microwave Power Calibration Techniques at the National Bureau of Standards, R. F. Desch and R. E. Larson, *IEEE Trans. Instr. Meas.,* vol. IM-12, no. 1, pp. 29–33, June, 1963.

621 I II — Measurement of Power, H. J. Carlin, chap. III, pp. 135–220, "Handbook of Microwave Measurements," 3d edition (M. Sucher and J. Fox, editors), Polytechnic Press, Polytechnic Institute of Brooklyn, N.Y., 1963.

622 I II — A Variable Impedance Power Meter, and Adjustable Reflection Coefficient Standard, G. F. Engen, *J. Res. NBS,* vol. 68C, no. 1, pp. 7–24, January–March, 1964.

*623 I II — A DC-RF Substitution Error in Dual Element Bolometer Mounts, G. F. Engen, *IEEE Trans. Instr. Meas.,* vol. IM-13, nos. 2, 3, pp. 58–64, June–September, 1964.

624 II — A Quick, Accurate Method for Measuring Thermistor-mount Efficiency and Calibration Factor, R. F. Pramann, *ISA Conference Proc.,* vol. 20, part I, preprint 42.1-4-65, 1965.

*625 I I S II III — Radio Frequency Power Measurements, A. Y. Rumfelt and L. B. Elwell, *Proc. IEEE,* vol. 55, no. 6, pp. 837–850, June, 1967.
This paper has an extensive list of references on power standards and measurements at microwave frequencies. Included in this paper is a short survey of various types of rf power-measurement devices.

626 I II — Experimental Confirmation of Barretter Substitution Error, J. W. Adams and R. F. Desch, *IEEE Trans. Microwave Theory and Techniques,* vol. MTT-16, no. 3, pp. 201–202, March, 1968.

627 I II — A Method of Determining the Mismatch Correction in Microwave Power Measurements, G. F. Engen, *IEEE Trans. Instr. Meas.,* vol. IM-17, no. 4, pp. 392–395, December, 1968.

628 II III — Accuracy of a Temperature-compensated Precision RF Power Bridge, E. E. Aslan, *IEEE Trans. Instr. Meas.,* vol. IM-18, no. 3, pp. 232–236, September, 1969.

629 I II — An Evaluation of the "Back-to-Back" Method of Measuring Adaptor Efficiency, G. F. Engen, *IEEE Trans. Instr. Meas.,* vol. IM-19, no. 1, pp. 18–22, February, 1970.

630 I II — Microwave Electrostatic Wattmeter, H. M. Barlow and W. W. Wizner, *Proc. IEE* (*London*), vol. 117, no. 1, pp. 249–254, January, 1970.

631 I II — The NBS Type II Power Measurement System, N. T. Larsen and F. R. Clague, paper 712, *Proc. 25th Ann. ISA Conf.,* vol. 25, part 3, October, 1970.

IMPEDANCE

Approximately 1 — 40 GHz (rectangular waveguide).

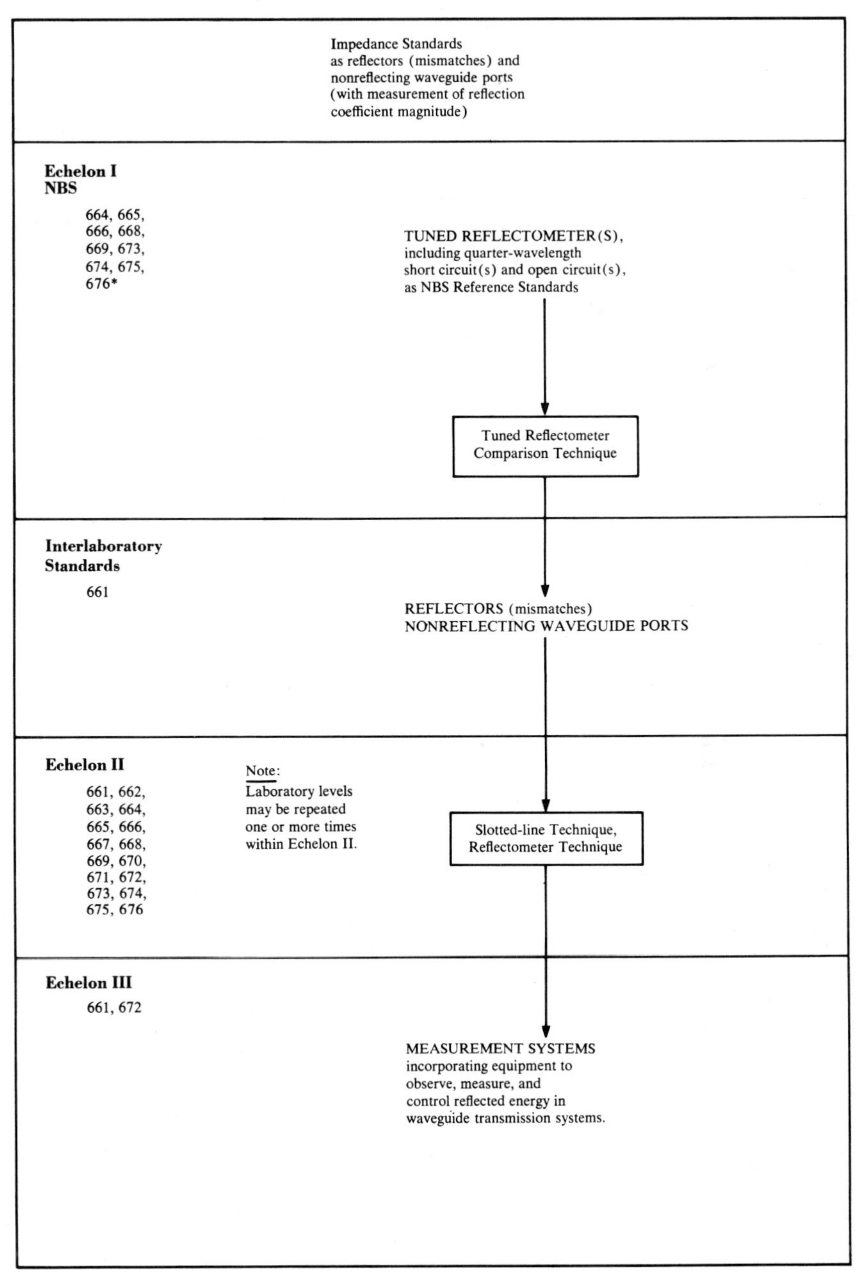

*These numbers refer to the list of references.

Approximately 1 to 40 GHz, Rectangular Waveguide

20. Impedance

661 I S II III Manufacturers of laboratory-type microwave equipment usually have available, upon request, a variety of technical information on their products, as well as informative literature on specialized topics of waveguide apparatus suitable for impedance standards and measurements.

662 II Measurements of Standing Waves, E. M. Porcell, chap. 8, pp. 473–514, and Measurement of Impedance, L. B. Young, chap. 9, pp. 515–560, "Technique of Microwave Measurements, Radiation Laboratory Series" (C. G. Montgomery, editor), McGraw-Hill Book Company, New York, 1947.

663 II Measurement of Impedance, chap. 5, pp. 235–312, "Microwave Measurements," E. L. Ginzton, McGraw-Hill Book Company, New York, 1957.

664 I II Recently Developed Microwave Impedance Standards and Methods of Measurements, R. W. Beatty and D. M. Kerns, *IRE Trans. Instr.*, vol. I-7, nos. 3, 4, pp. 319–321, December, 1958.

665 I II Microwave Reflectometer Techniques, G. F. Engen and R. W. Beatty, *IRE Trans. Microwave Theory and Techniques,* vol. MTT-7, no. 3, pp. 351–355, July, 1959.

666 I II Table of Magnitude of Reflection Coefficient Versus Return Loss ($L_R = 20 \log_{10} 1/|\Gamma|$), R. W. Beatty and W. J. Anson, *NBS Tech. Note* 72, Sept. 19, 1960.

667 II Microwave Impedance Calibration Service, *NBS Tech. News Bull.*, vol. 45, no. 8, pp. 136–137, August, 1961.

**668* I II A Guide to the Use of the Modified Reflectometer Technique of VSWR Measurement, W. J. Anson, *J. Res. NBS,* vol. 65C, no. 4, pp. 217–223, October–December, 1961.

669 I II Microwave Measurements in the NBS Electronic Calibration Center, R. E. Larson, *Proc. IEE (London)*, vol. 109, part B, supplement 23, pp. 644–650, 1962.

670 II Measurement of Standing Wave Ratio, A. B. Giordano, 3d edition, chap. II, pp. 73–133, "Handbook of Microwave Measurements" (M. Sucher and J. Fox, editors), Polytechnic Press, Polytechnic Institute of Brooklyn, N.Y., 1963.

**671* II Precise Reflection Coefficient Measurements with an Untuned Reflectometer, W. E. Little and D. A. Ellerbruch, *J. Res. NBS*, vol. 70C, no. 3, pp. 165–168, July–September, 1966.

672 II III A swept-frequency technique for measurement of reflection coefficient magnitude and of phase is described in An Advanced New Network Analyzer for Sweep-measuring Amplitude and Phase from 0.1 to 12.4 GHz, O. T. Dennison, *Hewlett-Packard J.*, vol. 18, no. 6, pp. 2–10, February, 1967; also, as auxiliary equipment: An Automatic Network Analyzer System, R. A. Hackborn, *Microwave J.*, vol. 11, no. 5, pp. 45–52, May, 1968.

**673* I II Impedance Measurements and Standards for Uniconductor Waveguide, R. W. Beatty, *Proc. IEEE,* vol. 55, no. 6, pp. 933–941, June, 1967.

674 I II A Graph of Return Loss versus Frequency for Quarter-wavelength Short-circuited Waveguide Impedance Standards, R. W. Beatty and B. C. Yates, *IEEE Trans. Microwave Theory and Techniques,* vol. MTT-17, no. 5, pp. 282–284, May, 1969.

675 I II A Semi-automatic Method for the Precision Measurement of Microwave Impedance, A. Jurkas, *IEEE Trans. Instr. Meas.*, vol. IM-18, no. 4, pp. 283–289, December, 1969.

676 I II A Calorimetric Method of Measuring High Reflection Coefficients at Microwave Frequencies, G. Rietto, *IEEE Trans. Instr. Meas.,* vol. IM-19, no. 4, pp. 364–368, November, 1970.

PHASE SHIFT

Approximately 1 – 40 GHz (rectangular waveguide). Measurements at NBS limited to certain frequencies.

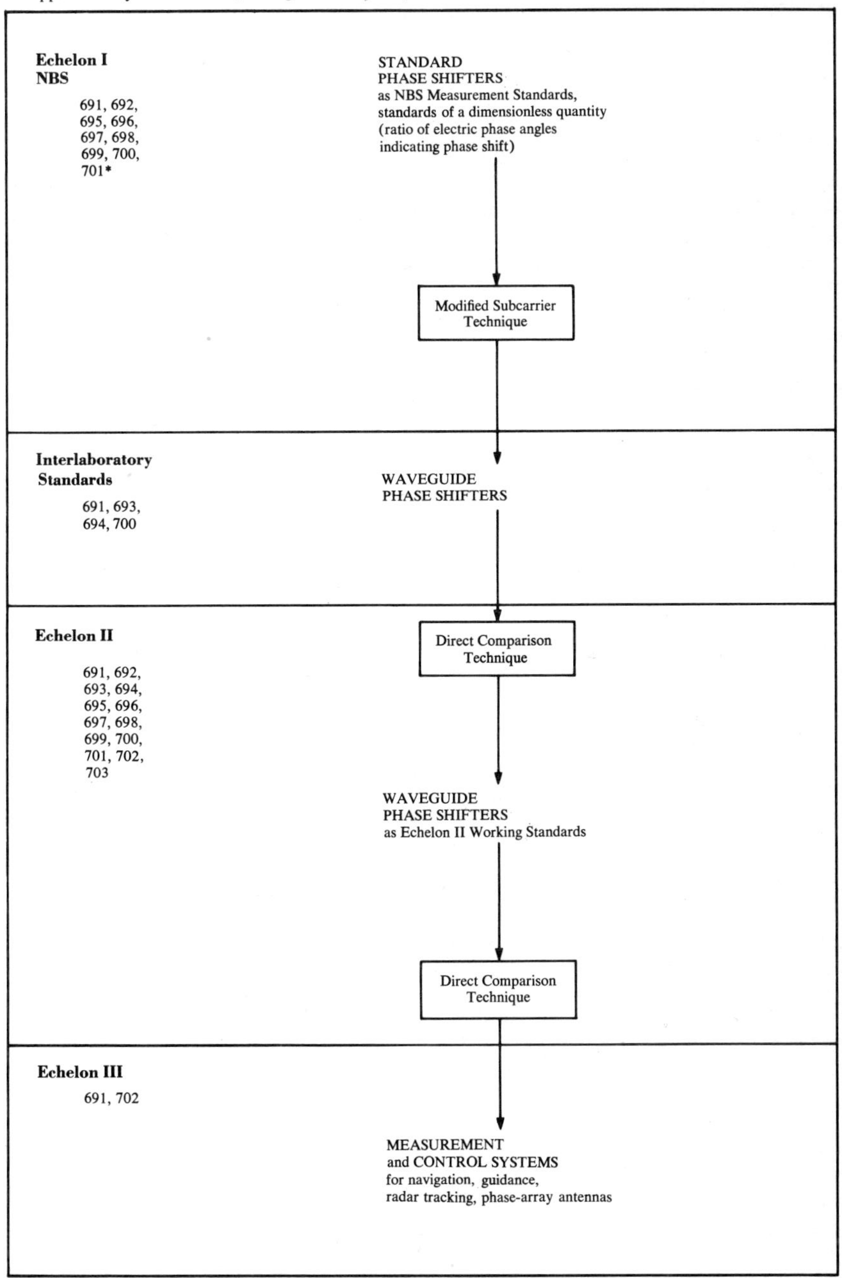

*These numbers refer to the list of references.

Approximately 1 to 40 GHz, Rectangular Waveguide (measurements at NBS limited to certain waveguide sizes)

21. Phase Shift

691 I I S II III — Manufacturers of laboratory-type microwave equipment usually have available, upon request, a variety of technical information on their products, as well as informative literature on specialized topics of waveguide apparatus suitable for phase-shift standards and measurements.

692 I II — A Method of Measuring Phase at Microwave Frequencies, S. D. Robertson, *Bell System Tech. J.*, vol. 28, no. 1, pp. 99–103, January, 1949.

693 I S II — A New Precision Waveguide Phase Shifter, E. F. Barnett, *Hewlett-Packard J.*, vol. 6, no. 5, pp. 3–4, January, 1955.

694 I S II — A New Precision X-band Phase-shifter, E. F. Barnett, *IRE Trans. Instr.*, vol. PGI-4, pp. 150–154, October, 1955.

695 I II — Precision Microwave Phase Shift Measurements, M. Magid, *IRE Trans. Instr.*, vol. I-7, nos. 3, 4, pp. 321–331, December, 1958.

696 I II — A Modulated Subcarrier Technique of Measuring Microwave Phase Shift, G. E. Shafer, *IRE Trans. Instr.*, vol. I–9, no. 2, pp. 217–219, September, 1960.

**697* I II — Mismatch Errors in Microwave Phase-shift Measurements, G. E. Schafer, *IRE Trans. Microwave Theory and Techniques*, vol. MTT-8, no. 6, pp. 617–622, November, 1960.

698 I II — Error Analysis of a Standard Microwave Phase Shifter, G. E. Schafer and R. W. Beatty, *J. Res. NBS*, vol. 64C, no. 4, pp. 261–265, October–December, 1960.

699 I II — Evaluation of a Microwave Phase Measurement System, D. A. Ellerbruch, *J. Res. NBS*, vol. 69C, no. 1, pp. 55–65, January–March, 1965.

**700* I I S II — UHF and Microwave Phase-shift Measurements, D. A. Ellerbruch, *Proc. IEEE*, vol. 55, no. 6, pp. 960–969, June, 1967. This paper has an extensive list of references on phase-shift measurements at microwave frequencies. Included in this paper is a short survey of various types of phase shifters.

701 I II — Calibration of Phase Shifters at Radio Frequencies, *NBS Tech. News Bull.*, vol. 53, no. 6, pp. 130–131, June, 1969.

702 II III — An Octave-band Microwave Phase Comparator, G. R. Deily and R. L. Herbstritt, *IEEE Trans. Instr. Meas.*, vol. IM-18, no. 4, pp. 290–294, December, 1969.

703 II — Universal Microwave Phase-Measuring System, W. P. Ernst, *IEEE Trans. Instr. Meas.*, vol. IM-19, no. 4, pp. 354–357, November, 1970.

ATTENUATION

Approximately 1 – 40 GHz (rectangular waveguide, also coaxial line).

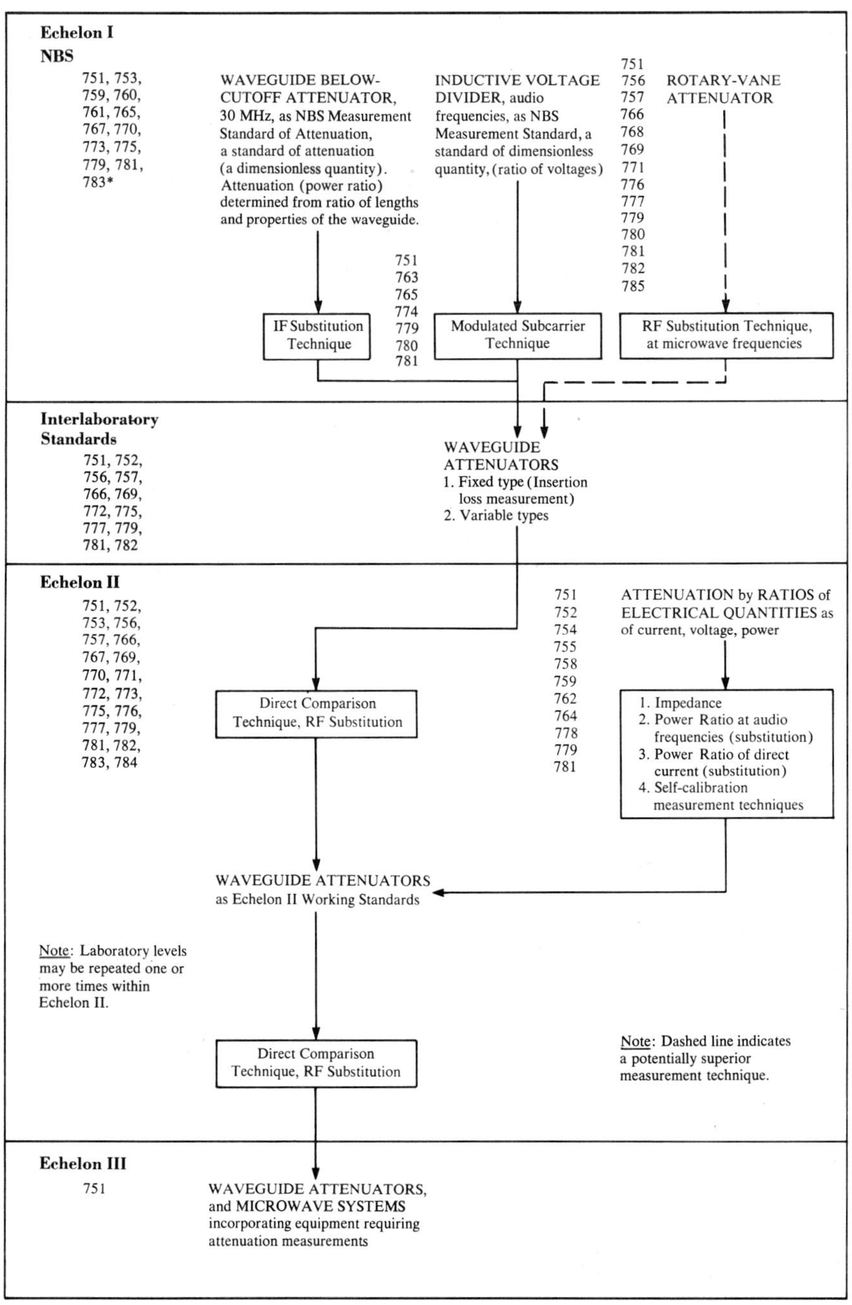

*These numbers refer to the list of references.

Approximately 1 to 40 GHz, Rectangular Waveguide, Also Coaxial Line

22. Attenuation

751 I I S II III — Manufacturers of laboratory-type microwave equipment usually have available, upon request, a variety of technical information on their products, as well as informative literature on specialized topics of waveguide apparatus suitable for attenuation standards and measurements.

752 I S II — Microwave Attenuators—Cutoff Attenuators, R. N. Griesheimer, chap. 11, pp. 679–719; Microwave Attenuators—Resistive Attenuators, E. Weber and R. N. Griesheimer, chap. 12, pp. 720–803; The Measurement of Attenuation, E. Weber, chap. 13, pp. 804–853, of "Technique of Microwave Measurements, Radiation Laboratory Series" (C. G. Montgomery, editor), McGraw-Hill Book Company, New York, 1947.

753 I II — A Standard of Attenuation for Microwave Measurements, R. E. Granthan and J. J. Freeman, *AIEE Trans.* (*Communication and Electronics*), vol. 67, pp. 329–335, 1948.

754 II — Determination of Attenuation from Impedance Measurements, R. W. Beatty, *Proc. IRE,* vol. 38, no. 8, pp. 895–897, August, 1950.

755 II — A-M System Measures Microwave Attenuation, J. Korewick, *Electronics,* 27, no. 1, pp. 175–177, January, 1954.

756 I I S II — Broadband Rotary Wave Guide Attenuator, B. P. Hand, *Electronics,* vol. 27, no. 1, pp. 184–185, January, 1954.

757 I I S II — A Precision Wave Guide Attenuator Which Obeys a Mathematical Law, B. P. Hand, *Hewlett-Packard J.,* vol. 6, no. 5, pp. 1–2, January, 1955.

758 II — The Calibration of Microwave Attenuators by an Absolute Method, E. Laverick, *IRE Trans. Microwave Theory and Techniques,* vol. MTT-5, no. 4, pp. 250–254, October, 1957.

759 I II — Microwave Attenuation Measurements with Accuracies from 0.0001 to 0.06 Decibel over a Range of 0.01 to 50 Decibels, G. F. Engen and R. W. Beatty, *J. Res. NBS,* vol. 64C, no. 2, pp. 139–145, April–June, 1960.

**760* I — A Precision RF Attenuation Calibration System, C. M. Allred and C. C. Cook, *IRE Trans, Instr.,* vol. I-9, no. 2, pp. 268–274, September, 1960.

761 I — Comparison of Two Techniques for Measuring Microwave Attenuation, *NBS Tech. News Bull.,* vol. 44, no. 11, pp. 192–193, November, 1960.

762 II — An Accurate Attenuation Measuring System with Great Dynamic Range, B. O. Weinschel, *Microwave J.,* vol. 4, no. 9, pp. 77–83, September, 1961.

**763* I — A Modulated Sub-carrier Technique of Measuring Microwave Attenuation, G. E. Schafer and R. R. Bowman, *Proc. IEE* (*London*), vol. 109, part B, supplement 23, pp. 783–786, 1962.

764 II — A Method for the Self-calibration of Attenuation Measuring Systems, R. L. Peck, *J. Res. NBS,* vol. 66C, no. 1, pp. 13–18, January–March, 1962.

765 I — Microwave Measurements in the NBS Electronic Calibration Center, R. E. Larson, *Proc. IEE* (*London*), vol. 109, part B, supplement 23, pp. 644–650, 1962.

766 I I S II — Analysis of Rotation Errors of a Waveguide Rotary-vane Attenuator, W. Larson, *IRE International Convention Record,* part 3, pp. 213–219, 1962.

767 I II — The Measurement of Arbitrary Linear Microwave Two-ports, H. M. Altschuler, *Proc. IEE* (*London*), vol. 109, part B, supplement 23, pp. 704–712, May, 1962.

768 I — An Absolute Microwave Attenuator, P. F. Mariner, *Proc. IEE* (*London*), vol. 109, part B (*Electronic and Communication Engineering*), pp. 415–419, September, 1962.

769 I I S II — A High-accuracy Microwave-attenuation Standard for Use in Primary Calibration Laboratories, A. V. James, *IRE Trans. Instr.,* vol. I-11, nos. 3, 4, pp. 285–290, December, 1962.

770 A Precision Attenuation Standard for X-band, R. F. Clark and B. J. Dean,
I *IRE Trans. Instr.*, vol. I-11, nos. 3, 4, pp. 291–293, December, 1962.
II

771 Table of Attenuation Error as a Function of Wave-angle Error for Rotary
I Vane Attenuators, W. Larson, *NBS Tech. Note* 177, May 20, 1963.
II

772 Attenuation, B. Rudner and S. W. Rosenthal, 3d edition, chap. VII, pp.
I S 377–416, "Handbook of Microwave Measurements" (M. Sucher and J.
II Fox, editors), Polytechnic Press, Polytechnic Institute of Brooklyn, N.Y., 1963.

773 A Standard Attenuator and the Precise Measurement of Attenuation, D. L.
I Hallway and F. P. Kelly, *IEEE Trans. Instr. Meas.*, vol. IM-13, no. 1,
II pp. 33–44, March, 1964.

774 Further Analysis of the Modulated Subcarrier Technique of Attenuation
I Measurement, W. E. Little, *IEEE Trans. Instr. Meas.*, vol. IM-13, nos. 2, 3, pp. 71–76, June–September, 1964.

***775** Effect of Connectors and Adapters on Accurate Attenuation Measurements
I at Microwave Frequencies, R. W. Beatty, *IEEE Trans. Instr. Meas.*, vol.
I S IM-13, no. 4, pp. 272–284, December, 1964.
II

776 Table of Attenuation as a Function of Vane Angle for Rotary-vane At-
I tenuators ($A = -40 \log_{10} \cos \theta$), W. Larson, *NBS Tech. Note* 229, Jan.
II 7, 1965.

777 Gearing Errors as Related to Alignment Techniques of the Rotary-vane
I Attenuator, W. Larson, *IEEE Trans. Instr. Meas.*, vol. IM-14, no. 3, pp.
I S 117–123, September, 1965.
II

778 A Precision DC Potentiometer Microwave Insertion Loss Test Set, C. T.
II Stelzried, M. S. Reid, and S. M. Petty, *IEEE Trans. Instr. Meas.*, vol. IM-15, no. 3, pp. 98–104, September, 1966.

779 Microwave Attenuation Measurements and Standards, R. W. Beatty, NBS
I Monograph 97, Apr. 3, 1967.
I S This paper has an extensive list of references on waveguide attenuation
II standards and measurements.

780 Variable-type Rotary-vane Microwave Attenuators Calibrated by Modulated
I Subcarrier Technique, *NBS Tech. News Bull.*, vol. 51, no. 5, pp. 96–97, May, 1967.

***781** RF Attenuation, D. Russell and W. Larson, *Proc. IEEE*, vol. 55, no.
I 6, pp. 942–959, June, 1967.
I S This paper has an extensive list of references on microwave attenuation
II standards and measurements.

782 Analysis of Rotationally Misaligned Stators in the Rotary-vane Attenuator,
I W. Larson, *IEEE Trans. Instr. Meas.*, vol. IM-10, no. 3, pp. 225–231,
I S September, 1967.
II

783 A Two-channel Off-null Technique for Measuring Small Changes of At-
I tenuation, T. Nemoto, R. W. Beatty, and G. H. Fentress, *IEEE Trans.*
II *Microwave Theory and Techniques*, vol. MTT-17, no. 7, pp. 396–397, July, 1969.

784 Superheterodyne Measurement of Microwave Attenuation at a 10 kHz
II Intermediate Frequency, R. F. Clark, *IEEE Trans. Instr. Meas.*, vol. IM-18, no. 3, pp. 225–231, September, 1969.

785 Rotary-vane Attenuator with an Optical Readout, W. E. Little, W. Larson,
I B. J. Kinder, *J. Res. NBS*, vol. 75C, no. 1, pp. 1–5, January–March, 1971.

NOISE
Approximately 1 – 40 GHz (rectangular waveguide).
Measurements at NBS limited to certain frequencies.

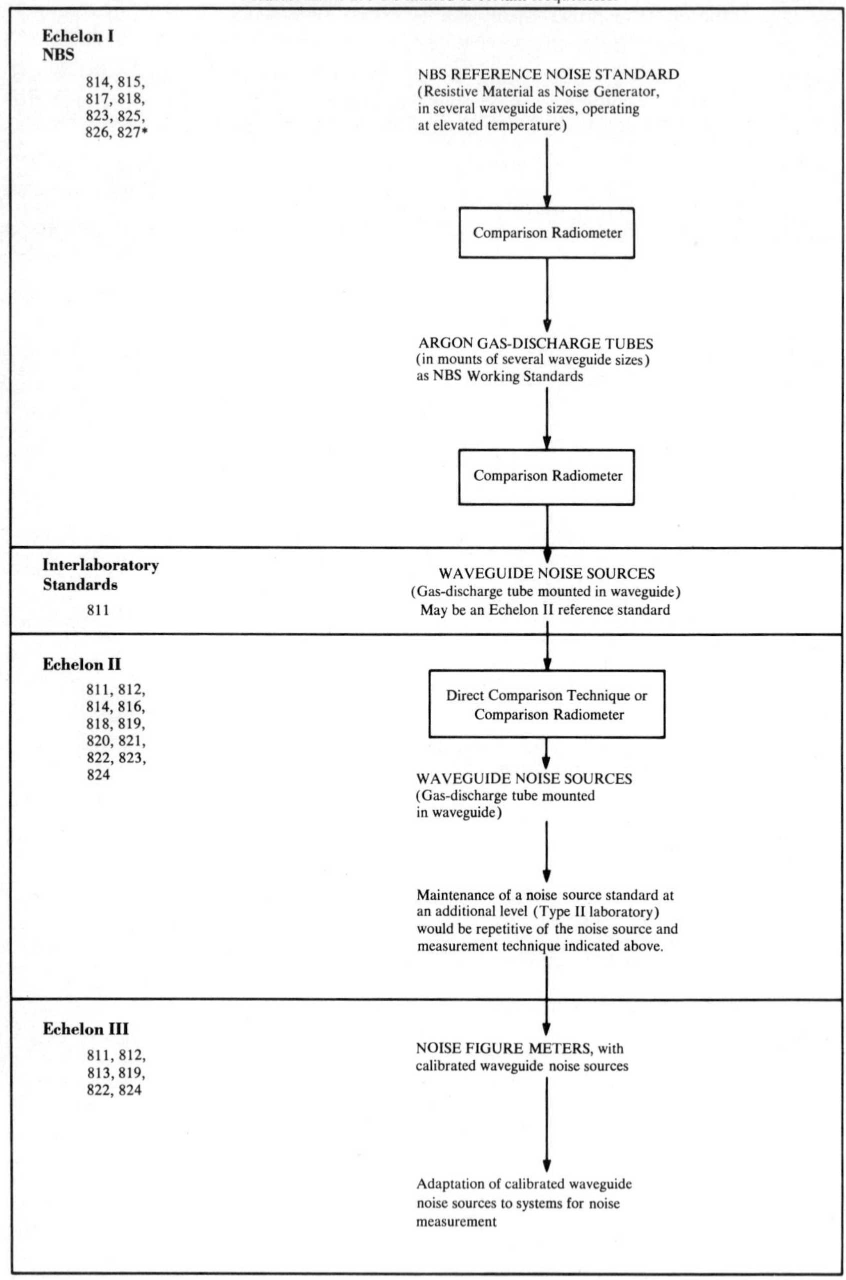

*These numbers refer to the list of references.

Approximately 1 to 40 GHz, Rectangular Waveguide (measurements at NBS limited to certain waveguide sizes and coaxial line)

23. Noise

811 I S II III — Manufacturers of laboratory-type microwave equipment usually have available, upon request, a variety of technical information on their products, as well as informative literature on specialized topics of waveguide apparatus suitable for noise standards and measurements.

812 II III — An Automatic Noise Figure for Improving Microwave Device Performance, H. C. Poulter; and Noise Figure and Its Measurements, B. M. Oliver, *Hewlett-Packard J.*, vol. 9, no. 5, pp. 1–8, January, 1958.

813 III — Automatic Indication of Receiver Noise Figure, T. G. Haneman and A. J. Hendler, *Topics in Noise,* Airborne, Instruments Laboratory, pp. 5–11, August, 1960.

814 I II — Electrical Noise, J. J. Freeman, *Electro-Technology,* vol. 66, no. 5, pp. 126–144, November, 1960.

815 I — Microwave Measurements in the NBS Electronic Calibration Center, R. E. Larson, *Proc. IEEE* (*London*), vol. 109, part B, supplement 23, pp. 644–650, 1962.

816 II — Subtle Difference in System Noise Measurement and Calibration of Noise Standards, T. Mukaihata, B. L. Walsh, Jr., M. F. Bottjer, and E. B. Roberts, *IRE Trans. Microwave Theory and Techniques,* vol. MTT-10, no. 6, pp. 506–516, November, 1962.

817 I — Calibration of Microwave Noise Sources, *NBS Tech. News Bull.,* vol. 47, no. 2, pp. 31–34, February, 1963.

**818* I II — Measurement of Effective Temperatures of Microwave Noise Sources, J. J. Wells, W. C. Daywitt, and C. K. S. Miller, *IEEE Trans. Instr. Meas.,* vol. IM-13, no. 1, pp. 17–28, March, 1964.

819 II III — A Survey of Techniques in Microwave Noise Measurement, T. Mukaihata, *ISA Trans.,* vol. 3, no. 4, pp. 342–352, October, 1964.

820 II — Calibration of Gas-discharge Noise Sources in an Industrial Laboratory, R. A. Andrews, Jr., *ISA Conference Proc.,* vol. 20, part I, preprint 42.1-1-65, 1965.

821 II — Noise Comparators and Standards for S and X Bands, G. J. Halford, *IEEE Trans. Instr. Meas.,* vol. IM-15, no. 4, pp. 310–317, December, 1966.

822 II III — Noise Figure Primer, *Hewlett-Packard Application Note* 57, Hewlett-Packard Co., June, 1967.

**823* I II — Noise Standards, Measurements, and Receiver Noise Definitions, C. K. S. Miller, W. C. Daywitt, and M. G. Arthur, *Proc. IEEE,* vol. 55, no. 6, pp. 865–877, June, 1967.
This paper has an extensive list of references on noise standards and noise measurements.

824 II III — New Equation Analyzes Mismatch Errors in Noise Measurements, W. E. Pastori, *Microwave,* vol. 7, no. 4, pp. 58–63, April, 1968.

825 I — A Method of Calibrating Coaxial Noise Sources in Terms of a Waveguide Standard, G. F. Engen, *IEEE Trans. Microwave Theory and Techniques,* vol. MTT-16, no. 9, pp. 636–639, September, 1968.

826 I — Noise Sources in Four Waveguide Sizes, *NBS Tech. News Bull.,* vol. 53, no. 1, p. 16, January, 1969.

827 I — Calibration of Coaxial Noise Sources Fitted with 14 mm Precision Connectors, *NBS Tech. News Bull.,* vol. 54, no. 3, pp. 62–63, March, 1970.

Approximately 1 to 40 GHz and Higher

GENERAL REFERENCES

841 "Technique of Microwave Measurements, Radiation Laboratory Series," C. G. Montgomery (editor), McGraw-Hill Book Company, New York, 1947.

842 "Microwave Measurements." E. L. Ginzton, McGraw-Hill Book Company, New York, 1957.

843 Mechanical Design and Manufacture of Waveguide Structures, A. F. Harvey, *IRE Trans. Microwave Theory and Techniques,* vol. MTT-7, no. 4, pp. 402–422, October, 1959.
This paper has an extensive list of references on the mechanical design and fabrication of microwave components that are used as standards and as components in measurement systems.

844 "Microwave Theory and Measurements," Engineering Staff of Hewlett-Packard Co., Prentice-Hall, Inc., Englewood Cliffs, N.J., 1962.

845 "Handbook of Microwave Measurement," M. Sucher and J. Fox (editors), vol. I, Polytechnic Press, Polytechnic Institute of Brooklyn, N.Y., 1963.

846 The System of Electromagnetic Quantities at Frequencies above 1 GHz, R. W. Beatty, *Metrologia,* vol. 2, no. 1, pp. 46–54, January, 1966.

847 "Handbook of Electronic Instruments and Measurement Techniques," H. E. Thomas and C. A. Clarke, Prentice-Hall, Inc., Englewood Cliffs, N.J., 1967.

848 Radio-frequency Measurements in the NBS Institute for Basic Standards, R. S. Powers and W. F. Snyder (editors), *NBS Tech. Note* 373, June, 1969.

849 An Introduction to the Description and Evaluation of Microwave Systems Using Terminal Invariant Parameters, G. F. Engen, NBS Monograph 112, October, 1969.

850 A valuable source of information on standards and precision-measurement techniques at radio frequencies is being made available by the Technical Committee on Electromagnetic Measurement—State of the Art, IEEE Group on Instrumentation and Measurement. Information on reports by this committee may be obtained from:

The Institute of Electrical and Electronics Engineers, Inc.
345 East 47th Street
New York, N.Y. 10017

CHART OF BASIC STANDARDS AND TRACEABILITY OF FREQUENCY

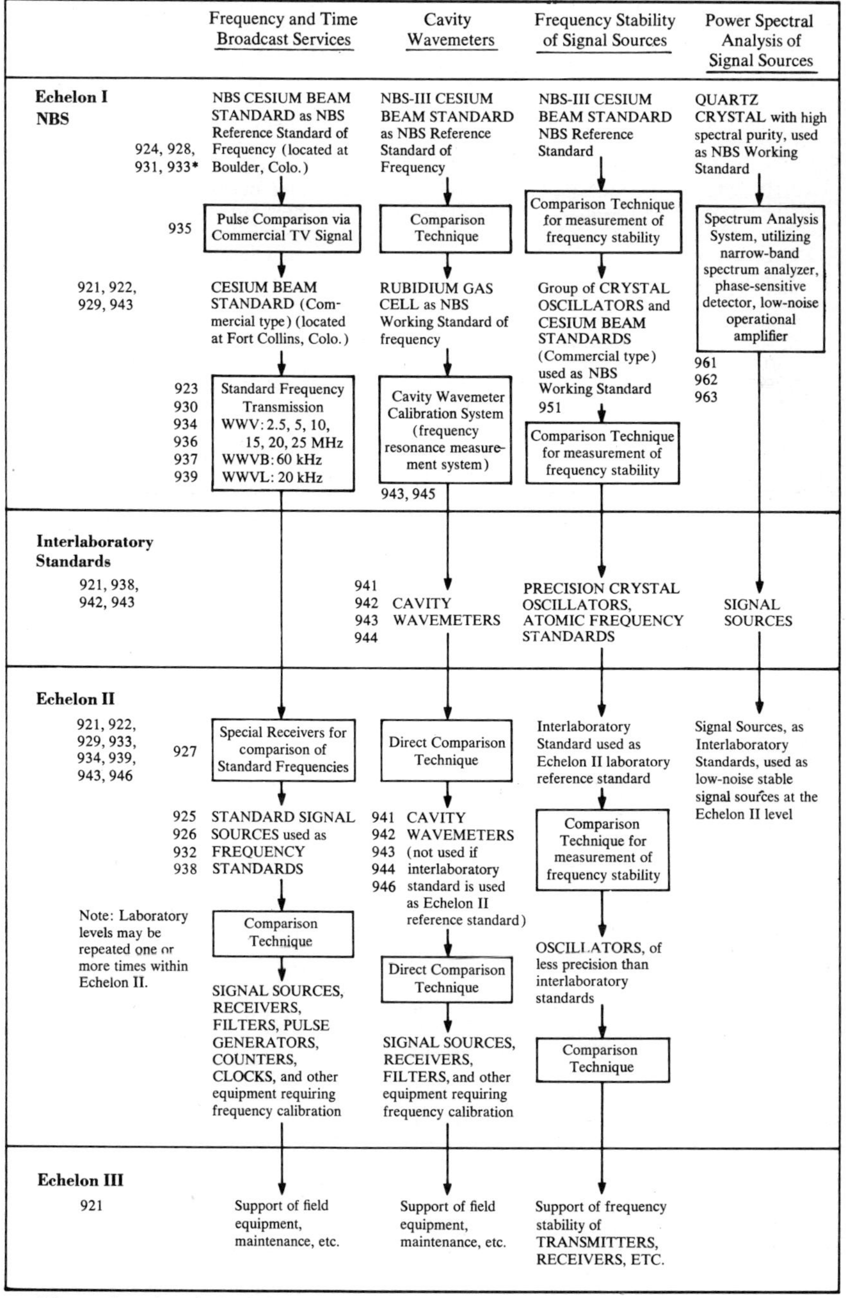

*These numbers refer to the list of references.

Frequency

921 Manufacturers of laboratory-type radio equipment usually have available,
I upon request, a variety of technical information on their products, as
I S well as informative literature on specialized topics of apparatus suitable
II for frequency standards and measurements.
III

Frequency and Time Broadcast Services

922 Frequency and Time Standards, F. D. Lewis, *Proc. IRE,* vol. 43, no.
I 9, pp. 1046–1068, September, 1955.
II This paper contains an extensive list of references on various types of frequency standards that had been developed up to the year 1955.

923 National Standards of Time and Frequency in the United States, Cor-
I respondence by NBS, *Proc. IRE,* vol. 48, no. 1, pp. 105–106, January, 1960.

924 A Comparison of Atomic Beam Frequency Standards, R. C. Mockler and
I C. S. Snider, *Nature,* vol. 187, no. 4738, pp. 681–682, Aug. 20, 1960.

925 Miniature Transistorized Crystal-controlled Precision Oscillators, W. L.
II Smith, *IRE Trans. Instr.,* vol. I-9, no. 2, pp. 141–148, September, 1960.

926 Performance of Precision Quartz-crystal Controlled Frequency Generators,
II R. A. Sykes, W. L. Smith, and W. J. Spencer, *IRE Trans. Instr.,* vol. I-11, nos. 3, 4, pp. 243–247, December, 1962.

927 A VLF Comparator for Relating Local Frequency to U.S. Standards,
II *Hewlett-Packard J.,* vol. 16, no. 2, pp. 1–8, October, 1964.

928 Cesium Beam Atomic Time and Frequency Standards, R. E. Beehler,
I R. C. Mockler, and J. M. Richardson, *Metrologia,* vol. 1, no. 3, pp. 114–131, July, 1965.
This paper has a very extensive list of references on atomic frequency and time standards to 1965.

929 Frequency and Time Standards, *Hewlett-Packard Application Note* 52,
I Hewlett-Packard Co., printing of November, 1965.
II

930 LF-VLF Frequency and Time Services of the National Bureau of Standards,
I D. H. Andrews, *Proc. IEEE Trans. Instr. Meas.,* vol. IM-14, no. 4, pp. 233–237, December, 1965.

931 An Intercomparison of Atomic Standards, R. E. Beehler, et al., *Proc. IEEE,*
I vol. 54, no. 2, pp. 301–302, February, 1966.

932 Quartz Frequency Standards, E. A. Gerber and R. A. Sykes, *Proc. IEEE,*
II vol. 55, no. 6, pp. 783–791, June, 1967.
This paper has an extensive list of references on developments in quartz frequency standards in recent years.

933 A Historical Review of Atomic Frequency Standards, R. H. Beehler, *Proc.*
I *IEEE,* vol. 55, no. 6, pp. 792–805, June, 1967.
II Although this survey paper is a historical sketch, it contains an extensive list of literature references that describes the various types of atomic frequency standards.

934 Distribution of Standard Frequency and Time Signals, A. H. Morgan,
I *Proc. IEEE,* vol. 55, no. 6, pp. 827–836, June, 1967.
II This paper has an extensive list of references on the distribution of standard frequency and time signals.

935 Microsecond Clock Comparison by Means of TV Synchronizing Pulses,
I J. Tolman, V. Ptaček, A. Součcek, and R. Stecher, *IEEE Trans. Instr. Meas.,* vol. IM-16, no. 3, pp. 247–254, September, 1967.

936 Standard Time and Frequency: Its Generation, Control, and Dissemination
I from the National Bureau of Standards Time and Frequency Division, J. B. Milton, *NBS Tech. Note* 379, August, 1969.

937 NBS Frequency and Time Broadcast Services, *NBS Special Publ.* 236,
I 1971 edition.

938 Frequency Meter, Comparator, Phase Meter—Three in One, A. Delagrange
I S and R. Davis, *Electronics,* vol. 43, no. 4, pp. 122–124, Feb. 16, 1970.
II

939 The Use of Television Signals for Time and Frequency Dissemination,
I D. D. Davis, J. L. Jeperson, and G. Kamas, *IEEE Proc. Letters,* vol.
II 58, no. 6, pp. 931–933, June, 1970.

Cavity Wavemeters

941 I S II High Q Resonant Cavities for Microwave Testing, I. G. Wilson, C. W. Schramm, and J. P. Kinzer, *Bell System Tech. J.*, vol. 25, no. 3, pp. 408–434, July, 1946.

942 I S II Frequency Measurements, L. B. Young, portion of chap. 6, pp. 375–407 of "Technique of Microwave Measurements, Radiation Laboratory Series" (C. G. Montgomery, editor), McGraw-Hill Book Company, New York, 1947.

943 I I S II Microwave Frequency Measurements and Standards, B. F. Husten and H. Lyons, *AIEE Trans.*, vol. 67, part I, pp. 321–328, 1948.

944 I S II Accurate Microwave Wavemeters with Convenient Tables, H. E. Bussey and A. J. Estin, *Rev. Sci. Instr.*, vol. 31, no. 4, pp. 410–413, April, 1960.

945 I Microwave Measurements in the NBS Electronic Calibration Center, R. F. Larson, *Proc. IEE (London)*, vol. 109, part B, supplement 23, pp. 644–650, 1962.

946 II Frequency and Wavelength, H. Klipper, chap. 1, pp. 1–69, of "Handbook of Microwave Measurements," 3d edition (M. Sucher and J. Fox, editors), Polytechnic Press, Polytechnic Institute of Brooklyn, N.Y., 1963.

Frequency Stability of Signal Sources

951 I Frequency Stability Calibration of Signal Sources, *NBS Tech. News Bull.*, vol. 49, no. 6, p. 89, June, 1965.

Power Spectral Analysis

961 I The Power Spectrum and Its Importance in Precise Frequency Measurements, J. A. Barnes and R. C. Mockler, *IRE Trans. Instr.*, vol. I-9, no. 2, pp. 149–155, September, 1960.

962 I A High-resolution Ammonia-maser-spectrum Analyser, J. A. Barnes and L. E. Heim, *IRE Trans. Instr.*, vol. I-10, no. 1, pp. 4–8, June, 1961.

963 I Power Spectrum Analysis of Signal Sources, *NBS Tech. News Bull.*, vol. 51, no. 6, pp. 112–113, June, 1967.

FUTURE DEVELOPMENT OF BASIC ELECTRICAL STANDARDS

Numerous programs are under development or being considered for the future to further the measurement art in the field of applied electronics. Such programs are in progress at the National Bureau of Standards, in industrial laboratories, and in the metrology laboratories of the Department of Defense. Of interest in these areas are:

1. Accurate measurements of rise time, shape, duration, and other characteristics of pulses, particularly for pulses of very short duration—of the order of nanoseconds
2. High rf power
3. Extension of frequency and magnitude ranges
4. Increased accuracy of measurements*
5. Swept-frequency measurement techniques
6. Measurements of balanced-line standards and instruments

* Significant steps have come in recent years with new approaches to obtain greater precision and accuracy of measurement and to gain greater simplicity of operation. In general, the technique involved is that of ratio measurement—the concept is old, but new and fresh approaches have brought on many improvements. These newer ratio-measurement devices and comparators permit ratios of magnitudes or small differences in magnitudes to be measured with great resolution and precision. Moreover, when the technique is coupled to a standard that has a known value of high accuracy of a dimensional quantity, the resultant ratio measurements will yield measurements with but little degradation of accuracy. These new developments cover a wide frequency range, extending from dc upward into radio frequencies. The accompanying lists of literature references cite a number of these developments of recent years.

7. New-concept approaches to present-day measurement problems*
8. Problems bearing upon automated measurement techniques
9. Standards and measurement techniques in microelectronics

* A new approach to calibration processes and the impact upon the National Measurement System is being taken by the National Bureau of Standards. It had its beginnings in the development of a measurement-analysis program, sometimes called the "pilot program" for mass calibration. (See P. E. Pontius, Measurement Philosophy of the Pilot Program for Mass Calibration, *NBS Tech. Note* 288, May 6, 1966; P. E. Pontius and J. M. Cameron, Realistic Uncertainties and the Mass Measurement Process, an Illustrated Review, NBS Monograph 103, Aug. 15, 1967.) In such a calibration process it is possible to apply many of the concepts of statistical quality control beyond the environment of the standards laboratory and into field operations.

Today's technology requires higher accuracy of calibrations than heretofore. The fact that a standard has been calibrated by a national laboratory does not mean that it will retain the measured value to a high degree of accuracy for an indefinite period or even a called-out period of time. What is desirable is a control process that will allow monitoring of the calibration as the standard is used beyond the confines of the calibrating laboratory.

Chapter 4

Accuracy and Precision*

THOMAS L. ZAPF

National Bureau of Standards, Boulder, Colorado

INTRODUCTION

Technical people everywhere find measurements to be a part of their daily work. The instruments they use to make measurements must be carefully chosen so that the measurement results will be correct within acceptable limits, and useful in further work. The best choice is usually made by those who are well acquainted with the characteristics of instruments (including inherent errors) and the general characteristics of measurement data.

The correctness, or accuracy, of measurement results must be determined, i.e., measured or estimated, and it must be described so others may understand. Thus, a vocabulary, including a certain amount of technical jargon, has built up over many years in the areas of specification writing, error analysis, and quality control. Much of the vocabulary has a basis in statistics, and it is to the statistician that one should go for carefully considered definitions of technical terms in these areas. The reader should be alert to the differences between terms that serve well as topical headings (accuracy, precision, etc.) and terms having refined technical definitions for use with numbers (limits of error, the standard deviation, etc.).

The topics in this chapter have been chosen to give the reader an understanding of many of the basic concepts, procedures, and mathematical tools used by metrologists to ascertain the accuracy and the precision of measurements.

In the next section of this chapter some common errors in electrical and electronic instruments are discussed to call attention to the many elementary errors that arise in instruments themselves, and those directly related to their use. Then, we consider the characteristics of errors in measurements, and discuss what is meant by a measurement method, a measurement process, systematic and random errors, accuracy, and precision. The last section, on statistical methods, presents basic information, formulas, and procedures for the treatment of random errors in measurements.

The chapter should serve as an introduction to precision and accuracy for electronics engineers and technicians interested in electronic instrumentation. References mentioned in the text are listed at the end of the chapter.

ERRORS IN INSTRUMENTS

1. Sources of Error in Instruments In this section we will discuss briefly many recognizable sources of error in electronic instruments that employ electrical deflecting instruments as readout devices or as null indicators. Some of the sources of error to be mentioned will be absent in equipment with digital readout devices, of course, but others will appear. The purpose of this discussion is to bring to mind the large number of elementary sources of error in (or related to) electronic instruments, so that the reader will understand that errors in instrument readings are resultants of many elementary components. Some of the elementary errors will vary from one reading to another, others will remain relatively constant, and others will change slowly over a long period of time.

Division marks may be incorrectly located on the scale of an instrument, perhaps from errors in marking the cardinal points, or from improper spacing of subdivision marks between cardinal points. Scales in many electronic instruments are printed in large lots in conformance with a known scale law or master scale. After manufacture, the instruments are checked for acceptance within specified tolerances in the manufacturer's quality-control laboratory. Instruments having scale errors larger than permitted by the tolerances would be reworked. Sometimes an apparent error is caused by a bent pointer, an iron filing in the gap of the magnet (in permanent-magnet moving-coil instruments), or perhaps a fiber sticking upward from the scale interfering with movement of the pointer. In the absence of flaws such as these, scale errors can be measured by comparing the readings of the instrument with those of a more accurate one. The errors are then known, and corrections can be applied whenever the instrument is used.

Pivot friction is a common source of error in instruments having moving elements that rotate on pivots in jeweled bearings. Through use, or abuse, the points on pivots become flattened, and the bearings worn and dirty. The effect of pivot friction is seen when the pointer position changes in a jerky manner when the measured quantity is gradually changed. To eliminate the effects of pivot friction, it is good practice to tap an instrument gently before reading it.

Some instruments are designed for use with their scales horizontal, others vertical. The balance of the moving system may be such as to yield different readings if the position is changed—hence a possible error. To avoid this error, the instrument should be used in the same position as calibrated.

Deflecting torque on the moving system (in many instruments) is opposed by the torque from flat spiral springs. In many instruments the springs also conduct current to and from the moving system. The stress on the springs is well below their elastic limit, but in practice some "creeping" may be noticed, a result of slight yield in the spring when stressed. The trouble is revealed when the instrument is deenergized; the pointer then may return to a point slightly upscale, returning to zero only after a minute or so. Obviously, such effects can cause errors.

A mechanical zero-adjusting mechanism is to be found on most electronic measuring instruments, and on some a separate electrical "zero set" is provided also. Neglecting to set these adjustments before taking readings can cause errors. Zero settings should be checked frequently during a series of measurements, and at the finish.

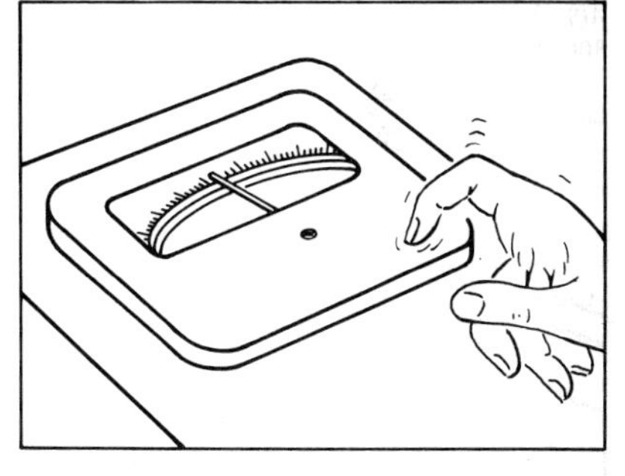

Fig. 1. Gentle tapping reduces the effect of pivot friction.

The aging effects in vacuum tubes and heating effects in transistors used in electronic instruments are largely eliminated by good circuit design. Nevertheless, instruments do sometimes exhibit a long-term drift. Instruments should be calibrated frequently enough to detect drift (from whatever cause) before errors become intolerable. If warm-up effects exist, the procedure for both calibrating and using the instrument should be specified so that the effects do not cause errors in measurement results. Often this can be accomplished by taking the readings quickly, before warm-up can occur. In other cases it may be best to let the instrument attain temperature equilibrium before reading.

Many components in electronic instruments are sensitive to changes in temperature. Laboratory instruments of best quality are usually designed for best accuracy at, or near, 23°C. If an instrument is to be used at temperatures of more than, say, 5°C above or below the design temperature, it would be advisable to recalibrate at the desired temperature. Springs, magnets, transistors, resistors, and other components can be affected by heating, whether it be from ambient conditions or from self-heating, i.e., from power dissipated in the component itself.

Most instruments are frequency-sensitive; i.e., their response depends on the frequency of the applied quantity (current, voltage, or power). Errors can result if the frequency at time of use differs from that used for the calibration. Calibrations using swept-frequency techniques yielding a graph, or an extensive table, of instrument response vs. frequency can be very useful in correcting for errors from differences in frequency.

Waveform errors are particularly troublesome in some instruments. For example, an instrument intended for measuring the effective (root mean square) value of a sine waveform may inherently respond to the average value of the rectified waveform, or perhaps to the peak value of the rectified waveform, but the scale is marked to indicate the effective value of the sine wave. If a nonsinusoidal waveform is measured, the readings may not (and generally will not) be correct. Harris,[1] pp. 454–468, treats this problem in some detail, as part of an introduction to various kinds of electronic instruments. A good introductory discussion of vacuum-tube voltmeters, diode voltmeters, and rectifier voltmeters is to be found in Chap. 1 of Ref. 2.

2. Errors in Reading Instruments It is particularly appropriate to consider some errors that arise in reading instrument scales. First, let us discuss parallax errors.

The parallax error in reading a deflecting instrument arises from the apparent displacement of the pointer corresponding to different positions of the observer's eye. The usual means by which parallax is eliminated is the familiar antiparallax mirror, a reflecting plane arc adjacent to the scale of the instrument and underneath the pointer. To eliminate parallax, the observer aligns the pointer with its image in the mirror, thus fixing the observer's line of sight relative to the pointer of the instrument. The observer then reads the instrument by associating the position of the pointer with the nearby scale markings, or adjusts auxiliary apparatus to deflect the pointer to a particular division mark, in which case continuous attention to parallax is necessary. (See Fig. 2.)

It has been found that scale-reading errors are minimized when the width of the pointer and the width of the division marks are both about one-tenth of the interval between marks.[3] This ratio is commonly found in electrical and electronic instruments of the best quality. It has been the experience of the author and his colleagues that an observer can usually estimate correctly to the nearest 0.1 scale division, on instruments having well-designed scales, and he is nearly always correct within ±0.2 scale division. An error in reading of 0.1 division at the 100 division mark on a 100-division scale will be an error of 0.1 percent of the measured quantity, but a 0.1 division error at the quarter-scale point will be an error of 0.4 percent of the measured quantity. For best accuracy, instruments should be chosen so that readings will be taken from the upper half of the scale. This and other sources of error in reading instruments are discussed by Weaver[3] and Harris,[1] pp. 116–120.

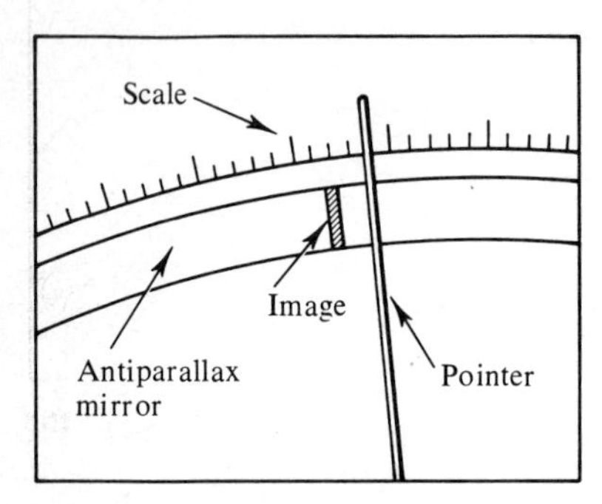

Fig. 2. To eliminate parallax, the observer aligns the pointer with its image in the mirror.

3. Correcting for Known Errors The choice of a measuring instrument for a particular measurement job should be made, if possible, after a preliminary analysis of errors has been done. If it is possible to apply corrections to the instrument readings to correct for known errors, then this should be done. Ideally the remaining errors in the instrument should be small relative to the errors from other equipment or other sources of error in the measurement process.

One function of national standardizing laboratories is to determine the corrections to the nominal values of standards of measurement used by manufacturers and metrology laboratories where, in turn, corrections are assigned to other standards and instruments. In the United States a chain of measurements can be traced from the National Bureau of Standards to most instruments used for measuring defined quantities. However, not every instrument is provided with a set of corrections. Many instruments are merely checked to ensure that their readings are within acceptable tolerances. The manufacturer then warrants that the inaccuracy of the readings is within stated limits. If the user needs better accuracy, either he must have the instrument calibrated (i.e., have the corrections determined) and then apply the corrections, or he must seek a higher-quality instrument. If he does neither of these, he can only allow for the possibility of error in his instrument by widening the gap between the limits of error associated with the results of his work. The advantages of applying corrections for systematic errors in electrical instruments are discussed by F. L. Hermach.[4]

In addition to instrument errors, errors in measurements arise from other sources, too. One needs only to mention that errors, both variable and fixed, occur in the repeated use of standards, bridges, transformers, and other measuring equipment, to understand that in nearly every measurement there are at least several sources of error. Intentional or unintentional variations in measurement *procedures* can cause errors. In this chapter we cannot undertake a detailed examination of errors in specific equipment, or in specific procedures. Instead, we will consider "errors in measurements" in a general way, i.e., by their characteristics as evident from looking at data. For an extensive survey of experimental design, error analysis, and probability and statistics the reader should see E. Bright Wilson, Jr.[5]

ERRORS IN MEASUREMENTS

4. Errors, Corrections, and Residual Errors The reading R of a measuring instrument would be correct if it were to equal exactly the true value τ of the quantity being measured. Generally speaking, instrument readings are seldom absolutely correct. The difference $R - \tau$ is the error in the reading. The reading can be corrected by algebraically adding a correction C to the reading R. Thus the correction is the negative of the error and is ordinarily determined by measurement by the manufacturer or by a calibration laboratory. Corrections are applied to readings to offset the effect of error, and the corrected reading is then taken as a *measure* of the true value.

A standard of measurement, such as a standard resistor or a standard attenuator, embodies a unit of measurement. The nominal value N, or marked value, is usually a round number such as 100 Ω or 20 dB. Rarely does a standard embody *exactly* the round-number nominal value marked (often engraved) on the standard, but instead it possesses more, or less, of the quantity. Thus, the nominal value is ordinarily slightly in error and can be corrected by adding a correction C that has been determined by accurate measurement in a calibration laboratory. The result, $N + C = T$, is a measure of the true value τ of the unit embodied by the standard. The letter T is used here to denote a "measure" of the true value to call attention to the fact that it may not (and, in general, probably will not) equal exactly the true value τ. Thus the difference $T - \tau$ is an error of smaller magnitude and unknown sign remaining after the correction has been applied. Of course, a calibration laboratory may report its measurement of the true value directly, e.g., 100.023 Ω or 19.988 dB, rather than an algebraically additive "correction to nominal," +0.023 Ω or −0.012 dB. Alternatively, correction *factors* may be reported, e.g., as 100(1.00023) Ω, or 20(0.9994) dB.

In general, a measurement result X will be in error and may be corrected to yield a measure of the true value, i.e., $X + C = T$. Unfortunately, even after the application of corrections to counter the effect of determinate errors, there may remain a residual error, i.e., an error of unknown magnitude and unknown sign. We have already shown that there are many sources of variation (and error) in the use of deflecting instruments, such as environmental changes, pivot friction, self-heating effects, spring fatigue, and observational errors in reading the scale. It is helpful now to consider the general behavior of residual errors when repeated readings are taken, e.g., from the same instrument or from different instruments, or when a number of standards of measurement are used in succession in a measurement process. But first, what is meant by "measurement process"?

5. Measurement Methods and Measurement Processes A measurement result is a product of a measurement *process*, which is considered to be a particular realization of a specified measurement *method*. The specification of the method states the *kinds* of standards, instruments, and other equipment of importance, the way they are to be interconnected, the conditions under which the measurements are to be made, and the procedure to be followed. The method of measurement should be specified clearly enough so that the *true value* can be measured with accuracy sufficient to satisfy the needs. Certainly, the treatment of end effects, connection errors, conditions, etc., should be explained in the specification of the method. When particular instruments, standards, and other equipment are used under particular conditions by particular observers to obtain measurement results, the measurement process should (but may not always) satisfy the needs.

Whenever a measurement process is used repeatedly, it is generally found that the measurement results $x_1, x_2, \ldots, x_n$ differ by small amounts. Such differences are evidence of errors that vary from measurement to measurement. The application of a single correction C to all the measurement results will not reduce the variations in the results. Rather, it will make the average of the results a better estimate of the true value τ. Where do corrections come from? They are, themselves, the results of careful calibrations (of instruments, or standards) or the results of calculations based on measurements.

Whenever corrections are available for application to readings or other "raw" data to improve results, they should be applied, of course. From here on, we shall stipulate that all appropriate corrections have been applied, leaving only residual errors for further consideration. Thus a set of results $x_1, x_2, \ldots, x_n$ will be henceforward a set of corrected data, and we shall be interested in the characteristics of corrected data.

The importance of defining exactly what is meant by a "repetition of the process" can be understood by considering the following hypothetical situations. Suppose we are asked to measure, by a specified method, "errors in vacuum-tube voltmeters of the 1 percent accuracy class at the top scale point on the 300-V range, at 1 MHz." The specifications for the method include tolerances allowable on environmental conditions, electric and magnetic fields, etc., and also state that "a well-regulated, calibrated signal generator (limits of error, ± 0.2 percent of output voltage) shall be used." The specifications also tell how to connect the instrument (a vacuum-tube voltmeter) to the generator, maximum lead length, procedures, and many other things. We want to obtain a measure of the errors in vacuum-tube voltmeters, and also a measure of the variation of results in repetitions of our measurement process (which is a particular realization of the specified method). We decide (tentatively, at least) to take 20 measurements at irregular intervals over a period of 5 days. Now, let us consider ways in which instruments can be chosen. Let us consider three situations.

If only one instrument is used, the set of 20 results $x_1, x_2, \ldots, x_{20}$ from measurements of the single fixed quantity from this particular measurement process (in which readings are repetitively taken from a single instrument) can be treated as a *sample,* of size 20, from a larger *population* of results that might have been, or could be, obtained. Such a population is conceptually infinite, although practical limitations (lack of time, wear in equipment, observer fatigue, etc.) usually prohibit acquiring more than, say, a few hundred results before some significant change must be made. It is important to understand that, in this situation, the results of repetitions are from a measuring process in which no changes were made in any of the equipment.

Next, consider that 20 instruments are to be used, all of the same make and model, and each is to be used in the process only once. Each of the 20 readings (in the 20 repetitions of the process) comes from a different instrument. Most people would agree that larger variations among the x values are to be expected, now. The measurement process is different to the extent that a different instrument is *required* in each repetition. For *this* process a set of data is a sample from a population of data that could be taken (using the process) with all instruments of the same make and model. The population is large, but finite.

Finally, suppose that the instruments are to include all makes, and all appropriate models, available in this country. This is quite a different process, again, with an added problem, namely, how to choose the instruments that will constitute a sample from the different makes and models. Assuming that the matter is settled by stipulating some orderly or perhaps a "random" manner of selection, a set of data from this process is a sample from a population of much larger (but finite) size. Indeed, a set of 20 may not be large enough to include all makes and models even once. The variations in the results are likely to be larger than if only one manufacturer's product were used.

The three situations correspond to three different measurement processes based on one measurement method. The scope of each process is different, and the data (measurement results) must be considered as samples from different statistical populations. After the process has been adequately specified (including exactly what is involved in repetitions of the process), it is possible to speak meaningfully of systematic errors and random errors.

6. Systematic Errors and Random Errors Errors may be classified in many ways for different purposes. It is usually desirable, however, to distinguish as well as possible between systematic errors and random errors in measurement processes. First, we shall consider what is meant by "systematic errors."

The classification "systematic errors" embraces those errors that remain constant through all repetitions of a measurement process, or produce a drift, trend, cyclic, or other predictable pattern among repeated measurement results. Errors that remain constant through all repetitions of a measurement process are not ordinarily evident from looking at data. Constant errors in measurement results can exist, and their magnitude and sign may remain unknown until comparisons are made with results from other processes or other methods. The metrologist can (and should) determine *limits* of systematic error so that the uncertainty of the measurement result may be better understood by others who must make use of the result. Often it is necessary to determine limits of systematic error by rather subjective means. However, estimates made by an experienced metrologist who is familiar with the particular measurement process are generally accepted.

TABLE 1 Data from Measurements of Electromotive Force of a Particular Unsaturated Standard Cell*

Date	*Electromotive Force, V*
Mar. 1960	1.019 33
Jan. 1961	1.019 29
Jul. 1961	1.019 26
Feb. 1962	1.019 25
Jan. 1963	1.019 20
Jul. 1963	1.019 18
Nov. 1963	1.019 16
May 1964	1.019 14
Aug. 1964	1.019 12
Feb. 1965	1.019 10
Aug. 1965	1.019 07
Aug. 1966	1.019 02

* Data supplied by B. A. Wickoff, Electromagnetics Division, Institute for Basic Standards, National Bureau of Standards.

Systematic errors that are evident from the data, i.e., trends and cyclical variations, may be correctable. Examine the data on a standard cell in Table 1. Each successive test yields a value lower than all previous values. In this case the measurement process was known to be in good control, and so the cell was suspected. It was checked frequently, and finally discarded. If the cell had been used as a standard from March, 1960, until July, 1963, say, without recalibration on the assumption that the assigned value (1.01933 V) was valid during the entire period, there would be an increasing error in the measurements, reaching about 150 μV in July, 1963. By more frequent calibration, the errors from the unidirectional drift in the cell's voltage were limited to 50 μV or less.

A drift, a trend, or a cyclical variation in data can often be correlated with a similarly changing environmental factor such as temperature or humidity, or factors associated with the equipment (or the operation of it) such as the applied power, frequency, or line voltage. The search for causes of systematic errors in measurement process can be a difficult task. It requires a rather complete knowledge of the specifications of the measurement method and measurement process, including the characteristics of the particular equipment used. The burden of the search is squarely on the shoulders of the metrologist in charge of the measurement process. He must use his resources, including ingenuity, to find the causes of error, and then take corrective action. For example, if drift is found to be correlated with frequency, the test frequency should be controlled within narrower tolerances, or if the dependence on frequency is known and the frequency is measured at the time each measurement is made, each measurement result can be corrected to yield the result that would have been obtained at the specified frequency.

Sometimes the presence of systematic errors is known, but for one reason or another, corrections cannot be (or simply *are not*) made. Then it is customary to include in the limits of systematic error associated with the measurement results an allowance for error of this sort. In this case the metrologist should include in his report a discussion on the nature of the systematic errors and their effects.

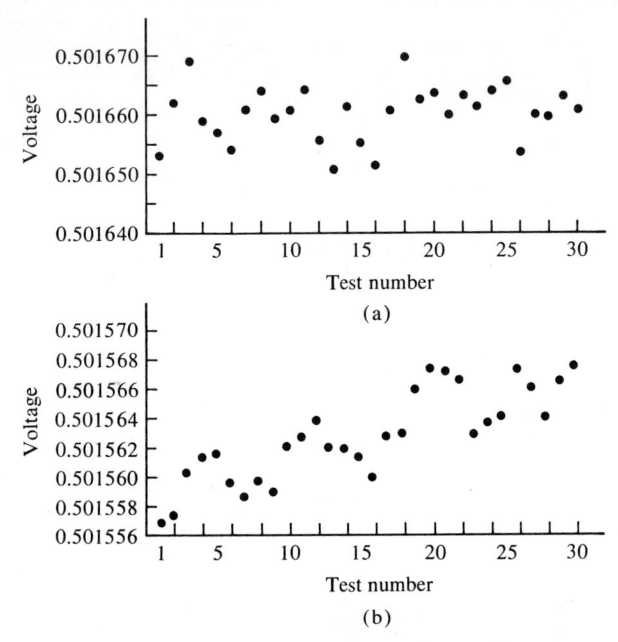

Fig. 3. Experimental data plotted in the order taken. Although representing results of many readings of the same measurement, the data shown in (*a*) varies significantly from point to point in an unpredictable manner. This demonstrates the action of random causes resulting in differences between measurements, even though each point is within the expected overall accuracy of the system. There is no serious evidence of systematic errors such as drifts, trends, or cyclic variations, but in (*b*) while the same random variation still exists, a drift (or nonrandom error) is also evident.

Random errors presumably result from a number of relatively small and independent error sources. Random errors, as a class, can now be defined as nonsystematic errors, i.e., those residual errors exhibited by repeated measurement results that vary in an irregular manner without discernible and predictable pattern. "Randomness" has been found to be one of the most elusive of all concepts to define and, as a property, one of the most difficult to distinguish sharply from "nonrandomness."

The presence of nonrandom errors is more or less evident from an examination of measurement results plotted graphically in the order taken. Figure 3*a* shows a graph of data from part of an experiment on noise measurements. The graph shows no evidence of serious systematic effects. There seems to be no predictable drift or cyclic variation. In Fig. 3*b*, however, an upward drift is clearly evident.

When the results appear to be random, independent, and spread somewhat symmetrically about a central value, and when small deviations from the central value are more frequent than large ones, the "normal law of error" (to be discussed later) is customarily used as a basis for describing the distribution of results. Statistical methods are available for treating random errors in measurements.

One of the most readable and interesting articles discussing systematic and random errors is by Dorsey and Eisenhart, On Absolute Measurement, reprinted as Paper 1.3, p. 49, of Ref. 6. In the same reference, Paper 1.4 is a reprint of an article by Youden on Systematic Errors in Physical Constants, containing an introduction to the design of experiments for detecting systematic errors, and the entire Sec. 2 is devoted to the design of calibration experiments. An elementary introduction to some of the characteristics of measurement data is given in Ref. 7.

TABLE 2 Sets of Data from Two Slightly Different Measurement Processes in Experiments on Radio-frequency Noise Measurements*

For condition B a noise source was *in* the circuit, whereas it was *not* in the circuit for condition A. The difference between the averages is caused by a small deliberate change in level required as part of the procedures.

Test No.	Voltage (condition A), V	Voltage (condition B), V
1	0.501 110	0.501 182
2	0.501 112	0.501 197
3	0.501 110	0.501 182
4	0.501 110	0.501 183
5	0.501 009	0.501 186
6	0.501 110	0.501 187
7	0.501 110	0.501 178
8	0.501 111	0.501 195
9	0.501 109	0.501 191
10	0.501 112	0.501 188
	Avg. 0.501 110	0.501 187

* Data supplied by M. G. Arthur, Electromagnetics Division, Institute for Basic Standards, National Bureau of Standards.

7. The Meaning of Precision and Accuracy In metrology the terms "accuracy" and "precision" are considered as characteristics of the measuring process. Accuracy refers to the typical "closeness to the true value," and "precision" refers to the typical "closeness together" of measurement results in the (conceptually) large population of results that might have been, or could be, obtained.[8] A small set of measurement results may be considered as a sample from the population. For further discussion of the meaning of "population" and "sample" see Chap. 1 of Ref. 9, which is reprinted as Paper 5.1 in Ref. 6. When measurements of the same quantity are repeated, the dispersion of the results can be seen by examining the data. A set of data that shows little variation may be said to "exhibit" greater precision than a set of data showing larger variation. For example, observe the variations in the data in the left column of Table 2 and compare with the large variations in the right column. The sets of data are from measurements of voltage of two slightly different measurement processes corresponding to conditions A and B. It must be understood that a single set of measurement data from a measurement process will exhibit greater or less precision than that which is characteristic of the measurement process (considering the conceptually infinitely large population of data that might have been, or could be, obtained). Thus, we distinguish between the *apparent* precision of a set, or sample, of data, and the precision of the measurement process. The precision of a measurement process can be visualized by means of a graphical "distribution" of the population of measurement results showing the probability density as a function of the measured values. Figure 5 is an example of a distribution, one that will be discussed in detail later. The probability of occurrence of measured values within a chosen interval on the scale of measured values is given by the area under the distribution curve within the interval.

Terms like "high precision" and "low precision" leave much to be desired. The "high" and "low" modifiers must be considered relative to some known value of precision. Furthermore, in discussing precision, it is customary to think of the small differences among the results, which are really related directly to *imprecision* rather than *precision.*

The term "accuracy" in measurements refers to the typical closeness of a measurement result x (or an average $\bar{x}$) to the true value τ. Associated with a *particular* measurement result there is some (perhaps unknown) error. We conjecture or make inferences about the magnitude of the error, i.e., of the "accuracy," from our knowledge of the measurement process, or the method of measurement that produced it. Conceptually, as used in metrology, accuracy comprises both precision and conformance with the true value. The term "accurary" is frequently used to denote a small difference from the true value, really the "inaccuracy" of a measurement. Advertisements for electronic instruments commonly contain statements such as "the *accuracy* is ±0.1 percent of full scale." What is intended is that "the limits of *inaccuracy* are ±0.1 percent of full scale." This inversion of meaning is common, and rarely causes real misunderstanding, but it is well to be aware of it. The negative and positive limits are intended, presumably, as outer bounds for the errors that may reside in, or be caused by, the instrument, giving rise to the term "limits of error." Thus, one could say "the limits of error are ±0.1 percent of full scale." Numerical measures of impression and numerical limits of systematic error are needed to describe the accuracy of measurements; so it is important that all metrologists use the terms "accuracy" and "precision" in a consistent way.

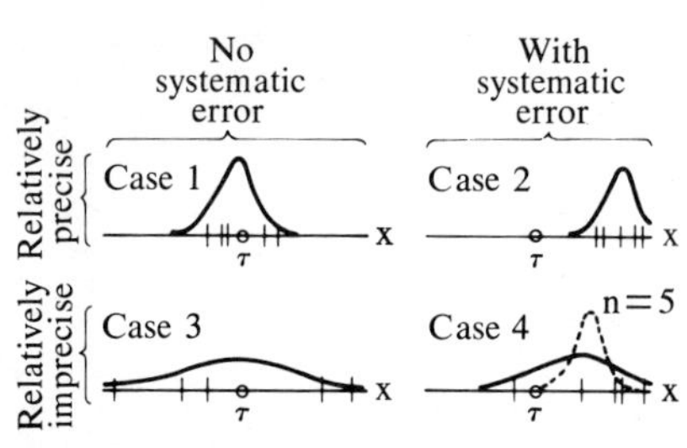

Fig. 4. Four typical cases. The horizontal lines are scales of values of a measured quantity with the true value τ indicated by a circle. In each case the five measured values marked on the scale are a sample from a large population having a distribution indicated by the curve. The dashed curve in case 4 indicates the distribution of *means* of five values. See text for discussion.

Before discussing statistical methods, it is instructive to distinguish between random errors and systematic errors, and between precision and accuracy, in a few cases typical of different measurement processes. Figure 4 shows four drawings, each of which depicts a population distribution (the smooth bell-shaped curve), and a set of five individual measurement results from the population indicated by marks on the horizontal line. The meaning of the dashed curve marked "$n = 5$" in case 4 will be discussed later. In "case 1" each of the five values is relatively close to the true value τ and to each other. In this case the measurement process was relatively precise and relatively accurate, as indicated by the narrowness of the bell-shaped distribution and its location (nearly centered on τ). Each individual result in the set of five exhibits relatively good accuracy, and so would the arithmetic mean of the group, if it were shown.

In case 2 none of the results is relatively close to the true value. The five results are close together, however, and we see that the population distribution is relatively narrow but its center is relatively far from the true value τ. Therefore, it can be said that the measurement process is precise, but not accurate, and the five values exhibit this well. Here the distinction between accuracy and precision is quite clear.

In case 3 the individual results do not all exhibit good accuracy, but the mean of the five would exhibit good accuracy if it were shown. The precision of the measurement process is relatively poor in this case, as indicated by the relatively wide population distribution. Although the mean of the particular set of five exhibits good accuracy in this case, and the mean of the population is very close to τ, the measurement process cannot be called accurate because of the relatively poor precision. In this case the distinction between the concept of "good accuracy" and "freedom from systematic error" can be seen.

In case 4, although one of the results happens to be near the true value, the accuracy exhibited by most of the individual measurement results is relatively poor, the accuracy exhibited by the mean of the set is relatively poor, and the precision exhibited by the set is relatively poor. Clearly, the accuracy of the measurement process is relatively poor in case 4, but this conclusion must be reached by looking at the population distribution (the smooth curve) rather than the distribution of the particular set of five values, and the conclusion most certainly should *not* be based on only one or a few values.

Only in case 1 can the measurement process be called accurate. In case 2 the accuracy of the measurement process can be improved by correcting the systematic error. In case 3 the accuracy can be improved only by improving the precision, and in case 4 both factors need to be improved.

In the figure associated with case 4 the dashed curve indicates the distribution of *means* from sets (i.e., random samples) of five values. The better precision of the mean of five independent measurement values over that of a single measurement value is evident. However, such a mean may actually be "less accurate" in the sense that, given sufficient systematic error, the probability of a mean of n measurements being really close to the true value τ may actually be considerably less than that of a single measurement. This situation is illustrated in case 4, wherein it is seen that the probability density for individual measurements (the smooth curve) is relatively high in the vicinity of τ, whereas the probability density at τ is quite small for means of five results (the dashed curve). An interesting elaboration, On the Meaning of Precision and Accuracy by R. B. Murphy, is reprinted as Paper 6.1 of Ref. 6.

8. Reducing Systematic Errors It is clear that when measurements of greatest accuracy are to be made, it is necessary to define the measurement process rather well and to state exactly what constitutes a repetition of the measurement. Only then can the separation of random and systematic errors be done in a meaningful way. Suppose an instrument with a scale and pointer reads erroneously because the "zero" adjustment is not properly set. The error will affect the recorded value and every further use that is made of it. It is a constant error in further use. If the measurement is repeated, and the adjustment still is not made, the result will be in error again, the same amount—a typical systematic error, regular and predictable in effect, although its size may be unknown.

When a systematic error is known to exist, as in this case, the metrologist must state the limits to systematic error that he is allowing to exist in the measurement process. This gives the user of the measurement results (and the recipient of the metrologist's statement) information that he needs, along with a measure of the imprecision, to judge the accuracy associated with the results.

However, if the zero adjustment is carefully set before each repetition of the measurement, the small residual error from this particular source of error is likely to be different each time. After many repetitions of the measurements, it becomes apparent that the errors are distributed normally (i.e., that they fit the so-called "normal distribution," which will be discussed later), and the sample standard deviation (also to be discussed later) would be a good measure of their dispersion.

The systematic error from the zero adjustment has been reduced or eliminated. The random errors in the measurements may be slightly larger than they were before. The systematic error has been reduced at the expense of a slight increase in random errors by the alteration in procedure.

Means of a number of such readings (readjusting the "zero" each time) would be expected to exhibit more precision; i.e., they would show less variability than single readings. This kind of change in the measurement method is an improvement. The metrologist should strive to ensure that *all* systematic errors are reduced to negligible size or removed entirely, leaving only random errors which can be treated in more objective ways.

Some instruments draw power from the measurement circuit, thereby disturbing it and, perhaps, causing undesired or unknown changes. Sometimes the connections between the instrument and the circuit are ill-defined or produce an error that is difficult to correct. Perhaps environmental conditions affect the performance of an instrument. Whether the errors from such causes can be called systematic or random obviously depends on the answer to the question, "what is a repetition of the measurement?" We have seen that the determination of limits of systematic error is sometimes rather subjective, i.e., depends on the judgment of the metrologist. The treatment of random errors can be done much more objectively by using statistical methods.

STATISTICAL METHODS IN MEASUREMENTS

9. The Population and the Sample Measurements of a quantity are usually taken in groups or sets, perhaps all on one day, or all in a few weeks. Each measurement in a set is a measure of the quantity. The groups of measurement results may be treated statistically as samples of measurement results from a very large population of results that might have been made. The statistical formulas and procedures to be discussed all depend for their strict validity on *independence* of the errors of the measurements concerned. When independence is lacking, more sophisticated statistical methods must be used than are to be found in this chapter. Reference 10, for example, shows the increased difficulties that arise when there is a lack of independence.

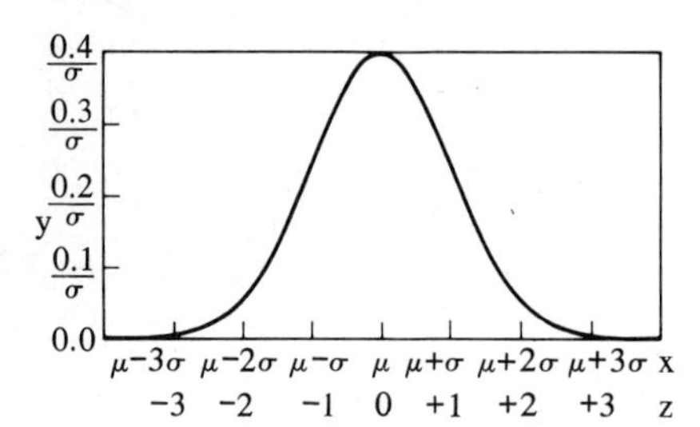

Fig. 5. The normal distribution. This bell-shaped curve is based on the "normal law of error," a mathematical equation that descibes the dispersion of measurement results about the mean of the population of results from many, but not all, measurement processes. The probability density y is shown as a function of the measured value x. A scale of z is shown also (refer to text for explanation).

The characteristics of the population can be considered as the limits of sample characteristics as the sample size approaches infinity. Statistical methods based on sampling can be used to estimate the characteristics of the distribution of measurement results. The characteristic *shape* of the distribution of a population of measurement results is generally assumed to fit the normal curve (see Fig. 5) unless it is known or the data themselves suggest it to be otherwise, in which case it may be appropriate to subject the data to a suitable "normalizing transformation" before undertaking their analysis. A discussion of normalizing transformations for a variety of nonnormal data is available in Chap. 20 of Ref. 9.

The other characteristics of the distribution are (1) a measure of location (such as the population mean μ) and (2) a measure of imprecision (such as the standard deviation σ). *Estimates* of μ and σ are obtained by computation, using data from sets (samples) of measurements. As a measure of location, the *estimate* of μ is generally obtained by computing the arithmetic mean $\bar{x}$ of a set of n measurement results $x_1, x_2, \ldots, x_n$, i.e, $\bar{x} = (x_1 + x_2 + \ldots + x_n)/n$, or in abbreviated form,

$$\bar{x} = \frac{\sum_{i=1}^{n} x_i}{n}$$

The mean is a single value that represents the location of the set. In the example given in the previous section, the data points for condition B (Table 2) are "reduced" to a single value, the arithmetic mean, having a value of 0.501187 V. This one number describes the *location* of the set of data, but it does not describe the *dispersion.*

10. Measures of Dispersion There are several measures of dispersion of data that have gained popularity for one reason or another. The relative merits of the various measures of dispersion may be judged by the extent to which the information contained in the data is incorporated in the measure of dispersion, by the simplicity or complexity of use, or by other means.

Perhaps the simplest measure of dispersion for samples is the *range* w, the difference between the largest and the smallest of the measured values,

$$w = x_L - x_S$$

Because only two values enter into the computation of w, when the sample size is large, much information is lost. For very small samples (five or less, say), the range is a useful and easily computed measure of dispersion. However, the range has a serious weakness that prevents it from receiving a recommendation for general use, namely, that ranges of sets involving different numbers of measurements are not directly comparable. The range of a set of measurements tends to grow steadily with the number of measurements. When a new measurement is added to a set, the range of the new set may be the same or greater but is never less than the range of the first set.

The *mean deviation* is a measure of dispersion that makes use of all the measurement data. The mean deviation is computed as the mean of the absolute values of all deviations from the mean,

$$a = \frac{\sum_{i=1}^{n} |x_i - \bar{x}|}{n}$$

It is an easily computed measure of dispersion, but it is not as generally useful as the sample standard deviation s and its square, the sample variance s^2, which is of great usefulness in mathematical treatments involving "mean squares," such as in the method of least squares and the analysis of variance.

The *standard deviation* is the most popular measure of dispersion, although it is a little more difficult to compute than others. The population standard deviation is the value approached by the *positive* square root of the mean of the deviations squared as the number of measurements is infinitely increased,

$$\sigma = \operatorname*{limit}_{n \to \infty} \sqrt{\frac{\sum_{i=1}^{n} (x_i - \mu)^2}{n}}$$

The square of the standard deviation is called the variance. The points of inflection *on the normal curve* occur at $\mu \pm \sigma$. Hence, if the value of σ is known, the scale of the normal curve may be easily visualized; however, it must be emphasized that this is a characteristic of the *normal curve* and *not* a general property of the standard deviation σ of a population distribution.

Figure 5 shows a normal curve. It is evident that the curve is symmetrical and is completely described by μ and σ. The vertical scale is the probability density. The *probability of occurrence* of values of x between any two chosen limits is given by the area under the curve between those limits. In Fig. 5 the curve, which depicts the "normal law of error," is so scaled that the total area under the curve is unity, corresponding to a probability of 1 (i.e., 100 percent) that a measured value will fall somewhere between $\mu - \infty$ and $\mu + \infty$. Although the tails of the curve extend infinitely in both directions, it is obvious that the probability of values outside of the interval $\mu \pm 3\sigma$ is quite small (actually, less than 0.3 percent).

Let us consider a simple example wherein a knowledge of the standard deviation of existing random errors in a measurement process can be of help in selecting an instrument for use in taking data. First, the meaning of "least count" should be understood. If the observer estimates readings to tenths of a division, the interval "one-tenth division" is said to be the least count of the reading. The readings are limited to discrete values spaced by the least count. The quantity,

TABLE 3 Probability of Deviations in the Normal Distribution*

P (expressed in percent) is the probability of occurrence of deviations between $-z$ and $+z$, where z is the standard normal variable.

z	P, %	z	P, %
0.5	38.29	1.8	92.81
0.6	45.15	1.9	94.26
0.7	51.61	2.0	95.45
0.8	57.63	2.1	96.43
0.9	63.19	2.2	97.22
1.0	68.27	2.3	97.86
1.1	72.87	2.4	98.36
1.2	76.99	2.5	98.76
1.3	80.64	2.6	99.07
1.4	83.85	2.7	99.31
1.5	86.64	2.8	99.49
1.6	89.04	2.9	99.63
1.7	91.09	3.0	99.73

* From Tables of Normal Probability Functions, National Bureau of Standards Applied Mathematics Series 23.

as measured by the instrument, may exhibit random variation described by a standard deviation. If this standard deviation is small relative to the least count of the reading, the same reading will be observed for each repetition of the measurement process. On the other hand, if the standard deviation is very large relative to the least count, the extra digits recorded may be worthless. Whenever possible, it is recommended that the instrument be chosen so that the least count of the readings will be from 0.2 to 0.3 times the standard deviation of the readings. This choice will force the imprecision from scale reading to be small relative to the imprecision from other sources of error.

Tables of probability for the normal distribution are usually shown as functions of the "standard normal variable," as in Table 3. The standard normal variable is

$$z = \frac{x - \mu}{\sigma}$$

where x is any normally distributed variable. The formula is used to transform the scale of values of x (which may be in any units, i.e., volts, amperes, ohms, decibels, millimeters, scale divisions, etc.) to values of z which can be looked up in tables. Table 3 shows the probability between limits of $-z$ and $+z$ for a number of values of z ranging from 0.5 to 3.0. The standard deviation of the variable z is, of course, 1.

Consider the following problem. A method has been developed for the measurement of rf power (from a constant-power source) dissipated in a load, and the process is in good control; i.e., no drifts, trends, or cyclic effects are evident in repetitions, and the random variations are acceptably small. The standard deviation of the process has been found to be $\sigma = 5.1$ mW. Many measurements have been made, and the population mean μ is known to be 1,362.9 mW. The question is asked, "Within what limits can I expect to find 90 percent of the measurements?" Using Table 3, we find that z is about 1.65 for $P = 90$ percent. Now the limits can be computed as $\mu \pm z\sigma$, i.e., 1,362.9 mW ± 8.4 mW. The upper and lower limits are 1,371.3 and 1,354.5 mW. Suppose a newly measured value is recorded as 1,354.3 mW. This value is outside the 90 percent limits. We see it is slightly lower than the lower limit. We expect 10 percent of our results to be outside the limits, and this result may well be one of them. If we had chosen to work with 91 percent probability, instead of 90 percent, the new result would have been just within the limits 1,354.2 and 1,371.6 mW.

A group of measurement results can be considered as a sample from a large population of results that might have been obtained. Then, *estimates* of the population mean and the population standard deviation can be computed from the sample data. The symbol $\bar{x}$ denotes a sample mean, and s denotes a sample standard deviation. Thus,

$$\bar{x} = \frac{\sum_{i=1}^{n} x_i}{n}$$

is an *estimate* of the population mean μ. Similarly,

$$s = \sqrt{\frac{\sum_{i=1}^{n} (x_i - \bar{x})^2}{n - 1}}$$

is an *estimate* of the population standard deviation σ.

The above formulas can be applied to any set of data. When the set of data is a random sample from a measurement process that is in good control (i.e., the data are independent and within predicted bounds), the value of s is a valid estimate of σ. The use of $n - 1$ in the denominator of the formula for s requires some explanation. It is the number of *degrees of freedom* left over from the computation of s after the mean $\bar{x}$ has been computed from the sample of size n. When the value of μ is known and the errors $x_i - \mu$ of the n measurements are independent,

$$\frac{\sum_{i=1}^{n} (x_i - \mu)^2}{n}$$

provides an unbiased estimate of σ^2. But there are only $n - 1$ independent deviations $(x_i - \bar{x})$ from the sample mean $\bar{x}$.

When desk calculators are used for computing s, and μ is not much larger than σ, there is some advantage in using one of the following formulas:

$$s = \sqrt{\frac{1}{n - 1}\left[\Sigma x^2 - \frac{(\Sigma x)^2}{n}\right]}$$

or

$$s = \sqrt{\frac{1}{n(n - 1)}\left[n\Sigma x^2 - (\Sigma x)^2\right]}$$

The terms Σx^2 and Σx can be accumulated simultaneously on many machines. If μ is much larger than σ, it is advisable to subtract a constant x_a from all values of x. The constant x_a should be a rounded-off value of about the same size as the x values. This will result in fewer significant figures in values of $(x - x_a)$ than in x, which is desired in the use of the formulas. The values of $(x - x_a)$ can then be used, instead of x, in the above formulas. The variance of $(x - x_a)$ is the same as the variance of x. However, because of the possibility of round-off errors, neither of the two formulas immediately above should be used with automatic electronic computers. Instead, the formulas for s based on $\Sigma(x - \bar{x})^2$ introduced earlier should be used.

When a measurement process is in good statistical control, there is a definite advantage in making a number n of measurements and computing the mean. The mean is more precise than the individual measurements. In fact, the *standard error of the mean* (also called the standard deviation of the mean) is $\sqrt{n}$ times smaller than the standard deviation of the population for independent data, i.e.,

$$\sigma_{\bar{x}} = \frac{\sigma}{\sqrt{n}}$$

If, however, the n measurements $x_1, x_2, \ldots, x_n$ are not independent but have errors that are intercorrelated, then the standard error of their mean may be somewhat, or even considerably, larger or smaller than the value given by the expression above for the case of independence. Indeed, in the extreme case of n measurements that are perfectly *positively* correlated, they are all sensibly the same measurement, and $\sigma_{\bar{x}} \to \sigma$, the standard deviation of a single measurement; and with maximum average *negative* correlation, $\sigma_{\bar{x}} \to 0$. In general, if the arithmetic mean of the $n(n-1)/2$ correlation coefficients among them is $\bar{\rho}$, then the standard error of the arithmetic mean of the x's will be

$$\frac{\sigma}{\sqrt{n}} [1 + (n - 1)\bar{\rho}]^{1/2}$$

as indicated at the bottom of the fourth page of Paper 5.3, p. 334, in Ref. 6. For information on the treatment of correlated data, refer to Chap. 6 of Ref. 11, or Chap. 11 of Ref. 12.

The standard error of the mean may be computed from the above formula, if σ is known. If σ is not known, it can be *estimated* by computation from

$$s_{\bar{x}} = \frac{s}{\sqrt{n}}$$

for independent data. If the n measurements involved are not independent but are such that the arithmetic mean of the $n(n-1)/2$ correlation coefficients among them is $\bar{\rho}$, then s^2 is no longer an (unbiased) estimator of σ^2, but rather of $\sigma^2(1 - \bar{\rho})$. Hence the above formula for $s_{\bar{x}}$ will tend to underestimate $\sigma/\sqrt{n}$ when $\bar{\rho} > 0$, and hence to "doubly" underestimate the actual $\sigma_{\bar{x}}$ in this case. It should be understood that whereas "independent" implies "uncorrelated," the converse is *not* true. For *further* discussion of this point the reader should see Ref. 13.

The standard error of the mean is a measure of the dispersion of means, from samples of size n, that would exist if many such means (from the same size of sample) were computed. One should always keep in mind that $\sigma_{\bar{x}}$ is a function of sample size n as well as the standard deviation (of the population) σ. For a statement of $\sigma_{\bar{x}}$ to be meaningful, n must be stated, also. Thus, the value of $\sigma_{\bar{x}}$ for a series of measurements can be made smaller by taking more measurements. Of course, there are practical limits to the improvement that can be obtained. For example, it may be uneconomical to take more measurements. Repetition may not diminish systematic errors, and it is often a matter of judgment whether it is worthwhile improving the precision of the results (by increasing the number of measurements) when the range of random errors is about the same size as the possible systematic error. Also, one needs to satisfy himself that the data may be regarded as independent.

For many years the *probable error* was quite popular as a measure of imprecision (often with very inadequate information regarding the method whereby a purported value of "probable error" was obtained). The intended criterion is that the probability is 50 percent for occurrence of a deviation greater than the "probable error."

The theory of probability and its applications in statistics can be an interesting subject for study, and Ref. 14 provides an introduction to the basic concepts. For the advanced student, Ref. 15 is a chapter-length compendium of fundamentals of statistical probability theory and calculus. It contains a section on the principal sampling distributions of statistics, and a multiplicity of references at the end, of which 50 through 132 guide the reader to principal collections of mathematical tables and specialized tables of value in probability and statistical theory and practice.

11. Confidence Levels and Confidence Limits In statistics, and in metrology, confidence in the result from measurements is expressed by stating confidence limits, and a confidence coefficient γ (also called confidence level), which is a number between 0 (or 0 percent) and 1.00 (or 100 percent). Confidence limits for the mean μ of a measurement population are usually laid off from the mean x of a set of measurement results from this population. For example, 95 percent confidence limits for the mean of the population giving rise to the 10 values in our previous example, with mean $\bar{x} = 0.501187$ V, were determined from the sample standard deviation s. They were found to be (0.501187 ± 0.000004) V using the formula involving t and s given below.

In a particular sample the limits will bracket the population mean, or they will not. The confidence level γ is the proportion of such samples (with the limits recomputed for each sample) for which limits *will* bracket the population mean. The previous sentence states what is meant by *confidence level* as used in mathematical statistics. It is important to understand that "confidence level" is a refined concept and not merely a "vague feeling." Fifty and 90 percent confidence intervals for μ from samples of size 4, and 50 percent confidence intervals for μ corresponding to sample sizes of 4, 100, and 1,000, are shown in Figs. 1-8 and 1-9 of Chap. 1 of Ref 9, which is reprinted as Paper 5.1 in Ref. 6.

When σ is known, confidence limits for the mean from samples of size n can be computed simply using tables of the standard normal variable z such as Table 3 (where P in the table equals γ for this purpose). Then, the limits

$$\bar{x} \pm z \frac{\sigma}{\sqrt{n}}$$

will include the population mean with confidence $\gamma(=P)$. Note that the limits are a function of the sample size as well as the value of z for a chosen γ.

In cases where σ is not known but can be estimated by computing s, confidence limits can be derived using "Student's t" ("Student" was the pen name of W. S. Gosset, a chemist). This procedure is valid *only* if the data are independent. If this is not certainly known, the limits are "hopeful estimates." Table 4 shows t as a function of γ and degrees of freedom, or sample size n, for the case in which the number of degrees of freedom available for the determination of dispersion is $n - 1$, the mean already having been determined from the data. More extensive tables of t can be found in many texts, e.g., Table 9.2, p. 240, of Ref. 5, or Table 2-2 in Sec. 5.2, p. 296, of Ref. 6, or Table A-4 in Sec. 5 of Ref. 9.

The population mean is included within the limits

$$\bar{x} \pm t \frac{s}{\sqrt{n}}$$

with confidence γ. To illustrate the use of this formula, let us use the data from the voltage-measurement example, with which we are already somewhat familiar. The reader can verify that $s = 0.000006$ V for the data from condition B, Table 2. The table of Student's t shows that, for $n = 10$ and $\gamma = 0.95$, $t = 2.26$. Substituting, the limits are (0.501187 ± 0.000004) V. When a new sample is taken, the limits must be recomputed, because the value of s will be different. The user of the equipment can say, however, that for 95 percent of the samples (with limits recomputed for each sample) the limits will bracket the population mean. The choice of confidence level should be made by the user of the measurement results in accord with technical or economic factors of which he may be aware.

Examination of a table of Student's t will show that, for a chosen γ, t approaches z as the sample size is increased to infinity. For small sample sizes, values of t can be quite large, however, and in repeated small samples of the same fixed size, the variation of s from sample to sample will result in confidence intervals whose widths fluctuate noticeably, and vary considerably when $n < 10$, say, as shown for $n = 4$ in Figs. 1-8 and 1-9 of Chap. 1 of Ref. 9, which is reprinted as Paper 5.1 in Ref. 6. This is an unsatisfactory feature of confidence intervals in small samples that points up the advantage of using a known value of σ whenever possible, or a pooled estimate thereof from previous samples of the same kind computed as indicated in Paper 5.2, p. 316, of Ref. 6.

TABLE 4 Student's *t*

Values of t are given in the body of the table for several values of confidence level γ and degrees of freedom ν (or sample size n, where $\nu = n - 1$).

n	ν	γ (two-tail)		
		0.90	0.95	0.99
2	1	6.31	12.71	63.66
3	2	2.92	4.30	9.93
4	3	2.35	3.18	5.84
5	4	2.13	2.78	4.60
6	5	2.02	2.57	4.03
7	6	1.94	2.45	3.71
8	7	1.90	2.37	3.50
9	8	1.86	2.31	3.36
10	9	1.83	2.26	3.25
15	14	1.76	2.15	2.98
20	19	1.73	2.09	2.86
30	29	1.70	2.04	2.76
100	99	1.66	1.98	2.63
∞	∞	1.64	1.96	2.58

12. Control Charts When repetitive measurements are made in a calibration laboratory or on a production line, and all known systematic effects are believed to have been removed, the presumptions that "only random errors remain" and that "the random errors are within acceptable bounds" need to be tested at frequent intervals. The criterion for deciding when it is safe "to proceed for the present *as if*" only random errors remain is provided by *control charts* and associated techniques for judging the statistical significance of apparent trends, fluctuations, and other indications of possible nonrandomness. Control charts are graphical indicators of variability that provide visual evidence of statistical control, or the lack of it.

To obtain verification of the quality of a measurement process, the metrologist should use a "check standard" and keep control charts on the check standard. The check standard should be selected for best stability. A small group of standards of ordinary stability can be used for this purpose; the mean of the group would be expected to exhibit better stability than a single standard. The check standard is measured frequently as if it were an item to be routinely calibrated, and preferably through indirect comparison with other items and standards. An illustration of control charts on the mean and standard deviation of a check standard for mass is given in Paper 1.1 of Ref. 6. The use of indirect comparison to give "realistic repetitions" of measurements of a check standard is emphasized in Sec. 4.1(*b*) of Paper 1.2 and illustrated in Paper 1.4 of Ref. 6.

Control charts are usually prepared for either individual measurement results x or the mean $\bar{x}$ of a group of measurement results, and either the computed standard deviation s of a group or the range w of a group. A "group" of measurements should be reasonably coherent and deemed likely to exhibit only randomness within the group. Variations from group to group that are out of control will be recognizable on the control charts, and corrective action can be taken. In

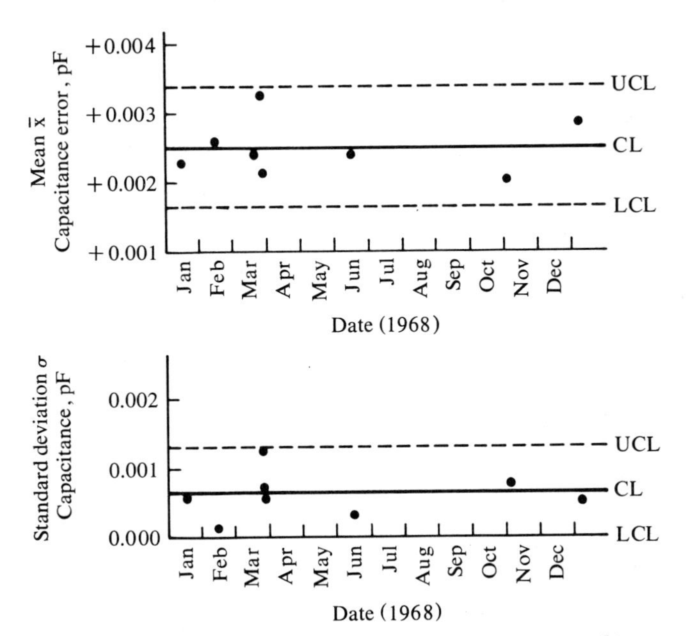

Fig. 6. A set of control charts. (*a*) Control chart for means, (*b*) control chart for the standard deviations. Both (*a*) and (*b*) computed from sets of six measurements of errors in a particular 50-pF capacitor at 100 kHz over a period of about 1 year. (*Data supplied by R. N. Jones, Electromagnetics Division, Institute for Basic Standards, National Bureau of Standards.*)

calibration laboratories an appropriate group may be a set of five measurements, taken one each day. At the end of the week the control charts would indicate the validity of the work done during the week and would give timely notice of trouble.

A control chart is prepared on graph paper by making a scale of the controlled-variable quantity on the vertical axis vs. order (or time) on the horizontal axis. Horizontal lines are drawn to denote the central line and upper and lower control limits, as shown in Fig. 6. As values of the quantity become available, they are plotted on the chart; thus the control chart is maintained as a continuing record of the process. The scattering of points above and below the central line is indicative of the variability of the process with respect to the quantity plotted. Charts may be used to monitor the measured value, the mean of a number of measured values, the computed standard deviation of the values in a group, the computed range of values in a group, etc. Control charts are not difficult to construct, and they can be developed to meet the requirements of many different measurement processes.

Other examples of the use of control charts can be found in Sec. 5.2 of Ref. 6 and in Refs. 11 and 16. Formulas and tables for locating the central line and the upper and lower control limits may be found in Chap. 18 of Ref. 9 and Part 3 of Ref. 16. Care must be taken to avoid misusing the formulas and tables. Especially, the difference between s and σ must be kept in mind; the tables in Refs. 9 and 16 are based on the formula $\sigma^2 = \Sigma(x - \bar{x})^2/n$ used for convenience by workers in quality control, rather than $s^2 = \Sigma(x - \bar{x})^2/(n - 1)$, which is preferred as an unbiased estimate of σ^2.

This chapter has dealt with the general aspects of precision and accuracy in measurements, and many problems of concern to those who must use instruments. The wide variety of electronic instruments available today, the complexity of their construction, and the serious need for greatest accuracy in electronic measurements require a good knowledge of the general characteristic of measurement data, as well as an understanding of the basic design of many types of electronic instruments. Technical details and circuitry of many types of electronic instruments are discussed in the chapters that follow.

The author acknowledges, with thanks, many helpful comments from Dr. Churchill Eisenhart (NBS, Gaithersburg), and some technical discussions with Dr. E. L. Crow (ITS, Boulder) and Dr. S. Jarvis, Jr. (NBS, Boulder) as well as colleagues in the Electromagnetics Division at NBS, Boulder.

REFERENCES

1. Harris, F. K.: "Electrical Measurements," John Wiley & Sons, Inc., New York, 1952.
2. Terman, F. E., and J. M. Pettit: "Electronic Measurements," McGraw-Hill Book Company, New York, 1952.
3. Weaver, F. D.: Scale and Reading Errors of Electrical Indicators, *Instruments and Automation,* vol. 27, no. 11, November, 1954.
4. Hermach, F. L.: An Analysis of Errors in the Calibration of Electrical Instruments, *AIEE Trans. Communication and Electronics,* May, 1961.
5. Wilson, E. Bright, Jr.: "An Introduction to Scientific Research," McGraw-Hill Book Company, New York, 1952.
6. Ku, H. H. (ed.): "Precision Measurement and Calibration: Selected NBS Papers on Statistical Concepts and Procedures," NBS Special Publication 300, vol. 1, 1969.
7. Youden, W. J.: "Experimentation and Measurement," National Science Teachers Association Vistas of Science Series, Scholastic Book Services, New York, 1962.
8. Eisenhart, C.: Realistic Evaluation of the Precision and Accuracy of Instrument Calibration Systems, *J. Res. NBS,* vol. 67C, no. 2 (April–June, 1963). Reprinted as Paper 1.2, p. 21, of Ref. 6.
9. Natrella, M. G.: "Experimental Statistics, NBS Handbook 91," Government Printing Office, Washington, D.C., 1963, reprinted with corrections, 1966.
10. Allan, D. W.: Statistics of Atomic Frequency Standards, *Proc. IEEE,* vol. 54, no. 2, pp. 221–230, February, 1966.
11. Crow, E. L., F. A. Davis, and M. W. Maxfield: "Statistics Manual," Dover Publications, Inc., New York, 1960.
12. Dixon, W. J., and F. J. Massey: "Introduction to Statistical Analysis," 2d ed., McGraw-Hill Book Company, New York, 1957.
13. Gibbons, J. D.: Mutually Exclusive Events, Independence and Zero Correlation, *Am. Statistician,* vol. 22, no. 5, pp. 31–32, December, 1968.
14. Mosteller, F., R. E. K. Rourke, and G. B. Thomas, Jr.: "Probability with Statistical Applications," Addison-Wesley Publishing Company, Inc., Reading, Mass., 1961.
15. Eisenhart, C., and M. Zelen: Elements of Probability, part 1, chap. 12 (pp. 1–163 through 1–197) of E. U. Condon and H. Odishaw (eds.), "Handbook of Physics," 2d ed., McGraw-Hill Book Company, New York, 1967.
16. American Society for Testing and Materials, Committee E-11: "ASTM Manual on Quality Control of Materials," Special Technical Publication 15-C, ASTM, Philadelphia, Pa., 1951.

Section Two

Fundamentals of Electronic-measurement Instruments

All devices that use electric circuitry to perform and display measurements have certain things in common. In the first place, there are only certain phenomena that can be detected and translated into *useful* electric signals for introduction to the instrument, which then manipulates the signal so that it can present information, corresponding to the original physical situation, for human or machine interpretation. Voltmeters, oscilloscopes, graphic recorders, and other devices all have basic elements, and differ only in the particular way each step is accomplished. This section looks at each of these fundamental elements in detail, so that the overall and general case is presented without limiting the discussion to defining a particular instrument. In later chapters the details associated with individual instruments are discussed, but then without including the general material presented here.

In this section it should be remembered that any quantity that can be represented by an electric signal can be measured and presented to the human senses. For example, a heart beat is measured by causing the "beating" to generate a voltage which, after proper processing, is then used to drive a pen on a chart. What the medical specialist is really using is a special "voltmeter," which has all the elements discussed in this chapter. Similarly, there are many devices that present mechanical, biological, and physical information which are in reality just special designs of such electric-circuit elements; the user may not even be aware that he is using an electric instrument designed for a special purpose. An understanding of these elements, however, makes the use of these devices more pertinent and less mysterious.

The designs of electronic measurement instruments are constantly being improved. New devices perform the same functions described here, though perhaps in a faster, more accurate, more sensitive, or more reliable manner, or in a way that requires less skill by the operator. In any of these new designs, however, the fundamental basis for the operation of the device is described here.

Chapter 5

Electrical Measurements

EDWARD W. ERNST, Ph.D.

Department of Electrical Engineering, Univeristy of Illinois, Urbana, Illinois

INTRODUCTION

Although the human senses can detect and measure many physical quantities, they are completely unsuited for detection or measurement of electrical quantities. Thus, instruments which respond to electrical quantities and display this response in a form suitable for human interpretation are required. Of the many electrical quantities of interest to engineers and scientists, and the many quantities which instruments have been designed to measure, a careful examination shows there are four which can be sensed or measured directly:

1. Voltage
2. Current
3. Power
4. Time interval

The ability to measure these allows us to make measurements of other electrical quantities of interest.

1. Voltage and Current Measurement The electronic voltmeter, the cathode-ray oscilloscope, and electrostatic voltmeter are three frequently used voltage-sensing instruments. The PMMC (permanent-magnet moving-coil) movement which forms the basis for a large portion of the direct-current indicating instruments is an instrument which responds to the average current applied to the terminals. The electrodynamometer ammeter and the various iron-vane ammeters are other examples of current-sensing devices.

The relationship between current and voltage given by Ohm's law,

$$V = IR \quad (1)$$

permits voltages to be measured by sensing current values and currents to be measured by sensing voltage values. These relationships are shown in Fig. 1. For example, if a resistance R_1 is placed in series with a current-sensing meter (such as a PMMC movement), the voltage across the combination V_1 will be the value of the current measured multiplied by R_1. If R_1 is 20,000 Ω and the meter yields a full-scale deflection for a current I_1 of 50 μA, then full-scale deflection will occur when V_1 is 1 V; if R_2 is 0.050 Ω and the meter yields a full-scale deflection for a voltage of 50 mV, full-scale deflection will occur when I_2 is 1 A.

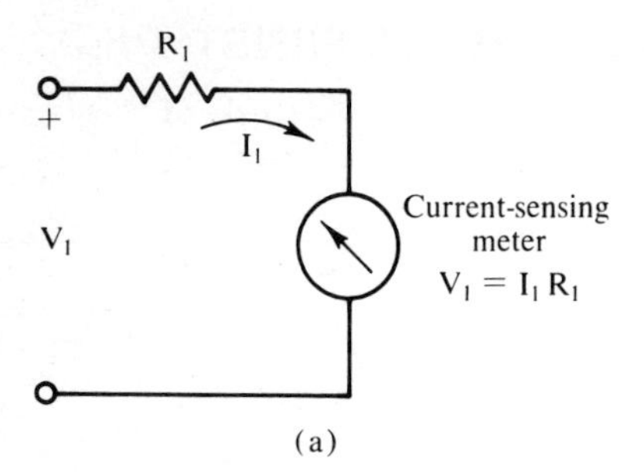

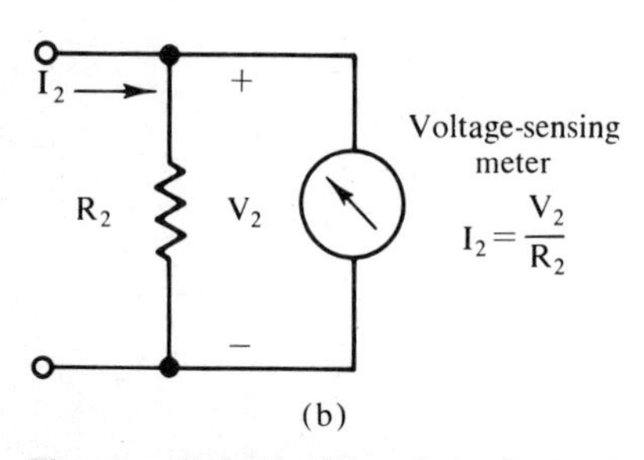

Fig. 1. Relationships between voltage and current measurements. (*a*) Voltmeter using current-sensing meter. (*b*) Ammeter using voltage-sensing meter.

2. Power Measurement The principal method used for directly sensing electrical power is to determine the heating effect associated with the dissipation of electrical power in a resistance. However, it is interesting to note that the most common method of measuring electrical power at direct and low frequencies, the electrodynamometer wattmeter, senses the product of two currents. This yields an indication of electrical power delivered to a load only because the currents are made proportional to the current and the voltage to the load, respectively.

3. Time-interval Measurement Time interval, a basic quantity in electrical measurements, in one sense is not an electrical quantity. It is one of the basic physical quantities needed for a description of physical phenomena in many fields of study. As many electrical phenomena are functions of time, this quantity is of considerable importance in the studies of electrical phenomena. The ability to determine time interval as it is related to an electrical phenomenon is interrelated with the ability to determine the beginning and the end of the time interval of interest. This usually requires that a magnitude, such as a voltage or current, be measured as a function of time so the time interval between appropriately selected points can be determined.

4. Magnetic Measurement Magnetic flux is a basic quantity for magnetic measurements. This quantity, although quite different, is analogous to electric flux for electrical measurements; another related quantity is magnetomotive force. Magnetic measurements are more difficult to make and less accurate than electrical measurements for two principal reasons. First, magnetic flux as such is not measured; rather some effect produced by the flux or a change of the flux is measured. Second, magnetic flux must be considered as a distributed parameter rather than a lumped parameter; that is, it is difficult to confine the flux definitely to a localized area. (Electric current is readily confined to electrical conductors.) The definitions for the two magnetic quantities mentioned indicate the dependence of magnetic measurements on electrical measurements. The unit of magnetic flux is the weber. A *weber* is the *magnetic flux* which, linking a circuit of 1 turn, produces a voltage in the circuit of 1 volt as the flux is reduced to zero at a uniform rate in 1 second. A current of 1 ampere in a 1-turn circuit yields a *magnetomotive force* of 1 *ampere-turn.*

The definitions strongly suggest that measurements of the *change* of magnetic flux can be readily measured; a coil of one or more turns located and oriented such that the magnetic flux to be measured passes through the coil is connected to an appropriate means for voltage measurement. If a coil is moved from a location with no magnetic flux to an area of magnetic flux, a change of the magnetic flux through the coil will occur; that the voltage produced is dependent on the *time rate of change* of the flux poses special problems. The measurement of a steady magnetic flux may be accomplished by noting the force on a permanent magnet immersed in the magnetic flux; the force will be proportional to the *magnetic-flux density.* The presence of magnetic flux produces other measurable effects; one of these is the "Hall effect." If a strip of conducting material carries an electric current in a direction which is normal to the direction of magnetic flux, a voltage between the two sides of the conductor is produced. The *direction* of the voltage is normal to the directions of both the magnetic flux and the current; the magnitude of the voltage is proportional to the product of the current and the magnetic-flux density.

5. Electrical Units The ability to detect or measure the electrical quantities noted above can be used as the basis for measuring other electrical quantities of interest. These may be grouped in several different ways. For convenience, they are grouped here into three categories.

1. The electrical characteristics of signals
   Examples: voltage, current, frequency, phase
2. The electrical characteristics of components
   Examples: resistance, capacitance, inductance, impedance, admittance
3. The electrical characteristics of systems
   Examples: gain, frequency response, nonlinear distortion

MEASUREMENT OF SIGNALS

The characteristics of electrical signals of interest are the measures of signal magnitude (current, voltage, or power) associated with an electrical signal and the measures of signal shape. The shape of an electrical signal can be described in either of two ways. One is a description of its characteristics in the *time domain,* in which the emphasis is on the amplitude of the signal as a function of time. The other is the description of its characteristics in the *frequency domain,* in which the emphasis is on the description of the magnitude and relative phase of the energy which may be found at various frequencies in the spectrum for the particular signal under consideration. Full knowledge of one description will allow determination of the other. However, the methods of measuring each of the characterizations are quite different. Figure 2 indicates the interrelationship of these two descriptions.

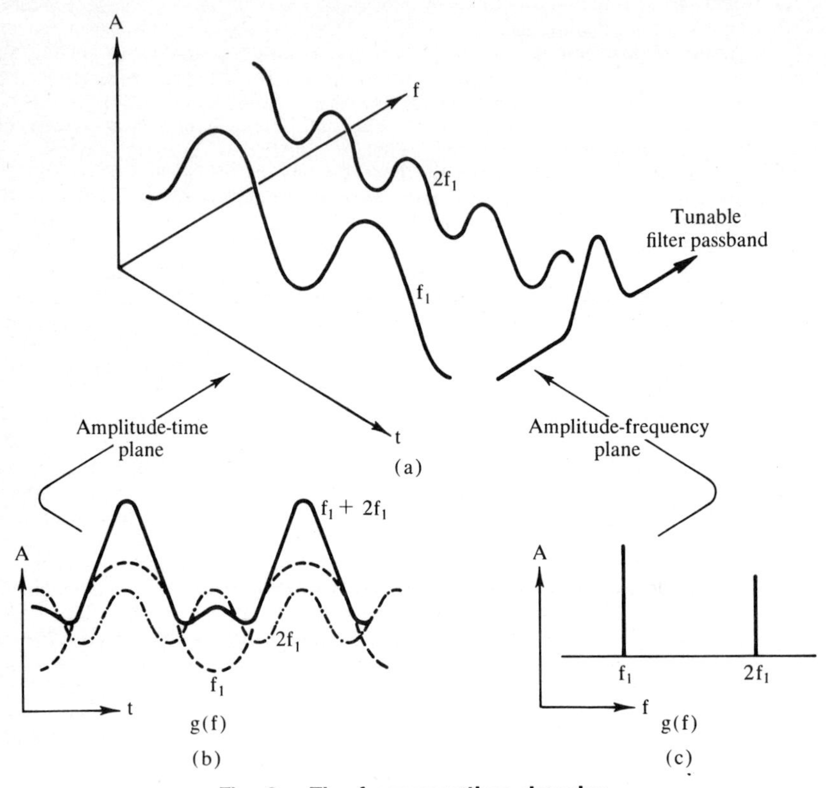

Fig. 2. The frequency/time domains.

TIME DOMAIN

Time-domain measurements will emphasize the following characteristics.

6. Frequency The rate at which a signal shape is repeated in time is known as frequency. As electrical signals are repeated rapidly, the frequency is usually given in terms of the number of repetitions which occur in a second. The unit of frequency is the hertz; a signal with a frequency of 1 hertz has exactly 1 repetition in 1 second. Thus the task of determining the frequency of a signal becomes that of establishing a known time interval and determining the number of repetitions that would occur within a 1-second time interval. The frequency of the signal shown in Fig. 3*b* is greater than that of the signal shown in Fig. 3*a*; the signal shown in Fig. 3*c* has a frequency which varies with time.

7. Phase One aspect of a comparison of two signals which have the same frequency and shape involves knowing whether the repetitions of the signal occur at essentially the same time or whether one is displaced from the other along the time axis. The two sinusoidal signals shown in Fig. 4 are displaced from one another by a phase difference ϕ. The displacement along the time axis could be given as a fraction of a complete period for the signal. When this fractional period is expressed in terms of radians or degrees, for which a full period of displacement is 2 π radians or 360°, respectively, the measurement of phase is equivalent to a time-interval measurement together with some computation.

8. Waveform For the time interval which represents the period over which the signal does not repeat, it is of interest to know something of the way in which the signal varies. If the variation is one which can be expressed as a regular mathematical function, such as a sine or cosine signal, then this is an adequate description of the shape of the signal during the time interval. If some such simple characterization of the variation of the signal during the time interval is not possible, it is necessary to describe the signal variation by giving the variation of amplitude as a function of time in considerable detail. A pulse signal, for example, is described in terms of the width of the pulse, the rise time, the flatness of the top, and the fall time if the pulse is of a somewhat regular shape. Other waveforms are described by other terms which are equally descriptive. The cath-

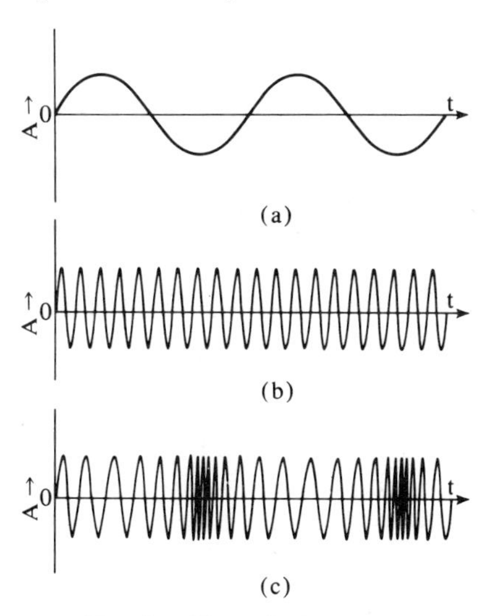

Fig. 3. Sinusoidal signals.

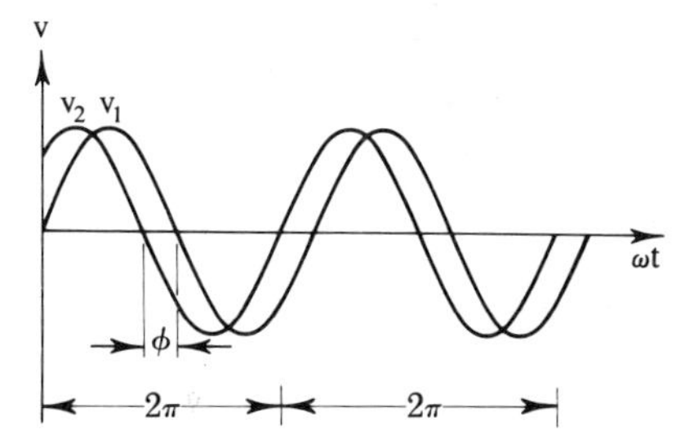

Fig. 4. Phase relationships for sinusoidal signals.

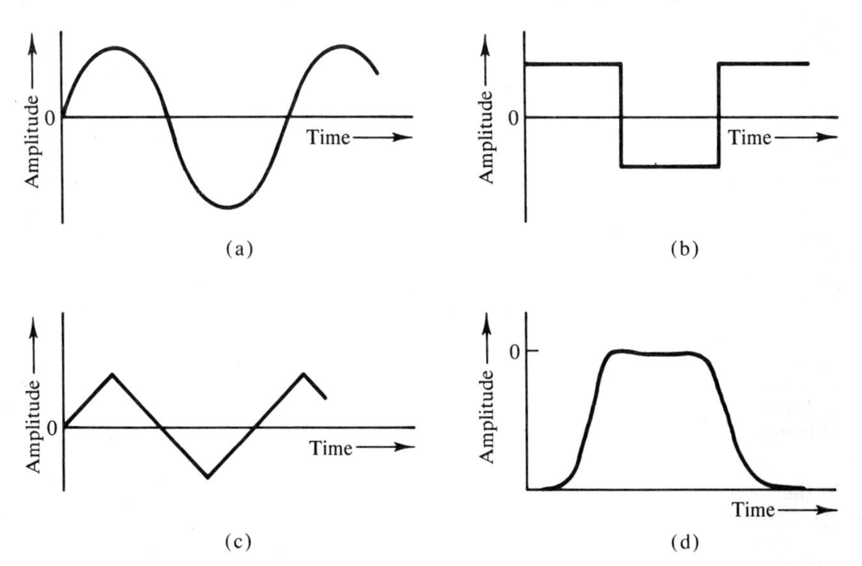

Fig. 5. Typical waveforms. (*a*) Sinusoidal signal. (*b*) Square-wave signal. (*c*) Triangle-wave signal. (*d*) Pulse signal.

ode-ray oscilloscope is the most widely used instrument for determining the characteristics of the signal in the time domain. See Fig. 5 for typical waveforms.

FREQUENCY DOMAIN

Frequency-domain characteristics of signals are expressed in terms of the sinusoidal signals which, when summed, would yield a signal having the same time-domain characteristics as the signal under study. For example, in Fig. 2*b* the waveform shown in the A vs. t plane may be represented as the sum of two sinusoids with frequencies f_1 and $2f_2$. The representation in Fig. 2*c* shows that two frequencies are present and the signal at f_1 is larger than the signal at $2f_1$. Figure 6*a* shows the waveform resulting from the addition of cos ωt and $-\sin 2\ \omega t$. That is, the

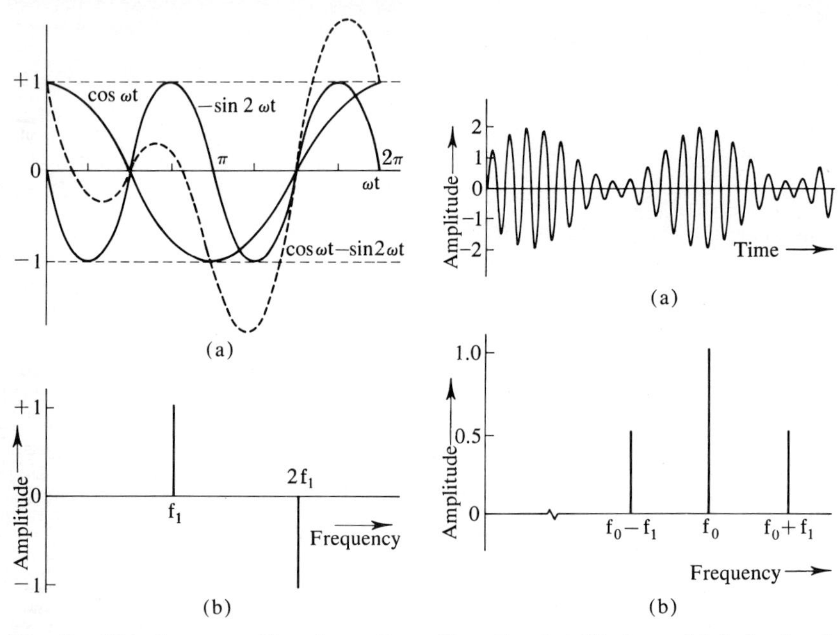

Fig. 6. Waveform resulting from the addition of cos ωf **and** $-\sin 2\ \omega f$. (*a*) Time domain. (*b*) Frequency domain.

Fig. 7. Amplitude-modulated signal, $m = 1.0$. (*a*) Time domain. (*b*) Frequency domain.

dotted waveform on the amplitude vs. time plot (time domain) may be represented as ($\omega = 2\ \pi f$)

$$v(t) = \cos \omega t - \sin 2\omega t \tag{2}$$

In a plot of amplitude vs. frequency (frequency domain), this signal would be shown as two lines as in Fig. 6*b*. Figure 7*a* is a time-domain plot of a sinusoid at $\omega_0(2\pi f_0)$ which has been amplitude-modulated by another sinusoid at $\omega_1(2\pi f_1)$. This may be represented as

$$v(t) = A_0(1 + \cos \omega_1 t) \cos \omega_0 t \tag{3}$$

In the frequency-domain plot of Fig. 7*b* this signal is shown as three lines representing frequency components at $(f_0 - f_1)$, f_0, $(f_0 + f_1)$. Note that the signal at f_0 has twice the magnitude of the other two components. The signal may be represented as

$$v(t) = A_0 \cos \omega_0 t + \frac{A_0}{2} \cos (\omega_0 - \omega_1)t + \frac{A_0}{2} \cos (\omega_0 + \omega_1)t \tag{4}$$

Trigonometric identities can be used to show that the two representations for $v(t)$ are equivalent.

Thus, given a nonsinusoidal signal, it is possible to produce that same signal by adding together a number of sinusoidal signals with a given frequency, amplitude, and phase for each. The measurement of the frequency-domain characteristics of a signal is the inverse of this process. That is, it is necessary to perform measurements to determine the frequency, magnitude, and relative phase of each of the sinusoidal frequency components which constitute the signal under study. It is necessary to select the frequency component of the signal to be measured from all those which constitute the signal and determine its magnitude; in some situations the phase of this component with respect to the phase of the fundamental or lowest-frequency component present in the signal is also needed. The wave analyzer and the spectrum analyzer are the principal instruments used for determining the frequency-domain characteristics of signals. However, these instruments are suited for determining only the frequency and the magnitude of each of the components.

MEASUREMENT OF COMPONENTS

For two-terminal circuit elements, the characteristics which are most frequently of interest are those characterized by the ratio of the voltage across the device to the current through the device, which is the "impedance" (or its reciprocal, which is the "admittance").

TABLE 1 Characteristics of Two-terminal Elements

Resistance $R = \dfrac{v}{i}$

Capacitance $C = \dfrac{i}{dv/dt}$

Inductance $L = \dfrac{v}{di/dt}$

Conductance $G = \dfrac{i}{v}$

Impedance $Z = \dfrac{v}{i} = \dfrac{|v|}{|i|}\text{(phase shift)} = |Z|\underline{/\theta} = R + jX$

Admittance $Y = \dfrac{i}{v} = |Y|\underline{/\theta} = G + jB$

$$Q = \frac{\text{peak energy stored}}{\text{energy dissipated/radian}}$$

$$Q = \frac{\omega L}{R} \text{ for series } RL$$

$$Q = \frac{\omega C}{G} \text{ for parallel } CG$$

Dissipation factor $D = \dfrac{1}{Q}$

9. Linear Components Resistance, capacitance, and inductance are three characteristics of a circuit element's impedance of interest (see Table 1). In principle, it is possible to measure each of these three quantities directly by measuring the voltage and current (or time rate of change of voltage or current as required by the defining expressions). However, the difficulty of doing this and the accuracy with which it may be done make other methods for determining these quantities more attractive. One of the most widely used methods for determining these characteristics is the bridge or comparison method shown diagrammatically in Fig. 8. In a bridge measurement the values of three elements of the bridge are known and are adjusted so that the voltage across the unknown element is equal to the voltage across the corresponding element K_3. When the currents associated with the unknown elements and the corresponding elements become either equal or in some known ratio which creates equality of voltage between terminals A and B, this, together with knowledge of the current ratio and the value of the other components, allows a value to be assigned to the unknown quantity with considerable accuracy. The voltage across the unknown element U is equal to that across K_3 when the detector indicates a null voltage. This condition is referred to as "balance," and when this condition is obtained, the complex impedances represented by the four elements of the bridge are related by

$$K_2U = K_1K_3$$

or

$$U = \frac{K_1K_3}{K_2}$$

The concepts of impedance and admittance, noted in Table 1, are valid only in terms of sinusoidal currents or voltages impressed on the element, and the use of bridges with sinusoidal signals to measure impedance and/or admittance permits equivalent values of R, G, X, and B to be determined.

Both R and Z are defined as the ratio of the voltage across a component to the current through the component. This definition of R assumes that the voltage

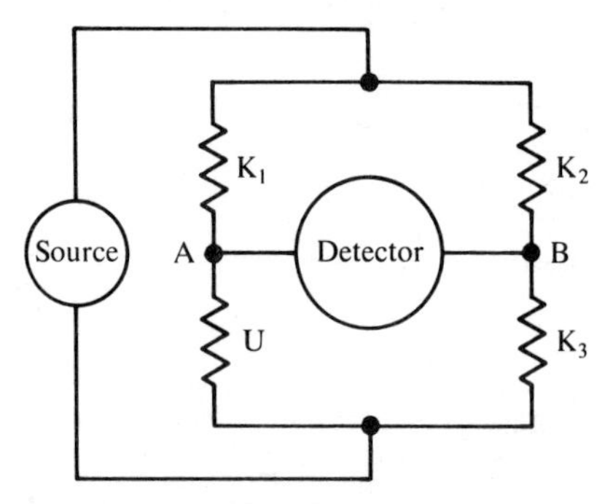

Fig. 8. Bridge method of measurement. U = component of unknown value. K_1, K_2, K_3 = components of known value.

and current waveforms are of the same shape and phase and R is the ratio of the *magnitudes* of v and i. The definition of Z assumes only that the voltage and current waveforms are of the same shape (sinusoid) but may differ in phase. Thus the impedance Z must indicate the ratio of the magnitudes of v and i *and* the relative phase between the two sinusoids. This is written as

$$Z = |Z|\underline{/\theta_Z} \tag{5}$$

where $|Z|$ is the ratio of the magnitudes of v and i and θ_Z is the phase by which v leads i. Z is also written as

$$Z = R + jX \tag{6}$$

$R = |Z| \cos \theta_Z$, the resistance; $X = |Z| \sin \theta_Z$, the reactance; j is defined as $\sqrt{-1}$, which is an impossible quantity and therefore called the "imaginary" coefficient. It defines those elements which are at 90° to the "real," or energy-dissipating, elements. Equations of this form are called "complex," with a "real" and an "imaginary" component. Then

$$|Z| = \sqrt{R^2 + X^2} \qquad \theta_Z = \arctan\frac{X}{R} \tag{7}$$

Thus, if the voltage is resolved into a component in phase with the current and a component with a phase shift of $+90°$ with respect to the current, R is the ratio of the magnitude of the in-phase component to the magnitude of the current and X is the ratio of the magnitude of the out-of-phase component to the magnitude of the current.

It is often helpful to use the ratio of current to voltage; this is the reciprocal of R or Z. The reciprocal of R is G, the conductance. The reciprocal of Z is Y, the admittance. Thus,

$$Y = G + jB \qquad \text{the admittance} \tag{8}$$
$$G = |Y| \cos \theta_Y \qquad \text{the conductance} \tag{9}$$
$$B = |Y| \sin \theta_Y \qquad \text{the susceptance} \tag{10}$$

If the current is resolved into a component in phase with the voltage and a component with a phase shift of $+90°$ with respect to the voltage, G is the ratio of the magnitude of the in-phase component to the magnitude of the voltage and B is the ratio of the magnitude of the out-of-phase component to the magnitude of the voltage.

For the same component $|Y|\,|Z| = 1$ and $\theta_Y + \theta_Z = 0$. For pure inductance, the impedance is a reactance. That is,

$$Z_L = jX_L = j\omega L = \omega L \angle 90° \tag{11}$$

For a capacitor

$$Z_C = jXC = -j\frac{1}{\omega C} = \frac{1}{\omega C} \angle -90° \tag{12}$$
$$Y_C = jB_C = j\omega C = \omega C \angle 90° \tag{13}$$

ω is a function of frequency f and is defined as

$$\omega = 2\pi f \tag{14}$$

If f is known, the value of L or C can be determined from a knowledge of Z or Y. Although the quantities just described are adequate to describe the characteristics of a two-terminal linear element, the concept of a quality factor Q or a dissipation factor D is a useful one measured by some instruments.

The Q of an element or a network is a measure of the *quality* of the element as an energy-storage device. The measure which is expressed by Q is the ratio of the energy stored by the element to the energy dissipated in a particular time interval. The definition shown in Table 1 is in terms of a sinusoidal signal. For this case, the energy stored varies with time during a period of the signal, as does the instantaneous energy dissipated. Thus the Q is defined as the ratio of the maximum value of the energy stored to the average energy dissipated in a time interval corresponding to 1 radian of phase for the signal. A large Q is associated with sharp resonance characteristics. The dissipation factor D is simply the reciprocal of Q and is most frequently used with capacitors.

10. Nonlinear Components Components such as resistors, inductors, and capacitors are *linear* elements, and as such the ratio of the voltage to the current is invariant with the magnitude of either the voltage or the current. Other components of interest may be *nonlinear,* and for these the ratio of the voltage to the current is dependent on the magnitude of the current or voltage. Figure 9 shows current vs. voltage plots for a linear component, a resistor, and a nonlinear component, a diode. For two-terminal nonlinear circuit elements, such as diodes, or for circuit elements which have more than two terminals and may be nonlinear, such as transistors or vacuum tubes, other characteristics related to the ratio of terminal voltages to terminal currents or to the ratio of current at one terminal to current at another terminal or the voltage at one terminal pair to the voltage at another terminal pair are often desired.

Figure 10 shows the schematic representation of a typical three-terminal element, a transistor. The ratio of the input voltage and current v_1/i_1 or the output voltage and current v_2/i_2 is of interest. The ratio of output current to input current i_2/i_1 and the ratio of input voltage to output voltage v_1/v_2 is also of interest.

For nonlinear elements, such as the diode and transistor, the ratio of related changes in the values of voltages and currents may be of considerable interest. Figure 11 shows an expanded portion of the *iv* characteristics for the diode shown

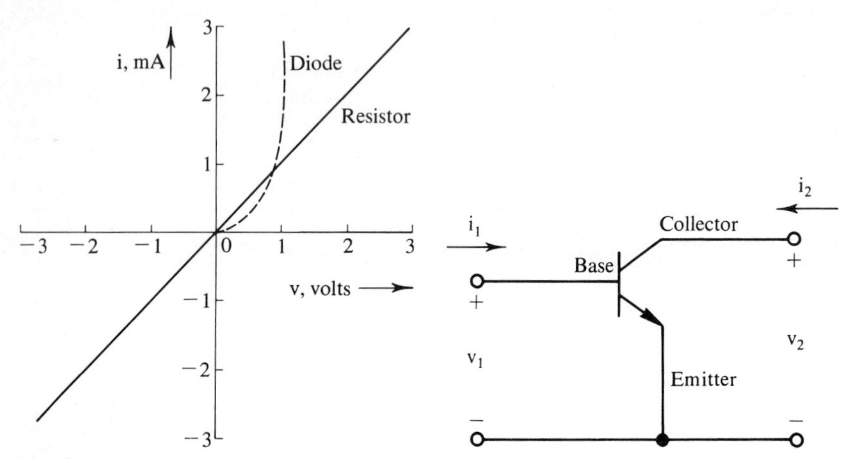

Fig. 9. ***i* vs. *v* for a linear and nonlinear component.**

Fig. 10. Transistor, common-emitter configuration.

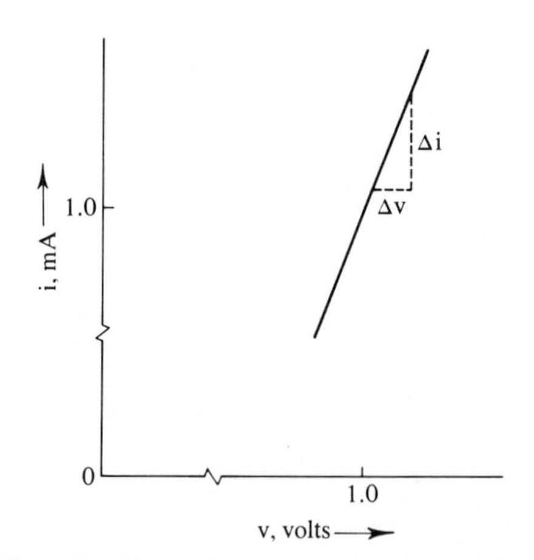

Fig. 11. Expanded *i* vs. *v* plot for a diode.

in Fig. 9. Although i/v is not constant, it appears that the ratio of *changes* in i to *changes* in v, $\Delta i/\Delta v$, is the same within the portion of the *iv* plot shown. A ratio such as this is often denoted as an *incremental* or *dynamic* parameter. For example, for the diode, $\Delta i/\Delta v$ is the *dynamic conductance* g_p. The *dynamic resistance* r_p is the reciprocal.

$$r_p = \frac{1}{g_p} = \frac{\Delta v}{\Delta i} \tag{15}$$

This same concept may be applied to other elements such as the transistor. The h parameters* for a transistor are ratios of increments of current and voltage. The transistor in Fig. 10 is shown in a common-emitter configuration, denoting that the emitter terminal is common to both the input and output ports.

The h parameters for the configuration of Fig. 10 are as follows:

$$h_{ie} = \frac{\Delta v_1}{\Delta i_1} \qquad \text{with } v_2 \text{ constant } (\Delta v_2 = 0)$$
$$h_{fe} = \frac{\Delta i_2}{\Delta i_1}$$
$$h_{oe} = \frac{\Delta i_2}{\Delta v_2} \qquad \text{with } i_1 \text{ constant } (\Delta i_1 = 0)$$
$$h_{re} = \frac{\Delta v_1}{\Delta v_2}$$

The particular ratios of interest and the conditions under which the ratio is of greatest interest (and under which it is measured) vary considerably from device to device. It should be noted that, since the quantity of interest is expressed in terms of a ratio, such measurements can be readily made with instruments designed to compare voltages or currents.

MEASUREMENTS OF SYSTEMS

The measurements of the electrical characteristics of larger functional units, such as amplifiers, attenuators, and filters, or of complete electrical systems, such as

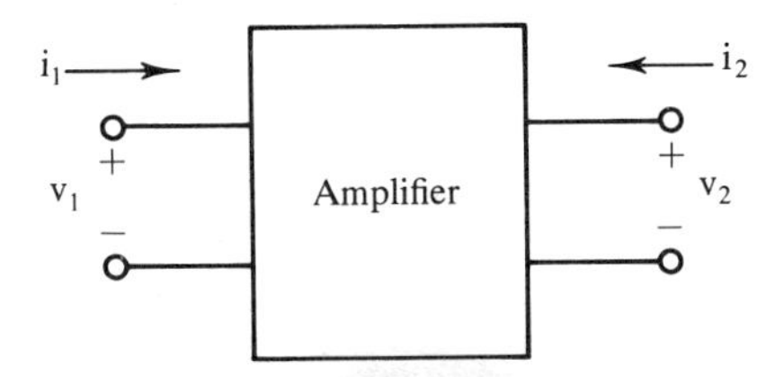

Fig. 12. The amplifier as a system.

receivers, transmitters, radar systems, and television units, require determining the characteristics of electrical signals at particular points in the unit under test or the characteristics of a particular terminal pair considered as a two-terminal element. In addition, some measurements are given by the ratio of two voltages, two currents, or a voltage and a current. *Amplification* or *attenuation* is the ratio of the signal at one port (terminal pair) to the signal at another port. When this quantity is determined at each of several frequencies over a range, and the relationship as a function of frequency is noted, this gives a frequency-response characteristic of the unit.

11. Amplification Under certain test conditions which are external to the amplifier, the *voltage amplification* A of the amplifier shown in Fig. 12 may be given as

$$A = \frac{v_2}{v_1} \tag{16}$$

* The h (hybrid) parameters are a mixed group of ratios; that is, one of the group is the ratio of currents, another is the ratio of voltages, a third is the ratio of a current to a voltage, and the fourth is the ratio of a voltage to a current. The h parameters express the interrelationship between changes in voltage and current at the designated terminal pairs. Other groups of ratios can be (and are) used to show the interrelationship. The convenience this particular group offers for some applications is the principal reason for its use.

12. Frequency Response The *frequency response* of the voltage amplification may be noted as the value of A as a function of frequency. If the input v_1 is a sinusoid, v_2 should also be a sinusoid of the same frequency. However, they may not be of the same phase, and A will then have both a magnitude and a phase. The output v_2 may be composed of several frequencies even though the input is a single-frequency signal; this is evidence of *nonlinear distortion* in the amplifier. The determination of *nonlinear distortion* involves measurements of the size of the various frequency signal components present at the output of a unit with a single-frequency signal input and determination of the ratio of the amplitude of the various components to that of the fundamental frequency component.

13. Noise Figure The *noise figure* for a unit such as an amplifier is described as the ratio of the noise (or unwanted signal) power measured with and without the unit connected. This may also be determined by measuring the amplitude of a noise signal at the input required to increase the output noise power by a given amount. In either case, it should be recognized that the measurement required is a power measurement.

DIMENSIONS OF ELECTRICAL MEASUREMENTS

The measurement of an electrical quantity has several dimensions:

1. The electrical quantity to be measured
2. The magnitude of the electrical quantity
3. The frequency at which the electrical quantity is to be measured
4. The accuracy with which the electrical quantity is to be measured

Other dimensions may involve various environmental parameters and the time available for making the measurement. Each measuring instrument occupies a place in this multidimensional space determined by its position along each of the appropriate dimensions.

Chapter 6

Transducers

EDWIN C. JONES, Jr., Ph.D.

Iowa State University, Ames, Iowa

INTRODUCTION

In general terms, a transducer is a device that is capable of transforming energy from one form to another. Thus a loudspeaker, which transforms an electrical signal to an acoustic signal, is called an electroacoustic transducer. In the field of instrumentation systems, it is wise to restrict this definition slightly, and to define a transducer as a device that develops a usable electrical output signal in response to a specific physical phenomenon.

In this handbook, devices that transform a variety of physical effects to electrical signals will be considered. The reason for this is that information is more readily transmitted and processed in an electrical format than by any other means. Modern digital computers are making such systems ever more important. Such a transducer normally consists of two important and closely related parts—the *sensing element* and the *transduction element*. There may also be many auxiliary parts, such as electrical amplifiers and other signal processors, power supplies, calibrating and/or reference elements, and mechanical mounting features.

The sensing element is that part of the transducer which responds to a physical effect, or to a change in that effect. It must be closely related to the effect and be capable of responding without materially distorting the effect that is being measured. It must also be free of responses to other physical effects. Some transducers require more than one sensing element; that is, a succession of conversions is necessary to achieve an electrical signal.

The "transduction element" is that part of the transducer which transforms the sensing-element response to an electrical signal. Often it is indistinguishable from the sensing element. An example of this is the thermocouple, in which the presence of heat creates a voltage at the junction of two dissimilar metals.

Transducers may be classified as (1) *self-generating* or (2) *externally powered.* Self-generating transducers develop their own voltage or current, absorbing all the energy needed for this from the energy in the phenomena being measured. Externally powered transducers must have power supplied from some external source, though they may also absorb some energy from the system being measured.

ELECTRICAL PHENOMENA EMPLOYED BY TRANSDUCERS

Twelve different electrical phenomena may be identified and considered for use as transduction elements. These may be combined with appropriate sensing elements to provide many different transducers. These are as follows:

1. Capacitive
2. Electromagnetic
3. Inductive
4. Ionization
5. Photoresistive or photoconductive
6. Photoelectric or photoemissive
7. Photovoltaic
8. Piezoelectric
9. Potentiometric
10. Resistive
11. Thermoelectric or thermovoltaic
12. Variable medium—permittivity or resistivity

1. Capacitive The sensing element converts the effect into a change of capacitance of a device. This is done either by changing the separation of the two plates or by changing the relative proportion of two dielectric media with differing dielectric constants. The capacitance in turn is measured either in a bridge or by measuring the effect of the changed capacitance on the performance of a circuit, such as the frequency of an oscillator or the resonant frequency of a tuned circuit. These are externally powered devices. See Fig. 1 for a schematic example of a capacitive transducer.

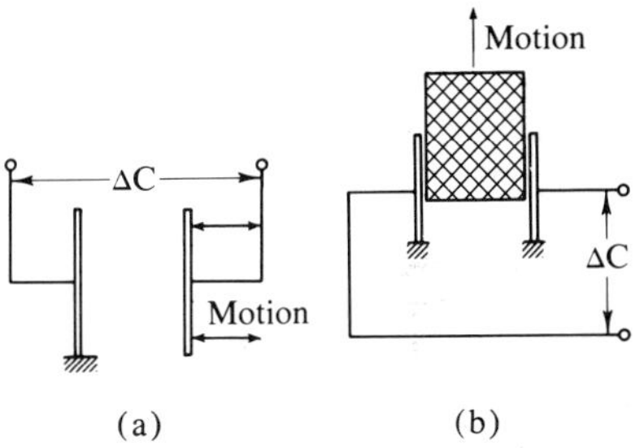

Fig. 1. Capacitive transduction elements. (*a*) Fixed dielectric, one movable capacitor plate. (*b*) Fixed capacitor plates, movable dielectric.

2. Electromagnetic The sensing element converts the effect into a voltage induced in a coil. This voltage is induced by a changing magnetic field, which in turn is related to the sensing element. The voltage may be measured directly. These are self-generating devices, but electromagnets require external power. See Fig. 2 for a schematic example of an electromagnetic transducer.

3. Inductive The sensing element converts the effect into a change in the self-, or mutual, inductance of a coil or coil set. This may be done either by a change in the position of a magnetic core or by relative motion between the coils. The inductance in turn may be measured on a bridge or by measuring the effect of the changed inductance on the performance of a circuit, such as the frequency of an oscillator, the resonant frequency of a tuned circuit, or the voltage or current change in a circuit. These are externally powered devices (see Fig. 3).

4. Ionization The sensing element converts the effect into some type of change in the ionized gases in an otherwise evacuated chamber. In turn this is measured as a change in current, resistance, or voltage in an electric circuit. These are externally powered devices (see Fig. 4).

5. Photoresistive or Photoconductive Some substances, when illuminated, experience a change in electrical resistance. Usually these are semiconductors. The physical effect to be measured may be light, or it may be converted first to an equivalent illumination from some other effect. In either case, the change in resistance may be monitored by a Wheatstone bridge or by the change in current or voltage in some circuit. These are externally powered devices (see Fig. 5).

6. Photoelectric or Photoemissive Some substances, when illuminated, emit a stream of electrons that is proportional to the illumination. Such materials may be placed in an evacuated chamber, and the electron beam may be collected on a plate, where it appears as an electric current. These are externally powered because of the necessity of supplying a voltage to the pair of plates necessary for operation (see Fig. 6).

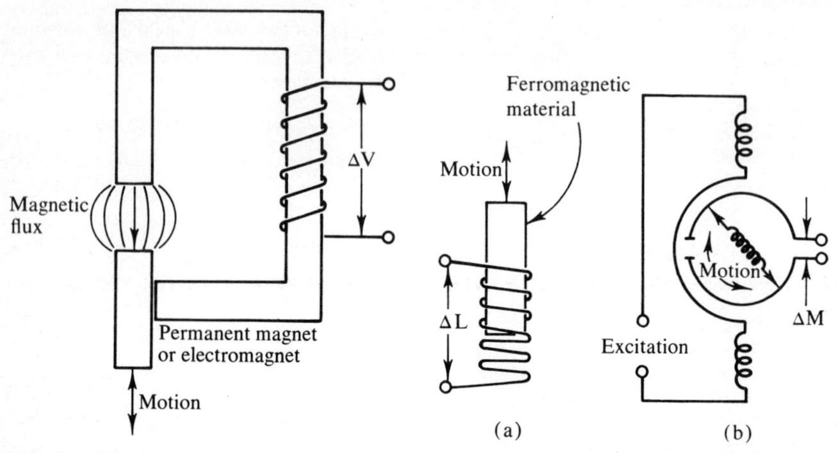

Fig. 2. Electromagnetic transduction element.

Fig. 3. Inductive transduction elements. Either technique may be used for either rotational or translational motion. (*a*) Variable self-inductance. (*b*) Variable mutual inductance.

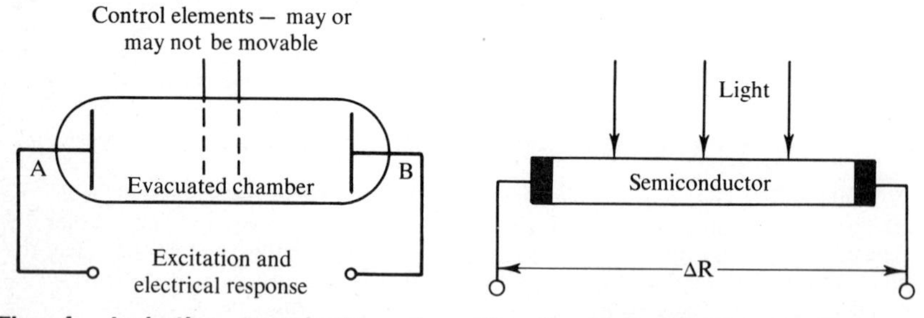

Fig. 4. Ionization transduction element.

Fig. 5. Photoresistive or photoconductive transduction element.

7. Photovoltaic When junctions between certain dissimilar materials are illuminated, a voltage is developed. This can be measured directly. It is a self-generating system when used to measure illumination levels, and an externally powered system when the light in turn is controlled by some other physical effect which is the unknown to be measured (see Fig. 7).

8. Piezoelectric Certain crystals have the property that when they are subjected to mechanical stress, a voltage is developed. This can be measured directly, in which case such a device is self-generating. The crystal may also be used as a frequency-determination element in an oscillator, and the effect of stress is to change the frequency of oscillation. This can be measured, in which case the device is externally powered (see Fig. 8).

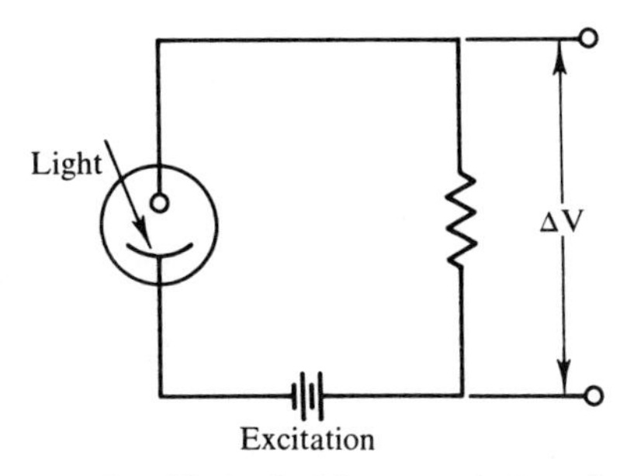

Fig. 6. Photoelectric or photoemissive transduction element.

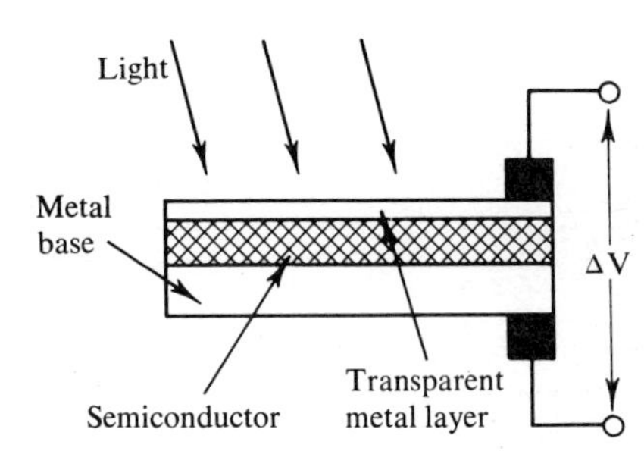

Fig. 7. Photovoltaic transduction element.

9. Potentiometric The sensing element may be arranged to cause the movable contact of the resistance element of a potentiometer to change positions, thus changing the output voltage. This may be measured directly. Such devices are externally powered (see Fig. 9).

10. Resistive The sensing element may be made to change the resistance of a device through changes caused by other physical effects. Examples are many and are represented by strain gages, temperature-sensitive resistors, and motion to move a contact on a rheostat. These resistance changes are measured, either by monitoring

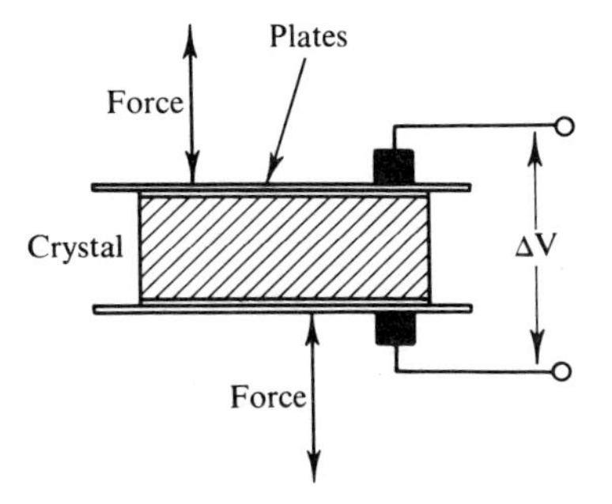

Fig. 8. Piezoelectric transduction elements. The forces may be compressive, tension, bending, or shear.

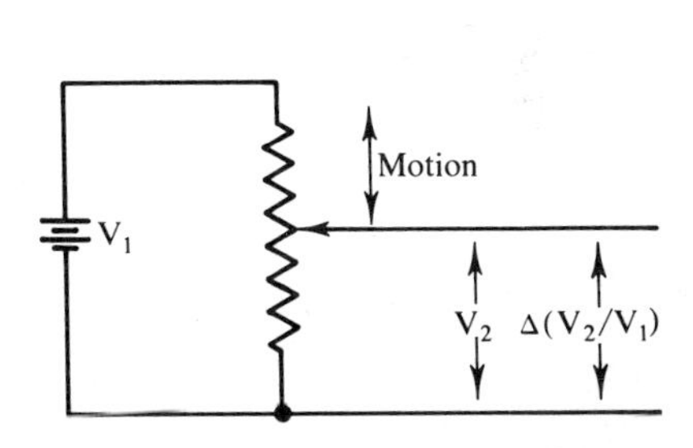

Fig. 9. Potentiometric transducer.

current and/or voltage, or directly, as with a Wheatstone bridge. These are externally powered devices (see Fig. 10).

11. Thermoelectric or Thermovoltaic If the two junctions between wires made of two different metals are kept at different temperatures, and if one of the wires is opened, a voltage will appear between the two leads. This may be measured directly. These are self-generating devices, though often energy must be supplied to the reference junction to keep its temperature constant (see Fig. 11).

12. Variable Medium—Permittivity or Resistivity These devices are similar in nature to the resistive and capacitive devices, but the difference is that the material of which the resistor is made or of which the capacitor dielectric is made is one whose resistivity or permittivity may be changed in accordance with some physical effect, such as moisture. The resistance and capacitance changes are measured as with resistive and capacitive transduction elements. These are externally powered devices (see Fig. 12).

This division into 12 groups is somewhat arbitrary, as some groups could be combined with others, while some groups could be further subdivided. But it does provide a useful framework for choosing and in particular for considering whether or not external power will be needed for the transducer.

Another very important difference between self-generating and externally powered devices is that it is not possible to use self-generating devices to convert information

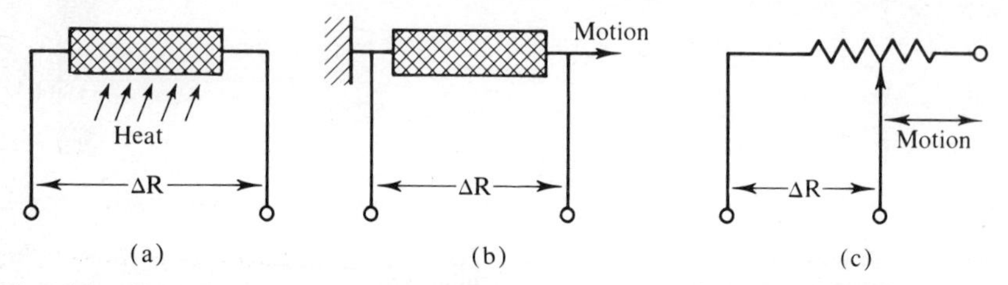

Fig. 10. Resistive transduction elements. (*a*) Temperature-sensitive resistor. (*b*) Strain gage or stress-sensitive resistor. (*c*) Movable-contact rheostat or variable resistor.

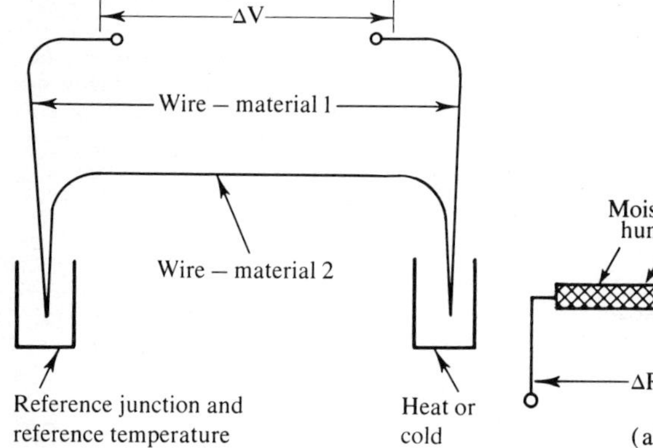

Fig. 11. Thermoelectric transduction element.

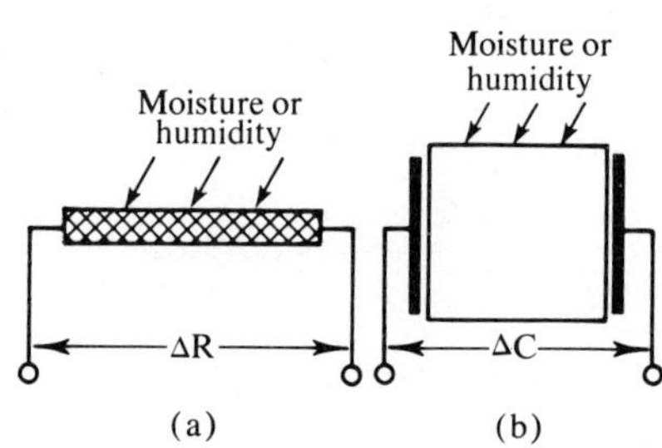

Fig. 12. Variable-resistivity or -permittivity transduction elements. (*a*) Moisture-sensitive resistor. (*b*) Capacitor with moisture-sensitive dielectric.

formats, e.g., analog to digital, or modulation. However, it is possible, and often desirable, to use externally powered devices in which information-format conversion is possible.

TRANSDUCER SELECTION CONSIDERATIONS

It is possible for an instrumentation engineer to choose from a wide variety of models when he must specify a transducer.* In addition to questions of cost, he must give careful attention to the considerations that are listed below, as follows:

1. Sensitivity
2. Range

* The ISA "Transducer Compendium" (Ref. 7) lists specific data on some 1,250 different transducers.

3. Physical properties
4. Loading effects and distortion
5. Frequency response
6. Electrical output format
7. Output impedance
8. Power requirements
9. Noise
10. Error or accuracy
11. Calibration
12. Environment

1. *Sensitivity.* Sensitivity is defined as the ratio of the output per unit input. This must be large enough so that the resolution of the system will be satisfactory.

2. *Range.* The expected minimum and maximum values of the effect to be measured must be known, and a transducer that will respond over this range must be chosen. If this is not possible, two or more transducers will be necessary, with provision for switching from one to the other, and for protection of the one not in use.

3. *Physical Properties.* The arrangements for mounting the transducer in the system to be measured, for protecting it, and for making and shielding electrical connections must be understood and evaluated.

4. *Loading Effects and Distortion.* All transducers will absorb some energy from the effect under study. The designer must be certain that this is negligible or, if this is not possible, that it will be possible to compensate the readings for this loss. It may be that the transducer will so completely change the conditions of operation that the data it yields will be useless and misleading. This is called "distortion" and must, of course, be minimized. If these precautions are not taken, significant systematic errors will be the result.

5. *Frequency Response.* The sensing element and transduction element must both be able to respond accurately at the maximum rate of change of the effect under study. If this is not assured, a serious loss of information will occur, and the data obtained will normally be invalid.

6. *Electrical Output Format.* The form of the output signal must be compatible with the rest of the system, or it must be possible to convert it. For example, a direct voltage would not be satisfactory if all amplifiers must be capacitively coupled.

7. *Output Impedance.* The output impedance of the transducer must be such that it is compatible with the succeeding electrical stages of the system. If this is not true, additional amplifiers at additional cost will be necessary.

8. *Power Requirements.* Externally powered transducers must be supplied with power. It is necessary to ensure that enough power, and at the right current and/or voltage, is available.

9. *Noise.* Noise is defined as any undesired "signal" in a system. It should be distinguished from "distortion," which is an unwanted modification of a desired signal. The types of noise are as follows:

A desired response but to an undesired signal
An undesired response to the desired signal
An undesired response to an undesired signal

The undesired responses will be signals that are virtually impossible to separate from the desired responses, and so a transducer must be chosen that will be free of these in the environment where it is to be used. Undesired signals may or may not be present in a particular environment, but all possible undesired signals must be identified and their effects on proposed transducers must be evaluated.

10. *Error or Accuracy.* The manufacturer usually evaluates the accuracy or degree of uncertainty with which a transducer is expected to respond. This is quoted under specified conditions, and the user must also ensure that the conditions under which he will be using the transducer are such that the stated accuracy either applies or can be modified to correct for differing conditions.

11. *Calibration.* The properties of some transducers drift with time and aging.

This can be compensated by recalibration, but the frequency and the desirability of this must be evaluated.

12. *Environment.* The performance of many transducers is critically affected by environmental factors such as temperature, humidity, and dirt. These must be considered before a transducer is specified, and the conditions must be appropriate for the transducer.

Research and development in the transducer industry has traditionally been very productive. Many new forms and rapid improvements of old forms are continuously reported. It is important for a prospective user to search the manufacturers' most recent catalogs in order to obtain current and complete information about available models.

One of the most successful improvements in transducers is the incorporation of much of the electronic processing circuitry into the basic unit. This is made possible by improvements in integrated-circuit technology. An example of major changes made by this technology is in piezoelectric-effect transducers. These normally have a very high output impedance, of the order of gigaohms (10^9), and this leads to severe electrical problems. But the possibility of placing an electronic amplifier on an integrated-circuit chip within 1 in. of the crystal greatly reduces these problems and provides a usable signal with a low output impedance. Consequently, piezoelectric transducers are becoming much more common than formerly. Use of transducers with built-in electronics will usually enable the instrumentation engineer to develop a more reliable, responsive, and accurate system.

TRANSDUCER DESCRIPTIONS

In this handbook, transducers will be divided first according to the general class of phenomena—thermal, mechanical, etc.—and then by specific phenomena within

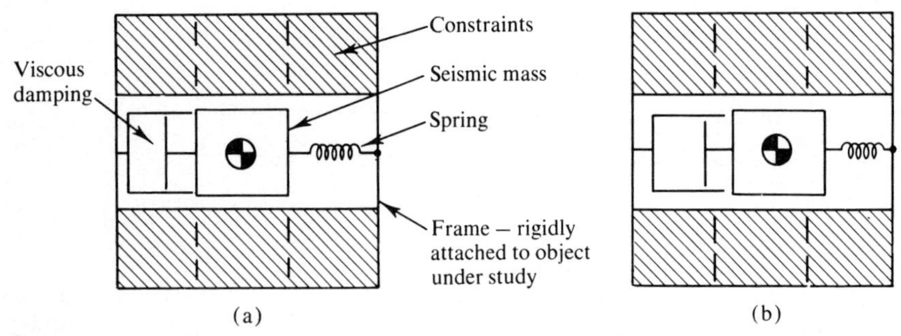

Fig. 13. The seismic mass used as a sensing element. (*a*) Rest position of accelerometer—constant velocity. (*b*) Object and frame accelerated to the left.

a class. Each transducer within a specific class will be described by its sensing element, its transduction element, and other appropriate information. This will be done in one paragraph. The intent is to give the handbook user the information he needs to choose a type of transducer to do a particular job. He is then expected to consult catalogs or manufacturers for specific information. References 3 to 7 all contain listings of manufacturers of various items. Most of these are issued annually. Other similar lists are available.

13. Acceleration

PHENOMENON: Acceleration, linear or angular.

COMMON NAME: Accelerometer.

All accelerometers use a seismic mass as a sensing element (see Fig. 13). This figure illustrates a linear accelerometer; angular accelerometers use a disk or cylinder that is suspended so that it may rotate with respect to the frame. The frame of any accelerometer is in turn attached rigidly to the device whose motion is being studied. In addition to a seismic mass, any accelerometer must have a restraining and restoring spring, and a viscous damping mechanism, normally the fluid in which the mass is suspended. The mass must be constrained to move only in those directions in which it is desired to measure acceleration. All the units described develop a voltage that is proportional to acceleration and that can be transmitted and processed accordingly.

Piezoelectric. In an accelerometer with a piezoelectric crystal used as the transduction element, the motion of the mass is restrained in large part by the crystal, which acts as a spring. The deformation of the crystal causes a voltage to be developed. These are relatively inexpensive and rugged devices. They are, however, somewhat temperature-sensitive, and are subject to hysteresis error. Their output impedance is high, usually in the gigaohm range. Typical frequency responses are from 10 Hz to 50 kHz. Typical sensitivities vary from 10 to 100 mV per g, where g is the acceleration of gravity, or 9.82 m/s/s. Current developments include the incorporation of integrated-circuit signal processors right with the transduction element, so that practical units with high signal strength and low output impedance can be obtained. The devices are individually calibrated by the manufacturer.

Linear Variable-differential Transformer Unit. These are inductive transduction-element devices that require an ac excitation. The excitation frequency must be at least ten times the highest expected frequency component in the acceleration to be measured. Their frequency response is limited to about 50 Hz. The unit can respond to accelerations from 0.1 to 500g. The magnitude of the output voltage depends on the type of excitation and the associated circuits. These are capable of very fine resolution. The principal source of error is usually stray magnetic fields, which induce unwanted voltages in the wires.

Potentiometer. Accelerometers may be built with a potentiometric or resistive transduction element. The mass is coupled mechanically to the movable contact. These are low-cost and are typically free of undesired responses, especially to accelerations in other than the intended direction. Frequency response is limited to about 10 Hz. The unit can respond to accelerations from 0.1 to more than 100g, but provision must be made to protect the mechanical linkage from accelerations greater than the intended range of the instrument.

Strain Gage. Strain gages are resistive transduction elements. (Strain gages are fully described in Sec. 17.) However, they do not have the sliding contacts of potentiometric devices. The frequency response is limited to about 350 Hz. The unit can be made to respond to accelerations from less than 0.1 to more than 100g, and the ouput voltages are typically in the range 20 to 600 mV, depending on the excitation, with bonded gages usually giving lower outputs. The units are relatively free from transverse effects.

14. Velocity

PHENOMENON: Speed or velocity, angular or linear.

COMMON NAMES: Linear velocity transducer; angular tachometer.

Velocity, whether linear or angular, can be measured by connecting the output voltage of an accelerometer to an integrating circuit. Provided initial conditions are properly accounted for, this gives a relatively noise free indication of velocity and allows the use of the accelerometer for more than one measurement. This is valid for either linear or angular velocity.

Velocity may be measured by two independent measurements, one of distance or displacement, the other of time. Division of distance by time gives the average velocity over the interval. Provided this is short enough, a reasonably good approximation of velocity is obtained. However, as the time and distance both become smaller, the errors of measurement become more significant. This method may be used for either linear or angular velocity.

Linear velocity may be measured when there is a related angular velocity, as by a speedometer in an automobile. This method uses the techniques of angular-velocity measurement.

Electromagnetic Velocity Transducer. An inductive type of velocity transducer is typified in Fig. 14. The sensing element is the rod that is rigidly coupled to the device whose motion is being studied, and it is a permanent magnet. The motion of the magnet induces a voltage in the coil, and the amplitude of the voltage is directly proportional to the velocity, while the polarity determines the direction of motion. Such a device can be used for velocity measurement only over a displacement range dictated by the coil length. The maintenance requirements are negligible, because there are no mechanical surfaces or contacts. The sensitivity is usually stated in millivolts per inches per second or in equivalent voltage-to-time units. These devices are susceptible to the noise caused by stray magnetic fields, and these must be carefully considered. The frequency response will be limited by inductive effects in the coil, and is usually stated.

Other types of electromagnetic velocity transducers incorporate a fixed electromagnet or permanent magnet with a moving coil. These effectively interchange the roles of the parts shown in Fig. 14. A third type of construction suspends a seismic

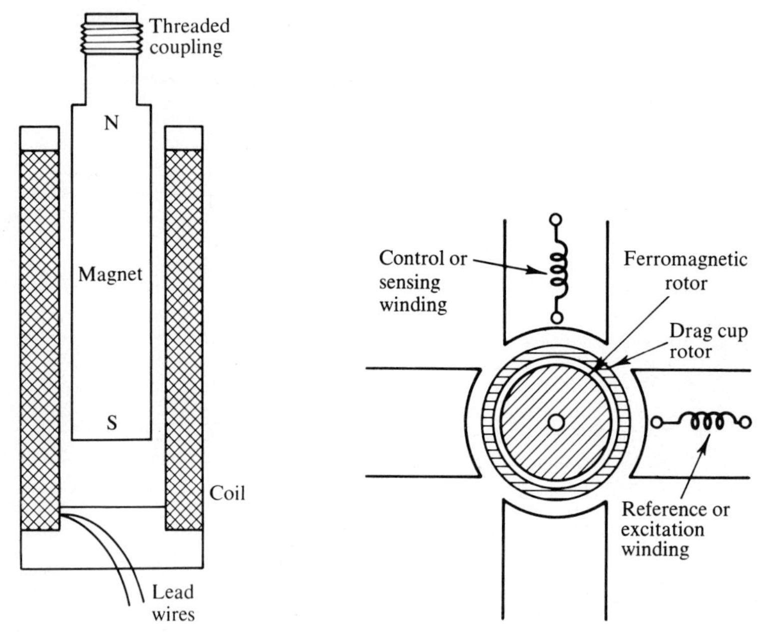

Fig. 14. Electromagnetic velocity transducer.

Fig. 15. Induction tachometer with drag-cup rotor.

mass which is also a magnet, and the frame is rigidly attached to the object whose velocity is being measured. The self-resonant frequencies of the seismic mass are typically 10 to 15 Hz. If operation at frequencies above about 20 Hz occurs, the mass is relatively stationary, and the frame moving in its magnetic field will have a velocity-proportional induced voltage. This does, of course, have good frequency-response characteristics. Both these systems have the disadvantage that connections must be made to the moving member, a problem avoided by the technique of construction shown in Fig. 14.

Inductive Tachometer. A variable-magnetic-coupling tachometer is indicated in Fig. 15. The rotor is made of both ferromagnetic and a highly conductive material, as either a "squirrel-cage" or "drag-cup" rotor. The stator has two coils. One coil is excited with an alternating voltage, and the second is used to sense the output. The motion of the rotor causes a speed-related voltage to be induced in the second winding. This voltage is directly proportional to velocity at low rpm, but ferromagnetic saturation causes a reduction in this voltage at high velocity.

These are rugged and inexpensive, and require little maintenance. One problem is that they are hard to calibrate. The output voltage is directly proportional to speed and to the excitation voltage. Consequently, to maintain calibration, the reference supply voltage must be held constant. The signal is free of ripple voltage, a very important advantage in some situations, and it is of a constant frequency.

Electromagnetic Tachometer. A variety of different tachometers using the electromagnetic principle exists. Three of these are indicated in Fig. 16. Other types are possible but are rarely used.

The *dc tachometer* uses a permanent-magnet stator and has a coil connected to the rotor. The connections to the coil are through brushes to a commutator. The reason for this is to develop a direct voltage with the unit. The amplitude of this voltage is directly proportional to velocity, and the polarity is determined by the direction of rotation. This latter is the chief advantage of this unit. The brushes and commutator require careful, periodic maintenance. The output voltage is typically 10 mV/rpm and can be measured with conventional dc instruments that are calibrated directly in rpm.

The *ac-magnet tachometer* has a rotating magnet, which may either be permanent or electromagnetic, and a coil wound on the stator. The rotation of the magnet

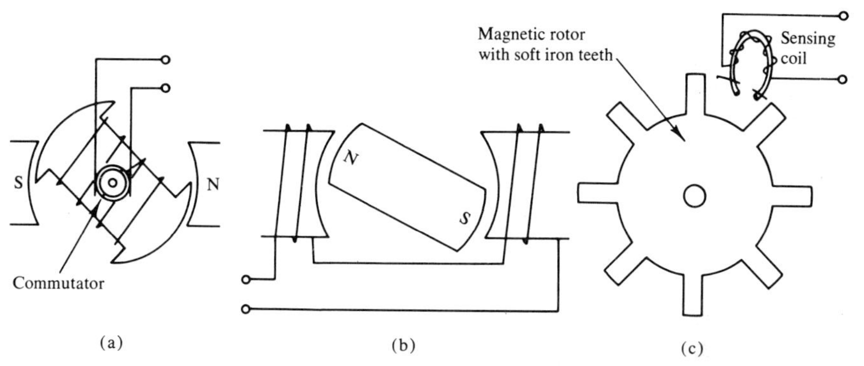

Fig. 16. Electromagnetic tachometers. (*a*) Dc tachometer. (*b*) Ac-magnet tachometer. (*c*) Toothed-rotor tachometer or revolution counter.

causes a voltage to be induced in the coil. The amplitude and the frequency of this voltage are both proportional to the angular velocity, and hence either of two electrical properties may be used to indicate speed. But modern electrical instruments such as counters make it desirable to use frequency, since this is not affected by temperature, impedance of meters, and other systematic errors that can and do affect voltage readings.

A *toothed-rotor* or *variable-reluctance* tachometer is the third principal type. As the rotor moves, the tooth passes through the air gap, changing its reluctance and inducing a voltage in its winding. Normally these are pulses, with a variety of waveshapes. However, this is not important, as this tachometer is always connected to an electronic counter, whose requirement is merely that the amplitude be great enough to trigger a count. A typical rotor has 60 teeth. Thus, if the counter counts the pulses developed in 1 s, the counter will display the angular velocity in rpm. This is probably the most common type of tachometer in use today. It is simple, rugged, maintenance-free, and easy to calibrate and to transmit information from.

Photoelectric Tachometer. A tachometer that develops a chain of pulses that indicates angular velocity may be built by a combination of a photoconductive or photovoltaic device, a disk or sector with a specified pattern of opaque and translucent areas, and a light source. The light source and the photoelectric device are rigidly attached to the frame, while the disk or sector rotates with the device under study. The light is passed only by the translucent portions, and at those instants a voltage is developed (photovoltaic device) or the current (photoconductive device) increases. The number of pulses developed in a specified time interval will then be a measure of angular velocity. These pulses are normally counted with an electronic counter. This system has two very important advantages. The first is that the output format is digital, and this means that if the tachometer is a part of a digital instrumentation system, no analog-to-digital conversions will be necessary. The second is the fact that the pulse amplitudes are constant. This simplifies the electronic circuitry. A disadvantage is that the light sources must be replaced from time to time. A typical specified lifetime is 50,000 h.

15. Position

PHENOMENON: Position relative to a reference.

COMMON NAMES: Angular, rotation or linear, translation or displacement.

A variety of terms is used to describe position measurements. The first is the idea of *absolute* and *incremental* positions. Absolute refers to location with respect to a specific reference position or angular position with respect to a specific reference. Incremental refers to a change in location, usually within a specified time interval.

In general, position measurements must be made with externally powered transducers. The reason for this is that often there will be no motion or any other mechanism that can provide an adequate amount of power to drive a transducer. This means that a wide variety of techniques can be used to develop position transducers, and consequently, many varieties exist. Only the more commonly used devices will be described here. The measurement of force or torque is in many respects similar to that of position measurement.

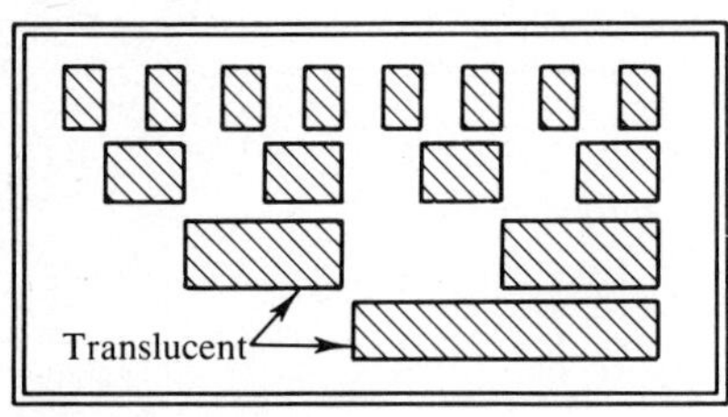

Fig. 17. Pattern of translucent and opaque sectors used in optical encoders. The photoelectric sensor is placed on one side, the light source on the other. The same pattern may also be used by using the shaded areas as conducting areas, and the remainder as insulated areas, and contacting these areas with sliding contacts.

One general method to determine position involves the use of a velocity transducer. The output signal from this circuit can be integrated in an appropriate electronic circuit, and the result of this is to give position information. The change in the values of the integral gives incremental displacement or rotation, but if absolute values are needed, initial conditions must be carefully considered. This method is especially adaptable to tachometers having a digital output, because the integrator becomes a counter which counts the total number of pulses in the specified time interval. It is less adaptable with analog circuits because, if the position changes slowly, the drift in the electronic circuits of the integrator may introduce errors into the measurement.

Most practical transducers require a mechanical linkage between the device under observation and the sensing element. This becomes one of the major sources of error and problems in all the devices, especially linear-position transducers. Backlash, which is mechanical slippage or hysteresis that occurs when the device changes direction, is one of the more important. Alignment can be a major source of error and maintenance problems, and normally provision should be made to adjust this from time to time.

Optical Encoders. A sector or disk that is mounted on a shaft may be designed with a pattern of opaque and translucent areas, and on either side may be placed a light source and a photoelectric sensor. The pattern of illuminated sensors then carries the information as to the location of the device. A similar arrangement is possible for translational motion, as indicated in Fig. 17. The figure shows a possible sector or pattern of opaque and translucent areas. The number of levels in the encoding determines the accuracy with which the device operates. A variety of codes is available, each of which has advantages and disadvantages. These encoders have two very important advantages. The first is that they give a true digital output. The second is that no mechanical contact is involved, hence few problems of wear and alignment. A disadvantage is that lights do burn out; however, manufacturers rate lamps for lifetimes like 50,000 h.

Resistive Digital Encoders. A sector or disk mounted on a shaft, or a linear sector may be designed with a pattern of contacts and insulated areas, arranged in a pattern of the same general type shown in Fig. 17. Fingers or electrical contacts may then ride on these surfaces, and those circuits which are complete will give a digital indication of the position of the device at that instant. These are relatively inexpensive, can be made to any desired accuracy provided the sector is large enough to hold the required number of rows for binary numbers, and are quite adequate for slowly moving systems. The principal problem is maintenance of the contacts and wear of the contactors. There is often an unavoidable ambiguity of one digit in the least significant binary digit.

Inductance-variation Transducers. A position transducer connected by a mechanical linkage to the core of a coil or set of coils is a simple, rugged device using the inductive-transduction principle. A variation of this is to vary the core in such a manner that two inductances are varied, one to increase, the other to decrease. These two inductors are two of the four arms of a Wheatstone bridge.

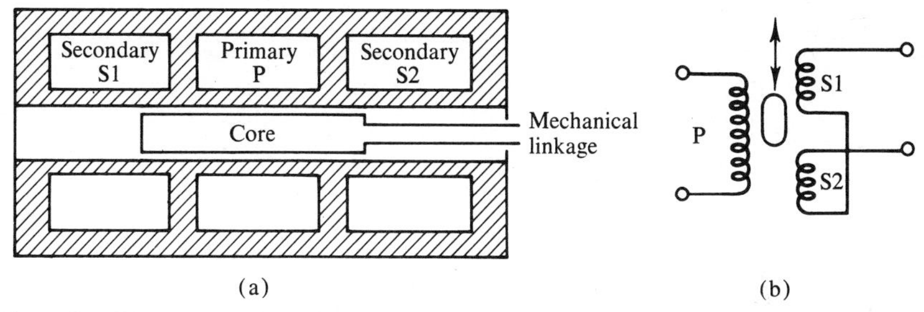

Fig. 18. Linear variable-differential transformer (LVDT) transducer. (*a*) Basic construction features of linear variable-differential transformer. (*b*) Schematic diagram of linear variable-differential transformer.

This technique gives greater sensitivity than the single-inductance method. It is also possible to vary the mutual inductance between two coils by this principle. In all cases, the accuracy is about 1.0 percent in typical applications.

Linear Variable-differential Transformer. The LVDT uses a mechanical linkage and the inductive-transduction principle. The linkage causes the core position to move, as indicated in Fig. 18. The distinguishing feature of the differential transformer is the connection of the two secondary windings, labeled with S. These coils are connected so that the output voltage is zero when the core is at the reference position. Motion of the core in either direction causes the voltage to increase. The two directions are distinguished by a 180° phase shift in the voltage as it passes through the reference position. This use of the differential principle makes it possible to build a transducer with a resolution as fine as 50 μin. These units are characterized by simplicity and ruggedness, and by being small and lightweight, stable, and easy to align and maintain. The excitation frequency must be at least ten times the maximum expected signal frequency. They exhibit a linear response over a wide input range. They are sensitive to stray magnetic fields, but shielding is possible.

Rotary Variable-differential Transformer. The RVDT is the application of the differential-transformer transduction principle to rotary motion. A specially shaped core is rotated around an axis marking the center of a coaxial-coil assembly. Careful core design produces an output voltage proportional to angular position over a relatively large range. Its characteristics and use are similar to those of the LVDT.

Synchros. Synchros are normally used in control systems, but they have properties useful in instrumentation systems. A synchro is a rotary-position transducer built on the inductive principle. It has a three-phase stator winding and a single-phase rotor winding. When the stator is excited from a three-phase source, often 400 Hz, the rotor output voltage is constant in amplitude, and its phase varies directly with position.

Resolvers. Resolvers are normally used in control systems but find transducer applications. A resolver is a rotary-position transducer built on the inductive principle. The stator has a two-phase winding, as does the rotor. The voltage developed by one rotor winding is proportional to the sine of the position angle with respect to the reference; the voltage developed by the second is proportional to the cosine of this position angle. The unused (if any) rotor winding must be short-circuited for proper operation.

Induction Potentiometer. This device comes from the control-system field. It is a variable-coupling transformer built something like a resolver, but with specially designed pole pieces so that the output voltage is directly proportional to the angular displacement from the reference, rather than to a trigonometric function of that angle. Usually it has only one rotor winding and cannot rotate more than 90° either way from the reference position.

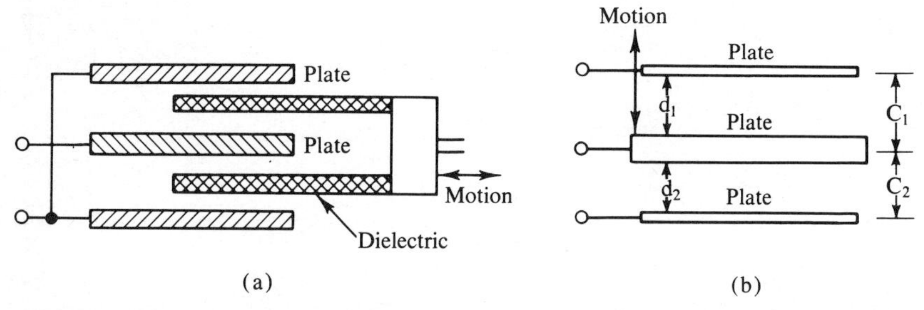

Fig. 19. Capacitive-displacement transducers. (*a*) Moving-dielectric-displacement transducer. The plates and the dielectric may be either rectangular or cylindrical. In the latter case this represents a cross-section view. (*b*) Differential capacitor-displacement transducer.

Microsyns. This device comes from the control-system field. It consists of specially arranged windings on four poles and operates much like a differential transformer. The device needs but one pair of excitation connections, and the output voltage is taken from the stator, as are the excitation leads. Thus no rotor connections are needed, a decided advantage. But the linear range of operation is quite limited, often only 10° or less from the reference position in either direction.

Capacitive-displacement Transducers. Figure 19 shows two different arrangements of a moving dielectric for a capacitive transducer. The mechanical linkage moves the dielectric in each case. The first is a conventional translation. The second provides a differential capacitance and when used as two of the arms of a Wheatstone bridge provides much greater sensitivity. Capacitive-displacement transducers have the effect that they require extremely small forces for operation and thus are useful in very small systems. They have good (as high as 50 kHz) frequency-response characteristics and high output impedance. On the other hand, the metallic parts of the capacitor must be insulated from each other, and in general the frames must be grounded. Care must be taken in this regard, especially with regard to dirt and similar contaminants which can affect the operation severely. Resolution of 100 μin. is possible.

Capacitive-rotation Transducers. The relative rotation of two plates of a capacitor makes a good position transducer. Figure 20 shows a two-plate capacitor and a differential arrangement. These require small torques for operation and are useful in small systems. All comments for capacitive-displacement transducers apply to these as well.

Resistive and Potentiometric Transducers. A very simple transducer for position or angular position may be built by mechanically linking the device under study to a variable resistor, as indicated in Fig. 21. Normally the resistors are wirewound. The resolution is limited to 0.002 in. or 0.2° of arc at best. A considerable force or torque is typically needed to drive these, and frequency responses are limited to less than 5 Hz. The chief source of problems is the sliding contact, which can be contaminated, wear out, become misaligned, and generate noise. These are inexpensive and are widely used where requirements are not especially severe.

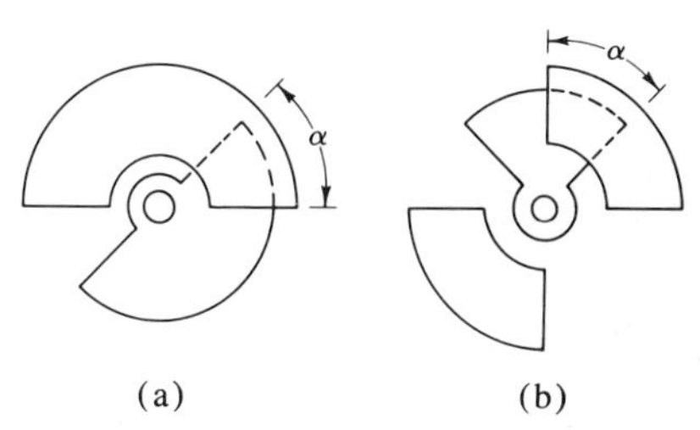

Fig. 20. Capacitive-rotary-motion-displacement transducers. (*a*) Two-plate rotary-motion capacitor. (*b*) Differential rotary-motion capacitor.

16. Force (Pressure)

PHENOMENON: Force, torque.

COMMON NAMES: Load cell, dynamometer, scales.

Tranducers for force and torque measurement are very similar in operation to those for displacement and rotation measurements. The essential difference is that force transducers depend for their operation on very small displacements of elastic sensors, while displacement transducers require motion with a minimum of force. As a consequence of this, a typical force transducer is composed of a sensor designed to respond to a force by converting this to an equivalent small displacement, and then a displacement

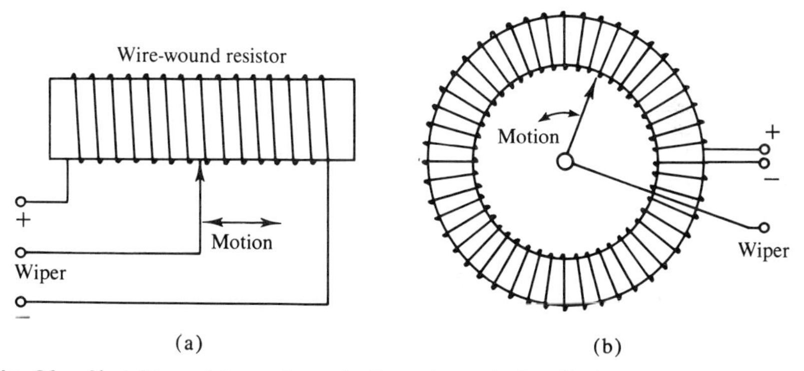

Fig. 21. Variable-resistance transduction elements for displacement transducers. (*a*) Resistive transducer for linear-displacement transducers. This may be used either with potentiometric or resistive transduction elements. (*b*) Resistive transducer for rotational-displacement transducers. This may be used either with resistive or potentiometric transduction elements.

transducer to convert this to an electrical signal. For this reason, this discussion will be concerned primarily with the basic sensing elements, and the user is asked to read the section on displacement transducers or on strain gages for additional information.

Force and torque measurements tend to be very difficult. The primary reasons for this are related to the small displacements involved. This means that the mating surfaces or contact areas between the sensing element and device under study must be carefully maintained. If not, hysteresis will develop and invalid data will result. Force and torque transducers are also susceptible to components

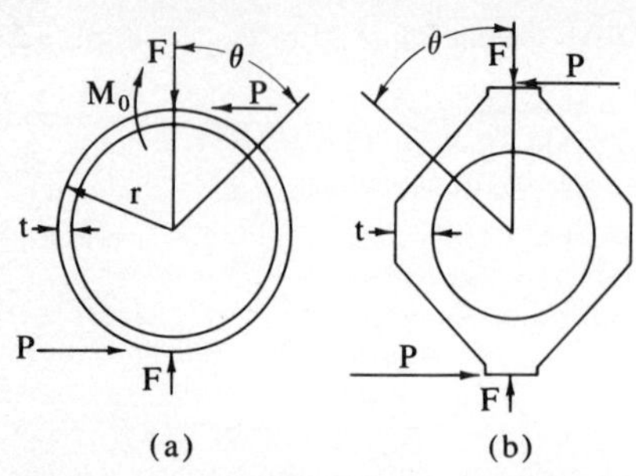

Fig. 22. Two types of rings used as force- or torque-sensing elements. Strain gages are used as transduction elements. (*a*) Circular proving ring for force (F) or torque (P) sensing. M_0 is a restraining torque that prevents rotation. A strain gage placed at $\theta = 39.6°$ will have an output proportional to P and independent of F. A gage on $\theta = 90°$ will have an output proportional to F and independent of P. (*b*) Octagonal proving ring. When θ is approximately 50°, a strain gage on this surface will give an output proportional to P and independent of F. A gage on the surface at $\theta = 90°$ will give an output proportional to F and independent of P.

in other than the desired direction, and much effort must be expended to place the transducers so that these effects will be compensated.

Rings. Figure 22 shows several forms of (proving) rings that are used as displacement-sensing elements. The usual transduction element with one of these is a strain gage, mounted in special places called strain nodes. At these nodes, the restraining moment M_0 is directly proportional to only one of the applied forces P or F.[14] Thus the strain at this point is directly related to the unknown force.

Beams. Beams that can be bent by unknown forces make good sensing elements. The deflection may be sensed and transduced by an LVDT, a strain gage, or piezoelectric transducers. The technique is illustrated in Fig. 23. The cantilever beam is especially useful because it can be readily arranged to respond to two forces, or to components at right angles to its transverse axis.

Columns. Columns may be bent by unknown forces, and the resulting displacements or strains may be transduced by strain gages. Figure 24 shows typical column arrangements.

Piezoelectric. A column-type sensing element may be combined with a piezoelectric crystal to produce a very sensitive and practical force transducer. The incorporation into these devices of integrated-circuit electronics makes them very useful. One of the disadvantages with a piezoelectric crystal is that it operates only in compression. If the transducer must

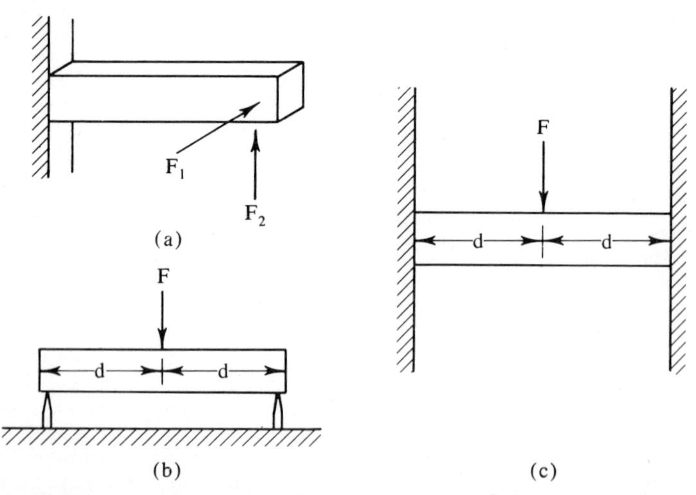

Fig. 23. Beams used to sense a force. The beam deflection is proportional to the force to be measured, and is measured with a displacement transducer. (*a*) Cantilever beam. (*b*) Supported beam. (*c*) Restrained beam.

respond to tension forces, then the crystal must be "preloaded"; i.e., it must exist in a state of initial (bias) compression. But these devices have a very good frequency response, responding to forces of duration less than 0.1 ms.

Diaphragm. A diaphragm is a circular plate that is clamped. A force applied at the center produces a good deflection characteristic. Transduction elements include LVDTs and capacitive transduction elements. The latter are more common, and the resulting transducers are rugged and relatively inexpensive.

Torque Tube. A cylinder, which may be either solid or hollow, will be twisted by an applied torque. The resulting strains may be transduced by strain gages located at 45° angles to the axis. One gage will be in tension, the other in compression. Thin-walled cylinders have the greater sensitivities (see Fig. 25).

17. Stress-Strain

PHENOMENON: Stress and strain.

COMMON NAMES: Strain gage.

Stress is, on a relative or per-unit basis, the force applied to a device that tends to cause a deformation, and strain is, again on a relative or per-unit basis, the resulting deformation. Generally, this is a displacement and can be sensed by ordinary displacement transducers. But special sensors have been developed especially for this problem, and it seems logical to treat these separately. In addition, strain gages are used as sensing elements in other types of transducers.

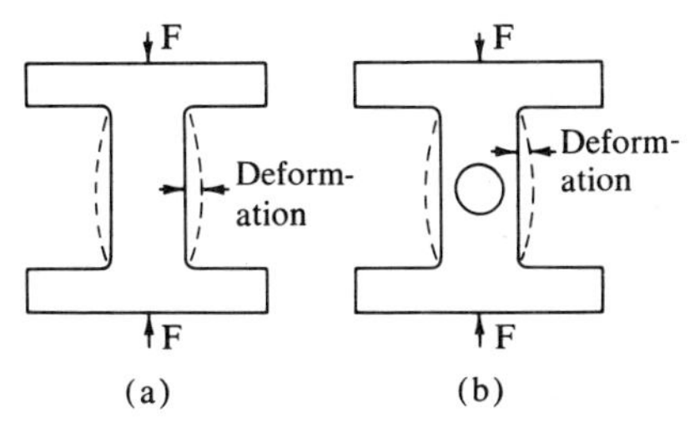

Fig. 24. Columns used to convert forces to strain-gage readings. (*a*) Cylindrical column. The cylinder may be hollow or solid. (*b*) Rectangular column with stress-concentration hole.

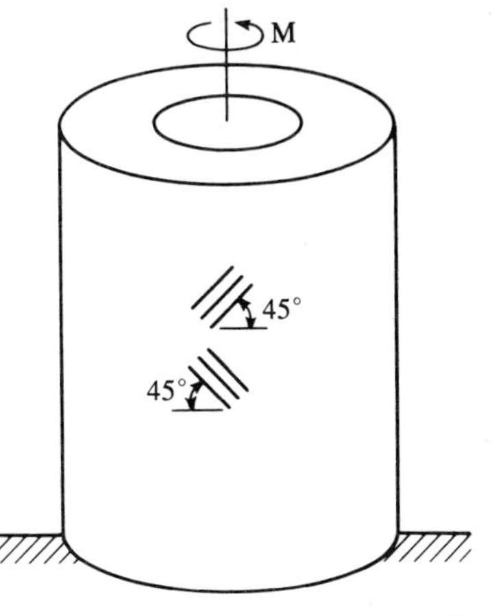

Fig. 25. Torque tube with strain gages mounted at 45° angles to measure *M*. One gage will indicate compression, the other tension. The gages can be used as two arms of a Wheatstone bridge.

Stress is measured in units of force per unit area, usually pounds per square inch or newtons per square meter. Strain is dimensionless, being measured in inches per inch or other relative units. The usual symbol for stress is s, for strain ϵ. If a material is stressed within the elastic limit,

$$s = E\epsilon \tag{1}$$

where E = modulus of elasticity

Strain gages all make use of the same physical phenomenon, called the "piezoresistance effect." A wire or semiconductor, when itself strained, will experience a change in resistance. Resistance change happens for two reasons and depends upon the definition of resistance

$$R = \rho \frac{l}{A} \tag{2}$$

where ρ = resistivity
l = length of material
A = cross-section area of material

The first is that, when the wire is in tension, it is elongated and the area is reduced. The second is a change in the resistivity ρ under tension. Strain gages are usable in either tension or compression, and exhibit little if any hysteresis effects.

Unbonded Strain Gages. An unbonded strain gage is an arrangement of wires mounted on insulated pins and stretched between two members. A simplified view is shown in Fig. 26. These are seldom used for strain measurements but do find application in accelerometers, pressure transducers, and similar apparatus.

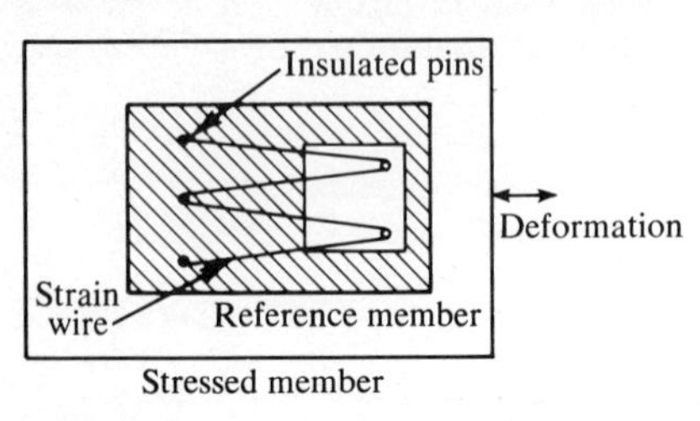

Fig. 26. Unbonded strain gage.

Bonded Strain Gages. Most strain gages are made by embedding the wires into a substrate of paper, plastic, nitrocellulose, or phenolic, and cementing or bonding this assembly to the member whose strain is to be measured. (This is a difficult operation, and the manufacturer's recommendations must be carefully followed.) The three principal types of construction are indicated in Fig. 27. Wire gages employ special materials in their construction such as platinum alloys, constantan, manganin, or Nichrome, of thickness 0.0005 to 0.0010 in. in diameter. Foil gages are usually less than 0.001 in. thick. Both must be securely fastened to the substrate so that the deformation will be transmitted to the gage. Semiconductor gages are made of silicon, with various types of doping to achieve a wide variety of effects.

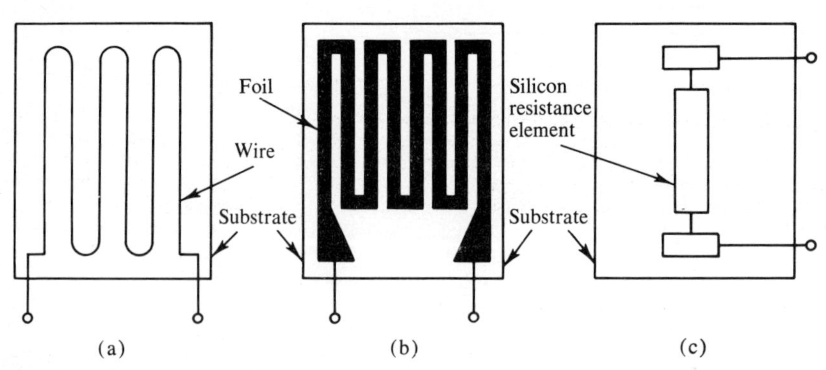

Fig. 27. Three types of strain gages using bonded attachment techniques. (*a*) Wire strain gage. (*b*) Foil strain gage. (*c*) Semiconductor strain gage.

Strain gages measure strain in only one direction, and are little affected by transverse strains. If it is desired to measure strains along more than one axis, a pattern or "rosette" of gages can be used. Two common patterns are shown in Fig. 28. For the rectangular rosette, the angle θ of the principal stress axis is given by

$$\tan 2\theta = \frac{2\epsilon_2 - \epsilon_1 - \epsilon_3}{\epsilon_1 - \epsilon_3} \tag{3}$$

where the ϵ's are the strains measured by the three gages. θ is less than 90° if $\epsilon_2 > (\epsilon_1 + \epsilon_3)/2$, and greater than 90° if it does not hold. For the delta rosette,

$$\tan 2\theta = \frac{\sqrt{3}\,(\epsilon_3 - \epsilon_2)}{2\epsilon_1 - \epsilon_2 - \epsilon_3} \tag{4}$$

and θ is less than 90° if $\epsilon_3 > \epsilon_2$, and greater than 90° if the converse holds.

Several problems with strain gages exist. They are fragile and must be handled carefully. Proper mounting is essential. The resistance can be measured only by sending a current through the wire, and this generates heat. Heat also causes a resistance change, which will lead to a systematic error unless corrected. The usual method for correction is to mount a second "dummy" gage in a location where its

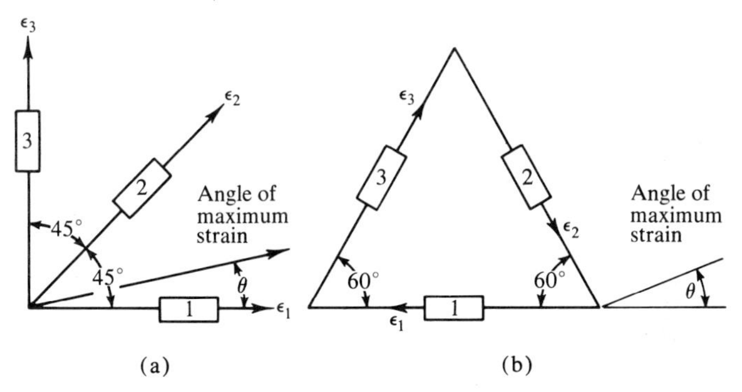

Fig. 28. Rosette patterns for strain-gage location. (*a*) Rectangular rosette for maximum strain determination. (*b*) Delta or triaxial rosette for maximum strain determination.

temperature effects are identical with those of the first but where no strain will exist. The difference in resistance changes is then used as the resistance change caused by strain only. Another problem is the thermally generated voltages at the contacts. With dc gage circuits, this can be reduced only by proper choice of leads and by keeping them clean. The problem is insignificant in ac gage circuits.

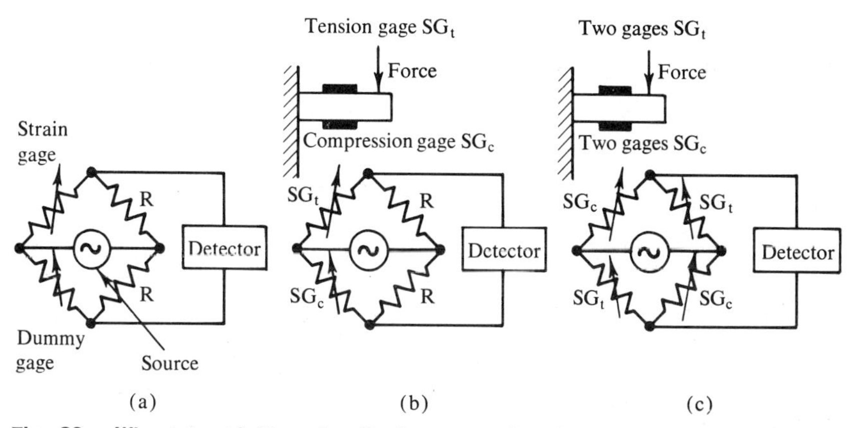

Fig. 29. Wheatstone-bridge circuits for measuring the resistance or resistance change of strain gages. (*a*) Strain-gage circuit with dummy gage for temperature compensation. (*b*) Strain-gage circuit with two active arms and temperature compensation. (*c*) Strain-gage circuit with four active arms.

Almost without exception, the resistances of the strain gages are measured with Wheatstone-bridge circuits. Either ac or dc excitation is possible. An ac excitation is preferable with situations where amplifiers must be used, because ac amplifiers are easier to build than dc. But dc excitation is better if the information must be transmitted over long cables for readout purposes. Figure 29 shows three possible arrangements of the bridge circuitry. The gages marked as compression gages in the latter two circuits also play the part of temperature-compensation gages, provided they see the same temperature as the tension gages. The use of more than one gage in a bridge gives a greater sensitivity, and thus generally more accurate strain measurements. Some strain-gage circuits employ pulse circuitry for excitation rather than either ac or dc systems. The advantage of this is that it allows high-peak short-duration pulses to be applied. This gives greater sensitivity in the output, and in the intervals when no current flows, the gage is dissipating the heat that was developed.

THERMODYNAMIC PROPERTIES

18. Thermodynamics *Temperature* is defined as the thermal state of a body and is a function of the mean kinetic energy of the molecules of a substance. *Heat* is a form of energy. Heat can be transferred from one body to a second when the temperature of the first is greater than that of the second. The result is commonly called *heat flow*. The three methods for this are as follows:

1. Conduction—heat transfer by thermal diffusion through a solid or through motionless fluids
2. Convection—heat transfer caused by fluid motion
3. Radiation—heat transfer through electromagnetic radiation

The term *thermal conductivity* expresses the relative ability of a substance to transfer heat by conduction; the term *insulation resistivity* is a reciprocal concept which expresses the relative ability of a substance to prevent heat transfer by conduction.

Temperature is currently defined according to an internationally agreed upon set of states of matter. These are stated in *degrees Kelvin* (°K), the only unit officially adopted by the International System of Units (SI). The scale is called the International Practical Temperature Scale (IPTS 68).

Temperature, °K	*Physical Effect*
13.81	Triple point of equilibrium hydrogen
17.042	Boiling point of equilibrium hydrogen at a pressure of $25/76$ standard atmosphere
20.28	Boiling point of equilibrium hydrogen at a pressure of 1 standard atmosphere
27.102	Boiling point of neon at a pressure of 1 standard atmosphere
54.361	Triple point of oxygen
90.188	Boiling point of oxygen at a pressure of 1 standard atmosphere
273.16	Triple point of water
373.15	Boiling point of water
505.1181	Freezing point of tin
692.73	Freezing point of zinc
903.89	Freezing point of antimony
1235.08	Freezing point of silver
1337.58	Freezing point of gold

Although not officially recognized by SI, temperatures are commonly expressed in Celsius (formerly centigrade). The temperatures given may be converted by the relation °C = °K − 273.15.

Calibration standards and transfer standards are provided by platinum resistance thermometers between the range of 13.81 and 903.89°K, by thermocouples made of a junction of platinum wire with a wire made of the alloy containing 90 percent platinum and 10 percent rhodium between 903.89 and 1337.58°K, and with optical pyrometers above 1337.58°K.

The most important problem that the instrumentation engineer who needs to measure temperature must solve is to ensure that the temperature-sensing device is in fact at the same temperature as the subject for measurement. The difficulty in this arises from a number of concerns. One is the fact that often it is necessary to protect the sensing element from the environment in which it operates, or to cement or otherwise secure it in place. Materials commonly used for both these purposes commonly have low thermal conductivity, and consequently the temperature of the sensing element may differ considerably from that of the environment. The sensing element may absorb a significant amount of energy from the environment, and thus change the temperature being measured. The sensing element may not be capable of responding adequately to rapid rates of change of temperature. The recommendations of the manufacturers must normally be carefully followed so that the errors resulting from these sources are acceptably small.

THERMODYNAMIC TRANSDUCERS

19. Heat-flow Measurement If one wishes to measure heat flow, or to measure thermal conductivity by measuring the temperature change caused by a known heat flow, one must immediately plan to measure temperature. This is the most practical approach, and as a consequence, all the information given in the following sections for temperature measurement applies directly to heat-flow measurement. The temperature information is used in conjunction with known heat flow and dimensions to find thermal conductivity, or with dimensions and known thermal conductivity to find heat flow.

20. Thermoresistive Thermometers Many substances have the property that their resistivity changes with temperature. Some of these find application as temperature-sensing devices. Metallic conductors usually have a resistivity that increases with increasing temperature. The changes are small but nearly linear over a wide temperature range. Thermometers made from these are called "resistance thermometers."

Semiconductors—silicon, germanium, and carbon—have a resistivity that decreases with increasing temperature. These are called either by their primary element name or "semiconductor thermometers."

Special mixtures of various elements, usually sintered metallic oxides, sulfides, and selenides, have a resistivity that is high and also increases with decreasing temperature. The relation is very nonlinear, but the changes in resistivity are large. These materials are called "thermistors" and find wide application.

Resistance Thermometers. Coils of wire made of platinum, nickel, certain nickel alloys, or tungsten, and certain metallic films are the most common resistance thermometers. Platinum resistance thermometers are the most accurate temperature transducers available, and thus are used as the calibration standard in the International Practical Temperature Scale. They are stable, readily calibrated, rugged, and lightweight. In addition to standards applications, they are used in many laboratory and industrial applications. They are expensive. Platinum resistance thermometers have good thermal time constants, even with ceramic coatings required for mechanical and environmental protection. Platinum resistance thermometers are used from 10 to 1350°K (−263 to 1077°C). Typical resistances vary from less than 0.1 to more than 10,000 Ω.

Nickel and nickel-alloy resistance thermometers are used from 170 to 600°K (−103 to 327°C). They are less expensive than platinum, and are used in many industrial applications.

Tungsten resistance thermometers are being rapidly improved, and as their properties become well established, they will become quite common. It is expected that tungsten resistance thermometers will be especially useful at higher temperatures.

The user of a resistance thermometer must measure its resistance and from this infer the unknown temperature. This may be done through the use of published calibration curves either for the individual thermometer or for the particular type of thermometer. For platinum, the properties are sufficiently well known that power series or other empirical mathematical expressions have been developed to permit the user to determine the temperature from the resistance. One problem with these is that because of their complexity the equations usually require iterative solutions for temperature.

One form of this empirical equation for platinum is called the Callendar-Van Dusen equation. This uses degrees Celsius for the temperature t:

$$R_t = R_0 \left\{1 + \alpha \left[t + \delta\left(1 - \frac{t}{100}\right)\frac{t}{100} + \beta\left(1 - \frac{t}{100}\right)\left(\frac{t}{100}\right)^3\right]\right\} \tag{5}$$

where R_t = resistance at some temperature t
R_0 = ice-point resistance (0°C or 273.15°K)
α = temperature coefficient of resistance near 0°C
δ = Callendar constant
β = Van Dusen constant

Typical values are $\alpha = 3.926 \times 10^{-3}$, $\delta = 1.491$, and $\beta = 0.1103$. This equation often appears in another form:

$$R_t = R_0 \left[1 + At + Bt^2 + Ct^3\left(1 - \frac{t}{100}\right)\right] \tag{6}$$

In this equation, R_t and R_0 are as previously defined. It may be shown through algebraic expansion of the Callendar-Van Dusen equation and comparison of coefficients that

$$A = \alpha + 0.01\alpha\delta$$
$$B = -\alpha\delta \times 10^{-4}$$
$$C = \alpha\beta \times 10^{-6}$$

Consequently, typical values for these constants are

$$A = 3.985 \times 10^{-3}$$
$$B = -5.856 \times 10^{-7}$$
$$C = 4.330 \times 10^{-10}$$

From knowledge of the resistance at the unknown temperature and at the reference temperature, one can then solve either of these equations for t.

Either of these equations is sufficiently accurate for most applications over the range 90 to 900°K (−183 to 627°C). Outside this range, they may be used with reduced accuracy, or more sophisticated empirical equations are available. The International Practical Temperature Scale now uses a power series with 20 terms, each coefficient having 16 significant figures, over the range 13.81 to 273.15°K, and a modified Callendar-Van Dusen equation over the range 273.15 to 903.89°K. Normally, carefully written digital-computer programs are necessary when these equations are employed.

Semiconductor Thermometers. Crystals of germanium with controlled impurity concentrations have found application in cryogenic temperature measurement, especially below 25°K. They are usable to 100°K. These have large temperature-resistivity coefficients and are thus very sensitive in this range. They are repeatable within 0.01°, but the units must be individually calibrated.

Silicon crystals are now being used in the range 225 to 525°K (−48 to 252°C). In this range, their resistance increases with increasing temperature, and the relation is reasonably linear. These must be individually calibrated.

Carbon resistors like those commonly found in much electronic circuitry are also used as temperature-sensing elements. These are readily available, inexpensive, rugged, small, and sensitive. Common sizes vary from ¼ to 1 W, 10 to 500 Ω. They have a large negative temperature coefficient of resistivity below 60°K. These are not so reproducible as germanium, but they do exhibit good frequency-response characteristics.

Thermistors. Most thermistors have a resistivity that decreases with increasing temperature (a negative resistivity coefficient), though some with a positive resistivity coefficient are available. Thermistors are usable between 200 and 600°K, and special units are used outside this range. Some thermistors will show a resistance that varies in a ratio of 1,000:1 as the temperature goes from 273 to 600°K (0 to 327°C). This large change makes them very sensitive. They are also reproducible, show good frequency responses, and are inexpensive and rugged. They do drift with age and must be calibrated according to the manufacturer's recommendations. An empirical relation between resistance and temperature is

$$R = R_0 \exp\left[\beta\left(\frac{1}{t} - \frac{1}{T_0}\right)\right] \tag{7}$$

where R_0 = resistance at some reference temperature
T_0 = reference temperature, °K
β = empirical constant, typically 3500 to 4500°K
R = desired resistance
t = unknown temperature, °K

Resistance Measurement in Thermoresistive Thermometry. The first question that must be answered when a resistance-measurement technique is chosen is to determine the time interval between readings, or what is closely related, determine whether rapidly changing temperatures will be measured or equilibrium conditions are needed. The most accurate resistance-measurement technique is normally the Wheatstone bridge. This is a null measurement and must be taken under equilibrium conditions, or at least conditions that are changing slowly compared with the reading time. The latter is typically several seconds or longer. Figure 30 shows two common bridge circuits. The reason for the use of a three-wire or four-wire cable instead of a two-wire cable to the sensing resistor is to get a set of leads whose resistance changes caused by heating in the operational environment will cancel. In the system showing a four-wire cable, the leads A and A' can be interchanged, and also those marked B and B'. A second resistance (temperature) reading is made, and the two results are averaged. This reduces systematic error caused by lead-resistance variation. Alternating or direct excitation may be used with these bridges.

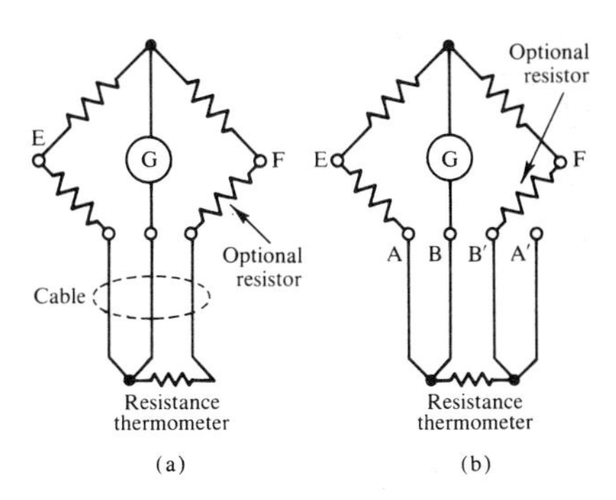

Fig. 30. Wheatstone-bridge resistance-measurement circuits for use in resistance thermometry. In both circuits, the bridge excitation is applied between points E and F. (*a*) Siemens three-lead cable for Wheatstone-bridge measurement of resistance of thermometer. (*b*) Floating-potential-lead arrangement. Leads at A and A' and at B and B' can be interchanged to provide two measurements of resistance.

When temperatures are to be read at rapid intervals, some type of direct reading is necessary. The readout may be a digital or deflecting meter; it may be converted internally for telemetry or computer processing. Figure 31 shows four possible circuit arrangements. In this case, the bridge is operated as an unbalanced bridge, and the output voltage E_0 is related to the excitation voltage E_s by

$$E_0 = E_s \frac{R_2(R_A + R_T) - R_1R_3}{(R_2 + R_3)(R_1 + R_T + R_A)} \tag{8}$$

R_A is a trimming resistor for adjusting the bridge to balance at one end of the temperature range. For the voltage divider,

$$E_0 = E_s \frac{R}{R_T + R} \tag{9}$$

Knowledge by measurement of E_0 and E_s permits a determination of R_T in either of these circuits, and thus the temperature. In the other two, the voltage E_0

produced by the constant current or the current I_0 produced by the constant voltage is taken as a measure of the resistance R_T. The latter three circuits are most appropriate with thermistors and semiconductor thermometers where large resistance changes increase the sensitivity of these inherently insensitive circuits.

In all these systems, current must flow through the resistance thermometer. This causes heating of the wire, which can be an important source of systematic error. The amount of heat so generated and its effect must be considered. Another problem is thermoelectric voltages at the junctions of dissimilar materials. These

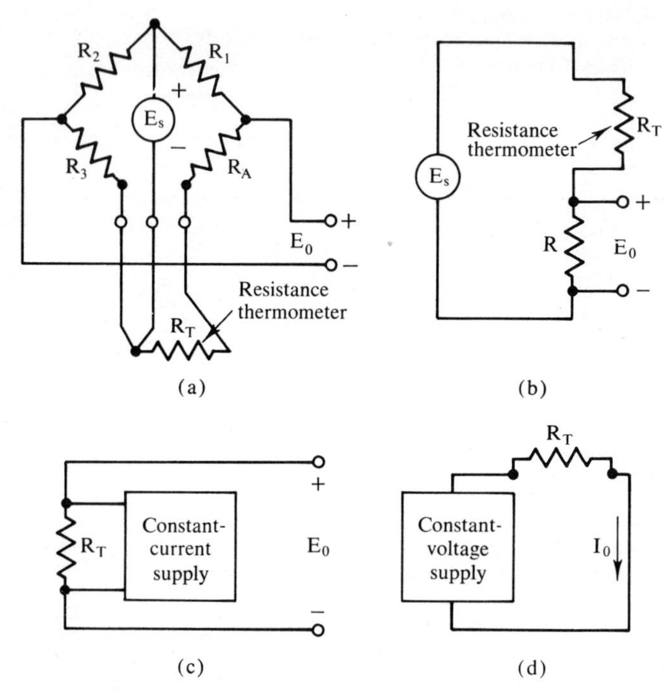

Fig. 31. Four circuits for direct reading of temperatures as either voltages or currents in thermoresistive thermometry. (*a*) Unbalanced bridge for resistance measurements. (*b*) Voltage divider for resistance measurements. (*c*) Voltage-drop system for resistance measurement. (*d*) Current-flow system for resistance measurement.

cause problems only with direct excitation. Manufacturers usually provide good guidelines on the reduction and elimination of these problems.

21. Thermocouples At a junction between two dissimilar metals, a voltage will be developed. The magnitude of this voltage is a function of the junction temperature. This is called the Seebeck effect, and it is the basis for the thermocouple, a very widely used electrical thermometer. In these devices, sensing and transduction take place in the same element, so that these are not externally powered.

Two other effects are associated with the Seebeck effect. The flow of electric current through a junction of two dissimilar metals will either heat or cool the junction. This is called the *Peltier* effect, and it depends on the current direction. The flow of electric current through a wire along which a temperature gradient exists will either heat or cool the wire. This is called the *Thomson* effect, and it also depends on the current direction. Both of these are independent of normal

I^2R heating and can be sources of systematic error in thermocouple circuits. The current must be kept small.

Since an electric circuit must be closed so that this Seebeck (thermoelectric) voltage can be measured, it will be necessary to have at least two junctions. One is usually called the reference-temperature junction. The temperatures and voltages at all junctions must be considered. This has led to the development of three principles of thermoelectric thermometry.

1. *Law of Homogeneous Circuits.* An electric current cannot be sustained in a circuit of a single homogeneous metal, regardless of variations in section, by the application of heat alone. This leads to the conclusion that the thermoelectric voltages developed are dependent only on the junction temperatures and are independent of temperature gradients and distributions along the wires.

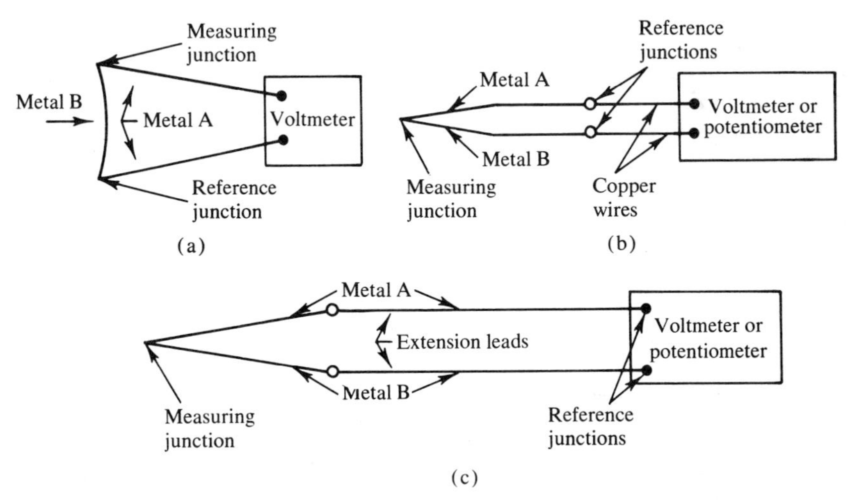

Fig. 32. Three possible wiring techniques for connection of a thermocouple to a voltmeter, potentiometer, or other voltage-measurement device. (*a*) Basic thermocouple instrumentation circuit. (*b*) A thermocouple connected to the indicating instrument with copper wires. Other material such as aluminum could be used, but both must be made of the same material. (*c*) A thermocouple connected to its indicating instrument with extension leads. The extension leads have thermoelectric properties virtually identical with the properties of the thermocouple wire itself, and must not be interchanged.

2. *Law of Intermediate Metals.* If in a circuit of solid conductors the temperature is uniform from any point P to a second point Q, the algebraic sum of the thermoelectric voltages in the entire circuit is independent of this part, and is the same as if P and Q were in contact. As a consequence, the device for measuring the voltage may be placed at any practical place in the circuit provided the two junctions thus introduced are at the same temperature.

3. *Law of Intermediate Temperatures.* The thermoelectric voltage developed by a thermocouple with its junctions at temperatures T_1 and T_3 is the algebraic sum of the voltages of identical thermocouples, one working between temperatures T_1 and T_2 and the second working between temperatures T_2 and T_3. This principle makes it possible to change the reference-junction temperatures of a thermocouple whose calibration is known, and it is also used in calibration procedures.

Wiring and Reference Junctions. Three different wiring techniques are commonly used to connect a thermocouple to a measuring instrument. These are illustrated in Fig. 32. The first technique is useful when the indicator is close to the environment being studied. It is not practical when long runs of rather expensive thermocouple wire must be used. The second technique is desirable when the two reference junctions can be maintained at the same temperature and are physically close to the environment under study. Each of the two extension wires required in the third technique is made of material that has thermoelectric properties that are virtually identical with those of the thermocouple wire to which it will be connected. When extension leads are used, the type that is designed for the thermocouple in use must be specified, and the individual wires must be connected to the proper thermocouple leads. Reversal of these in wiring is a major source of error in the use of thermocouples. The two reference junctions must be at the same temperature in this case as well.

The most common laboratory method for maintaining a reference-junction temperature is to insulate the junction electrically though not thermally, and place this junction in a vacuum flask filled with an ice-water mixture. This is not always practical in industrial environments. Consequently, many measuring instruments have automatic compensators to adjust the indicator for changes in reference-junction temperature. These are designed to operate over a limited temperature range which must be compatible with the environment of the indicator.

Thermocouple Voltage Measurement. The direct voltages developed by thermocouples are small, usually in the millivolt range. The effective output resistance of the devices and leads is often rather high, and as a consequence, the indicator must be a high-input-impedance device. Potentiometers have long been the most commonly used indicators. Because they are null instruments, they require no current from the thermocouple when a measurement is being made. The potentiometer may be read in millivolts, and the reading converted to temperature. Some potentiometers are designed for use with particular types of thermocouples and consequently are calibrated directly in temperature units.

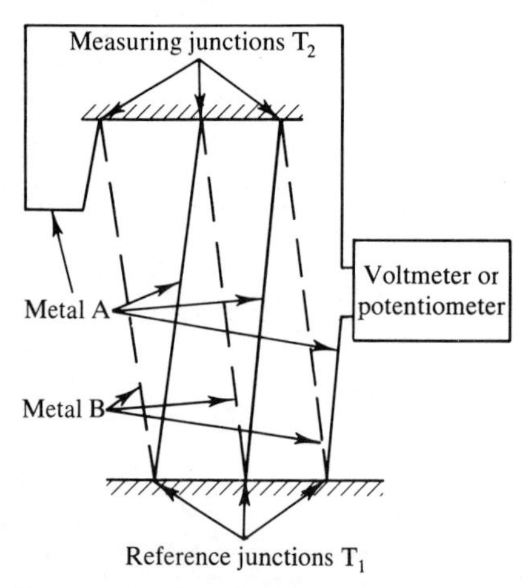

Fig. 33. Thermopile connection for increasing the voltage magnitude. Another use of this technique is to determine average temperature.

Modern electronics is having a major effect on thermoelectric thermometry. Many electronic voltmeters now have input impedances of the order of 100 MΩ or more. These are now very commonly used with thermocouples, especially the digital-readout types. Some digital meters are calibrated directly in temperature units.

Thermocouples are also used as transducers in automated systems in which a computer may perform a central role. Such systems need analog-digital processors to convert the low-level thermoelectric voltages to proper format for the computer, and these are common items with many manufacturers.

Thermopiles. One way to increase the voltage to be measured is to connect several thermocouples in series, as indicated in Fig. 33. This is called a thermopile. An alternative reason is to locate the several junctions throughout the region under study so that average temperatures may be obtained with one indicator. The chief disadvantages of a thermopile are that burnout of one unit renders all units inoperative, and it is not possible to ground all the units.

22. Thermocouple Materials Certain kinds of thermocouples are so widely used that they have been given "type" designations, and extensive tables are available for these, either from the National Bureau of Standards or from the manufacturers.

The type designations have become the defining characteristics, and the composition of the materials is sometimes altered slightly so that the devices continue to match the published curves.

Type S. Platinum vs. Platinum-Rhodium. A thermocouple of platinum vs. 10RhPt, an alloy composed of 10 percent rhodium and 90 percent platinum, is used to define IPTS 68 from 903.89 to 1337.58°K. These thermocouples are also used in industrial, aerospace, and laboratory situations. They may be used to a temperature as high as 1775°K (1502°C). These are rugged, reliable, resistant to oxidation, and highly repeatable. They are also expensive, and develop very small output voltages. With the reference at 273°K (0°C), the voltage at 1273°K (1000°C) is about 10 mV. These become quite insensitive at low temperatures, especially below 273°K, and should not be used in chemically "reducing" atmospheres.

Type R. Platinum vs. Platinum-Rhodium. A thermocouple of platinum vs. 13RhPt, an alloy composed of 13 percent rhodium and 87 percent platinum, has been used but is less common today. Its calibration curve differs from that of the type S thermocouple, but its general properties and areas of application are similar.

Type J. Iron-Constantan. Constantan is an alloy composed of copper and nickel, with some trace impurities. The exact composition varies among manufacturers because it must be matched to a particular type of iron in order that it will conform to the published calibration tables. These may be used to temperatures of 1050°K (777°C) in oxidizing atmospheres, and to 1250°K (977°C) in reducing atmospheres. The voltage developed between junctions at 0 and 500°C is about 30 mV. These are relatively low in cost and are widely used. Wire sizes vary from No. 8 to No. 30 AWG.

Type T. Copper-Constantan. These are used over the range 85 to 600°K (−188 to 327°C). The constantan used is called "Adams constantan," and it is formulated to be used with soft or annealed bare copper wire. These are available in small sizes. The voltage developed between junctions at 0 and 320°C is about 15 mV.

*Type K. Chromel-Alumel.** These are used primarily in the range 975 to 1500°K (702 to 1277°C), though they may be used at much lower temperatures. They should not be used in reducing atmospheres. These are large, coming in either No. 8 or No. 14 AWG wire sizes.

Type E. Chromel-Constantan. These have a large thermoelectric voltage, developing more than 70 mV between junctions at 0 and 1000°C. They may be used for differential temperature measurements, especially in heat-flow studies, and may be used to temperatures as high as 1530°K (1257°C).

Type B. Platinum 70 Rhodium 30 vs. Platinum 94 Rhodium 6. The numbers in the description indicate the percentages of the metals in the two alloys used in this very recently developed thermocouple. It is designed for use at temperatures higher than the limits of the type R and S thermocouples, and may be used continuously from 1700 to 1978°K (1427 to 1705°C) in oxidizing atmospheres, and to 2075°K (1802°C) on an intermittent basis.

Tungsten vs. Tungsten-Rhenium. Though no type designation has been assigned, these thermocouples are designed for use at temperatures as high as 3000°K (2727°C), as are other combinations of tungsten, iridium, and rhenium, or alloys of these metals.

Cryogenic Temperatures. Copper, silver, gold, Chromel, Alumel, constantan, and an alloy of cobalt and copper are being used as thermocouple materials in the cryogenic region, below 100°K (−173°C).

23. Quartz Thermometers Quartz crystals are often employed as the frequency determination of electronic oscillators. These are temperature-sensitive, and this fact is used to build thermometers. Sensitivities as high as 1.0 kHz/°C frequency change at a center frequency of 25 to 30 MHz can be achieved. The signal

* Chromel is an alloy of nickel and chromium; Alumel is an alloy of nickel, manganese, aluminum, and silicon. Both names are registered trademarks of Hoskins Manufacturing Co.

is transmitted to a counter, whose display either may be frequency or may be calibrated in temperature units. Such devices operate between 225 and 500°K (−48 and 227°C).

PRESSURE IN FLUIDS

This section is devoted to the measurement of pressure in fluids, and only devices giving an electrical output are considered. Pressure in solids may be measured by some adaptations of the variable-medium devices used for high-pressure measurement, especially the magnetostrictive devices. Pressure on the surface of solids is measured by force transducers, and the force is divided by the appropriate area.

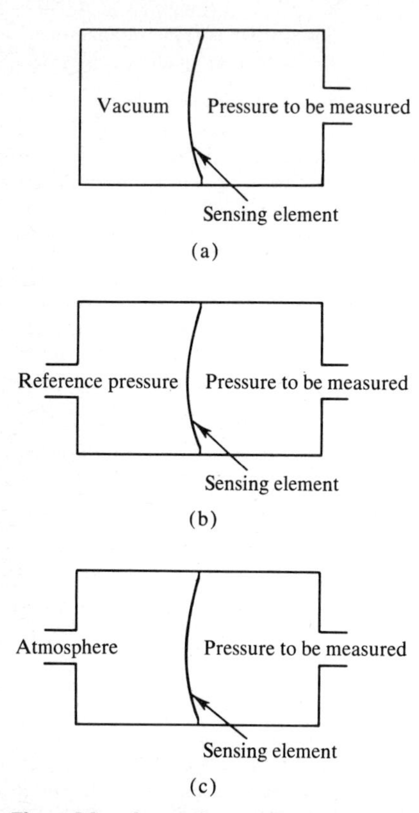

Fig. 34. General configuration of systems for pressure measurement in the medium-pressure range. (*a*) Absolute pressure. (*b*) Differential pressure. (*c*) Gage pressure.

Fluid pressure is expressed in a wide variety of units: pounds per square inch (psi), kilograms per square centimeter or square meter (kg/cm^2 or kg/m^2), newtons per square meter (N/m^2), and atmospheres. One atmosphere is 14.696 psi, or 1.033 kg/cm^2, or 101,325 N/m^2. Low pressures (vacuum measurements) are commonly expressed in "liquid head" units, usually millimeters of mercury (mm Hg), or "Torr." A Torr is equal to 1 millimeter of mercury at a temperature of 273.15°K (0°C). One atmosphere is equal to 760.00 mm Hg or 760.00 Torr.

Pressure-measurement techniques are conveniently divided into three regions, corresponding to pressure range. These divisions are somewhat arbitrary and may overlap. They are:

1. Low pressure—vacuum (below 1.0 Torr)
2. Medium pressures—1 to 10^6 Torr
3. High pressures—above 10^6 Torr, or above 10^3 atm

In the low-pressure region, pressures are expressed relative to absolute zero pressure (perfect vacuum). In the medium-pressure range, three different types of pressure expression are common:

1. Absolute (a)
2. Differential (d)
3. Gage (g)

Absolute pressures are expressed relative to perfect vacuum as zero, differential pressures as the difference between pressures existing in two different regions, and gage pressures as a differential pressure when one region is the atmosphere. Figure 34 illustrates configurations for each of these. In the high-pressure region, the difference between gage and absolute pressures becomes negligible. It is wise, when pressures in the medium range are expressed, to distinguish between the three types by adding a g, a, or d to the units, e.g., psig for pounds per square inch, gage.

24. Low-pressure (Vacuum) Measurement

Thermal Gages. In the pressure range 10^{-4} to 1.0 Torr, the thermal conductivity of a gas varies with pressure. This has led to the development of pressure transducers, using heated electric wires in the region near the sensing element, and both thermoelectric and temperature vs. resistance devices as transduction elements.

Thermocouple Gage. In Fig. 35, the filament is heated to a temperature of 50 to 400°C by a known, constant current. The voltage developed by the thermocouple is a function of the temperature, which in turn is determined by the heat

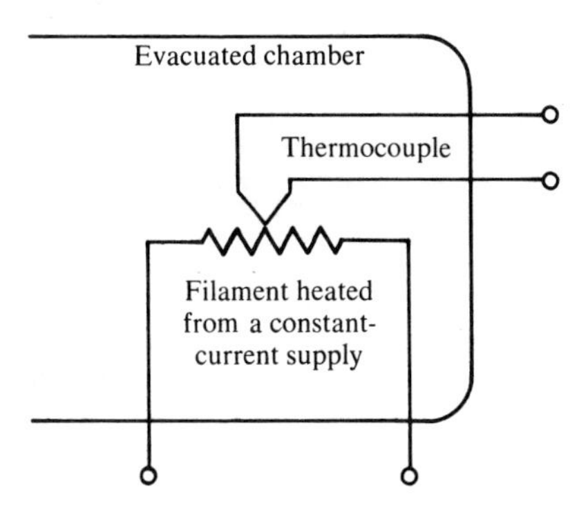

Fig. 35. Thermocouple gage for low-pressure determination.

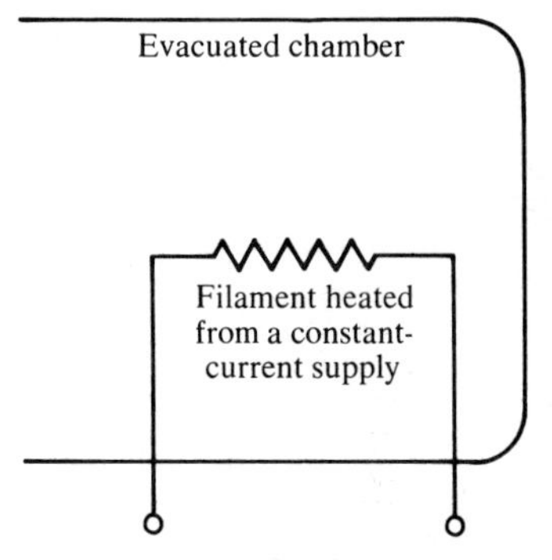

Fig. 36. Pirani gage for low-pressure measurement. The voltage across the filament varies with pressure.

flow from the filament. These must be individually calibrated, must be checked frequently, and must be recalibrated for measurement of different gases. They are rugged and inexpensive.

Pirani Gage. Figure 36 shows a heated filament. The constant-current supply develops a voltage proportional to the resistance of the wire, which in turn depends on the heat transfer in the gas. These are rugged, inexpensive, and generally more accurate than thermocouple gages. But they must be individually calibrated and checked frequently.

Ionization Gages. Positive ions will be produced by a stream of electrons in a gas. The rate of ion production will be dependent on the pressure and the number of electrons. The resulting gages are usable over the range 10^{-12} to 10^{-3} Torr, and with modification, to 10^{-17} Torr. A problem with all hot-cathode devices is that operation with a heated filament at too high a pressure, usually about 0.1 Torr, will burn out the gage.

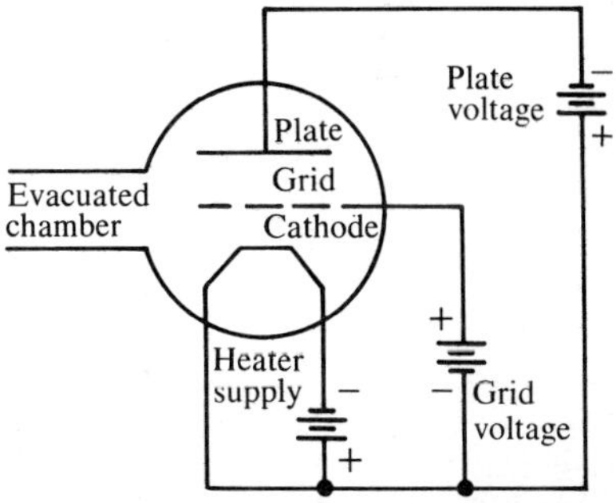

Triode Thermionic Gage. A three-electrode gage is illustrated in Fig. 37. The cathode, grid, and anode (plate) are concentric, with the cathode at the center. The cathode is heated and emits electrons. These are accelerated toward the grid by the positive voltage. Because of the small area of the grid, most electrons pass through, creating positive ions in the region between the grid and anode. These ions in turn are collected by the anode, and the ratio of plate to grid current is proportional to pressure.

Plate voltage
Plate
Grid
Evacuated chamber
Cathode
Heater supply
Grid voltage

Fig. 37. Schematic connections of an ionization gage. In the conventional gage, the three electrodes are concentric, with the cathode innermost. In the Bayard-Alpert gage, the plate (anode) is innermost.

These gages must be calibrated by individual gases, and checked occasionally. They must be carefully installed—in particular, adsorbed gases must be eliminated. They are usable from 10^{-8} to 10^{-3} Torr. Voltages required are in the range 50 to 300 V.

Bayard-Alpert Gage. This gage is similar in principle to the conventional ionization gage, but the anode is made the innermost electrode, with the cathode on the outside. This makes it possible to extend the lower limit down to 10^{-10} Torr, and further modifications, including electron-multiplying anodes, of this idea have extended the range down to 10^{-17} Torr.

Magnetic-field Ionization Gages. To increase their sensitivity, some gages have a magnetic field that increases the length of travel of an electron, thus increasing the number of collisions and resultant ionizations. Some are designed for measurement of total pressure, that is, the sum of the pressures of all constituent gases of the region under study. Others are designed for partial-pressure measurement, that is, for measurement of pressure caused by particular components in the system. All these require magnetic fields from 100 to 10,000 gauss (0.01 to 1.0 weber/m^2).

Lafferty Magnetron Gage. This gage measures total pressure over the range 10^{-14} to 10^{-5} Torr, and can be extended to 10^{-17} Torr with an electron-multiplying anode.

Penning or Philips Gage, Redhead Gage. The Penning Gage eliminates the heated filament and depends on the electron discharge in the field around a cold cathode. A power supply of 2,000 to 3,000 V is required, and the range is 10^{-7} to 10^{-3} Torr. Modifications by Redhead permit use down to 10^{-13} Torr.

Omegatron, Mass Spectrometer. A mass spectrometer is a device that selectively accelerates ions having a certain charge-to-mass ratio in a spiral path. A magnetic field of the order of 2,000 gauss is required. The electric field must be alternating at the cyclotron resonance frequency of the ion of interest—typically this is of the order of 1.0 MHz. Thus this device will measure *partial pressure,* and changes of the field frequency will permit various components to be analyzed. The version that has been developed for pressure measurements is called an "omegatron." These are also useful for *leak detection.* A gas—usually helium—not present in the system can be sprayed over the walls, and a response at its charge-to-mass ratio indicates a leak.

*Alphatron.** This is an ionization gage in which the ions are produced by alpha particles from a radioactive source. No heated filament is required, and the source remains constant for many years. The range is 10^{-3} to 10^{+3} Torr. It is sensitive to composition, and finds some application as a leak detector.

25. Medium-pressure Measurement Pressure transducers that are designed to operate in this range depend on a sensing element that produces mechanical motion that is a function of the pressure. The mechanical motion is then measured either by a motion transducer or by a force transducer.

Sensing elements include:

1. Bellows
2. Bourdon tube
3. Capsule
4. Diaphragm

Figure 38 shows the essential features of each of these. A sensing element is normally connected through a length of tubing to the environment to be studied. The tubing and the sensing element must be made of materials that will withstand the pressures involved, and the thermal and chemical environment as well.

Bellows are typically used in low-pressure measurements. They give a long stroke and are sensitive to small changes in pressure. They are susceptible to vibration. They can be used with inductive, electromagnetic, resistive, and potentiometric transducers as motion-measurement transducers.

Bourdon tubes develop rotary motion. These are most commonly used to build gages that read directly through a mechanical linkage, but they also are used with reluctive, resistive, potentiometric, and electromagnetic transducers as motion-measurement devices that develop an electrical output. They are somewhat sensitive to vibration, but less so than bellows. The principal advantage of a Bourdon tube is that it gives a maximum mechanical motion for a given volume of the gages listed.

* Registered trademark, National Research Corporation.

Capsules, or aneroids, are similar to both diaphragms and bellows and have many characteristics of each. They may be used over wide pressure ranges with capacitive, inductive, and electromagnetic transducers to measure the motion.

Diaphragms are made in a wide variety of styles. All are circular, but the variations in mounting, cross section, and support other than on the periphery have made many options available to the user. These can be used throughout the pressure range defined as "medium." The motion or force detectors may be capacitive, piezoelectric, electromagnetic, inductive, resistive, or photoelectric. The resistive category includes strain gages, which are commonly used. They may be bonded directly to the diaphragm, or a secondary motion sensor may also be employed. Piezoelectric transducers are common at higher pressures, and also in microphones.

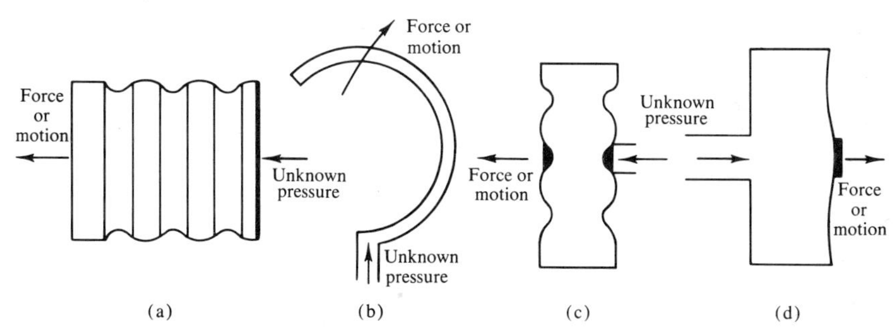

Fig. 38. Four common sensing elements for pressure determination in the medium-pressure range. (*a*) Bellows. (*b*) Bourdon tube. Many styles are available. (*c*) Capsule or aneroid. (*d*) Diaphragm. Many styles are available.

26. High-pressure Measurements In this pressure range, magnetostrictive devices have found application. But the most common is the Bridgman gage. Bridgman discovered empirically that the resistance of some types of fine wire varies with pressure according to a linear relation

$$R = R_A(1 + b\,\Delta p)$$

where R_A = resistance at, say, 1 atm
Δp = pressure change
b = coefficient of resistance change

Typical values for b are of the order of 3×10^{-6} per atmosphere pressure change. Gages made with this principle are used to pressures as high as 10^5 atm. Wheatstone bridges are used as the electrical output devices.

FLUID FLOW

27. Flowmeters Flowmeters are used to measure either the *volume flow rate* or the *mass flow rate*, i.e., either the volume or the mass of fluid transported in a specified time interval. Mass flowmeters require a construction that responds to the momentum of the flow and to the velocity; from this mass flow rate is determined. These are less common than volume flowmeters.

Volume flowmeters are designed to measure the flow velocity. From this and a separate measurement of fluid density, flow mass can be determined. In the case of liquids, volume flow and mass flow are closely related because of the incompressible nature of the liquid. In the case of gases, which are compressible, care must be taken to use appropriate density and volume data. Manufacturers usually specify how these are to be taken.

An important constant for fluid flow is the *Reynolds number.* This is a dimensionless constant,

$$N_R = \frac{Vd\rho}{\mu}$$

where N_R = Reynolds number
V = flow velocity
d = pipe diameter
ρ = fluid density
μ = fluid viscosity

Consistent units must be used, and any unit system is acceptable. A Reynolds number below about 2,000 indicates viscous or laminar flow, above 4,000 turbulent flow. Between these limits, the flow is in transition. The magnitude of this constant is important in flowmeter selection. Some other items to consider in the choice of a flowmeter include:

1. Chemical nature of the fluid.
2. Temperature.
3. Contaminants that may be present.
4. Flowmeter location. Most must be installed in a straight section of pipe. Some can be used only horizontally, others only vertically. Others may be used in any orientation.
5. Backflow. This is often a cleaning technique. The unit must be acceptable or protected in some manner if this will occur.

Flowmeters are examples of transducers that often require several stages of transduction to get an electrical signal which is related to the fluid velocity. An exception is the electromagnetic flowmeter, which gives a direct conversion to an electrical signal. Most of the others convert the velocity information to another form of information, which in turn is sensed by thermal, pressure, or mechanical transducers. For this reason, the magnetic flowmeter will be discussed only in this section. For the others, the user is asked to study also the relevant sections on the other types of transducers required by the process.

28. Electromagnetic Flowmeter This device, also called a magnetic flowmeter, uses the electromagnetic-transduction principle. A conductor that moves in a magnetic field will experience an induced voltage. The direction of the voltage is perpendicular to both the field and the flow; the magnitude is proportional to the product of the velocity and the field strength. Figure 39 illustrates the principle.

The magnetic field may be developed by either a permanent magnet or an electromagnet excited from an ac or dc source. But direct current may cause electrolysis. The coils may be outside the pipe or inside but usually are outside. The pipe must be nonconducting and nonmagnetic, though sometimes nonconductive liners in stainless-steel pipes are used.

These devices cannot be used with nonconducting fluids. The fluid whose flow is to be measured must have a minimum conductivity of the order of 10^{-8} mho/cm. They can be used for a wide range of flow rates, and have the advantage of minimum obstruction to flow. They are generally expensive, reliable, and accurate.

29. Fluid Velocity—Pressure Sensing An obstruction added in a fluid line will cause a pressure drop, and this may be used for velocity determination. Volume flow is then found from knowledge of the pipe dimensions.

The three principal obstructions are the nozzle, orifice, and venturi. These are illustrated in Fig. 40. All should be installed in a straight section of pipe. The venturi requires the most space and gives the best results—accuracy, resistance to wear from abrasive fluids, and low pressure loss. The nozzle requires less space and gives results nearly as good as the venturi. It is, however, difficult to install. The orifice requires the least space and is inexpensive. However, it offers lower accuracy, greater pressure loss, and low resistance to wear from abrasive fluids.

In all cases, the volume flow rate is given by an equation of the form

$$Q = CA\left(\frac{2g}{\rho}\Delta p\right)^{1/2}$$

where Q = volume flow rate
A = area at smallest diameter of constriction
g = gravitational acceleration
ρ = fluid density
C = flow coefficient; it depends on the Reynolds number and the compressibility, and is usually supplied by the manufacturer
Δp = pressure change across transducer

If the fluid is compressible, the density at the inlet is used. The pressure change is frequently measured with a differential-pressure gage, as this permits operation with but one gage.

These meters are generally used for turbulent flow where the Reynolds number is greater than 15,000, though modifications permit use at lower flow rates.

30. Fluid Velocity—Mechanical Sensing Many flowmeters use mechanical obstructions to flow, and mechanical transducers for flow measurement.

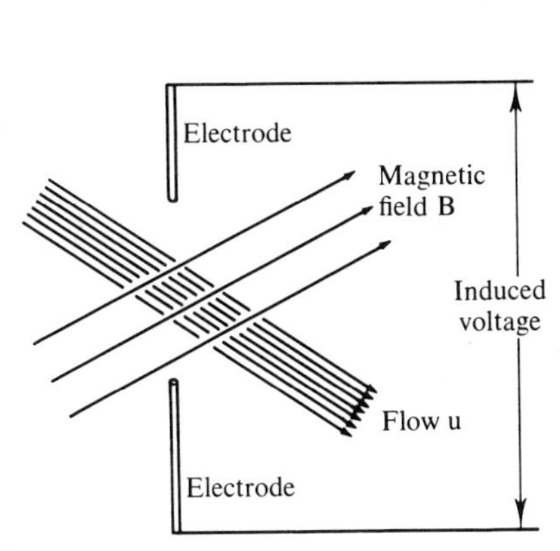

Fig. 39. Electromagnetic-flowmeter principles. The induced voltage is proportional to the produce of the flow velocity u and the magnetic-field strength B. This voltage is perpendicular to both the other quantities.

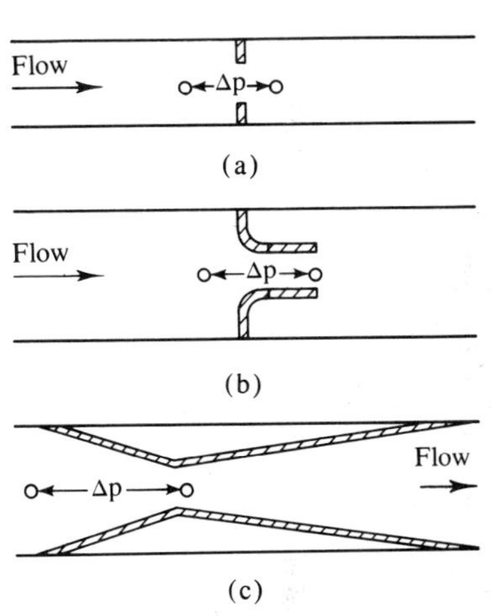

Fig. 40. Obstructions for differential-pressure measurement used in flowmeters. (*a*) Orifice or orifice plate. (*b*) Nozzle. (*c*) Venturi.

Rotameter. A weight may be mounted in a tapered vertical section of pipe. The flow will cause the weight to rise; the amount of rise is proportional to volume flow rate. The rise is measured by a displacement transducer. These handle a wide variety of fluids and can be made to give linear readings.

Vane. A leaf mounted in a position to obstruct a part of the flow will be rotated. The amount of rotation is proportional to the flow and can be measured with an angular-displacement transducer.

Propeller or Turbine. A propeller or turbine may be mounted in the pipe. The flow causes the device to rotate, and the rotational velocity is proportional to flow. Usually this velocity is measured by mounting a tachometer on the same shaft, and measuring, digitally, the frequency of the voltage that is developed. These present bearing-wear problems, and lose accuracy at low flow rates. The turbines are expensive and find application in specialized situations.

31. Hot-wire Anemometer Some flowmeters add a small quantity of a substance to the basic flow, or change its state, especially its temperature. The resulting effects are then used to build flow transducers.

If a wire that is heated electrically is placed in the flow stream, heat will be transferred to the fluid in a manner that is dependent on the flow velocity. Such wires are usually heated from constant-current sources and are commonly made of tungsten or platinum. The devices are most commonly employed for research involving gases. Frequency responses higher than 10 kHz are possible. An equation which gives flow velocity is as follows:

$$V = \frac{1}{b^2\rho}\left(\frac{I^2R}{T_w - T_f}\right)^2 = \frac{1}{b^2\rho}\left\{\frac{I^2R_0[1 + \alpha(T_w - T_0)]}{T_w - T_f}\right\}^2$$

where V = flow velocity
ρ = fluid density
I = heating current
R = resistance of heated wire
R_0 = resistance of wire at its reference temperature
T_w = hot-wire temperature
T_0 = reference temperature of resistance wire
T_f = fluid temperature
a, b = calibration constants
α = resistivity coefficient of wire

Calibration of these is difficult. Resistance can be measured by measuring the voltage across the heated wire with a potentiometer or an oscilloscope.

32. Nucleonic Sensing Elements Flowmeters have been built for specialized problems by developing radioactive particles in the fluid. This may be done either by adding a trace amount of a radioactive substance to the flow, or by irradiating the flow from a source placed near the pipe or tube. In either case, the number of particles moving past a counter in a predetermined time is found, and this information indicates the flow rate. These offer no obstruction to the flow and provide a means for studying complex flow conditions.

LIGHT AND RADIATION

Electromagnetic and particle radiation are usually sensed by devices such as the radiometer, light meter, Geiger counter, and scintillation counter.

As the frequency of electromagnetic-energy propagation increases to values higher than the frequency of radio and radar signals, direct electrical-measurement techniques become impractical. Common names of these electromagnetic-energy signals are listed below, together with the corresponding wavelengths. All such signals have the property that, in vacuo, the product of the wavelength λ and frequency f is equal to the velocity of light, 3.00×10^8. Short wavelengths are frequently expressed in angstrom units (Å). One angstrom unit is 10^{-8} meter. The divisions given are somewhat arbitrary, but generally accepted:

Infrared	7000 Å $< \lambda <$ 1.0 mm
Visible light	4000 Å $< \lambda <$ 7000 Å
Ultraviolet	10 Å $< \lambda <$ 4000 Å
X-ray	0.1 Å $< \lambda <$ 10 Å
Gamma ray	10^{-3} Å $< \lambda <$ 0.1 Å
Cosmic ray	$\lambda < 10^{-3}$ Å

The term radiation also includes certain types of particle. Alpha rays, which are helium nuclei, beta rays, which are electrons, and neutron streams are the most important of these.

33. Light Transducers

Optical Sensing Elements. The term "optical" literally refers to study of the human eye, and as such it implies visible light. But in practice, the term "light" is used to describe radiation from the infrared to the ultraviolet region, and so the term "optical" is applied to these regions also. The techniques are developed from those originally used for visible-light measurement, and it is this characteristic that unifies the ideas.

Photoconductive Sensing Elements. The resistivity of most semiconductors is sensitive to electromagnetic radiation; in general it decreases with increasing illumination, though not linearly. Figure 5 shows a typical arrangement for application of this effect. Common materials include cadmium sulfide, cadmium selenide, germanium, lead sulfide, selenium, silicon, and thallium sulfide. Cadmium sulfide is used in some photographic exposure meters. Spectral responses of these devices go from the infrared to the x-ray region. They are externally powered and require individual calibration. They are generally rugged, though certain types must be protected from radiation in certain parts of the spectrum, and from excessive amounts of radiation. Voltage limits must be observed.

A variation of this technique is the photodiode or phototransistor. A lens is arranged to illuminate the semiconductor junction, and the current is thus related to the light. The transistors are especially useful because the second, unilluminated junction becomes the first stage of an electronic amplifier. These are being developed rapidly and are becoming very commonly used devices.

All photoconductive devices are very sensitive to manufacturing techniques; this accounts in part for the wide variation of reported properties for seemingly similar devices. One possible source of error is that radiation at frequencies outside that of interest can reduce or quench the photoconductive current.

Photoemissive Sensing Elements. Certain substances will, upon radiation impingement, emit electrons. These are used in a wide variety of optical transducers. In general, they are diodes whose cathodes are photoemissive (see Fig. 6). The cathode and anode are mounted in an evacuated or gas-filled envelope. The envelope is transparent to the radiation to be measured. Typical anode voltages vary from 10 to 500 V.

A wide variety of photoemissive materials is found. They are formulated to be responsive in particular portions of the spectrum and can be made to respond to very low levels of illumination. They are sensitive to fabrication techniques, and consequently, reported properties vary widely. Many can be damaged by excessive radiation. In some cases, the damage is reversible, provided special treatments are followed.

An important application of the photoemissive effect is the photomultiplier tube. These consist of a photoemissive cathode and a sequence of anodes, operating at successively higher voltages. An electron emitted from the cathode is attracted to the first anode, which emits more than one electron as a result. This is called secondary emission. These electrons are attracted to the second anode, where even more electrons are emitted, and so on. Electron multiplications ranging from 10^3 to 10^{12} are possible.

Photovoltaic Sensing Elements. These self-generating transducers are used as power sources, e.g., in satellites and in measurement systems. The essential element is a semiconductor. The voltages developed are temperature-dependent, an important possible source of error. These can be built to exhibit linear operation or to exhibit operation that approaches logarithmic. The latter is useful when several orders of magnitude of radiation must be measured without changing ranges. These are dependent upon fabrication techniques and are generally rugged and reliable but are insensitive at low levels of radiation.

Thermal Sensing Elements. A leaf of silver or gold may be blackened, and thus it will absorb radiation and be heated. The temperature is then measured usually with a thermocouple, and is a function of the radiation. These are used in the infrared region.

34. Radiation Transducers.

Ionization-type Sensing Elements. High-frequency short-wavelength radiation can produce ionization of certain materials. Alpha and beta rays can also cause ionization. As a result of this ionization, secondary sensing elements may be needed.

Ionization Chamber. The ionization chamber is designed to measure the energy level of incoming radiation. The basic construction is illustrated in Fig. 4. The anode and cathode may also be concentric. The anode voltage is high enough to ensure collection of the electrons produced by the ionization, but low enough to prevent secondary ionization. The resulting anode current is proportional to the level of incoming radiation.

Geiger Counter. The basic construction of the Geiger counter is illustrated in Fig. 4. It is similar to the ionization chamber, but the anode voltage is much higher. Radiation, or alpha and beta particles, will cause ionization, and thus a voltage pulse in the output circuitry. The number of pulses is counted, either audibly with a loudspeaker or electronically with a digital counter, and is a measure of the number of particles or photons received, without regard to energy level. The upper limit is of the order of 10^4 counts per second.

Scintillation Counter. A scintillation counter is made with a crystal that emits a flash of light when struck by a photon or particle. The intensity of the light is proportional to the energy level; the number of flashes is proportional to the number of photons or particles. The light is measured with a photemissive system, usually incorporating a photomultiplier tube.

Solid-state Ionization Sensing Elements. A system for counting the number of particles or photons whose energy level exceeds about 1,000 electron volts is built by using extrinsic semiconductors mounted so that the radiation ionizes an atom in the crystal, and a pulse appears in the output circuitry. Operation is normally at liquid-nitrogen temperatures. Counting rates above 10^6 per second are possible.

Neutron Sensing Elements. Neutrons do not cause ionization. Neutron detectors require an arrangement to produce alpha or beta rays, which are then counted in one of the systems described in preceding paragraphs. An atomic reaction is necessary, and the techniques vary with the energy level of the neutrons.

SOUND TRANSDUCERS (MICROPHONES)

A microphone is a special type of pressure transducer, and the material in the section on pressure dealing with "medium-pressure" measurement should also be read. Invariably the sensing element is a diaphragm, as illustrated in Fig. 38*d*. A variety of transduction elements are available. The range of pressures to be measured is normally small compared with ambient (atmospheric) pressure, even for the most intense sounds. Desirable characteristics include linearity over a wide range of amplitudes and frequencies. Directional patterns must be considered.

Sound-pressure levels are commonly expressed in logarithmic units called decibels (dB). For a reference pressure p_0 and a measured pressure p,

$$\text{Pressure level (dB)} = 20 \log_{10} \frac{p}{p_0}$$

The most common pressure reference is 2.0×10^{-5} N/m², or 2.0×10^{-4} dyne/cm², or 2.9×10^{-9} psi. This reference corresponds to the lowest audible sound in a normal human ear. A pressure of 90 dB, or 0.632 N/m², is normally the maximum sustained level human beings can tolerate (threshold of pain).

The sensitivity of a microphone is a measure of the voltage developed per unit sound pressure. It is given by

$$\text{Sensitivity (dB)} = 20 \log_{10} (\text{voltage output}) + 74 \text{ dB} - (\text{applied sound pressure in dB})$$

Thus a sensitivity of −20 dB means that a voltage of 0.1 V will be developed by a sound signal of pressure level 74 dB, or 1.0 dyne/cm², which is the reference condition for sensitivity.

Carbon Microphone. The moving diaphragm is mounted so as to compress together grains of carbon, thus changing the resistance in a circuit. The device is externally powered from a constant-voltage source, and the resulting current is thus a function of the sound pressure. The most common application of these is in telephones. Their frequency range is limited to a maximum of about 5 kHz. The output impedance is low, and the sensitivity is high, about −40 dB. These find little application in sound measurement.

Capacitive Microphone. The moving diaphragm is used as one plate of a capacitor. A constant charge is maintained on the plates from a 200- to 500-V supply, and the changes in capacitance cause a change in the capacitor voltage. An emitter or cathode follower is usually located close to the microphone, reducing the inherently high output impedance and reducing the distortion caused by noise. These are expensive, but accurate, instruments. They are used for precision measurements, and as standards. They operate to 50 kHz and are reasonably sensitive. A typical sensitivity is −50 dB. The high-voltage supply, however, is often inconvenient to provide.

Dynamic Microphone. These use the electromagnetic-transduction principle. A coil of wire is attached to the diaphragm, and moves in the field of a permanent magnet. They are self-generating. They have low sensitivity, typically −80 dB, and a low output impedance. Their frequency response is limited to about 20 kHz. These find field application but are seldom used in precision measurements.

Inductive Microphone. The diaphragm is ferromagnetic, and its motion changes the self-inductance of a coil. These changes are usually measured in a bridge circuit. The frequency response is limited to a fraction of the excitation frequency of the bridge. These can be designed to operate in hot and dirty environments.

Magnetostrictive Microphone. The diaphragm causes changes in the magnetic properties of certain materials. In turn, these changes appear as changes in dimension, which are sensed by displacement transducers. These have low output impedance, low sensitivity (−100 dB), and operate in the ultrasonic region. They find application in underwater transducers.

Piezoelectric Microphone. These self-generating microphones have been developed for use in a wide variety of situations. The problems of piezoelectric devices in general apply. These problems include high output impedance, temperature dependence, and vibration sensitivity. Microphones built with this transduction element have a frequency response extending to the ultrasonic region, above 100 kHz, and they have a low sensitivity, −50 to −100 dB. They also are very linear over a wide range of amplitudes and are widely used in sound-measurement systems.

HUMIDITY

Humidity is commonly expressed by either of two terms. *Absolute humidity* is the amount of water vapor contained in an air sample, and *relative humidity,* usually expressed in percent, is the ratio of the absolute humidity to the amount of water vapor contained in air under saturated conditions, or the maximum possible absolute humidity. The maximum possible moisture content increases rapidly with temperature. *Dew point* is the temperature at which, if a given air sample is cooled, its relative humidity becomes 100 percent, and condensation occurs. Psychrometric tables relate dew point, relative humidity, and absolute humidity.*

Dew Point. Dew point is frequently measured with a small cooling system. Often "Peltier" cooling is employed. The device is cooled until condensation occurs, and the resulting temperature is measured. Thermocouples or other electrical thermometers may be employed.

35. Relative Humidity Several materials exhibit changes in electrical properties that are caused by humidity. These are frequently used in transducers that are designed and calibrated to read relative humidity directly.

Resistive Hygrometer. Some hygroscopic salts exhibit a change in resistivity with humidity. The most common is lithium chloride. This, with a binder, may be coated on a wire or on electrodes. Resulting resistance changes cover a wide range, e.g., 10^4 to 10^8 Ω as the humidity changes from 100 to 0 percent. This makes it impractical to design a single element to operate from 1 to 100 percent relative humidity. Instead, several elements are used, each in a narrow range, with provision for switching elements. Resistance is measured either with a Wheatstone bridge or by a combination of current and voltage measurements.

Most of these must not be exposed to conditions of 100 percent humidity, as

* See Ref. 10 for an example of psychrometric tables.

the resulting condensation may damage the device. Either they must operate in a constant-temperature environment or temperature corrections must be made. These are accurate to within ±2.5 percent or ±1.5 percent in some cases. Response times are typically of the order of a few seconds. These are currently the most common electronic hygrometers.

Capacitive Hygrometer. Some hygroscopic materials exhibit a change in dielectric constant with humidity changes. In addition, the presence of water vapor in air changes the dielectric constant of the mixture. In either case, the changes are small, and the change in capacitance is usually measured by including it as the frequency-determining element in an oscillator, heterodyning this signal with a beat-frequency oscillator, and measuring the resulting difference frequency. These have response times of about 1 s.

Microwave Refractometer. For secondary standards, a system consisting of two cavities, each of which is coupled to a klystron, may be employed. One cavity contains dry air, the other the mixture to be measured. The change in dielectric constant changes the frequency of one oscillator. This difference is measured electronically. The complexity of the devices precludes their use except in very special situations.

Aluminum-oxide Hygrometer. The aluminum-oxide coating on anodized aluminum exhibits a change in dielectric constant and a change in resistivity with a change in humidity. A hygrometer that uses this is built by using the base aluminum as one electrode and depositing a very thin electrode—usually gold—on the opposite side of the oxide. This thin electrode is porous to the air-vapor mixture. The resulting changes in resistivity and capacitance lead to a complex impedance change, which is measured with a bridge or related methods. Errors are less than ±3 percent and response times are about 10 s. The changes are large, but often only one sensing element is needed for the entire range to be covered. This hygrometer is rapidly becoming a very important component in electronic systems.

Crystal Hygrometer. Some crystals are hygroscopic, and others may be coated with a hygroscopic material. The crystals are used as frequency-determination elements in electronic oscillators. Frequency shifts with humidity are measured electronically. These are useful if a telemetry system is needed, because the frequency range can be chosen as a standard telemetry frequency.

REFERENCES

1. Stein, P. K.: The Engineering of Measuring Systems, *J. Metals,* October, 1969, pp. 40–47.
2. Stein, P. K.: "The Response of Transducers to their Environment," Publication No. 17, Measurement Engineering Laboratory, Mechanical Engineering Department, Arizona State University, Tempe, Ariz., October, 1969.
3. *Science;* "1969–70 Guide to Scientific Instruments," American Association for the Advancement of Science, Sept. 23, 1969. (A similar volume is published annually.)
4. *Industrial Research:* "1970 Instruments Specified," Industrial Research, Inc., Nov. 20, 1969. (A similar volume is published annually.)
5. *Electronic Engineers Masters* "1969–70 Buying Guide," United Technical Publications, Inc. (A similar volume is published annually.)
6. *Annual Source Directory of Electronic Instrument Digest,* Kiver Publications, Inc. (A similar volume is published annually.)
7. Harvey, G. F. (ed.): "ISA Transducer Compendium," 2d ed., Part 1 (1969), Part 2 (1970), Part 3 (1971), Plenum Press, New York.
8. Norton, H. N.: "Handbook of Transducers for Electronic Measuring Systems," Prentice-Hall, Inc., Englewood Cliffs, N.J., 1969.
9. Holman, J. P., "Experimental Methods for Engineers," McGraw-Hill Book Company, New York, 1966.
10. Tuve, G. L., and L. C. Domholdt: "Engineering Experimentation," McGraw-Hill Book Company, New York, 1966.
11. Gibson, J. E., and F. B. Tuteur: "Control System Components," McGraw-Hill Book Company, New York, 1958.

12. Lion, K. S.: "Instrumentation in Scientific Research," McGraw-Hill Book Company, New York, 1959.
13. Bartholomew, D.: "Electrical Measurements and Instrumentation," Allyn and Bacon, Inc., Boston, 1963.
14. Cook, N. H., and E. Rabinowicz: "Physical Measurement and Analysis," Addison-Wesley Publishing Company, Inc., Reading, Mass., 1963.
15. "Kearfott Technical Information for the Engineer," no. 1, 10th ed., Kearfott Products Division, General Precision Systems, Inc., 1967.
16. Notes on Linear Variable Differential Transformers, *Bulletin* AA-1A, Schaevitz Engineering, Pennsauken, N.J., 1955.
17. "Precision Measurement and Calibration—Temperature," National Bureau of Standards Special Publication 300, vol. 2, Government Printing Office, Washington, D.C., 1968.
18. Hix, C. F., and R. P. Alley: "Physical Laws and Effects," John Wiley & Sons, Inc., New York, 1958.
19. Neswald, R.: The New Look in Force Transducers, *Electron. Prod.,* in two parts, February and March, 1970.
20. Doebelin, E.: "Measurement Systems," McGraw-Hill Book Company, New York, 1966.
21. Iltis, R.: Solid State Sensors: Strain Gages, *Control Eng.,* January, 1970.
22. Preliminary Draft of Text of International Practical Temperature Scale of 1968, *Metrologia,* April, 1969.
23. Benedict, R. P.: International Practical Temperature Scale of 1968, *Leeds and Northrup Tech. J.,* no. 6, spring, 1969.
24. Finch, D. I.: General Principles of Thermoelectric Thermometry, *Leeds and Northrup Techn. Publi.* D1.1000, 1969.
25. Kirk, W. H.: Thermocouple Primer, reprinted by Westinghouse Technical Information from *Instruments and Control Systems,* 1968.
26. Alpert, D., R. S. Buritz, and W. A. Rogers: Studies of Limiting Factors on the Attainment of Ultra-high Vacua, *Westinghouse Res. Labs. Res. Rept.* R-94436-4-B, 1952.

Chapter 7

Signal Transmission, Amplification, and Mixing

EDWIN C. JONES, Jr., Ph.D.

Iowa State University, Ames, Iowa

INTRODUCTION

The signals developed by the transducers contain the information needed for processing by the rest of the instrumentation system. The signal is usually a voltage, though some transducers develop a current. These voltages or currents have a limited number of properties that are used to carry the information. The two most important are the amplitude and frequency of the signal. Often the polarity is of significance. Many transducers develop signals in the millivolt (10^{-3}) or microvolt (10^{-6}) range. A fundamental problem that must be solved is to prevent this signal from being contaminated by noise, which is defined as any extraneous signal that interferes with the properties of interest in the desired signal. A second fundamental problem is distortion, which is defined as any change of the signal content by the processing equipment.

The signal developed by the transducer must first be sensed; that is, it must be made available on a pair of conductors. It must then be transmitted to the point of use, for interpretation. To do these, it may be necessary to perform one or more processes on the signal. These include linear processing such as

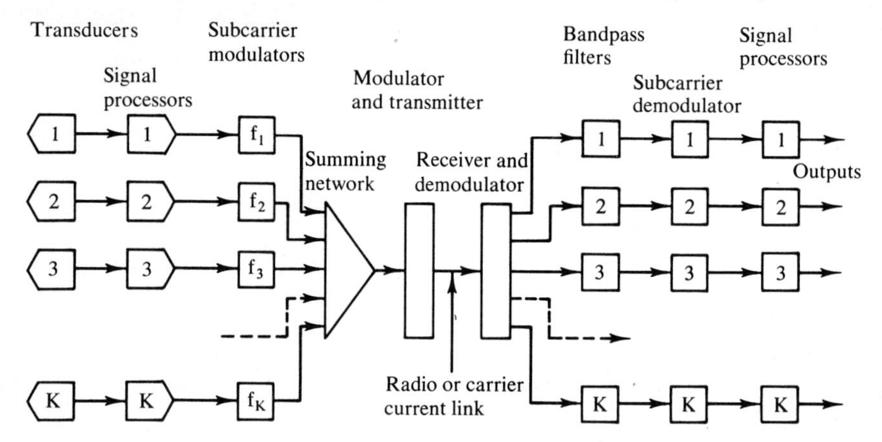

Fig. 1. A signal-transmission system.

amplification, attenuation, integration, differentiation, addition, and subtraction, and nonlinear processing, such as modulation, detection, conversion between digital and analog forms, sampling, clipping, clamping, and logarithmic processes.

Frequently the transducers are located at a considerable distance from the point at which the signal is to be interpreted. It is desirable to design the system so that the outputs of all transducers can be transmitted together and that, where it is available, use of existing communication links is made. This leads to the concept of a telemetry or multiplex system, which is a convenient way to describe the interrelationship of the parts of a signal-transmission system. When the system being measured is close to the data-processing equipment, this telemetry system may not exist. A block diagram of a signal-transmission system is shown as Fig. 1.

Virtually all the components of the general system that is depicted can be purchased, so that the instrument engineer's primary responsibility is to ensure that the various components operate together as intended. The various sections of this chapter are concerned with noise and distortion, wire and cables, linear signal processing, nonlinear signal processing, and some special topics.

WIRE, CABLE, AND CONNECTORS

1. Wire Copper is the conductor that usually is used to connect electrical equipment together. Some aluminum is used, but at present this is confined to power-distribution systems where large amounts of power are needed. Although aluminum is light in weight, its relatively high resistance requires a much greater volume of material than is needed with copper for equivalent resistance.

Copper wire is sized according to the American wire gage (AWG) system. For solid wire, size 30 is assigned a diameter of 0.0100 in. An increase of one in the gage number divides the diameter by 1.123; a decrease of one multiplies the diameter by this amount. This value is very close (within 0.1 percent) to the sixth root of 2, and as a consequence, a change of six gage numbers either halves or doubles the diameter and divides or multiplies the area and resistance per unit length by 4. A change of three gage numbers divides or multiplies the resistance per unit length by 2.* A partial wire table is included as Table 1.

TABLE 1 Partial Wire Table for Annealed Soft Copper Single-strand Wire

AWG	Diameter		Cross section, in.^{2}	Ω/1,000 ft at 20°C	Ft/lb
	In.	Mils			
10	0.1019	101.9	0.008155	0.9988	31.82
11	0.0907	90.7	0.00646	1.26	40.2
12	0.0808	80.8	0.00513	1.59	50.6
13	0.0720	72.0	0.00407	2.00	63.7
14	0.0641	64.1	0.00323	2.52	80.4
15	0.0571	57.1	0.00256	3.18	101
16	0.0508	50.8	0.00203	4.02	128
17	0.0453	45.3	0.00161	5.05	161
18	0.0403	40.3	0.00128	6.39	203
19	0.0359	35.9	0.00101	8.05	256
20	0.0320	32.0	0.000804	10.1	323
21	0.0285	28.5	0.000638	12.8	407
22	0.0253	25.3	0.000503	16.2	516
23	0.0226	22.6	0.000401	20.3	647
24	0.0201	20.1	0.000317	25.7	818
25	0.0179	17.9	0.000252	32.4	1,030
26	0.0159	15.9	0.000199	41.0	1,310
27	0.0142	14.2	0.000158	51.4	1,640
28	0.0126	12.6	0.000125	65.3	2,080
29	0.0113	11.3	0.000100	81.2	2,590
30	0.0100	10.0	0.0000785	104	3,300

Stranded copper wire is used in many installations. The reason for this is that it is more flexible than solid wire and thus is less susceptible to breakage when mechanical motion is involved. Stranding is done so that the effective current-carrying cross section of a given wire size is identical with that of solid wire. Hence the total diameter of the strands together is increased by 10 to 20 percent.

2. Cable When many signals are to be transmitted over the same route, it is often desirable to obtain a cable, which is a collection of insulated wire bound together with a plastic sleeve or ties, color-coded for identification purposes. Such cables can be purchased in a variety of sizes. They may contain as many as 60 wires or 60 pairs of wires in one bundle. Some cables are shielded, which means that a conducting wrapper is placed around the entire assembly. This reduces the electromagnetic effects that otherwise are induced in a wire and that cause noise voltages to be transmitted to the rest of the system.

* A complete wire table may be found in Ref. 1 and in many other handbooks and manufacturer's publications.

3. Coaxial Cable Coaxial cable is a form of wire construction in which the conductors are concentric (see Fig. 2). Coaxial cables have the advantage that the electric and magnetic fields associated with the signal propagating along the cable are contained entirely within the cable, and the signals on the wire are affected very little by stray fields through which the cable passes. Coaxial cable is much more expensive than ordinary wire. At frequencies above 1.0 MHz it is usually essential to use coaxial cable to avoid the effects of unwanted electric and magnetic fields. It is also essential to use it when very small signals are being transmitted.

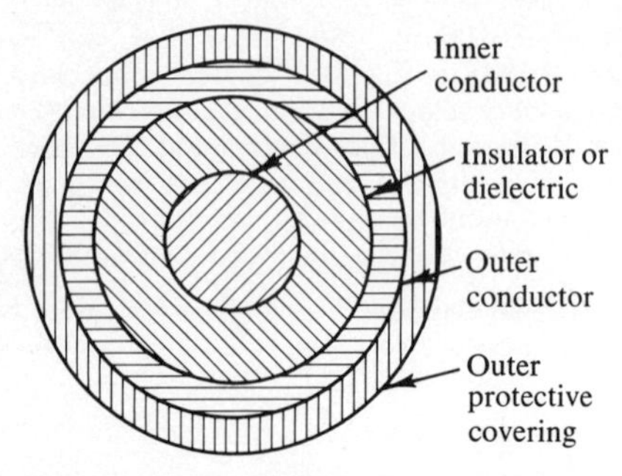

Fig. 2. Cross section of coaxial cable.

Coaxial cable is commonly identified by a code developed for use in military purchasing specifications. A typical nomenclature is RG-mn/U, or RG-mnj/U. The mn is a two-digit number that specifies the cable. If present, the j is a letter that identifies an improved version of a particular cable. There is no pattern to the choice of digits, and the best way to determine the specifications is to consult a manufacturer's catalog.

4. Choice and Installation of Cables In addition to the consideration of signal strength and frequency components, other factors influence the type of wire or cable to be used. These include:

1. *Insulation Breakdown Voltage.* This is the voltage that will cause the insulation to fail. It should be at least ten times the expected signal strength in wire or cable.

2. *Insulation Leakage Resistance.* This is the ratio of the voltage on a wire or cable to the current that flows through the insulation to another conductor. It should be at least one hundred times as high as the input impedance of the following stage of the system.

3. *Temperature Range.* This is the range over which the cable will maintain its specified electrical and mechanical properties.

4. *Environmental Range.* Wire and cables are designed to operate in specified environments of humidity, chemicals, gases, and pressure. These must be considered so that adequate cable is chosen.

5. *Capacitance.* The conductors in a wire or cable are separated by insulation and thus act as a capacitor. This is particularly important in coaxial cable or large bundled cables. This capacitance will distort some signals, especially when long runs or high-frequency signals are transmitted.

6. *Bending Characteristics.* When a cable is installed, it will usually be necessary to bend or flex it. This mechanical characteristic must be considered.

When a wire or cable is installed, care must be taken that it is mechanically secure. If not, its motion may in time damage or destroy the cable, and the motion may also introduce noise into the system.

5. Connectors A connector is a device used to fasten together, both electrically and mechanically, two components of an instrumentation system. It serves a number of purposes, including:

1. Providing an electrical path for a signal
2. Providing mechanical support for a part of the system
3. Providing a means of disconnecting components of the system when it is necessary to service the system
4. Providing a place to insert test signals into the system

Some of the problems associated with instruments involve connectors. Among these are as follows:

1. Fastening together the wrong pair of connectors.

2. Electrical or mechanical breakdown of the connector. Electrical breakdown is caused either when the voltage is larger than the connector's rating or when

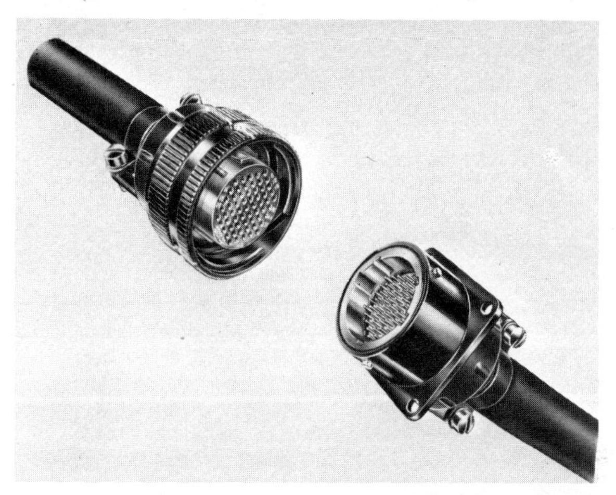

Fig. 3. Amphenol 224 series Ultra-Mite Hi-Density cable connectors. Widely used for instrumentation, calculators, and nonenvironmental systems.

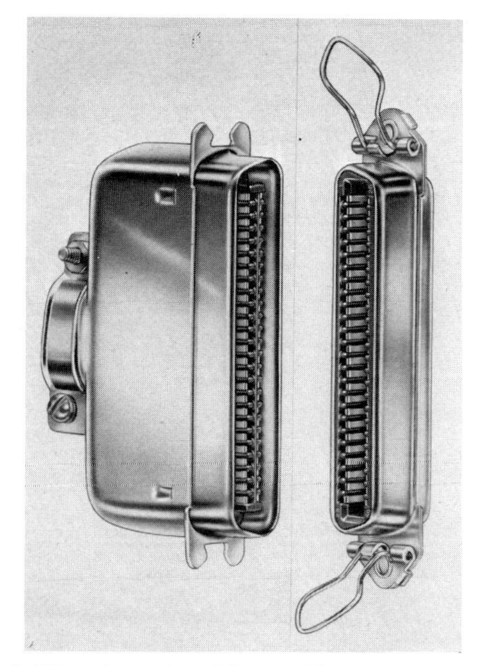

Fig. 4. Amphenol 57 series microribbon cable-to-panel connectors. Provides interconnections for up to 50 circuits. Spring clip holds plug firmly in mated position.

the current exceeds the specifications. Mechanical breakdown is caused by excessive strain on the connector or the wire close to the connector, by wearing away of the contacts, and by abuse or misuse of the devices themselves.

Some types of connectors that are commonly used are as follows:

1. *Cable-to-Cable.* Occasionally it is necessary to splice together two cables to complete a run. When this is done, the male connector is normally connected

to the load or receiving end of the path, and the female connector to the source or sending end of the path (see Fig. 3).

2. *Rack-to-Cable.* Equipment is normally mounted in a cabinet that is commonly called a rack. Rack-to-cable connectors are the connectors used to terminate a cable at the rack. One half of the connector is fastened to the cable, the other half to the rack. The rack portion is sometimes called a receptacle, and from this the signals are distributed throughout the rack as needed. The cable portion is often called a plug (see Fig. 4).

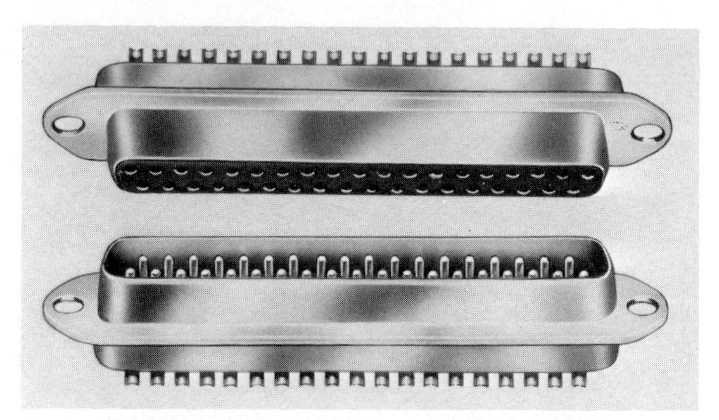

Fig. 5. Amphenol Min-Rac 17 series fixed-contact connector for rack-and-panel use. Ideal for communications equipment, computers, instruments, and control systems.

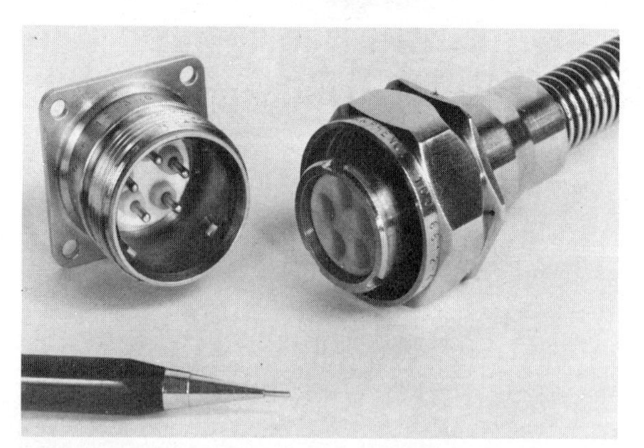

Fig. 6. Amphenol 1200 to −85°F specially designed hermetic engine connector.

3. *Rack-to-Panel.* Some cabinets or racks are designed so that the various circuits are connected to drawers that may be pulled out for service or replacement. A rack-and-panel connector is one that connects the inside rear of the rack to the drawer when the drawer is fully inserted (see Fig. 5).

4. *Feedthrough.* A connector designed to transmit a signal through a wall or bulkhead between regions. The terminals are usually double-ended (see Fig. 6).

5. *Coaxial Cable.* A connector used as either a cable-to-cable or rack-to-cable junction between coaxial-cable elements. Each cable normally requires its own connector, and each style of cable requires its own series of connectors.

The vocabulary associated with connectors has a number of terms that should be defined:

1. *Male Connector.* That part of a connector which is inserted into a connector. Normally it is the portion connected to the "load" rather than the "transmitting" side of the system.
2. *Female Connector.* That part of a connector which receives the male connector. Normally it is the portion connected to the source (transmitting) side of the system.
3. *Hermaphroditic Connector.* A connector in which both members are identical at the mating faces. It normally includes provision to maintain correct polarity, hot-lead protection, and environmental characteristics.
4. *Polarized Connector.* A connector combination that can be connected in only one manner. The use of polarized plugs and receptacles throughout reduces instrumentation problems.
5. *Soldered Connection.* A connection in which the wire is fastened to the connector by melted solder.
6. *Crimped Connection.* A connection in which the wire is fastened to the connector by mechanical compression.
7. *Wrapped Connection.* A connection in which a solid wire is wrapped about four times around a square or V-shaped terminal with a special tool.

When an instrumentation system is being engineered, it is important to give considerable attention to the cables and connectors. The use of polarized connectors is strongly recommended. If it is necessary to use more than one connector, different styles should be chosen, so that there is no chance to make incorrect connections. Power leads should not be connected in the same cable as signal leads, unless there is no feasible alternative. The various manufacturer's catalogs contain much information about currently available styles, their environmental characteristics, and their mechanical and electrical ratings.

LINEAR SIGNAL PROCESSING

Transducers develop electrical signals that are quantitative representations of some physical effect. They are sometimes called electrical "analogs" of that effect. These electrical signals may be manipulated in the same sense that mathematical functions are manipulated, though this is done by certain electric networks. The signals may be added or subtracted, multiplied or divided, differentiated or integrated; and operations such as exponentiation, logarithms, and trigonometric functions of the variables are possible.

Some electric networks are adequately described by the principle of superposition;[2] networks having this property are called *linear signal processors.* Superposition requires that the network have the properties of "additivity" and "homogeneity" as follows:

1. *Additivity.* The response to a number of independent excitations may be computed by adding the responses to each excitation with all other excitations reduced to zero.
2. *Homogeneity.* If all excitations are multiplied by a constant, the response is multiplied by that same constant.

Circuits that add or subtract signals, circuits that amplify or attenuate, and circuits that differentiate or integrate may be considered linear.

Electronic circuits are inherently nonlinear. But for certain ranges of their operating currents and voltages, they may be operated as linear devices. If the user takes careful precautions to keep the equipment in its linear range, it is then possible to use electronic circuits to amplify signals, and also to build a wide variety of signal processors.

The analysis and design of these circuits are usually done with "equivalent" circuits. An equivalent circuit for a transistor, tube, or any other device is a collection of electric-circuit elements—resistors, capacitors, etc.—that has the same properties as the original device. The designer replaces the device in his circuit with its equivalent, and solves the network using conventional circuit analysis.*

One type of new circuit element often appears in an equivalent circuit. It relates the current through or the voltage across one pair of terminals to the voltage across or the current through another portion of the circuit. This is called a controlled or dependent[4] source, which is a circuit model that describes this effect. This effect accounts for the possibility of power amplification. Four types of controlled source must be considered. Figure 7 illustrates these. The analysis of circuits that contain controlled sources is in all essential respects done just like the analysis of circuits that do not contain them. When the Kirchhoff's law (i.e., the sum of *all* voltages in a closed circuit is zero, or the sum of all currents leaving a node is zero) equations are written, the controlled source will be included. It is then

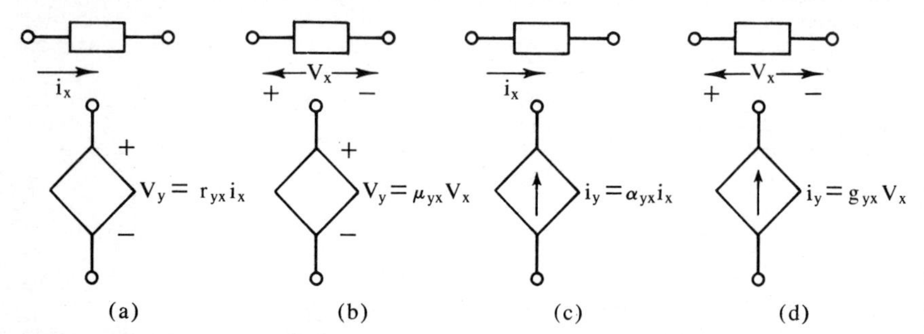

Fig. 7. Controlled- or dependent-source models. (*a*) Current-controlled voltage source (CCVS). (*b*) Voltage-controlled voltage source (VCVS). (*c*) Current-controlled current source (CCCS). (*d*) Voltage-controlled current source (VCCS).

necessary to substitute a relation for the controlling variable into the basic equation, and proceed. An example illustrating the method is included below.

AMPLIFIERS

6. Amplifier Terminology Amplifiers are used widely in instrumentation systems, and many different types are available. In this section definitions of the more common types are given. A designer may build one of these from basic components, but it is also possible and often better engineering to purchase one from a reliable manufacturer. For the most part these terms find a common definition throughout the industry.

AUDIO (AF): An amplifier designed to amplify signals whose frequency spectrum lies essentially in the audio range, or about 20 Hz to 20 kHz.

ANTENNA: An amplifier designed to amplify signals that are received on an antenna. They must be quite noise-free because of the low level of the input signals.

CHARGE: An amplifier designed to accept and amplify signals from very high impedance sources such as piezoelectric transducers.

COMPRESSORS: An amplifier designed to give an output range that is much less than the input range. Usually the output signal is proportional to the logarithm of the input signal.

CONTROL: An amplifier that is designed to serve as a power amplifier and to drive control elements such as lamps or relays. Linearity is not so important as power and heat considerations.

CURRENT: An amplifier that accepts a current as an input signal and develops an output current that is proportional to it.

* See Ref. 3. This is an excellent description of all that is involved in the process of determining these equivalent circuits.

DC: A direct-coupled amplifier. There are no capacitors between stages, and thus it will handle very low frequencies down to direct currents and/or voltages.

DECADE: An amplifier whose gain is adjustable in discrete steps that are multiples of 10.

DISTRIBUTED: An amplifier that uses techniques of distributed circuits (delay lines, etc.) to achieve a large gain over a very wide range of frequencies, often to 500 MHz or higher.

DISTRIBUTION: An amplifier designed for distribution of closed-circuit television signals.

IF: Intermediate-frequency amplifier. These are designed to give a high gain over a very narrow frequency range, usually a small fraction of a decade of frequency, and are used in communication systems.

ISOLATION: An amplifier designed to isolate one part of a system so that it is unaffected by events in another part. This is also called buffering.

LINEAR: An amplifier whose output signal is directly proportional to the input signal.

LOGARITHMIC: An amplifier whose output signal is proportional to the logarithm of the input signal.

MIXING: An amplifier whose input signals (two or more) are processed in some way to get the output signal. Common operations include addition, subtraction, and multiplication.

NARROW BAND: An amplifier designed to amplify signals over a very narrow range of frequencies. The frequency range may or may not be adjustable.

OPERATIONAL: A high-gain direct-coupled amplifier that is used as a "building block" in many instrumentation systems.

PHOTOCELL: An amplifier designed to respond to the output voltage developed by photocells.

POWER: An amplifier designed primarily to deliver a substantial amount of power to some load. Examples might include motors, relays, loudspeakers, and lamps.

PULSE: An amplifier designed to reproduce pulses (short-duration signals) faithfully.

RF: A radio-frequency amplifier; one that is designed to amplify signals at frequencies from about 100 kHz to 1,000 Mhz. (No one amplifier covers the entire range.)

SAMPLE AND HOLD: An amplifier used to digitize (convert to discrete format) continuous signals. At specified intervals, it produces an output proportional to the instantaneous value of the input, and holds this value until the next interval.

TRANSDUCER: An amplifier designed to work with a particular type of transducer. Sometimes specific transducers are listed, e.g., a thermocouple amplifier.

ULTRASONIC: An amplifier designed to work in the ultrasonic frequency range, about 20 to 150 kHz.

VIDEO: An amplifier designed to operate in the video-frequency range, often as wide as 10 Hz to 10 MHz.

WIDEBAND: A general term that describes amplifiers designed to operate over a wide range of frequencies, usually several decades of frequency.

7. Transistors in Amplifiers The transistor, either alone or as part of an integrated circuit, is the main element in almost all instrument amplifiers. Therefore, this discussion emphasizes this form of amplifier rather than vacuum tubes. A similar discussion is appropriate for vacuum-tube amplifiers, however, and only the specific circuit elements change while the concepts are the same.

The transistor is a three-terminal electric-circuit component that has become the central element around which electronic circuits are built. It is made of a semiconducting material, usually germanium or silicon, and comes in a wide variety of capabilities and ratings. The two principal types are the bipolar-junction transistor (BJT) and the field-effect transistor (FET). In general, there are two types of semiconductor, *n*-type and *p*-type. Material that contains an excess of electrons as charge carriers, caused by proper mixing of elements having a valence of 5 with the germanium or silicon, are called *n*-type. Materials containing an excess of electron deficiencies, or holes, caused by use of elements with a valence

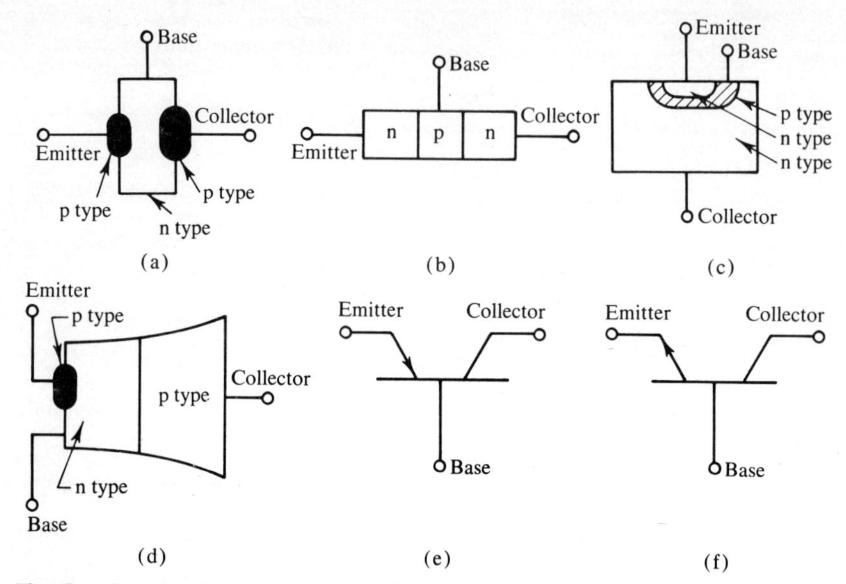

Fig. 8. Junction-transistor construction and symbols. (*a*) *pnp* alloy transistor. (*b*) *npn* rate-grown transistor. (*e*) *pnp* planar-diffused transistor. (*d*) *pnp* mesa transistor. (*e*) *pnp* transistor, symbol, and notation. (*f*) *npn* transistor, symbol, and notation.

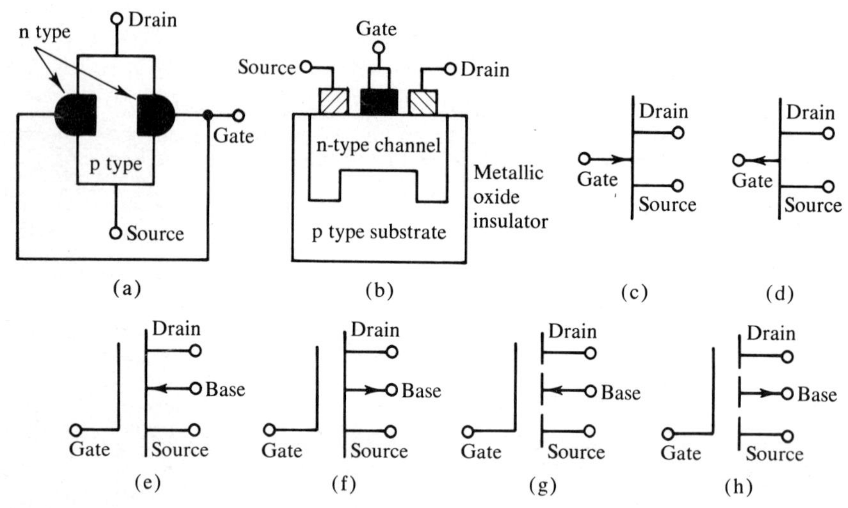

Fig. 9. Field-effect transistor (FET) construction and symbols. In many commercial models, the base is internally connected to the source, and the one available terminal is called the source. (*a*) *p*-channel depletion-mode FET. (*b*) *n*-channel insulated-gate FET (MOSFET). (*c*) *n*-channel FET, depletion-mode, symbol and notation. (*d*) *p*-channel FET, depletion-mode, symbol and notation. (*e*) *n*-channel MOSFET, depletion-mode, symbol and notation. (*f*) *p*-channel MOSFET, depletion-mode, symbol and notation. (*g*) *n*-channel MOSFET, enhancement-mode symbol and notation. (*h*) *p*-channel MOSFET, enhancement-mode, symbol and notation.

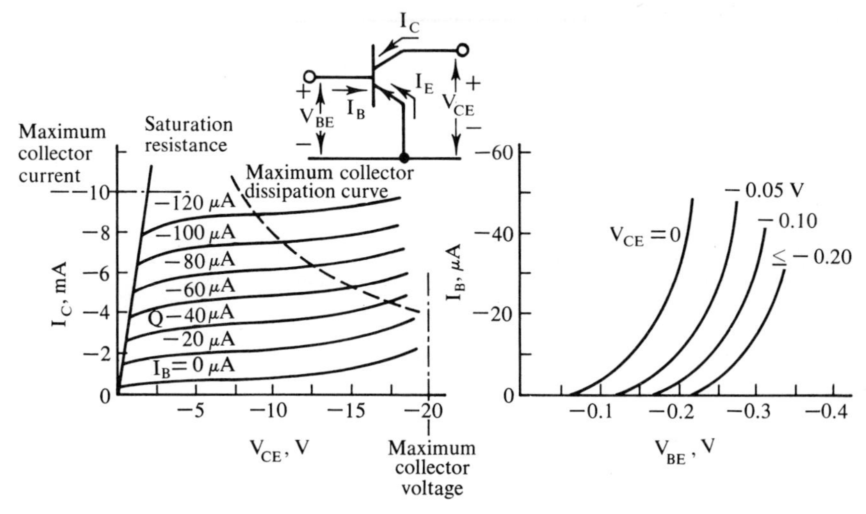

Fig. 10. Typical characteristic curves, *npn* silicon-junction transistor. The curves for a *pnp* silicon transistor would have the same shape, but polarities are reversed.

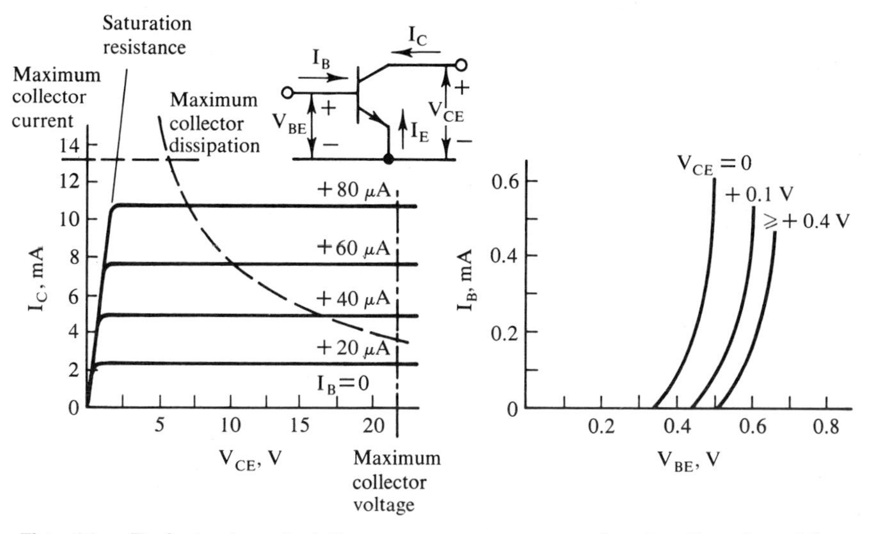

Fig. 11. Typical characteristics curves, *pnp* germanium-junction transistor. The curves for an *npn* germanium transistor would have the same shape, but all polarities would be reversed.

of 3 as controlled impurities, are called *p*-type.[5,6] Figure 8 shows pictorial diagrams of the construction of junction transistors and defines the names ordinarily associated with the terminals. Figure 9 presents similar information for the field-effect transistor.

Figures 10 and 11 show typical pictures of the characteristic volt-ampere curves for junction transistors. These are shown in the commonly employed common-emitter configuration and may be readily obtained with the aid of special attachments for many commercially available oscilloscopes or with special-purpose oscilloscopes. It is not typical for the manufacturer to supply these curves. Instead he usually provides certain specifications and limitations, and many of these are listed or illustrated on the curves.

Figure 12 is drawn to show typical characteristic curves for FET's. These again are not typically supplied but may be obtained with modifications of the equipment used for obtaining junction-transistor curves or with special equipment designed for picturing FET curves. Again, common specifications and limitations that the manufacturer supplies are illustrated.

When a transistor is used as the central element in an amplifier or other signal processor, it must first be "biased." The reason for this is best understood by realizing what an amplifier is. An amplifier is a signal processor that accepts an input signal and increases the magnitude of certain essential features of the signal

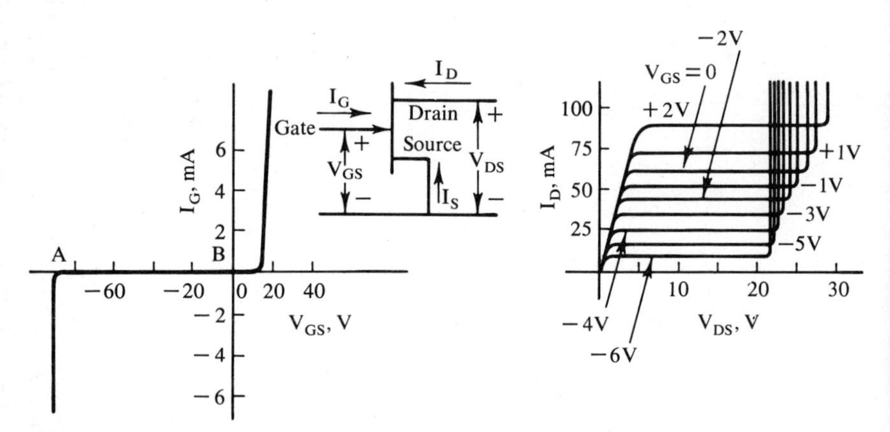

Fig. 12. Typical characteristic curves for an *n*-channel field-effect transistor. Curves for a *p*-channel transistor would have a similar appearance, but all polarities would be reversed. Junction field-effect transistors cannot operate with V_{GS} positive. They must operate with this voltage negative. Such operation is called depletion-mode operation. Some MOSFETs are designed to operate with this voltage positive. This is called enhancement-mode operation. The principal difference between junction FETs and MOSFETs is that in the region *AB* the latter have currents three to four orders of magnitude lower.

without introducing appreciable distortion. Probably the most common are voltage amplifiers, which multiply the signal-voltage strength by some constant called the amplifier gain. Other common types include power and current amplifiers. In this process, the bias supply served two purposes. The first is to supply the required power. It is not possible to get adequate power from the signal source, and hence the bias supply must provide the additional power required by succeeding operations or stages. In this sense the signal is controlling the power delivered from the bias supply. The second purpose is to force the transistor into a region of operation where the desired linearity is possible. Figures 10, 11, and 12 all show that there is a region in which, to a very good approximation, small changes in one (control) variable produce proportional changes in another variable. For example, in Fig. 10, if the circuit is adjusted to have the transistor operating at the point *Q* when the signal is zero, then small changes in the base current representing changes in the signal information will cause corresponding changes in the collector current. The latter changes will be much greater, and thus amplification is possible.

From Figs. 10 and 11 it may be seen that linear junction-transistor operation is possible when two conditions are met. The first is that the base-emitter junction must be "forward-biased," i.e., the base is positive with respect to the emitter in *npn* transistors, and negative in *pnp* transistors. Normally, this voltage will be about 0.4 V for germanium transistors, and 0.7 V for silicon transistors. The second is that in *npn* transistors, the collector is positive with respect to the emitter, while in *pnp* transistors, this voltage must be negative. The effect of this is to put a reverse bias on the collector-base junction. Figure 13 shows methods for biasing transistors to appropriate conditions using a single power or bias supply.

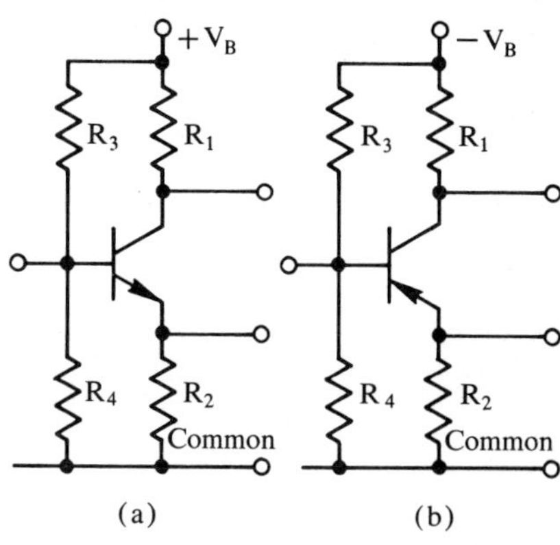

Fig. 13. Bias supplies for transistors. (*a*) Bias supply for *npn* transistor. This arrangement can also be used for *n*-channel FETs. (*b*) Bias supply for *pnp* transistor or for *p*-channel FET.

Bias considerations for FETs are similar. When the transistor is *n*-channel, the drain is positive with respect to the source. *p*-channel transistors require that the drain be negative with respect to the source. If the transistor is to be operated in the *depletion* mode, the polarity of the gate with respect to the source is opposite that of the drain-source voltage. FETs operated in the *enhancement* mode require that both these polarities be the same. The bias diagrams for FETs are essentially identical with those for junction transistors, except that in some cases, the resistors labeled R_3 and/or R_4 may be eliminated. This results from and maintains the high input impedance of these circuits.*

In the computation of the currents and voltages at the operating point, two different models are commonly used. The Ebers-Moll model is a set of equations relating the appropriate currents and voltages.[8] This is typically used in computer-aided analysis and design programs but is quite difficult to use unless a digital computer is available. A model making use of ideal diodes is often adequate for operating-point calculations and will be described here.

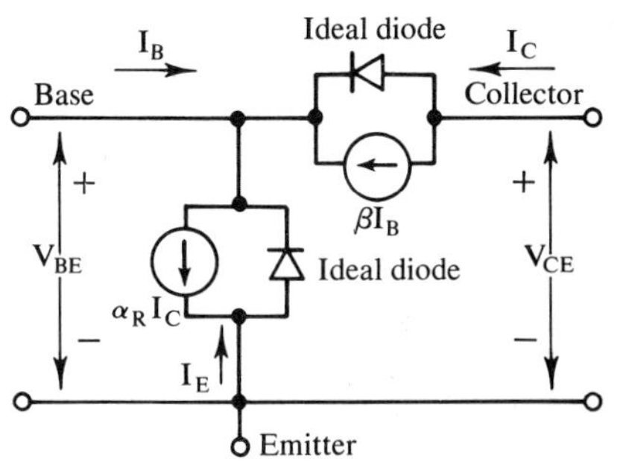

Fig. 14. Ideal-diode model for *pnp* transistor. For *npn* transistors, the two diodes must be reversed. The same model may also be used for FETs. The model shown is usable for *p*-channel FETs with the *gate* in place of the *base*, the *source* in place of the *emitter*, and the *drain* in place of the *collector*. For *n*-channel FETs, the diodes must be reversed, but the substitutions are the same. Definitions: β is the ratio of the collector to the base currents and is usually furnished by the manufacturer. α_R is the ratio of collector current to emitter current. To a good approximation, this is usually set to unity.

Figure 14 shows an ideal-diode equivalent circuit (model) for transistors. For operating-point calculations, the circuit containing a transistor may be redrawn with this model replacing the transistor, and the resulting equivalent circuit is analyzed. Analysis must proceed by the "breakpoint" or "assumed-states" method. In this, the diode is considered as either an open or a short circuit. If the solution violates the assumed condition, the solution is not valid and must be repeated with different assumptions. See the following example and Fig. 15.

* See Ref. 7, pp. 374–386, for an excellent and detailed discussion of general considerations in biasing and stability of operating points.

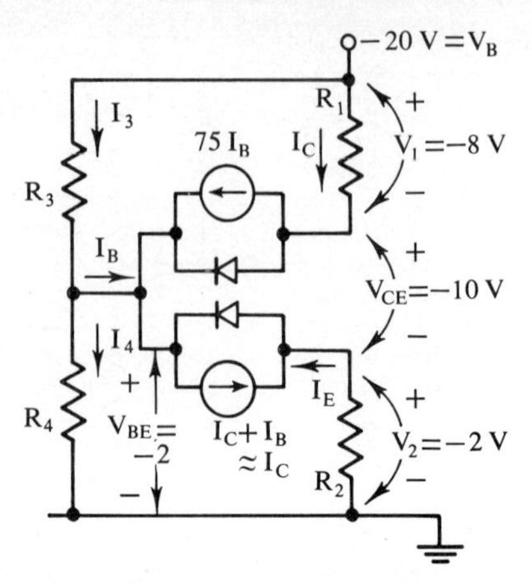

Fig. 15. Sample operating-point calculation for *pnp* transistor.

Example: Operating-point Calculation. It is desired to operate a *pnp* transistor subject to the following specifications:

$$V_B = -20 \text{ V}$$
$$V_{CE} = -10 \text{ V}$$
$$V_{BE} = -2 \text{ V}$$
$$I_B = -0.1 \text{ mA}$$

The transistor chosen has $\beta = 75$. Choose suitable 5 percent tolerance resistors.

The drawing shows the equivalent circuit and defines certain additional symbols. A logical order of computations is shown.

1. $I_C = \beta I_B = 75(-0.1) = -7.5$ mA
2. $I_E = -(I_B + I_C) = +7.6$ mA
3. $R_2 = 2.0$ V/7.6 mA = 263 Ω
4. $R_1 = 8.0$ V/7.5 mA = 1.07 kΩ
5. Choose $I_4 = -0.1$ mA; then $I_3 = -0.2$ mA
6. $R_4 = -2.0$ V/−0.1 mA = 20 kΩ
7. $R_3 = -18$ V/−0.2 mA = 90 kΩ

The nearest 5 percent tolerance components are

$$R_1 = 1.1 \text{ k}\Omega$$
$$R_2 = 270\ \Omega$$
$$R_3 = 91 \text{ k}\Omega$$
$$R_4 = 20 \text{ k}\Omega$$

The maximum power dissipated by any of these resistors is less than 0.5 W.

AMPLIFIER ANALYSIS AND DESIGN

When the transistor or vacuum tube has been biased to a suitable "operating point," it is necessary to consider the effect of signals on the amplifier. A signal will cause changes of current and voltage away from the operating point. These changes may be represented and studied by combinations of resistors, capacitors, and controlled sources. Figure 16 shows two common equivalent circuits for junction transistors, and Fig. 17 shows similar circuits for FETs. The numbers are typical values, and the circuit forms are identical for *pnp* or *npn* junction transistors, and *n*- or *p*-channel FETs. The example of Fig. 18 shows the use of one of these. For an analysis of this type, fixed power-supply voltages are "unchanging," and thus for small-signal analysis, these power busses are effectively considered by connecting them to a point of zero voltage. This is usually called "ac ground." The example that is given does not consider the effects of the various capacitors on low- and high-frequency response, but this is readily done through the use of standard techniques of circuit analysis. Normally nodal (current into a junction equals current out of the junction or node) analysis is superior to mesh (loop) analysis in which current in a continuous path is constant.

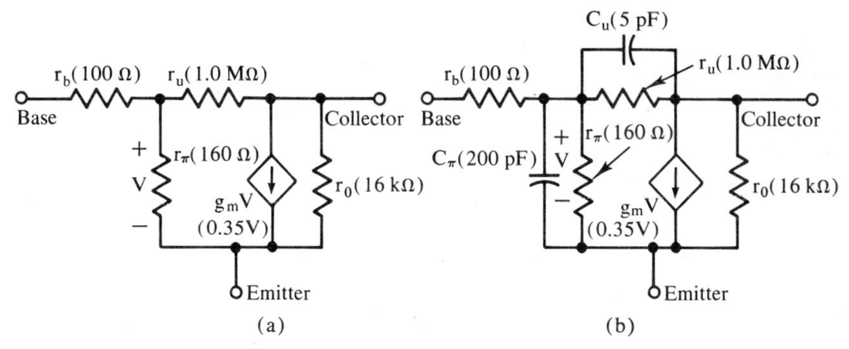

Fig. 16. Equivalent circuits for bipolar junction transistors. (Typical element values are shown in parentheses.) (*a*) Low-frequency hybrid-π equivalent circuit for junction transistor. (*b*) Hybrid-π equivalent circuit to use at mid- and higher-frequency ranges for junction transistor.

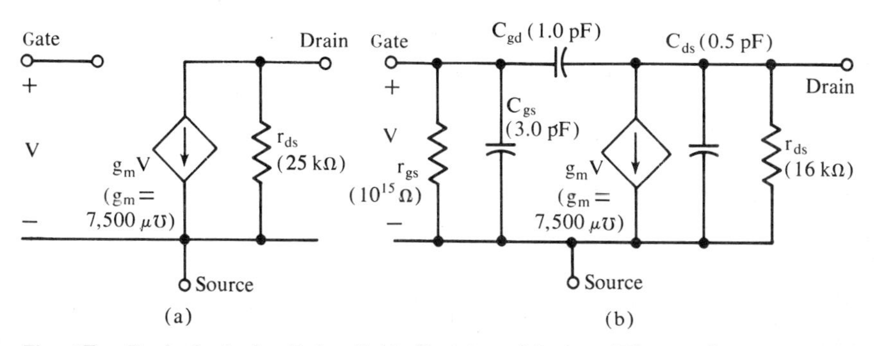

Fig. 17. Equivalent circuit for field-effect transistors. (The numbers in parentheses are typical element values.) (*a*) Low- and midfrequency hybrid-π equivalent circuit for FET. (*b*) High-frequency hybrid-π equivalent circuit for an FET.

To design an amplifier, the engineer must consider several items. These include:

1. Voltage, current, or power gain required
2. Range of frequencies over which operation is needed
3. Maximum signal amplitude, especially at the output
4. Minimum signal amplitude, especially at the input
5. Current and voltage ratings of the available power supply
6. Power dissipation by each element and by the total circuit
7. Physical size and weight
8. Output impedance of source and input impedance of the following portion of the system*

* In Ref. 9 Shea gives a wealth of circuits for doing various types of amplification, and the use of this handbook is recommended for difficult situations.

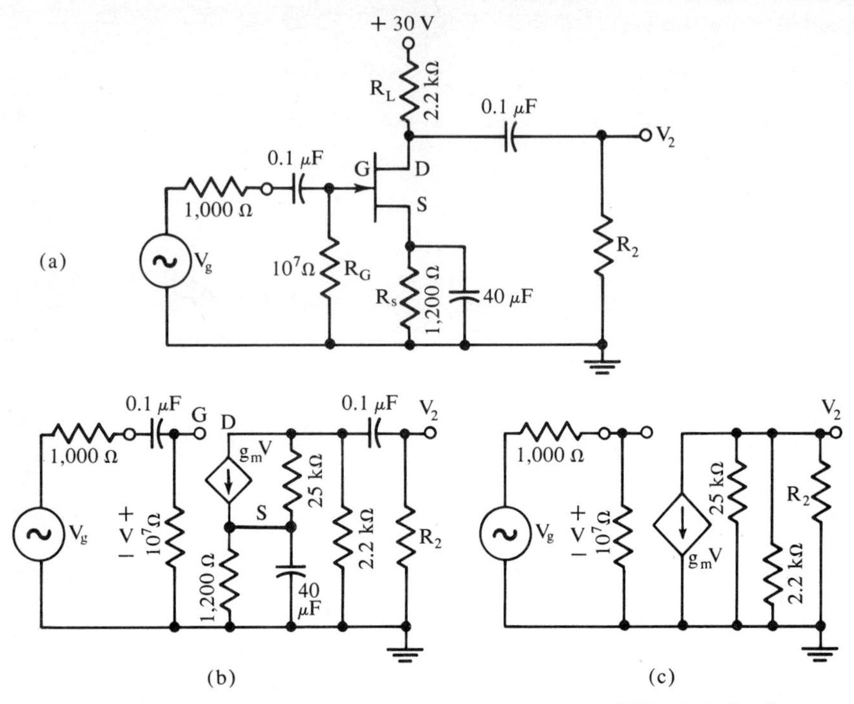

Fig. 18. Example of amplifier-gain calculation with an FET. (*a*) Single-stage FET amplifier. (*b*) Complete small-signal equivalent circuit, using model of Fig. 17*a*. (*c*) Midfrequency small-signal equivalent circuit—capacitive reactances have been assumed small compared with all resistances, and thus source node is effectively connected to ground. The specification is that this stage shall have a voltage gain, here defined as the magnitude of the ratio of V_2 to V_g, of 10 *V/V*. The only variable that is adjustable is R_2, since all other elements are determined as a part of either the voltage source or the necessary biasing network for the FET. It is here assumed that the specification means mid-frequency gain, i.e., gain at frequencies above those at which the capacitors affect the operation.

Part *b* shows an equivalent circuit. Previous results are used for the parameters. At frequencies above 1,000 Hz the reactances of the capacitors are small compared with the associated resistors. With this information it is possible to draw part *c*. This is used for the analysis. From Fig. 17*a*, the value of g_m is $7{,}500 \times 10^{-3}$ mhos.

Solution: a. $V \approx V_g$, since the source impedance is much smaller than R_G.

b. By Kirchhoff's current law, we can write this equation at the node designated V_2:

$$g_m V = -V_2 \left(\frac{1}{25 \times 10^3} + \frac{1}{2.2 \times 10^3} + \frac{1}{R_2} \right)$$

This equation is then solved for V_2/V, and this is set to −10. The one unknown is R_2, and an algebraic solution for this gives 3.9 k Ω.

OPERATIONAL AMPLIFIERS

One of the most important building blocks for modern instrumentation and control circuits is the "operational amplifier." This is the term applied to a high-gain direct-coupled (no capacitors) amplifier that originally was developed for use in analog computers. With this unit, the instrumentation engineer can build amplifiers with stable gain characteristics, summing circuits, integrating circuits, filters, and also nonlinear circuits such as comparators, digital-to-analog or analog-to-digital converters, and gates.[10–13]

The more common types of operational amplifier include:

1. Differential amplifier
2. Chopper-stabilized
3. FET-input
4. Linear integrated-circuit amplifiers

These amplifiers are available with gains varying from about 10^4 to 10^{14} with output impedances varying from 1,000 Ω down to virtually zero, and bandwidths (the frequency at which the gain is reduced to unity) varying from 1.0 to above 30 MHz. Virtually all have two input (signal) terminals, connected in a differential manner. Figure 19 shows a typical arrangement and set of labels for the terminals of an operational amplifier.

The terminals labeled $+V$ and $-V$ are designed for power-supply connection. Often recommended numerical values are used in place of V. It is possible to buy power supplies that will give the user the capability of supplying both of these from one unit. Their use is recommended because this means that variations in one voltage will be compensated for by variations in the other. Care must be taken to keep these voltages below or at the recommended value.

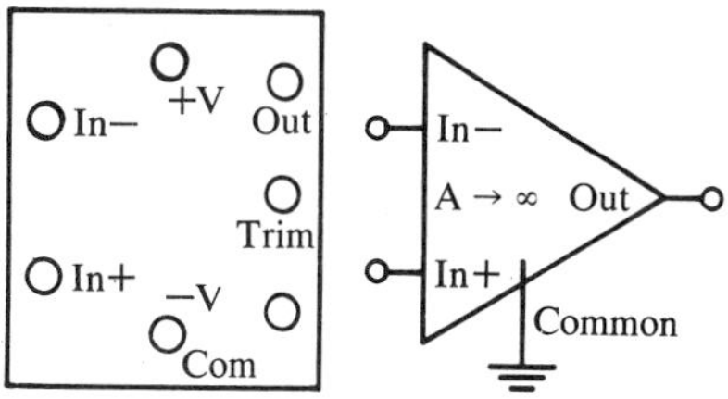

The terminal labeled "com" or "gnd" (common or ground) is available as the common lead in a circuit. In some commercial units it is not internally connected to the amplifier, but in most units it is connected.

The terminal labeled "trim" is designed to connect a compensating voltage into the amplifier. One of the errors that can exist is an output voltage that is different from zero when the input is zero. This is intolerable in a direct-coupled amplifier. The specification sheet issued with each amplifier will contain detailed directions for the use of this terminal. These must be followed carefully.

Fig. 19. Typical lead arrangement for operational amplifier, and most common symbol for small-signal analysis.

The terminal labeled "out" is the output lead. From this point the signal is available for further processing by remaining parts of the system.

The terminal or terminals labeled "in" or "in+" and "in−" or similar names are available to connect a signal to the amplifier. When two are present, the one labeled "in+" is used when it is not desired to invert (shift phase by 180°) the signal. The terminal labeled "in−" is used when such a phase shift is needed. Care must be taken not to interchange these terminals, so that the circuit will perform as intended.

In addition to trimming problems, another source of error is the drift that is exhibited by these amplifiers. This is usually caused by temperature variations, and the measures that are taken to reduce this problem are largely responsible for the wide variation of operational-amplifier prices. The other causes of variation are bandwidth and open-loop gain. The user needs to analyze his requirements carefully so as to obtain a satisfactory unit.

The analysis of circuits containing operational amplifiers is quite similar to that of other circuits, but two simplifications help this considerably. The first is that the current flowing into the two input terminals is negligible compared with that in any other part of the circuit. The second is that the gain A of the amplifier is much greater than unity or, as it more commonly appears, that the reciprocal of A is much less than unity, or nearly zero. This shows in the design equations in that all results are independent of A, as shown in the six common circuits of Fig. 20 through 25, inclusive. In all six of these figures, only the small-signal behavior-determination elements are shown. The amplifier must also have power-supply and trimming connections, but they are omitted here for clarity.

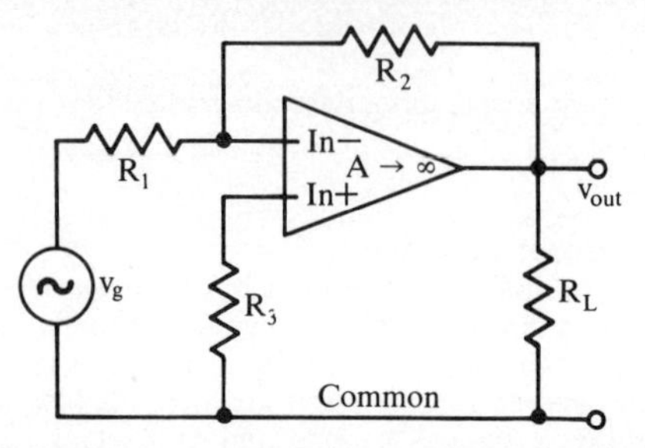

Fig. 20. Inverting amplifier implemented with one differential operational amplifier. The input impedance of this circuit is approximately equal to R_1, which should include the output impedance of the source. The output impedance is generally low. $v_{out} = -v_g(R_2/R_1)$; R_L may be eliminated. R_3 should be approximately equal to the effective parallel-resistance equivalent of R_1 and R_2 for maximum freedom from drift.

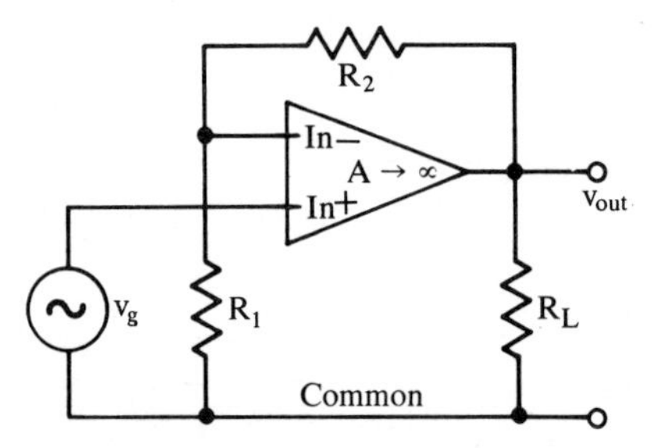

Fig. 21. Noninverting amplifier implemented with one differential amplifier. When R_2 is made zero, the circuit becomes a unity-gain voltage follower with a very high input impedance and a low output impedance. $v_{out} = v_g[(R_1 + R_2)/R_1]$; R_L may be eliminated.

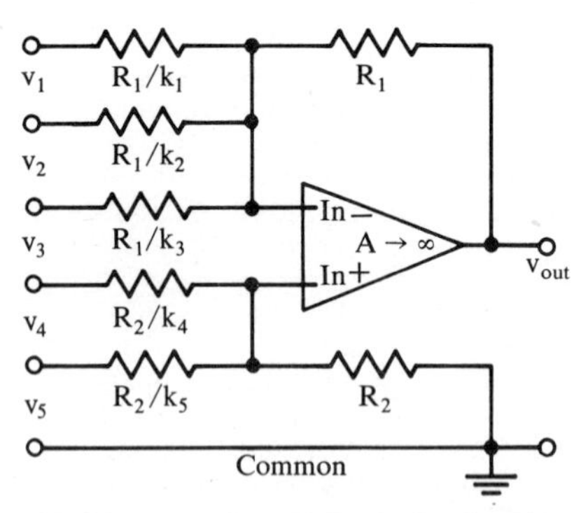

Fig. 22. Sum and difference amplifier implemented with one differential operational amplifier. $v_{out} = k_4v_4 + k_5v_5 - (k_1v_1 + k_2v_2 + k_3v_3)$. Restriction:

$$k_1 + k_2 + k_3 = k_4 + k_5$$

No restriction on number of inputs. Voltages are measured with respect to a common.

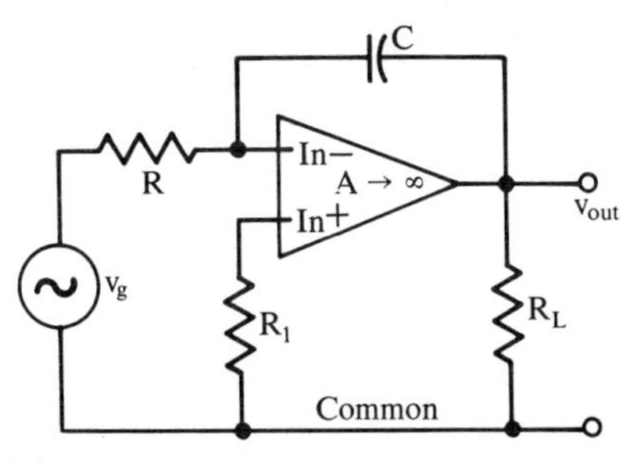

Fig. 23. An integrating circuit implemented with one differential operational amplifier. $v_{out} = -1/RC \int^t v_g(t)\, dt$. R_1 should be approximately equal to R_L. R_L may represent the input impedance of the following stage of the system. It is often necessary to shunt C with a very large resistor in order to achieve a satisfactory trim or balance arrangement.

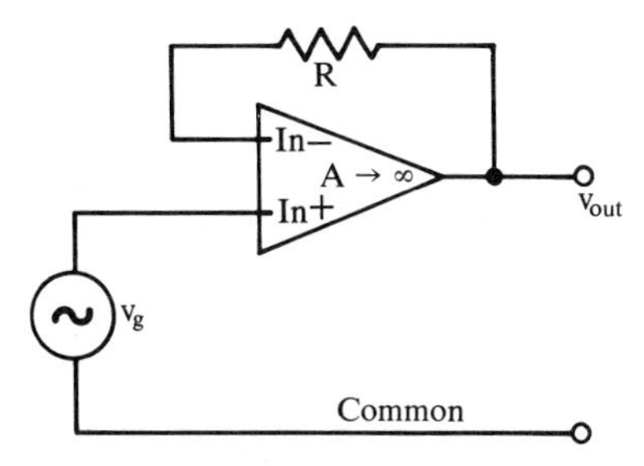

Fig. 24. Unity-gain buffer amplifier. R should be equal to the output impedance of the source. This circuit has an exceptionally high input impedance and is thus useful when the source has a high impedance and it is impossible to draw any power from the source. $V_{out} = V_g$.

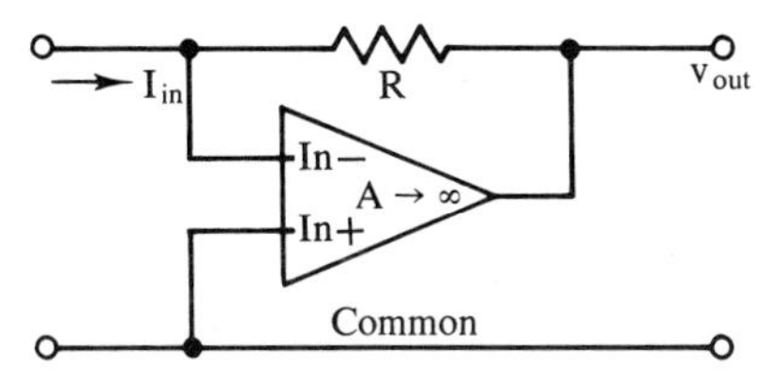

Fig. 25. Current-to-voltage transducer. In this circuit, $v_{out} = -I_{in}R$. The output voltage is thus proportional to a signal current, and this provides a good way of using the signal current to drive a recorder or some other circuit. The output and input impedances are both very low.

INTEGRATED CIRCUITS IN AMPLIFIERS

Electronic technology has developed so that it is now possible for a single structure of semiconductor to incorporate many components—resistors, transistors, diodes, and capacitors. A wide variety of techniques for implementation exists, but they are usually called by the generic term "integrated circuits." It is this development more than any other that is making it practical for the instrumentation engineer to specify and purchase complete units, rather than to design and build his own from components. The electronic engineer who designs these integrated circuits must of course view these from a perspective rather different from that for discrete-component circuits, but from the viewpoint of the instrumentation engineer there is little difference, except that the newer techniques yield lower size and weight requirements, require less power, and are generally more reliable.[15]

VACUUM TUBES

Since the invention of the transistor in 1948, the impending death of vacuum tubes has been discussed. But much instrumentation is still being produced with tubes, and many good pieces of equipment in use today are constructed with tubes. Tubes perform exactly the same types of function in a circuit as transistors—they amplify, switch, rectify, etc. In application in a device, however, tubes are quite different to deal with. They are much larger, in general, than transistors, and since the stream of electrons that is required for their operation requires a very hot element inside the tube for its production, a separate pair of wires to conduct electricity to a "filament" is required. This, plus the generally higher voltages and currents employed, is responsible for the fact that much more heat is produced by tube-operated equipment than by transistorized equipment.

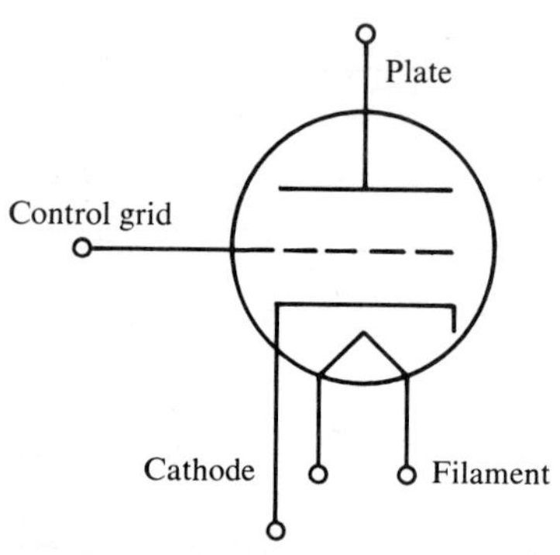

Fig. 26. Symbol for a vacuum triode. Tubes that have more than one control grid will have an appropriate number of dashed lines.

Tubes contain a number of electrical elements in an evacuated glass envelope. These are:

1. *Filament.* This is the element that heats the cathode.
2. *Cathode.* This is the element that emits a stream of electrons.
3. *Anode or Plate.* This is the element that receives the electron beam; it is normally operated positively with respect to the cathode.
4. *Control Grids.* These are elements interspersed between the plate and cathode. The voltages applied to them control the electron-beam flow and make various actions possible. A tube with no control grids is called a diode. With one grid, it is a triode; with two, a tetrode; with three, a pentode; etc. Figure 26 shows the common symbol for a triode. Symbols for other tubes are similar; the principal difference is the number of dotted lines that represent the control grids.*

NONLINEAR SIGNAL PROCESSING AND MIXING

Electronic circuits may be used to perform many operations on electronic signals. The combination, other than by addition or subtraction, of two or more signals to produce some desired effect or new signal is generally called mixing, and circuits that do this are called mixers. Mixers may multiply two signals, or take the ratio. They may determine whether the amplitude exceeds a particular level, or which of a group of signals is the strongest. They may determine whether or not signals from two or more sources are present simultaneously or in a particular sequence. In general, they may perform mathematical and common logical operations.

The responsibility of the instrumentation engineer is to decide what operations need to be done, and he must be able to describe quantitatively the signals that will be available. Packaged circuits or instruments for doing these functions are available from a variety of sources; and if he wishes to build his own, circuits for many mixers may be found in Reich.[17]

* Reference 16 contains a good discussion of the application of tubes to electronic circuits.

8. Digital-to-Analog Format Conversion The signals that are developed by most transducers and that carry the needed information are called "continuous" or "analog" signals. This means that their amplitudes change in a smooth fashion between levels; for example, consider a sine wave. The signals that are processed by digital computers and by some electronic instruments such as counters, however, are called "digital" or "discrete" signals. This means that their amplitudes exist in certain levels or ranges only, and these are well differentiated. The simplest and most practical digital signal exists in one of two states. In the case of a transistor, the collector may be nonconducting (the transistor is turned off), or it may have a current exceeding some threshold value (e.g., 10 mA). The states of the transistor then represent "off" and "on," or "0" and "1." Such signals are called "binary digits" or "bits." Numbers are frequently represented in binary format rather than decimal format, as this is the way digital computers are built.[22] On the other hand, virtually all transducers develop continuous signals. (While some research is being done in order to develop transducers that give digital outputs, these are usually available only in special situations.[21]) Consequently, it is necessary

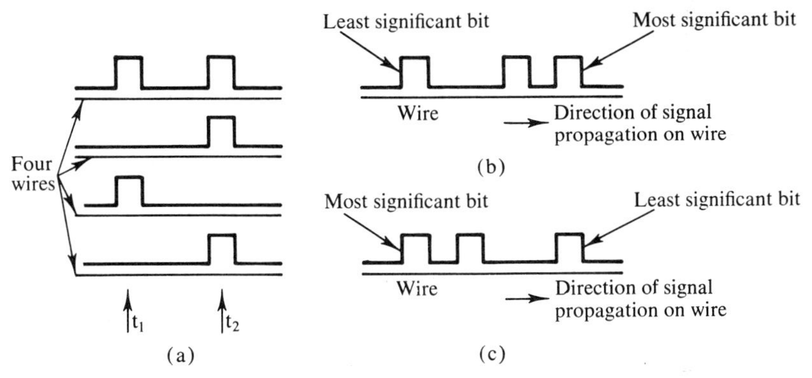

Fig. 27. Three possible formats for digital-number transfer along wire or cable. (*a*) Digital-number format—parallel representation. At instants t_1, t_2, etc., signals are present simultaneously on all wires. The signals shown represent two 4-bit numbers. (*b*) Digital-number format—serial representation, most significant bit first. (*c*) Digital-number format—serial representation, least significant bit first.

for a modern instrumentation system to have analog-to-digital converters to convert the signals from the transducers to digital format for computer processing, and digital-to-analog converters to convert the computer output so that information can be returned to the transducers, to graphical displays, etc.

Digital signals may exist in either of two types of format—"serial" or "parallel." Figure 27 illustrates these. It is of course essential for the designer to ensure that he is using the format required by his equipment. It is relatively easy to convert between these, and special hardware is readily available.

9. Digital-to-Analog Conversion A common method for digital-to-analog conversion for parallel signals employs a resistive divider used as a summing network in conjunction with a set of electronic switches. Figure 28 illustrates the concept. It is possible to show through use of ordinary circuit analysis that the output voltage V_{out} is equal to $\frac{1}{2}V$ when the most significant bit is nonzero and all others are zero, is equal to $\frac{1}{4}V$ when the second most significant bit is nonzero and all others are zero, is equal to $\frac{1}{8}V$ when the third most significant bit is nonzero and all others are zero, etc. Whether the various binary digits to be converted are zero or one determines the settings of the electronic switches. Superposition then tells us that V_{out} is the sum of the voltages developed by each of the nonzero bits, and hence is an analog representation of the binary signal. This analog signal varies between 0 and V. The voltage reference supply must be a precision source so that good conversion accuracy may be achieved. Variations of this circuit permit an analog signal to vary between $-V$ and $+V$ and are useful when the algebraic sign of a quantity is significant.

10. Feedback Analog-to-Digital Conversion The preceding technique for digital-to-analog conversion may also be used as an analog-to-digital converter by combining it in a feedback loop with a comparator, as shown in Fig. 29. The action of

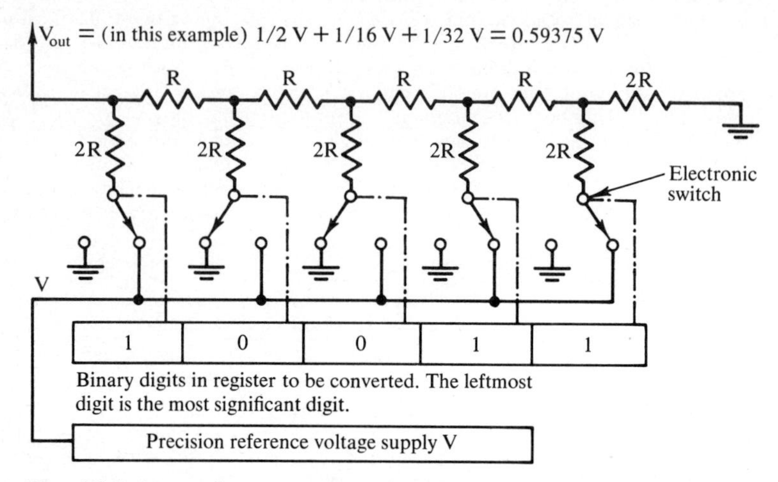

Fig. 28. Digital-to-analog converter using divider-summing network. The sample is for a 5-bit word, but the principle may be extended to longer words.

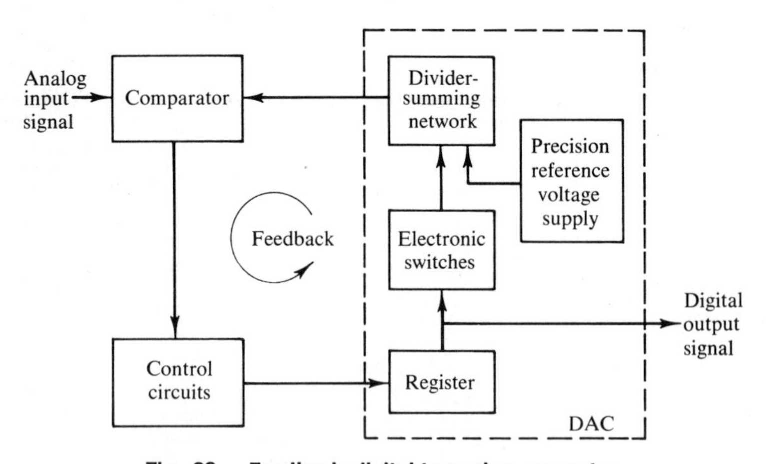

Fig. 29. Feedback digital-to-analog converter.

the comparator is to determine whether the analog input signal is larger or smaller than the divider-network output, and thus to modify the digital number held in the register. When the difference is acceptably small, the digital output is obtained from the register. The method is slow but relatively inexpensive and adequate for many applications.

11. Successive-approximation Analog-to-Digital Conversion The most common analog-to-digital converter is the "successive-approximation" system. The block diagram of Fig. 30 shows the general technique. The comparator may be an operational amplifier that operates without any feedback. The digital output is stored in the register or transmitted to another part of the system for further processing.

12. Miscellaneous Nonlinear Processing Concepts Electronic circuits are also used to perform many other types of signal processing. A few of the more important ones that are available are listed and defined here. Reich[17] has a good description and circuits for many of these.

Modulation. This is the process by which the characteristics of one signal (carrier) are varied in accordance with the information carried by another signal. The principal types are amplitude modulation (AM), frequency modulation (FM), and pulse-code modulation (PCM). Schwartz[23] is a good reference for this material.

Detection. This is the process by which the information is recovered from a modulated signal. The process varies in accordance with the modulation technique. Again, Schwartz[23] contains much information.

Heterodyning. This is a technique that may be used in either modulation or detection. It is implemented by building a circuit that multiplies signals of two

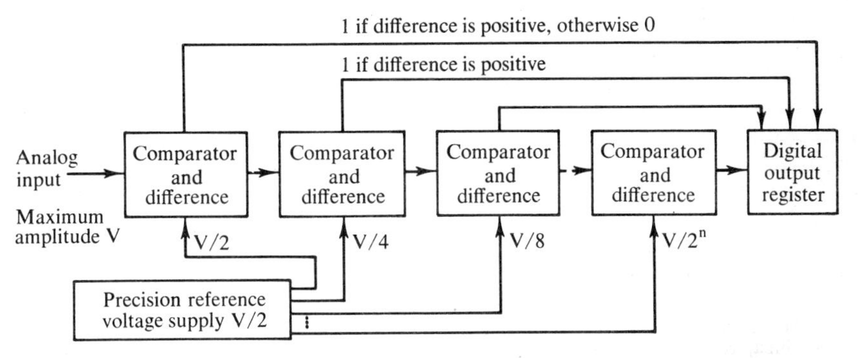

Fig. 30. A successive-approximation analog-to-digital converter. The first comparator subtracts $V/2$ from the analog input. If the difference is positive, a 1 is placed in the most significant bit of the register, and the difference is transmitted to the next comparator. If the difference is negative, the signal itself is transmitted to the next comparator. In either case, $V/4$ is subtracted, and the process is repeated for n stages of conversion.

different frequencies together. In the result will be new signals at new frequencies, including the sum and/or difference frequency of the two basic signals. This is the basic process used in telemetry or multiplex systems. Schwartz[23] is again recommended as a basic reference.

Sampling. The process by which a signal is monitored only at specified intervals. The sampler output is set according to the instantaneous signal level and is held there until the next sample point. The frequency at which the signal is sampled must be at least two times as high as the frequency components in the signal; otherwise information will be lost.

Triggering. This is the process by which a relatively short duration, large-amplitude signal is developed and transmitted to another circuit to initiate a desired action. One example is the initiation of the trace of the electron beam in a cathode-ray tube such as in an oscilloscope.

Gate. A gate is a switch that closes on command to allow the transmission of a signal or opens to prevent this transmission. Principal types include the NAND, AND, OR, and NOR gates. The AND gate transmits information if and only if all of a certain set of conditions are met. The OR gate transmits information if any one of a set of conditions is met. The NAND gate transmits information if the conditions AND are not met—the name is a shorthand notation for NOT

AND. Similarly, the NOR means NOT OR, and transmits information if the OR conditions are not met.

Clipping. This is the process of eliminating any portion of a signal that exceeds some specified value. The process is also called amplitude comparison.

Clamping. This is the process by which the signal (voltage) variations at some point in a circuit are forced to take place relative to a constant or direct reference voltage. This reference may be zero, but more commonly a clamping circuit is used to ensure that all variations in voltage are such as to maintain a constant polarity.

Correlation. This is the process by which signals are compared and a correlation coefficient is measured.

REFERENCES

1. Fink, D. G., and J. Carroll: "Standard Handbook for Electrical Engineers," 10th ed., McGraw-Hill Book Company, New York, 1968.
2. Friedland, B., O. Wing, and R. Ash: "Principles of Linear Networks," p. 40, McGraw-Hill Book Company, New York, 1961.
3. Anner, G. E.: "Elementary Nonlinear Electronic Circuits," Prentice-Hall, Inc., Englewood Cliffs, N.J., 1967.
4. Angelo, E. J.: "Electronics: BJT's, FET's, and Microcircuits," McGraw-Hill Book Company, New York, 1969.
5. Wedlock, B. D., and J. K. Roberge: "Electronic Components and Measurements," Prentice-Hall, Inc., Englewood Cliffs, N.J., 1969.
6. Adler, R. B., A. C. Smith, and R. L. Longini: "Introduction to Semiconductor Physics," John Wiley & Sons, Inc., New York, 1964. (This is Volume I of the 7-volume set published by the Semiconductor Electronics Education Committee.)
7. Chua, L. O.: "Introduction to Nonlinear Network Theory," pp. 374–386, McGraw-Hill Book Company, New York, 1968.
8. Searle, C. L., et al.: "Elementary Circuit Properties of Transistors," pp. 37–51, John Wiley & Sons, New York, 1964. (This is Volume III of the 7-volume set published by the Semiconductor Electronics Education Committee.)
9. Shea, R.: "Amplifier Handbook," McGraw-Hill Book Company, New York, 1966.
10. Huelsman, L. P.: "Theory and Design of Active RC Circuits," McGraw-Hill Book Company, New York, 1968.
11. Burr-Brown Research Corporation Staff: "Handbook of Operational Amplifier Applications," Tucson, Ariz., 1963.
12. Philbrick Researches, Inc., Staff: "Applications Manual for Computing Amplifiers," 2d ed., Nimrod Press, Boston, Mass., 1966.
13. Morrison, C. F., Jr.: "Generalized Instrumentation for Research and Teaching," Washington State University, Pullman, Wash., 1964.
14. General Electric Company Staff, J. F. Cleary (ed.): "Transistor Manual," 7th ed., General Electric Company, Syracuse, N.Y., 1966.
15. RCA Staff: "RCA Linear Integrated Circuit Fundamentals," RCA, Inc., Harrison, N.J., 1966.
16. Spangenberg, K. R.: "Fundamentals of Electron Devices," McGraw-Hill Book Company, New York, 1957.
17. Reich, H. J.: "Functional Circuits and Oscillators," D. Van Nostrand Company, Inc., Princeton, N.J., 1961.
18. Stadtfeld, N.: "Information Display Concepts," Tektronix, Inc., Beaverton, Ore., 1968.
19. Digital Equipment Corporation Staff: "Digital Logic Handbook," Digital Equipment Corporation, Maynard, Mass., 1970.
20. Aniebona, E. N., and R. T. Brathwaite: A Review of Analog-to-Digital Conversion, *Computer Design*, December, 1969.
21. Sherwood, W. M.: The Search for a True Digital Transducer, *Control Eng.*, October, 1969.
22. Bartholomew, D.: "Electrical Measurements and Instrumentation," Allyn and Bacon, Inc., Boston, 1963.
23. Schwartz, M.: "Information, Transmission, Modulation, and Noise," 2d ed., McGraw-Hill Book Company, New York, 1970.

Chapter 8

Output Devices

EDWARD W. ERNST, Ph.D.

Department of Electrical Engineering, University of Illinois, Urbana, Illinois

INTRODUCTION

The result of a measurement must be displayed for observation or recorded (for later observation) if it is to be useful. The wide variety of means for displaying or recording a measurement is a reflection of the output devices as well as the available capability. In assessing the differences between various output devices, two factors appear to be significant: (1) the expected use of the output and (2) the information content of the output. The first of these concerns itself with such questions as: Is the output for human observation? Is a record needed? Is it to be an input to a computer or other data-processing system? The second factor considers such questions as: Is a single value for the output all that is needed? Is the value as a function of time needed? What is the frequency content of the signal at the output?

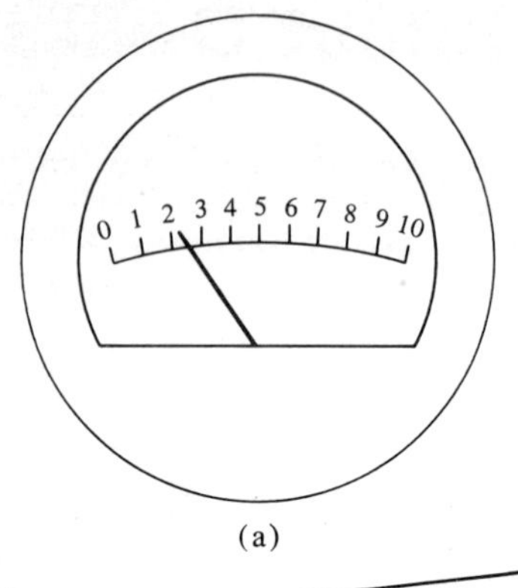

(a)

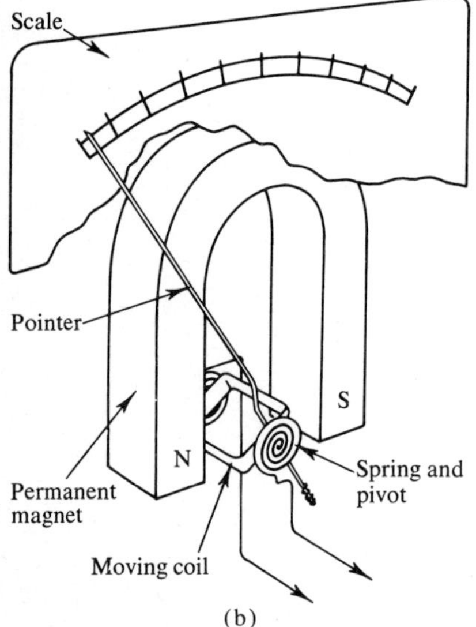

(b)

Fig. 1. Scale and pointer—dial-indicators instrument. (*a*) Scale and pointer. (*b*) Mechanism (PMMC movement).

SINGLE-NUMBER OUTPUT DEVICES

One group of output devices is that designed to indicate the value of some particular quantity under conditions such that the value to be measured can be regarded as invariant during the time over which the measurement is made. To represent the value obtained from such a measurement, a single number—the value—is all that is needed. The title "single-number output devices" is given to this group. The time for which the number represents the value of the quantity may be relatively brief, and an additional reading may be taken after a short interval to represent a new value of the quantity. However, each value is obtained as a single number.

1. Indicating Instruments The simplest form of output device is that which displays a number indicating the value of the measured quantity. Dial-type indicating instruments are an important class of these single-number output devices. The value of the measured quantity is shown as the position of a pointer against a scale (Fig. 1). The torque which causes the pointer to be displaced from the zero position is derived from the current or voltage applied to the instrument; the displacement is opposed by a restraining spring. If the restraining torque from the spring increases linearly with the deflection angle, the deflection of the pointer is a direct indication of the deflection torque.

The movable part of the indicating instrument, which includes the pointer, must be held in position so that it rotates freely about the axis of rotation but does not move in other directions. The taut-band suspension (Fig. 2) supports the movable coil (or other movable element) with flat metal ribbon kept in tension by some sort of spring arrangement. The tension must be such that the position of the movable element is independent of the orientation (horizontal or vertical) of the device. The flat-ribbon support also acts as the restraining spring. As the pointer rotates, the flat-ribbon support twists. In addition, the current to the coil may be conducted through the flat-ribbon support. This form of support offers no friction but requires that the movable element have extremely low mass to reduce tension required, and hence the force required for full-scale deflection.

Another method used for suspension in dial devices is the pivot-and-jewel bearings illustrated in Fig. 3. A hardened-steel pivot together with a sapphire jewel gives a relatively low but nonzero friction. The helical-wound restraining spring can also be used to conduct current to the coil. The friction of the support introduces some error; careful design and manufacture *can* reduce this to less than 0.2 percent of the full-scale deflection. As the area of contact in the pivot-and-jewel is small,

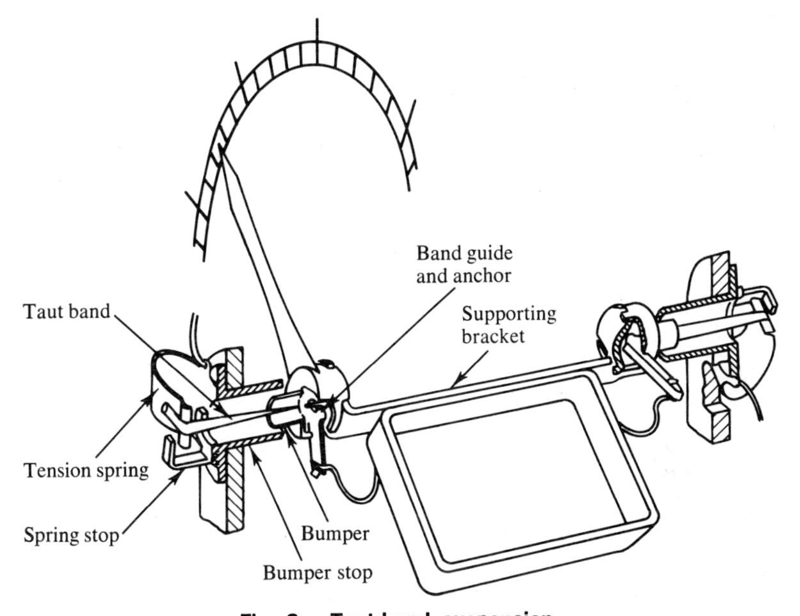

Fig. 2. Taut-band suspension.

the mechanical stress is large, and the added stress which results from mechanical shock (dropping the device, for example) may damage the support.

For either type of support, the repeated flexing of the springs occurring in normal usage could cause fatigue or permanent "set." Careful control of the materials used and the manufacture of the springs can eliminate these as serious problems. These are delicate, precision devices. Damage caused by abuse can result in complete failure or, more often, a significant loss of accuracy.

Proper damping is essential to a good dial-indicating instrument. With very little damping, the pointer may swing beyond the correct reading—then back too far in the opposite direction—and settle to rest after many oscillations. This is time-consuming and annoying. *Damping* is introduced to reduce these swings as the pointer seeks a final position. Damping may be accomplished by use of a lightweight vane, mounted on the moving element, which moves in a close-fitting, stationary chamber. As the air must move from one part of the chamber to another through a narrow opening when the pointer (and hence the vane) moves, rapid movements are impeded. Damping may also be obtained in a permanent-magnet moving-coil (PMMC) instrument by winding the coil on an aluminum frame. The circulating currents set up in the frame as the coil deflects give a retarding torque proportional to the velocity. If the resistance connected across the terminals is low (a shunt for an ammeter, for example), the circulating currents set up as the coil deflects give a similar retarding torque.

Although the deflection for a device of this type is a function of the current or voltage applied to the terminals, it may be desirable to use the meter to indicate the value of some other quantity which is converted to the current or voltage by means of a *transducer*. In this case, the dial should be calibrated in terms of the desired quantity (say, temperature) rather than current; for some applications the same meter is used to indicate values of several quantities, and multiple scales

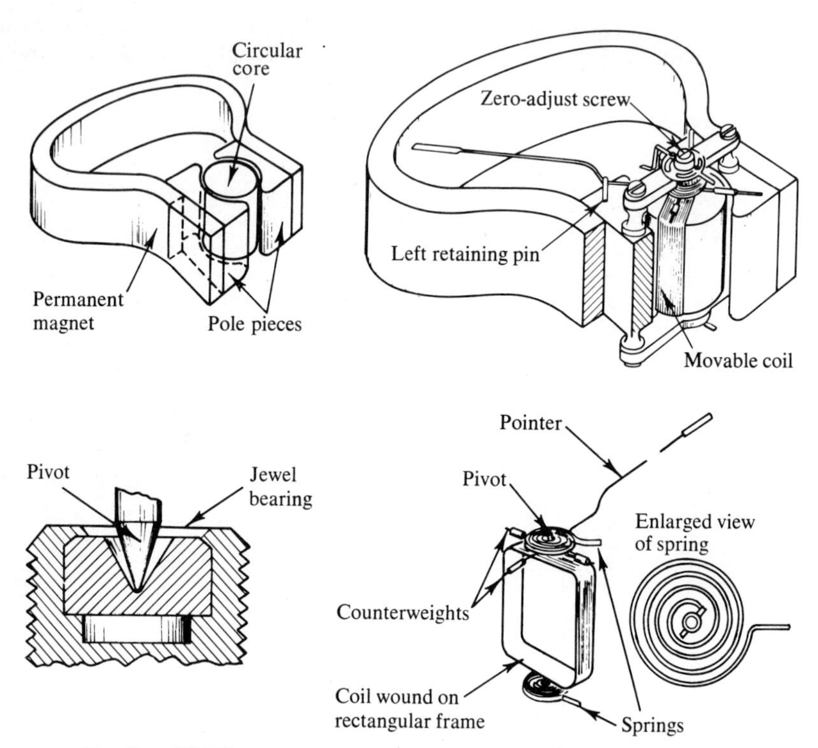

Fig. 3. PMMC movement, pivot-and-jewel bearing construction.

are used. It should be recognized that individual differences between supposedly identical indicating devices of this type produce errors if identical scales are used on all instruments of the same type. To achieve the improved accuracy that individually calibrated scales yield, some instrument scales are marked for the particular unit.

Although the several types of dial-and-pointer indicating instruments respond in different ways to the applied signals, all these devices are connected to and become part of the electric circuit. Table 1 compares important features of the three major meter movements. Each movement is discussed in detail beginning on p. 8-5.

2. Permanent-magnet Moving-coil Meter A frequently used indicating instrument is the permanent-magnet moving-coil (PMMC), which responds to the average value of the current (direct current) passing through the terminals of the meter. The PMMC movement (Fig. 3) has a coil of wire suspended in the field of a permanent magnet. When a current is passed through the coil, a torque is produced which causes the coil to rotate; the rotation is opposed by the restraining

TABLE 1 Meter Movements

Name	Responds to	Accuracy (full-scale), %	Relative power consumption	Frequency	Applications
Iron vane.......	Average of square (rms)	½–2	Medium	25–2,500 Hz	Sinusoidal current and voltage
PMMC (d'Arsonval)	Average of signal	½–2	Low	Dc	Direct current and voltage
Electrodynamometer	Average of square (rms)	½–2	High	Dc–2,500 Hz	Direct and alternating current and voltage

spring. The torque is proportional to the current in the coil; the deflection of the pointer—rotation of the coil—is proportional to the *average* vlaue of the current, and a value for the average current may be read against a linear scale. The deflection can be calibrated to show any desired quantity. That is, the scale may be calibrated to indicate current, voltage, resistance, power, temperature, displacement, velocity, or other measured quantity. For some of these, the scales are not linear, even though the deflection is linearly proportional to the current through

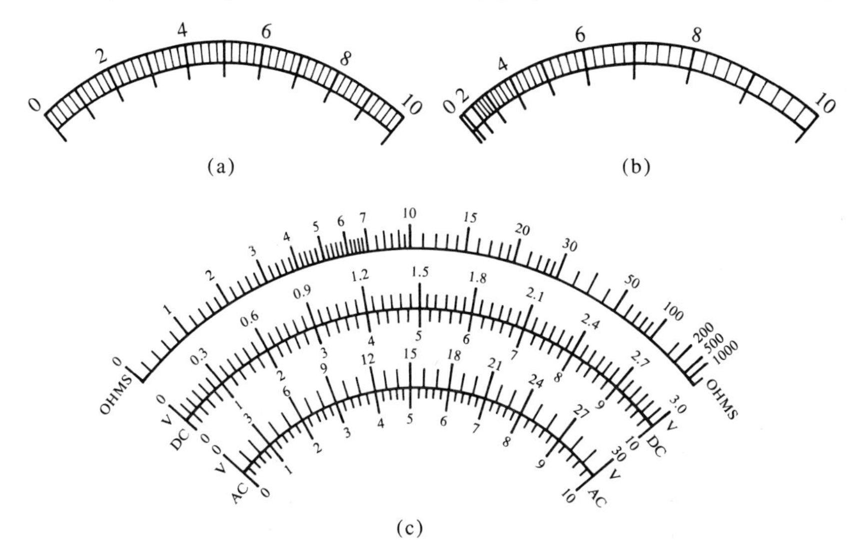

Fig. 4. Scales for indicating instrument. (*a*) Linear scale. (*b*) Square-law scale. (*c*) Typical multimeter scale.

the device. If the shape of the magnet poles is altered, the deflection will no longer be proportional to the average current in the coil. This is used to expand a selected portion of the scale or to cause the deflection vs. current relation to approximate some relationship other than a linear one (see Fig. 4).

The PMMC movement is used to indicate the value of a direct current or voltage. It is also frequently used to indicate the output of an instrument designed to measure other quantities such as ac voltage, power, or resistance. The measuring instrument produces a direct current whose value is a function of the quantity

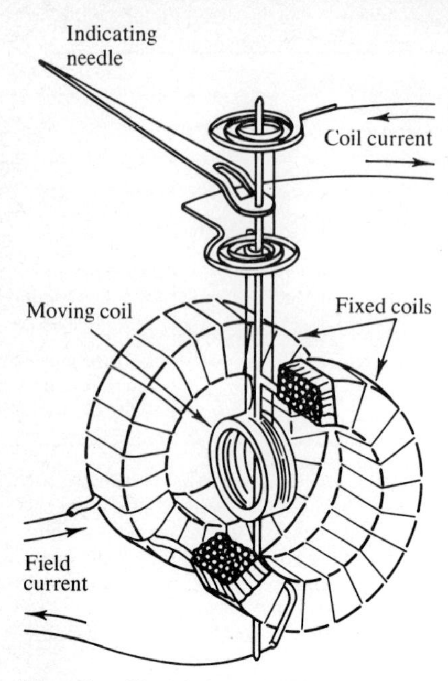

Fig. 5. Electrodynamometer movement.

to be measured. The PMMC movement then responds to the direct current. The basic PMMC movement is available in a variety of sizes and shapes, with accuracy ranging from ½ to 2 percent of the full-scale reading.

3. Electrodynamometer Meter The electrodynamometer movement (Fig. 5) has a coil of wire suspended in the magnetic field produced by another coil of wire. The torque on the movable coil is proportional to the product of the current in the movable coil and the strength of the magnetic field produced by the fixed coil. As the magnetic-field strength is proportional to the current in the coil, the torque is proportional to the *product* of the currents in the two coils. If the coils are connected in series, the torque will be proportional to the square of the current. The deflection will then be proportional to the average of the square of the current.

4. Iron Vane The iron-vane movement (Fig. 6) has two soft-iron pieces in the magnetic field produced by a coil of wire. One iron piece is fixed; the other is movable. The two iron pieces are magnetized in a like manner by the current in the coil; thus a repelling force is developed in them, proportional to the square of the current in the coil, which tends to move them apart. A spring attached to the moving piece—or vane—opposes the motion of the vane

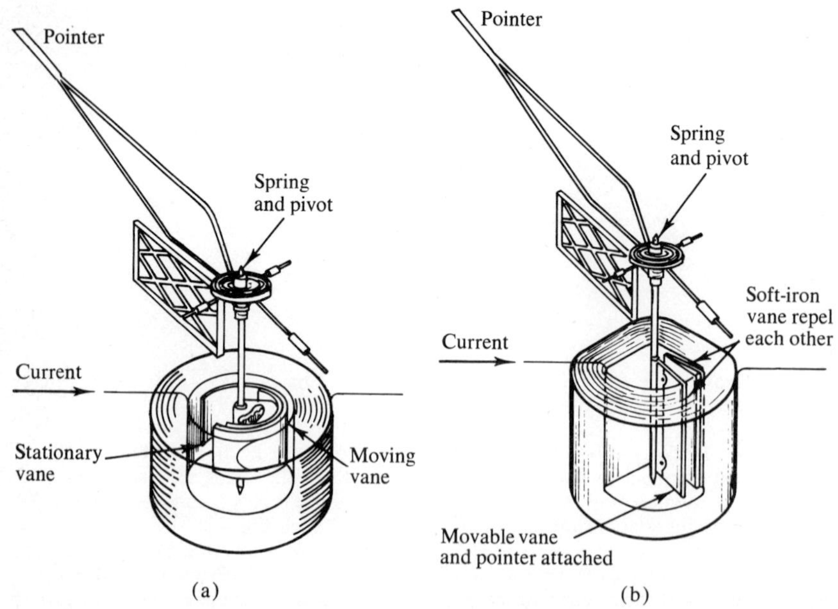

Fig. 6. Iron-vane movement. (*a*) Concentric vane. (*b*) Radial vane.

and permits the scale to be calibrated in terms of average value of the square of the current.

The response of both the electrodynamometer and the iron-vane movments is a function of the mean square of the current applied to the terminals. The scale may be calibrated to indicate the square root of the mean-square value or in terms of the *root-mean-square* (rms) value of the quantity being measured (Fig. 4*b*). These instruments are basically independent of signal waveform. They are dependent on frequency, with higher frequencies yielding larger errors. Thus the high-frequency components of a complex waveform will not be indicated correctly and the reading will not be entirely independent of waveform, particularly if appreciable signal components are present at high frequencies. The particular value varies with individual designs, and the usable frequency may be as high as 2,500 Hz, although 125 Hz is the more usual high-frequency limit. Changes in the position and shape of the coils or the iron vanes can alter the relationship between the deflection and the current applied to the terminals in much the same manner as changes in the shape of the magnet poles alter the relationship for a PMMC device.

These devices are used to display the value of an alternating current or voltage. These indicating instruments are also available in various sizes and shapes with an accuracy from ½ to 2 percent of the full-scale value.

5. Digital-display Units Another output device which indicates the value of the measured quantity as a number is the digital-display device which indicates the value directly in decimal digits. The number of digits corresponds to the significant figures needed to represent the value. The basic element in a digital display is the display for a single digit; *N*-digit displays are simply single-digit displays grouped together. Figure 7 shows a multiple-digit display. A single-digit display is capable of indicating the numbers from 0 to 9; in some instances a decimal point may be displayed. The input to the digit display is either a code on one or more input lines, indicating the particular number to be displayed, or the excitation of one of ten input lines designating the number to be displayed.

8 4 2 1 0 3

Fig. 7. Multiple-digit display.

TABLE 2 Binary Code for Digital-display Unit

Digit displayed	Line no. 1	2	3	4
0	0	0	0	0
1	0	0	0	1
2	0	0	1	0
3	0	0	1	1
4	0	1	0	0
5	0	1	0	1
6	0	1	1	0
7	0	1	1	1
8	1	0	0	0
9	1	0	0	1

0 indicates the line *is not* excited.
1 indicates the line is excited.

A typical binary code on four input lines is shown in Table 2. The digit displayed will depend on which combination of "excitation" and "noexcitation" is present at a particular time; the decoding circuits are part of the display unit (see Sec. 15). Several methods for displaying the digits are shown in Fig. 8, as follows:

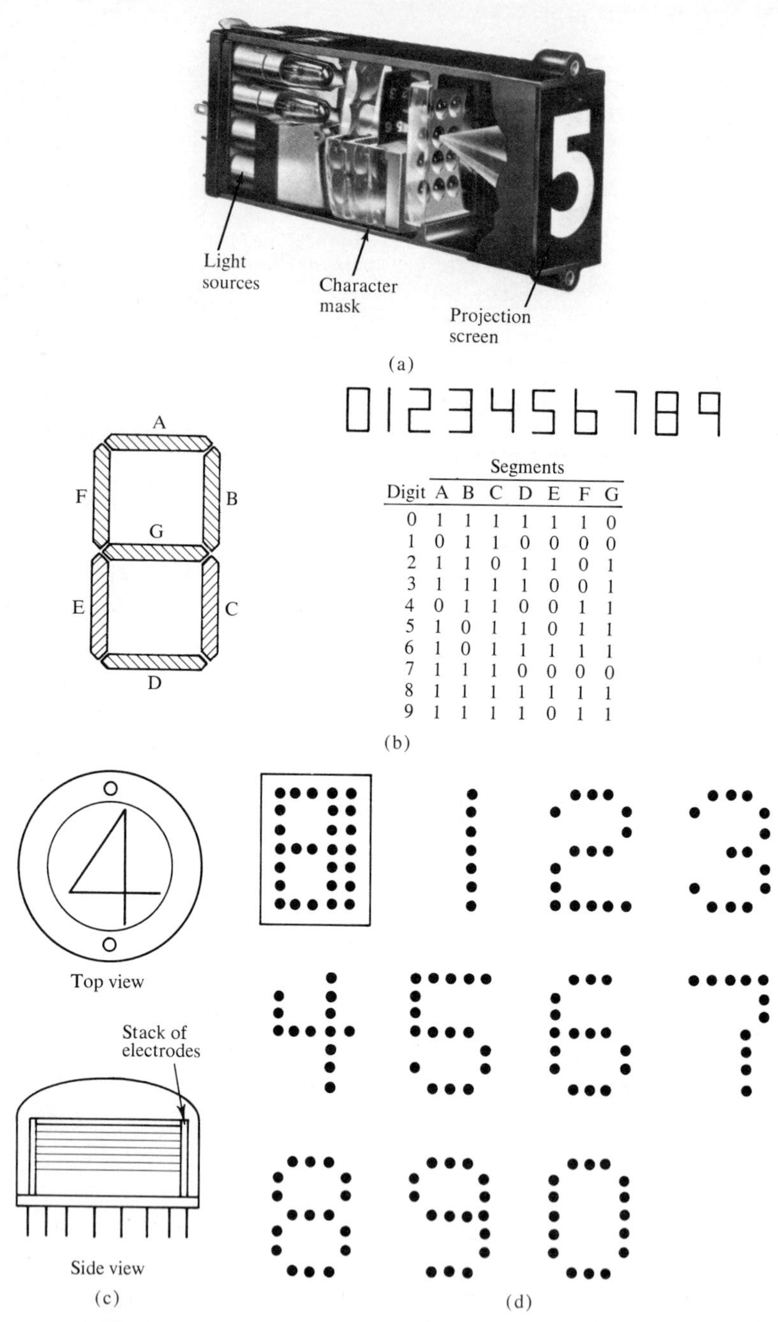

Digit	A	B	C	D	E	F	G
0	1	1	1	1	1	1	0
1	0	1	1	0	0	0	0
2	1	1	0	1	1	0	1
3	1	1	1	1	0	0	1
4	0	1	1	0	0	1	1
5	1	0	1	1	0	1	1
6	1	0	1	1	1	1	1
7	1	1	1	0	0	0	0
8	1	1	1	1	1	1	1
9	1	1	1	1	0	1	1

(Columns A–G under "Segments")

Fig. 8. Digital-display methods. Digits are displayed as an illuminated character against a dark background. (*a*) Rear-projection display. (*b*) Segment display; the 1 in the table indicates the segments which are illuminated for each digit. (*c*) Gaseous-glow display. (*d*) Dot-matrix display. The upper left shows the entire matrix of 27 dots used for a number display.

Fig. 8*a*. A projection display projects the desired digit on a small screen by means of an optical system and an appropriate mask. Each digit appears at the same plane.

Fig. 8*b*. A segmented display forms the digit to be displayed by illuminating selected segments from a group. As all the available segments are in the same plane, all digits will be displayed in the same plane. Both electroluminescent elements and incandescent filaments have been used for this type of display.

Fig. 8*c*. Gaseous-glow display tubes have a set of electrodes, each shaped in the form of a digit. The selected electrode is surrounded by a gaseous discharge, or glow, when the digit is selected. The electrodes are stacked one behind the other; hence the various digits will appear at different planes.

Fig. 8*d*. A grid of illuminated dots may be used to form the digit to be displayed. Although larger versions of this approach use a grid of incandescent light bulbs, the units used as output devices in electronic instruments are light-emitting diodes.

Additional information such as the sign and the units associated with the quantity displayed can be given by adding additional "digits" (display units) to the display. A well-designed digital display is flexible and relatively easy to interpret. Digital-display units are used as the output devices for digital measuring instruments.

TIME-DOMAIN OUTPUT DEVICES

If the values the quantity takes on as a function of time are needed, the indicating instrument or digital-display device is no longer satisfactory except for very slowly

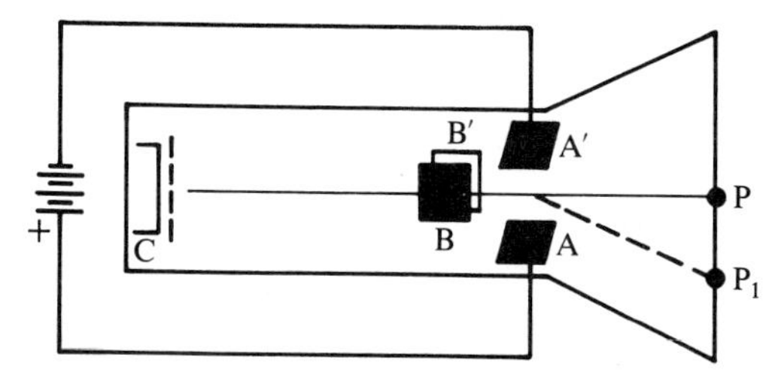

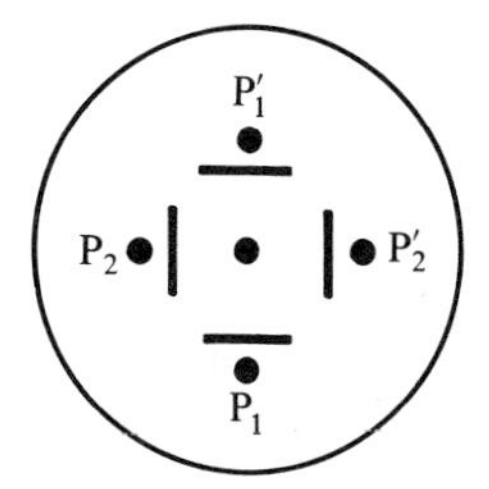

Fig. 9. Cathode-ray tube.

changing quantities—those for which values at intervals of once each several seconds are satisfactory. It is then necessary to describe the value of the quantity as a function of time; for many uses, the variation with time, such as the signal waveform or shape, is the desired information. One device for displaying values which are functions of time is the cathode-ray tube.

6. The Cathode-ray Tube Figure 9 is a simplified pictorial diagram of the CRT. At the left end of the CRT is a heated cathode C emitting electrons which are then accelerated down the neck of the CRT tube by an "electron gun." This beam of electrons is produced continuously. When a potential difference is applied to the metal plates A and A', which, spatially, are in a horizontal position, the beam of electrons, being a stream of negative charges, will be electrostatically deflected during the time they are between the plates A and A'. Thus, if no voltages are present on any of the plates, the beam of electrons will be deflected downward to a different point P. It should be evident that if the polarity of the battery is reversed, the vertical electric field between the plates A and A' will be reversed so that now the beam of electrons will be deflected vertically upward to a position P_1'. Hence the CRT is sensitive to the polarity of the deflecting voltage. Also, it is sensitive to the amplitude of the deflecting voltage, since this varies the magnitude of the electric field.

The two plates A and A' are called the *vertical-deflection plates.* Now, if the potential difference of the battery is applied to the two plates B and B', the beam of electrons can be deflected horizontally to a position P_2 or P_2', depending on whether the + terminal of the battery is connected to B' or B, respectively. The plates B and B' are called the *horizontal-deflection plates.*

Clearly, then, it is possible to position the beam of electrons to a spot anywhere on the screen by simultaneously applying voltages to both sets of deflection plates. Furthermore, if the magnitudes of these applied voltages are continuously varied, the spot will trace out a path, or "display," that will be observable from the persistence of the phosphors on the oscilloscope screen. If the magnitudes of these voltages are varied very rapidly, the human eye will not be able to follow the spot as a single entity, and an observer will see a display of the complete path traced out by the spot. This is a result of the persistence of vision and a small persistence of screen fluorescence, creating the illusion of a continuous line, instead of producing just a succession of images of the spot.

The trace on the CRT plots the value of one quantity vs. the value of another quantity. As the "writing" is accomplished by a beam of electrons moved to various positions on the screen by electrical signals, variations of the observed value which occur in extremely small time intervals (as short as 10 ns) may be observed on a cathode-ray tube. The characteristics of some of the more common phosphors used in a CRT are shown in Table 3. It may be seen from the table that the intensity of the image produced by the electron beam decays rapidly for most phosphors. Thus the image on the CRT will not remain after the electron beam has traced it but will decay rapidly (in a few milliseconds) except for the long-persistence phosphorescence of the P2 or P7 phosphor. If the trace can be repeated at intervals of a few milliseconds or faster, the observed display will appear to be of constant intensity. Thus the cathode ray is effective for displaying a repetitive pattern. With a longer period of repetition, the screen persistence needed increases. As the decay time in Table 3 is the time required to decay to 0.1 percent of the initial intensity, a repetition period greater than about one-tenth of the decay time will produce a definite flicker.

The cathode-ray tube is available with screen sizes ranging from 1 in. in diameter to rectangular screens with 27-in. diagonal. The CRT used in electronic instruments is usually the smaller size, with the 5-in.-diameter screen or a rectangular shape of equivalent size the most popular. Cathode-ray tubes of this size have been made with a flat screen (as opposed to the spherical screen found in larger-sized CRTs) to aid in making quantitative observations. A graticule is usually used with a CRT to allow the deflection to be measured. This is usually in the form of a rectangular grid 10 by 10 cm, 8 by 10 cm, or 6 by 10 cm with lines at 1-cm intervals and division of 2 mm (⅕ cm) indicated along the axes. Although the graticule may be scribed on a transparent sheet and attached to the outside of the CRT faceplate, some CRTs used in electronic instruments have the graticule placed on the inside of the CRT faceplate in the same plane as the phosphor. The internal graticule avoids errors caused by parallax, which exists when the graticule is external to the tube and separated from the phosphor by the thickness of the glass faceplate.

The widely used instrument, the cathode-ray oscilloscope (CRO), has been designed to utilize the properties of the CRT as an output device. The CRT is also used with other instruments and is the display device for a television receiver.

The resolution of the CRT is limited by the size of the spot produced by the beam of electrons. In a CRT with a 10- by 10-cm screen, the resolution will be approximately 1 mm (1 percent of full-scale deflection).

7. Storage Tubes The storage cathode-ray tube or storage tube is capable of storing the visual image on the screen for periods as long as an hour with no appreciable loss of intensity. Thus with a storage tube the pattern produced by a nonrepetitive signal may be examined in detail. The stored pattern may be readily erased so that another signal pattern may be examined. A storage tube can also be operated without using the storage feature, and in this mode of operation

TABLE 3 CRT Phosphor Data Chart

Phosphor	Fluorescence (phosphorescence)	Relative luminance*	Relative photographic writing speed†	Decay to 0.1 %, ms	Relative burn resistance	Comments
P1	Yellowish-green	0.50	0.20	95	Medium	Replaced by P31 in most applications
P2	Bluish-green (yellowish-green)	0.55	0.40	120‡	Medium high	Good compromise for high- and low-speed applications
P4	White	0.50	0.40	20	Medium high	Television displays
P7	Blue (yellowish-green)	0.35	0.75	1,500‡	Medium	Long decay, double-layer screen
P11	Purplish-blue	0.15	1.00	20	Medium	For photographic applications
P15	Bluish-green	0.15	0.15	0.05	Very high	Very short decay for flying-spot scanner use
P31	Yellowish-green	1.00	0.50	32	High	General-purpose, brightest available phosphor

* Taken with a spectra brightness spot meter which incorporates a CIE standard eye filter. Representative of 10-kV aluminized screens. P31 as reference.

† P11 as reference with Polaroid 410 film. Representative of 10-kV aluminized screens.

‡ Low level lasts over 1 min under conditions of low ambient illumination.

the characteristics are similar to those of a standard cathode-ray tube. Some storage tubes permit split-screen operation in which either the upper or lower half of the screen, or both, may exhibit storage capability. Another characteristic available with some storage tubes is variable persistence. This allows the effective persistence of the screen to be varied from about 0.2 s to more than a minute. This is useful for observing repetitive waveforms with long periods.

RECORDING OUTPUT DEVICES

8. Cathode-ray-tube Photographs For some applications, an output device which provides a record of the measured quantity as a function of time (or some other variable) is desired for later observation. For quantities which are observed on the screen of a cathode-ray tube, a photograph of the observed pattern may be a desirable output record. Several cameras have been designed for this purpose. The cameras can use several films, including the rapid-development Polaroid Land films, 35-mm color transparencies, and black-and-white negative films.

The exposure to be used depends on many factors: the type of film, the photographic characteristics of the cathode-ray tube, and the particular signal to be recorded. A stationary pattern generated by a repetitive signal and a synchronized sweep is relatively easy to photograph. Though it is necessary only to open the shutter long enough to photograph one complete sweep, the difficulty of obtaining a shutter time corresponding exactly to one complete sweep makes it desirable to keep the shutter open long enough to include at least five complete sweeps. Beyond this minimum time, neither the exposure time nor the aperture opening (f stop) is particularly critical. The camera exposure can be kept relatively constant when the exposure time is increased by decreasing the aperture size (increase f-stop number). The wide exposure latitude of most films will give an acceptable recording over a wide range of f-stop numbers. A range of four f stops (exposure range of 16:1) with the same shutter speed will all produce acceptable recordings, for example.

The setting of the CRO intensity control has a great effect on the exposure required. Unfortunately, the eye is not a satisfactory judge of trace intensity. Signal frequency and sweep repetition rate appear to have relatively little effect on exposure requirements. However, increased signal amplitudes cause the spot to move more rapidly and will require more exposure for an invariant recording. The exposure latitude of the film gnerally makes it unnecessary to adjust the exposure for signal amplitude.

Because of the large number of factors influencing the quality of the recording, experience with the particular camera-CRO combination is usually the best guide. Table 4 gives some characteristics of films used for recording CRO traces, and Table 5 is a rough guide to those recording these traces for the first time. This table provides approximate shutter speed and f-stop settings for some films and classes of cathode-ray tubes.

9. Direct-writing Recorders The direct-writing recorder allows variations in amplitude as a function of time to be recorded directly. The record is available without further processing, is prepared in real time, and may be stored for long periods of time. Many of the devices in this class are based on the movement used in the PMMC indicating meter. Conceptually, the direct-writing recorder may be thought of as a PMMC movement with a pen or other marking device on the end of the pointer. The pen moves across and marks on a paper which moves at a constant rate transverse to the pen motion.

Although the PMMC indicating meter has been designed to respond to direct current and to suppress the response to alternating current, the PMMC mechanism used in the direct-writing recorder has been designed to respond to low-frequency alternating current as well as direct current. Thus the direct-writing recorder gives full-scale deflection for signal frequencies to about 50 Hz. The most outstanding difference to be found among these devices is the writing method used.

TABLE 4 Photorecording Film and Paper Characteristics

Type and manufacturer	Spectral characteristic	ASA speed index	Max photographic writing rate, cm/μs	CRT recording applications	Special characteristics
Polaroid Land films:					
Polaroid 47, 107	Panchromatic	3,000	625	Stationary patterns and high-speed transients	10-s development, very high speed
High-speed negative films:					
AGFA Isopan Record	Panchromatic	1,250	600	35-mm continuous motion recording and high-speed transients	Very high speed, somewhat grainy. Rodinal developer recommended. Available in 100-ft bulk only
Kodak Tri-X Pan	Panchromatic	400	375	Same as above	High speed, fine grain
Medium-speed negative films:					
Kodak Verichrome Pan	Panchromatic	160	70	Roll-film exposures of stationary patterns; low-speed transients	Fine grain; wide gray-scale range
Color films:					
Kodak High Speed Ektachrome	Color film	160	Does not apply	May be used to record stationary patterns and continuous motion records in color when used with appropriate phosphors and filters	High-speed color film; positive color transparencies
Ansco Super Ansochrome	Color film	.....	Does not apply	Same as above	High-speed color film; positive color transparencies

TABLE 5 Guide to Exposure Settings for Stationary Patterns

General oscilloscope type	Polaroid types 42, 44, 55P/N Plus X, Verichrome Pan Super XX	Polaroid T-47, 107 Tri-X, Royal Pan
Accelerating voltage below 5,000 V.	1/5 s at $f/4$	1/10 s at $f/5.6$
Accelerating voltage between 6,000 and 12,000 V.	1/10 s at $f/5.6$	1/25 s at $f/8$
Accelerating voltage above 12,000 V.	1/10 s at $f/8$	1/25 s at $f/11$

NOTE: These exposures are suggested for first trials using the P1, P2, and P31 phosphors with the standard green filter in place, using medium-intensity settings. For P11 phosphor and for oscilloscopes without filter, use less exposure or reduced spot intensity.

1. Ink writing on paper with preprinted scales is one of the most common writing methods used. It operates over a wide range of recording speeds and has little friction between the stylus tip and the paper. As the paper used is "ordinary" paper, the paper cost is quite low. The recordings may also be readily reproduced by many common copying processes. The ink may splatter at high writing rates and may cause blotches from too much ink at low speeds; if allowed to stand, the pen may clog. To help alleviate some of the disadvantages of the gravity or capillary ink systems, a variable-pressure ink system has been used that pumps the exact amount of ink for the writing speed. Such a system introduces added complexity as contrasted with the simplicity of a gravity or capillary ink system.

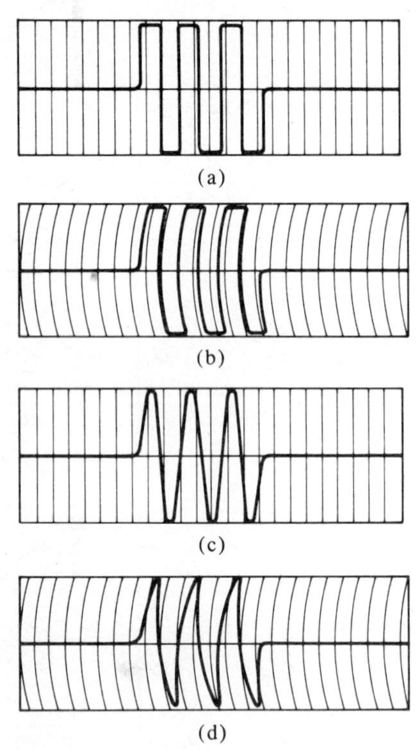

Fig. 10. Curvilinear and rectilinear coordinates. (*a*) Rectilinear reproduced square waves. (*b*) Curvilinear reproduced square waves. (*c*) Rectilinear reproduced sine waves. (*d*) Curvilinear reproduced sine waves.

2. A heated stylus writing on special paper is free of many of the difficulties of ink writing. The heated stylus melts a thin, white, waxlike coating on a black-paper base. Since the paper required is special, the cost for the paper is considerably higher than for paper used with ink marking. Also, the special paper may be marked by other than the heating process and it is somewhat more limited in the methods that can be used for reproduction. The system is quite reliable and offers high-contrast traces.

3. The electric stylus marking on special paper has a wide range of recording speeds, low stylus friction, and long stylus life. Current conducted from the stylus through the coating causes a change in the coating to form the mark. The paper has a special coating, and the cost is much higher than for regular paper. Some electrical marking processes depend on an electrical discharge, and electrical interference with other equipment may be experienced.

4. Optical recording by means of a light beam writing on photosensitive paper allows higher frequencies to be recorded and permits a relatively large chart with good resolution. The paper cost is very high, and as the writing process is a photographic one, the record is not immediately available but must be developed.

A second difference between these devices is the coordinates of the trace produced (Fig. 10). Curvilinear coordinates are those in which a line of constant time is the arc described by the tip of the pointer. It is frequently found with the various ink-marking methods. Rectilinear coordinates, in which a line of constant time is a straight line perpendicular to the time axis, are usually associated with

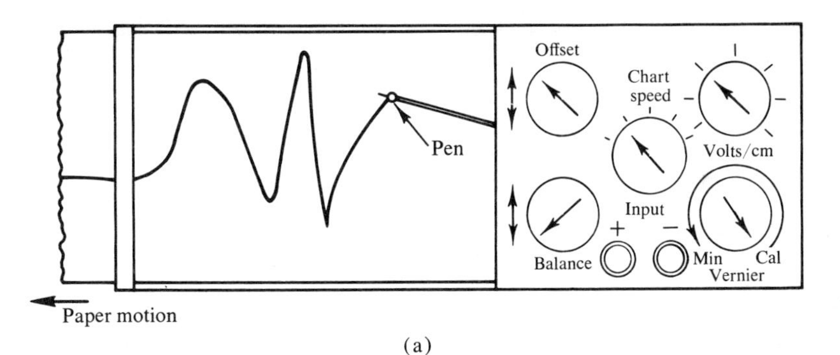

(a)

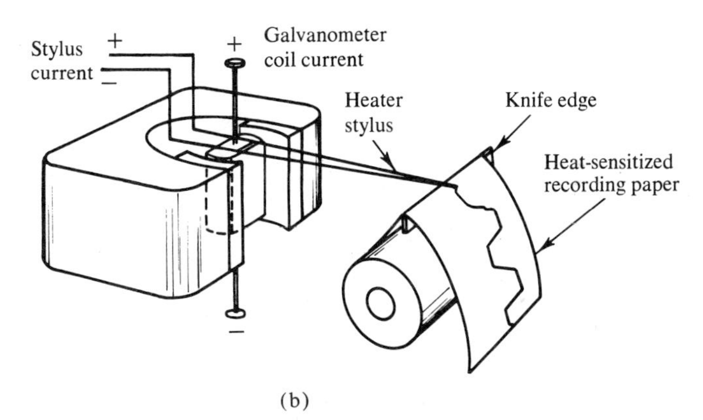

(b)

Fig. 11. Direct-writing recorder. (*a*) Front. (*b*) Mechanism (thermal writing).

thermal or electric writing. However, either curvilinear or rectilinear coordinates may be found with any of the marking methods.

Beyond the differences in the writing and basic deflection mechanisms, chart-drive mechanisms offer a wide variety of chart speeds including 1 to 100 mm/s. Amplifiers are normally used to increase the input signal to the level needed to drive the deflection system. Thus the sensitivity can range from 1 mV/cm to 100 V/cm. The dc offset allows a deviation from a fixed level to be recorded by subtracting a fixed value from the signal before it is recorded. Thus the amplitude scale on the chart may have a total span of 10 mV and range from 1.000 to 1.010 V. Figure 11 shows the controls and principal units of this device.

10. Strip-chart Recorders An output device very similar to the direct-writing recorder is the strip-chart recorder shown in Fig. 12. In terms of performance, the principal differences between the two are response time and chart speed. Typically, the strip-chart recorder responds to signals with frequencies less than 1.0 Hz and has chart speeds in the range from 1.0 cm/h to 100 cm/min.

The pen (or marking stylus) of a strip-chart recorder is moved across the paper by a null-balance servosystem. This produces a motion of the pen perpendicular

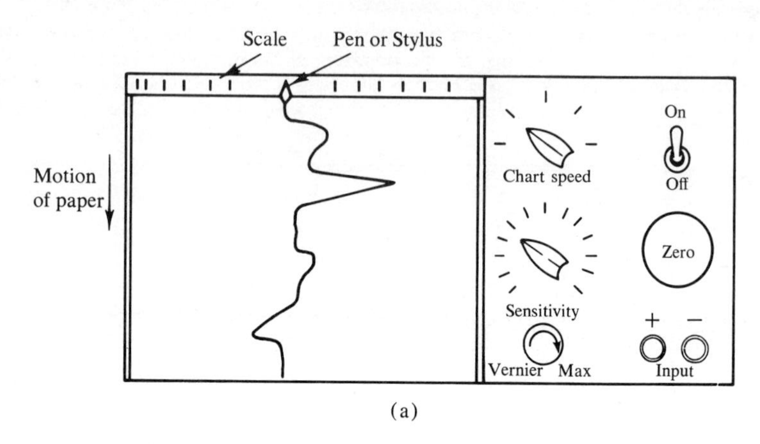

(a)

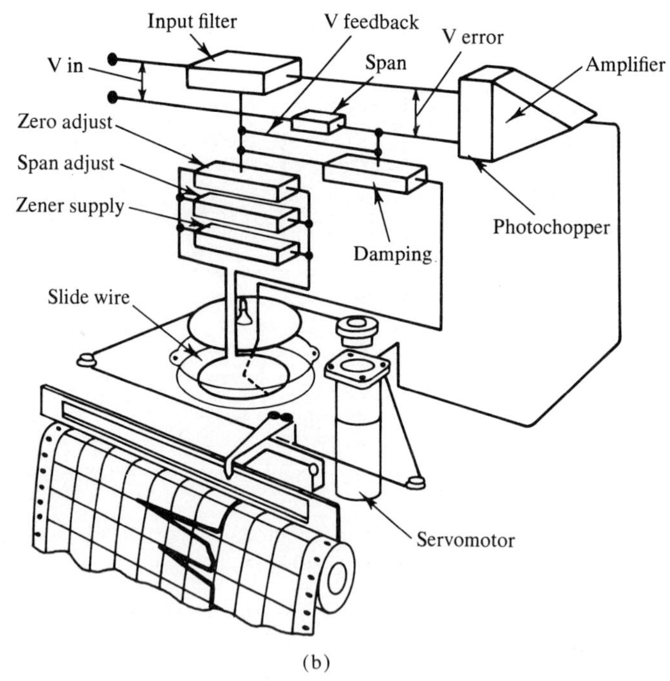

(b)

Fig. 12. Strip-chart recorder. (*a*) Front. (*b*) Servosystem pen drive.

to the direction of motion of the paper, giving rectilinear coordinates. This also allows the pen to be moved across a wider chart than may be easily accomplished with a PMMC-device recorder, and chart widths up to 11 in. are available. Note that the signal input is the input to an amplifier. Thus these output devices require little power from the source. Strip-chart recorders are available which use ink, thermal, or electric marking. In addition to the capillary and pressure ink systems found in direct-writing recorders, a ball-point pen and nylon-fiber-tip marking pen are available with some strip-chart recorders. These pens are simple and reduce the problems of clogging and splatter associated with capillary and gravity ink systems. The strip-chart recorder is used to record variations in signal levels that change relatively slowly and for which a record over an extended period of time is desired. Strip-chart recorders are available with a wide variety of characteristics including accuracy from 0.2 to 2 percent of the full-scale reading.

11. PMMC Chart Recorders Both the direct-writing recorder and the servo-drive strip-chart recorder should be considered high-performance devices, and as a consequence, they may be costly. A chart recorder with limited frequency response

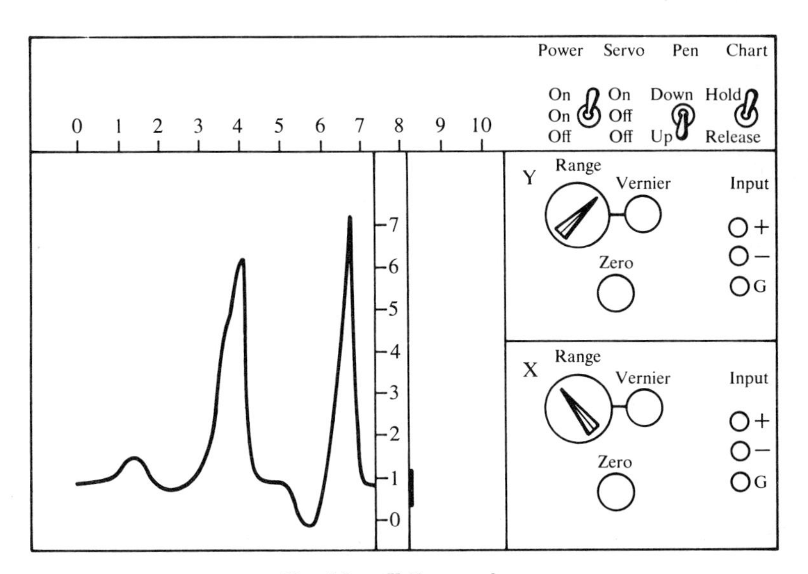

Fig. 13. *X-Y* **recorder.**

(dc to less than 1 Hz), low chart speeds (1 to 100 cm/h), and the simple PMMC mechanism offers reduced performance (including an accuracy of about 1 to 2 percent), reduced cost, and high reliability. Marking methods include ink, electric marking, and pressure-sensitive. The pressure-sensitive method uses special paper which is marked by the pressure of a stylus against the paper. As the pressures required are incompatible with the forces available from a PMMC mechanism, the stylus is pressed against the paper at intervals of one to several seconds. A mark is made on the paper corresponding to the position of the stylus each time the stylus is pressed against the paper. The stylus (pointer of the PMMC mechanism) is free to move in response to the signal to be recorded. The PMMC mechanism used frequently requires a 1-mA current for full-scale deflection; thus the recorder may be connected wherever a 0- to 1-mA PMMC indicating instrument can be used.

12. ***X-Y*** **Recorders** The *X-Y* recorder shown in Fig. 13 automatically plots the value of a dependent variable vs. an independent variable directly on conventional graph paper using electrical signals as information for both variables. In all *X-Y* recorders, both the *X* and *Y* axes are under control of a servosystem that positions the marking pen to the successive points on a graph. This allows high accuracy (0.1 to 0.25 percent) and a broad range of sensitivity (0.1 mV/in. to 100 V/in.)

for both axes. The maximum writing rate is usually less thaan 20 in./s, and the upper frequency limit of about 1.0 Hz limits signals to be recorded to slowly varying ones.

The pen is mounted on a support parallel to one axis of the plot. The position of the pen on the support—along the parallel axis—is determined by the servosystem for that axis. In some devices, the paper is held in place and the support is moved along the other axis under control of the servosystem for that axis. In other devices, the pen support is held fixed and the paper is moved along the other axis under control of the servosystem for that axis. Either approach will produce the same plot of one variable vs. a second variable.

Both ink and electric marking systems are used with *X-Y* recorders. Although standard 8½ by 11 and 11 by 17 graph papers are the sizes most frequently used, other sizes are available.

MACHINE-INTERPRETABLE OUTPUTS

The output devices described in the preceding sections provide an output that requires interpretation by a human being. In some instances, however, it is necessary that the output data be recorded in a form to be "read" by a machine. These "machine-interpretable outputs" occur in a variety of forms, including:

1. Magnetic tape
2. Punched paper tape
3. Punched cards
4. Electrical signals

A signal recorded in analog form on magnetic tape may be used to drive an appropriate output device including a cathode-ray tube, a recorder, or an indicating instrument. A signal recorded in digital form—that is, encoded in a discrete, distinctive pattern—on magnetic tape, punched paper tape, or punched cards can be used to activate an output device designed to respond to digital signals such as a digital-display unit, a printer, or a digital computer.

It is important to recognize that the form of output suitable for subsequent machine interpretation is not suitable for human interpretation, and the converse is also true. Thus a special class of output devices is needed to meet these requirements.

13. Analog Magnetic Tape Magnetic tape used to record analog signals is one form of a machine-interpretable output. Although magnetic-tape recording is used for a variety of special purposes, including voice and music recording and video recording of television programs, the recorders used for these applications are considered special-purpose recorders designed for a special purpose. The *instrumentation recorder* is a general-purpose electronic instrument used to record data in the form of an analog electrical signal for later evaluation. Standards for instrumentation recording have been established by the Inter-Range Instrumentation Group (IRIG). Compatibility and exchange of recorded data between various magnetic-recording systems require this standardization.*

Three recording methods have been specified to meet various requirements: (1) direct recording, (2) frequency-modulation recording, and (3) pulse recording. Direct and FM recording meet the needs of the majority of applications; pulse recording is used for more specialized purposes. Magnetic tape ¼, ½, or 1 in. in width is moved past the recording (and playback) heads at speeds of 1⅞, 3¾, 7½, 15, 30, 60, and 120 in./s. The higher speeds are used for recording larger bandwidths; the slower speeds for increasing the recording time.

Figure 14 is a simplified diagram of the magnetic-recording process showing one recording head. A number of separate recording heads may be positioned across the width of the magnetic tape, increasing the data that may be recorded

* "IRIG Telemetry Standards," Document 106–66, March, 1966, Defense Documentation Center for Scientific and Technical Information, Conover Station, Alexandria, Va.

on a single tape. Each head records on a separate track or position on the tape. The individual track width is 0.050 in. and the parallel, multiple tracks are spaced 0.070 in. center to center. The number of tracks that can be recorded on a tape depends on the tape width. The ½-in.-width tape permits 7 tracks, and the 1-in.-width tape allows 14 tracks.

The considerable development and design effort devoted to the magnetic-tape recorder has made this device a precision electronic instrument. Although most of the discussion in this section is concerned with the form of the recorded data

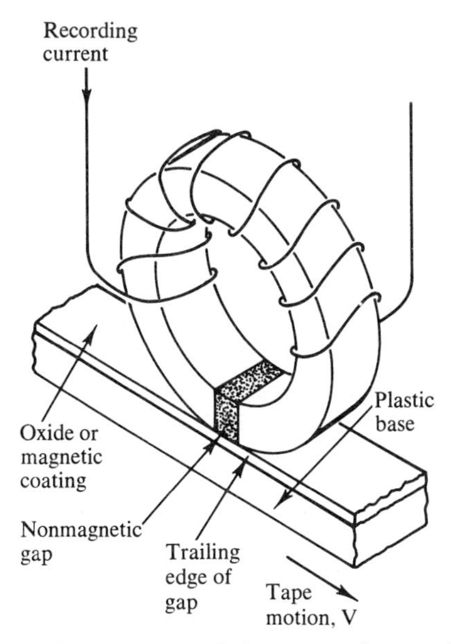

Fig. 14. Simplified diagram of the magnetic-recording process.

and the capability of a magnetic-tape recorder as an output device, it is helpful to consider the principal parts of the device:

1. The data are recorded on a *magnetic tape*. This is a ribbon of plastic (usually polyester) 0.0001 in. thick on which an emulsion of highly refined magnetic oxides is placed. Differences in the emulsion and the binder and the manufacturing process will produce noticeable differences in the data-recording characteristics of the tape.

2. Recording of the data on the tape occurs at the point where the *tape-recorder head* contacts the tape. Thus the head is an electromagnetic transducer which converts an electrical signal to a magnetic signal. Figure 14 suggests the general form of the head. However, the high performance expected from heads used in instrumentation recorders is based on improved materials and manufacturing methods.

3. The tape must be moved past the recording heads by the *tape-transport mechanism*. This part of the device must move the tape by the heads at a constant, predetermined speed and provide for handling the tape without straining, distorting, or wearing the tape.

4. The *electronics* conditions and applies the input data to the record heads. It should present a relatively high impedance to the source of the data; it provides the frequency response needed to assume a constant-flux recording characteristic over the required bandwidth.

The magnetic-tape recorder used as an output device and the magnetic-tape reproducer used to reproduce the recorded data will both include the four major parts outlined above. However, record and reproduce electronics will differ considerably from one another. Basic construction of both record (write) and reproduce (read) heads is similar but may differ in detail. The different methods of recording require different electronics but may use the same tape, heads, and tape transport.

Direct recording provides the greatest bandwidth available from a magnetic-tape recorder, as may be seen in Table 6. It requires only relatively simple, moderately priced electronics.

TABLE 6 Parameters for Direct Record and FM Record

Tape speed, in./s	Direct-record passband, Hz	FM-record modulation frequency, Hz
1⅞	100–7,500	Dc–625
3¾	100–15,000	Dc–1,250
7½	100–30,000	Dc–2,500
15	100–60,000	Dc–5,000
30	200–125,000	Dc–10,000
60	300–250,000	Dc–20,000
120	300–500,000	Dc–40,000

With this recording method, the intensity of magnetization on tape is made proportional to the instantaneous *amplitude* of the input signal.

In the *reproduce* process, however, a signal is induced from tape to heads *only* in response to *changes* in flux on the recorded tape; the direct-record process cannot, therefore, extend down to dc and is limited to frequencies above 50 to 100 Hz.

This direct-recording method is also characterized by some amplitude instability, caused primarily by random surface inhomogeneities in the tape. These variations are normally a few percent at the lower recording frequencies and can exceed as much as 10 percent near upper bandwidth limits. Occasional momentary signal decreases of over 50 percent may occur; these are commonly referred to as "dropouts."

Uses for direct recording, then, have a common requirement: economy, with a maximum bandwidth, in applications where amplitude-variation errors are not critical. Typical applications include audio recording, where the human ear averages any amplitude-variation errors, or recordings where the signal's frequency, not amplitude, is of primary importance.

Frequency-modulation recording (FM) overcomes some of the basic limitations of the direct-recording process, but at the expense of high-frequency bandwidth; response does, however, extend down to dc, as may be seen in Table 6. This recording technique significantly improves the signal-amplitude stability, since it is now proportional to carrier deviation, rather than the intensity of magnetization on tape.

In the FM-recording method, a carrier oscillator is frequency-modulated by the input signal. The oscillator's center frequency corresponds to a zero-level input, with deviation from that center frequency being proportional to the amplitude of the input signal.

FM recording is used primarily when the dc component of the input signal is to be preserved, or when the amplitude variations of the direct-recording method cannot be tolerated. Accuracy of the reproduced signal is another factor in favor of FM recording, being in the order of 1 percent, vs. 5 percent for the direct-recording process.

If data from several separate sources are to be recorded, they could be recorded on a one data source for one track basis. It would also be possible to multiplex the several data signals into a single data signal that would be received on one track. Thus, multiplexing allows several signals to share the same data track. FM recording offers a way to record several data signals on the same track without elaborate external multiplexing; thus the characteristics of FM recording are used to achieve multiplexing. The carrier frequency for FM recording is selected near the middle of the recorder frequency response for the given tape speed. This allows all the modulation products to be recorded. If, however, several carriers were used, they could be recorded (and reproduced) simultaneously, provided the portion of the spectrum (bandwidth) occupied by each carrier and its modulation

TABLE 7 Proportional Subcarrier Channels*

Channel	Center frequencies, Hz	Deviation limit, Hz	Upper deviation limit, Hz	Nominal frequency response, Hz
1	400	370	430	6
2	560	518	602	8
3	730	675	785	11
4	960	888	1,032	14
5	1,300	1,202	1,398	20
6	1,700	1,572	1,828	25
7	2,300	2,127	2,473	35
8	3,000	2,775	3,225	45
9	3,900	3,607	4,193	59
10	5,400	4,995	5,805	81
11	7,350	6,799	7,901	110
12	10,500	9,712	11,288	160
13	14,500	13,412	15,588	220
14	22,000	20,350	23,650	330
15	30,000	27,750	32,250	450
16	40,000	37,000	43,000	600
17	52,500	48,562	56,438	790
18	70,000	64,750	75,250	1,050
19	93,000	86,025	99,975	1,395
20	124,000	114,700	133,300	1,860
21	165,000	152,625	177,375	2,475

* IRIG 7.5 per cent proportional subcarrier channels.

products does not overlap. This can be accomplished if the modulating frequency is kept low. Table 7 shows the carrier frequencies and the modulation bandwidths for a group of 21 "channels." Each channel records the data from a separate data source. The tape speed used must be adequate to record frequencies from about 300 to 200 KHz. Examination of the direct-record parameters from Table 6 shows that a tape speed of 60 in./s would be satisfactory.

14. Digital Output Devices The wide use of the digital computer for storage and processing of experimental data has created the need for output devices which provide a record that can be used as a direct input to a computer.

One of the distinguishing characteristics of a digital device is the way in which the values of quantities are represented. In an analog device signal amplitudes are used to represent values directly; in a digital device a *code* is used to represent the value. The code used usually has several digits; increasing the number of digits increases the number of increments that can be expressed by the code. The decimal-number system is an example of a digital representation of a value. That is, the number *DDD* can represent the value of a quantity such as a voltage. The symbol *D* stands for a decimal digit from 0 to 9. Thus *DDD* can represent any of 1,000 values from 000 to 999. Rather than allow each digit to take on any of 10 different values (as in the decimal system), digital output devices use a *binary* code in which the individual digit can take on only two values. Thus *BBB* can represent only eight values from 0 to 7 if *B* is a binary-code element. By increasing the number of digits it is possible to represent both very large and very small values exactly. This increased precision is achieved at the expense of a more complex form for representing the value. In an analog format the value is given by the amplitude of a single signal; in a digital format the value is given by evaluating the amplitudes of *several* signals. Digital output devices produce an output record that has the values encoded in a digital format. This is usually a binary digital format. It is necessary that the input to these digital output devices be a digital-coded signal.

TABLE 8 BCD Codes

Decimal value	8-4-2-1 code	4-2-2-1 code	2-4-2-1 code
0	0000	0000	0000
1	0001	0001	0001
2	0010	0010	0010
3	0011	0011	0011
4	0100	1000	0100
5	0101	1001	0101
6	0110	1010	0110
7	0111	1011	0111
8	1000	1110	1110
9	1001	1111	1111

15. Binary-coded Decimal (BCD) Codes The decimal system, commonly used for representing values of quantities, is a digital system. However, the decimal system requires that each digit be able to take on any one of ten different values; most digital circuits operate in a binary system capable of taking on only two different values. One means of translating between the two systems is to encode each decimal digit by a group of binary digits. A minimum of four binary digits are required to create codes for the ten values of a single decimal digit. Several codes are in common use. These are designated by a set of four numbers which give the weight assigned to the presence of a binary 1 in that position. Three of these are 8-4-2-1, 4-2-2-1, 2-4-2-1. Table 8 shows the coding for each of these three BCD codes for the decimal-digit values (0 to 9). It should be noted that other codes are possible.

16. Analog-to-Digital Converter Some signals are produced for input to an output device in a digital format; others are analog signals and must be converted to a digital format by an analog-to-digital converter. The output of an analog-to-digital converter will represent an analog signal by samples of the signal amplitude. The sampling rate—the measurements of the analog-signal values are made at this rate—must be greater than twice the highest-frequency component present in the signal. Thus a signal with components up to 100 Hz should be sampled a minimum of 200 times per second. A second characteristic of the analog-to-digital conversion is the quantification of the signal level which occurs. The digital code representing a particular sampled value indicates which one of the finite number of amplitudes is to be assigned to that sample; it does not represent a continuous range of values. The increment from one value to the next is the resolution of the digital code which is usually some form of binary code. Thus, a larger number of binary digits in the code indicates a finer resolution. The sampling rate and the resolution are chosen to meet the requirements of the signal to be recorded. The particular coding chosen will be influenced by the digital output device to be used.

For example, consider an analog-to-digital converter which converts signals between 0.0 and 4.095 V to a 12-bit binary code. The input to the analog-to-digital converter is a single terminal pair at which the value of the signal is presented. The output is a set of 12 terminals; each terminal will be either HI (10 V) or LO (0 V). If HI is represented by 1 and LO is represented by 0, then the value at the output (represented by the voltage pattern) may be represented on paper as a set of 12 digits, each of which may be 1 or 0. Each digit is assigned a "weight" corresponding to a power of 2. Starting with the rightmost digit, the weight increases to the left. The value of a digit (either 0 or 1) is multiplied by the weight. Thus, the smallest value that can be represented is 000 000 000 000, which represents zero volts; the largest value is 111 111 111 111, which represents 4,095 or $(2{,}048 \times 1 + 1{,}024 \times 1 + 512 \times 1 + 256 \times 1 + 128 \times 1 + 64 \times 1 + 32 \times 1 + 16 \times 1 + 8 \times 1 + 4 \times 1 + 2 \times 1 + 1 \times 1)$ or $(2^{11} \times 1 + 2^{10} \times 1 + 2^{9} \times 1 + 2^{8} \times 1 + 2^{7} \times 1 + 2^{6} \times 1 + 2^{5} \times 1 + 2^{4} \times 1 + 2^{3} \times 1 + 2^{2} \times 1 + 2^{1} \times 1 + 2^{0} \times 1)$ or 4.095 V. The code 000 000 000 001 represents 1 or 0.001 V. The number 000 000 100 001 represents 33 or 0.033 V; the number 001 111 101 000 represents 1,000 or 1.000 V. That is, the values of the input signal can be represented in *increments* of 1 mV from 0 to 4.095 V.

17. Digital Computer One of the uses of an electronic digital computer is as an output device which receives values from other electronic instruments and processes these values for control, display, or storage. Although the computer has a much greater role in an instrumentation system than as an output device (when a computer is included as part of an instrumentation system, the computer is usually in control), its function as an output device, however, will be considered here. When information is to be furnished to a computer from an analog-to-digital converter or other instrument which provides the information in a digital format, it is necessary that the signals furnished be compatible with the signals in the computer. The hardware that is necessary to achieve the match is the *interface.* Some of the considerations are (1) logic levels, (2) coding, (3) timing. These are discussed in the paragraphs that follow.

Many *logic levels* are used in both computers and instruments. With a binary system, one of the two levels is usually zero volts (0 ± 0.50). The other may be positive or negative; magnitudes of 3, 5, 6, 10, or 12 are common. This gives the two binary states required for each line or "digit." *Level converters* are used in the interface to allow instruments with different logic levels to communicate. One level converter is needed for each digit in the code.

The combination of logic levels on the data lines is the *code* for a given value. There are many ways in which an N-digit binary code can be interpreted. Although it is most convenient if the data to the computer are encoded in the same form used by the computer, it is possible to use the computer to translate from one code pattern to another.

The values which are encoded and used for input to the computer are samples of the data. Thus the time at which the sample is obtained must be considered, as the signal measured may be varying with time and the computer is not ready to receive the information at all times. One aspect of computer control of the measuring system may be seen here. The computer signals the measuring device when the data are to be sampled. When the sample has been obtained and converted, the coded value can be transmitted to the computer. It is critical that the time at which these events (sampling and transmission) are initiated be related to other events (switching of signals, etc.) so the value sampled is representative of the data desired and the computer is ready to accept the data.

Other considerations of the interface include noise and interference rejection, power and impedance requirements of the instruments, and suitable interconnecting cables.

18. Digital Printer For some requirements, a device which will print the measured value is needed. An electrically actuated typewriter (e.g., the common Teletype machines) or a multiple-column printer (e.g., line printers) may be used. This output requires human interpretation, even though a digital-coded input is required.

19. Punched Paper Tape The punched-paper-tape record most frequently used is a 1-in.-wide paper tape with eight punched positions across the width. The pattern of holes (or no holes) represented by the eight positions across the width of the tape encodes a particular value. Figure 15 shows a punched paper tape. Each value is given as an 8-bit binary code. The USASCII (American Code for Information Interchange) code is frequently used. Table 9 indicates the USASCII Standard character set. The numbers given in the 8-bit octal and 6-bit octal columns are in octal code, where the numbers from 0 to 7 are used to represent

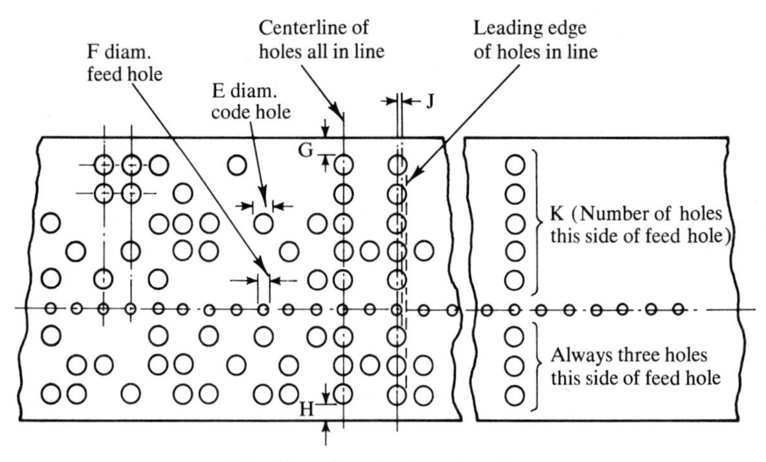

Fig. 15. Punched paper tape.

the patterns of three adjacent holes (or no holes). The coding is shown in Table 10.

Thus, a 6-bit octal code of 32 (Z in the character set) represents a hole pattern of 011010; the 8-bit octal code of 332 (also Z) represents a hole pattern of 11011010.

If increased resolution is needed, several characters can be used to represent the complete code for a value. One example is the use of several successive characters to represent decimal digits. Thus, a six-decimal-digit value uses six characters on a tape. The density of recording along the axis of the tape is 10 characters per inch. A given paper-tape punch operates from very slow rates to a maximum value which is determined by the characteristics of the punch. The maximum varies from 10 to about 500 characters per second.

20. Punched Cards Data to be recorded can be encoded on the familiar punched card shown in Fig. 16. Each card can store 80 alphanumeric values; the speed of punching can be as high as several hundred cards per minute. Each column of the 80-column card can be used to represent a character. There are 12 positions that can be punched; 10 of these are shown by the numbers 0 to 9 on the card; the 11 position is just above the zero and the 12 position toward the top edge. Table 11 shows the pattern of punches that encode the various characters. Where more than one number is shown in the "card-code zone number"

TABLE 9 USASCII* Character Set

Character	8-bit octal	6-bit octal	Character	8-bit octal	6-bit octal
A	301	01	!	241	41
B	302	02	"	242	42
C	303	03	#	243	43
D	304	04	$	244	44
E	305	05	%	245	45
F	306	06	&	246	46
G	307	07	'	247	47
H	310	10	(	250	50
I	311	11	)	251	51
J	312	12	*	252	52
K	313	13	+	253	53
L	314	14	,	254	54
M	315	15	-	255	55
N	316	16	.	256	56
O	317	17	/	257	57
P	320	20	:	272	72
Q	321	21	;	273	73
R	322	22	<	274	74
S	323	23	=	275	75
T	324	24	>	276	76
U	325	25	?	277	77
V	326	26	@	300	
W	327	27	[	333	33
X	330	30	\	334	34
Y	331	31	]	335	35
Z	332	32	↑	336	36
0	260	60	←	337	37
1	261	61	Leader/Trailer	200	
2	262	62	LINE FEED	212	
3	263	63	Carriage RETURN	215	
4	264	64	SPACE	240	40
5	265	65	RUBOUT	377	
6	266	66	Blank	000	
7	267	67	BELL	207	
8	270	70	TAB	211	
9	271	71	FORM	214	

* An abbreviation for USA Standard Code for Information Interchange.

column, each of these positions is punched. The card in Fig. 16 has several characters punched, and the character is printed at the top of the column.

21. Magnetic Tape (Digital) The digital-magnetic-tape record is usually ½ in. wide and has either 7 or 9 recording tracks. Figure 17 is a diagram of a 9-track tape. The pattern recorded on the several tracks across the tape is the code for

TABLE 10

Octal	*Binary*
0	000
1	001
2	010
3	011
4	100
5	101
6	110
7	111

TABLE 11 Code for Punched Card

Card-code zone no.	IBM 29 keyboard character	IBM 26 keyboard character	Card-code zone no.	IBM 29 keyboard character	IBM 26 keyboard character
NONE	SPACE	SPACE	11 –	– Minus or hyphen	– Minus or hyphen
– 1	1	1	11 1	J	J
– 2	2	2	11 2	K	K
– 3	3	3	11 3	L	L
– 4	4	4	11 4	M	M
– 5	5	5	11 5	N	N
– 6	6	6	11 6	O	O
– 7	7	7	11 7	P	P
– 8	8	8	11 8	Q	Q
– 9	9	9	11 9	R	R
– 8·2	: Colon*	None assigned	11 8·2	! Exclamation*	None assigned
– 8·3	# Number sign	= Equal sign	11 8·3	$ Dollar sign	$ Dollar sign
– 8·4	@ At sign	' Apostrophe	11 8·4	* Asterisk	* Asterisk
– 8·5	' Apostrophe*	None assigned	11 8·5	) Parenthesis*	None assigned
– 8·6	= Equal sign*	None assigned	11 8·6	; Semicolon*	None assigned
– 8·7	" Quotation mark*	None assigned	11 8·7	¬ Logical NOT*	None assigned
0 –	0	0	12 –	& Ampersand	+ Plus
0 1	/ Slash	/ Slash	12 1	A	A
0 2	S	S	12 2	B	B
0 3	T	T	12 3	C	C
0 4	U	U	12 4	D	D
0 5	V	V	12 5	E	E
0 6	W	W	12 6	F	F
0 7	X	X	12 7	G	G
0 8	Y	Y	12 8	H	H
0 9	Z	Z	12 9	I	I
0 8·2	None assigned	None assigned	12 8·2	¢ Cent sign*	None assigned
0 8·3	, Comma	, Comma	12 8·3	. Period	. Period
0 8·4	% Percent	(Parenthesis	12 8·4	< Less than	) Parenthesis
0 8·5	— Underscore*	None assigned	12 8·5	(Parenthesis*	None assigned
0 8·6	> Greater than*	None assigned	12 8·6	+ Plus sign*	None assigned
0 8·7	? Question mark*	None assigned	12 8·7	| Vertical bar*	None assigned

a character. The recording density along the axis of the tape is from 200 to 1,600 characters per inch. With tape speeds as high as 200 in./s, recording rates up to 320,000 characters per second may be realized. Whenever the recording rate is variable and not particularly high, the incremental tape recorder should be considered. This device will record one character at a time—at any recording rate from zero to the maximum (about 600 characters per second). The incremental

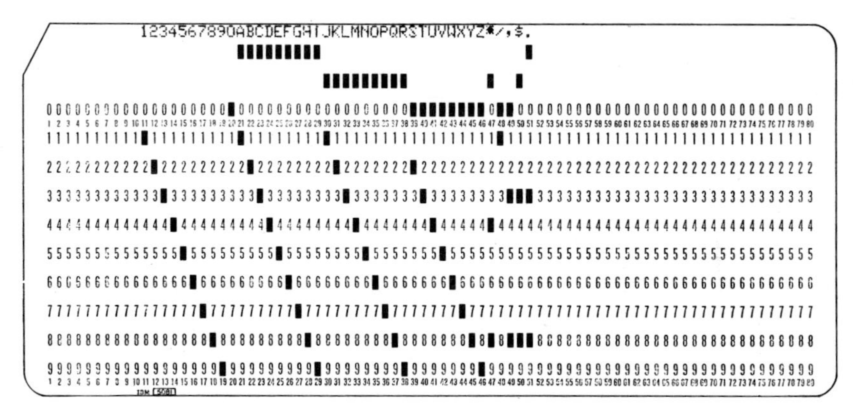

Fig. 16. Punched card.

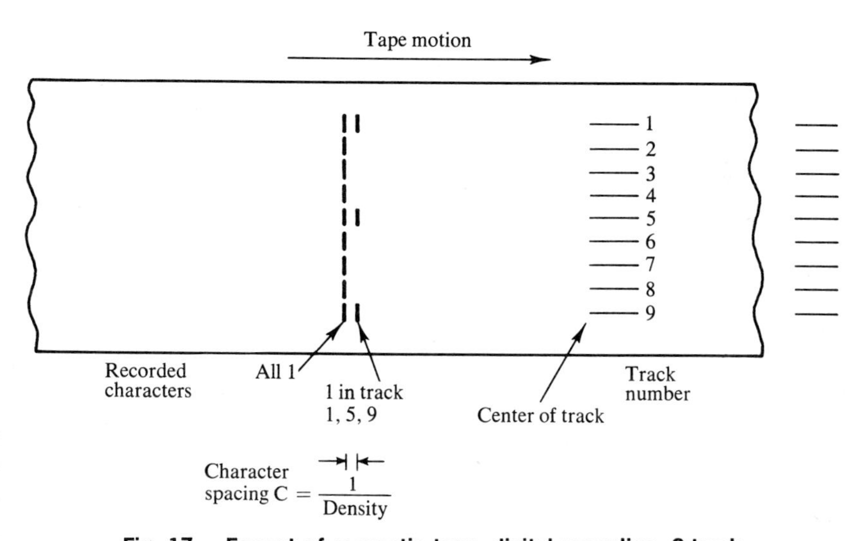

Fig. 17. Format of magnetic tape, digital recording, 9-track.

recorder finds application when the data rate is low or when the data are in bursts. Under these conditions, a continuous-motion tape would have a record with variable density and irregular sample length. For high data rates the continuous-motion tape recorder is necessary. To allow the data record to have constant density and regular sample length, it may be necessary to buffer the data by collecting them in a buffer memory until a fixed amount has been acquired. The high performance available from a quality continuous-motion recorder is usually accompanied by a larger cost than for an incremental recorder.

Section Three

Fundamentals of Signal-generation Instruments

All electric signal-generating devices have certain fundamental elements in common: the conversion of a direct, or constant, voltage to a particular periodically varying voltage, the manipulation of that voltage to a desired wave shape, and the precise control of the magnitude and frequency of that voltage. Many special instruments can be made that perform these functions in order to achieve a specific result, but they all contain the same basic building blocks. These basic elements are discussed separately in this section to make the understanding of the general situation easier. This allows the detailed discussions of individual instruments, later in this book, to concentrate on the specific nature of the particular device without the necessity of reviewing these general concepts for each case.

Electronic signal-generating device designs are constantly being improved. The improvements consist of ways to perform the basic instrument tasks faster, more accurately, more reliably, or in a way that creates a purer wave shape and/or more stable frequency. At the same time newer instrument trends are to automate the operation of devices such as these by special programming features in the instrument or in combination with a computer. In all these situations the fundamental signal-generating elements maintain their basic identity and role. It is therefore important to understand these elements by themselves, before proceeding to the more complex special-purpose instruments that make use of them.

Chapter **9**

Introduction to Electronic Signal Generation

D. H. SCHUSTER, Ph.D.

Departments of Psychology and Computer Science,
Iowa State University, Ames, Iowa

BASIC CONCEPTS IN OSCILLATORS

1. Introduction A voltage or current with deliberately induced and time-varying characteristics is called a signal. Signals can be generated by a variety of electronic devices and circuits. Such a signal-producing device may be called an oscillator, signal generator, function generator, pulse generator, or signal synthesizer as appropriate. All these devices are basically energy converters in that dc (direct-current) power usually is fed into the device and a time-varying signal as a function of time [$f(t)$] is the result or output. Refer to Fig. 1. While the input power usually is dc, it need not be. In addition, dc power typically comes from the 60-Hz ac supply main commonly available. The output signal often is a periodic signal that repeats itself over a given time period; one exception is the random-noise generator.

Techniques for generating signals vary from simple to complex, but they almost always have feedback in some form to control the frequency or period, as well as the amplitude or level of the output signal. Therefore, an understanding of feedback is fundamental to a basic comprehension of oscillators. An example of feedback is an oscillating public-address system that has a howl or squeal in it when the gain is turned up too high. Feedback is shown in Fig. 1 as a line from the output to a box labeled "feedback" going back to modify the input to the amplifier.

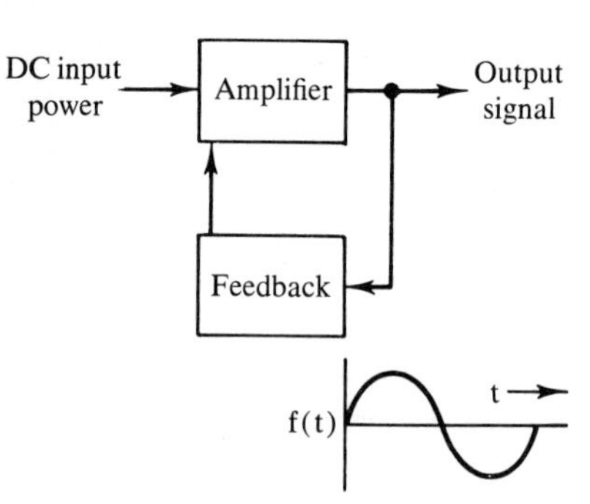

Fig. 1. Basic signal generation.

2. Feedback In Fig. 1, part of the output signal is returned (or fed back) to the input of the same device. There the feedback modifies the control voltage that determines the magnitude and shape of the output. If a voltage fed back to the input is of the same polarity or phase as that already there, it is called "positive" feedback and reinforces the action. If the input signal to the device is making it conduct current, positive feedback will make it conduct more. The more it conducts, the greater the signal is fed back to make it even more so. This continues until the device cannot conduct more no matter what happens at the input. This event is known as saturation.

When a device so saturated encounters an input tendency to reduce the conduction, it will similarly be fed back to reinforce the input action and to shut off the device. The process can be repeated indefinitely. This completes one cycle of an oscillator and shows how positive feedback causes the basic oscillation. An example is the howling public-address system mentioned previously.

Feedback may also be negative. In Fig. 1, if the effect of the part of the signal returned to the input of the amplifier is such as to reduce the magnitude or shape of the output signal, the feedback is said to be "negative." An example of negative feedback is the conventional thermostat in the heating system of a house. When the temperature in the house becomes low enough, a contact in the thermostat closes. This energizes the flow of gas to the furnace and the ignition circuit. Then the furnace turns on and produces heat to warm the house, which also increases the temperature of the thermostat. The thermostat, when sufficiently warm, opens and deenergizes the control circuit to the furnace. Thus the room temperature is kept relatively constant, with only minor variations in the average as the thermostat and furnace operate. Feedback may be more complex than Fig. 1 indicates. Negative feedback in general is used to control the level or amplitude of an output signal from a basic signal generator as in Fig. 1.

3. Gain Gain is another term that needs definition. Gain refers to the basic property of amplification in an active circuit. "Gain" means that the signal is larger at the output than at the input. For example, a 1-Watt signal presented at the input to the amplifier in Fig. 2 has increased to 2 W at the output. Gain is defined as the ratio of magnitude of the output signal to the input signal, and ignores the phase or shape of the waveform. In our example, gain is the ratio of 2 W output over 1 W input, producing an amplification ratio or gain of 2.0.

Typically gain is measured in "decibels," a ratio based on common logarithms. Consider the power-gain ratio of 2 above. The gain in decibels (dB) is $10 \log_{10}$ (output power/input power) = 10 log 2/1 = 10×0.301 = 3.01 dB. If the input and output resistances of the amplifier are the same, the dB power gain can be expressed as dB gain = 20 log (output voltage/input voltage).

4. Phase Shift In addition to gain and feedback, the phase of the feedback signal is an important characteristic in understanding oscillators. In Fig. 2, the output signal is merely an amplified version of the input signal, but it has the same waveshape, a sine wave that starts at zero time. Amplifiers typically produce 180° of phase change: the output signal is inverted with respect to the input. If we take equal-sized signals and look merely at phase changes, Fig. 3 is illuminating. The reference sine wave starting at zero time is shown in Fig. 3*a*. An inverted sine wave starts by going negative and is shown in Fig. 3*b*, representing 180° phase shift with respect to *a*. Figure 3*c* shows a cosine wave, a sine wave phase-shifted by 90° or halfway between the amount of phase shift between the first signals shown in Fig. 3. Such a phase change, for instance, might be seen across a tuned transformer or a resistor-capacitor combination under certain circumstances. Shifting a sine wave by 360° merely advances it one cycle farther along in the series. This is equivalent to zero degrees phase shift, as one sine wave is like any other. The usual amount of phase shift in an oscillator is zero or 180°.

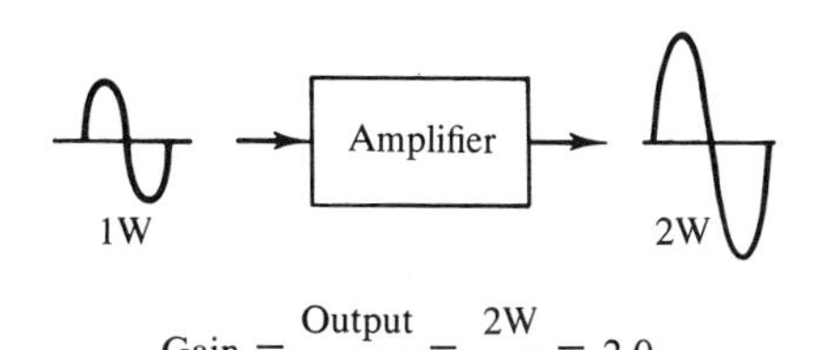

Fig. 2. Definition of gain.

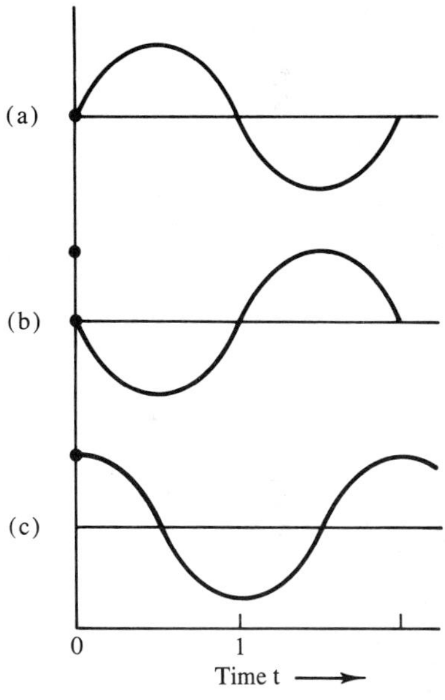

Fig. 3. Definition of phase shift. (*a*) Sine wave. (*b*) Inverted sine. (*c*) Cosine wave.

5. General An oscillator is basically a sinusoidal signal source, regardless of the frequency range. An example of a simple oscillator circuit and its time-varying output is shown in Fig. 4.

The amplifier usually is a single transistor or vacuum tube to change the level of the input signal, to make up for the losses of the circuit, and to supply output signal power. Sometimes other devices are used to provide gain or amplification. Oscillators modify the phase of the feedback signal to control the period or frequency of the output signal. Negative feedback or limiting is used to control the output amplitude.

Oscillators are categorized into two types, LC (L = inductance and C = capacitance) or RC (R = resistance and C = capacitance). These are the two basic types of feedback networks used to control the frequency or period* of the oscillator.

A variety of techniques for generating signals will be introduced in this chapter and discussed in greater detail in subsequent chapters. This is to give the reader an appreciation of the different techniques before getting himself immersed too deeply in details.

SIMPLE OSCILLATORS

6. Hartley Oscillator Figure 4 illustrates the circuit for the common Hartley transistor oscillator. This circuit was selected for discussion first because of its

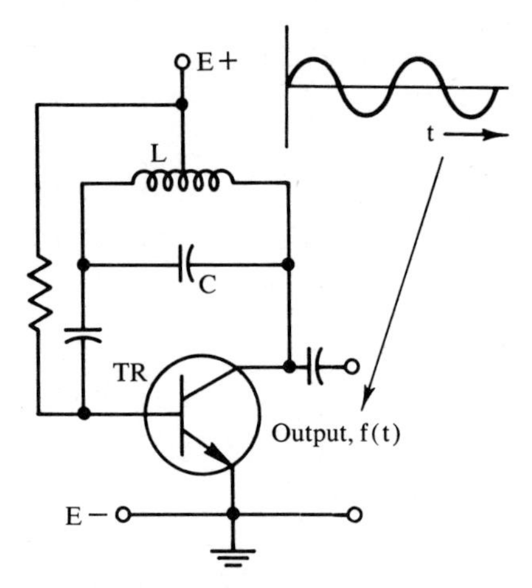

Fig. 4. Hartley oscillator.

circuit simplicity and its widespread use. It is a low-precision oscillator used in audio tone-generating circuits for code practice or telephone work. Other uses are for generating radio-frequency signals for test purposes in radio and TV. Where measures are taken to increase the accuracy of frequency, the Hartley oscillator circuit is also used in precision signal generators.

The purpose of the transistor in Fig. 4 is to supply output signal power and to make up for the circuit's power losses. The transistor also supplies 180° of phase shift, such that if a positive-going sine wave is applied to the base of the transistor, a larger-amplitude but negative-going sine wave will result at the plate. Dc power is supplied to the transistor through the connections labeled $E+$ and $E-$, and the transistor converts this dc power to signal ac power $f(t)$. The frequency at which oscillations take place in this circuit is determined primarily by the combination of the inductance L and capacitance C. The formula for frequency of oscillation is

$$f = \frac{1}{2\pi \sqrt{LC}}$$

* Frequency f and period T for a periodic signal are inversely related: $f = 1/T$.

A constant-amplitude sine wave is obtained by transistor characteristics not apparent in the circuit. As successively larger currents are applied to the base, the output current at the collector becomes progressively smaller even though further amplified; the gain diminishes. A second factor is losses in the input circuit. The base normally draws a slight signal current. As the base is driven to larger and larger current swings, it draws progressively more current. This base-emitter diode of the transistor absorbs signal power. Thus the decreasing gain and the increasing base-current losses are nonlinear characteristics of the circuit to hold the amplitude of the output signal reasonably constant.

7. Phase-shift Oscillator Figure 5 shows a transistorized *RC* phase-shift oscillator. In the circuit, gain to compensate for circuit losses and to supply output power is furnished by a transistor *TR*. The phase-shift network has three sets of identical capacitors *C* and resistors *R* in series to provide the necessary 180° total phase shift and determine the output frequency.

The circuit is an energy converter in that dc power supplied to the terminals labeled *E* is converted into ac power at the output as a regularly time-varying

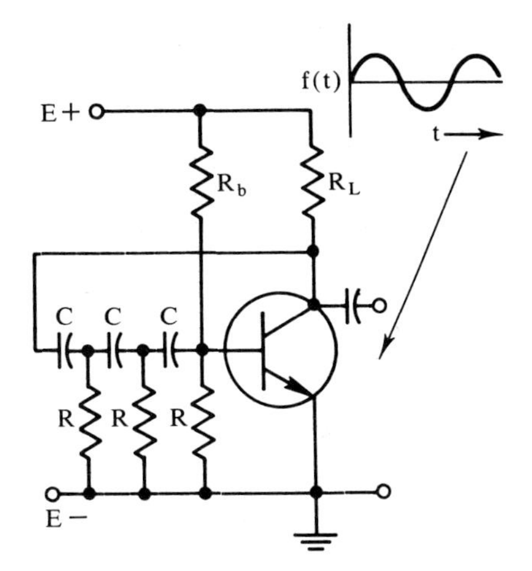

Fig. 5. RC-phase-shift oscillator.

signal $f(t)$. The transistor *TR* supplies an appreciable power gain to amplify the applied signal and inverts it at the output. The load resistor R_L passes collector current; variations in collector current develop the output signal $f(t)$.

The feedback network consists of three pairs of elements *C* and *R*. Since the transistor supplies 180° of phase shift, this feedback network must supply an additional 180° of phase shift such that signals are fed back in phase to sustain steady oscillations. Signals at other frequencies will be fed back with a different phase shift so that the fed-back signal will not reinforce that originally supplied to the base of the transistor *TR*. The total of 180° phase shift for the three sections divides down to 60° per *RC* section. This is only an approximation, because of the loading of adjacent sections upon one another. The period is approximately given by $T = 15.4RC$ or $f = 1/(2\pi\sqrt{6}\,RC)$. For the derivation, see Seely.* It is not necessary that the resistances *R* and capacitors *C* be equal in each section, merely that the *RC* product per section be equal. For instance, to reduce loading effects by the next section, the resistance values per section actually might be *R*, 10*R*,

* S. Seely, "Electron-tube Circuits," 2d ed., pp. 413–414, McGraw-Hill Book Company, New York, 1958.

and 100*R*. The capacitors correspondingly would be *C*, 0.1*C*, and 0.01*C* to keep the *RC* product per section at unity (1.0*RC*).

8. Other Oscillators There are other types of oscillators, but basically they are merely variations on the above two types. For example, in the *LC* type of oscillator, other typical oscillators are the Colpitts, Clapp, and tuned-plate, tuned-grid. A crystal oscillator also is considered an *LC* oscillator, as its vibrating quartz crystal has an equivalent inductance and capacitance. Other widely used *RC* oscillators are the Wien-bridge and the twin-T oscillators. These merely use different combinations of resistance and capacitance in the feedback frequency-shaping network.

Finally amplifiers can be different from either of the simple transistor examples given above; electron tubes could be used instead of transistors. The amplifier could be replaced by several stages of amplification in series or a multivibrator where sine waves are produced by an *LC* feedback coupling or a tunnel diode for a completely different type of oscillator (negative resistance).

9. Applications of Oscillators The applications of oscillators are widespread indeed. The *LC* oscillator usually is used to generate frequencies in the radio-frequency (rf) range, and as such these oscillators are suitable for use in radio, radar, and TV equipment as well as in more complicated signal generators described later. *RC* oscillators are usually at a frequency in the audio-frequency (af) range and are used to provide test signals for audio-studio equipment, telephone equipment, hi-fi sets, etc.

SIGNAL GENERATORS

10. Signal Generation A signal generator includes a basic oscillator such as that described previously. The signal generator in addition usually has a number of

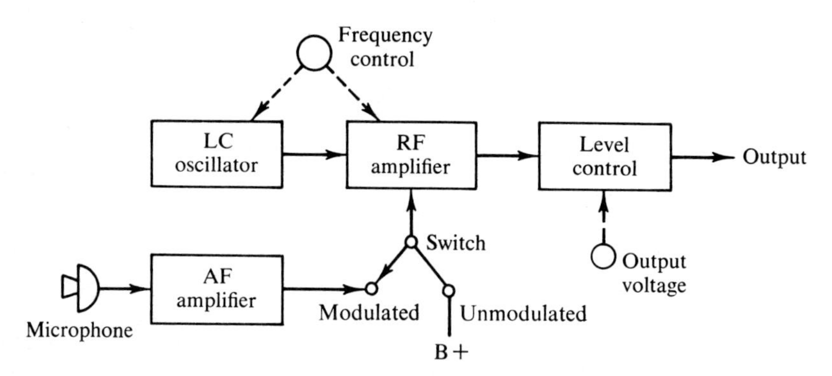

Fig. 6. Rf signal generator.

features that make it more useful and more versatile. The additions consist of such things as a wide and precisely controllable range of frequencies, methods of controlling the signal level precisely, and methods for modulating the signal. Modulating a signal makes its frequency or amplitude vary as a function of time, as determined by a second signal (see Fig. 6). Some oscillators have enough of these additional features so that they really could be called signal generators. Conversely, some signal generators have so few features beyond the bare necessity of an oscillator that they might well be simply called an oscillator. Where to draw the dividing line between an oscillator and a signal generator is not clear and is often a personal preference.

11. Applications The application of signal generators includes the uses of oscillators, as well as more refined purposes such as the measurement of the frequency and amplitude of other signals, checking their phase and time-varying characteristics.

When modulation is included, signal generators also are useful in producing test signals for troubleshooting purposes in TV, radar, radio, etc.

FUNCTION GENERATORS

12. Function Generation Function generators, as the name implies, generate specific types of waveforms or periodic functions according to some basic function of time, such as a sine wave or a square wave that cyclically repeats itself. The function generation may be accomplished by starting with a given waveshape and distorting it systematically, or by starting with a given function and integrating it over time to generate a new function. A typical example of these approaches is in the common sine-square triangular-wave generator. A third approach generates a function by following some given arbitrary curve. These approaches are discussed below.

13. Distortion Method The distortion approach starts with a sine wave from an oscillator and amplifies it to an extreme, so that the amplifier overloads symmetrically

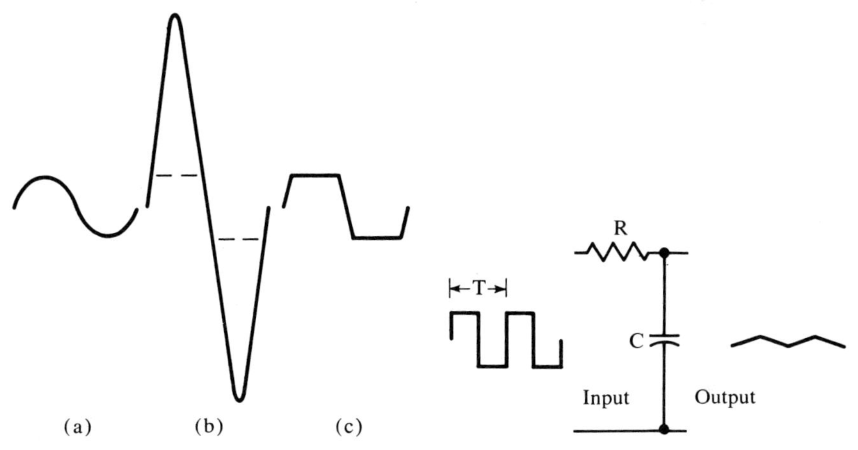

Fig. 7. Systematic distortion. (*a*) Input. (*b*) Amplified. (*c*) Clipped.

Fig. 8. Square-wave integration.

on both extremes (see Fig. 7). Only the resulting highly clipped center section of the original sine wave remains as an approximation to the desired square wave.

14. Integration Method The integration approach starts with an input waveform and integrates it over the time of one half period, or until the wave reverses itself. At this time the input waveform flips over and thus the time-integrated value reverses also.

Figure 8 represents such a simple circuit, where a square-wave input is sent into an RC integrator circuit. The product of the resistance R and capacitance C is long here compared with the time T for one complete cycle of the signal. Integration may be thought of as a process of continuous addition or accumulation. The capacitor C accumulates a charge of electrons because of the current through the resistor R. This charge of electrons makes its presence "felt" as a voltage across the capacitor, as the voltage $v = q/C$. This voltage slowly changes as the charging current continues to pile up in the capacitor.

This voltage acts to oppose the input voltage, so that true integration or continuous addition occurs only when the capacitor voltage is very small compared with the input voltage. This is realized when the RC product is much longer than the signal's period T. This effectively means that the signal reverses itself before the capacitor voltage becomes even a small fraction of the input.

15. Curve-follower Method Signals of an arbitrary or periodic nature may be generated with this method. Refer to Fig. 9. A graph of the desired signal is "followed" by the sensing probe as it moves evenly from left to right repetitively across the graph. The probe sweeps linearly and horizontally across the graph just like the sweep in an oscilloscope. In the vertical direction, the probe is sensitive to displacement above or below the desired curve line, and uses a displacement-sensitive servo to keep itself on the line. The desired electrical signal is the height of the probe (and curve) above the reference axis. This signal is amplified and fed to the output.

A related approach to generating arbitrary curves is the diode function generator. As above, a recurrent linear voltage sweep is used as input. Diodes are adjusted to conduct at various sweep voltages, and adjustable amounts of the diode currents are fed into a common summing amplifier. In this fashion the desired function is generated as a series of short straight-line segments. These are common in analog computers.

16. Applications Applications of function generators are many. For example, a square wave is used to check the frequency response of electronic systems such

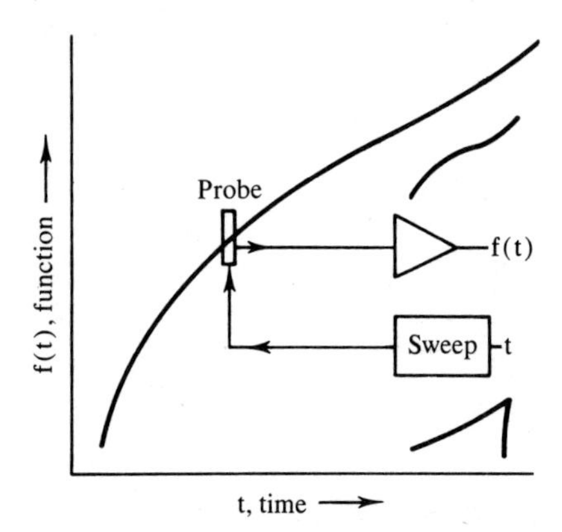

Fig. 9. Curve-follower diagram.

as a hi-fi set in the home. The square wave has a fundamental frequency corresponding to the sine wave with the same period as the square wave. In addition, the square wave has a large number of the odd harmonics* of this fundamental sine wave in decreasing proportions according to the harmonic number; that is, the higher the harmonic the smaller its amplitude in the square wave. These higher-frequency harmonics determine the sharpness of the corners in the square wave. This characteristic means that the square wave is suitable for checking the high-frequency response of a hi-fi system. Insufficient higher harmonics would show up as rounded corners on the square wave. Correspondingly, the low-frequency response of the system can be checked by the square-wave droop from input to output. A poor low-frequency response would show up as a sag of the square wave toward its center.

Triangular-shaped waves are used in general for a linear sweep of some type. For instance, it may be desirable to sweep a signal in amplitude or in frequency for certain purposes. For testing how well a component mechanically is able to withstand vibration, the amplitude of vibration applied to a test stand or "shake table" may be increased linearly in magnitude via a triangular wave such that the object being shaken has an increasingly greater and then decreasingly smaller range of

* A harmonic is a signal whose frequency is some integral multiple of the fundamental or first harmonic. Here the first odd harmonic would be a signal whose frequency was three times higher than the fundamental or lowest frequency.

amplitude. Another application of the triangular wave is to check the linearity of response in hi-fi amplifiers or systems in general. A linear amplifier is characterized by the fact that it will amplify both a small signal and a large signal with exactly the same gain. A triangular wave fed to such an amplifier would let one determine whether the amplifier indeed was linear throughout a wide range of amplitude signals on input. Change of gain would show up as a change in slope; the output signal would no longer be triangular.

PULSE GENERATORS

17. Pulse Generation A pulse can best be described as a fast change from the reference level of a voltage or current to a temporary level; this is followed by an equally rapid return to the original level (see Fig. 10). Perhaps the simplest way to generate a pulse is to close a switch or relay contact for a determined amount of time and then open the contact to turn the pulse off. The switch can be operated manually, electronically, or electrically by a relay. The electronic switch is known as a "one-shot" or monostable multivibrator. The adjective "monostable" in this case means that the multivibrator has a basic resting level from which it can be disturbed long enough to produce a pulse on a one-shot basis and then return to its quiescent state. See Chapter 10 for details.

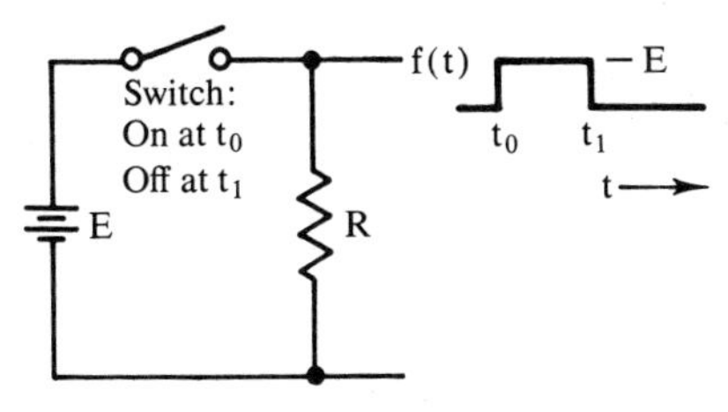

Fig 10. Pulse generation.

18. Applications People can flip switches to produce pulses as short as 0.1 s. Relays can be pulsed in the same range and also down to 0.001 s. Below this, electronics and the multivibrator take over. Pulses are quite useful for testing logic circuits and computers and generating noise for testing receivers.

FREQUENCY SYNTHESIZERS

19. Frequency Synthesis A frequency synthesizer basically is a system for generation of any single desired (sinusoidal) frequency with a high degree of accuracy from a highly stable master reference oscillator. Sometimes several reference oscillators are used, but the number of possible output frequencies greatly exceeds the number of oscillators. The desired output frequency is related by some precise function of subharmonic* and/or harmonic relationships to the basic stable oscillator. Many degrees of frequency division or harmonic generation may be used, so that the functions may be highly complex but also extremely accurate.

Figure 11 shows the basic method. The output of a stable oscillator is subdivided in several steps into precise subharmonics. The master oscillator, for instance, might have a frequency of 1 MHz, and each divider would subdivide this frequency by 10. Thus the output of the first divider would be 100 kHz, that of the next 10 kHz, that of the third 1 kHz or 1,000 Hz, and so on down possibly to 1-Hz increments. Each divider also provides harmonics of its own output frequency. A switching arrangement then picks out the proper harmonics, adds them, and puts them through a filter which passes only the desired single resulting frequency.

* A subharmonic is a signal whose frequency bears an integral fractional ratio, such as ½ or 1/10, to the fundamental signal.

The resulting signal is highly accurate in frequency, as it is limited only by the frequency accuracy of the original master oscillator. Consequently, considerable effort is usually expended to ensure the accuracy and stability of this master oscillator. Here one controls the frequency digitally by switches or by computer control. In certain circumstances this is highly desired, rather than setting an analog control, such as a capacitor shaft, to control an oscillator's frequency. A disadvantage is the high degree of circuit complexity associated with this type of frequency

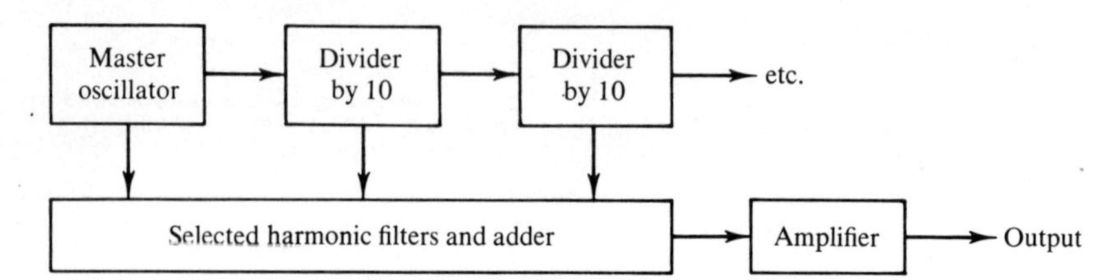

Fig. 11. Frequency synthesizer.

generator. However, the size of a frequency synthesizer can be reduced by miniaturization techniques utilizing integrated circuits (ICs). With the use of such devices the cost also can be reduced in spite of the complexity.

20. Applications The frequency synthesizer can be used wherever an accurate preset frequency is desired. For instance, it may be desirable to control the frequency of a signal generator digitally by relays. This is easily done in a frequency synthesizer. Frequency synthesizers are widely used in commercial two-way radio equipment where it is desirable to monitor communications on certain frequencies on a predetermined basis. Also, oscillators at different physical locations may be locked together in both frequency and phase under digital control, something that would be difficult to accomplish with other techniques. These phase-locked oscillators may then be swept together in frequency for measurement purposes.

Chapter 10

Sources of Electrical Signals

D. H. SCHUSTER, Ph.D.

Departments of Psychology and Computer Science,
Iowa State University, Ames, Iowa

OSCILLATORS

1. Introduction to Oscillators This chapter will cover basic sources of electrical signals. The last chapter covered the different types of devices that produce signals, and in this chapter we shall take a look at just the basic circuits themselves rather than complicated devices consisting of many simpler circuits. Specifically we shall consider circuits that produce sine waves, triangular waves, or square waves. This is a logical starting place, as more complicated devices use these simple circuits and devices as building blocks.

Important characteristics of oscillators are type of circuit to obtain control of frequency and amplification, accuracy of resulting frequency, power produced, power consumed, and some other minor characteristics, such as circuit complexity. These are listed in relative order of importance; type of circuit is so important that this may be the only descriptive phrase used, such as a "transistorized Colpitts oscillator." This chapter is organized in this fashion.

Major concerns of any type of oscillator circuit are how accurate it is and how stable the frequency is. The frequency is typically measured against some frequency standard such as a highly stable oscillator or radio station WWV, the primary frequency standard in this country. Knowing the effect of other variables on oscillator frequency is highly desirable. For instance, does the oscillator frequency change with time; that is, is it stable? Does the frequency change with temperature, with the supply voltage, with the amount of power taken out of the circuit? These characteristics will be discussed individually for the different circuits.

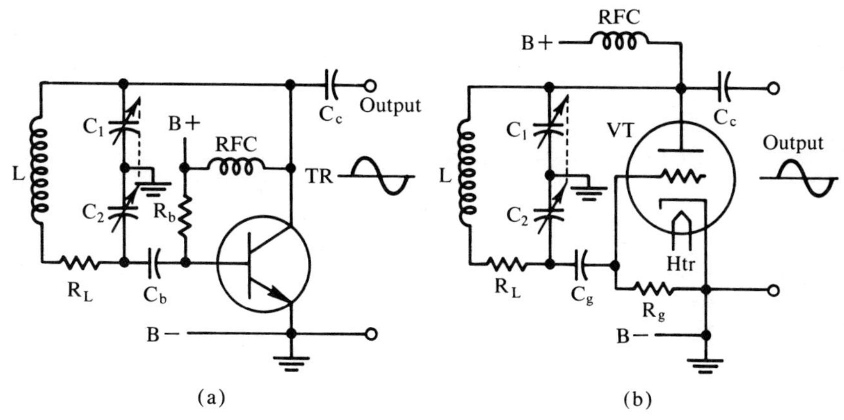

Fig. 1. Colpitts-oscillator circuit.

COLPITTS OSCILLATORS

2. Circuit Diagram Let us look in detail at a typical simple oscillator. Figure 1 gives a complete circuit diagram for the widely used Colpitts oscillator. The circuit is shown for both the transistorized version (*a*) and the corresponding circuit with a vacuum tube (*b*). There is an *LC* tank circuit which controls the basic frequency much as in the Hartley oscillator discussed previously (see Chap. 9, Sec. 3). However, instead of one capacitor two are connected in series with their mid-connection grounded. The inductance coil *L* is not tapped, and the connections are made just to its two terminals.

One purpose of this tapped *LC* combination, or "*LC* tank," is to provide 180° phase shift between the top and bottom connections of the coil *L*. This can be seen by referring to Fig. 2*a*. An unknown voltage V_x is assumed to exist at a given instant in time across the inductance *L*. This same voltage V_x exists across the series combination of C_1 and C_2, so that their sum is $V_1 + V_2 = V_x$ as shown in Fig. 2*b*.

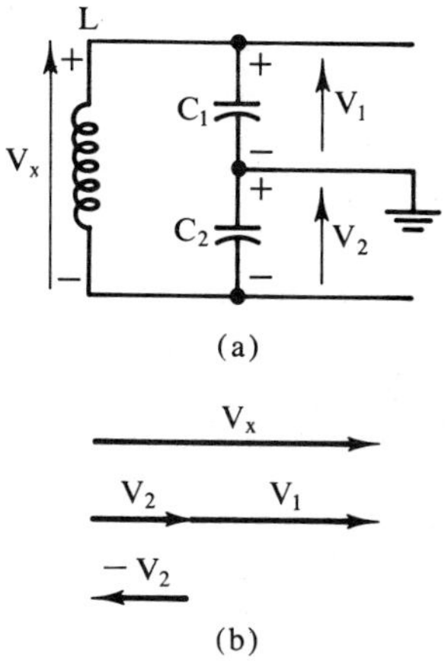

Fig. 2. Colpitts LC-tank voltages.

These same voltages appear at the transistor or tube terminals. The voltage V_1 is also output voltage from the transistor's collector (or tube's plate). Similarly, the voltage V_2 is also the input voltage to the transistor's base (or tube's grid). The active device, whether transistor or tube, has both a gain *G* and 180° phase shift from input to output. Thus the output voltage $V_1 = -GV_2$. If this requirement is met, the circuit will oscillate.

Referring again to Fig. 2*a*, when voltage V_1 is positive to ground, V_2 is negative because V_2 was defined as shown with its arrowhead grounded. Thus the *LC* tank acts as a phase inverter, providing 180° phase shift from top to bottom with reference to ground between C_1 and C_2.

Note that $V_1 > V_2$ by virtue of the active device's gain G. Solving for the input voltage in the above equation gives $-V_2 = V_1/G$. The LC tank also provides this voltage division or fractionation via the ratio of capacitative reactances of C_1 and C_2. The voltage across a capacitor is proportional to its reactance. Thus the ratio of voltages V_1 and V_2 equals that of the reactance XC_1 and XC_2, $V_1/V_2 = XC_1/XC_2$. In summary, the LC tank provides both 180° phase shift and voltage division.

Thus a signal applied to the transistor's base or grid of the triode would be amplified at the output but 180° out of phase with the input. This signal is applied to the tank circuit, and both reversed in phase and diminished in amplitude by the tank circuit to be presented back in phase at the input again. Oscillations build up and are sustained at a frequency determined by the LC product.

The effective circuit capacitance C is basically the resultant of C_1 and C_2 in series and is given by $1/C = 1/C_1 + 1/C_2$. Typically the capacitors are ganged (mounted on the same shaft) to ensure that they are moved together to maintain the proper voltage-dividing ratio between the output and the input circuits.

Coupling of the signal from the tank to the grid is done via an RC network, the grid resistor R_g and the grid capacitor C_g. For the transistor, the comparable elements are the base resistor R_b and the base capacitor C_b. This coupling network provides a dc isolation from the tank to the grid, such that when the grid is driven positive at the peak of the sine waves, the grid draws current which biases the tube for normal operation of the oscillator circuit. The plate connection is through a radio-frequency choke (RFC on the schematic) to keep the rf energy from being shorted to ground through the power supply labeled $B+$ and $B-$. Output energy is taken from the circuit at the plate by the coupling capacitor C_c.

3. Frequency Accuracy The frequency accuracy of the circuit is determined by several considerations. These are the LC tank's efficiency (or relative energy lost), relative stability under supply-voltage changes, effect-of-temperature changes, and dial-reading accuracy. Let us consider first the effect of resistive losses in the active device and tank circuit upon the frequency of oscillation.

The exact formula in the vacuum-tube case for the frequency of oscillation is

$$f = \frac{1}{2\pi}\sqrt{\frac{1}{LC}\,\frac{rC + r_pC_1}{r_pC_1}}$$

where r_p = tube plate resistance
r = equivalent tank resistance
C = equivalent tank capacitance as defined above

Here r refers to the effective loss resistance in the tank circuit. This loss resistance is not the dc resistance of the tank coil but includes it as one component. There are losses in the coil due to hysteresis and skin effects such that the high-frequency resistance of the coil is considerably more than its dc or low-frequency resistance. Minimizing the tank resistance r may be paraphrased as increasing the Q or figure of merit of the circuit. Stating this another way, when $r_p \gg r$, the right-hand term under the radical approaches unity (1), the efficiency of the circuit is high, and the frequency is determined by the square root of $1/LC$ to a high degree of accuracy.

Actual inductance and capacitors used in an oscillator may have a variation of 10 to 50 percent from their nominal or stated design value. Thus one reason for the variable capacitors C_1 and C_2 is to provide an adjustment so that the frequency may be set accurately when compared with some standard frequency. When precise values of inductance and capacitance must be obtained, "trimming" is used. For capacitors, this is usually done by adding a small capacity in parallel with the tank capacitor; this smaller capacitor has a value 10 to 50 percent of the larger capacitor being "trimmed" in this fashion. Trimming an inductance is accomplished by two possible means. One is to adjust the core position of a movable powdered-iron slug within the coil. The second method applies only to small inductances with an air core (no iron slug). Here the relatively few turns in the coil may be spread or compressed together to adjust the inductance value.

Typically the dial of an oscillator such as this one may be read to 2 or 3 percent. The accuracy of reading the dial may be increased by special techniques such as using a multiturn dial or a vernier scale. However, merely increasing the dial-reading accuracy is no guarantee that the frequency of the oscillator is what the dial claims. If too much power is taken out of the oscillator, this introduces an effective series resistance, the same as increasing the loss resistance r in the tank circuit. This would mean that the approximation would not be an accurate estimate of the oscillator frequency and could lead to inaccuracy.

A similar effect is due to a change in voltage. There is no term in the equation above for the effect of the supply voltage. However, the gain of the tube is a small but significant function of the supply voltage, so that when the supply voltage changes, the frequency of the oscillator will change slightly. A typical equation for this frequency shift might be $f_s = 0.001(E - E_n)$, where f_s is the frequency shift, E the actual voltage, and E_n the nominal power-supply voltage. Thus to ensure a high degree of accuracy in an oscillator, precautions must be taken to use only a minimum and constant amount of power to run the next stage and to ensure that the supply voltage remains constant. When these load and voltage-supply precautions are taken, the frequency of the oscillator is quite stable.

4. Applications Such oscillators as this are actually used as frequency references, sometimes called wavemeters. Here the accuracy of the dial may be something like 0.01 percent using special dials such as the multiturn one mentioned above. To ensure that the dial is being read accurately, a crystal oscillator, described later in this chapter, is used to calibrate the dial at certain points. The crystal oscillator is a highly accurate source of an ac signal and is used to calibrate or check a variable-frequency oscillator such as this Colpitts oscillator. For instance, a crystal oscillator could be used to check the oscillator at 1 MHz, 2 MHz, 3 MHz, and so on. The crystal oscillator would have a basic frequency of 1 MHz, but an output especially enriched to supply a wide spectrum of harmonics from the second at 2 MHz up, perhaps, through the hundredth harmonic. Thus the dial can be calibrated or the frequency known accurately at many reference points. Between these reference points, the frequency is assumed to change linearly.

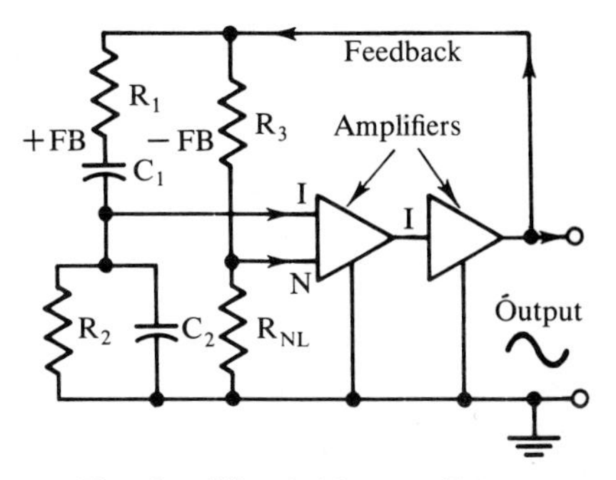

Fig. 3. Wien-bridge oscillator.

WIEN-BRIDGE OSCILLATOR

5. Circuit Diagram The Wien bridge (pronounced "ween" or "veen") is a typical audio oscillator, using an *RC* (resistive-capacitive) combination to determine its basic frequency of oscillation. Refer to Fig. 3. The circuit consists of two feedback paths labeled +FB for positive feedback and —FB for negative feedback, associated with two amplifiers. The amplifiers are shown as triangular symbols, and they can be transistors or vacuum tubes with one phase-inverting device in each amplifier.

The circuit uses a sensitive phase-shift-sensing circuit to determine the frequency of oscillation. This phase-shifting part of the circuit is the positive-feedback branch, consisting of the series resistor R_1 and capacitor C_1 tied to the parallel combination of R_2 and C_2. At some frequency, the phase shift across the series *RC* network of R_1 and C_1 is exactly offset by the phase shift of opposite sign from the shunt part of the circuit, R_2 and C_2. For convenience the two resistors R_1 and R_2 are usually made equal and switchable together in decades. Capacitors C_1 and C_2 are usually made equal also and ganged so they may be varied simultaneously.

The frequency at which the phase shift of the series branch is exactly offset by the phase shift of the parallel branch results in no net phase shift. A signal whose frequency results in this zero net phase shift will be amplified and fed back to the positive-feedback branch of the circuit. Other frequencies would be amplified and presented back out of phase, such that no regeneration would result from their going around the loop many times.

The letter *I* at the amplifier input means "inverting input," as a signal applied here would be inverted (phase-shifted by 180°) as well as amplified at the output. Two such amplifiers, as here, result in 360° phase shift, or no net inversion. The letter *N* means a "noninverting input."

The negative-feedback aspect consists of resistor R_3 and R_{NL} in series. The lower resistor R_{NL} is a nonlinear resistor, such as a common light bulb, whose resistance is some inverse function of its current. This branch of the circuit is used to control the signal amplitude and is fed into the noninverting (*N*) input of the first amplifiers; since the second amplifier is fed only in its inverting (*I*) input, the signal from the junction of the resistor R_3 and R_{NL} is shifted in phase by 180° and thus constitutes negative feedback or degeneration. As the amplitude of the signal fed back gets larger, R_{NL} decreases its resistance such that a smaller percentage of this increased signal is fed into the amplifier. Thus the voltage divider consisting of R_3 and R_{NL} is an automatic gain-controlling circuit to maintain a constant-amplitude signal out of the oscillator. The amplitude of the oscillation is regulated rather closely, typically from 1 to 5 percent, by this stratagem.

6. Frequency Accuracy The basic frequency of the device is given by $f = 1/R_1C_1$ when $R_1 = R_2$ and $C_1 = C_2$. This formula assumes that the two positive-feedback resistors are equal as are the associated capacitors. The formula is derived from the fact that at the frequency of oscillation, the capacitive reactances in the $+FB$ branch equal the value of their associated resistors.

7. Applications The Wien-bridge oscillator is the most widely used audio-oscillator circuit today. This is due to its circuit simplicity, range, and stability. As an audio test oscillator, the circuit uses ganged variable capacitors to cover slightly more than a 10:1 frequency range and switchable paired resistors with values in multiples of 10 to cover four to six decades of frequency, say from 10 Hz to 1 MHz. The output is a relatively pure sine wave with a stable amplitude.

With these good characteristics, the versatile Wien-bridge oscillator is widely used to supply af test signals. Uses include supplying a test signal to measure amplifier gain and phase shift vs. frequency (the "frequency response"); troubleshooting audio circuits in telephone, hi-fi, or studio; and other test equipment such as an af bridge to measure capacitance and inductance and to provide audio tones for various signaling/monitoring purposes.

CRYSTAL OSCILLATORS

8. Circuit Diagram Certain rock crystals are used in conjunction with oscillators to provide a highly stable source of electrical signals. The basic crystal material used is natural or synthetic quartz. A piece of crystalline quartz is cut, ground, polished, and lapped with at least one set of parallel surfaces. Electrodes are applied or plated to the set of parallel edges and connected to an oscillator circuit. The crystal vibrates mechanically when a voltage is applied. Physically it has the quality called piezoelectricity such that accompanying the mechanical vibrations are corresponding electrical vibrations. Thus the crystal can oscillate both mechanically and electrically.

Figure 4*a* shows an equivalent *LC* tank circuit for the crystal. This is a series-parallel circuit with a very low resistance; that is, *Q* is very high, indicating very low losses in the crystal *LC* tank. Since there are both series and parallel capacitances in this circuit, the crystal actually has two resonant frequencies close together. Which frequency is used depends upon the oscillator circuit. Figure 4*b* also shows a basic crystal-oscillator circuit. The oscillator usually is tuned electrically to its fundamental frequency, but occasionally the third or fifth overtone is used instead when a higher output frequency is wanted. For instance, the fifth harmonic of a crystal whose fundamental frequency was 5 MHz might be used to provide a 25-MHz oscillator by using the fifth overtone. This is done because of physical size and accuracy limitations; a stable 25-MHz crystal would be so thin as to be hard to manufacture. The range of crystal-oscillator frequencies is roughly 10 kHz to 10 MHz. Crystal thinness (e.g., 0.010 in.) sets the upper limit and crystal thickness (e.g., 1.0 in.) the lower frequency limit.

9. Accuracy The long-term accuracy of a crystal is much better than that of the simple *LC* or *RC* oscillators which we have discussed previously. Long-term frequency stability depends upon the care with which the crystal is cut and polished, the type of crystal cut, the maintenance of constant temperature and supply voltage, and also the final circuit adjustment. Unless a crystal is operated in a constant-temperature oven, a temperature change can cause a frequency change. When first operated, a crystal may age or change its frequency slightly. Typically accuracy may be 0.01 or 0.001 percent of the claimed frequency for the crystal. In use the crystal may have its frequency adjusted very slightly or trimmed by the means of a small shunt adjustable capacitor. The short-term frequency stability of the

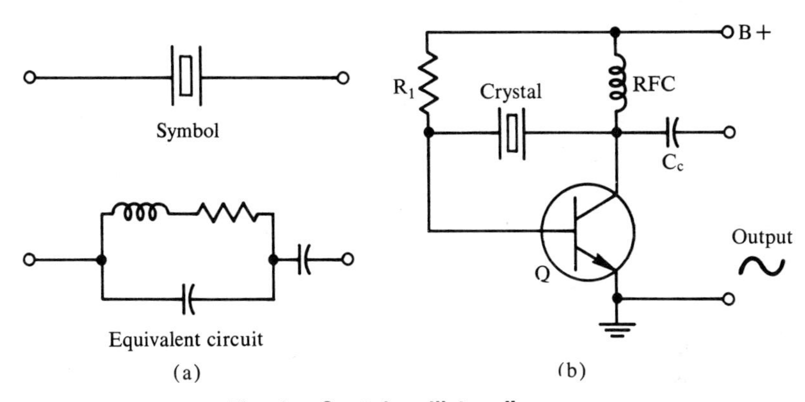

Fig. 4. Crystal-oscillator diagram.

crystal also is very good. The frequency of the crystal may be checked against some primary standard such as radio station WWV.

10. Applications Crystal oscillators are widely used as stable sources of rf signals. Such fixed-frequency oscillators are used in radio transmitters, in radio receivers or test equipment to transfer (or "heterodyne") one band of frequencies to another, and as accurate frequency standards in test equipment for calibrating and comparing other signals. Crystal oscillators also are used to generate a spectrum of crystal harmonic frequencies, starting with the crystal fundamental, then the second, third, fourth, etc., harmonic out through perhaps the hundredth harmonic (100 times the crystal fundamental frequency). This spectrum of evenly spaced frequencies can be used to check the accuracy of a radio receiver throughout its tuning range or in the technique of frequency generation under digital control called frequency synthesis (which see separately).

When used as a secondary frequency standard, the crystal and its oscillator circuit are installed in a temperature-controlled box. The temperature is held by a thermostat and heater to a constant temperature of, say, 120°F. The voltage supplied to the oscillator also is carefully regulated to minimize frequency variations caused by changes in the voltage supply.

Crystals are also used occasionally in conjunction with making bandpass filters for passing only a very narrow range of frequencies and rejecting all others. Typically such a circuit does not oscillate but merely amplifies the desired frequency.

MULTIVIBRATORS

11. General Characteristics Multivibrators are a special type of oscillator characterized by the use of two active devices, such as two transistors or two vacuum tubes, and an output of square waves or abrupt changes between two possible levels. There are three basic types of multivibrators with different stability conditions and input-output characteristics. The interstage coupling and biasing conditions also vary among the three types but will be discussed later under the respective circuit details.

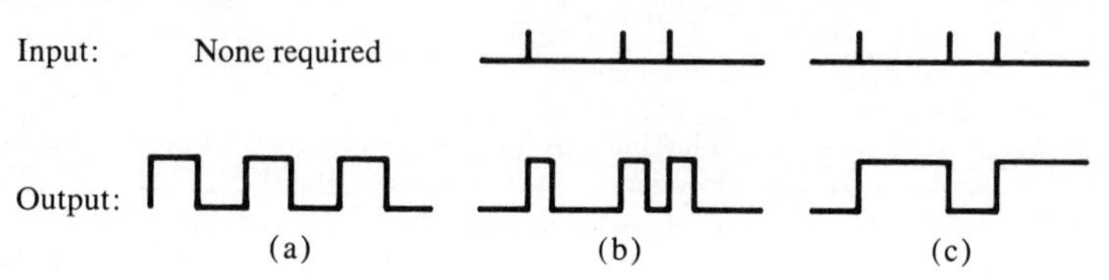

Fig. 5. Multivibrator characteristics. (*a*) Astable. (*b*) Monostable. (*c*) Bistable.

The first of multivibrator is the free-running, or astable, multivibrator (see Fig. 5*a*). This device needs no signal input but does require a power supply so that it may convert dc input energy into an output train of square waves.

The second type of multivibrator is the monostable, or one-shot, multivibrator (see Fig. 5*b*). This device has one stable condition to which it always returns if disturbed or excited by a signal input. The circuit will temporarily go to a transient state and then return after a predetermined timing interval.

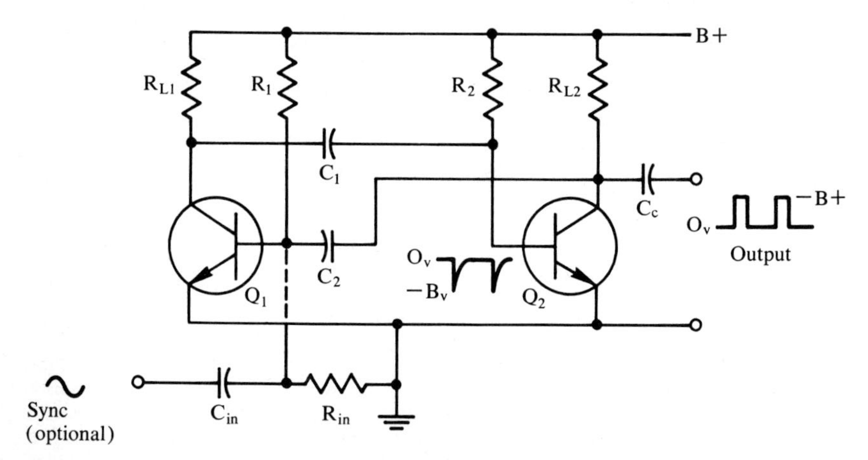

Fig. 6. Free-running multivibrator.

The bistable multivibrator is the third type, with two stable states from either of which it may be disturbed by an input pulse (see Fig. 5*c*). When disturbed by an input pulse, the device flips to its alternate stable state and remains there until the next input signal occurs. Other names for this type are flip-flop, Eccles-Jordan multivibrator, or binary counter. A related circuit is the Schmitt trigger.

12. Free-running Multivibrator In Fig. 6, note that there are two transistors, each supplying 180° of phase shift. The *RC* coupling networks from collector to the other base provide coupling and time delay but do not contribute to the required

360°of phase shift. Assume that transistor Q_1 is conducting (just turned on). Capacitor C_1 had just been charged to full-supply voltage; consequently when the collector voltage at Q_1 falls, this voltage coupled through C_1 reduces the base voltage of transistor Q_2, cutting it off. Transistor Q_2 had just been conducting and now is turned off. Capacitor C_2 had been discharged to approximately zero voltage since both the collector of transistor Q_2 and the base of transistor Q_1 were at approximately the same potential. When transistor Q_2 cuts off, the collector of Q_2 rises to the supply voltage. Since capacitor C_2 has no voltage across it initially, this full-supply voltage is coupled to the base of Q_1 turning it on even harder. Thus, positive feedback around the loop ensues until capacitor C_1 discharges, permitting Q_2 to turn on again. As soon as transistor Q_2 goes on, the state of affairs reverses and transistor Q_2 is on with transistor Q_1 off. And so the cycle continues; each transistor flips on and off alternately.

Note that the time at which transistor Q_2 turns on is determined at some point in the *RC* timing cycle, not necessarily the *RC* time constant. It will be about the same point in the cycle each time, whether it is exactly the *RC* time or, as is typical, somewhat longer. The *RC* cutoff timing typically is different for each transistor as shown here. However, these times may be the same, as in square waves.

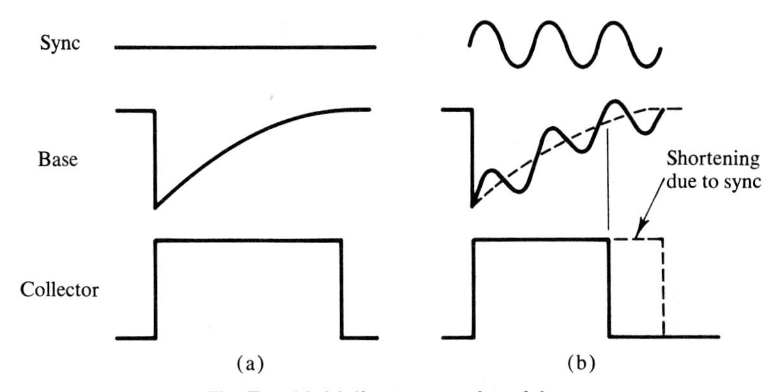

Fig 7. Multivibrator synchronizing.

Low-voltage pulses or sine waves may be coupled to the bases of the transistors to synchronize the turnover points in the cycle with the external frequency. Such a synchronizing signal ("sync") may be coupled as shown by the dashed line to Q_1 in Fig. 6.

The free-running multivibrator may be synchronized to the fundamental frequency of a sine wave in this manner or to some given subharmonic of the sine wave. Figure 7*a* shows the unsynchronized timing waveforms at Q_2 or Q_1 as in Fig. 6. Figure 7*b* shows these waveforms at transistor Q_1 with an added synchronizing signal. The resultant base signal is the instantaneous sum of the sync and *RC* decay voltages. Whenever this resultant signal crosses zero, the transistor of course turns on; once on, positive feedback keeps it on for a new half cycle. The synchronizing here is shown on the start of the third sync cycle; adjusting the resistance *R* would permit turning on the transistor at the end of the second complete sine wave. Triggering here is desirable as it is relatively immune to noise. The base signal has the highest positive slope here, and noise would have the least effect in advancing or retarding triggering.

Note that the natural or *RC* period of the multivibrator is shortened, not lengthened, by this synchronization. Note also that here only one timing period is controlled—a second *RC* coupling network (R_{in}, C_{in}) is required for the second transistor. Finally the range of subharmonics over which synchronization is practical is limited from 1:1 to 10:1 (10 sync cycles to multivibrator turn-on) because of noise and jitter.

13. Accuracy The accuracy of frequency of free-running astable multivibrators is rather poor, but in the neighborhood of 5 to 10 percent. Providing a constant charging current for the timing capacitors and using precision *RC* components can increase the accuracy to about 1.0 percent. However, the circuit may be synchronized or locked to a reference frequency with the resultant accuracy of this reference frequency.

14. Applications Free-running multivibrators are used as a source of constant-amplitude square-wave signals where an approximate frequency is desired. This makes for a convenient test oscillator.

ONE-SHOT MULTIVIBRATOR

15. Circuit Diagram Refer to Fig. 8 for circuit details of the one-shot, or monostable, multivibrator. Note first the difference in biasing conditions of the two transistors. Transistor Q_2 is normally biased on via a direct current through resistor

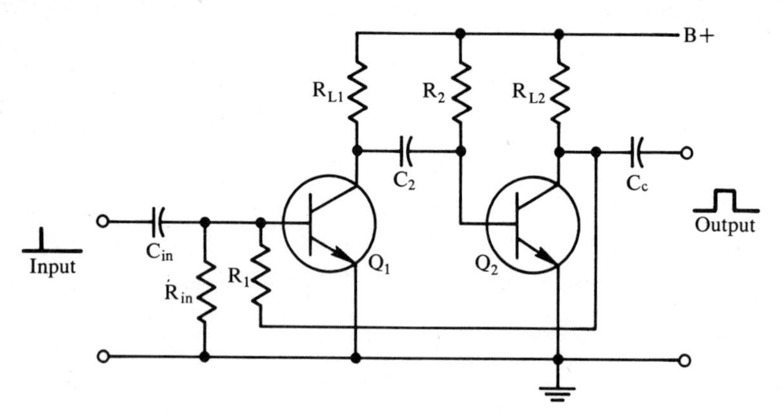

Fig. 8. One-shot multivibrator.

R_2. On the other hand, transistor Q_1 has its bias path through resistor R_1 to the collector of transistor Q_2. If the collector voltage of Q_2 is high (Q_2 cut off), bias current will flow to transistor Q_1. If the collector voltage of Q_2 is low (Q_2 conducting), the bias current to transistor Q_1 will be quite low, cutting off transistor Q_1. Thus the normal state of affairs is that the output transistor Q_2 is conducting, with its collector consequently at a low voltage close to zero. As a result, the input transistor Q_2 is normally biased off, or nonconducting.

This quiescent state of affairs is interrupted when a positive pulse appears at the input to the base of transistor Q_1. The positive pulse turns on transistor Q_1, and its collector voltage drops from its high cutoff condition to its low saturated condition. This large negative pulse cuts off transistor Q_2, with an accompanying amplified positive voltage swing at the output, representing the start of the output pulse. This positive-going and leading edge of the output pulse is directly coupled back to the base of the input transistor, reinforcing the effect of the positive trigger signal. Thus the collector of transistor Q_1 is driven more negative regeneratively. This state of affairs continues until the voltage across capacitor C_2 has leaked off and the base of transistor Q_2 goes positive, permitting this transistor to start conducting again. When Q_2 starts conducting, the output voltage starts decreasing, which is coupled regeneratively back through Q_1 to turn transistor Q_1 off again and leave Q_2 on again or saturated. This is the end of the pulse. The timing of the pulse width is determined primarily by the RC product of R_2C_2 but usually is some constant ratio longer than the calculated RC time constant.

16. Accuracy A 10 percent timing accuracy is also typical for the monostable multivibrator. This can be improved for a timing error of 1 percent or less by the use of precision components for R_2 and C_2, and by the use of a well-regulated power supply with low ripple or noise. The timing resistor R_2 is frequently made adjustable to trim the pulse width to a desired value. A synchronizing signal can be used, as discussed for free-running multivibrators, to lock or synchronize the time delay exactly to some external signal. In this case, the time delay of the one-shot is as precise as the sync signal's timing.

17. Applications Delay multivibrators are used to lengthen or delay an input pulse. Thus, by selecting R_2 and C_2, the circuit provides a short-term memory for transient input signals. For instance, in computers, one-shot multivibrators provide a precise timing delay for reference signals.

FLIP-FLOP MULTIVIBRATOR

18. Circuit Diagram Figure 9 shows the circuit details for a flip-flop, or bistable, multivibrator. Consider the dc bias condition for the base of each transistor first.

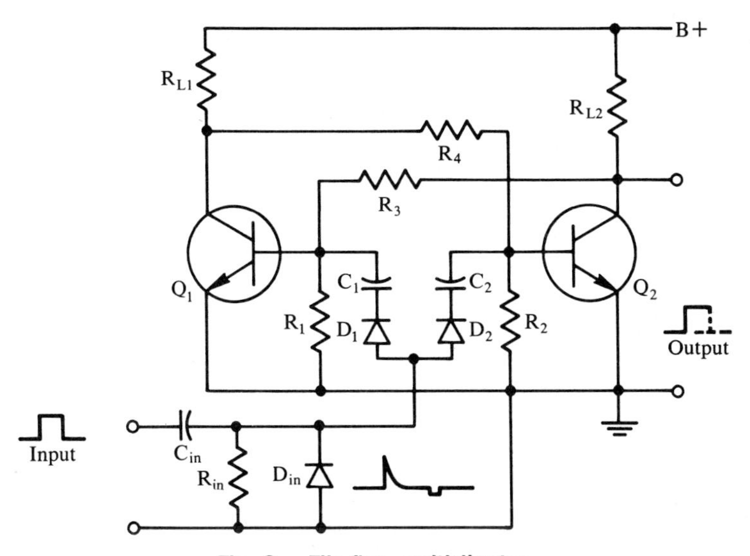

Fig. 9. Flip-flop multivibrator.

Ignore the coupling capacitors C_1 and C_2, and note that each base is connected both to ground and to the opposite collector through resistors. Whether one transistor will be on or not depend on the voltage at the alternate transistor's collector. Both transistors cannot be on simultaneously, as because of some initial transient, one of the two transistors will be off and the other one on.

The circuit will maintain itself in this quiescent condition until disturbed by a positive trigger pulse at the input. Note that the input circuitry in this case is a little more complicated than for the one-shot multivibrator. Square waves at the input are differentiated or changed to pairs of positive and negative spikes. A diode is included to eliminate negative-going spikes by providing a low-resistance path for them to ground. Thus only positive-going triggers, or spikes, will be applied through capacitors C_1 and C_2 to both bases. The series diodes prevent coupling from one base to the other. The effect of the positive-going spike will be nil on the transistor already conducting but will turn on the transistor that is cut off.

Assume, for the sake of argument, that transistor Q_1 is cut off and transistor Q_2 is conducting at the start. The positive trigger applied to the base of transistor Q_2 will have no effect, as this transistor is already fully conducting or saturated. The positive trigger applied to transistor Q_1, however, will drive it momentarily into condition. Its collector voltage, which was high just previously, now drops to a low level; this decrease in voltage is directly coupled to the base of transistor Q_2 and feeds regeneratively back to the base of the transistor Q_2, causing that transistor to be driven into full conduction and held there as long as the collector of transistor Q_2 stays positive. This situation will continue until a second positive input pulse arrives. At that point the bistable situation will reverse, or flip-flop.

The length of the output pulse has nothing to do with timing circuits in the flip-flop itself but is a function of spacing between the input trigger pulses. The collector of transistor Q_2 will go positive for one input pulse, negative for the next, positive for the third, and so on. Thus the output frequency is one-half of the input frequency. If the input is a steady stream of pulses, the device will produce an output frequency exactly half of the input frequency. If the stream of input pulses is aperiodic, the flip-flop still subdivides the input pulses exactly by two, giving rise to the name frequency counter or pulse counter.

19. Accuracy The accuracy of the binary flip-flop is perfect; that is, its output reverses state with each successive input pulse as long as the circuit is working normally. However, the circuit is somewhat sensitive to noise in that large noise pulses on the input line may trigger the flip-flop erroneously. To provide increased noise immunity, a sophisticated flip-flop known as a *J-K* clocked flip-flop is frequently used in computers. The additional immunity to noise is accomplished by requiring the signal and a clock pulse to be present simultaneously for the flip-flop to change state.

20. Applications Because of its perfection in precision, or counting accuracy, the bistable multivibrator finds many applications in counters and digital computers. If the monostable multivibrator provides a temporary memory, the bistable multivibrator provides a permanent memory of the input. The memory lasts until the next pulse or until the circuit is disturbed such as by shutting off the power supply or by a large noise pulse on the input line.

The flip-flop is the basis for counting in computers. Several flip-flops are connected in cascade, one flip-flop feeding the next. For example, if two are connected in series, a binary counter with four unique states results. That is, the circuit conditions start repeating after four input pulses have arrived. (For further information, refer to the digital section of this handbook.)

A related circuit is the Schmitt trigger. This is a flip-flop with a dc coupling resistor to just one transistor base instead of the diode-*RC* signal network shown in Fig. 9. This circuit is used to detect small changes in dc levels, and flips appropriately (changes state) whenever a threshold is passed.

CATHODE-COUPLED MULTIVIBRATOR

21. Circuit Diagram The cathodes or emitters of the two active elements in a multivibrator may be connected together with a common load resistor, especially in the cases of the monostable and bistable multivibrators. Figure 10 shows a cathode-coupled, vacuum-tube, one-shot multivibrator, where the two cathodes of the triodes are connected together with a common-cathode load resistor R_K.

First note the biasing arrangement of the two triodes in the diagram. Tube VT_1 has its grid connected with resistor R_{in} directly to ground. Tube VT_2 has its grid connected to B+ via a resistor R. Thus the second triode VT_2 will be on or conducting in the quiescent state, whereas input triode VT_1 will be biased off, because of the cathode current from triode VT_2 through the common resistance R_K.

The operation of the circuit parallels that of the one-shot multivibrator, as discussed previously. A positive input trigger will momentarily drive the input triode VT_1 from its normal cutoff condition into conduction slightly or momentarily. This slight conduction appears as a negative-going transient at the plate and is coupled via a capacitor C to the grid of the second triode. This negative spike decreases the plate current of the second triode momentarily; this decrease is coupled back via the common-cathode resistor R_K. This reduces the cathode bias on the first tube, permitting it to draw more current. The increased plate current from tube VT_1 means that its plate voltage decreases even further, and this is coupled regeneratively around the circuit. Tube VT_2 is cut off for the duration of the pulse and tube VT_1 is on, but not saturated, with its plate current being limited by the bias buildup of its own current through the resistor R_K. The duration of the pulse is determined primarily by the RC time constant of resistor R and capacitor C, and the point on the grid-bias curve where triode VT_2 comes back into conduction to shut off the pulse.

22. Applications This circuit, or its transistor counterpart, is used to advantage where it is desired to separate the signal-input and pulse-timing circuits. Compare the signal-input connections in Figs. 8 and 10. In Fig. 8, the signal and pulse

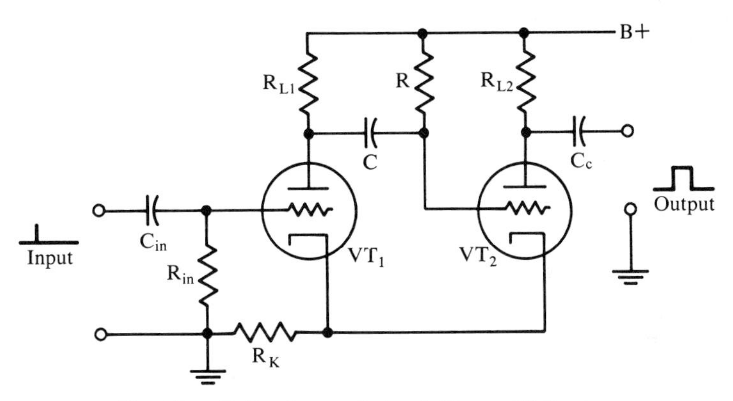

Fig. 10. Cathode-coupled astable multivibrator.

feedback signals have a common point at the base of the input transistor. It is possible for the output pulse to feed undesirably out on the signal-input line. This cannot happen in Fig. 10, where the trigger signal goes to the triode grid and the output-pulse feedback to the cathode, providing isolation between input and output. This input-output isolation is desirable in many cases.

The transistor analog of this circuit also provides input-output isolation, but not as much as the vacuum-tube version. The difference is due to the fact that the grid-cathode diode is an open circuit at most signal frequencies, while the base-emitter diode in a transistor has a small resistance which definitely produces coupling between base (signal) and emitter (feedback) circuits.

LINE FREQUENCY

23. Line-frequency Manipulation The frequency of an output signal may be tied exactly to the frequency of some input signal called a "line" frequency. The line frequency is typically the 60-Hz power supplied throughout the country on the power mains, or it may refer in unusual cases to some basic reference frequency such as 1 MHz in a frequency-standard oscillator. The line frequency may be manipulated, such as doubled or halved, such that the output frequency will bear some exact ratio to the input signal. For instance, if the common line frequency of 60 Hz were doubled, the output signal would be a 120-Hz signal and the accuracy would be one-half that of the 60-Hz power line, which is maintained to close standards in the United States.

24. Basic Techniques The basic techniques of line-frequency manipulation are frequency multiplication, frequency division, heterodyning, sweeping, and frequency synthesis. Parametric devices use a related technique. These basic techniques and circuits are described in detail in Chapter 12.

A basic definition of these processes is in order at this point. If frequency multiplication takes a harmonic of the basic or line frequency as the desired output, then frequency division does the opposite conceptually. For instance, if the input line frequency of 60 Hz were to be halved via frequency division, the output signal would be 30 Hz. Heterodyning combines the signals of two oscillators such that the output has the frequency components of the two inputs plus the harmonics and various cross products as well. Of these, the sum and difference frequencies are the most important, with the difference frequency the more generally used in superheterodyne receivers. For instance, if a broadcast station is transmitting on a frequency of 1,456 kHz and a local oscillator in a receiver is tuned to 1 MHz, the output of the heterodyne circuit will contain the transmitter and the local oscillator frequencies, their harmonics, and the sum and difference of the two input signals. Of most importance commercially is the widely used difference frequency of 456 kHz in AM broadcast receivers.

25. Sophisticated Frequency Manipulation Frequencies may be swept or manipulated in a special sense. An oscillator is swept by varying one of its controlling elements in some systematic fashion to produce a frequency that changes in a controllable fashion. For audio oscillators the sweeping may be done simply by a motor driving the tuning capacitor. At radio frequencies, the tuning may be done with a voltage-variable capacitor or varactor, that is, a capacitor whose capacitance is controlled electrically in response to some control signal.

Frequency synthesis is another complicated method of manipulating a fundamental or line frequency to generate other frequencies that bear some exact but controllable relationship to the input line frequency. Frequency-synthesis techniques require that the output of the oscillator be broken down, usually into tenths and hundredths of the original frequency. The frequency subdivision may be carried further in precise ratios. Then the output frequency is generated by combining harmonics of these precise subharmonics through appropriate filters and ignoring all the other subharmonics. The term frequency synthesis means to combine appropriately or to synthesize the desired, precise signal frequency.

More will be said about swept oscillators and frequency synthesis in Chapter 12.

26. Accuracy The accuracy of line-frequency-manipulation techniques is basically that of the original line-frequency input multiplied by the ratio of the output frequency to the original line frequency. The power companies state that the power-line frequency occasionally deviates from the nominal 60 Hz by 0.01 or 0.02 Hz for short periods. Most of the time the line frequency is even closer than this to 60 Hz. The accumulated error is within 1 or 2 s of time at the worst.

Efficiency of energy conversion in the frequency-manipulation processes is usually ignored or of small consequence as long as a significant amount of the output frequency is available. Putting it another way, line-frequency techniques are not usually used in the output stages in transmitters.

27. Applications Line-frequency multiplication is sometimes used to provide a known audio reference signal. For instance, doubling the 60-Hz line frequency in three successive stages would provide an audio reference tone of 480 Hz. Similarly the line frequency may be counted down, or divided, by 6 and 60 to provide 0.1- and 1-s reference pulses for timing.

Frequency heterodyning, sweeping, and synthesis typically are not employed at the power-line frequency of 60 Hz. (They are mentioned here because of their characteristic of manipulating frequency.) Heterodyning is widely used in radio receivers and special test equipment. Frequency sweeping is used in special test oscillators. Frequency synthesis is used in reference oscillators and commercial radio receivers of high quality.

MICROWAVE FREQUENCY GENERATION

28. Introduction Generating a signal at extremely high frequencies requires special devices and techniques. The frequencies from above 300 MHz to 100 gigahertz (GHz) are called microwave frequencies because their corresponding wavelengths are less than 1 m. For example, the wavelength (distance between the same points on the two successive waves) of a 3-GHz signal is 300/3,000* or 0.1 m or 10 cm. The usual transistor or vacuum-tube oscillator does not work well at microwave frequencies because of transit time or capacity effects. Transit time refers to the time taken by current carriers (electrons or holes) injected into the base region of a transistor to drift their way through this region. A similar definition holds for vacuum tubes for electrons going from the cathode

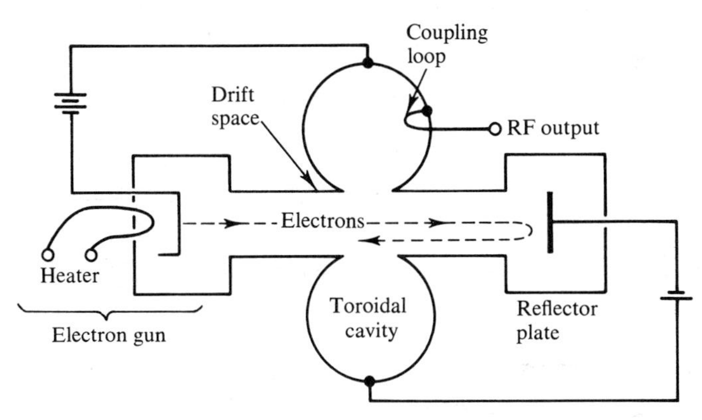

Fig. 11. Cross section of reflex klystron.

to the plate. Transit time produces an upper frequency limit for the device. If an input signal changes appreciably, e.g., reverses itself, before it has time to change the output due to transit-time delay, the output signal does not mirror the input waveshape. Because of drift-time delay and spreading, the device tends to "blur" or average a signal that is changing too fast and thus produces no output signal.

The inherent capacitance of the amplifying device produces a similar effect in limiting the maximum frequency at which amplification or oscillation can take place. The limitation here is that the output current must charge the capacitance of the device as well as produce output power. Above a cutoff frequency, the would-be signal power is used in making rapid current changes in the device capacitance, and none is available for output.

Special devices and techniques are used to bypass the transit-time and capacitance effects of tubes and transistors at microwave frequencies. Briefly, they are listed here and will be discussed in turn below: klystrons, backward-wave oscillators, and various solid-state devices such as LSA and tunnel diodes. The magnetron is a related device, but it is not used generally in test equipment, being generally reserved for the generation of microwave power at high levels.

29. Klystrons Figure 11 shows a cross-sectional view of a reflex klystron. The term "reflex oscillator" applies to this device because the electrons make two passes

* The prefix "giga" or "G" implies a multiplier of 10^9 or one billion. Thus 100 GHz equals 100,000,000,000 Hz, formerly cycles per second. The 300 in the numerator represents the speed of radio waves in vacuum, about 300 million meters per second.

through the cavity, hence the name reflex. Electrons are boiled off of the hot cathode of the electron gun and are accelerated by a high electric field between the cathode and the cavity. The cavity itself is a torus (doughnut) with its "hole" straddling the electron beam. A ringlike slit is cut in the torus where it straddles the electron beam. As the electrons drift the first time through the cavity under the influence of the applied electric field, they induce an rf signal in the surrounding cavity walls because of their passage as an electric current. Many electrons miss hitting the cavity walls and continue on. As the electrons near the reflector plate, they are repelled by its voltage, which is negative with respect to the cavity. The electrons actually turn around and enter the cavity a second time but this time going in a backward direction. Their cavity leaving and returning time corresponds to half a cycle at the signal frequency. If this turnaround time agrees with the half-cycle time for the resonant cavity (time for its natural frequency to change 180°), oscillations take place. The electrons eventually are lost via collision with the cavity wall.

The major frequency-determining element is the cavity, which essentially acts as a high-Q tank circuit at these microwave frequencies. This LC tank circuit has its own natural frequency of oscillation, and the electron turnaround time

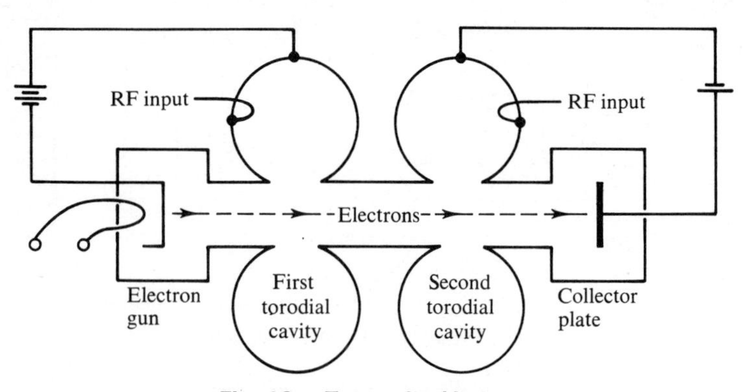

Fig. 12. Two-cavity klystron.

is adjusted to match it. A second determiner of frequency is cavity-to-plate distance and the voltage applied to the plate with respect to the cavity, which determines the speed with which the electrons reenter the cavity. This plate voltage often is varied automatically to tune the klystron over small ranges of frequency.

The klystron is not limited to having one resonant cavity as in the reflex klystron. A second cavity may be added, with rf energy introduced into the cavity closer to the cathode (see Fig. 12). The electrons drift in phase or in step with the applied frequency to the second cavity. The electron beam is velocity-modulated by the frequency of the first cavity. That is, some electrons are speeded up by the first cavity and others slowed down. The electrons bunch together as they drift between cavities. This bunching implies signal amplification. That is, the bunching in electron velocity implies added signal strength because the electrons have gone farther in the applied electric field. Thus amplified microwave energy may be taken out of the second cavity. If, in turn, this second cavity is coupled with a cable or waveguide back to the first cavity, oscillations will take place. Such a two-cavity klystron will produce microwave power at a higher level than the reflex klystron. High-power klystrons may have three or more cavities.

30. Power and Accuracy The amount of power generated by a reflex klystron is typically in the milliwatt level, as the device is very inefficient. Typical efficiency is 1 percent. As such, a reflex klystron finds uses as a test oscillator for microwave frequencies or as the local oscillator in radar superheterodyne receivers. Typical frequencies range from 0.5 to 50 GHz. The basic frequency accuracy of the device is essentially limited by the high-Q tank circuit and may be 1 percent or better. The device may be checked against frequency standards and automatically tuned or synchronized with such accurate frequency generators. The automatic tuning is accomplished with a frequency servo. The klystron frequency is compared with a reference frequency; the difference is amplified and controls the klystron plate voltage.

31. Applications Reflex klystrons are used as local oscillators in radar receivers and as low-power oscillators in microwave test equipment where only a few milliwatts of power is needed. Frequencies range from 1 to 10 GHz. The oscillator has its frequency closely controlled with a frequency servo. Multiple-cavity klystrons can supply kilowatts of pulse power at these extremely high frequencies.

32. Backward-wave Oscillator (BWO) This type of oscillator is one in which there is an energy-exchange interaction between a slow wave signal propagated on a helical structure surrounding an electron beam and the electron beam traveling down the tube in the middle. See Fig. 13 for a cross section of a BWO tube. A slow wave is one in which the electromagnetic wave is propagated at a velocity appreciably less than that of the speed of light in a vacuum; here the slow wave goes down the tube and through the helix at roughly one-tenth the speed of light.

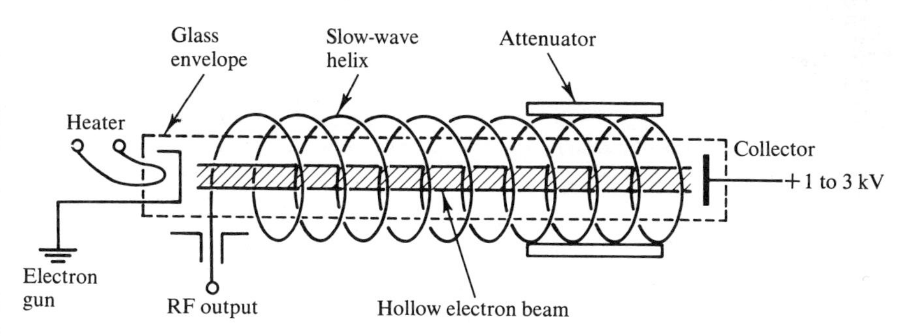

Fig. 13. Backward-wave oscillator.

The wave on the helix has to go around the circumference of the entire length of the wire in the helix, whereas its interaction with the electron tube progresses only at its net forward velocity. In other words, the slowing-down effect is the ratio of the axial length of the helix divided by the entire wire length in the circumference of the helix.

An energy exchange is possible only when the phase velocity, or speed with which the electromagnetic wave is moving down the length of the tube, is close to that of the velocity of the electron beam also traveling down the tube. This synchronism is a basic requirement for energy exchange, although for the electron beam to yield energy to the wave, the electron beam must be moving slightly faster than the wave. The electron beam gives up energy to the wave and in the process is slowed down slightly.

Starting at some arbitrary intermediate point on the helix, a wave could travel either forward or backward along the helix, as there are no directional couplers here to ensure that the wave proceeds in just one direction. Thus a traveling wave could be supported with two space harmonics or modes, one traveling in the forward mode from left to right in Fig. 13 or in the backward mode from right to left. In addition there is a third mode, an "imaginary" one in which the wave is stationary, but this is of little consequence as no power could be taken out of this component. It should be emphasized that these components relate to the phase velocities of the traveling-wave components and *not* to the actual group velocities of the waves. The wave group velocity for any interaction with the electron beam has to be going in the same direction as the electron beam.

Four possibilities exist. An input traveling wave with an average or group velocity could be injected at the left end of the helix, and it would have a group velocity directed to the right along the helix. In turn this traveling wave can have two components, a forward-wave and a backward wave component where the phase velocities are traveling to the right and left, respectively. The other two possibilities concern a traveling wave injected at the right end and proceeding to the left. It also would have a forward- and a backward-wave component, but in this case the group velocity would be in the direction opposite to that of the electron beam.

Figure 13 shows a cross section of a backward-wave oscillator (BWO) vacuum tube. An electron gun in a sealed glass envelope produces electrons in a hollow cylindrical beam. This is accelerated by a high voltage in the range of 1 to 3 kV by the positive voltage on the collector at the opposite end of the tube. The tube depends for its operation upon the backward mode of propagation of a traveling wave initiated near the electron-gun end of the tube by minute instabilities in the electron beam. The backward-wave mode of the traveling wave is essentially an unstable one because the positive-feedback nature of the interaction occurs at only a narrow range of frequencies. This unstable interaction proceeds to make a backward wave that builds up in amplitude with increasing distance from the collector. The amplitude of this backward wave is maximum near the electron gun and is coupled off the helix via a waveguide or coaxial connector to an external circuit.

As stated above, the wave being propagated in the tube at any particular instant can have both a forward and a backward component. There are no one-way streets for electrons in the device, but use is made of the fact that the forward-wave component of the traveling wave would be at a maximum amplitude near the collector end of the tube. Consequently an attenuator is placed around the helix at the collector end of the tube and attenuates any forward-wave components of the traveling wave. Since the backward wave is minimal at this end of the tube, the attenuator has almost no effect on the backward wave. Thus the attenuator serves to eliminate any forward-wave component or reflections from impedance mismatch, leaving the field open for the backward wave to grow progressively to the left. The attenuator, in practice, usually is a lossy insulator supporting the helix.

Not shown in Fig. 13 is an external focusing method, such as a long hollow dc-energized solenoid or alternatively permanent-magnet focusing to keep the electron beam from spreading radially.

33. Accuracy and Power The backward-wave oscillator can be tuned easily by changing the collector voltage; this determines the velocity of the electron beam. Since an oscillatory interaction occurs only where the velocity of the electron beam is slightly larger than the group velocity of the traveling wave, this provides precise tuning. The tuning accuracy is in the order of a few percent, and frequency stability is about 1 percent. The device can be referenced to stable and accurate frequency references through the use of a frequency servo, as described for klystrons. A tuning range of over 2:1 is usual. The amount of power output from the backward-wave oscillator varies from the milliwatt to the hundreds of watts level.

34. Applications BWOs find about the same uses as klystrons, as their frequency ranges and power levels overlap to some extent. However, their frequency extends beyond that of klystrons, 1 to 40 GHz at 100 to 15 mW, respectively.

SOLID-STATE MICROWAVE OSCILLATORS

Solid-state devices exist to generate signals primarily at microwave frequencies of 300 MHz and above. There are in general two basic types of solid-state devices. One type of microwave oscillator utilizes a bulk-effect phenomenon of transferred electrons, such as in the Gunn diode or limited-space-charge-accumulation (LSA) diode. In this case the term "diode" means only that the diode has two leads connected to it and does not carry the usual connotation of the nonlinear effect found at a typical diode junction. A second type uses a diode junction, a doping difference that forms a solid-state junction in the tunnel diode, avalanche diode, or Read diode.

35. Gunn Oscillators A Gunn diode is a gallium arsenide (GaAs) diode with the doping of carrier impurity uniform throughout. There is no doping differential to produce a diode junction in the typical sense, but while the doping is meant to be uniform, there are minor local variations in the doping concentration throughout the diode. The diode depends for its oscillations on a quantum-mechanical property: as the voltage across the diode is increased, the current increases linearly as one would expect in an ordinary resistor, but only at first (see Fig. 14). As a certain voltage V_p is reached, some of the carriers (electrons or holes) in the diode transfer abruptly to an excited state where their mobility is drastically decreased, such as by a factor of one-fiftieth. The decreased mobility is associated with a larger effective radius of electrostatic attraction for the current carrier. The excited and enlarged carrier cannot move through the solid-state crystal lattice anywhere nearly as fast as it did before under the push of the applied electric field. As the applied voltage is increased further, more and more of the current carriers hop into the

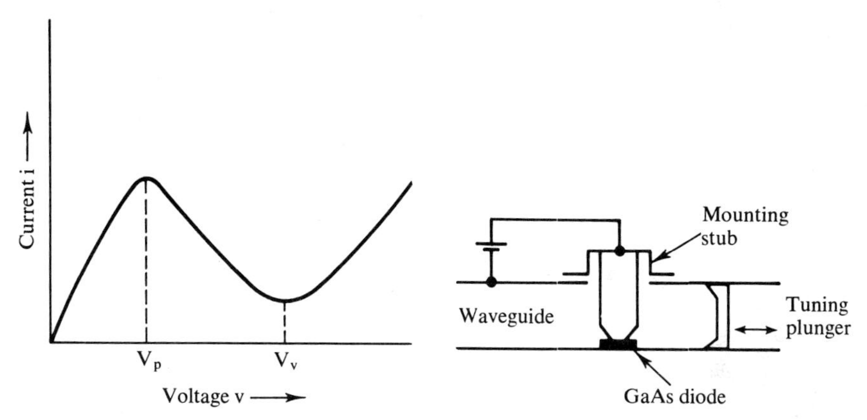

Fig. 14. Current-voltage characteristic of Gunn diode.

Fig. 15. Gunn-diode oscillator.

excited state until eventually, at some valley voltage V_v, all the current carriers are in the excited state and the current can again increase in a linear fashion. Between the peak voltage at which the carriers first start to jump into the excited state, and the valley voltage where all carriers are excited, the slope of the current vs. voltage graph shows a negative slope. This negative slope can be interpreted as a negative resistance; that is, as the voltage increases, the current through the device actually decreases in this range.

A useful interpretation of negative resistance is that such a device can supply power when operating in this region. Remember that a positive resistance absorbs power instead of generating it. As will be seen, a Gunn diode converts direct energy into alternating energy, and thus the term "negative resistance" fits.

As the current carriers leave at the instantaneous cathode, they behave as ordinary current carriers until the electric field is sufficient to separate the electrons and holes. Once the electrons and holes separate, they form a diode pair and continue drifting toward the instantaneous anode and there recombine to regain electrical neutrality in the device. It takes a finite amount of time for the carrier dipoles to drift to the anode. This transit time is proportional to the length of the diode, and the corresponding drift time sets a rough natural resonant frequency for the diode.

Figure 15 shows a typical mounting configuration for a Gunn oscillator. The rather small gallium arsenide diode is held against one side of a microwave waveguide by an electrically conductive mounting stub. The mounting stub is itself isolated as far as direct current is concerned from the wall of the waveguide, but the mounting stub at the radio frequencies concerned isolates the diode as a quarter-wave stub from the rest of the waveguide. The mounting stub also permits a dc bias voltage to be supplied as the basic energy source for the diode. The source voltage is adjusted for optimum frequency and power output. While tuning can be done to a certain extent by varying the voltage applied to the diode, which varies the transit time, tuning mechanically also is possible by a plunger which shortens or lengthens the tuning stub for which the diode is at the apex of a quarter-wave-length stub.

36. Frequency and Power Frequency ranges for this device run from 2 to 50 GHz typically. In a limited-space-charge-accumulation mode (LSA diode) where the applied voltage is very high to preclude dipole generation, the frequency can be extended from 50 to 100 GHz. The frequency of the oscillator is controlled by the *Q* of the waveguide and the power-supply voltage. Typically the accuracy may be from 1 to 5 percent, and the frequency may be varied over a decade

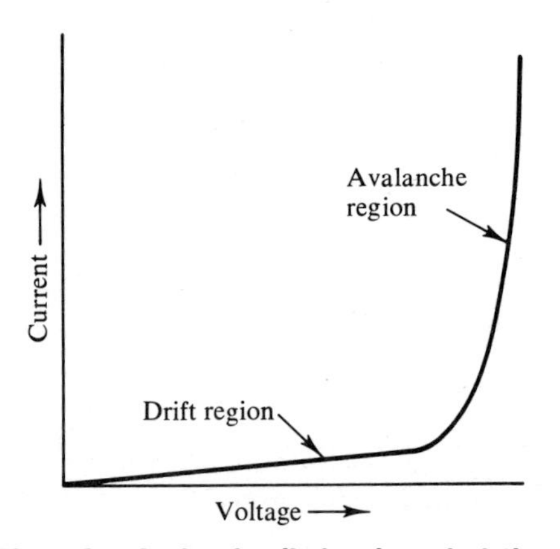

Fig. 16. Avalanche-diode characteristics.

by a combination of changing the waveguide dimensions and varying the applied voltage.

The power output of a Gunn oscillator, a bulk-effect device, may vary from the milliwatt to about the 0.1-W level as the current state of the art. Thinness of the diode limits both power and frequency. A typical Gunn diode may produce 50 mW power at 10 GHz with 2 to 5 percent power-conversion efficiency.

37. Applications Gunn diodes have been used experimentally as microwave-signal sources for microwave equipment. Their small size, simplicity, and voltage tunability are advantages. These diodes are used as low-power oscillators in microwave receivers and test equipment.

38. Avalanche Transit-time Oscillators The second major class of solid-state oscillators is that generically called the avalanche transit-time oscillator. The basic physical phenomenon here is to employ a reverse-biased junction diode and increase the voltage applied across it (see Fig. 16). As the voltage is increased, there comes a point at which many carriers are generated rather suddenly. The process is one of impact ionization, where a carrier accelerated by the electric field runs into a neighboring atom and jars loose an electron. In the avalanche mode more than one electron is jarred loose for each colliding electron entering the crystal lattice in that neighborhood. In a short period of time the carriers have multiplied exponentially in the so-called "avalanche" mode. The diode is operated at a constant dc voltage well into the avalanche region.

The current carriers generated by the avalanche process drift through the center intrinsic region of such an avalanching diode. They drift through this region with a time half of the characteristic period. Since the current carriers then are out of phase with the applied voltage, this is equivalent to a negative resistance in the rf region. Stated another way, the rate of carrier generation is maximum when the applied field is maximum, but the carriers drift through the intrinsic region at a rate such that they are out of phase by a transit-time delay with the applied voltage. As the current carriers drift, this is equivalent to an induced current that is out of phase at some frequency with the applied voltage.

A mounting arrangement similar to that shown previously for the bulk-effect diode is applicable here also. Other mounting details such as stub tuning also are similar.

39. Frequency and Power The frequency range of an avalanche transit-time oscillator is in the range of 10 to 50 GHz with an accuracy, as for the Gunn oscillator, tied to that of the waveguide. Power levels, however, are approximately an order of magnitude higher for the same frequency than for the Gunn oscillator. A typical device may produce 2 to 5 W at 10 GHz.

40. Applications In addition to the applications for Gunn devices, avalanche diodes may be used as oscillators in transmitters because of their higher output power. The device is not readily voltage-tuned, however, so that frequency is determined by the containing resonant structure, such as a waveguide.

41. Tunnel Diode The tunnel diode is a device related to the avalanche transit-time oscillator with a doping differential to produce a junction. However, it is a forward-biased solid-state diode that shows a negative-resistance characteristic at low forward-bias voltages such as 0.5 V. (See the discussion of negative resistance in Sec. 35.) The effect is quantum-mechanical in nature in that some electrons can "tunnel" under the potential barrier at the junction to get on the high-energy side.

The device can generate milliwatts of power from the af to the microwave region. The frequency accuracy depends upon the external circuit.

42. Applications The tunnel diode is used commercially in video and microwave amplifiers, low-power externally tuned oscillators, digital-computer logic, and low-amplitude signal detectors. Tunnel diodes are relatively insensitive to nuclear radiation, so that they are used in nuclear and space applications.

BIBLIOGRAPHY

Al-Moufti, M. N., S. V. Jaskolski, & T. K. Ishii: Calculating Gunn Diode Output, *Electronics,* vol. 41, no. 23, pp. 148–150, November 11, 1968.

Backward Wave Oscillators, *Proc. IRE,* vol 43, pp. 684–697, 1955.

Baldridge, D. E.: Sweep Generators for TV Service, *Electron. World,* vol. 80, no. 5, pp. 40–42, November, 1968.

Gewartouski, J. W.: Solid-state Microwave Power Sources, *Proc. Natl. Electron. Conf.,* vol. 23, pp. 358–363, October, 1967.

Heiserman, D. L.: Solid-state LSA Microwave Diodes, *Electron. World,* vol. 81, no. 2, pp. 40 et seq., February, 1969.

Monacchio, E. N., and A. L. Plevy: Testing of Audio Amplifiers, *Electron. World,* vol. 76, no. 1, pp. 74–76, July, 1966.

Niblack, W. K., and C. A. Levi: Microwave Power Diodes, *Electron. World,* vol. 82, no. 1, pp. 49–53, November, 1968.

Smith, F. P.: Crystal-saving Frequency Synthesizer, *Electron. World,* vol. 76, no. 6, pp. 46–48, December, 1966.

Special Issue on Semiconductor Bulk-effect and Transit-time Devices, *IEEE Trans. Electron. Devices,* vol. ED-13, January, 1966.

Uenohara, M.: Current Status of Bulk GaAs Oscillators and Amplifiers, *Proc. Natl. Electron. Conf.,* vol. 22, pp. 79–82, 1966.

Widman, D. L.: Microwave Sweep Oscillators for the Laboratory, *Electron. World,* vol. 80, no. 5, pp. 49–52, 1968.

Chapter 11

Function Generation

D. H. SCHUSTER, Ph.D.

Departments of Psychology and Computer Science,
Iowa State University, Ames, Iowa

1. Introduction A "function" means that one variable or quantity depends on a second variable; the first variable is a function of the second. For example, the common 60-Hz laboratory voltage is a function of time, $v = f(t)$ mathematically. This is read "v(voltage) is a function of t(time)."

Electrical periodic functions may be generated via the two techniques discussed earlier, systematic distortion and integration of input signals. The second general class of function generators consists of the servo curve follower and diode function generator.

2. Square-wave Generation The systematic-distortion concept is used to transform an input sine wave into an output square wave. The basic technique is to amplify the incoming sine wave by a large factor such that the amplifier will be highly nonlinear. Clipping limits the amplitude of the sine wave in both directions (see Chapter 9, Fig. 7, where just a small section of the center of the original sine wave is left). This process may be carried to a great extreme such as using an amplification factor of 1,000 or 1,000,000 to 1. This produces an extremely good approximation to a square wave.

Square waves are also produced with multivibrators, as discussed in Chap. 10, Sec. 3. They can be generated with low precision by the free-running multivibrator, or triggered with great precision in the bistable multivibrator.

3. Triangular Wave A second technique is one of integration, as commonly done with a square wave to produce a triangular wave. Figure 8 in Chapter 9 shows such an application. The output of the integrator reflects the *RC* time constant; that is, the capacitor has charged up and is approaching a limit. If the charging rate is low, the capacitor just begins to charge when the cycle reverses; thus a linear triangular wave is generated. For precision triangular-wave generation, precision *RC* components are required along with a constant-current charging source.

4. Sawtooth-wave Generation This is a special case of the symmetrical triangular wave in that the first halves of the waveforms are identical. For a sawtooth waveform, the second half is different. The signal abruptly switches to its initial level and repeats (see Fig. 1). The reset shorting switch usually has some resistance so that the reset time is finite but negligible compared with the rise time. The resulting sawtooth waveform is also called a ramp.

5. Pulse Generation Pulses may be generated in a variety of ways, depending on the speed and precision required. Electronically, pulses are usually formed with

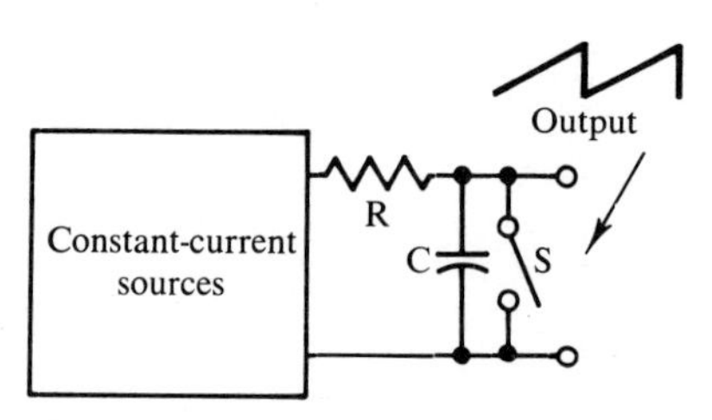

Fig. 1. Triangular-wave generation.

multivibrators, although sometimes a pulse-forming network and electronic switch are used for short, precise pulses.

From one point of view, square waves are pulses: on 50 percent of the time and off 50 percent of the time for a 50 percent duty cycle. Square waves need not be symmetrical; the output pulse could be on only 10 percent of the time and off 90 percent. A practical limit for an ordinary multivibrator is about 1 percent on time, unless speedup circuitry is added. With special high-speed charging/discharging arrangements, very short pulses and duty cycles can be made.

6. Curve Followers The third basic technique of generating a function is that of a curve follower. This is a servo device such that any arbitrary function $f(x)$ may be generated. The device starts with a plot of $f(x)$ vs. x on a servo table (see Chapter 9, Fig. 9). The arm positions back and forth horizontally corresponding to x. A piece of curved wire on the table is electrically contacted by the arm as it is moved back and forth. The arm contact is restrained to stay in contact with the wire on the graph paper, and whenever contact is broken, means are taken to ensure that contact is promptly renewed. Thus as the arm slides back and forth in response to the input x signal, the arm contact moves up and down to generate the function $f(x)$. A photoelectric device also may be used with cathode-ray tubes instead of this graphical two-way servo.

Note an interesting property of the curve follower that is different from the first two techniques of generating functions. The first two utilized periodic functions of time. Here no periodicity, no time function is involved. Stated another way, x is free to move arbitrarily, although it could be made time-related if desired. This relaxation is also true of diode function generators.

7. Diode Function Generators A fourth way of generating functions is to do it with a diode function generator which approximates a function with a series of straight-line segments. Since an operational amplifier is an integral part of this type of function generator, let us consider it briefly.

An operational amplifier is an inverting amplifier with extremely high gain and a frequency response flat from dc (0 Hz) to about 1,000 Hz typically. A triangular symbol, sometimes labeled "op amp," is used to represent an operational amplifier (see Fig. 2). The actual circuit gain is contrived to be the negative of the ratio of the feedback resistor R_f and an input resistor R_1.

The circuit gain for the op amp plus R_1 and R_f is derived as follows: The letter G refers to the grid input to the operational amplifier and is essentially at ground voltage in normal operation. Assume an input voltage x applied to resistor R_1 alone, neglecting R_2 and R_3 for the moment. The output voltage $f(x)$ then is due to x. Since an op amp inverts, $f(x)$ has a polarity opposite that of x. Assume a small error voltage e_G at the grid input G to the op amp, which also has a very high input resistance R_G compared with R_f and R_1. The error voltage e_G has two components, one due to current through R_1 and the other due to that through R_f. The op amp gain is called the constant K and is 100,000 to 10,000,000 typically. The output voltage $f(x) = -Ke_G$. With the feedback resistor R_f from output to grid input G, it should be obvious that e_G is forced to be very small and of opposite sign to $f(x)$.

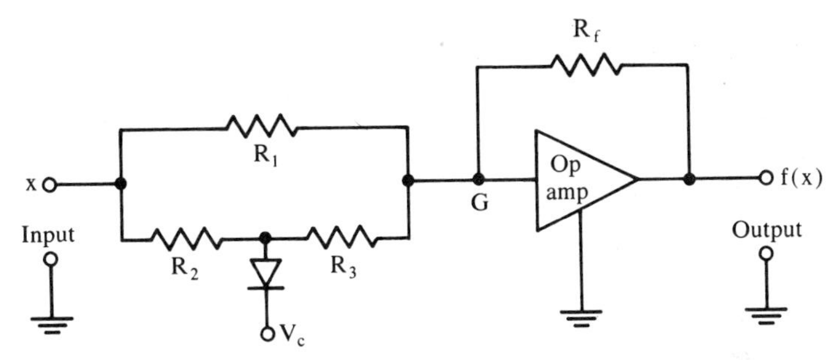

Fig. 2. Diode function generator.

The signal e_G is due to current through the two resistors R_1 and R_f. The feedback current through R_f is $f(x)/R_f$. Since point G is to be virtually at ground potential, these currents must cancel each other. This algebraically is $x/R_1 = -f(x)/R_f$. Solving for the output voltage leads to $f(x) = -xR_f/R_1$. Within the range of the op amp, this equation holds true independently for each input's contribution, so that the output results from the sum of all input currents. Hence this type of op amp is also called a "summer."

This diode function generator is composed of a number of resistors providing varying gains into an operational amplifier labeled "op amp" (see Fig. 2). The graphs in Fig. 3 show what happens. The amplifier output is the sum of the input signals multiplied by the gain through the various resistors. For instance, there is an output component f_1 due to resistor R_1. There is also an output component f_2 due to the series combination of equal resistors $R_3 + R_2$. Both components are shown separately in Fig. 2*a*, and their sum is shown in the output, Fig. 2*b*. The component due to R_1 is always present. The component due to the series resistors R_2 and R_3 is present until the input voltage x exceeds twice the cutoff voltage V_c. When the input voltage x is more than double V_c, the diode conducts, as the voltage at the function of the two equal resistors R_2 and R_3 is equal to V_c. Thus further increase in the input voltage x is no longer coupled through the series combination of R_2 and R_3.

A diode function generator may have 10 or 20 stages such as the one stage shown here by R_2 and R_3 in series. The gain for each is adjustable, and each

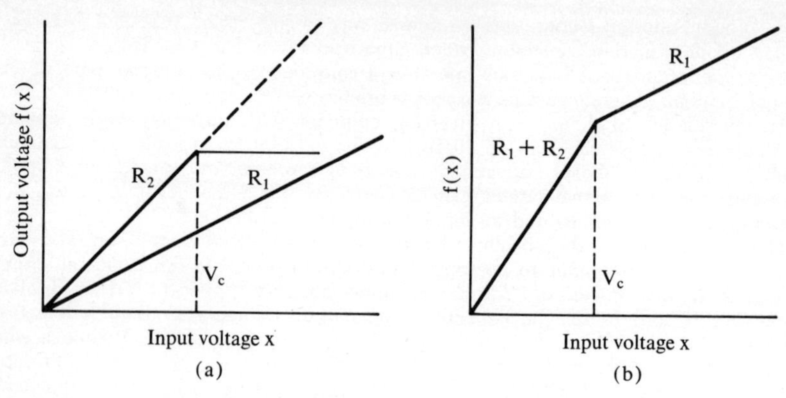

Fig. 3. Diode function generation.

breakpoint or cutoff voltage is adjustable. Thus functions may be synthesized by 10 or 20 line segments. As long as the function being synthesized in this fashion does not have any very steep slopes, the function may be generated with an arbitrary degree of accuracy such as 1 or 2 percent. The breakpoints obviously should be clustered where the slope of the function is changing the fastest.

BIBLIOGRAPHY

Bell, L. W.: "Digital Concepts," Tektronix, Inc., Beaverton, Ore., 1968.
"Digital Industrial handbook," Digital Equipment Corp., Maynard, Mass., 1967.

Chapter **12**

Frequency Manipulation

D. H. SCHUSTER, Ph.D.

**Departments of Psychology and Computer Science,
Iowa State University, Ames, Iowa**

1. Introduction This chapter deals with operations upon the frequency of a signal in some manner to generate a signal at a new frequency. There is a known and precise ratio between the original and new frequencies. Techniques to accomplish this are given below.

There are good reasons for being interested in frequency manipulation. A signal may be generated at one frequency for reasons of stability, reliability, convenience, or economy and then transformed to another frequency with other desired characteristics. A crystal oscillator is a good example. Such an oscillator is hard to make for radio-communications use in the frequency range of 30 to 150 MHz. A widely used solution to this problem is to generate a stable signal with a crystal oscillator at a frequency of say 15 MHz and "multiply" it by some exact ratio of say 2:1 or 9:1 as necessary to produce the desired output frequency. Thus a relatively stable high-frequency signal is practically obtained, even though the stability is affected adversely by this same ratio of frequency multiplication.

2. Frequency Multiplication Frequency multiplication means changing the frequency of a signal by some exact ratio such as 2:1 or 5:1. Two components are necessary to frequency multiplication; the first is some nonlinear or time-varying circuit that introduces harmonics in the output along with the fundamental or original line frequency, and the second is a resonant circuit tuned to the desired output frequency. Usually the frequency-selective element is an *LC* tank (inductance-capacitance), but occasionally it may be an *RC* (resistance-capacitance) bandpass or band-reject filter. The purpose of this filter is to pass only the desired output frequency to the load and reject other frequencies, especially the original or fundamental frequency.

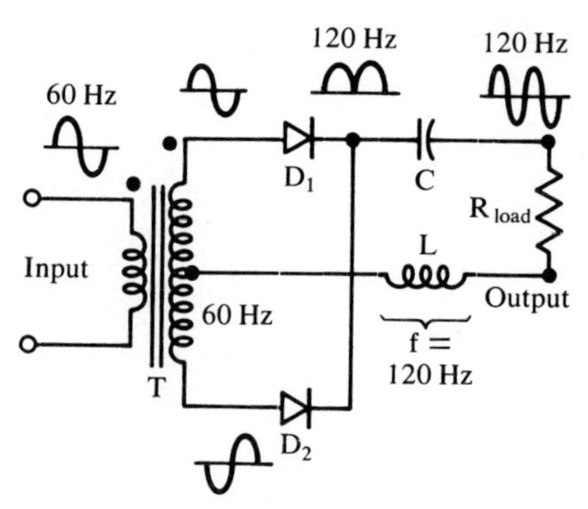

Fig. 1. Frequency-doubler circuit.

Figure 1 shows a simple-minded circuit to illustrate the point. The input is the basic line frequency, say 60 Hz. The output supplies a 120-Hz frequency into the resistance load. This circuit provides nonlinearity or distortion via full-wave rectification; the secondary of the transformer *T* is center-tapped to provide both a positive-going sine wave and a negative-going sine wave with respect to the center tap or reference point. The outputs of the two rectifiers D_1 and D_2 are added together without a ripple filter; the junction of the two rectifiers simply shows two positive-going halves of sine waves. (The negative component via diode D_2 was inverted.) This series of pulsating half sine waves has a basic repetition frequency of 120 Hz and is distorted in the sense that the negative part of the signal is a series of needle-sharp peaks and the positive parts are half sine waves. The purpose of the *LC* tank circuit is to eliminate the harmonics in the sharp negative peaks of this 120-Hz signal and pass only the desired second harmonic as a sine wave to the output as shown.

The *LC* tank is a narrow bandpass filter that is sharply tuned to 120 Hz. It acts similarly to a child's swing, which if left swinging keeps swinging back and forth and makes 120 complete swings or cycles per second. The pulsating-diode output, even though distorted and far from a sine wave, kicks the *LC* "swing" to produce a smooth sine-wave output. The *LC* tank absorbs energy on the positive peak, corresponding to the swing when kicked. The tank then delivers this stored energy to the load in the negative half cycle, much as the swing returns smoothly for its next "kick."

Frequency multiplication is not limited to even harmonics. Figure 2 shows a frequency tripler. A 1-MHz oscillator converts dc power from a power supply into a 1-MHz sine wave. This is fed to a nonlinear amplifier which distorts the signal symmetrically. The distortion in this case consists of flattening both the positive and negative peaks. This flattening process introduces predominantly odd harmonics. Thus output of the nonlinear amplifier would consist of the 1-MHz fundamental, plus the third harmonic somewhat smaller in amplitude, plus the fifth harmonic yet smaller in amplitude, and so on through the seventh, ninth, eleventh, etc. The amplitude of further harmonics would be quite small in comparison with the 1-MHz fundamental. The *LC* tank circuit is tuned to 3 MHz. It acts as a bandpass filter for the 3-MHz signal (which it also smooths out to a sine wave) and rejects the first (fundamental), fifth, seventh, ninth, etc., harmonics.

3. Applications Frequency multiplication is widely used in radio transmitters and sometimes in radio receivers for two-way communications. The signal frequency from a crystal oscillator typically may be doubled, tripled, or even quintupled in one frequency-multiplying stage. Several such stages may be cascaded together to produce even higher frequency-multiplication ratios such as 20:1 or 36:1.

4. Efficiency and Accuracy Efficiency of energy conversion of multiplying circuits is not very high, 10 or 20 percent being typical for a tripler. Efficiencies can be made somewhat higher but require additional effort. The accuracy of the 3-MHz output signal is directly related to the accuracy or frequency stability of the 1-MHz oscillator. For instance, if the 1-MHz oscillator were a secondary standard with 0.01 percent long-term accuracy, the accuracy of the 3-MHz output signal also would be 0.01 percent, which translates to a frequency tolerance of 300 Hz at the output of 3 MHz.

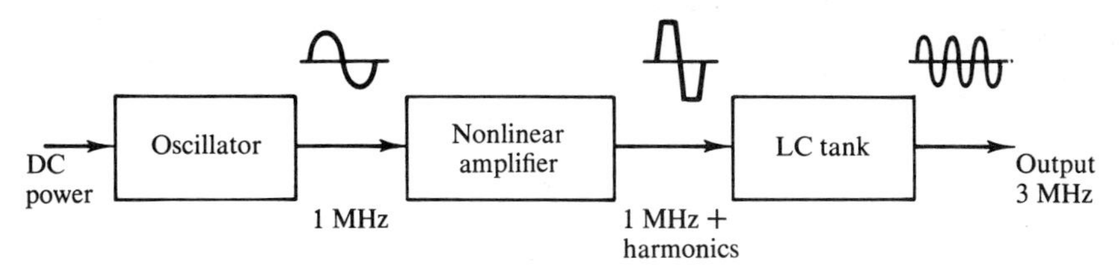

Fig. 2. Frequency tripler.

5. Frequency Division Frequency division is the opposite of frequency multiplication. The output frequency bears some exact fractional relationship to the input frequency, such as one-half, one-third, or one-tenth. There are two basic techniques to achieve frequency division, the countdown technique and the subharmonic-synchronization technique.

Figure 3 shows a binary countdown circuit. The circuit essentially is a bistable multivibrator or flip-flop with ac coupling for trigger input pulses. A series of positive and negative pulses or spikes as the input is reduced to a series of only positive pulses by the shunt diode. Alternate positive pulses turn on the transistor that is off. The two transistors are such that when one transistor turns on, the other circuit regeneratively is required to turn off. Thus the positive trigger will turn on only the transistor that is off and will have no effect on the transistor already on. Thus the multivibrator can change state only in response to a positive trigger. The series diodes are to steer the trigger pulses appropriately without letting the two transistors interact directly via the signal-coupling capacitors. (Refer to Sec. 2 and following in Chap. 11 for further discussion.)

The circuit can be arranged with 10 transistors in a ring to count down by a ratio of 10:1. In addition, stages such as the above may be cascaded, so that the frequency division continues to the power of 2. This type of circuit is used widely in digital computers.

6. Synchronized Subharmonic Oscillator An oscillator such as a Hartley oscillator can be synchronized or tied to the frequency of another oscillator operating at some exact ratio or fractional frequency away. For instance, a Hartley oscillator operating at a frequency of 300 kHz may be synchronized to that frequency by

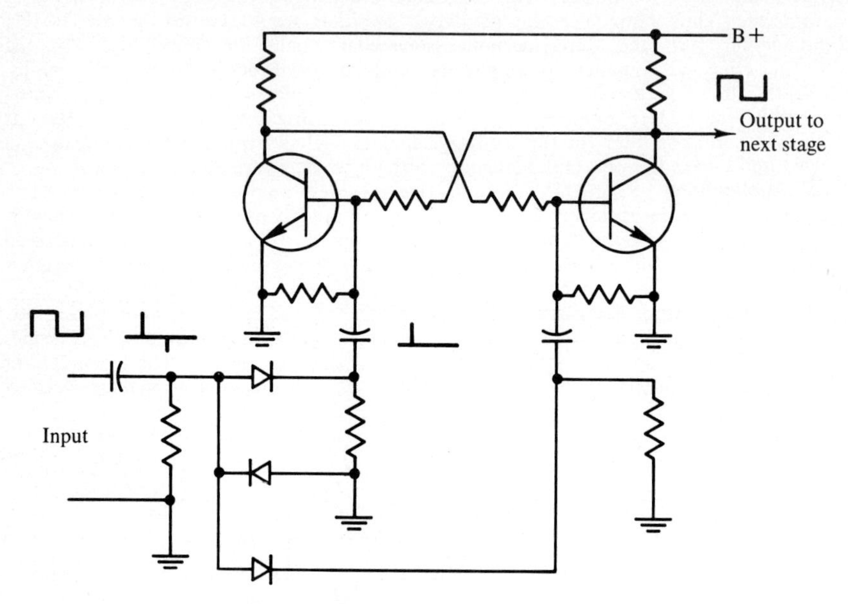

Fig. 3. Binary frequency counter.

an oscillator operating at the six times higher frequency of 1,800 kHz. Figure 4 shows the timing relationship. The large sine wave depicts the normal grid voltage at the desired subharmonic of 300 kHz. A small amount of the fundamental at 1,800 kHz is needed for accurate synchronization. In practice, the Hartley oscillator has its tank-circuit tuning varied until the frequency "locks" in stably.

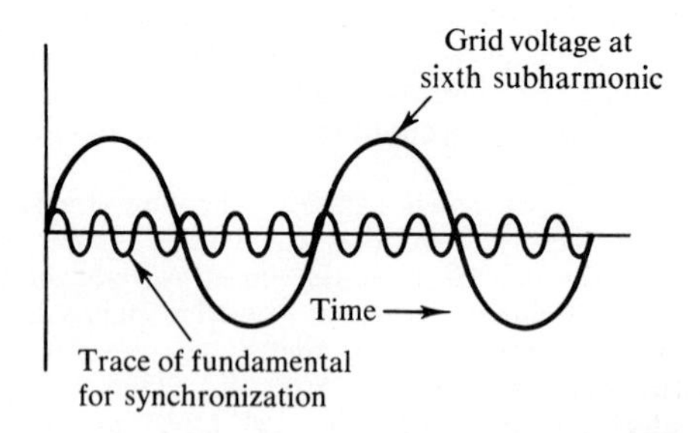

Fig. 4. Subharmonic oscillator synchronization.

It is interesting to note that the oscillator is only synchronized and not locked to the higher frequency. The difference between the terms "synchronized" and "locked" is shown by the following. If the reference oscillator of 1,800 kHz is shut off, the Hartley oscillator will continue to oscillate at a frequency of approximately 300 kHz, but only approximately so. It is no longer synchronized or tied in this fashion to the reference oscillator. The countdown circuits discussed previously, however, are locked or tied exactly to the basic reference frequency, and if the input signal stops, the output stops.

7. Heterodyning Heterodyning basically is a process by which the frequency outputs of two oscillators are combined in a mixer circuit and the resultant output signal is some selected algebraic combination of the two input frequencies. Heterodyning is widely used in receivers and transmitters; for instance, the local oscillator in most receivers commercially has its output combined with the incoming rf signal to produce an if signal. The process is sometimes called "beating" two signals together.

Heterodyning is basically a nonlinear process, as shown in Fig. 5. Two oscillators feed a mixer; one oscillator is usually fixed and the other is usually variable. A mixer may be a diode or a vacuum tube with highly nonlinear characteristics. The output of the mixer is a multitude of frequencies. The frequencies of interest are the sum and difference of the two input frequencies $f_1 + f_2$ and $f_1 - f_2$, but there are harmonics of both input frequencies, as well as harmonics of the sum and differences. Some sort of filter, such as an *LC* tank, must be used to select the desired signal from the many frequencies present in the mixer output. For example, in a typical AM radio receiver a frequency of 1,000 kHz is heterodyned (or "beat") with a local oscillator at a frequency of 1,456 kHz to produce the

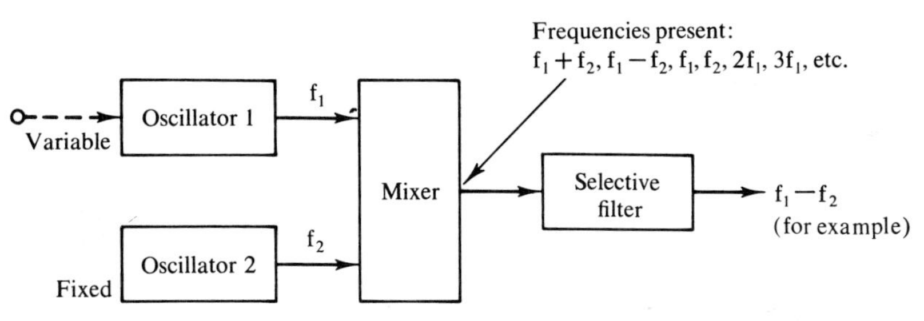

Fig. 5. Heterodyning process.

difference frequency of 456 kHz. A double-tuned transformer is the two-stage filter on the output to select this difference frequency.

The accuracy of the heterodyning process reflects the accuracy of both the input frequencies. The accuracy may be the worst possible combination of both inaccuracies, or in some cases it may be the best possible combination. Statistical averaging processes such as the root-mean-square (rms) process may be used to calculate the most likely accuracy of the resulting frequency.

As mentioned earlier, the heterodyne process finds many uses in receivers, transmitters, and test oscillators. Sometimes it is called a transfer oscillator, which means that a highly accurate oscillator is used to transfer a range of frequencies to a different range of frequencies measurable by another detector or receiver.

8. Sweeping Sweeping refers to another process for manipulating the output frequency of an oscillator. As Fig. 6 shows, a control changes the output frequency of an oscillator, usually in some predetermined fashion but not necessarily linearly. This sketch also shows that as the angle of the input shaft is turned, the output frequency changes in a determined fashion, in this case linearly.

Sweeping an oscillator frequency may be done in a number of ways, such as heterodyning the outputs of two oscillators as discussed above, by some mechanical means, or by an electronic-tuning device. Electronic tuning may be accomplished in several ways, such as by changing the capacitance or inductance electronically. A typical device for changing capacitance electronically is what is called a varactor diode, otherwise known as a voltage-variable capacitor. This refers to a diode that is dc-biased in the reverse direction, and whose capacitance is directly related to the voltage impressed across the diode. Thus by varying the dc bias across the diode, the capacitance is varied and is coupled to an oscillator to control its frequency. Refer to the next section for further details.

Sweeping a frequency finds uses in such purposes as testing the frequency response of a system. In this particular case the amplitude of the swept oscillator would be kept constant and a recorder would be used to record the amplitude of the response signal coming out of the system. By comparing the amplitude of the output with the input signal at each frequency, it is easy to plot a frequency-response curve for the system.

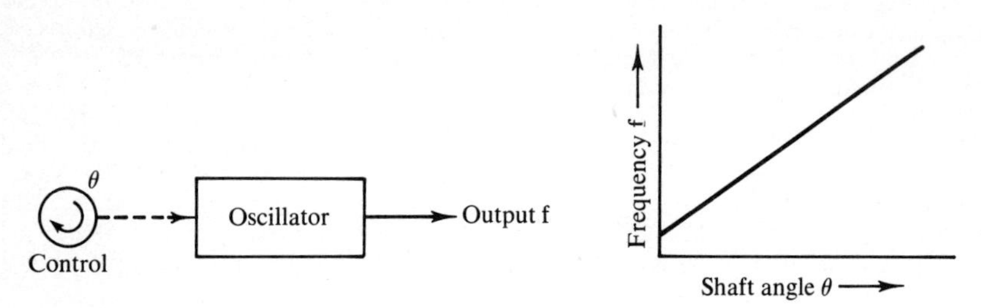

Fig. 6. Frequency sweeping.

9. Varactor Harmonic Generators The capacitance of a reverse-biased diode varies inversely as some function of the applied voltage. Use is made of this fact to control its capacitance. The diode also has a low series resistance so that losses at radio frequency are small or, correspondingly, the Q is high.

Refer to Fig. 7, which shows a varactor harmonic generator that will multiply the input frequency by the simple integral ratio of 3. This is also one type of frequency multiplier. Input power is coupled into the input side of the circuit and through the varactor diode D. The input circuit is series-resonant to f_1 at 144 MHz. The output circuit is tuned to the output frequency f_3, the third harmonic,

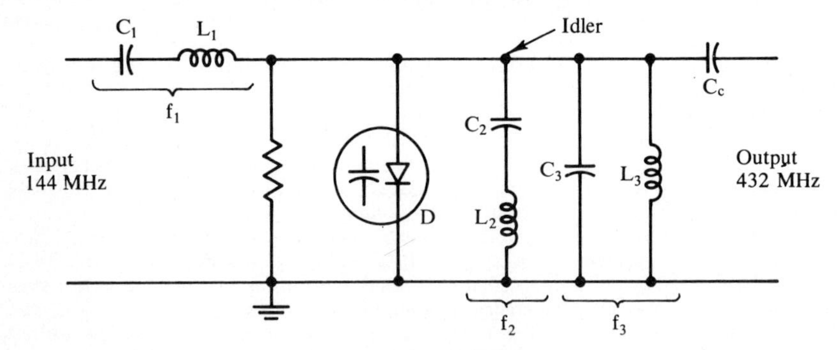

Fig. 7. Varactor tripler.

or 432 MHz. The "idler" circuit tuned to the second harmonic f_2 is necessary to operation of this circuit. The fundamental f_1 and second harmonic f_2 beat together to produce the third harmonic output f_3.

The diode absorbs little power, so that the losses in the circuit are small. Accordingly the conversion efficiency is high, approximately 50 percent for a frequency doubler or 30 percent for a frequency tripler. Frequency doublers or triplers may be coupled together in a chain or cascade fashion for higher-frequency multiplication ratios. For instance, in a doubler chain it has been possible to go from about 12 W of power at 70 MHz to 10 GHz with a power of about 0.1 W.

10. Synthesizers A frequency synthesizer is a rather complicated way of digitally generating any desired frequency within the range of this device (Fig. 8). A highly stable master oscillator has two outputs. First the oscillator's frequency is precisely subdivided by 10, and this in turn is subdivided again by 10, so that two accurate subharmonics are generated, the tenth and the hundredth. Here, the frequencies are 100 kHz, 10 kHz, and 1 kHz. These three frequencies in turn are fed into highly nonlinear devices so that a spectrum of frequencies is generated, starting with the input frequency and continuing with the second, third, and fourth harmonic up through the tenth and beyond. The output of the lowest-frequency spectrum generator would be the frequencies of 1, 2, 3, up through 9 and beyond kHz. The desired harmonic in this spectrum of precise subharmonics from the reference oscillator is picked off by a bandpass filter. The bandpass filter has its frequency selected by a series of switches and need only discriminate against the unwanted harmonics in favor of the desired harmonics by a fairly tolerant ratio. The output of the bandpass filters consists of the selected harmonic

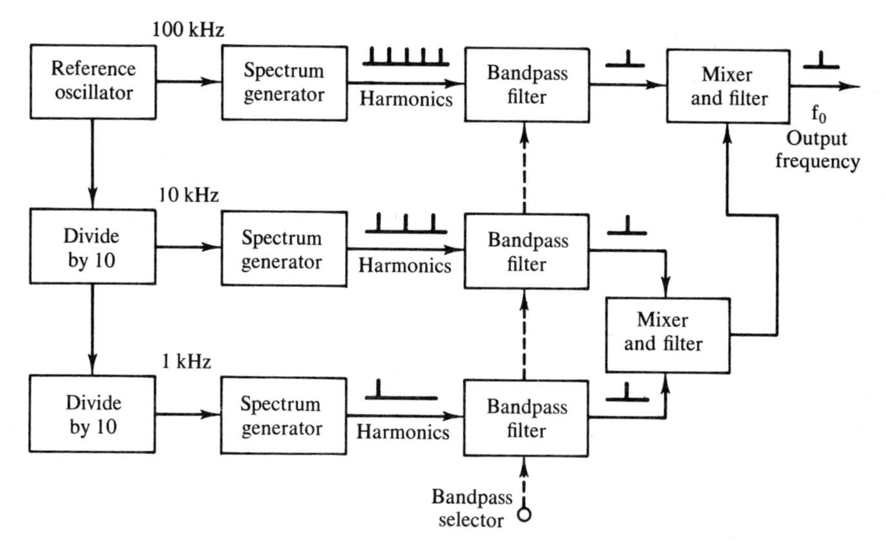

Fig. 8. Frequency synthesis.

of the three basic reference frequencies, all of which derive their accuracy from the master reference oscillator. The three selected harmonics are then combined in two stages with heterodyne mixers and filters, always picking the sum such that the output frequency is the sum of the three selected harmonics. For instance, we could have an output frequency of 247 kHz. This would consist of the second harmonic of the reference oscillator, the fourth harmonic from the tenth subharmonic, and the seventh harmonic of the hundredth subharmonic of the reference oscillator.

There are a number of uses for the extreme accuracy of such a frequency synthesizer. This concept is used in sophisticated transmitters and receivers, as a first use. A frequency-testing device may utilize a highly accurate secondary frequency standard as the reference oscillator, so that frequency variations are approximately 1 part in 10^{10}. The device is very useful for checking the frequency of any device. In addition, the device can be set up for automatic testing, since a frequency can be selected merely by setting up the appropriate switches rather than turning a dial or set of dials. The device also may be used to check out production equipment of transmitters and receivers. The device is programmable; that is, the switches may be operated by relays on a remote basis, such that the checking or testing of equipment may be done automatically under computer control. Spot frequencies may be selected for such purposes, or the frequency may be swept in the area of interest as discussed previously in frequency sweeping. The phase of the output frequency is also controllable on a programmable basis. For instance, two oscillators could be phase-locked together under remote control of one computer.

11. Parametric Devices Parametric devices depend for their operation on a periodic variation of some parameter such as capacitance, conductance, or resistance. Variable-resistance devices have been known for a long time, such as the diode mixer. Such circuits are lossy because of the characteristic of the resistance as a power dissipator. The variable-capacitance frequency multiplier shown above is another related device. Variable-inductance devices have also been known in the past, such as a saturable reactor or magnetic amplifier. Because of the frequency losses in the magnetization of iron, such devices are limited usually to the common line frequencies of 50, 60, or 400 Hz. This means that variable-capacitance devices are the major device for use at high frequencies. Such a capacitive device is known as a varactor, which is a solid-state reverse-biased diode. The capacitance of this device with high applied reverse voltage is low compared with its maximum capacity at zero applied voltages. This capacitive varactor also has the advantage of not dissipating power itself, as does the resistive diode mixer.

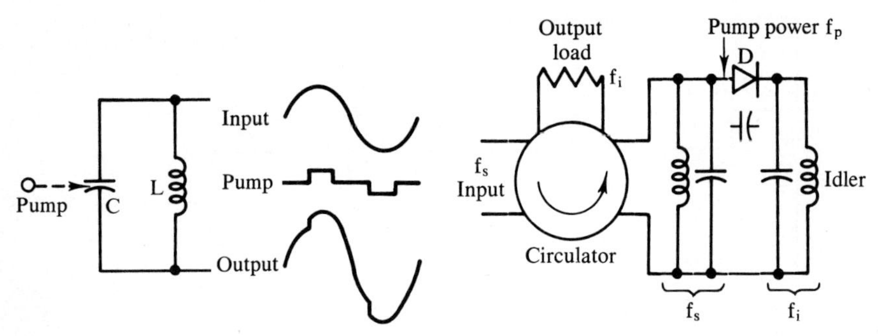

Fig. 9. Mechanically pumped resonant circuit.

Fig. 10. Parametric amplifier with circulator.

Three frequencies are always encountered in parametric devices. The first is the input signal frequency f_s, the second is the pump or source of power f_p, and the third is a related frequency at the idler frequency from which power is amplified and taken at the output f_o. This relationship always holds; namely, $f_p = f_s + f_o$. A familiar example of a parametric device that exhibits loss is the superheterodyne mixer, where one has the signal, pump, and idler frequency corresponding to the input, oscillator, and intermediate frequencies.

Figure 9 shows the basic concept of the operation of a parametric device. An LC resonant circuit is the heart of the device. The capacitance is varied by the spacing, changing the plates mechanically. The charge Q on a capacitor is constant unless there is some current flow. The following equation holds, where C is capacitance and V the voltage: $Q = CV = \text{constant}$. Thus as the spacing between the capacitor plates increases, the capacitance C decreases, and accordingly the impressed voltage V has to increase. The right part of Fig. 9 shows this relationship. There is an input sine wave, and the pump moves the capacitor plates apart at a square wave in phase with the signal frequency. The resultant output shows how the capacitor voltage is increased abruptly as the pump changes the capacitor-plate spacing.

At high frequencies it is impractical to use a square wave, but parametric devices work quite satisfactorily using a sine wave for pumping. The above degenerate case, where the output frequency equals that of the input, has the serious disadvantage that the pump frequency must be exactly twice the input frequency and exactly in phase with it. This requirement is called phase coherence.

The phase-coherent requirement can be relaxed where three frequencies are utilized rather than just two. Figure 10 shows a parametric amplifier using a circulator to separate the input and output or the signal and idler frequencies. The pump frequency is applied directly across the varactor diode *D*. The circuit effectively is a negative-conductance or negative-resistance amplifier, thus providing gain or amplification, with the previous frequency requirement holding that the three frequencies are yet related, $f_p = f_s + f_i$.

12. Masers The term, which comes from work by Gordon, Zeiger, and Townes in the United States in 1954,* is an acronym for microwave amplification by stimulated emission of radiation. The concept is based on atomic physics, the absorption and radiation of microwave energy at a narrow range of frequencies by certain substances. As with visible light, radiant energy can be absorbed by a substance and subsequently reradiated at the same frequency or at different frequencies. The maser utilizes the same physical characteristics, but with a frequency of interest in the far infrared or at microwave frequencies rather than taking place at visible-light frequencies. Thus the maser is an amplifying device that enhances a signal via an interaction with molecules to produce coherent radiation.

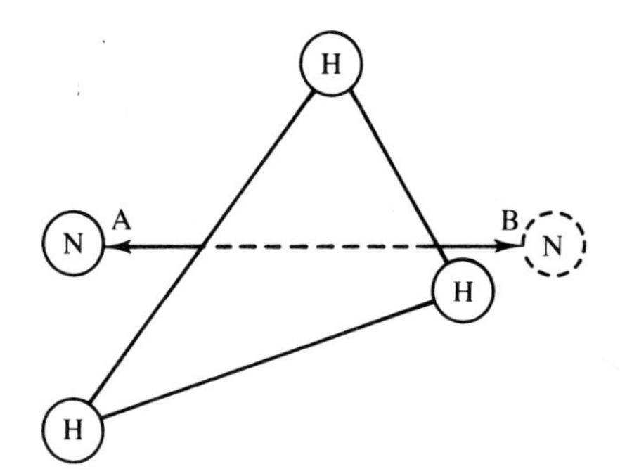

Fig. 11. Vibrating ammonia molecule.

The device has a number of interesting and special uses such as very-low-noise amplifiers and very-narrowband amplifiers and as a primary frequency standard as an oscillator.

13. Theory of the Ammonia Maser At rest, the four atoms in ammonia are almost in the same plane. The three hydrogen atoms define a plane, and at rest the nitrogen atom is almost in this same plane (see Fig. 11). When the ammonia molecule is excited by an incoming quantum of radiation, the nitrogen atom alternates between the two extreme positions *A* and *B*. It is a law of quantum mechanics that the number of atoms in two different energy states are in inverse proportion to the energies by an exponential relationship. Normally there would be a far greater number of molecules in the low-energy state than in the excited or high-energy state. The frequency required to produce the necessary energy is related via Planck's constant as follows: $f_{21} = dE_{21}/h$, where h is Planck's constant of 6.62×10^{-34} joule-seconds and the frequency is approximately 24 GHz for ammonia. After rearrangement, the number of molecules in each state can be written as follows: $n_1/n_2 = e(-dE_{21}/kT) = e(-hf_{21}/kT)$, where T is the absolute temperature in degrees Kelvin, n_1 and n_2 are the numbers of molecules in each state, dE_{21} is the energy change associated with excitation, and k is the atomic constant of 1.38×10^{-23} joules/degree.

* J. P. Gordon, H. Z. Zeiger, and C. H. Townes, The Maser—A New Type of Microwave Amplifier, *Phys. Rev.*, vol. 95, p. 282, 1955.

If some way could be found to remove molecules from the low-energy state, we would have an energy state where there would be more molecules in the excited state than the equilibrium demanded by the above equation. The equilibrium would soon be restored, however, because the excited molecules would decay to the low-energy state with the emission of a quantum of radiation at 24 GHz. But the decay would be random and would produce no useful work. However, if we put in energy at the same frequency at which the ammonia molecules decay into their low-energy state, we could stimulate radiation or induce emission. Moreover, there is an interesting quantum-mechanical property, that the incoming electromagnetic field of the signal, even though weak, interacts with the excited molecules and stimulates them to decay in phase or exact synchronism with the incoming weak field. Thus the output is an amplified wave at the incoming signal frequency and in phase with it.

14. Ammonia-maser Device Figure 12 shows the cross section of a simple ammonia maser. At the left is a source of ammonia molecules similar to the electron gun of a cathode-ray tube. The molecules are not ionized, but the ensuing molecular beam does consist of both resting or unexcited molecules and molecules in an excited state in equilibrium with the low-energy molecules. The purpose of the selector, usually called a focuser, is to disturb the equilibrium in the ammonia

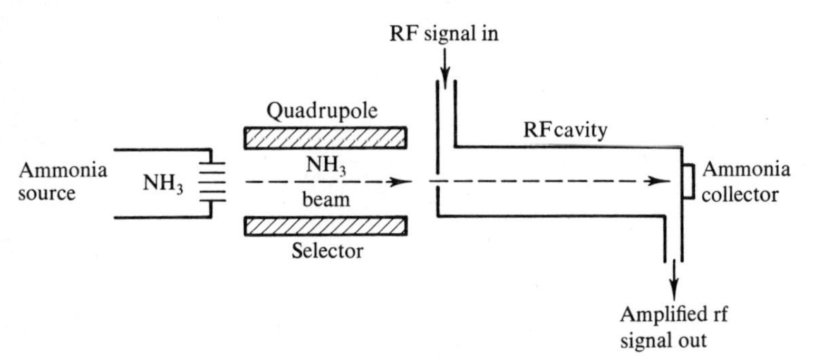

Fig. 12. Ammonia maser.

beam in a direction favorable to amplification. The selector is a pair of four electrodes called a quadrupole that attracts the unexcited molecules and pulls them away from the center of the molecular beam. The unexcited ammonia molecules in the presence of a static dc field have an induced charge upon them and when so charged are influenced or attracted to the selector and thus move out of the center of the molecular beam. The excited ammonia molecules, on the other hand, already have the nitrogen atom in either extreme position from the plane defined by the hydrogen atoms. As such, no further charge can be induced by persuading the nitrogen atom to move off its axis. It is already at one of two limits and alternates between them. So the excited molecules in the beam produced by the ammonia source remain in the center of the beam through the selector and enter the microwave cavity.

The beam of ammonia molecules entering the microwave cavity has a considerably higher proportion of excited molecules than equilibrium conditions demand. An interaction occurs in the cavity between the weak incoming signal and the excited ammonia molecules. The resulting interaction is one of stimulated radiation, as discussed previously. The rf input energy induces the excited molecules to relax, but in phase coherence with the incoming signal. Thus the incoming signal is amplified and present in greater energy at the output, the right part of the cavity, than at the left. The amplified rf signal is coupled out of the cavity at the far or right end. The ammonia beam is stopped or collected at this point, removed from the cavity, and returned to the ammonia source.

15. Ruby Maser In addition to changing the equilibrium distribution of unexcited and excited molecules via a selector or focusing device, the equilibrium can be disturbed by pumping or producing excited molecules with a frequency different from the one at which amplification is to take place. A restriction is placed on the other frequency; it has to be at a higher energy or higher frequency than the frequency at which amplification is to take place. Such a maser has three frequencies: the pump frequency, the signal frequency, and a third frequency, which results when the molecules which have gone from the excited frequency via the signal frequency to an intermediate level decay from this intermediate energy level to the original and unexcited level. A ruby maser typically is a device in which three-frequency maser action can take place. The doping level is rather critical; an active ruby will contain about 0.05 percent of chromium-atom doping. The ruby will be inactive if the doping level increases to 1 percent chromium atoms in the aluminum oxide matrix of the ruby crystal.

Figure 13 shows such a ruby maser with two types of crystals. The passive crystal above is to attenuate undesired signals and is built with about 1 percent

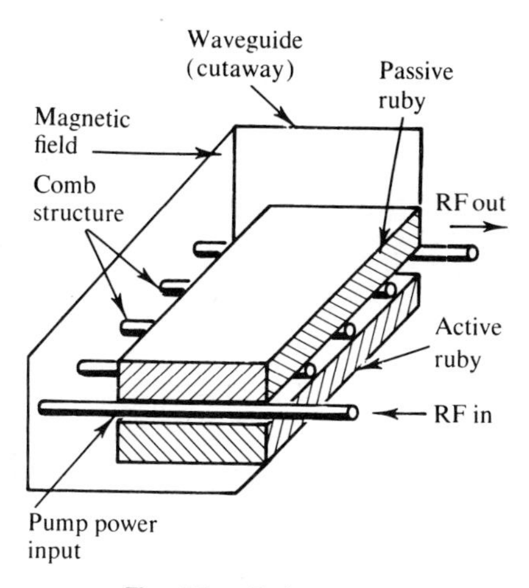

Fig. 13. Ruby maser.

chromic atoms. The active ruby crystal below is doped with about 0.05 percent chromium atoms in the aluminum oxide crystal lattice. The chromic atoms in a magnetic field oscillate in a paramagnetic mode at a frequency in the microwave region of about 19 GHz.

The incoming rf energy is slowed down to about 1 percent of the speed of light by a slow wave structure due to the comb or pins distributed linearly along the amplifying section of the waveguide. The amplified rf signal is taken out at the other end of the comb structure via the last long pin. The chromium atoms are excited by pump power conducted into the waveguide from the left. The chromium atoms decay to an intermediate level under stimulation from the weak incoming rf energy. The signal is amplified in a traveling-wave fashion; the amplified rf signal is taken out at the far end. The purpose of the passive ruby crystal is to attenuate drastically any back wave that may start either as a result of the spatial characteristic of the traveling wave or from reflections from improper terminations.

Both the ammonia and ruby masers can be used as very selective, low-noise amplifiers or as highly stable reference oscillators.

A related device is the laser, but at the much higher frequency of visible light.

Chapter 13

Signal-level Control and Modulation

D. H. SCHUSTER, Ph.D.

Departments of Psychology and Computer Science,
Iowa State University, Ames, Iowa

1. Introduction This chapter deals with controlling the level or amplitude of a signal. This can be done statically or dynamically. A relatively long term or static change in signal amplitude would be called "signal-level control." A short-term or dynamic change in signal amplitude as a function of another signal is called "amplitude modulation."

Adjusting signal level means that the signal must be either amplified or attenuated in order to bring the voltage or the power to some desired level. When the wanted output signal is to be larger than the input signal, this requires gain or amplification. When the output signal is to be smaller than the input signal, a loss is said to occur or the signal is attenuated.

2. Measurement of Gain There are two ways to express voltage gain or loss. The first of these is known as voltage gain and, as discussed above, may actually be a loss. This is simply the ratio of the output voltage to the input voltage, V.G. = e_o/e_{in}. Usually the input is adjusted or normalized to 1 V for this purpose, although the input voltage actually may be some arbitrary quantity such as 0.03 V.

The second way to express gain is to take the logarithm to the base 10 of the two ratios and multiply by a constant. The formula for decibels (dB) of voltage gain runs as follows: dB = $20 \log_{10} e_o/e_{in}$. DB gain assumes that the input and output impedances are constant or the same. This may not always be the case, and if so, a correction for different impedances must be included. The use of decibels (tenths of bels) comes about because they are units of a practical size and without decimal parts in many cases.

There are two ways of computing this gain formula; the above one was given for voltage. If power is being considered rather than voltage, the basic formula for decibels gain reads $dB_{power} = 10 \log_{10} p_o/p_{in}$.

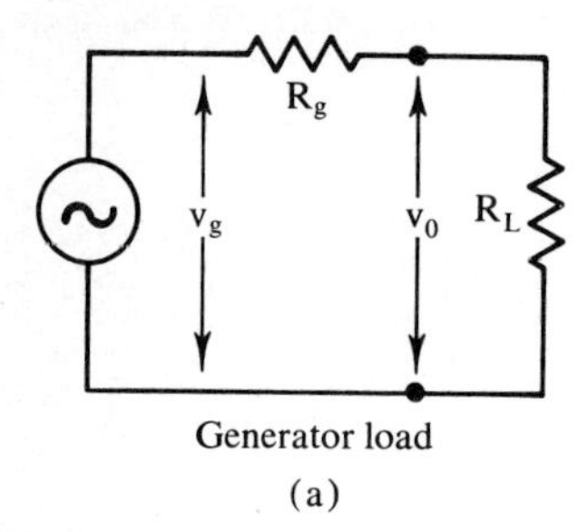

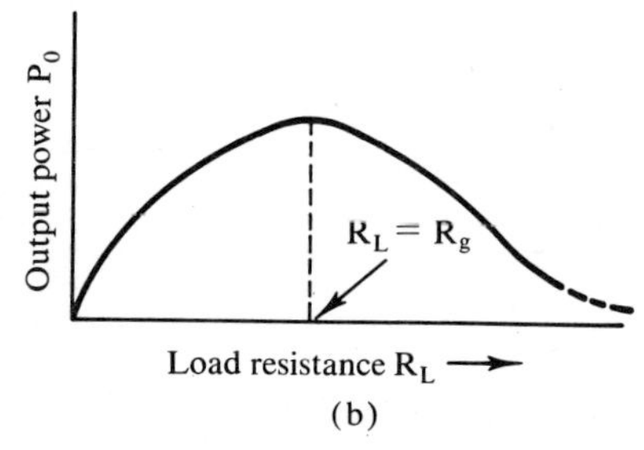

Fig. 1. Generator-load matching.

3. Signal Level Referred to a Standard Sometimes the abbreviation "dBm," which stands for decibels with respect to 1 mW, is used. This is a basic audio measurement and refers to a power level of 1 mW being dissipated in a 600-Ω resistor. This is typical of telephone lines. Occasionally other decibel measurements are used, such as dB(sp) in acoustics, where the "sp" refers to sound pressure at the typical limit of human hearing, a sound pressure of 0.0001 dyne/cm^2. Thus decibels are not restricted to measuring electrical voltage or power gain but are useful anywhere signals over large ranges are to be compared.

4. Impedance Matching Another relevant concept is that of impedance matching. This refers to making the load impedance match, or equal, the generator impedance. This is necessary in many cases with fast-rise-time pulses and in high-frequency circuitry. In many other cases, such as at audio frequency and intermediate frequency, or in amplifiers where impedance matching or power gain is not a problem, impedance matching is ignored. A generator can be likened to an equivalent circuit with a generator producing a voltage v_g across its internal impedance or resistance R_g. Refer to Fig. 1. The output terminals feed a load impedance, a resistor E_L. All physically real generators do indeed have at least some internal impedance or resistance, even though in many cases it is quite small compared with a typical load impedance. For a given generator resistance R_g, there is a nonlinear function expressing the amount of power P_L transferred to the load R_L as the resistance R_L is varied systematically starting near zero and proceeding to large values. The second sketch in Fig. 1 shows this relationship, and it has a definite maximum. The maximum power in the load R_L occurs when the load resistance just equals the generator resistance R_g. This is the pure-resistance case, and if there is a reactive component to the generator impedance, it must be offset by the complementary reactance in the load such that the two reactances cancel but the two resistive components remain equal. This procedure of making the load resistance equal to the generator resistance is called impedance matching. The penalty for this impedance matching is that one always dissipates half of the power in the generator and only half of the power from the generator is available to the load.

5. Amplification Amplification is defined simply as applying an input signal to an active device, such as a transistor or vacuum tube, and the resulting output-signal level is larger than the input signal. In such a case, a voltage gain is said to have occurred.

The general symbol for an amplifier without showing its internal connections is that of a large symmetrical triangle pointed toward the right (see Fig. 2). Occasionally one will find some notation such as "$G = 10$" written inside the triangle. This means that the voltage gain equals 10 V/V; the output is 10 times larger

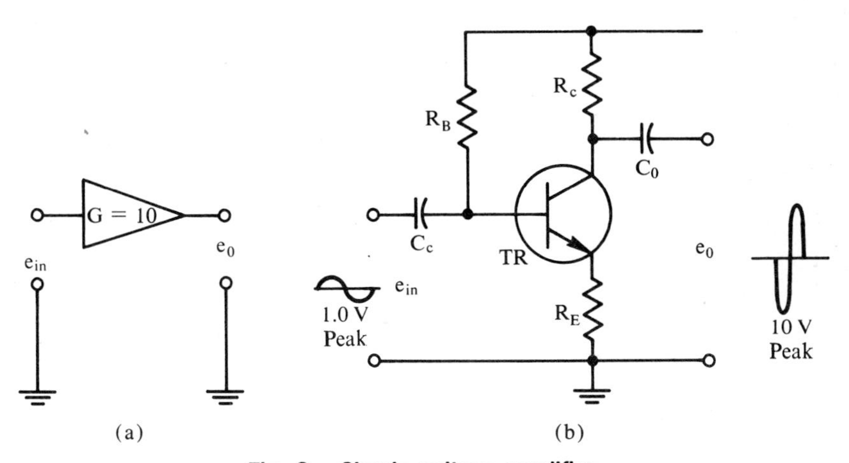

Fig. 2. Simple voltage amplifier.

than the input. If present, a minus sign means a phase change of 180° from input to output.

A simplified circuit diagram for an elementary amplifier is shown in Fig. 2. This is called a grounded-emitter transistor amplifier with an unbypassed emitter resistor R_e. An input voltage e_{in} is applied through a coupling capacitor to the base of the transistor *TR*. The amplified signal is obtained by a similar coupling capacitor from the collector of the transistor to the output terminal labeled e_o. The transistor uses controlled input current to control the output or collector current. The transistor essentially is a current-amplifying device, wherein a small alternating current applied to the base of the transistor is amplified many times and produces a much larger variation in the collector current. These variations are appropriately coupled to or from the transistor elements via capacitors.

Let us see what the gain of this simple amplifier means. Assume that a positive-going sine wave with a peak voltage of 1.0 V as shown is applied to the input of the transistor amplifier. At the output simultaneously is an amplified but inverted or negative-going sine wave with a peak voltage of 10 V. The voltage gain is computed by applying the previous formula, V.G. $= e_o/e_{in} = 10/1.0 = 10$. If one were to apply an input voltage of 0.18 V, the resultant output voltage would be the voltage gain times the input voltage, or 1.8 V. The power gain as measured in dB is dB $= 20 \log e_o/e_{in} = 20 \log 10/1.0 = 20 \log (10) = 20 \times 1.0 = 20$ dB. Remember that this formula assumes that the input and output impedances of this transistor amplifier are equal, an assumption only approximately met in this case.

To be a purist, one would have to add a correction factor 10 $\log_{10} R_{in}/R_o$. For voltage gain only, not power gain, this correction can be omitted.

The gain of a single stage as shown above may be insufficient for many purposes. A simple procedure is to couple a series of single stages together to make a multiple-stage amplifier. This results in a considerable increase in gain, since with appropriate impedance matching, the gain is simply the product of the gain for each individual stage under load. For instance, assuming equal input and output resistances for the above circuit, putting three of these in cascade would result in a voltage gain of 10^3 or 60 dB.

Unless suitable means are employed, multistage amplifiers in many cases tend to be multiple-stage oscillators. Negative feedback is utilized to stabilize the gain at a constant value as well as to eliminate possible oscillations in such amplifiers. Negative feedback may be either of two forms. A common type of feedback is to employ an *RC* coupling network (such as a large resistor in series with a capacitor) connected directly from the output of the multistage amplifier to its input. This requires 180° phase change between the two terminals. A second type of feedback is shown by the unbypassed emitter resistor R_e in the single-transistor amplifier circuit of Fig. 2*b*. The operation of this feedback may be appreciated as follows: The base-emitter diode can be considered separately from the collector-base diode. When the input voltage increases, the base-emitter diode

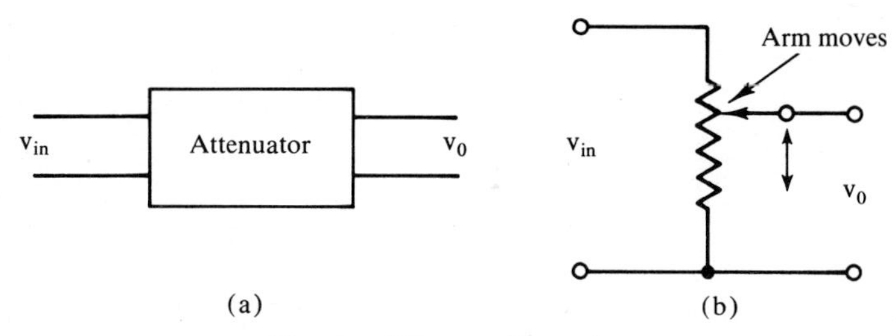

Fig. 3. Simple attenuator.

current increases, and consequently a portion of the input signal builds up across the emitter resistor R_e. This effectively is out of phase with the input signal, as a signal applied at the emitter would be amplified in phase at the collector. Thus bucking occurs; the effect of the input signal is diluted by the unbypassed resistor R_e. Both feedback methods are employed in practice. Other names are voltage feedback and current feedback.

6. Attenuation Attenuation refers to the fact that the output signal from a black box or electronic circuit is lower in amplitude or signal level than the signal applied to the input. For instance, in the diagram for Fig. 3, v_o would be lower in magnitude than v_{in}. As with an amplifier, the loss or attentuation can be expressed either as a linear ratio or in decibels. Sometimes a change in absolute level will be used to specify attenuation, such as the output signal is so many "dBm." This has the same meaning as before, namely, a 1-mW reference. Attenuations expressed in decibels are typically negative numbers; the minus sign means "loss," the opposite of "gain."

A simple way to implement a voltage loss is with a potentiometer, more simply called a "pot" (see Fig. 3). The input voltage to a pot is applied across the entire resistance, and the output voltage comes from a common terminal and the movable arm. The arm of this variable resistor can range smoothly from one end to the other. At the ground end, the output voltage is zero, and at the top end the output voltage equals the full input voltage v_{in}. Between these two extremes, an adjustable proportion of the input is available as output. In general, $v_o = \theta v_{in}$, where θ refers to the arm or wiper setting in percent of the total angular rotation over which resistance changes linearly.

Pots are widely used for control ratios of 10:1 up to approximately 1,000:1. A linear pot, wherein the resistance changed linearly with angular change, would be used with small ratios, and "log" pots would be utilized for large ratios where the resistance changed logarithmically as a function of rotation. A logarithmic resistance would be fabricated with small resistance changes toward the very top part of the pot and progressively larger resistance changes with rotation as the pot arm came close to the bottom end of the pot above.

A pot has simplicity and economy in its favor. Its disadvantages, however, are that the loss ratio may not be controlled as precisely as desired, that the output impedance or resistance varies considerably as a function of the angle of rotation, and that it may have some leakage of signal from input to output because the pot arm connection is in close proximity to the terminal for the input voltage. To get around these, the pot may be calibrated or adjusted to provide a precise ratio control. In addition, there are precision pots with a single turn or multiple turns, to provide a precise ratio control or voltage-dividing section. This sort of precision costs money. Compensating for the other disadvantages is complicated.

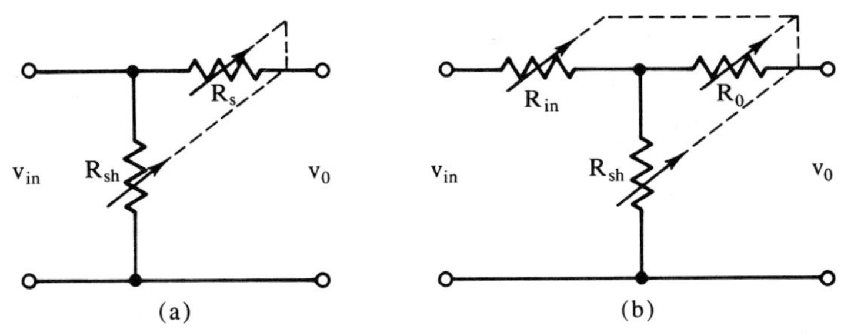

Fig. 4. Constant-impedance attenuators. (*a*) L pad, Z_o = constant. (*b*) T pad, $Z_{in} = Z_o$ = constant.

Maintaining a constant output impedance is of value in many cases, such as coupling a power amplifier to a hi-fi loudspeaker or in pulse work. Two schemes to control the output impedance are via the use of L and T pads. These are discussed below.

The L pad shown in Fig. 4 provides for a constant output impedance via the scheme of ganging two pots together. The name comes from its topological similarity to an inverted *L*. The shunt pot is arranged to be at a maximum when the series pot is at a minimum; this corresponds to minimum attenuation and maximum transfer of signal from input to output. As the pots are rotated together toward some intermediate value, the series resistance decreases and the shunt pot adds resistance to maintain a constant impedance to the load. When the pots are rotated to the minimum, the series pot is at a maximum and the shunt pot is at ground, and the constant load impedance is effected entirely by the series resistor.

The T pad shown in the second part of Fig. 4 provides both a constant output and a constant input impedance. The derivation of its name should be obvious from its connections. Pulse generators have this particular requirement that the pulse generator must "see" or be loaded by a constant impedance in spite of the fact that one wishes a variable output-signal level, also at constant impedance. The T pad does this well. All three pots are ganged together appropriately in a precise fashion to accomplish this. The T pad essentially is like an L pad as discussed above, but with the addition of an input arm to present a constant impedance to the source.

Attenuation may be accomplished in discrete steps or jumps with digital switches.

The advantages are that impedance matching is preserved via the use of individual T-pad sections used singly or in combination. Another advantage is the precision with which the attenuation can be controlled. Finally, leakage may be minimized by the use of electrostatic shields from one section to another. The impedance matching is ensured via the use of constant input-output impedance T-pad sections (refer to Fig. 5). The individual T pad may be switched in or out by the use of a ganged double-pole double-throw (DPDT) switch per section. Pushbutton switches usually are used for this. The fixed (nonadjustable) T pad is either completely in the circuit or would be bypassed by the switch. The attenuation in a digital attenuator such as this is simply the sum of the individual section losses measured in decibels. For instance, the loss in each section could be 20 dB, and so if both sections were joined in series by the switches, the total loss for both attenuators would be 20 + 20, or 40 dB. Note that the corresponding voltage-loss ratios would be 10 and 100 for the use of one and two sections appropriately.

7. Modulation Modulation consists of imposing information on a signal to be transmitted for the purpose of communicating with another person. Indian smoke signals are an early form of modulation or digital communication. When radio

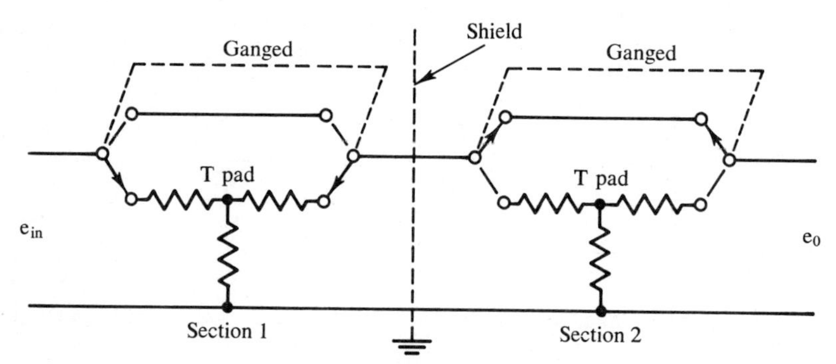

Fig. 5. Digital attenuator.

was first invented, Marconi transmitted information with a dot-dash system; that is, he either turned the radio transmitter on or left it off for short periods. The resulting Morse code, a series of dots and dashes, was a gross way of putting information or intelligence on the radio frequency transmitted. Two of the major types of modulation employed these days are amplitude and frequency modulation. In amplitude modulation (AM) the amplitude or intensity of the rf output signal itself varies in keeping with the intelligence or information being imposed, typically at an audio-frequency rate (see Fig. 6). In frequency modulation (FM), the frequency of the output signal is varied in keeping with the modulating information. Thus large or loud signals provide large excursions in frequency from a resting frequency, and high-frequency signals mean that such excursions in frequency deviation take place faster at a rate in keeping with the modulating signal.

Other types of modulation are phase modulation and single-sideband, where the carrier and one sideband are suppressed and just one sideband is transmitted from an original AM signal. There are several types of digital communication or pulse modulation. The modulating signal, or intelligence, is first converted to pulses. Then the rf carrier is pulsed appropriately for the type of pulse modulation used. The modulating pulses may control the amplitude, frequency, on-time, or phase of the carrier. Respectively, these are called pulse-amplitude modulation, frequency-shift keying, pulse-width modulation, and pulse-phase modulation.

Uses of modulation are many. Commercial radio on the low-frequency band uses AM and FM in the high-frequency band. Television uses AM for transmitting the picture information and FM for the sound information. Frequency-shift keying and pulse-phase modulation are widely used in commercial radio telegraphy.

8. Amplitude Modulation Figure 7 shows a simple scheme for amplitude modulation. Here an oscillator produces a frequency of 1 MHz, which is fed to an rf amplifier. A microphone produces an audio signal as the intelligence or information; this is amplified and applied to the rf amplifier via the modulation transformer. The modulator varies the effective voltage from the power supply such that the supply voltage to the rf amplifier may be doubled or cut to zero on audio peaks. When the power-supply voltage doubles, the corresponding amplitude

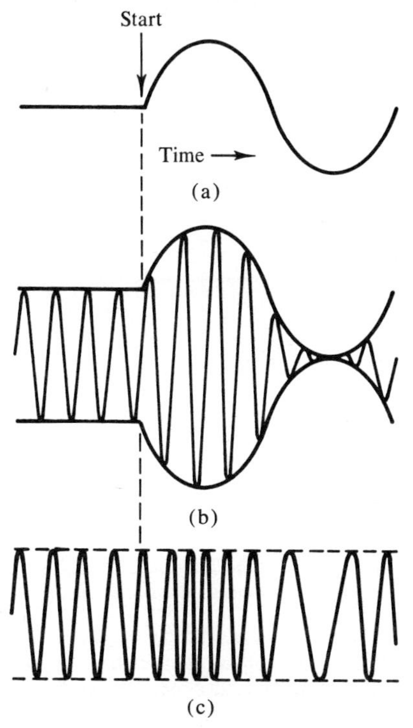

Fig. 6. Amplitude and frequency modulation. (*a*) Audio modulating signal. (*b*) Amplitude-modulated wave. (*c*) Frequency-modulated wave.

of the output rf signal also doubles. When the modulator cuts the power-supply voltage effectively to zero on the audio dips, the rf amplifier's output is zero. The output waveform from the amplifier thus is modulated radio frequency, with the frequency from the oscillator yet present but the amplitude or envelope of the carrier varying at a rate determined by the modulator and the voice signal from the microphone. Low-level audio signals produce small variations in the rf signal; large audio signals produce large peaks and valleys as shown in Fig. 6*b*.

Mathematically amplitude modulation can be expressed as $e_{out} = A(t) \cos w_o t$, where e_{out} is the modulated rf output voltage, $A(t)$ the envelope amplitude or rf signal level, w_o the frequency of the rf oscillator, and t the time. With no modulating signal present, the amplitude $A(t)$ is consant. Under modulation, however, $A(t) = 1 + \cos w_m t$, where w_m is the modulating signal frequency, typically af as in the example here. Thus under modulation, $e_{out} = (1 + \cos w_m t) \cos w_o t =$

$\cos w_o t + \cos w_m t \cos w_o t$. By using a trigonometric identity, this converts to $e_{out} = \cos w_o t + \cos(w_o \pm w_m)t$.

Thus the modulated rf output can be split into three frequency components, the original oscillator frequency yet at its previous amplitude, as well as two "sideband" frequencies. The upper sideband is the sum of the modulating and oscillator frequencies, whereas the lower sideband is the difference between the oscillator and the modulating frequencies. All the modulating information is contained in these sidebands and not in the constant-amplitude carrier. It is for this reason that both the carrier and one sideband may be suppressed and the remaining sideband transmitted. The information is later recovered with a special receiver for single-sideband (SSB) work.

The percentage of modulation is determined by the ratio of the peaks and valleys under modulation to the amplitude of the resting carrier. In the above case where the rf signal went to twice its resting amplitude on the audio peaks and to zero amplitude on the audio valleys, this is called 100 percent modulation. Most commercial AM transmitters operate with approximately 80 to 90 percent modulation

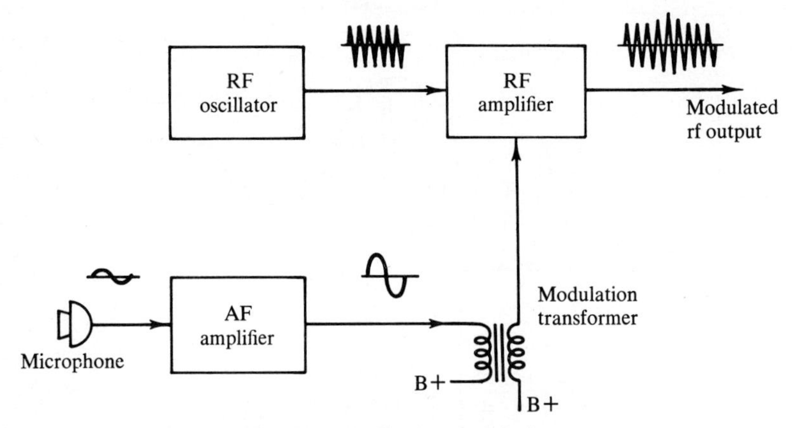

Fig. 7. Amplitude modulation.

as a practical limit. When 100 percent modulation is exceeded, spurious signals are generated at large amplitude because of the nonlinear aspects of the device at that point.

Amplitude modulation is used for commercial broadcast transmitters in the AM broadcast frequencies and from 550 to 1,600 kHz and for the video signal on TV transmitters. Many radio amateurs, or "hams," use amplitude modulation for their radio-telephone conversations. Many test oscillators will produce amplitude-modulated test signals to check out equipment.

9. AM-signal Detection Detection is the process whereby the intelligence or information imposed on an amplitude-modulated rf signal is recovered in a receiver. The process consists essentially of detecting the envelope which corresponds to the modulating signal and removing or stripping the carrier away. The sketch in Fig. 8 shows such a typical device. Modulated radio frequency from the transformer secondary encounters a diode *D*; this detector is a nonlinear device in that it leaves just half of the modulated rf waveform. The filter output cannot follow the rf signal and so integrates its gaps to leave only the envelop of the waveform, which is the desired information or recovered intelligence.

The sketch shows the commonly used diode detector. Radio-frequency energy is inductively coupled to a diode. There are other types of detectors, such as the product detector or an amplifier biased to cutoff; these all have the capability of being nonlinear and permitting only one half of the input rf waveform to get through; this is then filtered to leave only the low-frequency (audio) component as the desired information.

10. Frequency Modulation Frequency modulation is simply a deliberate variation of the frequency of an rf oscillator in keeping with the amplitude excursions of an input waveform. Refer to Fig. 6*c*, where on the positive peak of the sine wave, the frequency of the oscillator speeds up instantaneously in time. Thus a change in frequency of the frequency-modulated wave corresponds to a change in the amplitude of the input signal, and the rate of these frequency changes corresponds to the modulating frequency itself. Note that the amplitude of the modulated waveform itself stays constant, in contrast to amplitude modulation.

There are many uses of frequency modulation. For instance, there are commercial FM broadcast stations in the frequency range from 88 to 108 MHz. High fidelity is ensured by the wide bandwidth of 200 kHz and the fact that static from lightning or manmade interference causes little interference with FM signals. Most noise

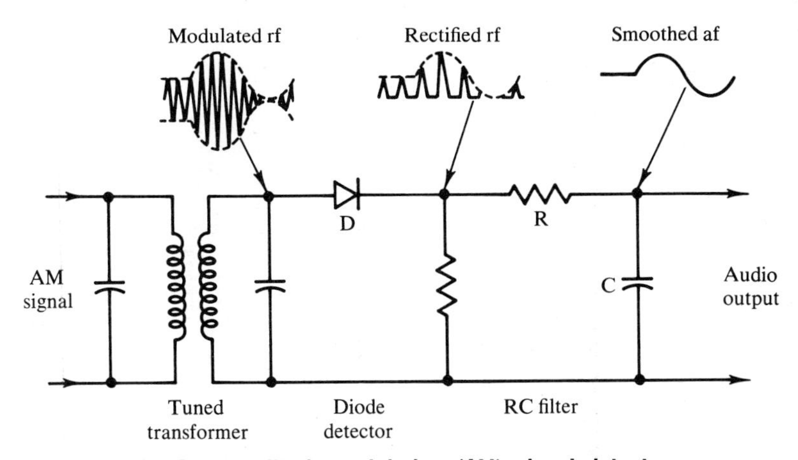

Fig. 8. Amplitude-modulation (AM) signal detector.

sources produce amplitude disturbances rather than frequency disturbances. In addition, an FM receiver designer takes pains to ensure insensitivity to variations in amplitude and sensitivity only to frequency excursions. Data frequently are sent over FM radio links, or telemetry, as when it is desired to relay the physical condition of an astronaut in space to earth for physiological-monitoring purposes. For instance, the astronaut's heartbeat and mental condition can be relayed in this fashion. Typically this is done with narrowband FM and a frequency spectrum of only 5 kHz instead of the wide bandwidth in commercial FM broadcasting. Sometimes a double FM process is used; a physical parameter such as heart rate is converted to FM audio-frequency changes, and these in turn are imposed as frequency excursions on the transmitted carrier. This results in what is called FM/FM telemetry. The major feature of this type of telemetry is the preservation of the dc levels of the signals with high fidelity, something that is hard to do with amplitude modulation.

11. FM-signal Generation The circuit in Fig. 9 shows a simplified Hartley oscillator that has a capacitance controlled by a microphone. Voice fluctuations vary the spacing in the capacitor to change the oscillator frequency.

What controls the change in capacitance can be one of a number of things. For instance, a condenser microphone could be used such that the ribbon in the microphone vibrates in response to voice variations; the ribbon can be fastened to one plate of the tank capacitor and the rest of the microphone connected to the other side of the oscillator tank circuit. Speaking into the microphone changes its capacitance. This in turn changes the resonant frequency of the oscillator and introduces the desired frequency change or frequency modulation. Another simple-minded scheme could be that the microphone would go through a conventional amplifier

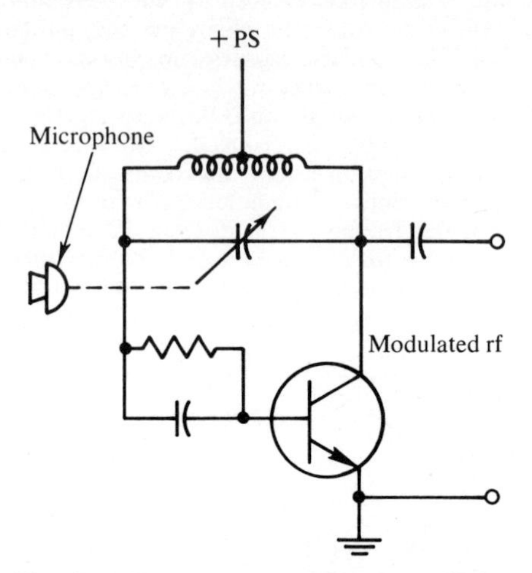

Fig. 9. Frequency-modulated oscillator.

and then the output speaker could be attached to one side of the *LC* tank capacitor to shake and change its capacitance to produce FM. Another scheme would be to use a varactor or voltage-variable diode, a back-biased diode whose capacitance is controlled by the applied audio voltage. More complicated schemes exist but are not discussed here.

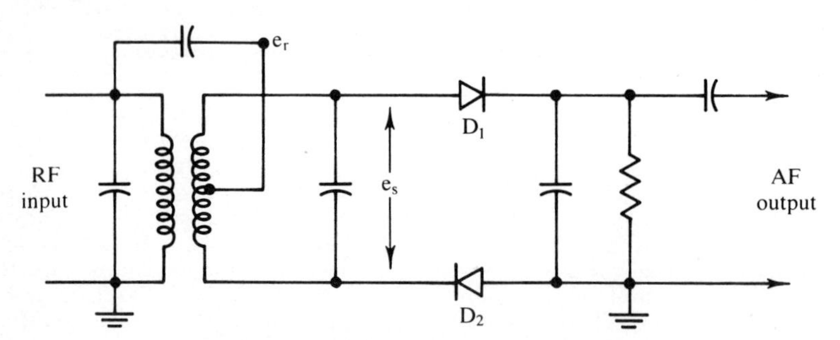

Fig. 10. Ratio detector for FM signals.

12. FM-signal Detection Detection of a frequency-modulated signal to recover the audio intelligence is more difficult than for amplitude modulation. A circuit called a frequency discriminator is used with a preceding limiter which ensures constant-amplitude signals. Figure 10 shows a simple frequency discriminator called a ratio detector.

The ratio detector utilizes the characteristic of a parallel-resonant circuit to shift the phase of a signal when its frequency is above or below its natural resonant frequency. There are two voltages of interest in the ratio detector (see Fig. 11). A reference voltage e_r is capacitatively coupled from the input rf signal. The secondary signal e_s is induced across the secondary of the doubly tuned transformer. The circuit shifts the phase of the resultant combined signal $e_r + e_s$ differently above and below the resonant frequency. This affects the voltages applied to the two diodes D_1 and D_2.

The secondary voltage e_s has a phase shift of 90° with respect to the reference voltage e_r from the primary because of normal transformer action. Half of the secondary voltage e_s leads the reference voltage, and because of the phase inversion, the voltage at the bottom lags the reference voltage by 90°. The voltage applied to each diode is the vector resultant of half of the secondary voltage e_s appropriately combined with the reference voltage e_r. The voltages applied to the diodes are of opposite phases but equal in magnitude at resonance.

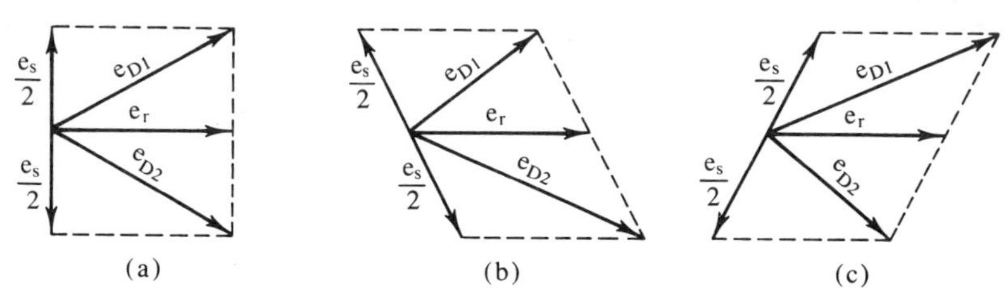

Fig. 11. Phase relationships in ratio detector. (*a*) At resonance. (*b*) Below resonance. (*c*) Above resonance.

Below its resonant frequency, the parallel-tuned resonant circuit here behaves inductively, and its secondary voltage e_s lags the reference voltage e_r by 90°. The second phase diagram (Fig. 11*b*) shows this case, and here the bottom diode D_2 receives a voltage larger than the voltage applied to the upper diode D_1. Above the resonant frequency the last phase diagram (Fig. 11*c*) shows that E_s leads the reference voltage E_e by 90° as the circuit is capacitive. In this case voltage applied to the top diode D_1 is larger than the voltage applied to D_2. Accordingly, above and below the resonance frequency the voltages applied to the two diodes change with a corresponding change in the dc output voltage. The changes in frequency excursion are thus detected and are reflected in corresponding change in output voltage. These are coupled via a capacitor to an audio amplifier as the af signal output.

Section Four

Using Electronic Instruments

The very act of using an electronic instrument can change the total circuit, of which the instrument has become a part, to such an extent that error can be introduced and completely extraneous information generated. The instrument, therefore, should not be used without consideration of its effect on the circuit and the circuit's effect on it.

This section deals with common problems encountered in the use of all instruments. Any instrument will be confronted with these problems whether it is a signal-measurement or signal-generating device. To ignore these potential problems is to risk not only grossly inaccurate results but damage to either the circuit or the instrument. This information, therefore, is intended not only to help the user protect his data and his equipment, but also to lead him to the proper selection of instruments in any application, based on its circuit use, operating environment, and component construction.

Chapter **14**

Impedance Considerations

K. D. BAKER, Ph.D., and D. A. BURT

Utah State University, Logan, Utah

INTRODUCTION

Electrical impedance may be defined as an apparent opposition to the flow of current in an electric circuit. Quantitatively, impedance (Z) is the ratio of the voltage (V) across a circuit to the current (I) flowing in the circuit (Ohm's law):

$$Z = \frac{V}{I} \tag{1}$$

An understanding of the impedance concept is important for proper usage of nearly all electrical measuring instruments and the correct interpretation of the measured values. Whenever a measuring instrument is connected to another device, attention should be given to the effect of the added loading (or changing the total impedance attached to the device) on the operation of the device, particularly with respect to the accuracy of the measured values.

Ideally, the application of a test instrument to the device under test would not disturb the operation of the device, and the measured values would be identical to those values in the device when the test instrument was not connected. Unfortunately, test instruments require extraction of energy from the device under test (by drawing a current) and thus modify the operation to varying degrees depending upon the impedance levels of both the test instrument and the device under test. For example, almost all electronic circuits will be affected by a voltage measurement using a common-type low-impedance multimeter. Typically voltage readings in a transistor circuit may be 10 to 20 percent low, while vacuum-tube circuits can be 50 percent low or worse. On the other hand, high-impedance electronic voltmeters such as a vacuum-tube voltmeter (VTVM) will read values that are not appreciably lower than the undisturbed circuit values in all but the highest-impedance circuits such as field-effect-transistor circuits.

In cases involving signal sources such as signal generators and pulse generators, the output-signal amplitude of the instrument is calibrated only when a specified impedance is connected to its output terminals. Any other value of impedance will result in magnitude errors unless corrections are made for the impedance level involved. Additionally, unless the impedance of the source is made equal to that of the load applied to its output terminals (achieving this condition is called impedance matching), troublesome signal reflections may occur, also resulting in calibration errors and in many cases spurious signals. Similar considerations are important in connecting output devices such as loudspeakers, indicating equipment (such as meters and recorders), and wattmeters.

Impedance-related problems of measurements are complicated by the fact that the impedance levels are dependent on the frequency and waveform of the signals. Often an instrument that does not affect the test device appreciably at low audio frequencies will be completely useless at a few hundred kilohertz because of drastic loading at these higher frequencies.

In the discussion that follows, an introduction to the impedance concept will be followed by specific problems and cases related to giving due consideration to the impedance aspects for proper measurement techniques.

THE IMPEDANCE CONCEPT

The current flowing in an electric circuit as a result of a given impressed voltage is determined by the circuit impedance; the higher the impedance, the more the circuit "impedes" the flow of current, hence the lower the value of current. A conceptual aid to the uninitiated reader is the analogy of the electrical system to the flow of water through a pipe system. The amount of water that flows through a pipe is dependent on two factors: the water pressure at the input and the critical characteristics of the pipe such as size, shape, and smoothness. The amount of water flow is analogous to the flow of electrons or the current through the electric circuit; the forcing pressure is analogous to the applied voltage, and the properties of the pipe that restrict or impede the water flow are analogous to the electrical impedance. Thus for a given pressure we can vary the water flow by varying water-system impedance by the setting of a valve. Similarly for a given voltage current can be controlled by varying the circuit impedance.

The impedance of electric circuits for the case of dc sources is simply the equivalent series resistance R in ohms defined by the ratio of the applied voltage V in volts to the resulting current I in amperes. This definition results from the familiar Ohm's law for dc circuits[1]

$$V = IR \quad (2)$$

Just as the current in a circuit that flows because of an impressed dc voltage is determined by the dc resistance, the current due to a time-varying voltage is determined by the circuit impedance presented to the time-varying signal (which involves circuit inductance and capacitance in addition to resistance). Hence the generalized definition of impedance Z is the ratio of the voltage across a circuit to the current flowing in the circuit (including time-varying effects)

$$Z = \frac{V}{I} \quad (3)$$

The commonly accepted units of impedance are ohms just as in the case of resistance for dc circuits.

For the important, common case of sinusoidally varying voltages (ac signals), the impedance Z of a circuit can be visualized as a complex number which is the sum of series resistance R and reactance X (see Fig. 1)

$$Z = R + jX \quad (4)$$

where the j preceding the reactance is literally $\sqrt{-1}$ and indicates that the current and voltage are 90° out of time phase in the reactance.*

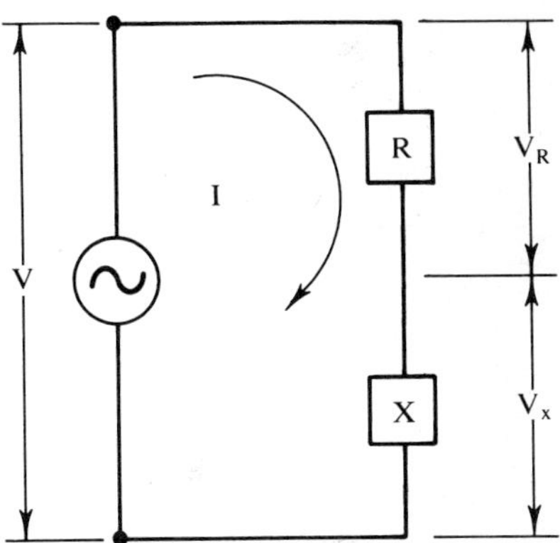

Fig. 1. Simple series circuit with resistance R and reactance X.

1. Impedance of Series Circuits The total applied voltage V in Fig. 1 must appear across the two series elements R and X. This simple circuit is denoted as a series circuit since there is only one path for the current I, which must necessarily flow through both R and X. By Ohm's law the voltage V_R across R must be IR and the voltage V_X across X must be IX. The total voltage across R and X, however, is not the simple sum $|V_R| + |V_X|$, because although the voltage across the resistance is in phase with the current, this is not true in the reactance where a 90° phase relationship exists as shown by the voltage and current plot in Fig. 2. As can be seen, the magnitude of the voltage across the circuit is not merely the sum of the magnitudes of the two voltage components but depends on the phase relationship as well. The instantaneous circuit voltage at any time is equal to the sum of the instantaneous component voltages (V_R and V_X) at the same time.

The impedance relationship $Z = R + jX$ can then be thought of as a basic definition of two components of impedance: a resistance R having the voltage in phase with the current and a reactance X having a voltage across it 90° out of phase with the current through it.

The impedance $R + jX$ can be visualized graphically as shown in Fig. 3 by plotting R along the horizontal axis (real axis) and X along the vertical axis (imaginary axis). X is plotted 90° with respect to R to portray the 90° phase

* Mathematically speaking, the resistance R is the real part and X is the imaginary part of the complex impedance Z.

relationship designated by the j preceding the X. Mathematically, since j is $\sqrt{-1}$, it plots 90° on the polar plot (by mathematical convention angles are measured counterclockwise).

The total impedance Z is a sum of the two components R and X, which are perpendicular. Thus, rather than merely forming the algebraic sum, the complex sum must be formed as shown in Fig. 3. This sum is represented by the length of the resultant arrow and the phase angle θ. This polar form of the impedance can be written as

$$Z = |Z| \angle \theta \tag{5}$$

where $|Z|$ is the ratio of the magnitude of V to I and $\angle\theta$, is the angle in electrical degrees that the current lags the voltage. For passive circuits θ will be between 90 and −90°. Negative angles mean that the current leads the voltage as a result of a negative reactance (reactance can be positive or negative). The two forms of the impedance Z are equivalent and can be transformed by fundamental, complex function operations.[2]

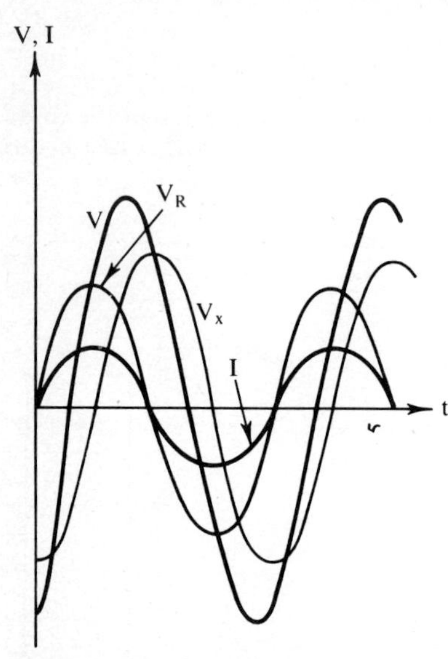

Fig. 2. Time plot of current I, voltage across the resistance V_R, voltage across the reactance V_X, and total circuit voltage V for the simple series.

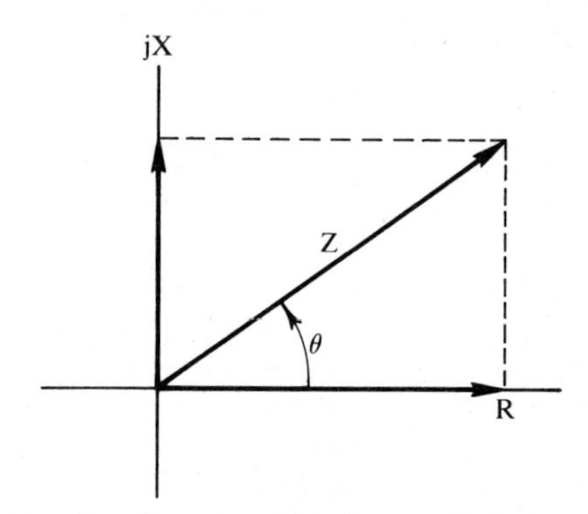

Fig. 3. Complex impedance diagram of series circuit. Resistance R is plotted on the horizontal axis, reactance X on the vertical axis, up being positive reactance and down negative reactance. The length of the arrow represents the magnitude in ohms. The angle θ is the impedance phase angle.

$$|Z| = \sqrt{X^2 + R^2} \tag{6}$$

$$\theta = \text{angle whose tangent is } \frac{X}{R} \tag{7}$$

If the impedance is stated in polar form ($|Z|\angle\theta$), the inverse operation to resistive and reactive components is

$$R = |Z| \cos \theta \tag{8}$$

$$X = |Z| \sin \theta \tag{9}$$

There are three basic types of passive circuit elements: resistance, capacitance, and inductance. The resistance, of course, is distinguished by voltage and current that are in phase ($\theta = 0°$), but capacitance results in a negative reactance ($\theta = -90°$) and inductance in a positive reactance ($\theta = +90°$). The total circuit reactance X is related to the total equivalent series inductance L and capacitance C by the relations[1,2]

$$X = X_L - X_C \tag{10}$$
$$X_L = 2\pi f L \tag{11}$$
$$X_C = \frac{1}{2\pi f C} \tag{12}$$

where f is the frequency of the sinusoidal applied voltage. The units of inductance and capacitance are henrys (H) and farads (F), respectively.

Fig. 4. Series RL circuit.

$X_L = 63\ \Omega$

$Z = 118.2$

$\theta = 32.2°$

$R = 100\ \Omega$

Fig. 5. Impedance diagram of Example 1.

Example 1: It is desired to find the impedance of a series circuit (Figs. 4 and 5) consisting of a 100-Ω resistor and 10-mH coil at a frequency of 1 kHz.

$$Z = R + jX \tag{4}$$
$$R = 100\ \Omega$$
$$X = 2\pi f L = (2\pi)(1{,}000)(0.01) = 63\ \Omega$$
$$Z = 100 + j63\ \Omega \text{ or } 118.2 \angle \theta$$

where $\theta = \arctan {}^{63}\!/_{100}$ or approximately 32.2°

Example 2: It is desired to find and plot in polar form the impedance of a series *RLC* circuit (Figs. 6 to 8) having values of

$$R = 50\ \Omega$$
$$L = 0.1\ \text{H}$$
$$C = 10\ \mu\text{F}$$
$$f = 100\ \text{Hz}$$
$$X_L = 2\pi f L = (2\pi)(100)(0.1) = 63\ \Omega$$
$$X_C = \frac{1}{2\pi f C} = \frac{1}{(2\pi)(100)(10^{-5})} = 159\ \Omega$$
$$X = X_L - X_C = -96\ \Omega$$
$$Z = 50 - j96\ \Omega$$
$$|Z| = \sqrt{R^2 + X^2} = \sqrt{(50^2) + (96)^2} = 108\ \Omega$$
$$\theta = \arctan \frac{X}{R} \left(\text{angle whose tangent is } \frac{X}{R}\right) = -{}^{96}\!/_{50}$$
$$\theta = -62.5°$$
$$Z = 108 \angle -62.5°\ \Omega$$

Example 3: The series *RLC* circuit shown in Fig. 9 has a 1-kHz signal of 1 V rms* applied across it. It is desired to find the resulting current.

* The root-mean-square (rms) value of a sinusoidally varying voltage is the effective value, which turns out to be 70.7 percent of the peak-voltage value.

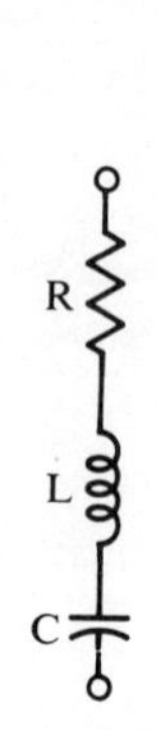

Fig. 6. Series RLC circuit.

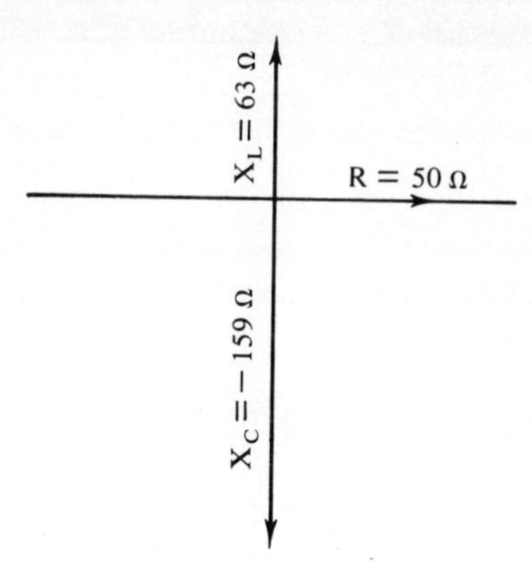

Fig. 7. Plot of individual impedance elements of Example 2.

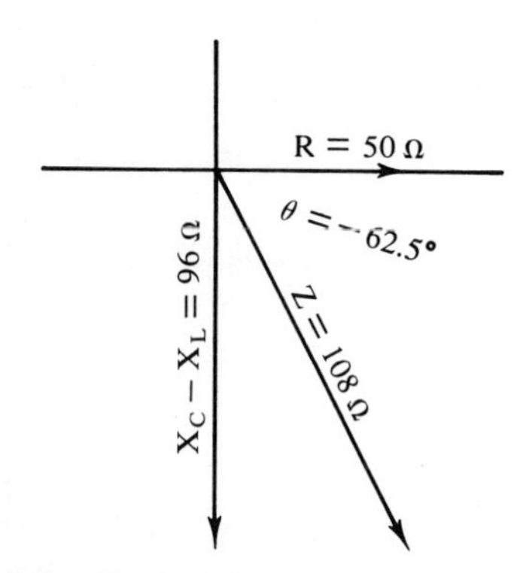

Fig. 8. Equivalent impedance plot for Fig. 7.

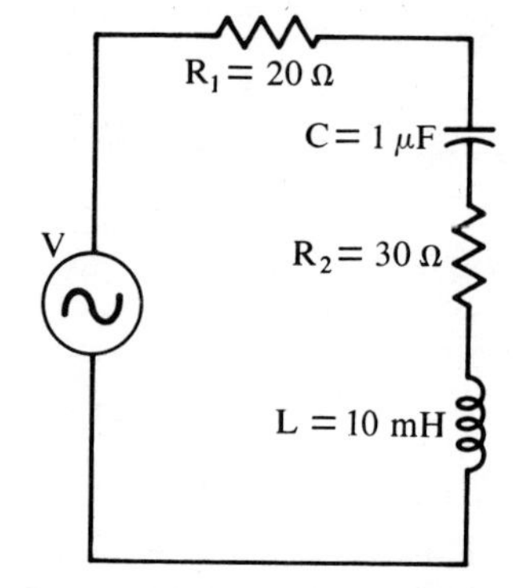

Fig. 9. Series RLC circuit of Example 3.

The total series impedance is

$$Z = R_1 + R_2 + j(X_L - X_C)$$

$$\text{where } X_L = 2\pi fL = (2\pi)(1{,}000)(10^{-2}) = 63\ \Omega$$

$$X_C = \frac{1}{2\pi fC} = \frac{1}{2(\pi)(1{,}000)(10^{-6})} = 159\ \Omega$$

$$Z = 20 + 30 + j(63 - 159) = 50 - j96 = 108\ \angle -62.5^\circ$$

The current therefore is, from Eq. (3),

$$I = \frac{V}{Z} = \frac{1}{108\ \angle -62.5^\circ} = 0.0092\ \angle 62.5^\circ\ \Omega$$

The magnitude of the current is 0.0092 A (9.2 mA), and the phase angle indicates that the current leads the voltage by 62.5°, as illustrated in Fig. 10.

2. Impedance of Parallel Circuits In contrast to the series circuit having the same current flowing through the circuit elements, the parallel or shunt circuit illustrated in Fig. 11 is characterized by a common voltage across the elements. The impedance of this parallel circuit can be found in equivalent series form, or as it is often said, the impedance can be combined by the expression

$$\frac{1}{Z_p} = \frac{1}{Z_1} + \frac{1}{Z_2} \qquad \text{or} \qquad Z_p = \frac{Z_1 Z_2}{Z_1 + Z_2} \tag{13}$$

The combination of more than two shunt-connected elements can be analyzed by repeated application of the two-element combination [Eq. (13)].

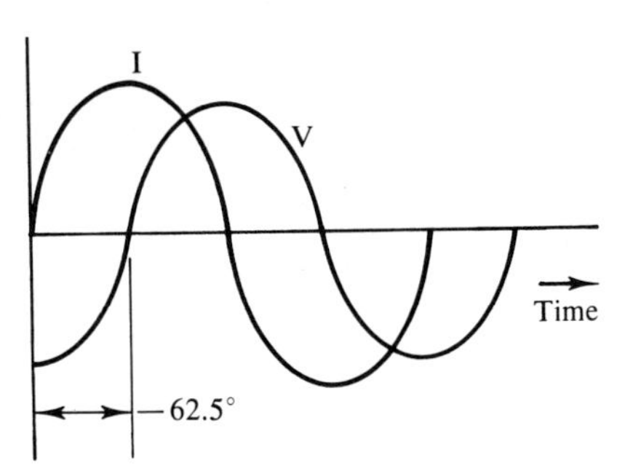

Fig. 10. Plots of current and voltage in Example 3.

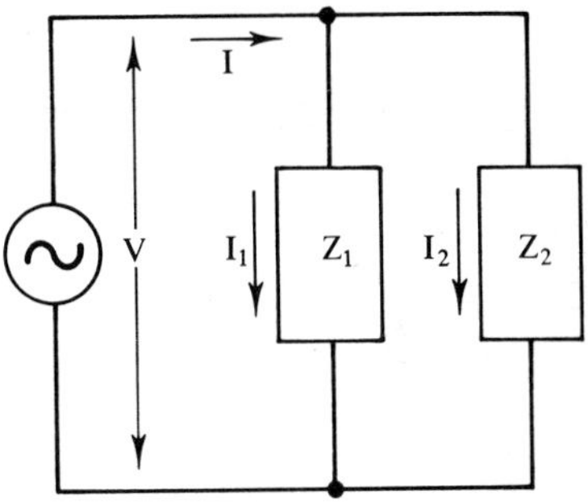

Fig. 11. Simple parallel circuit.

Example 4: It is desired to find the equivalent impedance of the parallel combination of a 1,000-Ω resistor and a 10-pF capacitor at 10 MHz.

$$Z_p = \frac{Z_1 Z_2}{Z_1 + Z_2}$$

where in this case,

$$Z_1 = 1{,}000\ \Omega$$

$$Z_2 = -jX_C = \frac{-j1}{2\pi f C} = \frac{-j1}{2\pi \times 10^7 \times 10^{-11}} = -j1{,}590\ \Omega$$

$$Z_p = \frac{(1{,}000)(-j1{,}590)}{1{,}000 - j1{,}590} = 1.59 \times 10^6 \angle -90^\circ$$

$$Z_p = 845 \angle -32.2^\circ\ \Omega$$

$$R = |Z| \cos\theta = 845 \cos(-32.2^\circ) = 716\ \Omega$$

$$X = |Z| \sin\theta = 845 \sin(-32.2^\circ) = -450\ \Omega$$

$$Z_p = (716 - j450)\ \Omega$$

INPUT AND OUTPUT IMPEDANCE

3. Input Impedance The input impedance of an electrical device is the ratio of voltage applied to the input terminals to the current flowing into the input terminals (see Fig. 12).

$$Z_{\text{in}} = \frac{V_{\text{in}}}{I_{\text{in}}} \tag{14}$$

In the case of dc applied voltages, the input impedance will be a resistance; however, for the ac-signal case, the general impedance including the phase relationship must be utilized. Only in the special case where the input current happens to be in phase with the applied voltage will the input impedance be a pure resistance (reactance equals zero). A low-input-impedance device will draw more current from a given applied voltage source than will a high-input-impedance device. The low-impedance device is said to "load" the source more heavily than the high-input-impedance device. It then follows that the input impedance of an instrument will determine the degree that the operation of any device is changed by the application of the test instrument. Accordingly, before connecting any test instrument, consideration should be given to the input impedance of the instrument and the consequences of connecting it to the circuit.

4. Output Impedance The output impedance of a device is the equivalent source impedance seen by the load. The output impedance has meaning only for an

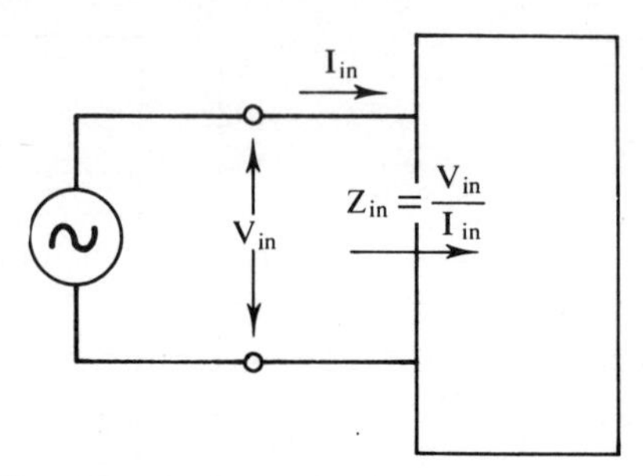

Fig. 12. Input impedance of a device.

active device at a pair of terminals considered as a signal source. The term "equivalent impedance" implies that the device can be represented by an equivalent circuit* (Thevenin's equivalent circuit) such as that shown in Fig. 13. Here the voltage source is the unloaded output voltage and Z_{out} is the impedance looking back into the device with all active sources replaced by their internal impedances.[3]

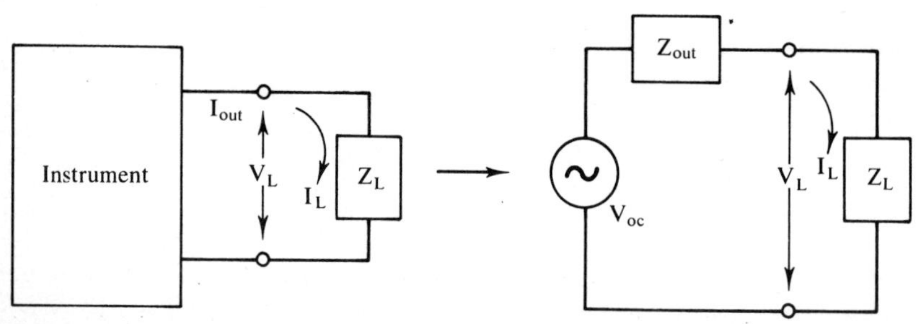

Fig. 13. The instrument can be replaced by the equivalent circuit for determining currents and voltages.

The output impedance can be stated in terms of the unloaded output voltage V_{oc} of the device and the loaded current I_L and voltage V_L as

$$Z_{\text{out}} = \frac{V_{oc} - V_L}{I_L} \tag{15}$$

This expression conveys the idea that the drop in the output voltage $(V_{oc} - V_L)$ as the device is loaded is determined directly by the output impedance.

The output impedance might be considered a measure of the susceptibility of the device to loading; i.e., the lower the output impedance, the less effect the

* The term equivalent circuit means that the circuit has the same voltages and currents as the original circuit, although the actual impedance elements may be different.

load will have on the output voltage. This can be seen by noting that the voltage drop across the output impedance for a given current will be less for lower output impedance; hence the output voltage will be higher.

5. Determination of Input and Output Impedances Input and output impedances of electronic devices may be determined by measuring the ratio of the appropriate voltage to current, or they may be calculated if the internal parameters of the instruments are known. Usually, however, this will not be necessary, since the instruction manual accompanying instruments used for measurements will list the input and output impedances which, at the design frequencies, approximate pure resistances. Statements such as "impedance of 50 ohms" and "50 ohm output impedance" imply that the reactance is essentially zero over the normal operating-frequency range.

The input and output impedances may not be adequately known for some applications. These parameters can normally be measured.

In the case of input impedance the definition is given in Eq. (14) $Z_{in} = V_{in}/I_{in}$. Thus, if the input voltage and current can be determined at their respective phase angles, the input impedance is specified. The most convenient method is to use an impedance bridge and actually measure impedance directly with the instrument activated and at the desired frequencies.

The output impedance can also be measured by an impedance bridge when the device can remain active but suppress its output so that it does not affect the bridge. The magnitude of the output impedance can be determined simply by noting the open-circuit output voltage and then loading it with a known impedance and measuring the loaded output voltage. The magnitude can then be calculated by following the equation (see Fig. 13)

$$|Z|_{out} = \frac{Z_L(V_{oc} - V_L)}{V_L} \tag{16}$$

When this method is used, care should be exercised not to exceed the output capabilities of the instrument.

EFFECTS OF INPUT AND OUTPUT IMPEDANCES ON MEASUREMENTS

In most measurement situations it is desirable that the test instrument not draw any appreciable power from the device being measured. This section will cover low-power measurements. The measurements involving intentional power transfer will be discussed in a following section. In the following discussion for low-insertion-power measurements the measuring device can be connected across the circuit (shunt-connected) or inserted in the circuit (series-connected).

6. Shunt-connected Instruments (Voltmeters, Oscilloscopes, etc.) For measurement or display of voltages in a circuit a test instrument such as a voltmeter or oscilloscope is normally connected across a circuit in shunt (parallel) with the elements as illustrated in Fig. 14. In this case the loading effect of the test instrument due to its finite input impedance must be taken into account. The voltage at point A with respect to point B will be modified by the current I_v drawn by the voltmeter. Only if this current is negligible compared with the circuit current I_c will the voltmeter read the same value that existed at A before the meter was connected. Ideally for these instruments, the input impedance should be infinite, i.e., should appear as an open circuit drawing no current and hence presenting no loading to the circuit. Although this condition is impossible to achieve, the loading effect of the instrument can usually be neglected if it is determined that the input impedance of the test instrument is very large compared with the output impedance of the device under test (usually a factor of 50 or more depending on the desired accuracy). Otherwise, corrections must be made for the loading effects. The voltage will be reduced from the unloaded output voltage of the device under test by a "voltage-divider" action. Referring to the equivalent circuit of Fig. 14*b*, the unloaded value V_{oc} will be related to the indicated value V_{ind} according to the relation

$$V_{ind} = \frac{V_{oc}Z_{in}}{Z_{in} + Z_{out}} \tag{17}$$

It should be borne in mind that Z_{out} and Z_{in} will, in general, be frequency-dependent because of their reactances, so that the indicated voltage will also depend

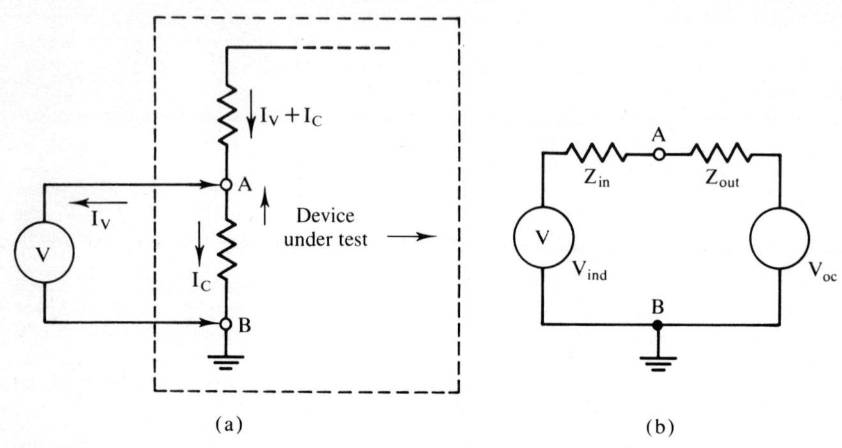

Fig. 14. (*a*) Voltmeter connected in shunt across circuit points *AB*. (*b*) Equivalent circuit of test setup of *a*.

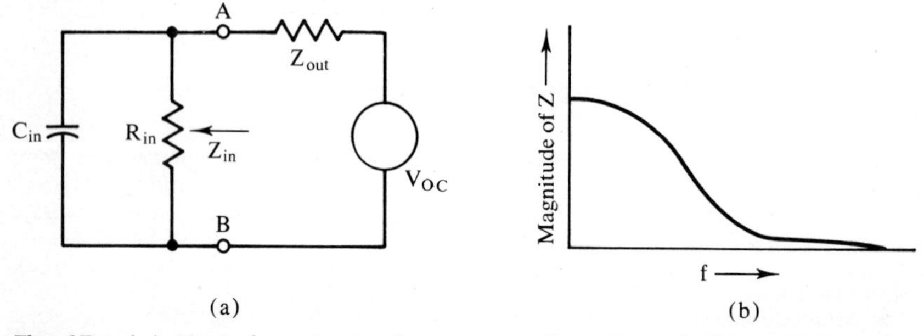

Fig. 15. (*a*) Equivalent circuit of test setup where Z_{in} includes a shunt capacitance. (*b*) Impedance magnitude of Z_{in} vs. frequency, illustrating that loading becomes more severe at higher frequencies.

on frequency. Generally, the shunting effect of Z_{in} becomes worse at higher frequencies (because of the input capacitance of the instrument),* giving a "high-frequency rolloff" or a reduction in impedance and hence more loading at the higher frequencies (see Fig. 15). Also as a consequence of the shunt capacitance,

* In the specifications of most test instruments, the input resistance and an effective shunting capacitance are given. The equivalent series impedance Z_{in} can be calculated by Eq. (13).

$$Z_{in} = \frac{Z_1 Z_2}{Z_1 + Z_2} = \frac{(R_{in})(-jX_{in})}{R_{in} - jX_{in}}$$

where $Z_1 = R_{in}$
$Z_2 = -jX_{in}$

sharply changing nonsinusoidal waveforms are rounded off because of the finite time it takes to charge the capacitance. This concept is illustrated in Fig. 16 for a square-wave source. In addition to the amplitude reduction due to instrumental loading, if the shunting due to the test instrument is severe, it may cause permanent damage to the circuit or device under test.

The loading effect of test instruments can be reduced at the expense of sensitivity by the use of a voltage-divider probe. A commonly used 10:1 probe is illustrated in Fig. 17. This device gives a 10:1 increase in impedance level but also attenuates signals by a factor of 10 (see Chapters 20, 22, and 24).

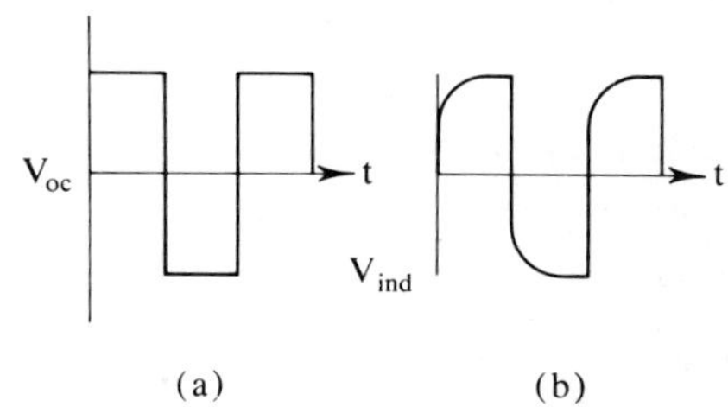

Fig. 16. (*a*) Square wave on circuit before instrument is connected. (*b*) Voltage is rounded because of shunt capacitance of the instrument.

Example 5: The voltage across a circuit having an output impedance of 100 kΩ is measured with a 20,000 Ω/V voltmeter. It is desired to find the percentage error in the reading due to the loading effect of the voltmeter on the 10-V range.

The input impedance of the voltmeter on the 10-V range is $Z_{in} = (20{,}000\ \Omega/\text{V}) \times (10\ \text{V}) = 200{,}000\ \Omega$. The indicated voltage will be [Eq. (17)]

$$V_{ind} = V_{oc}\frac{Z_{in}}{Z_{in} + Z_{out}} = V_{oc}\frac{200\ \text{k}\Omega}{300\ \text{k}\Omega} = 0.67\ V_{oc}$$

or 67 percent of the true, unloaded voltage value; therefore, the indicated reading (V_{ind}) will be 33 percent low.

The loading problem illustrated in Example 5 is typical of cases where a common-type voltmeter such as a small portable multimeter is used. Voltmeters of this type will usually seriously modify the normal in-use voltages in electronic circuits; however, they will not affect low-impedance circuits, such as power supplies. Voltmeters such as electronic voltmeters are available and should be used on high-impedance circuits to decrease this loading problem.

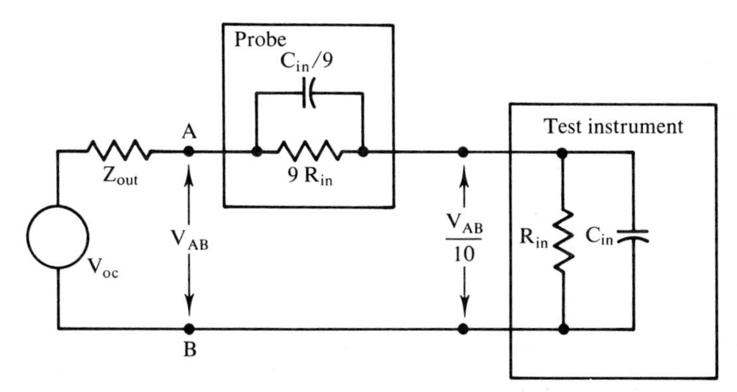

Fig. 17. A 10:1 voltage-divider probe for increase of input impedance of shunt-connected instruments.

Example 6: An oscilloscope having an input resistance of 1 MΩ shunted by a 50-pF capacitance is connected across a circuit having an effective output impedance of 10 kΩ. If the unloaded circuit voltage is a 1-V peak for a 100-kHz sine wave, what will be the voltage indicated on the oscilloscope? Repeat for 1-MHz sine wave.

The equivalent circuit for the system is shown in Fig. 18. The input impedance of the oscilloscope is a 1-MΩ resistor shunted by the capacitive reactance of the 50-pF capacitor. At 100 kHz

$$X_c = \frac{1}{2\pi fC} = \frac{1}{2\pi \times 10^5 \times (50 \times 10^{-12})} = 32{,}000\ \Omega$$

The parallel combination of R and $-jX_c$ will be

$$Z_{\text{in}} = \frac{R(-jX_c)}{R - jX_c} = \frac{10^6 \times (-j3.2 \times 10^4)}{10^6 - j3.2 \times 10^4} \approx -j3.2 \times 10^4\ \Omega$$

The indicated voltage V_{ind} then will be

$$V_{\text{ind}} = V_{oc}\frac{Z_{\text{in}}}{Z_{\text{in}} + Z_{\text{out}}} = 1.0 \times \frac{-j3.2 \times 10^4}{-j3.2 \times 10^4 \times 10^4}$$

$$= \frac{3.2 \times 10^4 \angle -90^\circ}{3.4 \times 10^4 \angle -73^\circ} = 0.94 \angle -17^\circ \text{ V}$$

This means that the magnitude of the indicated voltage will be 0.94 V (6 percent below true value) and shifted in phase by 17° lagging behind the unloaded value as shown.

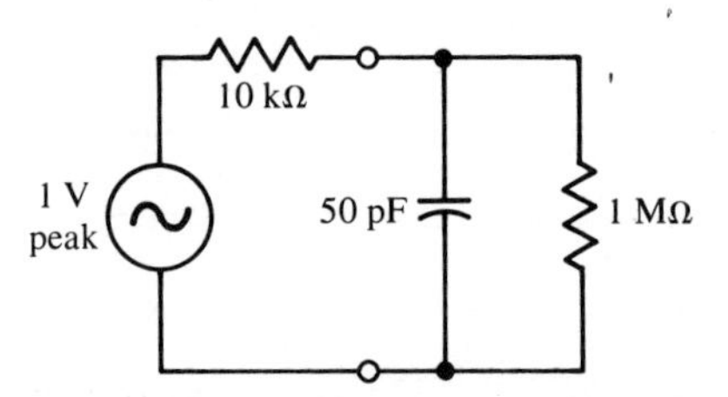

Fig. 18. Equivalent circuit of Example 6.

For the frequency of 1 MHz, the shunting reactance of the oscilloscope will be

$$X_c = \frac{1}{2\pi \times 10^6 \times 50 \times 10^{-12}} = 3{,}200\ \Omega$$

giving

$$Z_{\text{in}} = \frac{R(-jX_c)}{R - jX_c} = \frac{10^6(-j3.2 \times 10^3)}{10^6 - j3.2 \times 10^3} \approx -j3{,}200\ \Omega$$

$$V_{\text{ind}} = 1 \times \frac{-j3.2 \times 10^3}{10^4 - j3.2 \times 10^3} = \frac{3.2 \times 10^3 \angle -90^\circ}{1.0 \times 10^4 \angle -18^\circ} \approx 0.32 \angle -72^\circ$$

In this case, the observed voltage is less than a third of the unloaded value and lags by 72°. This typical case illustrates the increased shunting problem as the frequency increases.

The severe loading illustrated in this example could be lessened by the use of a voltage-divider probe. A 10:1 voltage-divider probe on the oscilloscope will result in an input impedance typically of 10 MΩ shunted by 5 pF. Use of the probe will give an input impedance then of about $-j32{,}000\ \Omega$ at 1 MHz, and the indicated voltage will be $0.94\angle 17^\circ$, the same as at 100 kHz without the probe. Account has to be taken of the factor-of-10 voltage reduction in the probe. This is easily done by increasing the oscilloscope gain by a factor of 10.

Example 7: Consider the effect of the oscilloscope on the circuit of Example 6 if the unloaded circuit voltage were a 1-V-peak, 250-kHz square wave.

The equivalent circuit of the system will be identical to Example 6. However, the problem cannot be solved by the sine-wave impedance techniques previously used. In this case sharp edges will be rounded as shown in Fig. 19, and a more meaningful concept is that of the rise time of the sharply changing waveform. An idea of the rise time is easily derived in terms of a time constant τ

$$\tau = RC_{sh} \tag{18}$$

where R is the resistance through which the capacitance C is charged. If the input resistance of the oscilloscope is high compared with R_{out}, R will be essentially R_{out}. Mathematically the time constant is the time required for the voltage waveform to change 63 percent of the total ultimate change. In about five time constants the voltage will be essentially to its final value. In the case here

$$\tau = 10^4 \times 50 \times 10^{-12} = 5 \times 10^{-7}\,\text{s} = 0.5\,\mu\text{s}$$

so the resulting waveform will be as shown in Fig. 19.

Example 8: As an example of circuit-performance deterioration due to shunting effects of test instruments more severe than those considered in the foregoing examples, consider the effect of connecting the oscilloscope across the tuned circuit consisting of a parallel 20-pF capacitor and 50-μH coil. The oscilloscope has input impedance consisting of 1 MΩ shunted by 50 pF capacitance.

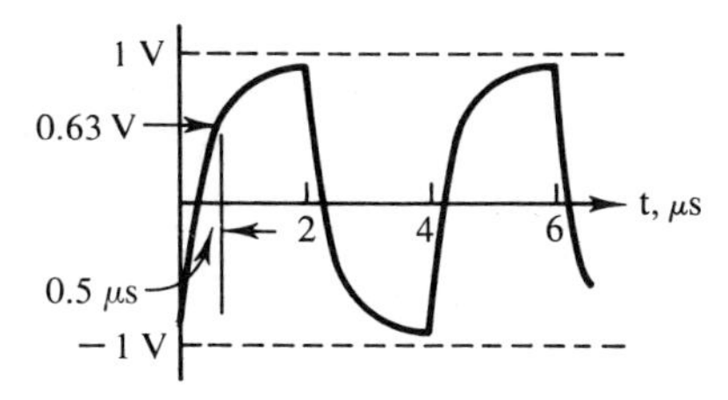

Fig. 19. Rounding of square wave by oscilloscope in Example 7.

Before the oscilloscope is connected, the tuned circuit resonates at a frequency of[1]

$$f_o = \frac{1}{2\pi\sqrt{LC}} = \frac{1}{2\pi\sqrt{20 \times 10^{-6} \times 50 \times 10^{-12}}} = 5\text{ MHz}$$

Application of the oscilloscope makes the total capacitance across the coil 100 pF and shifts the resonant point to

$$f_L = \frac{1}{2\pi\sqrt{20 \times 10^{-6} \times 100 \times 10^{-12}}} \approx 3.5\text{ Mhz}$$

Thus, if the circuit were a tank circuit of a 5-Mhz amplifier, its gain at 5 Mhz would drop off to nearly zero since the input capacitance of the oscilloscope shifted the resonant peak to 3.5 Mhz. If the tuned circuit were in an oscillator circuit, it would shift the oscillations to 3.5 Mhz or perhaps cause it to stop oscillating if it did not have sufficient drive at the new frequency.

The detuning of the resonant circuit could be lessened considerably by the use of a voltage-divider probe. However, rf circuits are always difficult to measure without detuning effects, with the problem becoming worse as the frequency is increased.

7. Series-connected Instruments (Ammeters, etc.) In a few measurement situations, rather than connecting the instrument in shunt with the circuit it is necessary to break the circuit and insert the instrument in series. A notable example is the ammeter for measurement of current as illustrated in Fig. 20. In this case the idealized value of instrument input impedance Z_A is opposite from the shunt-connected instrument described above; i.e., the ammeter should appear as a short cricuit ($Z_A = 0$). This can be seen from the equivalent circuits in Fig. 20. In order for the circuit to be undisturbed when the ammeter is added (Fig. 20*b*) the current I and voltage V_{in} should be the same as in Fig. 20*a*. This means that the voltage drop across the ammeter V_A must be negligible, which in turn means that the series impedance introduced by the ammeter must be negligible. All practical ammeters will have, of course, a nonzero input impedance; so in a measurement situation care must be taken to keep its impedance very much lower (say a factor of 50) than the circuit impedance. The actual factor required depends

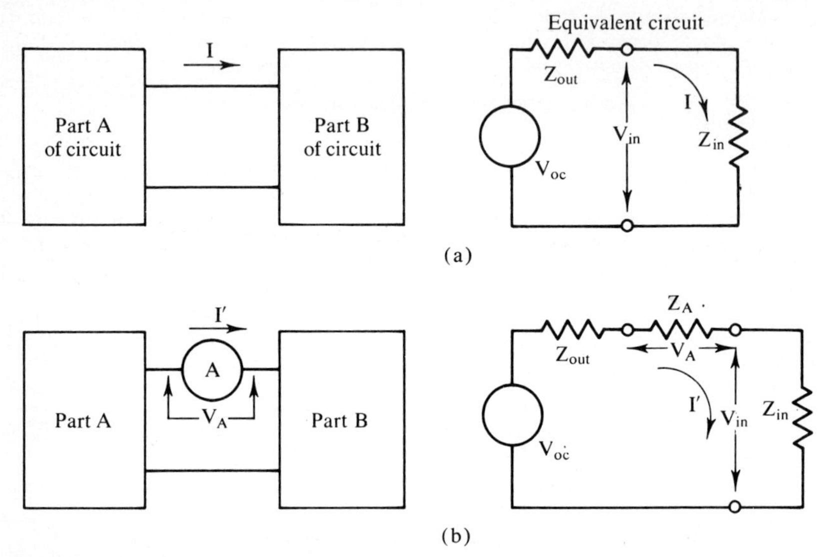

Fig. 20. Breaking circuit between *A* and *B* and inserting ammeter in series to measure current.

on the desired accuracy, and it should be borne in mind that corrections can be made for the impedances involved in most cases.

IMPEDANCE MATCHING

In many applications rather than attempting to make the input impedance of an instrument very high or low, it may be desirable to match the input impedance of the load device to the output impedance of the signal source.

8. Matching Output Impedance to Load Typical cases of impedance matching are most applications involving waveform generators (pulse generators, rf transmitters, etc.) which utilize a transmission line, commonly a coaxial cable, to transfer the energy from the source to the input of the device being excited. In addition, there are many relatively low frequency cases such as audio amplifiers driving loudspeakers and other electromechanical transducers where impedance matching is utilized for achieving high power transfer, proper damping, etc.

If the source has a purely resistive output impedance of $R\Omega$, an impedance match is achieved by making the load or the input impedance of the following device also equal to $R\Omega$. (Neglect, for the moment, the effect of any interconnecting cables, which will be discussed below.) This matched condition can be shown as being necessary for maximum power transference to the load.[3]

If the output impedance of the source contains some reactance ($Z_{out} = R_o + jX_o$), two so-called matched conditions are defined. The first, an image match, occurs where the load impedance is also equal to $R_o + jX_o$. The second case, which is usually more desirable, achieves maximum power transfer, a so-called conjugate or power match, by making the load resistance equal to that of the source and the load reactance equal in magnitude to the source reactance but opposite in sign; i.e., $Z_L = R_o - jX_o$ as shown in Fig. 21. Summing the total impedance around this circuit, X_o and X_c cancel to 0, leaving only R_o. This condition is equivalent to making the circuit series-resonant, and thus the remaining resistances R_o and R_L are matched, resulting in maximum power transfer.

9. Instrument Interconnections When interconnecting for rf or other ac signals, open wires are seldom used since they radiate, thereby losing energy and producing stray fields. These systems are subject to interference generation and pickup (see Chapters 15 and 17). Also the capacitive effects between the wires and surrounding objects may produce serious degrading effects. Usually a system of constant-impedance connectors and transmission lines such as coaxial cables or waveguides is used to transfer the energy more efficiently and predictably.* The effect of these transmission lines on the impedance must be considered for proper use of instruments.

In audio-frequency applications transmission lines as described above are not necessary and twisted-pair interconnections are common. At these low frequencies the effect of the wires on the impedances is small, and output and load impedances can be reasonably well matched, neglecting the interconnecting wires.

10. Effects of Transmission Lines—Matched Conditions All transmission lines have a basic parameter known as characteristic impedance Z_o that determines impedance levels. This characteristic impedance can be defined as the hypothetical input impedance to an infinitely long section of the transmission line. An interesting way to understand this concept is to consider feeding a signal into one end of a line which extends to infinity. Since an electrical signal has a finite propagation time, any signal starting at the input end of the line would never reach the other end. Thus the generator would never know what the load is on the other end of the line. The question then is, "If the generator has a known output voltage, what is the current that starts down the line?" This current is determined by the wire inductance and shunt capacitance of the line and is known as the characteristic impedance of the line. Over the most useful frequency range of transmission lines, this impedance is very nearly a constant resistance of relatively small magnitude, usually in the range of 25 to 600 Ω.

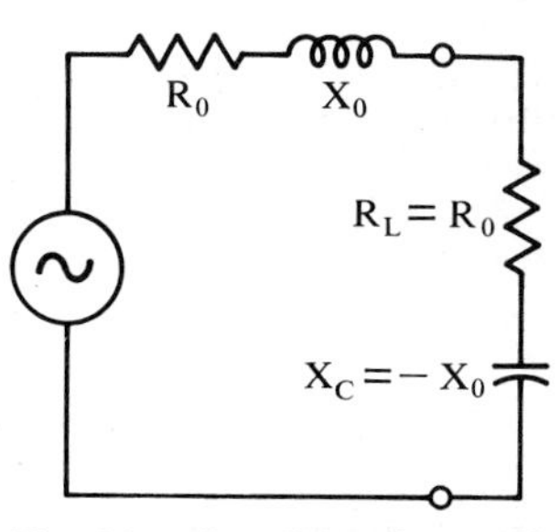

Fig. 21. Condition for maximum power transfer from generator to load R_L.

The most commonly encountered transmission systems have 50-Ω characteristic impedances and hence are called 50-Ω systems, for example, common coaxial cables such as RG8/U and RG58/U.[2] Also frequently encountered are 75- and 93-Ω systems. The input impedance of a transmission line of characteristic impedance Z_o, if terminated with an impedance Z_o, will also be Z_o. For example, the input impedance of a 50-Ω line with a 50-Ω resistor connected on the opposite end will be 50 Ω regardless of the length of the line.†

Most signal sources which have high-frequency components have output impedances that approximate 50 Ω resistance. If such a device is to be connected to a 50-Ω load, a matched system is simply achieved by use of a 50-Ω interconnecting

* Normally a coaxial cable is used for rf connections at frequencies to approximately 1 GHz. At frequencies above this the coaxial cable becomes too lossy for long distances and a hollow pipe known as a waveguide is utilized.

† Actually there is a small reactance associated with the power loss in the cable that is usually negligible if the lines are relatively short and used well below the maximum usable frequency. The power loss in the cable (attenuation) may be important for long cables or high frequencies. This loss is usually given in reference books in decibels per 100 ft at various frequencies.[2]

cable. In other cases, it may be desirable to transform the load and/or source impedance to values which will match common transmission lines by use of series reactance, impedance transformers, or other impedance-matching techniques.[4]

The transit of electrical signals down a transmission line takes a finite time; hence this delay time for signal propagation must be considered. For most coaxial cables, the velocity of propagation is approximately two-thirds that of light in free space, giving a value of about 2×10^8 m/s. This means a propagation time of about 0.16 μs = 160 ns per 100 ft of cable. (It takes 160 ns for a signal to travel 100 ft down this cable.)

EFFECTS OF IMPEDANCE MISMATCH

Unmatched systems present many difficulties. The input impedance of a transmission line terminated in an impedance other than its characteristic impedance is, in general, a much different value from the terminating impedance. The transmission line transforms the impedance in a complex manner that is a function of the line length, operating frequency, and the degree of mismatch on the line. The impedance transformation is due to the fact that all the energy incident on the load will not be absorbed as in the matched case; part of the energy will be reflected back up the line toward the source, resulting in standing waves on the line. As a consequence, the load on the generator is not known unless measured or calculated, the power to the load will be less than maximum, and the standing waves on the line will increase the line loss. For pulse sources, the reflections back and forth on an unmatched line system may be particularly bothersome.

The reflections are caused by the finite transit time down a line. When the generator sends a pulse down the line, it sends it into the characteristic impedance of the line. Thus the power sent down the line is independent of the load on the end of the line. When the pulse reaches the end of the line, if there is a mismatch some of the power will be reflected and a pulse will then be propagated back up the line. In the extreme case where the generator is also mismatched, there will be a large number of reflections or bounces back and forth on the line, causing multiple pulses on the output for each single input pulse.

A section of line shorter than a quarter wavelength which is unterminated (essentially open-circuited) and connected across a circuit will appear nearly as a capacitance shunting the circuit. (The capacitance of unterminated cables is listed in reference books; for example, RG58/U has 28.5 pF/ft.)[2] This effective shunting capacitance may have a detuning or other deleterious effect.

A final problem associated with unmatched systems is the fact that the calibrated output of signal generators is normally specified for a matched-load condition, i.e., when a resistance equal to the generator output impedance is connected to its output terminals. Under these matched conditions, equal voltage will appear across the load, and the internal impedance of the generator and the calibration should be correct. This means then that if the generator is essentially unloaded, its output voltage will be twice the listed value for matched output. If the effective load is smaller in magnitude than Z_0, the voltage at the output terminals will be less than the calibrated value. The corrections for unmatched values of impedance are the same as those of Eq. (13); and again, extreme loads (approaching short circuit) may distort the waveform.

REFERENCES

1. "The Radio Amateur's Handbook," 44th ed., American Radio Relay League, Newington, Conn., 1967.
2. "Reference Data for Radio Engineers," International Telephone and Telegraph Corp., New York.
3. Hamond, S. B.: "Electrical Engineering," McGraw-Hill Book Company, New York, 1961.
4. Terman, F. E.: "Radio Engineers' Handbook," McGraw-Hill Book Company, New York, 1943.

Chapter 15

Electrical Interference

D. A. BURT and K. D. BAKER, Ph.D.
Utah State University, Logan, Utah

INTRODUCTION

In a communication or measurement situation, any signal disturbance other than the desired signal is termed *interference*. These extraneous signals, which hinder the measurement of the desired signals, assume a variety of forms and can find many devious ways of getting into or out of electronic equipment. This chapter is devoted to describing these unwanted conditions and means of reducing or eliminating their effects.

GLOSSARY OF INTERFERENCE AND NOISE TERMINOLOGY

ATMOSPHERIC NOISE OR INTERFERENCE: Radio-wave disturbances originating in the atmosphere, principally because of lightning discharges. Also called "atmospherics" or simply "sferics."

COMMON-MODE INTERFERENCE: Conducted interference caused by voltage drops across wires (usually grounds) common to two circuits or systems.

CONDUCTED INTERFERENCE: Interference caused by direct coupling of extraneous signals through wires, components, etc.

COSMIC NOISE: Interference caused by radio waves emanating from extraterrestrial sources.

COUPLING: The transfer of power between two or more circuits or systems.

CROSSTALK: Electrical disturbances in one circuit as a result of coupling with other circuits.

ELECTROMAGNETIC INTERFERENCE (EMI): A general term for electrical interference throughout the frequency spectrum from subaudio up to microwave frequencies.

ELECTROSTATIC INDUCTION: Signals coupled to the measuring circuit through stray capacitances, also commonly called "capacitive pickup."

HUM: Electrical disturbance at the ac power-supply frequency or harmonics thereof.

IMPULSE NOISE: Noise generated in a discrete energy burst (not of random nature) which has an individual characteristic waveshape. This is normally the type of noise which is generated by rotating machinery such as a dc motor or generator.

INTERFERENCE: Extraneous signals, noises, etc., which hinder proper measurements in electronic systems.

MAGNETIC INDUCTION: Interference coupled to the measuring circuit by magnetic fields.

NOISE: Unwanted signals, commonly used to identify statistically random disturbances.

RADIATED INTERFERENCE: Interference transmitted from a source to another remote point with no apparent connection between the points.

RADIO-FREQUENCY INTERFERENCE (RFI): Electromagnetic interference (EMI) in the frequency band normally used for communications (approximately 10^4 to 10^{12} Hz).

RANDOM NOISE: Irregular signal whose instantaneous amplitude is distributed randomly with respect to time. Mathematically the distribution follows a normal or gaussian curve (also called gaussian noise).

SIGNAL-TO-NOISE RATIO: A ratio of signal level to noise level, usually in rms volts. The higher the signal-to-noise ratio, the less the importance of interference.

STATIC: Radio interference detectable as noise (crackling sound) in the audio stage of a receiver.

THERMAL NOISE: Random radio-frequency noise generated by thermal agitation of electrons in a resistor.

WHITE NOISE: An electrical signal whose frequency spectrum (power) is continuous and uniform.

INSTRUMENT NOISE

Internal noise is generated in all electronic equipment and limits the ultimate measurement sensitivity which can be achieved. Depending on the instrument bandwidth and input configuration, there is a theoretical noise due to thermal agitation given by

$$V_n = 2\sqrt{kTBR} \tag{1}$$

where V_n = noise voltage, rms
k = Boltzmann's constant, 1.38×10^{-23} J/°K
T = absolute temperature, °K
B = system bandwidth, Hz
R = resistance, Ω

Reduction of the noise beyond this theoretical value is not possible without changing the basic design of the instrument. As the instrument's sensitivity approaches this theoretical limit, the signal becomes masked by the noise.

Since noise introduced at the input of an amplifier, called "transducer" or "detector" noise, will be amplified by succeeding stages along with the signal, the noise associated with the input stage will usually determine the overall signal-to-noise ratio and therefore will be the limiting parameter for ultimate useful sensitivity or the minimum detectable signal.

Most instruments are designed to maintain a noise level below the sensitivity at which the instrument is intended to operate. Therefore, internal noise of the instrument is not evident at the output. This fact, however, determines the minimum measurable input signal. Operation can be extended to lower signal levels by additional amplification of the output down to the limit where the signal approaches the noise level as determined at the input of the instrument.* Once this limit is reached, further sensitivity cannot be achieved without reducing the input noise level. Only a few means are available to minimize the noise limitation introduced by the input characteristics of instrumentation. These are listed below.

1. Optimize the instrument noise figure to approach as nearly as possible the theoretical noise [Eq. (1)]. This can be accomplished in some cases by critical adjustment of the input circuitry (tuning, impedance level, etc.) and careful selection of low-noise-input devices, i.e., diode, tube, or transistor.
2. Use a low-noise preamplifier preceding the instrument.
3. Reduce system bandwidth or frequency response by filtering (if the nature of the desired signal will not be too seriously impaired).
4. Cool the input circuitry to reduce thermal-agitation noise.

RADIATED INTERFERENCE

All electrical equipment can radiate interfering signals, and with the proliferation of electrical equipment this radiation is becoming more and more serious. A radiated signal can be classified into three types: electric or high-impedance, magnetic or low-impedance, and plane-wave. The electric and magnetic coupling is most important when the radiating source is on the order of a few wavelengths or less away. This is called the *near-field* region. At larger separations the electric and magnetic fields become negligible and the plane-wave propagation takes over. This region is called the *far field*.

1. Electric or High-impedance Interference This interference is essentially capacitive coupling from sources which have high potentials and little or no current flow. The characteristic coupling from these sources is *directly* proportional to the frequency of the signal and inversely proportional to the separation distance from the source.

The coupling of energy from the source to the pickup circuit can be described in terms of an impedance Z_c coupling the two together as illustrated in Fig. 1. The actual energy coupled between the two circuits is determined not only by the coupling impedance but also by the source voltage V_s, the output impedance of the source Z_o, and the input impedance of the pickup point Z_{in} (see Chapter 14). It is difficult to assign exact numbers to the value of coupling impedance,

* The use of external amplifiers may complicate the calibration of the measurement stem.

since the exact configuration must be known. However, in general, for frequencies below about 10 MHz and distances from inches to several feet this impedance will be several thousand ohms, but decreases as the frequency increases.

Some of the more obvious ways of reducing the effects of this interference are to maintain low voltage and low impedance levels at both the source and the pickup, require large spacing, keep all radiating and pickup areas as small as possible, and limit the high-frequency response. Since these methods may not be adequate, shielding is also used. Proper shielding will be discussed later in this chapter.

2. Magnetic or Low-impedance Interference Magnetic interference is coupled into a circuit by the transformer action of stray magnetic fluxes. Sources for magnetic coupling are normally a loop or wire carrying a significant amount of current. The coupling between the source and receiver is *inversely* proportional to the frequency and distance. For frequencies below 1 MHz and distances ranging from inches to several feet, the coupling impedance can be on the order of a few ohms. Some methods of reducing these types of signals are to use low current and high impedance levels, require large spacing, keep current-carrying wires short, and eliminate low-frequency response. It is interesting to note the paradox that exists in considering the ways to reduce electric and magnetic noise. Some techniques that reduce the effects of one type of interference actually increase the other type. However, both types of noise may be reduced by increasing distance and by shielding.

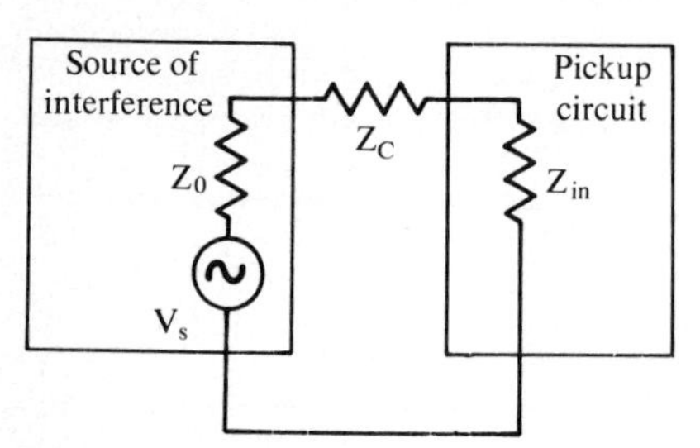

Fig. 1. Equivalent circuit illustrating interference coupling.

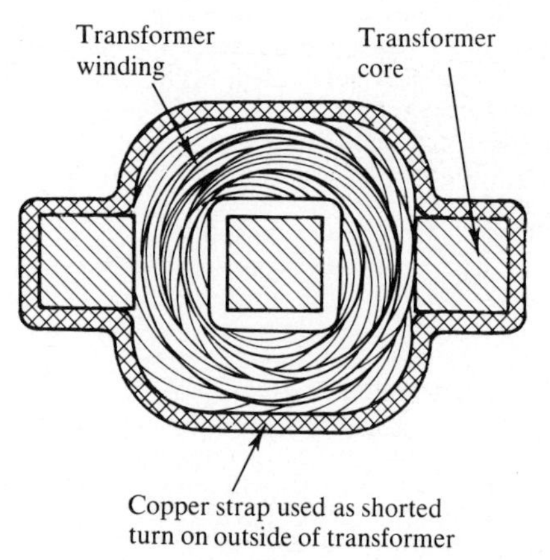

Fig. 2. Shorted turn on outside of transformer to attenuate stray magnetic fields.

Magnetic interference is the most difficult to shield against. Therefore, it is often easier to control this noise at the source. When attempting to eliminate stray magnetic fluxes, consider the principle that the magnetic flux produced in any closed path is proportional to the sum of the current enclosed by that path. Simply stated, this means that if there is a device that draws sufficient current to produce interfering fields, the power and return leads should be designed to run side by side in a twisted pair or a coaxial power cable. This simple procedure requires that the current which flows to the unit must flow back the same way so the sum of the current inside a closed path around the two wires is zero, thereby reducing the external magnetic fields.

Another common source of magnetic interference is the stray flux which may emanate from power transformers. A common method for minimizing these fields is to provide a shorted turn around the outside of the transformer core. This shorted turn must have low impedance and be wrapped in the same direction as the transformer windings, as shown in Fig. 2. Thus, leakage fluxes outside of the transformer will be attenuated by the short circuit caused by this shorted turn. The physical proximity is of utmost importance in determining the level of interference. In some cases, the interference can be reduced to a tolerable level only by physical separation and by proper orientation of wires.

3. Plane-wave Interference Radiated electromagnetic fields approximate a plane wave in the far field (all radio propagation is due to plane-wave propagation). The magnitude of the coupling impedance between the source and the receiver depends upon the sending and receiving configurations and their separation distance. At frequencies above 1 GHz practically all coupling is due to plane-wave propagation. Rejection of this interfering signal is again accomplished mainly by maintaining radiating and pickup points small in size and widely separated and by the use of shielding.

SHIELDING

One of the most important methods of eliminating interference is the use of shields at either the source or receiver or both. This technique is to enclose the device in a shield which must be designed to reflect and/or absorb electromagnetic energy which attempts to penetrate it. The design of the shield itself usually depends on the frequencies and types of interference which must be contained or excluded.

4. Plane-wave and Electric-field Shielding When a plane wave, or high-impedance electric signal, strikes a surface of high conductivity, the signal is essentially all reflected. Shielding then is effected by enclosing the object to be shielded in a completely closed, conductive surface. For this surface to be effective, it must have high conductivity and there can be no discontinuity or holes which approach a significant part of the wavelength of the signal which is to be rejected. This might appear to require a completely welded silver case. Because of skin effect (see Chapter 17), however, a silver plating will produce almost the same effective conductivity as would solid silver for most frequencies. For very high frequencies, some critical instruments will have silver-plated chassis and shields; however, in normal applications, most conductive metals will produce satisfactory results. To avoid heavy, bulky, solid metal boxes, metallic-wire mesh is often used as a shield material. Mesh having about 50 percent area and 60 or more strands per wavelength is nearly as effective as solid metal.

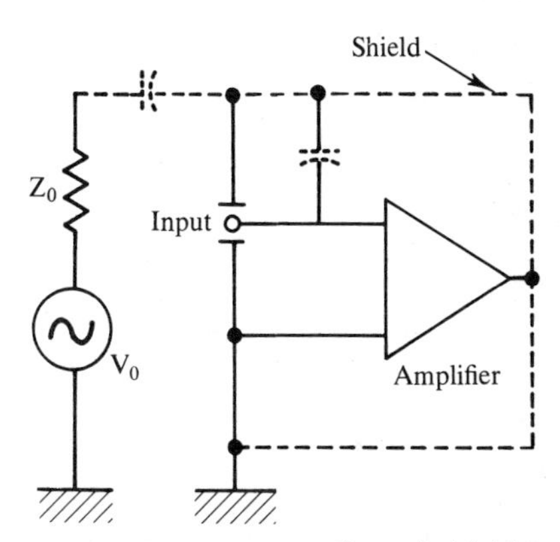

Fig. 3. Proper connection of shield to eliminate the effects of internal shunt capacitance to the shield.

In most instruments, the outer enclosure is made of metal and designed as the final shield. With the exception of floating inputs, this enclosure will be connected directly to the input-signal return or to the ground of the instrument. If the shield is maintained at the same potential as the ground point of the amplifier input, the interfering signal will be shunted out and will not affect the input. This can be seen by referring to Fig. 3, which shows an amplifier as an example. As can be seen, the interfering source will be coupled to the shield through stray capacitance, as will the input of the amplifier. As long as the shield is maintained at the same potential as the amplifier input, there will be no energy flow between the shield and the amplifier input. In effect the interfering signal coupled to the shield will be shunted out.

5. Magnetic Shielding Shielding to eliminate magnetic fields is more difficult than shielding for other types of interference because of the low coupling-impedance level. These fields may be static fields such as the earth's magnetic field or the time-varying fluxes which emanate from current loops in the near field. As stated previously, it is better to eliminate as much of the interference at the source as possible. Once a magnetic field has been reduced to a reasonable level, it becomes practical to use magnetic shielding for further reduction. The basis for magnetic shielding is to provide a low-reluctance path which will attenuate the field external to the sensitive device being shielded or conversely to reduce magnetic flux emanating from the instrument. The procedure then requires the use of a metal for shielding with high magnetic permeability such as transformer iron or Mumetal. The proper permeability and thickness must be selected, however, according to the strength of the field. If the permeability is too high for the cross-sectional area, the magnetic field may saturate the metal, resulting in a poor shield. A common procedure is to use a shield built up in layers, with an air gap or nonmagnetic material between each layer, the lowest-permeability metal being on the side of the shield with the source of the interference to avoid saturation. Depending on the strength of the field, many layers of shielding may be required. If the object to be shielded is large, this type of shielding can become both expensive and heavy quite rapidly.

Magnetic shields must be preformed without seams and then heat-treated to achieve their maximum capabilities. Any type of discontinuity can distort the magnetic path and cause leakage from that point. Bending metal even once can change its characteristics sufficiently to cause such irregularities.

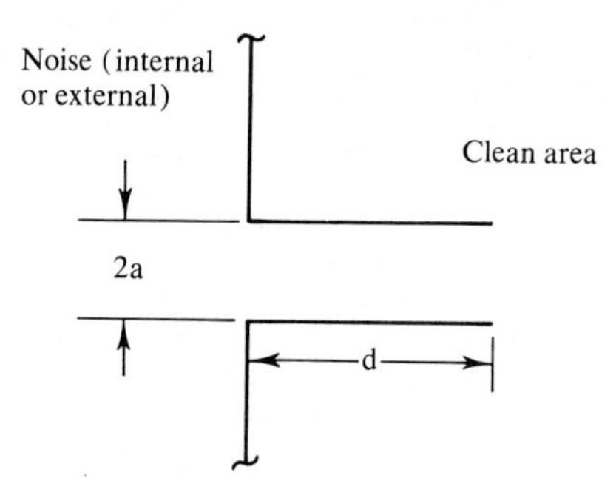

Fig. 4. Design for use of sleeve to provide a large hole in a shield.

$$\text{Attenuation} = 54.5 \frac{d}{\lambda_c} \left[1 - \left(\frac{\lambda_c}{\lambda}\right)^2\right]^{1/2} \quad \text{dB}$$

where λ_c = waveguide cutoff wavelength = $3.412a$
λ = wavelength of interfering signal
d = length of aperture, m
a = radius of aperture, m

General shielding is normally designed to eliminate electric fields and decrease magnetic fields to some degree. For this reason most instrument enclosures are made from mild steel. This gives a higher penetration loss than nonmagnetic materials but does not have quite the reflectivity of the higher-conductivity materials such as copper.

6. Holes in Shields Instrument setups normally require holes through the shield for ventilation. As a rule for good interference rejection, all uncovered holes should be less than ⅛ in. diameter. If larger holes are necessary, they should be covered with a fine wire mesh. In the case where it is necessary to have a large hole with no screen, the hole should be designed with protruding sleeves as shown in Fig. 4. This type of design acts as a waveguide beyond cutoff and will attenuate all signals below the cutoff frequency of the waveguide. The equations for determining the cutoff frequency and attenuation are given in Fig. 4. If the sleeve is made three times as long as the diameter, approximately 100 dB attenuation can be achieved for frequencies one-fifth of the cutoff frequency or below. At frequencies above the cutoff frequency, however, the sleeve becomes a waveguide and will allow signals to enter directly into the instrument. In a typical case a sleeve diameter of 2 cm and a length of 6 cm will have a cutoff frequency of about 9 GHz and attenuation of approximately 100 dB below 2 GHz.

7. Shield Bonds At joints in the shield and where access doors are necessary, continuous electrical and mechanical bonds are required. Therefore, the joints should be permanent where possible (by welding or brazing) or semipermanent with good, clean, machined, metallic surfaces bolted together with an rf gasket between them. The rf gasket will assure continuous low-impedance contact throughout the joint.

Bonding straps of copper or braid may be used where direct bonds are not possible, and these function reasonably well at lower frequencies. However, this type of bond is never as good as the direct bond. In general, since a low-impedance path between points is required, it can be accomplished only when the path length between the points is short in comparison with the wavelength being rejected.

CONDUCTED INTERFERENCE

Any wires which must penetrate the shield enclosure provide a path for conducting an interfering signal through the shield, thereby conveying the noise directly or, once the shield is penetrated, by radiation into the measuring system. This conducted interference can be reduced by proper filtering.

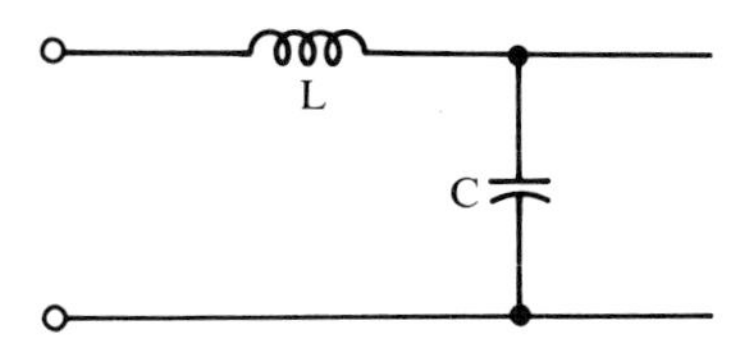

Fig. 5. Simple LC low-pass filter.

8. Filters Many filter designs are available for interference reduction. The choice of filter types is determined by the frequency and characteristics of the desired signals (pass characteristics) as well as the interference to be rejected. Accordingly, filters are classified as low-pass, high-pass, or bandpass, depending upon the range of desired frequencies to be transmitted.

The basic idea of the filter is to provide a high series impedance and a low-impedance shunt for the interfering signal. The filter should affect the desired signals as little as possible.

Low-pass filters are used in primary power leads to reduce high-frequency disturbances, the most common type of conducted interference. A simple low-pass filter is illustrated in Fig. 5, which uses a series inductor for high impedance for high frequencies and a capacitor to shunt the high frequencies to ground. Because of this low-pass characteristic of the filter, it introduces small insertion loss for the power currents and high insertion loss for higher-frequency interference currents.

In some cases, the filtering can be satisfactorily accomplished by a bypass capacitor. The most effective type of bypass capacitor is a feedthrough design.

Additional filter types are shown in Fig. 6. For high-frequency signal circuits, the low-frequency interference components can be reduced by the high-pass filter. The bandpass filter can be used to pass selectively a narrow-frequency-range signal, rejecting all other frequencies. This filter is particularly effective in suppressing undesired harmonics of the signal. A similar filter known as a bandstop or blocking filter (sometimes referred to as a "trap") can selectively attenuate a particularly bothersome interference of specific frequency.

If application of the simple filter types described above is insufficient, two or

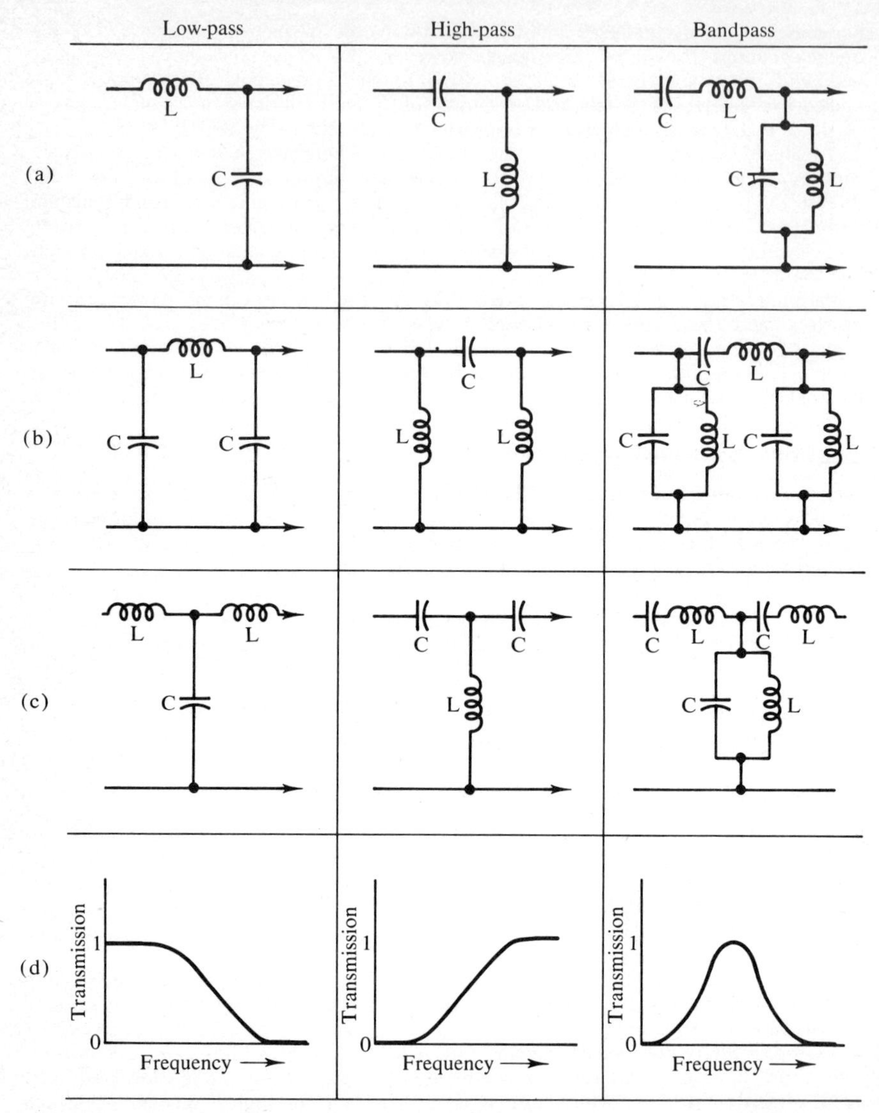

Fig. 6. Simple low-pass, high-pass, and bandpass filters. (*a*) L section. (*b*) π section. (*c*) T section. (*d*) The transmission factor as a function of frequency is a measure of the effectiveness of the filter. Ideally it would have a value of unity for desired frequencies and zero for interfering frequencies.

more filters can be placed in series or more sophisticated types of filters can be utilized.

Care must be utilized in installing filters, or their effectiveness in reducing the interference may be impaired or negated. It is important that no part of the wire be exposed within the shielded area prior to the filter, for this wire can radiate or receive noise and seriously reduce the effect of the filter. The proper method of applying filters is illustrated in Fig. 7. The filter should be placed as near the source of interference as possible and must be properly shielded and grounded to provide a low-impedance shunt for bypassing the interfering signal current without allowing it to couple energy into signal circuits. Attention must be given to inductive and capacitive coupling of interfering signals to other coils and leads by physical isolation, particularly of the input leads to the filter, and cleared output leads.

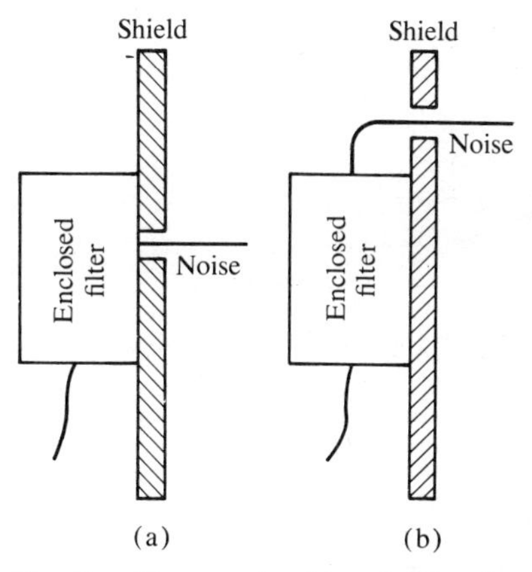

Fig. 7. Placement of input filter for any wires penetrating a shield. (*a*) Correct. (*b*) Incorrect.

COMMON-MODE INTERFERENCE

Common-mode interference is introduced by the inability to provide the same ground potential to an instrument and its signal source. This can be caused by long cables picking up signals, by electrostatic or magnetic coupling, or just by poor grounding, resulting in ground loops, as discussed in Chapter 16. An illustration of the common-mode interference problem is shown in Fig. 8*a*, illustrating an amplifier with input impedance Z_{in} connected by a cable to a distant transducer. The transducer ground *A* and amplifier ground *B* are widely separated and may therefore not be the same potential. This circuit can be represented by the equivalent circuit shown in Fig. 8b, where the difference potential between the output-transducer ground *A* and the amplifier ground *B* has been represented by a voltage source V_{cm} and series resistance Z_c. The transducer is represented by a voltage source V_{out} with an output impedance Z_{out}. The cable signal-conductor and return-lead impedances are represented by Z_A and Z_B, respectively.

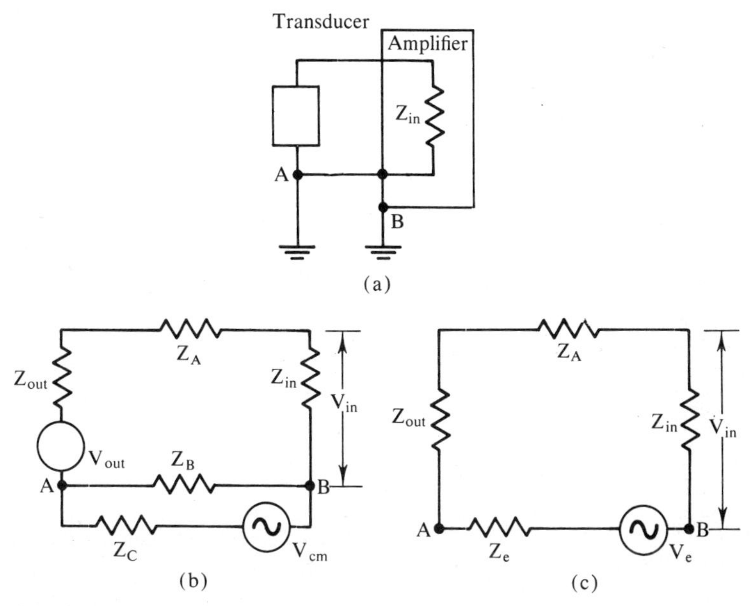

Fig. 8. Common-mode interference. (*a*) Typical amplifier with remote transducer. (*b*) Equivalent circuit of system of *a*. (*c*) Simplified equivalent circuit of *a*.

In order to simplify the analysis, assume for the moment that the transducer voltage V_{out} is zero. Now the interference voltage V_{in} due to the common-mode voltage can be readily determined from the equivalent circuit. The portion of the circuit containing the voltage source V_{cm} and impedances Z_C and Z_B can be replaced by a second equivalent circuit (Thevenin's equivalent) as shown in Fig. 8*c*, where V_e is the equivalent voltage source

$$V_e = V_{cm} \frac{Z_B}{Z_B + Z_C} \tag{2}$$

and the equivalent output impedance Z_e at point *AB* is

$$Z_e = \frac{Z_B Z_C}{Z_B + Z_C} \tag{3}$$

The voltage V_{in} now is simply the fraction of V_e that appears across Z_{in}:

$$V_{in} = \frac{V_e Z_{in}}{Z_{in} + Z_{out} + Z_A + Z_e}$$

If typical values are substituted into these equations, the seriousness of the problem can readily be seen. Assuming $Z_{in} = 10\ \text{M}\Omega$, $Z_{out} = 1{,}000\ \Omega$, $Z_A = Z_B = 10\ \Omega$, $Z_C = 1\ \Omega$, the following results are obtained:

$$V_e = V_{cm} \frac{10}{10 + 1} \approx V_{cm}$$

$$Z_e = \frac{10 \times 1}{10 + 1} \approx 1\ \Omega$$

$$V_{in} = V_{cm} \frac{10^7}{10^7 + 10^3 + 10 + 1} \approx V_{cm}$$

It is completely within the realm of possibility for V_{cm} on a long cable to be on the order 1 V. If sensitive (millivolt) readings are to be made, it is obviously impossible with this type of connection.

9. Reduction of Common-mode Interference by Use of Differential Inputs By the use of proper connections to differential inputs, the common-mode problem can be reduced. An instrument has a differential input if it responds to the algebraic difference between two separate input signals. Three commonly used types of differential inputs are illustrated in Figs. 9 through 11. Consider first the balanced input amplifier shown in Fig. 9*a* and its equivalent circuit in Fig. 9*b*. In this case neither input to the amplifier is grounded and the input impedance Z_{in} can be visualized as split and balanced to ground. As long as the input impedance is large compared with all other impedances, it is obvious that V_{cm} will essentially appear equally at each input with respect to ground; therefore, the common mode will cancel. If it were possible to make the system perfectly balanced by using a balanced-to-ground transducer or making $Z_{out} = Z_A = Z_B$, it is theoretically possible for the amplifier output to be independent of V_{cm}. Usually, however, in practical cases this is not completely possible.

The floating-input amplifier shown in Fig. 10 differs from the balanced-input case of Fig. 9 in that the inputs are isolated from ground with no intentional impedance connections to the ground system of the amplifier. Although the inputs are floating, in practice, both will have some finite leakage to ground. Normally, this leakage will be unbalanced to the extent that the leakage on one input terminal is negligible compared with that on the other. The equivalent circuit for this case is shown in Fig. 9*b*, where Z_I represents the leakage impedance. This equivalent circuit can be simplified to give Thevenin's equivalent identical to Fig. 8*c*. However, the equivalent voltage will be

$$V_e = V_{cm} \frac{Z_B}{Z_B + Z_C + Z_I} \tag{4}$$

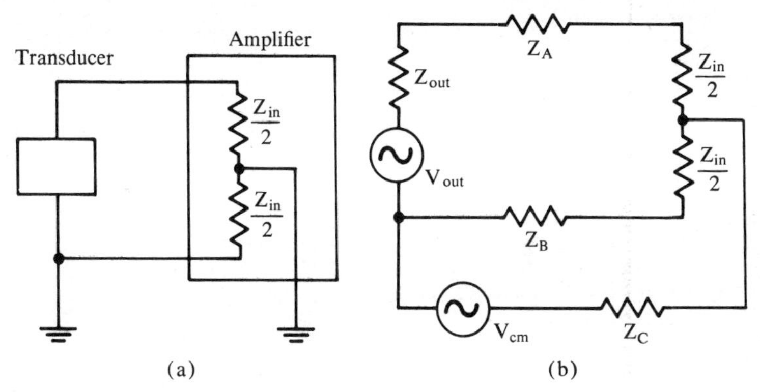

Fig. 9. Balanced input to ground amplifier. (*a*) Typical connection for balanced input to ground amplifier. (*b*) Equivalent circuit of *a*.

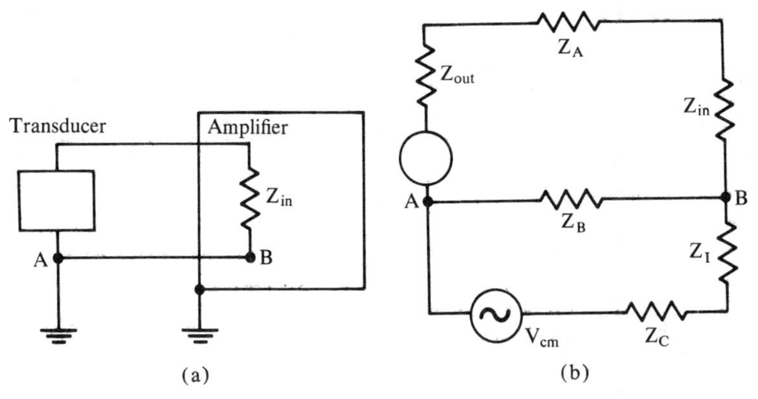

Fig. 10. Floating-input amplifier for reduction of common-mode interference. (*a*) Typical floating-input amplifier. (*b*) Equivalent circuit of *a*.

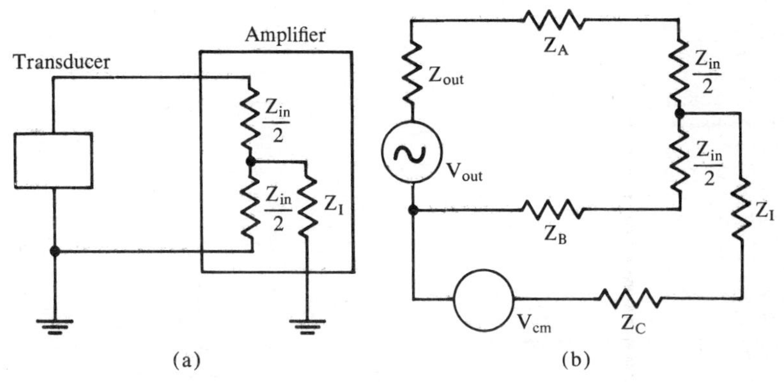

Fig. 11. Balanced differential amplifier with isolation to ground. (*a*) Typical connection for balanced differential amplifier. (*b*) Equivalent circuit for *a*.

It can be seen then that if Z_I can be maintained very large, V_e can be reduced to the point that the amplifier input voltage will be insignificant, since V_{cm} will appear almost entirely across Z_I. In practical cases it should be pointed out that Z_I will consist of the actual amplifier-leakage impedance in parallel with insulation and line impedance to ground. Any leakage on lines, such as any contamination or condensation, could reduce this impedance and cause difficulty.

The use of an amplifier that has a balanced floating input to ground, as shown in Fig. 11, combines the advantages of both prior systems and diminishes the disadvantages.

10. Guarding Guarding is a technique which is often used to reduce common-mode interference and also to reduce the effects of shunt capacitance and leakage.* The guarded connection for common-mode rejection is given in Fig. 12. This technique is essentially a floating input with a guard system for making negligible the leakage that limited the usefulness of the straight floating-input system. This isolation is achieved by enclosing the measuring or input section of the instrument

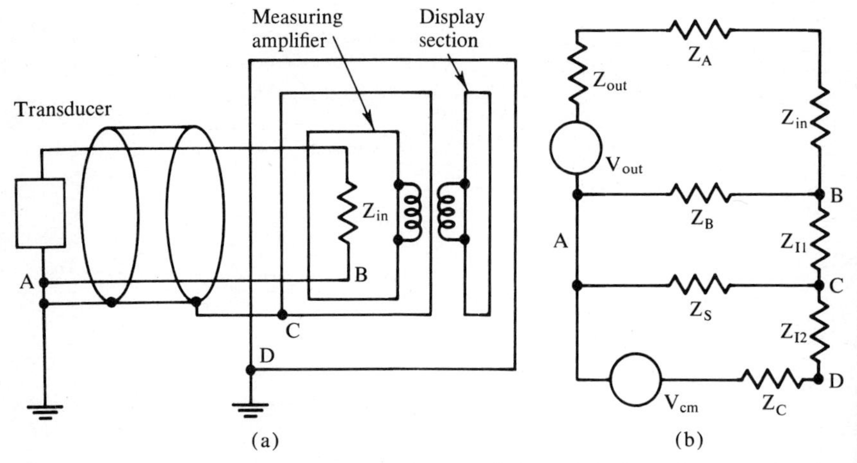

Fig. 12. Connection for guarded-section amplifier. (*a*) Typical connection for guarded-section amplifier. (*b*) Equivalent circuit of *a*.

in a shield that is isolated from ground. Also the guarded system effectively utilizes a cable shield. The equivalent circuit of this system is shown in Fig. 12*b*. Z_s represents the cable shield impedance, Z_{I_1} represents the isolation impedance from the amplifier from input *B* to the guard shield *C*, and Z_{I_2} represents the isolation impedance between the guard shield *C* and ground *D*. The common-mode voltage due to any potential difference between grounds *A* and *D* will be dropped across Z_2 because of the low-impedance path through the shield. Input *B* is further isolated by isolation impedance Z_{I_1}; thus the interference input to the amplifier is essentially nonexistent.

If it is not necessary to connect the source transducer to ground, an alternate solution is to leave the source ungrounded and connect its shield only to the cable shield of a differential unguarded amplifier. This will give the same results as the guarded amplifier if the impedance to ground at the transducer is maintained at a value comparable with the impedance Z_{I_2} of the guarded amplifier.

In the preceding examples it was shown that the common-mode interference was greatly reduced by making the isolation interference Z_I large in magnitude. In

* Another useful application of the guarding technique is the cancellation of leakage-impedance effects discussed in Chapter 17.

most instances Z_I is essentially a stray capacitance. Therefore, Z_I and its effectiveness in reducing common-mode interference will be less at higher frequencies.

CROSSTALK

In most practical instrumentation systems there will be different signals in different channels. Any time the signal from one channel appears in a second adjacent channel, it can be termed "crosstalk." This type of interference can be readily detected if the suspected interfering channel can be deactivated.

One instance of crosstalk occurs when the input of an instrument has a number of different input signals that can be selected, as shown in Fig. 13. In this case of two signals, when V_1 is selected as illustrated, V_2 is the unwanted signal; however,

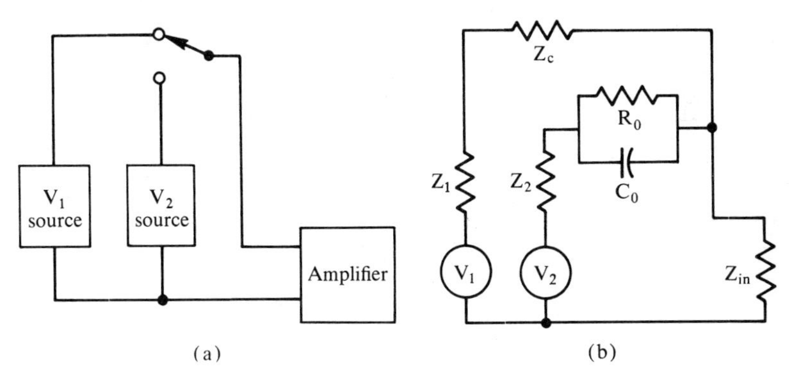

Fig. 13. Crosstalk in switch. (*a*) Typical switched-input amplifier. (*b*) Equivalent circuit of *a*.

the stray leakages in the switch can couple this voltage into the amplifier. An equivalent circuit of the two inputs V_1 and V_2 is shown in Fig. 13*b*, where

R_o = leakage resistance of open switch
C_o = stray capacitance of open switch
Z_1 = source 1 impedance
Z_2 = source 2 impedance
Z_c = contact impedance of closed switch
Z_{in} = input impedance of the amplifier

If Z_{in} is high, the voltage which will appear on the input due to V_2

$$\text{Coupled voltage} = \frac{V_2(Z_1 + Z_c)}{(Z_1 + Z_c + Z_2 + Z_0)} \tag{5}$$

where Z_o is impedance of R_o and C_o in parallel. At very low frequencies $Z_o \approx R_o$, and at high frequencies $Z_o \approx 1/\omega C_o$. From Eq. (5), it can be seen that to maintain minimum crosstalk, Z_1 should be small and Z_o as large as possible (usually Z_c and Z_2 will be negligibly small).

Very often crosstalk will appear between two separate amplifiers where an input on one amplifier will also produce an output on the second amplifier. The same arguments hold in this case as in the switched input amplifier. Any stray capacitance or resistance anywhere from the first amplifier to the second will cause coupling. Often the problem will be caused by something in common being shared by the two amplifiers such as a common power supply or using the same power or ground wire between them. The obvious solution to this problem is to require complete shielding between the two amplifiers and separate power supplies. Economics do not always make this possible. Therefore, leads common to the two amplifiers should not be allowed unless absolutely necessary. Situations involving common leads require that the leads be short and large enough that their impedance is insignificant. A common power supply then should have a low output impedance and separate leads taking power to each amplifier. Each of these leads can also be decoupled by using an appropriate filter.

CONTACT POTENTIAL

When two conductors of dissimilar materials are connected together, a voltage is generated at the junction which can be a source of constant static-offset interference. This voltage is a function of the temperature of the junction. In any realizable system where dissimilar metals are used in a circuit, more than one junction will always be involved. As shown in Fig. 14*a* most voltmeters will have copper wires (conductor 1) so that if a junction *A* is made with conductor 2 and the copper wire, the same junction in the reverse must be made by conductor 2 and the other copper meter lead at *B*. Thus, if the two junctions are at the same temperature, no net voltage will be produced, since the voltages generated

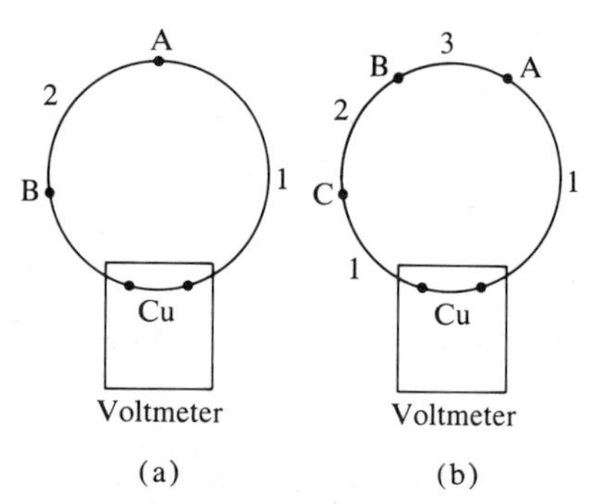

Fig. 14. Contact potential by thermocouple action. (*a*) Circuit with two dissimilar conductors. (*b*) Circuit with three dissimilar metals.

at the two junctions will cancel each other. If, as in Fig. 14*b*, a third homogeneous conductor 3 is inserted, as long as the temperatures of the three junctions are the same the sum of the contact potentials around the loop will still be equal to zero. As can be seen then, regardless of the number of junctions made, as long as all junctions are at the same temperature, no voltage will be produced. Problems can develop, however, if different points in the circuit are at different temperatures. In most instances, any problems can be forestalled by merely using the same conductor material throughout the system. When the thermoelectric effect is being exploited to measure temperature, one junction is held at a constant known temperature. The net voltage difference will then be a function of the temperature difference.

INSTRUMENT INTERCONNECTIONS

Any realizable system of instruments requires interconnecting wires or cables. Because of their length these wires and cables are prone to pick up noise. For instance, a cable may be of the proper length to be a receiving antenna for an rf signal, or the cable may form a large loop which will have large circulating currents flowing in it because of magnetic coupling.

The type of cabling used and the way it is connected therefore depend largely on the type of interference to be rejected. For instance, if the coupling is magnetic, all cable shields may be grounded on only one end. If it is rf interference, the cable should be grounded at intervals much less than a wavelength of the interfering signal.

In severe cases the cable may be double-shielded or shielded with a twisted pair of wires inside so that the outer shield can be grounded in several places to reduce rf pickup and the inner shield can be left open on one end of the twisted pair to reduce magnetic pickup. In general in all low-level circuits a properly shielded cable must be utilized to minimize interference pickup. Conversely, high-level circuits should use the proper shielded cable to minimize interference radiation.

The physical location and routing must be engineered properly to minimize the possibility of pickup. Low-level signal cables and wires must not run near or parallel to high-level signal or power cables. When low-level and high-level cables must be in proximity they should cross at right angles to each other.

Any cabling in a system which produces a loop should be routed to minimize the area of the loop and thus reduce magnetically induced interference. Another method of effectively reducing magnetic interference is to twist the wires tightly together (twisted pairs). This produces many small opposing loops which cancel the net magnetic pickup or transmission.

GENERAL CHARACTERISTICS AND SOURCES OF INTERFERENCE

Hum. This audio-frequency noise is prevalent because of ac power transmission and distribution systems. In the United States, the fundamental ac frequency is 60 Hz; hence, this frequency and its harmonics will characterize the hum. The magnitude of this interference at any location depends primarily on the proximity of power transformers and all power wires. In general, however, this type of interference will be appreciable in nearly every measurement situation in varying degrees of severity. One notable exception is that of measurements made in space.

Impulse Noise. This type of noise is normally generated any time the magnitude of a current is abruptly changed. The frequency spectrum is broad; therefore, it is very difficult to filter and is normally more easily controlled at the source. Common sources of impulse noise are dc and universal motors and generators (brush-type machines), automobile ignition systems, relays, dc-to-dc converters, etc. These sources may transfer energy to the measuring setup by radiation or conduction mechanisms.

Atmospheric Noise. This noise is generated in the atmosphere primarily by lightning discharges and is therefore dependent upon time of day, geographical location, and the weather. Its frequency characteristic covers a broad spectrum and is characterized by a crackling sound (static) in an AM receiver.

Cosmic Noise. There are many sources in space which transmit a wide band of random noise. One of the primary sources is the sun.

Thermal Noise. This signal is generated by the thermal agitation of electrons in a resistance. It is broadband random signal that defines the theoretical limit of sensitivity of an instrument.

Continuous Interference. A continuous type of interference may be narrowband as in the case of commercial radio, television, and amateur-radio transmitters, rf conduction-induction heaters, etc., or relatively broadband as in diathermy machines, x-ray machines, arcs and corona from high-voltage power lines, and other sources of arcs such as fluorescent mercury-vapor lighting fixtures, neon signs, and rotary machines with brushes or slip rings. The interference may be conducted or radiated.

Mechanically Generated Interference. The movement of conductors in a magnetic field is a source of interfering signal. Noise is also generated by flexing of coaxial cables, and production of static electricity due to friction. Another class of noise known as microphonics is generated by vibration and shock, particularly of electron tubes and phototubes.

SPECIFIC INTERFERENCE–SOURCE–REDUCTION TECHNIQUES

In most instances, reduction of noise and interference is most successful if sensitive instruments can be physically removed as far as possible from the interfering sources. Application of noise-suppression techniques at the sources, as described below for specific examples, provides an additional means of reducing noise and interference.

Relays, Controllers, Switching Devices

1. Shunt relay or switch contacts with a capacitor to reduce current surges. In general, a current-limiting resistor should be placed in series with the capacitor to prevent deterioration of the switching contacts.
2. Enclose switching device in a shield.

Electromechanical Vibrators

1. Shield the vibrator.
2. Use feedthrough capacitors or, if necessary, more elaborate filters for power leads passing through the shield. Filter components should all be within the shield, with leads passing through the shield via feedthrough capacitors.

Vibrating-type DC Voltage Regulators

1. Shield the regulator.
2. Locate the regulator as near the generator as possible.
3. Shield leads between regulator and generator.
4. Bypass input dc lead inside the shield with a capacitor, preferably a feedthrough capacitor.

DC-DC Converters and Inverters

1. Shield the unit.
2. Use low-pass filters on all leads passing through the shield (at minimum, use feedthrough capacitors).

Arc and Gaseous-discharge Devices—Mercury-arc Rectifiers, Thyratrons, Neon Signs, Fluorescent-lighting Fixtures, Arc Welders

1. Install bypass capacitors on lines.
2. Use special conductive coatings over glass.
3. Use shield cases.
4. Substitute incandescent lights for fluorescents.

Mechanically Induced Interference (Microphonics)

1. Support cables to reduce movement.
2. Use low-noise cables.
3. Use vibration and shock-damping mounts.
4. Select low-noise devices and hand-pick for lowest noise.

Electric Motors and Generators

1. Use a good shielded housing.
2. Bond housing to ground.
3. Use bypass capacitors at brushes.
4. Use a feedthrough capacitor at the armature terminal.
5. Shield terminals and interconnecting wiring.
6. Keep brushes in good condition.

RF Generators—Transmitters, Induction Heaters, Etc.

1. Use special multiple-shield enclosures.
2. Bypass and filter all lines entering or leaving the shield enclosures.
3. Use resonant traps for specific frequencies.

Ignition Noise (Internal-combustion Engine)

1. Place resistor (10 KΩ) in high-voltage lead near the coil, or use resistive ignition leads.
2. Use shielded internal-resistor spark plugs.
3. Shield the coil.
4. Use shielded ignition wires.
5. Use bypass capacitors on the dc lines into the coil and distributor.

Static, Corona, High-voltage Arc Discharges

1. Use conductive belts on machinery.
2. Use brush-to-ground drive shafts.
3. Electrically bond equipment together.
4. Eliminate sharp points and corners.
5. Use coatings and paint on rough surfaces.
6. Keep dry and free of contamination.
7. Pressurize high-voltage components or seal them in a hard vacuum.

SUMMARY

The reduction of interference can be accomplished in many ways. However, in general each method includes some form of physical placement, shielding, and filtering. The severity of the problem will determine the extent of the use of these principles. For instance, the problem may be solved by moving a sensitive instrument a few meters from a specific interfering source, or it may be necessary to place the whole measuring site in a remote area and use battery operation. Often laboratories have special low-noise measurement areas utilizing specially constructed multiply shielded rooms.

BIBLIOGRAPHY

Alvin, Arnold L.: Designing the RFI Shielded Package, *Electron. Ind.*, vol. 24, no. 1, pp. 80–83, January, 1965.

Buchman, A. S.: Noise Control in Low Level Data Systems, *Electromech. Design,* vol. 6, no. 9, pp. 64–81, September, 1962.

Buehler, W. E., and C. D. Lunden: Signature of Man-made High-frequency Radio Noise, *IEEE Trans. Electromagnetic Compatibility,* vol. EMC-8, no. 3, pp. 143–152, September, 1966.

Clark, Ralph L.: The Rationalization of United States Overseas Communications and Its Potential Impact on Electromagnetic Compatibility, *IEEE Trans. Electromagnetic Compatibility,* vol. EMC-8, no. 4, pp. 215–219, December, 1966.

Cook, Donald V.: RFI Suppression, Part I, *Electromech. Design,* vol. 11, no. 11, pp. 28–31, November, 1967.

Costa, David P.: RFI Suppression, Part II, *Electromech. Design,* vol. 11, no. 12, pp. 38–40, December, 1967.

Costa, David P.: RFI Suppression, Part III, *Electromech. Design,* vol. 12, no. 5, pp. 28–34, May, 1968.

Cowdell, Robert B.: Help Stamp Out EMI, *EDN Mag.*, vol. L63, Nov. 23, 1966.

Ehrreich, John E., and Melvin Nimoy: R. F. Shielding Performance of Reinforced Metal Filled Conductive Plastic Flat Gaskets, *IEEE Trans. Electromagnetic Compatibility,* March, 1965, pp. 50–54.

Ficchi, Rocco F.: "Electrical Interference," p. 262, Hayden Book Company, Inc., New York, 1964.

Flynn, George: From RFI to EMC . . . Cleaning Up the Spectrum. *Electron. Prod.*, vol. 10, no. 6, pp. 50–62, November, 1967.

"Grounding and Noise Reduction Practices for Instrumentation Systems," Scientific Data Systems.

"Instrumentation Grounding and Noise Minimization Handbook," Consolidated Systems Corporation, January, 1965.

Jambor, Schukantz, and Haber: Parallel Wire Susceptibility Testing for L.D. Signal Lines, *IEEE Trans. Electromagnetic Compatibility,* December, 1965, pp. 437–444.

Jarva, W.: Shielding Efficiency Calculation Methods, *EDN Circuit Packaging Issue,* October, 1963.

Jorgensen, C. M.: Electromagnetic-interference Shielding Techniques, *Electro-Technol. (New York)*, vol. 77, no. 5, pp. 95–96, May, 1966.

Klipec, Bruce E.: Reducing Electrical Noise in Instrument Circuits, *IEEE Trans. Ind. Gen. Appl.*, vol. IGA-3, no. 2, March/April, 1967.

Mayer, Ferdy: Electromagnetic Compatibility: Anti-interference Wires, Cables and Filters, *IEEE Trans. Electromagnetic Compatibility,* vol. EMC-8, no. 3, pp. 153–160, September, 1966.

"Military Specification Interference Control Requirements, Aeronautical Equipment (USAF)," with Amendment 1, June 17, 1959, MIL-I-26600.

Robinson, James G.: Fundamentals of EMI Shielding, *Electro-Technol.* (*New York*), vol. 77, no. 6, pp. 36–39, June, 1966.

Robinson, Trevor A.: The Role of Grounding in Eliminating Electronic Interference, *IEEE Spectrum,* vol. 2, no. 7, pp. 85–89, July, 1965.

Sabaroff, Samuel: Sources and Effects of Electrical Charge Accumulation and Dissipation on Spacecraft, *IEEE Trans. Electromagnetic Compatibility,* December, 1965, pp. 437–444.

Sclater, Neil: Systems Solution to EMI Problem Sought: DOD Seeks to Beat Increasing Interference by Having Compatibility Designed into Equipment, *Electron. Design,* no. 17, pp. 17–20, Aug. 16, 1967.

Sladek, Norbert J.: Electromagnetic-interference Control, *Electro-Technol.* (*New York*), vol. 78, no. 5, pp. 85–94, November, 1966.

Soldanels, Roy M.: Flexible Radio Frequency Bonding Configurations: Theoretical Analysis, Measurements, and Practical Applications, *IEEE Trans. Electromagnetic Compatibility,* vol. EMC-9, no. 3, December, 1967.

Spelman, Francis A.: Electrical Interference in Biomedical Systems, *IEEE Trans. Electromagnetic Compatibility,* December, 1965, pp. 428–436.

Thornwall, Joseph C.: Design Noise out of Spacecraft Payload: Good Circuit Design and Proper Layout Can Avoid Serious Troubles at Launching Time, *Electron. Design,* vol. 16, no. 8, pp. 64–68, Apr. 11, 1968.

Vogelman, Joseph H.: Predicting Electromagnetic Interference, *Electro-Technol.* (*New York*), vol. 75, no. 4, pp. 46–50, April, 1965.

White, Donald R. F.: Progress in EMC Instrumentation, *Electro-Technol.* (*New York*), vol. 74, no. 4, pp. 46–50, October, 1964.

White, J. V.: Wiring of Data Systems for Minimum Noise, *IEEE Trans. Radio Frequency Interference,* March, 1963, pp. 77–82.

Chapter **16**

Electrical Grounding

D. A. BURT and K. D. BAKER, Ph.D.
Utah State University, Logan, Utah

Even experienced electronics engineers on occasion have been known to say that there is some "black art" to building and using electronic equipment which does not oscillate or have some unwanted noise signal impressed upon it. In many cases, however, this "black art" is actually a good basic knowledge of how to ground all interconnecting systems properly.

Originally an electrical ground was a conducting connection between an electric circuit and the earth; however, the word has been rather loosely applied in the electronics industry as a point or points which are used as a zero-voltage reference.

In a measurement system, grounds are conventionally separated into three types:

1. *Power grounds:* the return path for electric current that provides the power necessary to operate the instrument.

2. *Signal grounds:* the reference point and return path for all signal currents.
3. *Chassis and shield grounds:* usually the chassis and outer metal case of instruments and cable shields.

The basic grounding criterion is the requirement that each type of ground have the same potential throughout the system. This requirement, however, is seldom if ever completely met in any practical system. For this reason this chapter is devoted to showing some of the sources of potentials appearing on the grounds and ways to minimize the problems caused by them.

AC POWER GROUNDS

One of the largest sources of electrical noise is ac power-distribution systems. For this reason it is important to have some understanding of the grounding practices in these distribution systems.

Power systems are normally separated into three groups:

1. Transmission lines which carry the power over long distances at high voltages, i.e., 34 kV and above.
2. Primary distribution lines which carry power to a test facility or a town in a relatively small area—ranging in voltages from 2.4 to 25 kV.
3. Facility distribution lines which normally operate at 120 to 240 V. In all cases these power lines are referenced to earth ground. This is done to prevent transient voltages due to arcing between grounds, to permit the use of lower insulation levels, and to aid in protective fusing.

Since these power lines are all referenced to earth ground, current will be flowing in the earth. This current will find and flow along the path of least resistance, thus producing potential drops in the earth and generating a magnetic flux. The potential drops make it impossible to connect to the earth at two different points and assume that they are and will remain at the same potential. The magnetic flux which is created will couple with a transformer action into long wires or loops of wire, thus generating low-impedance circulating currents which are difficult to eliminate.

High-voltage transmission lines are normally grounded at the generator end only. Over long lines, however, the capacitance of the wire to the earth can allow considerable current to flow through the earth.

For primary distribution lines the National Electrical Safety Code requires that the neutral conductor be connected to earth at least four times every mile. Under this system the current will divide and flow into the earth and the wire in proportion to the conductivity of each.

In facility distribution the neutral is grounded at the source and should not be grounded at the load. Unless there is a fault somewhere, there should be very little earth current due to the facility distribution.

Because of the extensive power systems throughout the world, it can be generally said that there will be ground currents almost everywhere. This is the 60-Hz signal that you see when you touch your finger to the input of an oscilloscope or the hum you hear when you touch the input of an audio amplifier. Since this signal is so prevalent, it must be considered in all interconnecting systems, especially if the systems are widely separated.

INSTRUMENT POWER INPUT

1. AC-powered Instruments Most quality instruments have a three-wire line cord. In the ac power line, one wire is the hot wire, the second is the common or power return, and the third is earth ground. Inside the instrument, the hot wire and the common go to a power transformer while the earth ground connects directly to the metal case. The third wire provides personnel safety by maintaining the instrument case at earth potential and should normally not be circumvented. While this third wire or earth ground is fine for safety in preventing electrical shock and in providing an overall grounded shield, it can cause problems when a number of instruments are all plugged into the power line and their cases are then all connected together. For instance, all the instrument grounds may be connected together to form a large loop. This loop then becomes a shorted turn, and the magnetic coupling to earth currents can produce large circulating currents. This is commonly referred to as a ground loop.

A large number of inexpensive commercial electronic items such as radios and television sets do not use internal power-supply transformers but derive the necessary voltages directly from the ac line. The chassis then may be connected to the ac common or to the high side of the line, depending on the orientation of the plug with respect to the socket. Thus, if the plug is inserted such that the chassis is connected to the hot side of the ac power, the chassis is hot with respect to earth ground; and unless a man is insulated from ground, he can receive a severe shock. If measurements are being made on this chassis with a quality instrument, a connection of the instrument ground to the hot chassis is a short circuit. Sparks, smoke, and a blown fuse will normally occur in that order. This type of equipment will always be completely encased in an insulating material and use an interlocking power cord to prevent shock to the user; however, a person working on the equipment must use due caution.

2. Battery-operated Instruments Rechargeable batteries and low-power-drain solid-state circuitry allow the instrument designer to design portable units which are completely isolated. Because of the isolation, this equipment offers a number of advantages in eliminating many of the problems associated with grounds. For instance, ground loops are readily eliminated, as is the problem of measuring a signal with respect to a point not at earth ground.

INSTRUMENT GROUNDS

3. Normal Input Grounds Signal ground paths vary, depending on the type of instrument; however, it is very important that no extraneous currents flow on them.

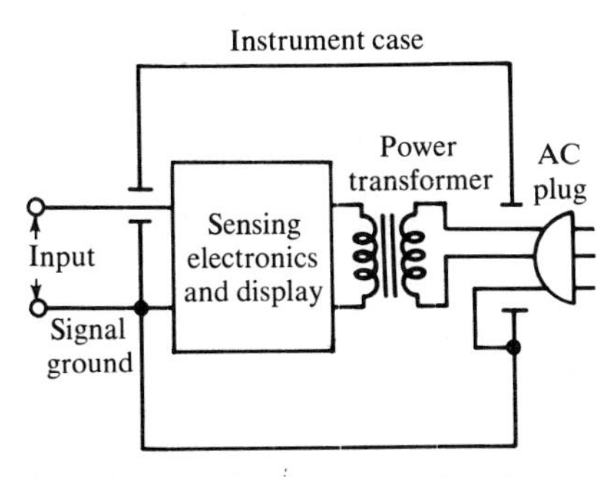

Fig. 1. Most common input and power grounds of measuring instruments.

A commonly used instrument is the measuring type such as a voltmeter, oscilloscope, or chart recorder. These instruments take some input quantity and display it to the operator. In general, this type of instrument has a complete ground system, as shown in Fig. 1.

It should be noted that the input of these instruments is referenced to case ground; and as stated in the previous section, this case ground is also tied to earth ground through the third wire of the ac power line. As long as the third wire is plugged in, the input ground should not be connected to any point which has a potential with respect to earth ground or it could produce disastrous consequences.

4. Differential Input Some measuring instruments have a differential (floating) input (signal ground isolated from case) and a case or shield ground as shown in Fig. 2. In this type of instrument, the signal that is displayed is the voltage difference between the two input signals. For example, if a 5-V signal were applied to the positive input with respect to case ground and a 3-V signal on the negative input, the only portion which would be sensed is the difference voltage (differential voltage) of 2 V. The part of the voltage which is common to both inputs is termed common-mode voltage and is not sensed. Since both input terminals are isolated, either terminal can be considered as signal ground. This reference terminal can be at an arbitrary voltage with respect to case ground as long as instrument voltage ratings are not exceeded.

5. Normal Ground for Output Type of Instrument An output-type instrument is the signal source which is to be connected to another instrument. Power supplies and signal generators normally fall in this category. Diagrams of these types of instruments are given in Fig. 3. For dc or low-frequency outputs, there is usually a plus and minus output terminal with a separate case terminal which can be connected where desired as shown in Fig. 3*a*. For rf generation or where there are high-frequency components, the

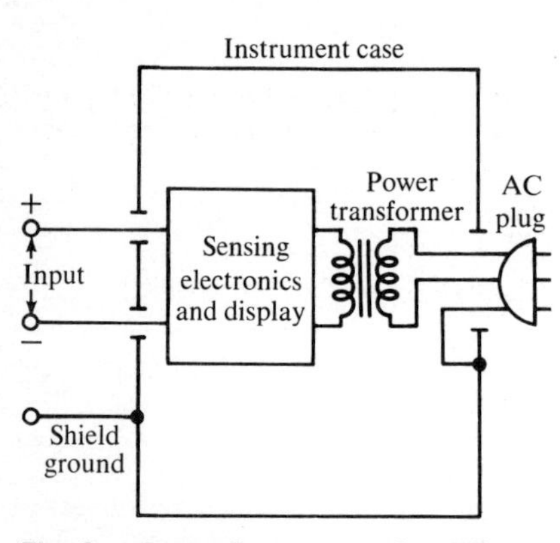

Fig. 2. Grounding system for differential-input devices.

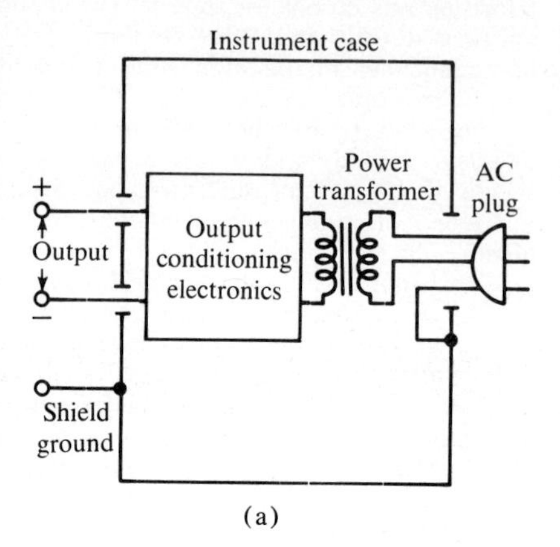

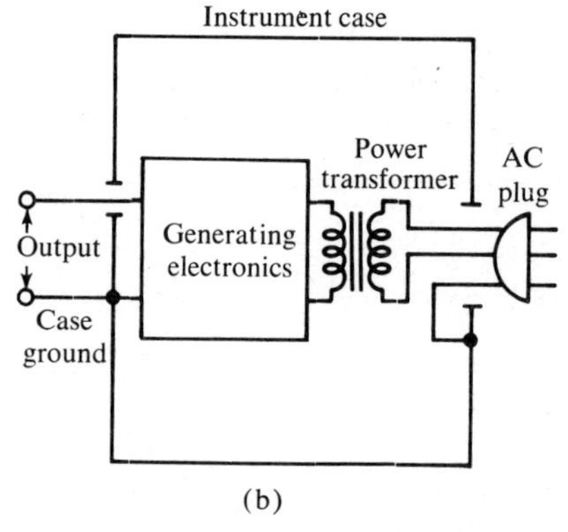

Fig. 3. Typical ground system for output-type instruments. (*a*) Ground system of low-frequency and dc output instruments. (*b*) Ground system of rf output instruments.

output will be on an rf connector where the outside or ground side of the connector is connected to the case, as shown in Fig. 3*b*.

6. Ground Connections in Measurement Systems An absolute general method of properly connecting the grounds of instruments together does not exist. Depending on the circumstances, there may be a number of ways which will produce satisfactory results. General guidelines for ground interconnections are:

1. Connect all grounds so that shield, power, and signal ground currents cannot intermix but can only flow in their respective ground paths.
2. Maintain short ground paths and use large conductors to minimize impedance between ground points.
3. Avoid multiple paths for ground currents.

4. Design each individual ground circuit in such a manner that high-level ground currents cannot flow in low-level input ground circuits.

In most instances it is not practical to adhere rigorously to all the foregoing rules at the same time. For example, all instruments should be connected to earth ground for safety purposes, and this requirement is often in conflict with the rule regarding multiple ground paths. In actual practice the foregoing "rules" are used as a guide, and all grounding is done in such a manner as to minimize the effects of compromising these rules. The best way to illustrate good grounding techniques is by the use of a number of examples.

An example of the grounding system typical of the internal connections of instruments is shown in Fig. 4. In this case the power and signal grounds are not isolated; however, care is taken to minimize the problems by proper ground design. The ground system runs in a continuous line from the high-level stage to the low-level stage in sequence with no doubling back. Even though a wire or chassis is designated a ground, it cannot be overemphasized that the same potential may not exist at all points, particularly at high frequencies. This is illustrated by the equivalent impedances Z_1, Z_2, and Z_3, which are the inductance and resistance of the interconnecting wires. Although these impedances need to be minimized by choice of short paths and large conductors, the current which flows through

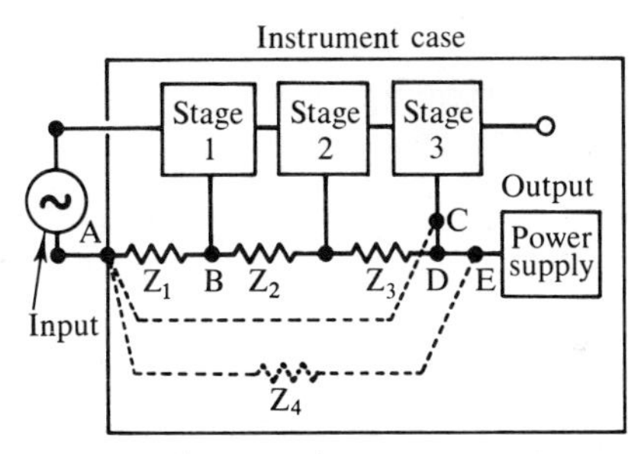

Fig. 4. Ground system inside an instrument.

these impedances may produce significant voltage drops, resulting in different potentials at the various ground points. Accordingly, a stage or instrument cannot be arbitrarily connected to any point considered ground. To illustrate the consequences of indiscriminate grounding, assume that stage 3 had been connected to point *A* instead of point *D* as the dotted line indicates. Now any signal and power currents which flow to stage 3 must pass through Z_1, Z_2, and Z_3. Often stage 3 is a high-level stage drawing large currents. These currents will produce a voltage drop in Z_1 which will be directly in series with the input of the first stage. Potential drops will also appear across Z_2 and Z_3 in series with the inputs of stage 2 and stage 3. These extraneous signals on the input can result in many serious problems. Depending on what the instrument may be, the system may oscillate or have a dc offset or many other spurious responses.

Note also that the power-supply ground should be connected first to the high-level stage as shown. If the power supply were connected to point *A*, as shown by the dotted line and Z_4, again the high-level current of stage 3 would be forced to flow through Z_1 and produce spurious responses. The low-level current from stage 1 will flow through Z_2 and Z_3 in the proper connection; however, this current is of such a low magnitude that the resulting signals in stages 2 and 3 are insignificant.

A classic illustration of the fallacy in assuming that ground is everywhere the same is encountered in the design of a simple power dc supply as shown in Fig. 5. Normally, in a well-designed power supply there will be very little ripple and noise on the output, between *A* and *B*. However, if by some chance it was more convenient to use point *C* as the ground reference, rather than point *D*, considerable ripple will appear in the output. This is because the current which flows through the rectifiers to charge the filter capacitor flows only for a small part of a cycle, producing short pulses of current many times greater than the direct output current of the supply. Since these current pulses will usually be at least several amperes, it takes very little resistance between *C* and *D* to produce a considerable voltage pulse in series with the output.

Many problems associated with measurement systems are a result of ground loops. The best definition of a ground loop is the inability to provide the same potential at two different ground points. This can be due to multiple-point grounding, magnetic pickup on a large wire loop, or electric pickup on a long wire. Whenever 60-Hz hum appears in a system, it can usually be traced to a ground loop. To illustrate the problems associated with a ground loop, refer to the system shown in Fig. 6. Proper procedures dictate that the power supply should be connected only to point *B*. If instead it were connected to both points *A* and *B* (dotted line), the high-level currents from stage 3 will split and flow both directions from point *B*. The amount of current flowing through each path will be proportional to the conductivity of each path. Again the relative conductivities could be such that the system would oscillate or produce erroneous results. The ground loop

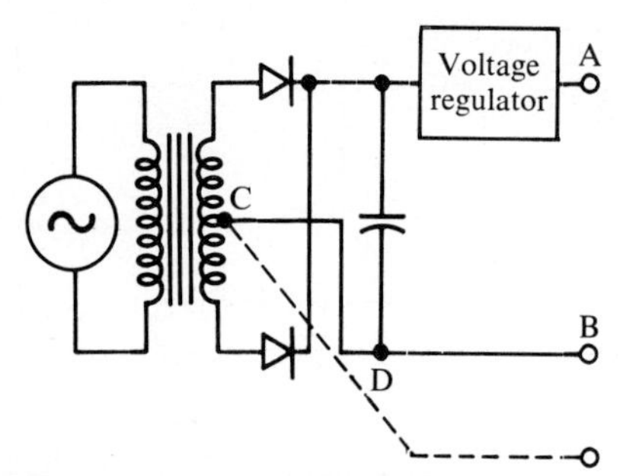

Fig. 5. Example of the use of proper and improper ground reference for a simple dc power supply.

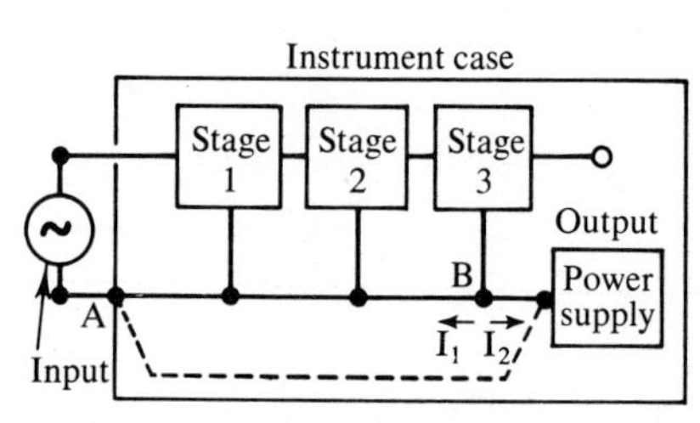

Fig. 6. Ground loop inside an instrument.

may produce additional interference in the presence of a changing magnetic field by inducing circulating currents in the loop. When this noise appears, because of long cables and widely separated ground points, it will normally appear at the signal ground and the signal input level at the same time. This is termed common-mode interference and requires special attention. This particulár situation is explained in Chapter 15.

A method of grounding known as single-point grounding is shown in Fig. 7. In this example the only ground impedance which is common to any of the stages is the output impedance of the power supply including the conductor to the common point. This usually can be made small enough to be insignificant.

The method of properly grounding a system consisting of an electronic instrument and an external power supply is illustrated in Fig. 8. Most good power supplies have three terminals: plus, minus, and a shield ground (the instrument cover). When connecting this power supply to other equipment, the plus and minus outputs are connected to the necessary power inputs and the shield ground is connected to the shield of the instrument as shown. This provides a continuous-shield system for minimizing interference pickup from external sources.

An example of the complete grounding system for a typical test setup is shown in Fig. 9. The electronic circuit under test is powered by a dc power supply and excited by an audio oscillator, and the output is observed with an oscilloscope. Multiple ground paths have been held to a minimum, and the shields have been

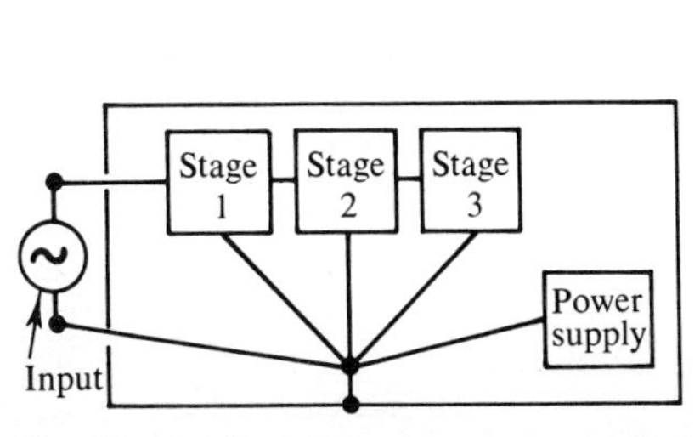

Fig. 7. Instrument stages connected to a common power supply with single-point grounding.

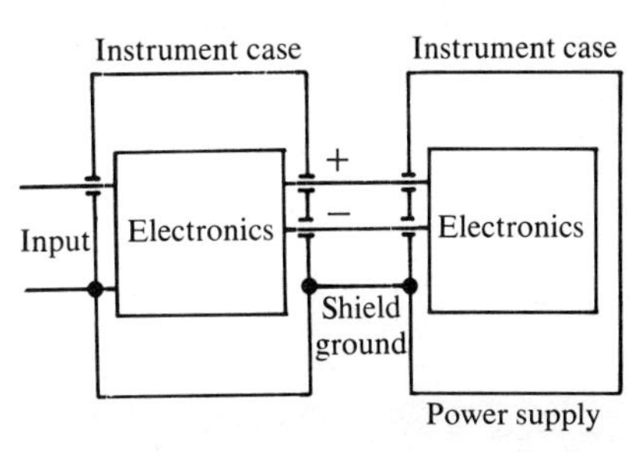

Fig. 8. Proper ground system for connecting external dc power supply to separate electronic instrument.

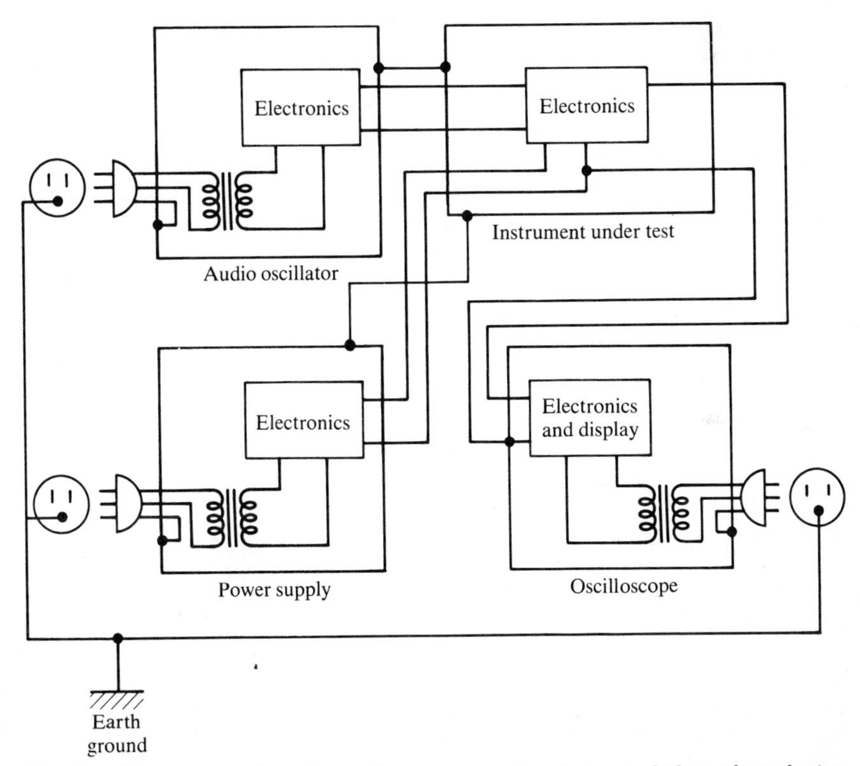

Fig. 9. Proper ground system of measurement setup consisting of an instrument being excited by an audio oscillator and observed by an oscilloscope.

connected together to eliminate external interference. This is relatively simple for this illustration, since most of the instruments have isolated inputs and outputs. There is one ground loop through the instrument cases and the earth ground pin on the power input. Under normal circumstances, since the shields are isolated from the other grounds, there are no significant currents flowing and this ground loop should have negligible effect as long as there is no strong magnetic field producing circulating currents.

Another interesting grounding system is a payload system for the idealized case in Fig. 10. All power grounds are tied together at one point, as are the positive power leads, so that no power leads are common between the instruments. Thus, only the battery is common between instruments. A dc-to-dc converter is used on each instrument so that power ground is completely isolated from signal or case ground, preventing the flow of power currents in the supporting structure or signal grounds. Each instrument has its own reference to shield ground at its input, and the signal and signal ground are run via a shielded twisted pair

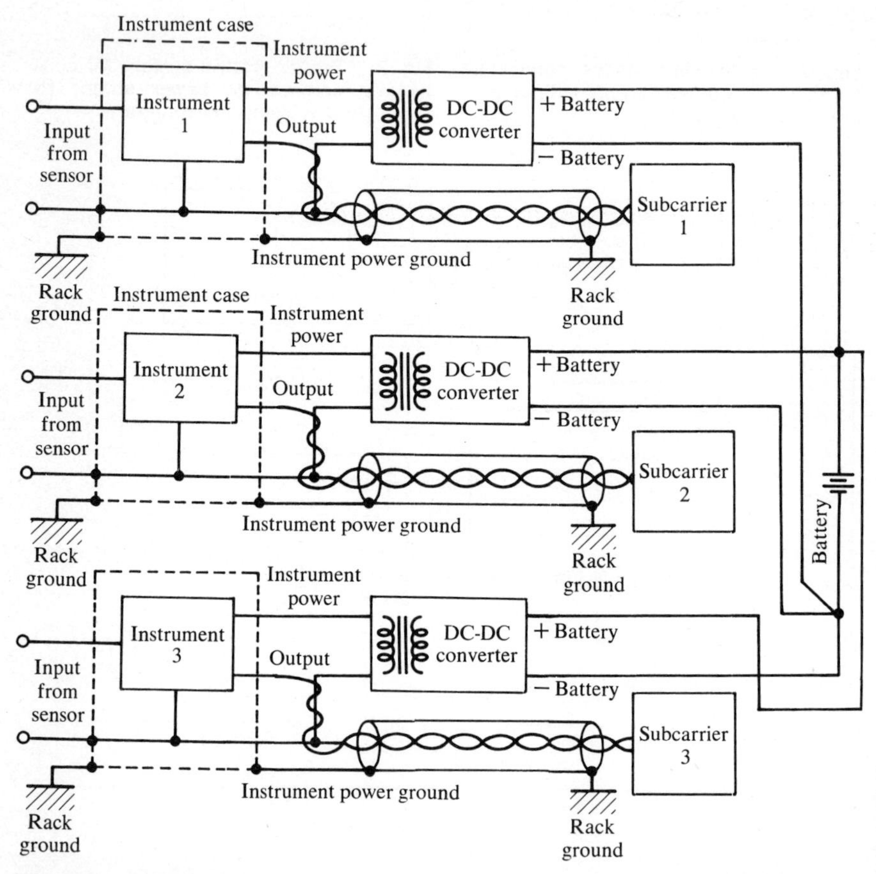

Fig. 10. Idealized connections for a remote measurement system utilized on a spacecraft system.

to a differential-input subcarrier oscillator. The shield may be grounded to the supporting structure at many points. Thus the twisted pair decreases magnetic coupling and the grounded shield decreases any electrostatic coupling which may come from any radiating source.

7. RF and Shield Grounds Rf grounding is difficult to accomplish because of the self-inductance of any grounding system used. A brute-force method of large metal grounding areas and short grounding wires normally provides the best system. The output and input terminals of most rf instruments are referenced directly to the metal case (shield ground) of the instruments. Separate instruments should be connected together with properly matched rf shielded cable, primarily to prevent standing waves and radiation from the cable (see Chap. 14).

When grounding cable shields, the necessary type of grounding depends on the frequencies involved, the length of line, and the sensitivity of the instrument. In general, however, a shield is not of much value unless it is grounded at least every 0.15 wavelength. This type of multiple-point grounding is not effective if the ground points used have high impedances between them. Because of the multiple grounding currents will be induced in the ground loops. The effect that these currents will have on the instruments should be evaluated. In many cases the instruments used will have no sensitivity to the induced frequencies and hence no problem.

However, in the case of video circuits where the frequency response will be from dc to several megahertz, there will invariably be some hum pickup. There are a few methods to reduce this hum, e.g., use of diode clamping circuit as utilized in the television industry to restore the dc level, and hum cancellation. This cancellation is accomplished by adding the proper-level out-of-phase signal to the system to cancel as much as possible the interfering hum.

All the preceding examples have shown sophisticated methods of grounding; however, it should be noted that a good brute-force method of large ground busbars or chassis should not be underrated. A typical example of this concept is the common practice used in large equipment racks such as a radar base or telemetry station. In these instances all the instruments are bolted together in metal consoles as individual units with large bonding straps connecting the consoles. Shield and signal grounds are tied together; however, these currents are normally small enough to not produce serious problems. The input power is isolated because each instrument has its own power transformer.

In many circuits, the chassis is used as ground, with each ground element connected with a short lead to the chassis near the component. This is paralleled in printed circuits, where one side of the printed board is a solid copper plate used as a ground.

BIBLIOGRAPHY

Alvin, Arnold L.: Designing the RFI Shielded Package, *Electron. Ind.,* vol. 24, no. 1, pp. 80–83, January, 1965.

Ek, Gayne R.: Grounding: Its Part in Practical Circuit Design, *EDN*, October, 1963, pp. 15–29.

Ficchi, Rocco F.: "Electrical Interference," p. 262, Hayden Book Company, Inc., New York, 1964,

Ficchi, Rocco F.: Grounding Design Guidelines, in EMC Handbook, *Electromech. Design,* vol. 11, no. 8, pp. 44–46, August, 1967.

"Grounding and Noise Reduction Practices for Instrumentation Systems," Scientific Data Systems, Santa Monica, Calif.

"Instrumentation Grounding and Noise Minimization Handbook," Consolidated Systems Corporation, January, 1965.

Robinson, James G.: Fundamentals of EMI Shielding, *Electro-Technol. (New York)*, vol. 77, no. 6, pp. 36–39, June, 1966.

Robinson, Trevor A.: The Role of Grounding in Eliminating Electronic Interference, *IEEE Spectrum,* vol. 2, no. 7, pp. 85–89, July, 1965.

Sladek, Norbert J.: Electromagnetic-interference Control, *Electro-Technol. (New York)*, vol. 78, no. 5, pp. 85–94, November, 1966.

Thornwall, Joseph C.: Design Noise out of Spacecraft Payload: Good Circuit Design and Proper Layout Can Avoid Serious Troubles at Launching Time, *Electron. Design,* vol. 16, no. 8, pp. 64–68, April, 1968.

White, Donald R. J.: Progress in EMC Instrumentation, *Electro-Technol. (New York)*, vol. 74, no. 4, pp. 46–50, October, 1964.

Chapter **17**

Distributed Parameters and Component Considerations

D. A. BURT and K. D. BAKER, Ph.D.
Utah State University, Logan, Utah

Distributed parameters are probably one of the largest contributors to the discrepancies between drawing-board design and actual working equipment. For this reason this chapter is devoted primarily to showing the magnitude of these parameters and some examples of the troubles that can occur because of them.

DC RESISTANCE

Dc resistance is the best-known and most thoroughly tabulated electrical parameter of materials. The formula for resistance R of a body of uniform cross-sectional area A and length L is simply

$$R = \rho \frac{L}{A}$$

where ρ is the volume resistivity of the material. The values of ρ for many materials have been tabulated in reference books[1] and hence will not be duplicated here.

The resistivity of all materials is a function of temperature. In general the resistance of semiconductors and insulators will decrease with increasing temperature, whereas the resistance of most metals will increase with increasing temperature. As an example, the resistivity of copper will increase approximately 0.4 percent per degree Celsius rise in temperature.

There is a simple rule of thumb that may be convenient for approximating the resistance of copper wire. The resistance of a copper wire 0.001 in. in diameter* and 1 ft long (a circular mil-foot) is approximately 10 Ω. Thus, if a known wire has a cross-sectional area of 100 circular mils (cmil) and a length of 1,000 ft, the approximate resistance will be

$$R \approx \frac{10 \times 1{,}000}{100} = 100\ \Omega$$

Wire sizes have been standardized according to American (B and S) gage, (the smaller the gage the larger the wire diameter).[2] Number 40 wire has close to 10 cmil cross-sectional area, and for every three wire sizes that area will approximately double. Accordingly, No. 37 wire will have approximately 20 cmil, No. 34 wire 40 cmil, etc. Thus the total resistance per foot will halve for each decrease of three wire sizes.

The effect of dc resistance with short wires will normally not be important if the wire is large enough to handle the current. However, for the transmission of power at longer distances, the wire resistance must be taken into account.

A classic example of the effects of wire resistance is the transmission of electrical power used throughout the world.† For instance, assume a small load of 10 A is required at 120 V (1.2 kW) 1 mile from the generator. If No. 6 wire were used, it would present a total resistance of approximately 4 Ω. Thus, 10 A flowing through the lines would then require a generator voltage of 160 V and produce a 400-W power loss in the wire just to deliver 1.2 kW at the load. However, if the voltage at the generator could be increased to 12,000 V and then stepped back down to 120 V at the load, the line current would be reduced to 0.1 A to supply the same power down the line. Under these conditions there would only be 0.04 W power loss in the line.

Anytime low-voltage power transmission is required, the wire resistance becomes very important. As another example, it may be necessary to transmit 10 A at 6 V to operate a rocket payload 1,000 ft away. If No. 6 wire is used, the resistance

* It is common to express the cross-sectional area of wires in circular mils, which is numerically equal to the square of the wire diameter in thousandths of an inch.

† Although the discussion has been strictly for dc resistance, this resistance is applicable for audio frequencies and below. The more complicated case of ac resistance at higher frequencies is discussed in the next section.

for a round trip, or 2,000 ft of wire, is approximately 0.8 Ω; 10-A current would produce an 8-V drop in the wire. It would then be necessary to supply 14 V at the input to obtain the required 6 V at the payload. Under some conditions this may be allowable; however, consider what happens if the payload should require a load which varies from 5 to 10 A. If 14 V were applied to provide 6 V at 10 A, the voltage at the payload would rise to 10 V under the 5-A load. Some equipment could, of course, be damaged by such a voltage overload.

On occasion it may be desirable to design a component which uses the wire resistance for current limiting, such as a coil to actuate a relay. In this case it must be kept in mind that power is being dissipated in the windings where the wire is densely wound. The coil design then must be able to dissipate the heat generated at a high enough rate to maintain the coil temperature within the temperature bounds of the insulation used on the wire.

In summary, it should be stated that the dc resistance must be taken into account anytime large currents are being transmitted, long-distance wire runs are necessary, or the power dissipated in the wire is appreciable for the given configuration.

AC RESISTANCE

At frequencies above the audio range, conductors present an effective resistance that is significantly higher than the simple dc resistance discussed above. This is so because the magnetic flux produced from the current in the wire does not all encircle the wire; there will be some internal flux in the conductor. As a result the impedance at the center of the wire is greater than near the surface. This effect is more pronounced at higher frequencies. At high frequencies, then, the current density in the conductor will be nonuniform and the effective resistance increases accordingly. A round wire will have a uniform distribution of current around the cylinder; however, the current density will be greatest at the surface and decrease toward the center. This phenomenon has been termed skin effect. The skin depth is defined as the depth at which the current density decreases to a value of $1/\epsilon$ or 37 percent of the surface current density. When this skin thickness is one-third or less than the radius of the conductor, the resistance is nearly the same as with a uniform current distribution in a hollow cylinder with the wall thickness equal to the skin depth. This skin depth can be calculated from the following equation (Ref. 2, p. 34):

$$\delta = \sqrt{\frac{\rho}{\pi f \mu}}$$

where δ = skin depth, m
$\mu = 4\pi \times 10^{-7}\mu_r$ H/m
μ_r = relative permeability of conductor material ($\mu_r = 1$ for copper and other nonmagnetic materials)
ρ = resistivity of conductor material, Ω-m
f = frequency, Hz

The ac resistance R_{ac} of a round wire with diameter D can be approximated in terms of the skin depth δ by

$$R_{ac} \approx \frac{L\rho}{\delta \pi D}$$

This approximation is reasonably accurate for ratios of diameter to skin depth greater than 3. If the conductor is copper and the length is given in feet and the diameter in inches, this equation numerically reduces to

$$R_{ac} = 0.996 \times 10^{-6} \frac{\sqrt{f}}{D} \qquad \Omega/\text{ft}$$

Example 1: What is the ac resistance per foot of a No. 18 cylindrical copper wire at 10 MHz? Compare this with the dc resistance. Assume the wire is at a temperature of 20°C.

$$R_{ac} = \frac{0.006 \times 10^{-6}}{0.0403} \sqrt{10^7}\ \Omega/\text{ft}$$
$$= 0.078\ \Omega/\text{ft}$$

Taking the value of the dc resistance from a standard wire table[2]

$$R_{dc} = 0.0063\ \Omega/\text{ft}$$

or the ac resistance is twelve times as great as the dc resistance.

As illustrated by the example, the effective resistance for radio frequencies is much higher than for direct current. For this reason the chassis and shields of rf instruments will often be plated with a higher-conductivity metal such as silver. Because of the skin effect the current will flow primarily in the thin layer of silver plating, thus reducing the effective resistance.

Another problem area occurs when trying to wind low-loss (high-Q) coils. The increased ac resistance greatly increases the loss of the coil. A special wire termed litz wire is often used at lower radio frequencies to decrease this resistance. Litz wire consists of multiple strands of tiny wires bundled together but insulated from each other. These strands are transposed such that any single conductor when averaged over a reasonable length will have as much distance in the center of the bundle as on the outside. Thus each wire will present the same impedance to the current, and the current will divide uniformly between the wires and effectively increase the total surface area. The effectiveness of this technique decreases at frequencies above several hundred kilohertz because of wire irregularities and capacitance between strands. This wire is seldom used above 2 MHz.

LEAKAGES

A problem which begins to take effect when very low level measurements are desired is the leakages that occur in materials that are normally considered insulators. These leakages result from finite resistance to ground accumulated throughout the system, i.e., wire insulation, etc.

Most instruments which measure very low currents require a high input impedance to develop a voltage which can be detected without requiring tremendous amplification. Normally this type of equipment requires all insulation to have greater than 10_{15} Ω resistance. Even the best insulation can become virtually a short circuit for low-level measurements if the surface becomes contaminated. One of the worst offenders is humidity. For this reason all leads which must present a high resistance must be kept short, clean, and dry. Another method of reducing the effects of dc leakages is the use of a guarded system as described in Sec. 3.

1. High-voltage Leakages At high voltages air or gases which surround a conductor will begin to ionize and produce a corona leakage. If the voltage gradient is high enough, the gases can completely break down (arc) and cause a low-resistance path due to the ionized gases. The voltage gradient is dependent not only on the voltage and spacing of conductors but on their shape as well. For example, in dry air at sea level an electrode gap of 0.2 in. for 1-in. spheres will arc at voltages above 20 kV, whereas two sharp points with the same gap will arc at approximately 6 kV.

As the gas pressure is decreased, the voltage required to initiate an arc for a given electrode spacing is decreased until a certain critical pressure is reached. As the pressure is decreased past this point, the arcing potential starts to increase. The minimum arcing voltage at the critical pressure is independent of the electrode spacing (Ref. 2, p. 118), although this critical pressure will depend on the electrode configuration. This means that any exposed electrodes with voltages greater than about 300 V can be expected to arc at some pressure between sea-level pressure and an absolute vacuum. For a gap of 0.2 in. the critical pressure will be about 1 mm of mercury or in the vicinity of 1/1,000 atm. Since the arcing voltage increases rapidly for pressures less than the critical pressure, an ultrahigh vacuum is often utilized for a high-voltage dielectric to prevent arcing in electric circuits.

This variation of arcing with pressure is usually the reason that some equipment can operate only to altitudes of 50,000 to 70,000 ft. This same equipment, however, might be very satisfactory if it were to be used at a much greater altitude.

High-voltage leakages can be minimized in a number of ways:

1. Conductors must have adequate spacing.
2. Sharp edges or points on conductors should be avoided.
3. All exposed surfaces can be insulated; for instance, high-voltage power transformers normally are filled with transformer oil. Silastics and other potting compounds are often used; however, care must be taken so that there is no contamination between the conducting surface and the potting compound, and there can be no voids in the potting.
4. All high voltages may be sealed in an airtight chamber and either pressurized or pumped to a high vacuum.

2. Stray Capacitance The conductors of an electrical system will have capacitive coupling to each other through what is termed stray capacitance. The magnitudes of these stray capacitances are difficult to calculate. A simple example will illustrate the stray-capacitance problem. The capacitance between two long parallel wires is given in the following equation (Ref. 2, p. 118):

$$C = \frac{3.677}{\log_{10}(2D/d)} \qquad \text{pF/ft}$$

where D = spacing between the wires

d = diameter of the wires (d is much less than D)

For a 2-in. spacing between two No. 24 wires, this gives a capacitance of 0.33 pF/in. While at first glance this may not seem to be such a large amount, consider the capacitive reactance between two 2-in. wires at 1 MHz.

$$X_c = \frac{1}{\omega c} = \frac{1}{(2\pi \times 10^6)(0.266 \times 10^{-12})} \simeq 600\ \text{k}\Omega$$

If one wire had a 5-V 1-MHz signal impressed on it and the other wire were the input of an amplifier with a 600-kΩ input impedance, a 2.5-V signal would be coupled to the amplifier. High-input-impedance amplifiers will have other shunt capacitances. When these shunt capacitances are taken into account, the problem is decreased. For instance, if the same amplifier had a 10-pF shunt capacitance on the input, a voltage of approximately 0.13 V would be impressed on the input of the amplifier.

Usually, the capacitance problems are worse than the simple case given, because of capacitances to other large metallic surfaces. The effect of other large surfaces can only increase the capacitance unless the surface is positioned as a shield, which then effectively shorts extraneous signals to ground. The effects of leakage capacitance can be reduced by short wires with wide spacing, shielding, and guarding.

3. Cancellation of Leakage Effects by Guarding The basic principle of canceling leakage effects by the guarding technique is to require the conductors to be at the same potential. If this is the case, there will be no current between conductors regardless of the impedance between them. The application of this concept is best illustrated by an example.

Example 2: It is desired to measure the volt-ampere characteristics of a high-impedance nonlinear resistance R_m which is a short distance from the measuring device by applying a slowly varying sweep voltage to it and detecting the current. Assume the impedance may vary from 10^{13} to 10^{14} Ω over a variation of voltage from 0 to 100 V.

Solution: The critical problems which will occur are due to the dc leakage and shunt capacitance between leads which connect the resistance and the instrument. For instance, a special low-capacitance coaxial cable has 6.5 pF/ft. If it were desired to make the measurement in 1 s and a cable 3 ft long were used, the displacement current due to the shunt capacitance would be

$$i = C\frac{dv}{dt}$$

where C is the total cable capacitance and dv/dt is the time rate of change of the voltage (in this linear case dv/dt = 100 V/1 s)

$$\begin{aligned} i &= (19.5 \times 10^{-12})(10^2) \\ &= 19.5 \times 10^{-10}\ \text{A} \end{aligned}$$

The current due to the resistance R_m measured would be less than 10^{-11} A. Even if the voltage were swept at such a slow rate that displacement currents became negligible, dc leakages could be on the same order of magnitude as the measured

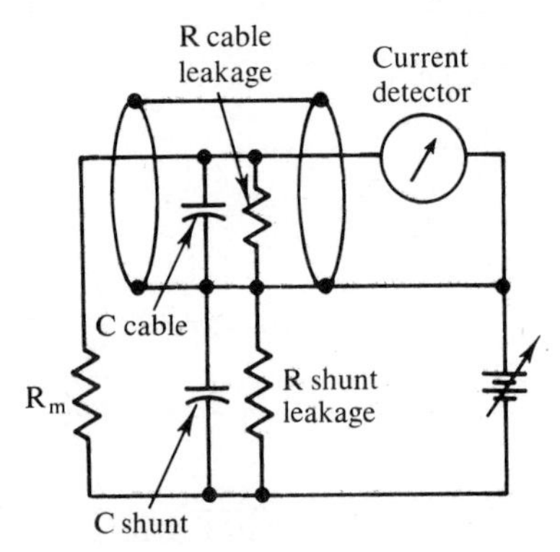

Fig. 1. Guarded system to eliminate leakage.

current. These problems can be eliminated by driving the shield of the cable at the same potential as the center conductor and allowing the current return on a third wire, as shown in Fig. 1. Thus there will be no current flow from the center conductor to the shield because there is no potential difference. Any current which flows from the shield to the third wire is not measured, as shown in Fig. 1.

4. Neutralization Another method to eliminate the effects of leakage currents is by a neutralization scheme. Leakage currents are canceled by applying a second current to the input of the amplifier, which has the same magnitude as the leakage but with the opposite polarity such that the total net current is zero. This is done as shown in Fig. 2 for the same measurement situation as discussed in Fig. 1. In this case, an opposite-polarity voltage which tracks the measuring voltage is applied to the input through R_{se} and C_{se}, which are made equivalent to the leakage resistance and capacitance of cable R_s and C_s. This technique, of course, requires a sensitive balance which is difficult to maintain.

5. Stray Inductance A magnetic field will exist about any conductor which carries a current. The coupling of this field to the conductor will always produce an inductance. This inductance is a function of the conductor configuration, where it is placed with respect to all other components, and the frequency of operation. It is difficult to calculate the exact inductance for a particular wire in a circuit. However, the following equations for a straight, round nonmagnetic wire should give the reader a feeling for the magnitude of the inductance involved. At low frequencies this self-inductance is given by the following equation:

$$L = 0.00508l\left(2.303 \log_{10}\frac{4l}{d} - 0.75\right) \quad \mu\text{H}$$

where l = length of wire, in.
d = diameter of wire, in.

At high frequencies the self-inductance decreases slightly because of skin effects to the following equation:

$$L = 0.00508l\left(2.303 \log_{10}\frac{4l}{d} - 1\right) \quad \mu\text{H}$$

For a 5-in.-long No. 20 wire, the high-frequency inductance will be approximately 0.14 μH, and the low-frequency inductance will be 0.15 μH (the resistance would be less than 0.01 Ω). At 10 MHz this wire would present an inductive reactance of approximately 9 Ω. It is obvious that for any length of wire at very high frequencies the wire impedance will become very high—approaching an open circuit.

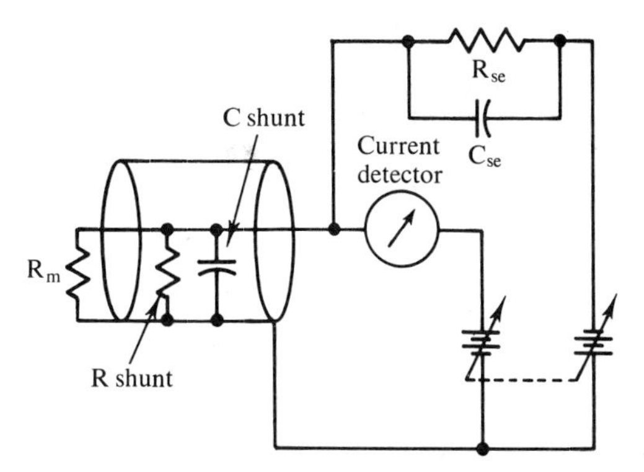

Fig. 2. Neutralization to reduce leakages.

The inductance of interconnecting leads is one of the serious high-frequency limitations in measurement situations. At frequencies up to about 1 MHz short, heavy wires may be satisfactory; however, above this a transmission line must be used. At microwave frequencies waveguide techniques are required.

COMPONENT STRAY PARAMETERS

Mistakes are often made by assuming that capacitors, resistors, and inductors exhibit the same capacitance, resistance, and inductances, respectively, at all frequencies, voltages, and currents. The changes that occur in these components due to these parameters are given in the following sections.

6. Resistors The characteristics of resistors depend on their physical construction. Most resistors are made either from resistive granules such as carbon or from some continuous resistive filament.

In granular construction there will be a small capacitance between the granules; thus at high frequencies this capacitance may shunt the resistive components to the extent that the resistor will appear as a leaky capacitor. As the frequency increases the lead inductance becomes dominant. At high voltages (600 to 1,000 V) the resistance of common carbon resistors will vary with voltage. This is caused by tiny arcs which will occur between the granules, again shunting out the resistance.

Filament resistors are made in many different ways. They can be wound from resistive wire, produced by carbon deposits, metal-etched, etc. Wirewound resistors require many turns of the filament on a form. This type of resistor will then have an inductance which is significant even at low frequencies. Some filament-wound resistors are designed to have as low an inductance as possible. This is accomplished by winding two filaments and connecting them in series so that the inductive field cancels. This method extends the frequency limit at which these resistors can operate. It is impossible to obtain perfect coupling between the two windings; therefore there will appear some leakage inductance which will eventually limit the upper frequency at which the resistors can be used.

7. Inductors Inductors consist of many turns of wire wound on a core. In various designs this core may vary from air to a magnetic material of high permeability. All inductors will exhibit a shunt capacitance and series resistance as shown in the eouivalent circuit of Fig. 3.

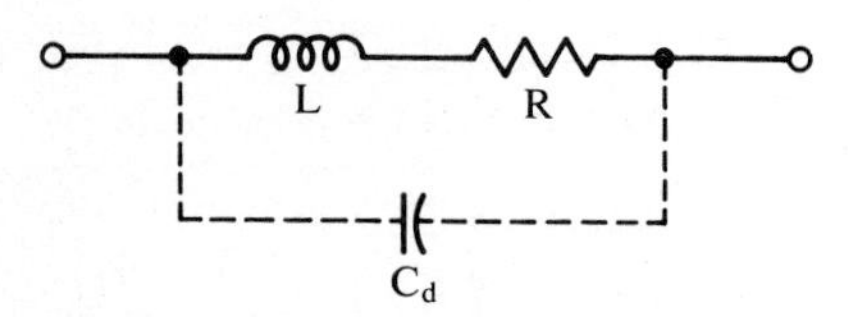

Fig. 3. Equivalent circuit of an inductor. L = inductance; R = resistance resulting from losses due to wire resistance, hysteresis loss, and eddy current in the core; C_d = equivalent distributed capacitance between windings.

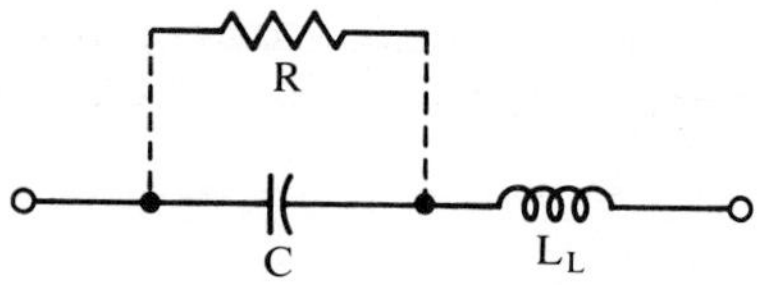

Fig. 4. Equivalent circuit of a capacitor. C = capacitance; L_L = lead inductance; R = resistance due to leakage and dielectric loss.

As the frequency is increased, two things will happen:

1. The resistance will increase because of skin effect, hysteresis, and eddy-current losses.

2. The distributed capacitance will determine a frequency at which the inductor will be self-resonant. At frequencies above this self-resonance, the inductor will appear capacitive.

When a magnetic material is used for the core, the inductance is also a function of the current through the coil. This is because the magnetic properties of all materials will vary with the current through the coil. Thus these inductors will only approximate linearity over small current variations. Sometimes an air gap is used in the core material to increase the range over which linearity can be achieved. This, of course, decreases the inductance per turn which can be achieved in any given inductor.

8. Capacitors Probably more varieties of capacitors are available than any other component. To describe the advantages and disadvantages of each is beyond the scope of this book. In general, however, all capacitors can be represented by the equivalent circuit shown in Fig. 4, and a few general comments are in order. The resistive loss of a given capacitor depends on the types of dielectric in the capacitor, the frequency of operation, and the applied voltage. Many dielectrics are very lossy at high frequencies. As the voltage increases, the capacitance may vary significantly with some dielectrics, and eventually a voltage breakdown will occur, limiting the amount of voltage that can be safely applied to a capacitor. All capacitors will have some internal inductance due to leads and connections which will limit the discharge rate and current flow. Special low-inductance capacitors are built for high discharge rates.

At microwave frequencies almost all components will appear inductive because of the connecting-lead inductance. At these frequencies special techniques such as cavities and waveguides must be used rather than lumped-circuit components.

ACTIVE DEVICES (TRANSISTORS, VACUUM TUBES, ETC.)

In general all electronic devices have stray parameters which normally degrade the action of the device. If the device is an amplifier such as a transistor or electronic tube, the effects of these stray parameters are varied and often depend on the circuit that they are in. This section cannot cover all these variations; however, a few basic ideas should be presented.

9. Junction Transistors The junction transistor is basically a low-impedance, current-amplifying device. Each transistor will have definite maximum ratings; and any time these ratings are exceeded, even if only for a microsecond, the device will usually be permanently destroyed.

10. FET and MOS Transistors Field-effect transistors are high-impedance, voltage-amplifying devices. Their major contribution to electronics is the extremely large input impedances which they present. Because of this high impedance, certain precautions should be taken when handling the devices. As an example, some MOS (metal-oxide semiconductor) FET transistors have input impedances of 10^{15} Ω. If only one electron per second were to collect on such an impedance, a voltage would be developed on the order of 0.2 mV. Thus infinitesimally small amounts of current can easily develop voltages which can destroy these transistors. When an instrument is built using these devices, the design engineer will do his best to protect them. The best protection designs will fail, however, under some conditions if the operator becomes careless. For instance, most protective circuits cannot cancel extremely fast pulses. A sudden arc or unintentional short in the circuit being tested can produce just such high-speed transients.

11. Integrated Circuits Integrated circuits are only an extension of the solid-state devices they contain. They contain MOS, FET, or junction transistors, depending on the type. Even the capacitors that may be in some integrated circuits are really reverse-biased diodes. Thus the same precautions must be used when handling these devices as for any other semiconductors, except that the operator might bear in mind that when a component in an integrated circuit is destroyed, the whole device is useless rather than just one component in a system built of discrete components.

12. Vacuum Tubes Tubes are normally high-impedance, high-voltage amplifying devices. The handling of tubes is not as critical as that of solid-state devices. Most tubes can take some overloading for a finite time without harm. Since tube circuits have high voltages, however, the operator should use due caution to prevent a serious shock.

13. Instrument Considerations Such a variety of instruments are available for measurements that no attempt will be made here to describe individual systems; however, it may be helpful to discuss briefly a few implications of instruments designed around different basic components. Because of the large impact that the introduction of solid-state circuits has had upon instruments, it would be difficult to avoid a comparison between these newer instruments and the earlier test instruments designed with electron tubes. The inclusion of semiconductors has eliminated the need in almost all cases of a power supply for filaments and the attendant high dissipation of heat. Additionally, the relatively high dc plate supply (B+) is eliminated. The elimination of these supplies and the much smaller possible packaging have made small portable battery-operated test equipment much more feasible. The advantages due to physical size and portability are obvious, but in addition these isolated instruments offer tremendous advantages for low-level, interference-free measurement situations. Solid-state circuitry, in addition to miniaturization and low-power operation, results in vast improvements in ruggedness and reliability. Anyone who has worked with vacuum-tube equipment knows that not only must burned-out tubes be replaced frequently but that they also become weak as they age and so must be frequently checked. This routine is eliminated in the newer solid-state instruments.

In the earlier development of solid-state devices, vacuum-tube equipment offered distinct advantages for high impedance levels, at radio frequencies, at high power levels, and for low-noise operation. With the continued development of devices, however, the advantages of tubes have by and large vanished.

A single remaining area where solid-state instruments are more vulnerable than their earlier counterparts is in the susceptibility to device damage due to impedance mismatch and overloading, voltage transients, and other abuse. Due consideration should be given to general careful usage practices and to precautions given in operating manuals.

REFERENCES

1. "Handbook of Chemistry and Physics," pp. 2588–2600, Chemical Rubber Publishing Co.
2. Terman, Frederick E.: "Radio Engineers' Handbook," p. 28, McGraw-Hill Book Company, New York, 1943.

Section Five

Instrumentation Systems

The word "system" is unusual, and yet universal, in that it has application across a broad spectrum of disciplines. It appears in names such as accounting system, weapon system, medical system, ecological system, communication system, transportation system, instrumentation system, and many others. Each of these names has particular meaning to the practitioners of the various disciplines. The term "systems approach" has often implied the application of a mysterious methodology or technique to the solution of a difficult problem. "Systems engineering" is often used in place of "systems approach" as a more specific description of the activity performed when attacking many of the vast problems confronting mankind. Environmental pollution, transportation, national defense, education, and many others appear to be appropriate candidates for the practitioners of "systems engineering."

The approach to the subject of this section is aimed at providing a broad view of the instrument-system spectrum. Because of space limitations, it is not possible to provide an exhaustive treatment for all types of instrument systems. Many of the factors identified as needing consideration have been demonstrated with examples of data-acquisition-system applications. These are probably as simple an example as is possible without unduly clouding the point being illustrated. This section is *not* intended to be a detailed design guide or to indicate specific problem solutions. It is intended to give the prospective system user something to think about and pointers on considerations in instrument-systems design.

Chapter 18

Instruments in Systems

EUGENE L. MLECZKO

Hewlett-Packard Company, Palo Alto, California

DEFINITION OF SYSTEM

A system is an aggregation or assemblage of objects united by some form of regular interaction or interdependence; a group of diverse units so combined by nature or art as to form an integral whole, and to function, operate, or move in unison, and often in obedience to some form of control. It is this definition of system which most appropriately describes in general terms the nature of the instrumentation systems which will be discussed in this chapter.

WHY SYSTEMS OF INSTRUMENTS?

One of the primary reasons a user should be interested in the application of a system approach to the solution of an instrumentation problem is that a system might just result in a synergistic interaction between the elements of the system. "Synergism" is the "cooperative action of discrete agencies such that the total effect is greater than the sum of the two effects taken independently." Synergistic action appears beneficial and thus desirable to the instrument user. Consequently, it is the user's desire for this enhanced functional operation or enhanced result which motivates the instrumentation user to consider assembling a system of instruments. The expectation that a combination of several instruments will perform a given measurement task better, faster, more accurately, or more economically is usually adequate motivation to justify a system of instruments. If this is not a sufficient answer to the question "Why systems of instruments?" perhaps an example or two might be in order.

Consider the case where it is necessary to measure a voltage output resulting from an operating parameter in a laboratory experiment. This voltage must be measured to a specified degree of precision. An instrument which will yield the desired precision is selected, purchased, and connected to the test item whose voltage is to be measured, and the measurement is made. So far, a single instrument, a voltmeter, has been used to make one measurement. There is nothing particularly systemic about this, although the necessity to measure a voltage can be one of several requirements for a systematic approach to this testing problem.

What does the average instrument user do in the laboratory when he has read the voltage? He will usually pick up his clipboard or a laboratory notebook and jot the reading down. What if a reading once every hour is required? This is not a particularly difficult constraint unless the data are needed for 24 hours of the day. The user can set a small alarm clock so that it goes off one minute before the time the reading is to be taken. When the alarm goes off, the user drops what he is doing and goes over to the voltmeter, takes the reading, writes it down on a sheet of paper, returns to his desk, winds the alarm, resets it for the next hour, and resumes his work. This cycle is repeated every hour until the user has acquired the data he needs. This may or may not be an onerous task for the user, depending upon how much interruption of his other duties and responsibilities he can tolerate, not to mention his patience.

If, however, the situation requires this piece of data be taken every 5 minutes instead of every hour, the problem assumes different proportions. This means that whatever the user is doing must be stopped, and a reading of the instrument taken every 5 minutes. The task becomes more substantial; the user has less time to do the creative work that he is probably trying to do and must spend more time in attending the instrument, taking the required readings.

If it were possible to print the record of the voltage read by the voltmeter automatically, it would certainly ease the user's work load. It might also be possible to cause the voltmeter to take a reading every 5 minutes automatically by means of a programming or clock control of the voltmeter-printer combination. If a continuous record of the voltage is required, instead of a printed one, it would be possible to use a strip-chart recorder for the application. In this case, the user is insisting on a printed record. If the user selected and used the traditional moving-coil voltmeter instrument to take the readings, there is very little chance of ever having that instrument appropriately and economically interfaced to a printer. However, if the user selected an electronic digital voltmeter having a coded digital output compatible with some form of printer, he would be one step closer to a system. All he has to do is select and connect a compatible printer to the voltmeter. With this accomplished, all that is needed is to push a "take a reading" button, and the voltmeter takes the reading and the printer prints it. The user has created a basic instrument system and dispensed with the necessity of writing down the information. All that remains is to set the alarm clock for every 5-minute interval and, when it rings, go over and punch the "take a reading" button in order to get printed data.

It would seem that, if the capability exists to take the information directly from the voltmeter and put it on a printer automatically, it should be possible to devise a means for programming the operation of the voltmeter-printer so readings can be taken and printed automatically. As a matter of fact, such programming means and hardware are readily available, and it is possible for the user to add a programmer to the voltmeter-printer combination.

The user started out with the voltmeter, which by itself is a stand-alone voltage-measuring device; he added a printer, which resulted in a two-instrument system. The need for taking periodic readings arises, and he eliminates the necessity of punching the button himself by adding a programmer. The result is a three-unit system which permits him to go on about his regular work while this system of instruments does the other task for him. Since the user has been relieved of the drudgery of periodically taking a reading, he has more time for his creative work. A block diagram of this system is shown in Fig. 1.

As the user's sophistication develops, he may find it necessary to take voltage readings every 5 minutes from ten different sources instead of one. Perhaps the most obvious solution to this problem is to buy nine more voltmeter-printer-programmer combinations. However, if consideration is given to the fact that the readings being taken previously used the equipment only briefly every 5 minutes, it would be economically very worthwhile and advantageous to utilize the original voltmeter, printer, and programmer to read the data from the nine new sources. This could be done during the intervals in the original reading sequence. Stated another way, if it were possible to connect the voltmeter to the 10 sources of voltage to be measured, systematically and sequentially, only one voltmeter, printer, and

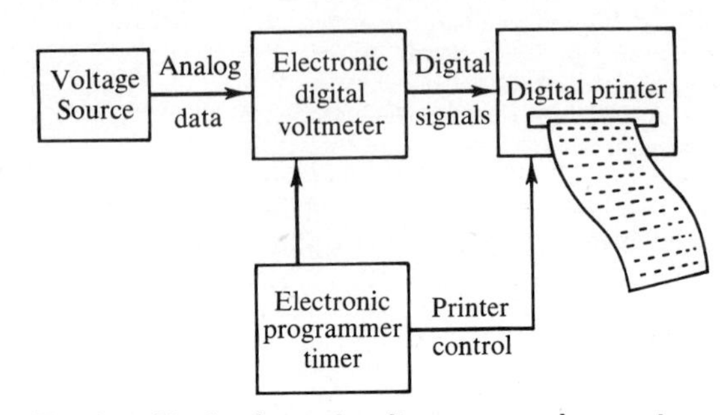

Fig. 1. Single-channel voltage-measuring system.

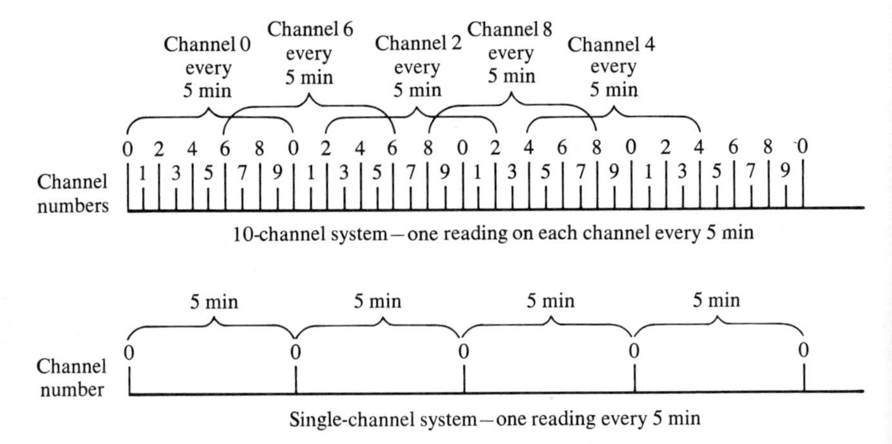

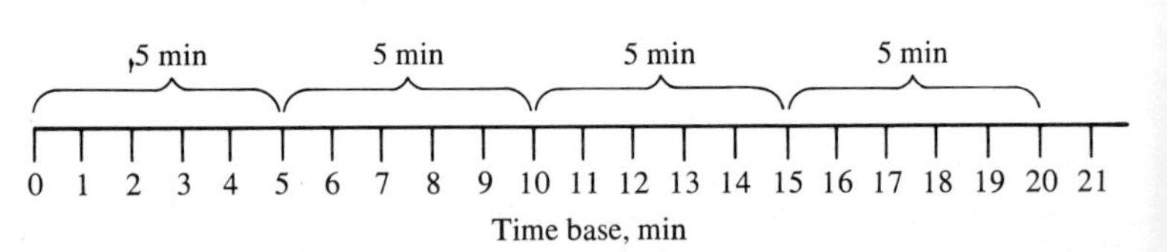

Fig. 2. Single-channel vs. 10-channel interleaved timing.

programmer would be needed to take all 10 of the required voltage readings. Fortunately, such devices are available and are called "scanners" or "multiplexers." Figure 2 depicts the interleaved relationship of the additional nine data sources.

The user can acquire a 10-channel scanner, which is just a switching device which connects the voltmeter in turn to each source of voltage to be read. After a reading is taken, it is switched to the next source of voltage, a reading is taken on it and switched to the next source, and so on until all 10 voltages have been read and their values printed. All this is now accomplished under the control of the programmer. The user has developed a system of four independent functioning instruments: a scanner, a voltmeter, a printer, and a means of programming the combination to take the required readings. The utility of the original voltmeter, printer, and programmer has been expanded tenfold by the addition of the scanner. A block diagram of this system arrangement is shown in Fig. 3.

The scanner sitting alone unconnected is of limited or no utility, as is the printer by itself; and the programmer is of no use without something to program. The voltmeter can do one thing: it can measure voltage. It is seen, therefore, that when these four functions are joined together, an instrument system has, in fact, been created. This system permits the user to measure voltages from 10 sources, to have those readings recorded on a printer, and to have this all take place under the control of the programmer. The result is a truly synergistic system. The total effect of all the elements of the system results in a greater utility than the sum of the individual effects by themselves.

This example shows graphically the advantages to be gained by the use of systems of instruments. When this system example is tested against the original definition of "system," it is seen that the system is in fact "an aggregation or

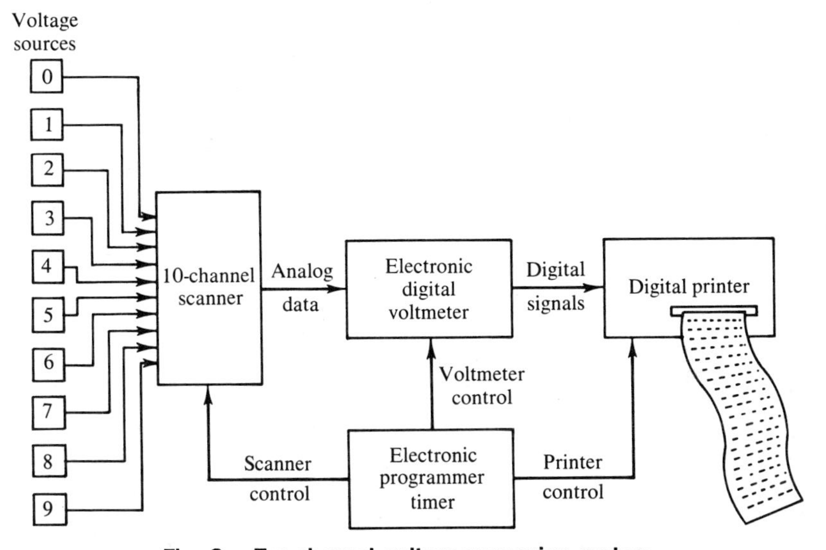

Fig. 3. Ten-channel voltage-measuring system.

assemblage" of instruments "united" to perform in a "regular interaction" and is made up of "a group of diverse units," and it is "so combined" by the art of the system designer "as to form an integral whole" and that it does "function, operate, or move in unison" in "obedience to some form of control" (the programmer).

It should be apparent from this example that the requirement for and assembly of such a system relied mainly on the application of common sense in the consideration and evaluation of the needs. It was then easy to act on those needs in a manner which resulted in satisfying them.

TYPES OF INSTRUMENT SYSTEMS

Three distinct classifications are possible for instrument systems:

1. The first classification deals with the "techniques" employed in implementing the systems. These techniques are analog, digital, and a combination of the two into analog-digital or hybrid systems. Analog systems handle analog signals, which may be thought of as continuous functions. It is not possible to measure an analog

value exactly but only with some degree of precision. Digital systems handle digital signals which represent discrete and exact digital values, even though the digital value may be an inexact representation of an analog value of interest. Hybrid systems accommodate signals of both types and perform conversions from one to the other in the normal course of system operation.

2. The second classification is concerned with the degree of versatility displayed by the system. Two distinct levels of versatility are usually encountered. These are the general-purpose system and the dedicated system. The first is easily adaptable to a wide variety of uses, as the name "general-purpose" signifies. The second is specifically structured for a particular purpose and is not readily adapted to any other use.

3. The third classification has to do with the purpose or application of the system. There can be many types of systems designed to meet a variety of purposes. Some of these are as follows: data acquisition, which is usually a very general-purpose system; stimulus-response; stimulus-response-control; and response-control, which are ordinarily very narrow in application range and thus of the dedicated type. "Automatic test" is also usually in the dedicated class of systems.

It should be evident that it is possible to have systems of any *purpose* designed with varying degrees of *versatility* and implemented in any of the three *techniques*. Examples of the techniques, versatility, and purposes follow—with some of the examples being applicable in more than one of the classifications. Where this occurs, it is noted.

TECHNIQUES

Examples of the three techniques of analog, digital, and hybrid used in implementing systems are described.

1. Analog Systems These are usually defined as ones which handle only analog signals and which carry the data through the system in analog form without conversion to some other method of signal representation. The input accepts an analog signal; the signal may be amplified by an analog amplifier, may be measured or characterized by some sort of analog device, and may have its output represented graphically in analog form. As noted earlier, the analog signal value cannot be measured exactly, but only with some degree of precision, because it is a continuous function.

For example, if one wishes to determine the efficiency of a single-acting-piston steam engine using the Rankine/vapor cycle, it is helpful to derive the pressure-volume diagram for the particular steam engine. This can be done in the following manner. A pressure transducer is applied to measure pressure in the cylinder of the steam engine under test. The output is an electrical signal proportional to pressure. A position transducer is applied to the engine mechanism in such a way as to derive relative piston position and thus the volume of the cylinder at any point in the stroke. If this output is also an electrical signal, proportional to cylinder volume, the user has two electrical-analog signals to feed to the input of the instrumentation system.

If the analog signals are large enough to be used without further amplification, the pressure-transducer signal is applied to the ordinate, or *Y*-axis input, while the position-transducer signal is applied to the abscissa, or *X*-axis input, of a suitable *X-Y* recorder to provide a plot of the pressure-volume diagram of the steam engine. The pressure transducer, however, might be of the strain-gage type, which could have an extremely low output signal—on the order of 10 to 30 mV full scale. If the *X-Y* recorder required a larger signal, it would then be necessary to amplify this analog output signal using an instrumentation amplifier of suitable gain to provide the required signal level for the recorder. In addition to the amplifier, the strain-gage transducer requires a source of excitation power and a bridge-balancing network. The latter items are customarily called "signal-conditioning" equipment and are discussed in greater detail below. The amplifier output signal is then connected to the *Y*-axis terminals of the *X-Y* recorder, and assuming that the position signal is of adequate amplitude, the system is completely defined.

In all respects, the information which is handled by this system is handled in analog form; the pressure parameter and the position parameter are converted from physical analogs to electrical signals in analog form. The electrical signals, in turn, are amplified as required and applied to the recorder, where the actual Rankine-cycle pressure-volume diagram of the steam engine is plotted graphically in analog form—that is, an analogous presentation is plotted on a piece of graph paper. This could be considered a dedicated system also, devoted to the task of acquiring and plotting Rankine-cycle pressure-volume diagrams. A block diagram of the Rankine-cycle dedicated system is shown in Fig. 4.

The all-analog parameter system is quite popular and is applied extensively in research, development, and production. Many scientific and technical users feel that they can easily interpret a graph in which one parameter is plotted against another. In many instances, parameters are plotted against time. A time dependency or variation with time is very rapidly comprehended at a glance by the experienced observer, whereas to read the same information out and interpret it from a printout is not as convenient. Therefore, particularly in the experimental or research and development type of environment, the all-analog systems are frequently preferred by the users—the basic advantage being that the information is maintained in analog format throughout and is presented in analog form for

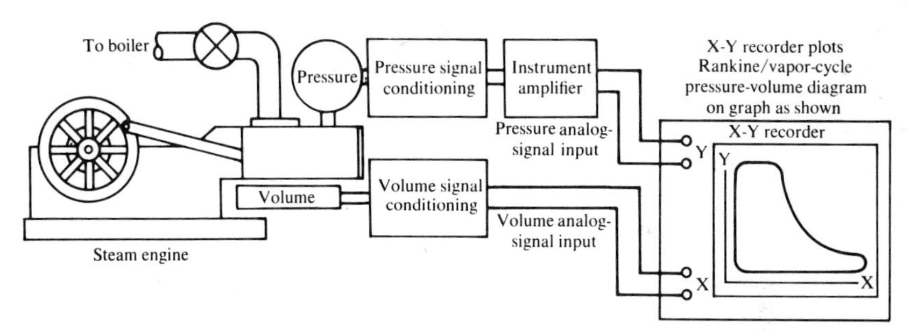

Fig. 4. Rankine-cycle dedicated measurement system.

interpretation. The principal disadvantage of all-analog systems is that accuracy of data is difficult to maintain. An accuracy of 1 percent overall is considered very good for such systems.

2. Digital Systems Instrument systems involving the use of all-digital parameters are not very common or as widely used as analog or analog-digital systems. This is because transducers providing a direct digital output are not as widely available as are analog transducers. The available digital transducers are really analog in nature, as their output is usually a variable frequency which is proportional to either temperature, pressure, or flow. The output frequency of the transducer is applied to a counter which counts the number of cycles and relates this directly to the temperature, pressure, or flow applied to the transducer. The output is then indicated in some digital form and also is made available on a printer, or is recorded directly on magnetic tape for future data retrieval by a computer. Barring unforeseen technological breakthroughs, it is not anticipated that use of direct-digital-output transducers will increase significantly except in the area of shaft-position and linear-position encoders. A variety of these can be found. They are chiefly useful where a great degree of accuracy or resolution of linear position or shaft rotation is needed. The output of these devices is usually in a binary code, with a unique code output for each increment of rotation or position.

3. Analog-Digital or Hybrid Systems The most commonly used instrument systems are analog-digital, hybrid, or mixed-parameter systems. All three names are used to describe the same basic type of system, which uses the best features of both the analog and digital techniques to solve instrument-system problems. In these, the information is acquired and partially operated on or conditioned in analog form and then converted to a digital form and further operated on digitally before final disposition. The trend is to move more and more in this direction, primarily because of the impetus being provided by computer control of instrument operations.

The digital computer operating in the digital domain can accept information only in digital form and operate on that information only digitally. It therefore becomes necessary for instrument systems to convert analog signals into their digital representations for the information to be operated on in the computer. Several of the ensuing system examples are of the hybrid type.

VERSATILITY AND PURPOSE

Several examples of instrument systems for various purposes are presented in essentially decreasing degrees of versatility starting with the most versatile or general-purpose system, the data-acquisition system.

4. Data Acquisition Perhaps the most important type of instrument system that is in general use today is the data-acquisition system. The need for data-acquisition systems comes from the necessity to measure and record large quantities of data which are derived from every phase of research, development, and production in today's complex technology. If the data must be acquired quickly and at specified time intervals while the test is in progress, the automatic data-acquisition system fills that need. As noted in a previous system example, the visual reading of instruments and the manual logging of the data from those readings are tedious tasks at best. With the possibility of human error ever-present, the use of automatic means of data acquisition becomes quite compelling and often economically attractive.

Data-acquisition systems can be assembled from a variety of instruments to take data from many types of data sources. However, the most common data-acquisition systems in use and available commercially today are applied to the measurement of voltage, frequency, and resistance. Standard data systems of this general nature are available from several instrument manufacturers. These systems are available both with and without computer control, depending upon the precision, speed, and other factors which may enter into the need for the data. It is possible to have a fully automatic system operating from a programmer, not necessarily a computer, that can easily take readings of ac or dc voltage, frequency, or resistance—from up to thousands of different sources. The readings from this multitude of sources can be printed out on a formatted output printer—such as a typewriter or teleprinter—or on a paper-tape strip printer, producing a printout similar to that of an adding machine. The data may be recorded on punched paper tape or on magnetic tape for further manipulation and retrieval by the computer after the completion of the data-acquisition cycle. Figure 5 shows a block diagram for a typical data-acquisition system.

Such a system can be utilized to acquire the data from other physical parameters—that is, other than voltage, frequency, or resistance—by the simple expedient of utilizing transducers to translate the physical phenomena (pressure, temperature, etc.) into an electrical signal which can, in turn, be acquired by the data-acquisition system. Pressure transducers are capable, for example, of converting the variations in pressure of a gas or fluid into an electrical signal (usually voltage, but occasionally frequency) proportional to the physical parameter (pressure) being measured. The proportional electrical signal is measured and recorded in such a manner that the user knows from previous calibration information that a given value of signal recorded on the printer, or on the magnetic tape, is equivalent to a given pressure in pounds per square inch or other appropriate units.

Signal Conditioning. In instrumentation situations where physical phenomena such as pressure or temperature are translated into electrical signals, it is frequently necessary to perform some operations on the signals to make them suitable for input to a data-acquisition system. These operations are customarily referred to as "signal conditioning" and may include application of excitation potentials or power to transducers such as strain gage or variable-reluctance devices. Bridge balancing and zero calibration are types of signal conditioning, as are amplification and/or filtering of the signal. Routing thermocouple signals through reference junctions is a form of signal conditioning. In short, any operation conducted on the signal to modify or enhance its utilization in a system is called "signal conditioning."

Where many hundreds of channels of data from physical phenomena are being instrumented, a substantial portion of the total system is devoted to the conditioning of the signals. This is because a conditioning package must usually be supplied for every transducer in the system. Each transducer displays a set of characteristics sufficiently different from that of similar transducers that a conditioning package must be assigned and calibrated for each one in order to derive accurate and useful information from each transducer. Figure 6 shows the application of some typical signal-conditioning equipment in a block-diagram form.

As a matter of fact, data-acquisition systems of this specific type where a physical parameter, such as pressure, is converted to a voltage, which is, in turn, measured and recorded, were used in the development of the gigantic rocket engines for the ballistic-missile weapon systems and for the propulsion systems used by the Apollo space vehicle for the manned-lunar-landing program. Many data-acquisition

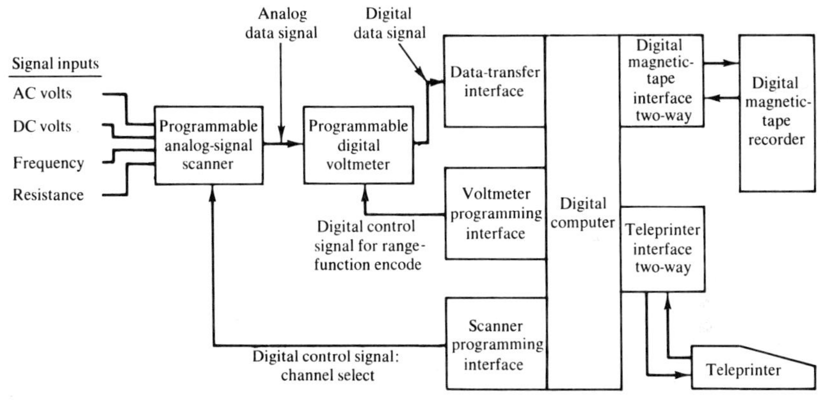

Fig. 5. Typical computer-controlled data-acquisition system.

systems have been utilized to monitor the operations of a variety of processes—for example, the temperature profile through a nuclear reactor. Here again, the conversion of a physical phenomenon to voltages, through the use of hundreds of thermocouples located throughout the core of a nuclear reactor, provides a means of measurement of the temperature readings, which are then scanned, measured, recorded, and manipulated as needed.

The use of data acquisition in laboratory automation is a common application. It may be desired to record the output from a number of analytical instruments in a chemical laboratory. Instruments such as gas chromatographs, pH meters, mass spectrometers, and infrared analyzers and other analytical instruments are interfaced to a data-acquisition system. Again, the conversion of some physical phenomenon to an electrical signal occurs. The signal, in turn, is scanned, measured, and recorded under the control of a programming means, either computer or otherwise, to achieve the desired result—automatic analysis and acquisition of needed data.

5. Stimulus-Response The stimulus-response system can be of the general-purpose or dedicated class. Such a system can be utilized in many types of applications and can assume many forms, dependent on the needs. A common use is in characterizing the performance of a device—for example, an amplifier. The system needs to stimulate the amplifier and measure the resulting output. It may be necessary to determine the frequency response of an amplifier. If the system is structured to provide a signal of varying frequency and constant amplitude to the amplifier under test, and provision is made to measure the output of the amplifier, everything needed is available in the system to make the test. For every given

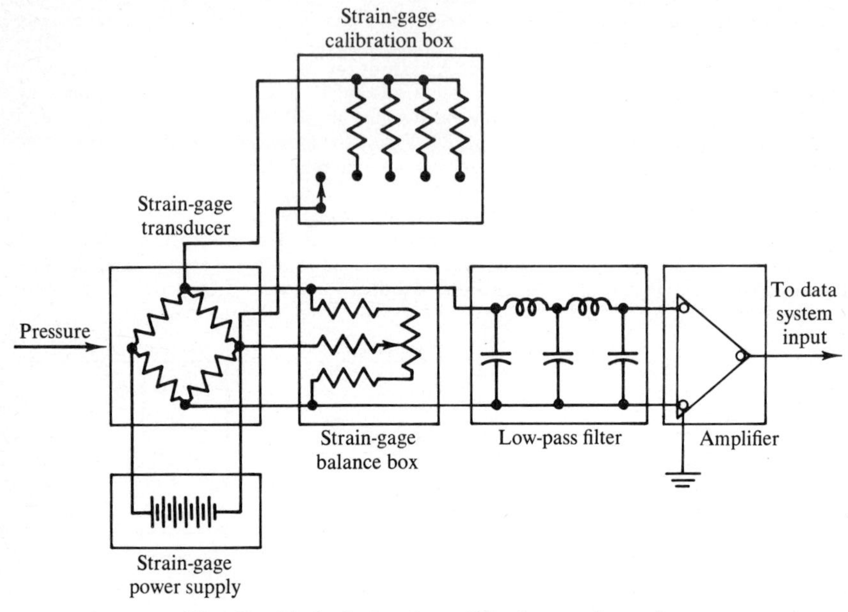

Fig. 6. Typical signal-conditioning equipment.

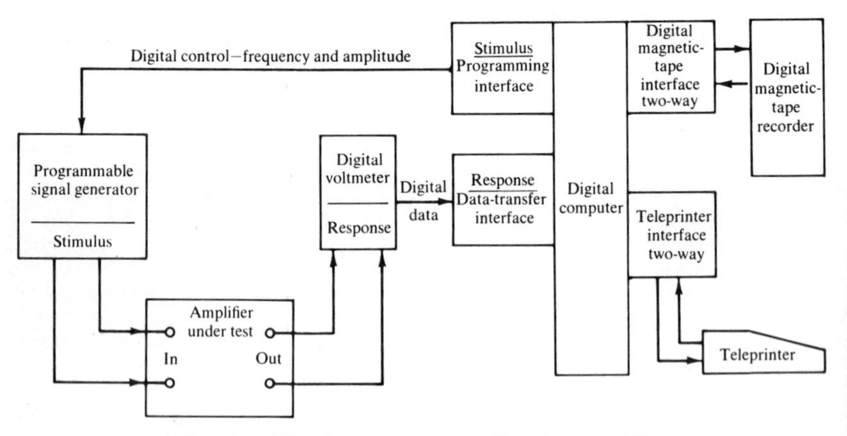

Fig. 7. Stimulus-response testing for amplifier.

stimulus on the input to the amplifier, a measurement of the output response is made; hence a stimulus-response type of instrument system results. Figure 7 shows an example of this type of system.

6. Stimulus-Response-Control Another type of instrument system is the stimulus-response-control system. This type is a variation of the stimulus-response system except that it has the additional feature of a control function and tends more toward the dedicated rather than general-purpose class. It is possible with this type of system to provide a means of automatically correcting the frequency response of the amplifier under test. This is done by providing a tuning head controlled by the system which can be attached to the amplifier to cause the amplifier to be tuned automatically to an appropriate response under a given stimulus. It should be noted that the item to be tested in this manner usually must be designed to accept automatic testing and setting or tuning of controls on it. Figure 8 depicts this type of system.

7. Response-Control The response-control system can "look" for a particular type of output from the equipment being monitored without regard to what the stimulus might be. Typically, the stimulus is not provided by the system as it was in the previous two examples. If a particular pattern or value of output appears, a control function is applied to the monitored equipment to provide a change in the output or response, hence a response-control instrument system. Such a system is usually involved in handling controls, limits, or alarms for process control. That is, if the pressure read on a system exceeds a given value—say,

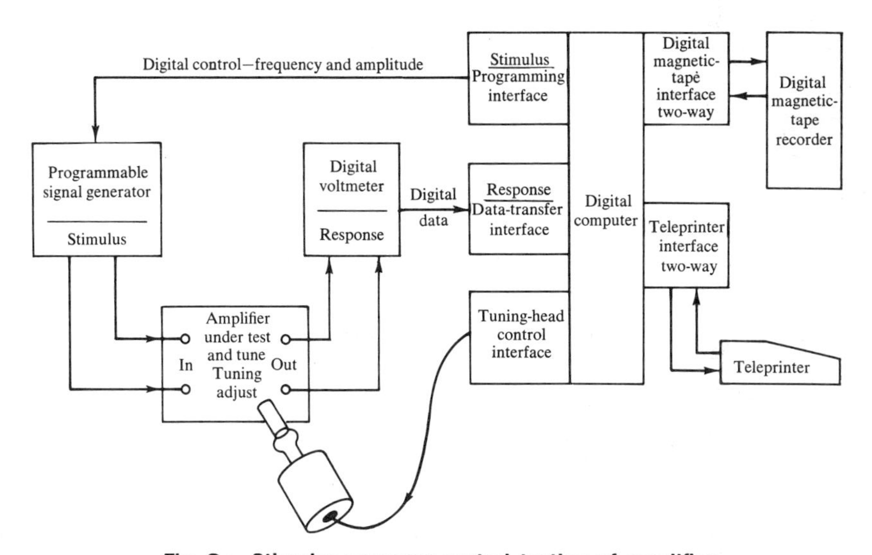

Fig. 8. Stimulus-response-control testing of amplifier.

a thousand pounds per square inch—then a control function is triggered by the system and either shuts off the pump supplying the pressure or performs some other action in relation to the response that is sought in order to control the process and not permit an overpressurization to take place. Figure 9 gives an example of this type of system.

8. Automatic Test Automatic test is broadly thought of as the ability to test an item comprehensively to determine all its characteristics with a minimum of human-operator intervention. The information desired from the test can vary from the minimum "go no-go" type of data presentation to completely characterized and recorded minutiae—all this being accomplished from a computer or coupler/controller. For example, if one wished to test an integrated-circuit operational amplifier automatically, it would be necessary to define a system which could provide an appropriate range of inputs to the amplifier, control the operation of the amplifier over a range of specified gains, measure the resulting output of the amplifier, and record all these parameters. This is really a highly specialized form of stimulus-

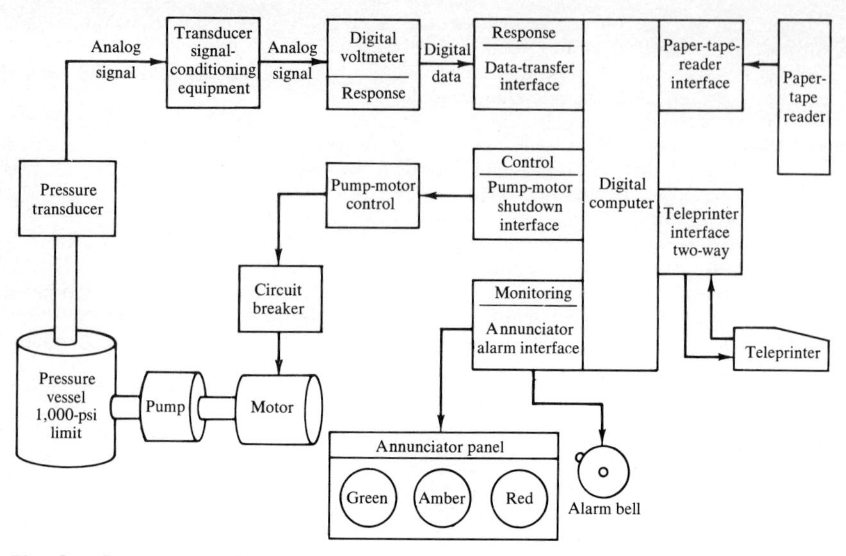

Fig. 9. Response-control system for overpressurization monitoring and control.

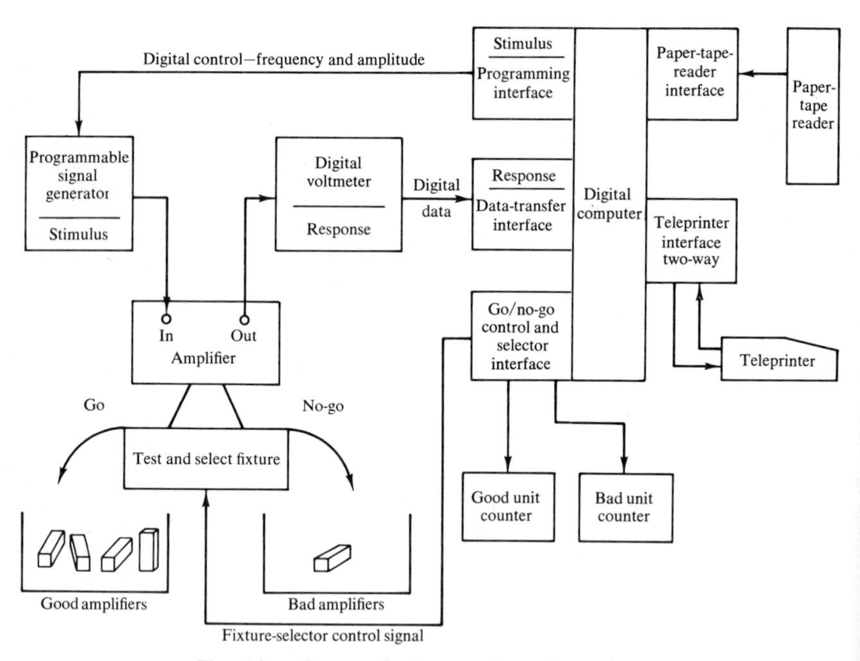

Fig. 10. Automatic test and sorting system.

response instrument system. In addition, or perhaps as an alternative, the system could provide a go no-go indication and automatic sorting. If the amplifier met all its requirements, it would be directed into a bin, indicating that it was ready to be packed for shipment. If the amplifier failed, it would be routed into another bin, indicating that the unit was rejected. It should be noted that, while stimulus and response systems are not necessarily always used for automatic test, automatic test will usually include stimulus as well as response functions. An example of an automatic test and sorting system is shown in Fig. 10.

9. Dedicated Systems In the previous examples, systems have been discussed which had analog inputs, such as voltage, frequency, or resistance, and digital inputs. However, there are many types of standard and custom-dedicated systems which can also accommodate special inputs and provide unique outputs depending on the application. Inputs and outputs can range from direct current through the audio- and radio-frequency regions of the spectrum on up through microwaves. A dedicated system can be defined as one which has been created for a particular purpose to solve a specific class of instrumentation problem and is therefore not readily adaptable for other uses. The system design has been optimized for the problem at hand and is not usually readily changeable by the user on a short turnaround basis to any other class of problem. Digital-logic test systems, acoustical-measuring systems, laboratory-analysis systems, and biomedical systems are all examples of dedicated systems.

Instrument systems accommodating signal frequencies up into the gigahertz region are frequently used in computer-controlled dedicated measurement applications of an automatic-test nature involving stimulus and response. They provide for complete measurement and characterization of microwave devices using methods which involve software-controlled calibration and completely computer-controlled internal error-correction techniques.

HOW TO RECOGNIZE WHEN A "SYSTEM" IS NEEDED

A question frequently asked is how does a user recognize when an instrumentation system is needed? Actually, this is quite easy to answer because there are so many reasons whereby a user can justify the application of a system approach to an instrumentation problem. For example, when the experiment or the process being instrumented demands that a structured and orderly series of repetitive measurements must be made, over some definable period of time, this is usually indicative of the necessity for a system.

A system should also be considered where a large number of measurements on many parameters, with a high degree of time correlation or time resolution, are needed. If, for example, some process requires that a hundred measurements be taken at the same (or virtually the same) point in time, it becomes evident that an observer looking at the various instruments and writing down the readings by hand is not going to provide a very well correlated time series of data. Under these circumstances then, a high-speed scanner, analog-to-digital converter, and recording media—such as magnetic-tape recording—probably are needed in order to achieve readings within an extremely short period of time.

The mere fact that 100 readings are required would tend to indicate that an instrument-system approach to the solution of the problem would be worthwhile. Even if the readings could be spread over a period of several minutes, an observer probably could not read and write down the readings with a requisite degree of accuracy.

Economics are also usually a factor involved in the decision to turn to an instrumentation system to solve a particular problem. The operating cost of an instrumentation system, including depreciation, is usually considerably less than the labor cost of an observer manually logging data over an extended period of time. The system is usually capable of doing data-logging operations faster and much more accurately and to a much greater degree of resolution than would be possible by a human operator.

When the user is working along and suddenly begins to realize that he has tied together more than one instrument in order to try to achieve a particular result, he has a good indication of system need. The voltmeter-printer-programmer-scanner combination discussed earlier is an excellent example of the kind of evolution in an operation which can point up the need for a system.

DEFINITION OF THE SYSTEM PROBLEM

When it has been recognized and determined that an instrumentation system is needed, some thought should be given to the considerations to be used in arriving at the best configuration for a system to solve the problem. The first system consideration is a complete definition of the problem that is to be solved by the application of the instrumentation system. The problem definition is the most important activity that one can carry out in preparing to specify an instrumentation system. Without a detailed definition of the problem, it is quite likely that some fundamental factor will be overlooked which can result in a system yielding less than optimum results.

In defining the problem, make a list of all the important factors affecting the problem; for example, identify and specify all the data inputs that are to be directed to the instrumentation system. This should include signal levels, frequency content, impedance levels, and any other factors that would help characterize the data inputs in terms of the nature of the problem that needs to be solved. If one can expect that some of the signals might have high common-mode voltages and unwanted normal-mode voltages associated with them, it is essential to recognize and specify this. Also, specify the magnitude and frequency content of the expected common-mode and normal-mode voltages. If the fact that a common-mode voltage will exist is known, it is possible to specify the appropriate type of signal-conditioning equipment—differential-input amplifier or guarded voltmeter—to permit the rejection of the common-mode voltage, while still being able to handle the desired normal-mode signal that is coming in on the lines. If it is known or suspected that undesired normal-mode noise or signals will exist on the signal circuits, filtering or integration techniques may be specified to remove or reduce the effect of these undesired signal elements from the signal circuits, leaving the desired signal to be processed as needed.

INSTRUMENTATION COMPLEXITY

The number of data inputs to the instrument system, the amount of conditioning or conversion which will be performed on the signal, and the resulting outputs of the instrument system will have a bearing on the instrumentation complexity of the system. If, for example, one can define the instrument system as requiring dc voltage measurements from only 100 different sources and at only one reading per second from any of the sources printed out on a standard strip printer, these requirements are considerably less demanding than if it is determined that the data to be taken from these 100 sources must be correlated within a 1-ms time frame and that this information must be recorded on magnetic tape in order to be subsequently processed in a computer.

The latter requirement implies a data-acquisition rate of 100 channels per 1 ms or 100,000 samples, or channels, per second, as opposed to the former system data rate of one sample or channel per second. The first system could be configured with any type of scanner, either stepping switch, crossbar, or reed relay. Any of these scanners would suit the requirements of taking one reading per second for the system; resulting in the 100 channels being sampled in a time frame of 100 s. The output of any of these scanners could then be connected to almost any digital voltmeter that could take readings at a rate faster than one per second.

On the other hand, a system, requiring that a sample of data from each of 100 channels be taken in a period of 1 ms, demands an extremely high-speed scanning device (or multiplexer), of necessity electronic in nature because none of the mechanical types noted previously could possibly operate at that speed. A high-speed electronic analog-to-digital converter would be needed which could keep pace with the multiplexer in order to convert the data in the time constraint specified. This latter system imposes many complexities on the instrumentation that do not exist in the slow-speed system. These variations in the instrumentation complexity have a direct bearing on instruments designed for system use.

SYSTEM INSTRUMENT REQUIREMENTS

If, in the previous example, the 100 channels of data to be recorded involved differing parameters—such as ac or dc voltage, frequency, or resistance—it is necessary to be able to provide remotely controllable function and range selection on the instrument in order to be able to measure the required parameters correctly. Such remote function and range selection or control of other instrument parameters has become known as "programmability."

Programmability is implemented on some instruments with analog control signals and on other instruments with digital control signals. With analog programming, an analog voltage of suitable magnitude is applied to the program line to accomplish the change. Analog programming is beset with many problems, but by far the most severe is susceptibility of the programmed instrument to noise entering on the analog program lines. The noise appears as a variation on the instrument output. It is difficult to suppress the incoming analog noise because the programming signal is also analog. Analog programming is also imprecise and slow.

Because of these reasons and the advent of digital computers and coupler/controllers, most new instrument designs today incorporate digital programming control. Digital control is faster, more precise, and less susceptible to noise. Digitally controlled and selected programming functions are thus an important requirement for any instrument to be used with a digital computer or coupler/controller.

It is essential that the instrument be controllable or programmable digitally by some commonly used code or at a minimum by special bit patterns. It is also essential in interfacing to a digital computer or coupler/controller that the data coming out of the instrument be presented in some common digital code, preferably in direct binary or binary-coded decimal. If an instrument meets the requirements of digital-data output and digital programmability, it can be said to be a "system instrument."

INTERFACING CONSIDERATIONS

10. Interfacing The single most important factor affecting the success or failure of instrumentation systems is the system interfacing. Assuming that the appropriate instruments have been properly selected for the job to be done and that the relationship of all the items to be used in the system is logical, then the manner in which the various items of the system are interconnected becomes of prime importance. This interconnection between equipment is commonly known as the "interface." Interfacing is important both in the analog side of the system as well as in the digital side of the system. A system can be all analog, or it can be all digital, or a mixture of the two, but in any event, a proper interface between various items of equipment making up the system is important regardless of the nature of the signals to be handled.

11. Grounding One of the most common sources of problems in interfacing various types of instruments, either analog or digital, is in the method of grounding. Grounding problems generally become apparent in the effects of either one or a combination of two problems. One is the common-mode problem caused by ground loops, and the other is the common-impedance problem where a number of different circuit elements or instruments are grounded through the same small conductor that has a substantial impedance to ground.

If, for example, an analog-signal ground and a digital-logic-circuit ground are both connected to the same conductor, which acts as a common impedance in both ground returns, it is entirely possible and, in fact, very likely that the switching transients from the digital-logic operation coupled through the common impedance in the ground return will appear in the analog-signal inputs. It is therefore very important to be sure all analog-signal grounds are isolated from power grounds and from digital-signal and power grounds. The common impedance in any of these paths should be kept as low as possible, and a final connection of all the grounds in the system should be made at one point where there can be as little common impedance as possible in the overall grounding scheme. This factor cannot be overemphasized.

More labor hours have probably been lost in instrument systems because of chasing problems that are the direct result of improper and ill-conceived grounding schemes than for any other single reason. Figure 11 shows the wrong way to effect a ground for the configuration of instruments demonstrated in the example, and Fig. 12 shows the right way.

When looking for a common grounding point that represents the ultimate ground for a system, the power-line ground or grounding contact in a grounded power-line receptacle is usually one of the poorest grounds that can be found. This is because it is often a small-diameter wire that runs all over the building before it finally ties into a water pipe or other effective grounding point—thus containing substantial

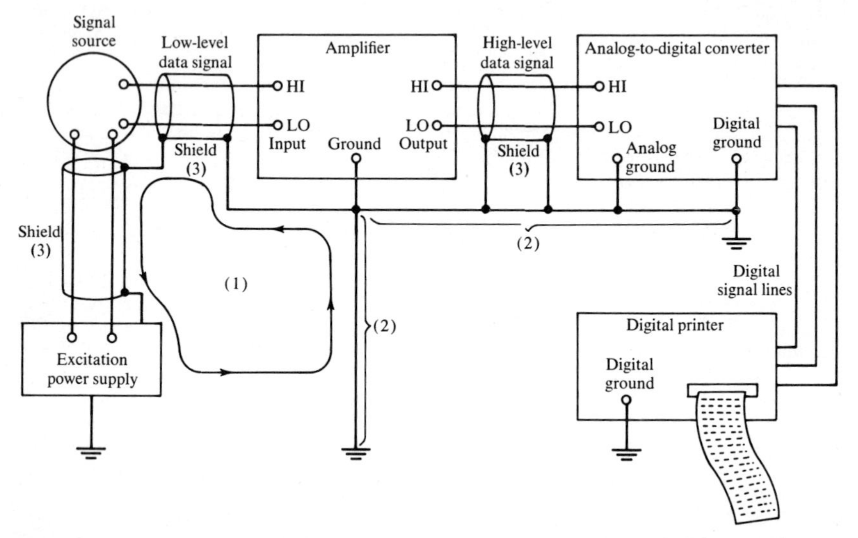

Fig. 11. Instrument grounding—common mistakes. (1) Ground loop will cause high circulating currents with result of high common-mode voltages in signal circuits. Noise problems and system instability can make system completely useless. (2) Large common impedances cause coupling of high-level data signal to amplifier input through cable shields. Amplifier can oscillate as result. Digital ground returns common to analog ground returns will couple digital switching noise into analog signal circuits. (3) Cable shields grounded at both ends virtually guarantee common-mode problems. See Fig. 12 for recommended method of grounding this system.

common impedance for all signals that are supposed to be at ground potential. The user should, wherever possible, pick up a ground connection that is independent of the power-system ground.

A water-pipe ground is frequently the best ground available. However, care must be exercised to be sure that an instrument in the system is not grounded through the power-cord grounding contact in a grounding power receptacle and also at the water pipe through a signal ground or a front-panel ground terminal. This will invariably result in a ground loop. If more than one instrument is involved, it will result in many ground loops which will cause untold problems to the user. Unfortunately, the easiest way to cure this problem is to disconnect the instrument from the power-line ground. However, local building and safety codes may not permit this, in which case the user must consult with the local plant engineer or electrician as to the best way to achieve the proper instrument ground while maintaining the safety and power-grounding requirements of the local building and safety codes.

ANALOG INTERFACES

First, consider some of the problems which are inherent in the interfacing of various analog devices. These devices may be used in dc measurement, microwave measurement, or in the audio field. Similar constraints and considerations apply in all these fields; so the comments to be presented here will be generally applicable for all of them.

12. Circuit Impedances and Loading Impedance-matching and circuit-loading considerations are of primary interest in the radio-frequency and microwave field but also apply where one analog device will be delivering a dc signal to another analog device. If the example mentioned earlier concerning the recording of the Rankine-cycle pressure-volume diagram is considered for a moment, several significant conditions can be identified.

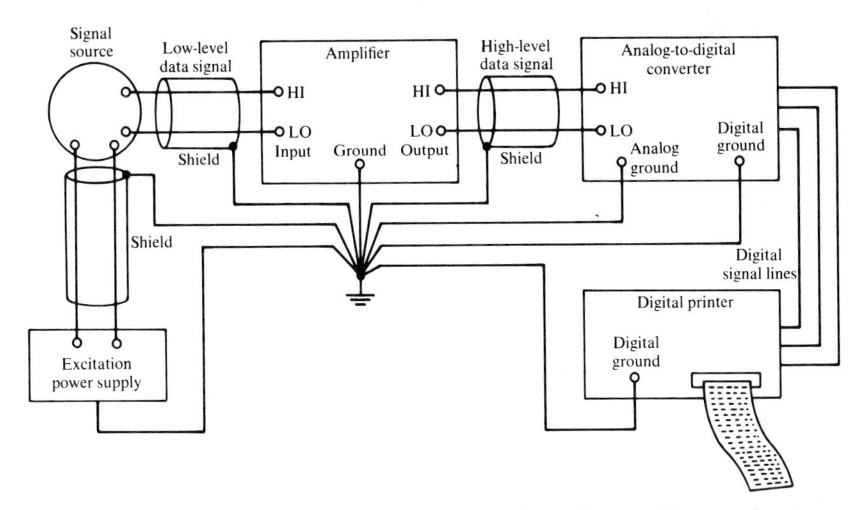

Fig. 12. Instrument grounding—recommended method. All grounds at one point only. At point of gain inflection. One wire per ground. No common impedances. No ground loops. No common analog-digital returns.

If the transducer being used to measure the pressure in the steam engine has a nominal internal impedance of 350 Ω and is connected directly to a recorder whose input impedance is 350 Ω, it should be immediately apparent that the output voltage recorded on the recorder will actually indicate only one-half of the open-circuit output voltage of the transducer. The other half of the open-circuit output voltage appears across the internal impedance of the transducer. The power transfer between the two devices may be optimized under this condition, but the power transfer is not the important item in this data-acquisition situation. The concern is not to get a maximum power transfer between the transducer and the recorder but to achieve a true representation of the output of the transducer in terms of its open-circuit voltage. It is this voltage which is representative of the pressure being applied to the transducer. The ideal instrumentation setup will achieve a measurement result which effectively does not disturb the circuit being measured. The data acquired would be identical, even if the instrument connection were not made. Thus we must interpose a means of maintaining and applying the true output voltage of the transducer to the recorder.

One way to do this would be to utilize a recorder with a potentiometric servocontrol for the pen drive which would have the requisite full-scale sensitivity of 30 mV. This type of recorder typically has a very high input impedance at the balance or null point when displaying the correct value of input voltage and a lower input impedance when the recorder is not in balance or is off null—that is, when the input voltage does not correspond instantaneously to the value of the voltage actually being displayed on the recorder. One consideration of the effect of these conditions would be the required or desired accuracy with which the output voltage of the transducer must be represented. If a recording with an accuracy of 1 percent or greater at all times is required, then the maximum load that can be applied to the transducer by the recorder must be at least one hundred times greater in value than the output impedance of the transducer itself. This is making no allowance for other sources of error in the system.

With a 350-Ω output impedance, it means that the loading applied to the transducer must be at least one hundred times greater, or greater than 35,000 Ω, in order to have a 1 percent or less effect on the accuracy of the output reading. It is usually desirable to include some margin of safety for error and for unknowns in the operation of the system. A typical practice would be to ensure that the input impedance of the instrument was perhaps three times greater than the 1 percent value—thus an impedance of 100,000 Ω input to the recording device would be appropriate in this case. The potentiometric or servo-driven graphic recorder can meet this requirement in most instances when in balance.

However, when the voltage input changes abruptly, the graphic-recorder pen-drive servo becomes unbalanced or off null. During this off-null condition and until the servo becomes balanced, the input impedance is low. This impedance can drop to 10,000 to 30,000 Ω under these conditions. It is apparent that the errors will be in the 1 to 3 percent range and will be variable or unpredictable in nature.

In order to ensure that the system accuracy will be unaffected during the entire period of unbalanced operation of the recorder, it is necessary to provide a constant input impedance for the transducer. If the constant impedance has to be 100,000 Ω or greater, it is apparent it will be necessary to interpose an amplifier between the transducer and the recorder in order to eliminate the effects of a fluctuating-load impedance on the transducer's output. A typical dc instrumentation amplifier capable of displaying an input impedance in excess of 100,000 Ω should also have a sufficiently low output impedance so that the variation in input impedance of the recorder will not have a detrimental effect in terms of loading the output of the amplifier. This will ensure that the output voltage recorded by the recorder will be independent of this loading condition. If the loading impedances can be made constant, the loading effect can be calculated and manually calibrated out of the results, or automatically calibrated and corrected by the computer.

If it is desired to consider 1 percent as the accuracy specification for a possible load as low as 10,000 Ω on the amplifier during periods of off balance for the recorder, it will require that the amplifier's output impedance be one-hundredth of that, or 100 Ω or less. If the same criterion of a one-third safety factor is applied to allow for unknown conditions which could affect the output, the dc amplifier should have an output impedance of less than 30 Ω. In practice, the output impedance of dc instrumentation amplifiers is typically below 1 Ω for an amplifier that is designed to deliver a reasonable amount of current into a reasonable load.

A reasonable amount of output current for a dc amplifier is 10 mA into a 1,000-Ω load. This means that the amplifier can swing a 10-V output across a 1,000-Ω load and still provide all the power necessary to do it precisely. If the internal impedance of the output circuit of the amplifier is 1,000 Ω and the graphic-recorder input impedance went as low as 10,000 Ω, errors as great as 10 percent in voltage swing or voltage displayed on the graphic recorder can be anticipated. These are the considerations that must be kept in mind when interfacing analog equipment where the voltage reading is the primary item of data desired. Figure 13 gives some examples of the magnitude of analog-circuit-loading errors.

The same circuit-loading considerations led to the development of the vacuum-tube voltmeter. This voltmeter displays the very high input impedances required to read the voltage in electronic circuitry properly, where the impedances are relatively high and are subject to loading by the instrument making the measurement. As noted earlier, maximum power transfer is not a consideration in voltage-measurement situations. Thus the characteristic impedances of the lines which may be used to connect the transducer to the voltage-measuring device are not particularly critical at dc and low-frequency ac signals.

However, in working in radio-frequency and in microwave measurements, characteristic impedances become very important. Typically, the matter of interest in these measurements is the amount of power being received or the amount of power being transmitted. Under these conditions, the line impedance matches must be

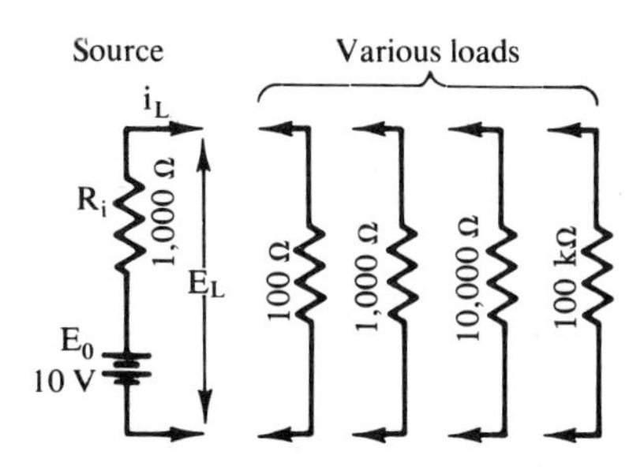

Load R, Ω	i_L, mA	E_L, V	Percent error in E_L	Calibration factor multiplier	Corrected E_L, V ($E_L \times$ C.F.)
0	10.000	0	00		
100	9.091	0.909	90.91	11.00	9.999
1,000	5.000	5.000	50.00	2.00	10.000
10,000	0.909	9.091	9.09	1.10	9.999
100,000	0.099	9.900	1.00	1.01	9.999
∞	0	10.000	0		

Fig. 13. Analog-circuit-loading errors. R_i, internal resistance of voltage source; E_o, open-circuit (no-load) voltage of source; E_L, apparent output voltage under load; i_L, load current. (NOTE: If load-resistor values are known and remain constant, the loading errors can be calibrated out. For example, multiplying the value of E_L by the calibration factors shown recovers the actual value of E_o to within 0.01 percent accuracy.)

scrupulously observed. If impedance mismatches are permitted, many detrimental effects—such as line reflections, high standing-wave ratios, and large reflected power components—can destroy or seriously impair the accuracy of the measurements which are being undertaken.

The examples given here of circuit impedance and loading problems are intended only to alert the user to the types of considerations which must be allowed for in the proper application and interconnection of instruments in systems. It is by no means a comprehensive recitation of all the types of problems that can be encountered.

13. Common-mode Noise Problems Another consideration related to analog-system applications is frequently troublesome to the user. This appears primarily in the voltage-measurement type of situation, which is really the most common sort of instrument system available to the average user. The question concerns common-mode noise-voltage problems which can affect the selection of the instruments or amplifiers to be used in a system. Common-mode voltages appear on instrument measurement circuits, of any length, when the source of the desired signal and the instrument to which it is connected are each grounded at different points. Alternating currents are induced from a variety of sources, including power lines and control circuitry in the vicinity of the measurement circuit. These currents appear in both conductors of the signal circuit and the ground and result in a potential difference appearing between the ground points of the signal source and the measuring instrument or amplifier. This, in turn, causes an unwanted voltage signal to appear at the instrument input terminals along with the real signal being measured. This unwanted voltage signal is known as ac common-mode pickup and is predominantly at the power-line frequency. The value of the common-mode voltages can approach several hundred volts. Signal sources yielding small signal voltages in the order of tens of millivolts, such as strain gages and thermocouples, can be completely obliterated by this interference. It is very difficult to separate this type of interference from the "normal mode," or desired measurement, signal if the signal is connected through a single-ended amplifier or to a single-ended instrument which is operating with one side of the input and output grounded. The instrument or amplifier sees the entire common-mode voltage magnitude across the input and cannot discriminate against this in favor of the desired signal due to the common ground. It should be pointed out that dc common-mode signals may also be present in measurement systems operating in the presence of large dc power-consuming loads such as aluminum-reducing pot lines.

In those situations where common-mode ground currents cannot be eliminated from the system, it is essential to prevent the common-mode ground currents from injecting an unwanted signal into the instrument input circuitry. As a rule, the instrument will be measuring signals from sources which are grounded at a remote point other than the instrument and cannot be easily disconnected. Attempts to break the ground loop are sometimes made by "floating" the instrument. A typical floating-instrument measurement setup is shown in Fig. 14. The instrument is measuring the signal between the two points *A* and *B* of the hypothetical source. The source has impedances R_{HI} and R_{LO} to the ground point *G*. Some examples of this type of source are grounded thermocouples and strain-gage bridges. These produce low signal amplitudes and because of the grounding are particularly sensitive to common-mode problems.

Looking at Fig. 14, the common-mode current flows in the loop formed by the source-ground leg resistance R_{LO} and the capacitance C_G between the LO side of the instrument input and the chassis. This produces an undesired common-mode voltage across R_{LO} which is effectively impressed on the signal measured by the instrument. R_{HI} contributes little in this situation because of the high input impedance of the instrument. Because of the low ground impedance R_G of the common-mode loop, the shield is largely ineffective and may, in fact, contribute to the unwanted noise because the ground loop it forms may induce still more noise in the signal leads. C_G is the primary circuit element here, and its value should be kept as low as possible to minimize the common-mode current in the signal circuit. Practical considerations, however, usually dictate a value for C_G of at least 0.1 μF, which results in a substantial common-mode signal. Floating the entire instrument instead of just the measurement circuit results in some improvement.

An instrument with a differential input is often used to help the common-mode problem. The differential input works best with balanced impedances and will not function properly with large unbalances or source impedance greater than a few hundred ohms. Frequently, the common-mode voltages encountered exceed the differential-input rating by five to ten times the maximum rated input of the input capability of the differential instrument. When this occurs, the instrument cannot be used.

The best solution is to enclose the entire measurement circuit of the instrument in a metallic guard which is insulated from the rest of the instrument. This isolates the measurement circuit from the rest of the instrument. The guard is operated at the potential of the signal-source ground by a direct connection. The instrument

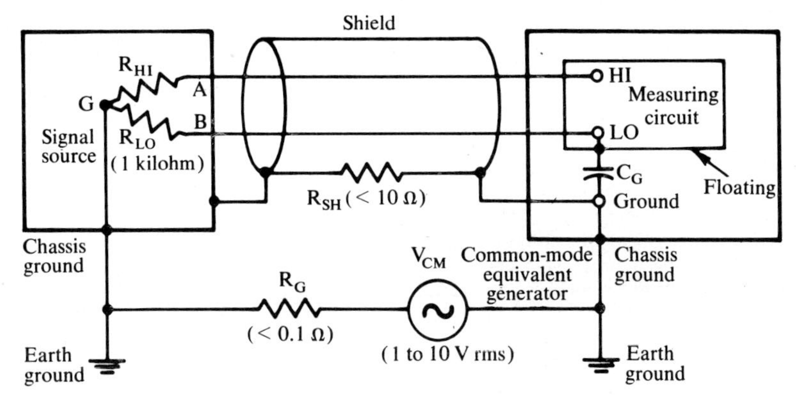

Fig. 14. Common-mode noise injection to floating instrument. R_{LO}, source-ground leg resistance; R_{SH}, shield or ground bus resistance; C_G, capacitance, measuring circuit to chassis ground (typically 0.1 μF).

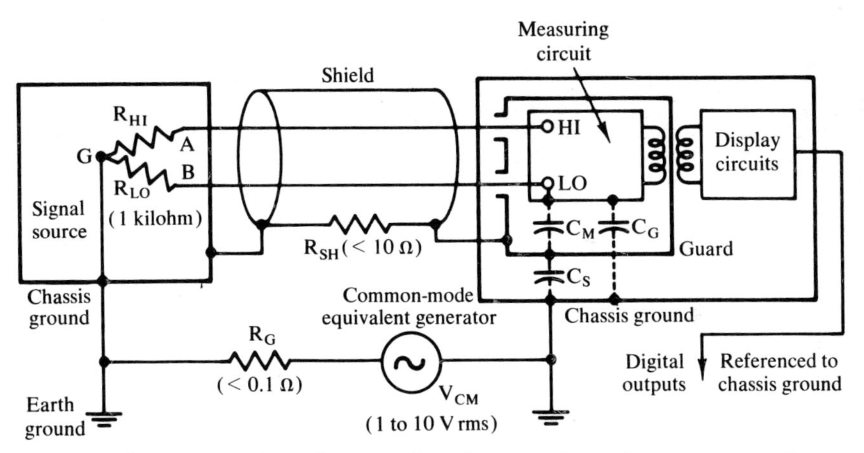

Fig. 15. Common-mode noise rejection by guarding. C_G, stray capacitance, measuring circuit to chassis (< 2.7 pF); C_M, stray capacitance, measuring circuit to guard (0.002 μF approximately); C_S, stray capacitance, measuring guard to chassis (0.003 μF approximately). Values given here are typical.

chassis is grounded normally and the common-mode currents are effectively shunted away from the measurement circuit through the guard circuit.

This arrangement is depicted in Fig. 15. The common-mode current flows in the loop formed by the shield and the stray capacitance C_S. The current flowing through C_M will be very small, thus resulting in a high rejection ratio, typically 160 dB. Imperfections of the guard shield resulting in some capacitance C_G between the measurement section and instrument ground will reduce the rejection ratio to approximately 120 dB. The result is that 10 V of 60-Hz common-mode noise will appear at the instrument input as a signal of 10 μV. The effect of this can be further reduced if the instrument incorporates integration in its measurement scheme.

Thus a guarded input to an instrument is the best solution for common-mode problems where system grounding cannot be controlled.

If the user is aware of the potential existence of this type of problem at the outset, it is possible to design a system to avoid these effects. In many cases, the simplest way to minimize this problem is to locate the signal circuitry as far away from any interfering sources as possible and be sure that the signal source and signal circuitry are not grounded at some distant point as well as at the amplifier or instrument, thus causing a ground loop. A ground loop is always the prime cause of common-mode interference problems. If the user can effectively control the grounding situation and the dressing or location of the instrument measurement circuitry so that common-mode voltages are not a problem, he can then use so-called "three-terminal" or "single-ended" amplifiers or instruments. In these devices, one side of the input and one side of the output are common and are usually grounded; and only one side of the input and the output is high with respect to ground. Under these conditions, the only point of grounding for one of the two signal conductors and for any shields of the shielded twisted pairs that may be necessary or needed for the signal circuitry is at the ground point of the single-ended amplifier or instrument. This is known as "gain-inflection-point grounding," because the only ground on the system is at the amplifier. Figure 16 shows a typical system block diagram for gain-inflection-point grounding.

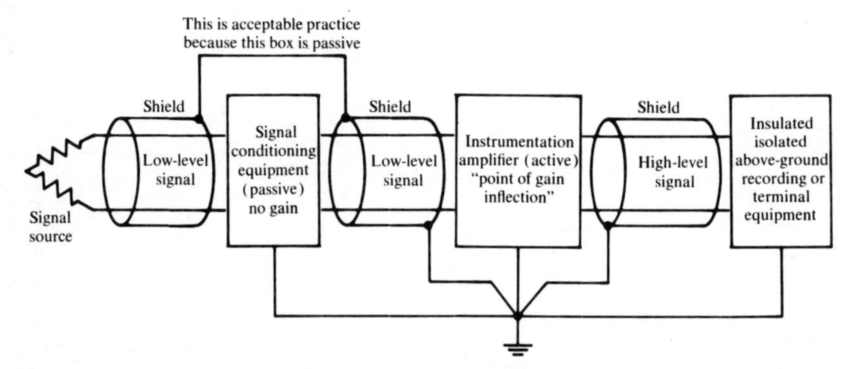

Fig. 16. Example of "gain-inflection-point grounding." (NOTE: Cable shields are not grounded to equipment cases of signal conditioning or recording or terminal equipment. The shields can be carried through the equipment without detrimental effects as long as insulation resistance is high. Equipment chassis grounds are brought to one point. Low-level signal-circuit and high-level signal-circuit shields are grounded with the equipment grounds at the ground closest to the "point of gain inflection," the amplifier ground. In cables of multiple-shielded pairs, the shields should also be insulated from each other.)

Unfortunately, there are many cases when the user cannot exercise this type of control. It is "unfortunate" because a three-terminal amplifier or instrument is usually a much less expensive device than a balanced differential or "guarded" input unit and thus has an economic advantage in a system or measurement situation being designed from scratch. Where the user cannot control the type of cable, its location, or a grounding situation, he will probably experience trouble, particularly where signal circuitry is already existing and installed and must be used. The worst possible common-mode problems are usually encountered here.

A thermocouple is another good case in point. In order to minimize the thermal delay in conducting the thermal signal to the thermocouple, it is common practice to create a physical metallic bond between the thermocouple junction and the surface of the device whose temperature is being measured. This intimate metallic contact between the thermocouple junction and the device under temperature measurement presents an uncontrolled ground situation which always results in common-mode signals significantly larger in magnitude than the actual millivolt signal level of the thermocouple itself.

Under these conditions, a differential-input or guarded amplifier or instrument is a must in order to be able to discriminate against the common-mode voltage which is present. Often poorly designed differential units are totally ineffective. Guarding is usually the answer. The user should be aware of the fact that there are several types of guarding techniques in practice for handling signals with common-mode content. Some applications may require the instrument and an associated scanner to withstand very high common-mode voltages from ±100 to 500 V peak or more without any damage to the equipment. Some equipment may not be able to withstand such high common-mode voltages without damage. Typical of these are the high-speed solid-state scanners, where the limit of common-mode voltage which can be safely tolerated by the equipment is often as low as ±10 V peak. Because of these equipment characteristics, the user must have an idea of what level of common-mode voltage to expect, so that when he puts his system together he does not inadvertently blast the equipment with a common-mode signal of such magnitude that damage results.

14. Time Correlation of Data Points As a rule, the user will encounter another criterion which must be considered in interfacing analog equipment. This is the question of time correlation of the measurements. For a single voltage measurement, or the measurement of a single parameter, time correlation is not an applicable consideration. The exact time of a measurement might need to be known. A clock which provides time marks or time codes for the measurement can be used to get these data. However, if there is a system requirement for measuring more than one voltage simultaneously, or within a certain time frame, the problem becomes more interesting. If a user, for example, must know the readings for 25 different parameters at exactly the same instant, this presents a different type of measurement problem than if he can be satisfied with the values of those 25 measurements spread over a 10-ms time frame or within a time frame of 1 s. This is the problem of designing the system to a specified value of time skew.

In the first example where all 25 readings must be made at the same time, the time skew which is permitted is 0. In the case where the 25 readings must all be made within a 10-ms time frame, the permitted time skew is 10 ms, and in the last case, it is 1 s. The obvious solution to the first case of no time skew permitted is to record all the readings simultaneously. To do this would require, in the worst case, 25 separate measurement and recording devices. This is obviously economically unattractive, and correlating the time of 25 recorders is not an insignificant task either. Another means must therefore be found to permit all the readings to be taken simultaneously and be recorded sequentially over some finite period of time after they have been taken.

One means for accomplishing this is to utilize a simultaneous sample and hold system. In this situation, there can be 25 separate sample and hold circuits which can all be triggered simultaneously so that they sample the data on each of the 25 points at the same time and then hold those data until such time as the hold circuits can be scanned, measured, and recorded. The period of time during which sampling is taking place is known as the "aperture time." This is typically very short, usually in the 50-ns range. The hold period is usually on the order of a few milliseconds. The rate of change of output from the hold circuit is known as "droop." If the hold period on the sample and hold circuits is long enough, it is possible to utilize a relatively slow measurement and recording device to record the voltage being held in each of them. Typically, however, the hold circuitry for a specified level of precision usually involves a time interval that is on the order of milliseconds. Under these conditions, it becomes necessary to utilize a scanning and measuring device of fairly high speed and a digital recording device in order to achieve the readings in a sufficiently short period of time so that the signals being held in the sample and hold circuitry do not degrade outside the limits of the precision required for the measurements.

If the group of 25 readings can tolerate a time skew of 1 s, any device which can scan the 25 parameters and convert the data into digital form and record them in digital form all in less than 1 s will provide the necessary capability to record all the data. However, if all 25 readings must be taken every 10 ms—that is, with an allowable time skew of 10 ms—an entirely different type of equipment operating at a much higher speed than for the previous example must be used in order to scan, read, convert, and record the data within 10 ms on a digital recording device. This same scanning, reading, converting, and recording scheme could probably be used to meet the requirement of zero skew time for the 25 readings by the addition of the sample and hold deskewing method. Thus it is important to take careful note of the time-correlation requirements of the data to be measured in order that appropriate means can be provided in the system to take care of the timing requirements.

15. Summary In summary, in defining analog interfacing problems for instrument systems, it is necessary to give proper consideration to the impedance levels and loading effects of the instrument circuits when voltages are to be measured and to give proper consideration to impedance matching where maximum power transfer is involved. It is essential to recognize and to pay particular attention to the existence and treatment of common-mode interference to the normal-mode signal. It is also necessary to pay strict attention to timing problems, time correlation, and time skew. All these analog interfacing considerations and their effects are important elements in the design for proper operation of the instrument system. There are certainly many other considerations which the user may encounter when he is trying to assemble the system. It is not possible to give a complete and exhaustive treatment of all these possibilities in this handbook, but it is certainly important to recognize that there may be other considerations and unusual effects which are not as common as the ones which were discussed by example here. It is worth remembering that these same analog considerations will apply in cases of either a completely analog system operating alone with both measurement inputs and measurement outputs in analog form or an analog system interfaced with a digital system where the outputs are presented in digital form.

ANALOG-DIGITAL CONVERSION

In joining analog and digital equipment together, it is necessary to take into consideration the techniques of analog-to-digital conversion. It is the conversion device which in the true sense provides an interface between the analog portion of the system and the digital portion of the system. Much analog information, which will be converted to a digital form for further processing, is usually converted first to a time-varying dc voltage. This technique is easily handled, accommodated, and understood and is almost universal in its application.

There are mechanical analog-to-digital conversion devices which utilize the conversion of an angular shaft position in a shaft-position encoder to give a digital output, and the conversion of a linear position along a linear digital encoder to yield a digital output. As shaft-position and linear-position encoders are not considered to be electronic instruments but are really a form of transducer, they will not be discussed in detail. It is, however, good to keep in mind the fact that they are available, in the event a direct translation from a mechanical position to a digital representation is needed.

16. Electronic Converters As noted earlier, various physical phenomena and electrical measurements can be converted to equivalent dc voltages, and it is these dc voltages which are, in turn, converted through the means of an analog-to-digital converter in order to get the data they represent into the digital operating domain.

There are four principal types of electronic analog-to-digital converters: the first is the successive-approximation type; the second, the continuous-balance type; the third, the ramp type—either single or dual; and the fourth, the integrating type. Each of these has its own unique characteristics and attributes. Some useful features are common to more than one of the types.

The integrating type of analog-to-digital converter is most useful when working with dc voltages having a high normal-mode noise content. Because a definite amount of time is required to perform the integration, the integrating types of analog-to-digital converters are relatively slow. A considerable degree of precision can, however, be developed with this type of converter.

The successive-approximation type of analog-to-digital converter at the other end of the spectrum is usually a high-speed type of converter and can yield a significant degree of resolution, depending upon how it is designed and how it is going to be applied. All these units can be designed to handle dc voltage inputs of various levels appropriate to the application for which they are going to be used. In addition, all of them will provide a coded digital output.

The most usual digital output is either binary or binary-coded decimal (BCD). The binary-coded decimal type of converter is most useful where it is desirable to handle a decimal output directly from the device. It is used frequently when the converter is embodied in the form of a digital voltmeter where a shaped electrode gaseous-discharge tube or other type of decimal numerical display is needed. It is important to note that binary-coded decimal output can be implemented with one of several codes. A discussion of the various codes used is given below. The user must know which output code is available from the instrument and other devices in the system when the instrument is being interfaced to a digital system, to be sure the data coming from the instrument are properly interpreted by the system.

Very few digital-voltmeter instruments have an output that is in binary. However, most analog-to-digital converters commonly used with computer systems have a binary output. This is most useful because computers applied in scientific applications usually carry out their internal operations in binary arithmetic and, having binary code available directly at the output of the analog-to-digital converter, eliminate the necessity of a code-conversion operation.

17. Converter-selection Criteria In considering the needs to be met in providing an analog-to-digital conversion device for use with a combination analog-digital system, some of the following criteria should be carefully considered to be sure the unit selected will, in fact, meet the requirements of the conversions:

1. It should be determined if there is going to be any common-mode voltage present in the input. If there is, the selection of an appropriate differential- or guarded-input type of converter should result in minimizing the effects of the common-mode signal. The integrating type of converter is particularly useful in eliminating unwanted normal-mode voltages imposed on the signal at power-line or other repetitive frequencies. It is also frequently useful to provide filtering or bandwidth control to help minimize the effects of unwanted signals or noise on the signal measurement at other than the power-line frequency.

2. The range of dc signals to be input to the converter should be known in order that a suitable selection of ranges is available to accommodate the signals. The ability of the converter to be overloaded without damage or to be overranged without adversely affecting its operation is important. A means of indicating the occurrence of overload or overrange is desirable. An automatic range-changing function could be useful. This would allow the converter to sense the input voltage and select a range yielding the greatest degree of resolution for that particular signal.

3. The degree of resolution required to present the measurement results properly must be considered.

4. If an integrating converter is to be used, the number and length of available sample periods for carrying out the integration should be known.

5. The input impedance of the device should be known to evaluate the loading effects on the circuit from which the voltage is to be measured.

6. If the analog-to-digital converter has range- or measurement-function controls, it is necessary to know if these can be programmed digitally from the digital system.

7. The type of programming and output digital codes used by the converter can substantially influence the design and operation of the interface between the analog and digital equipment.

DIGITAL CODES

In making the transition from the analog to the digital domain, it must be recognized by the user that representation of quantities or measurements is different in the digital domain from what it is in the analog domain. As noted earlier, an analog value cannot be measured exactly, but only with some degree of precision, because it is a continuous function. On the other hand, a digital value is discrete or exact, even though it may be an inexact representation of an analog value of interest. The analog domain is typically keyed to a decimal representation. In the decimal numbering system, each digit in a number can have a value from 0 to 9, and each digit is weighted according to its position, beginning with 1, 10, 100, 1,000, and so on. It is easy to perceive; if the three digits of a three-digit decimal number each have the value of 9, the total weighted value of that three-digit combination is 999, which is the highest value that can be represented by a three-digit decimal number. If the digits are valued 1, 2, 3, the decimal quantity is 123 because the 1 is assigned to the hundreds' position, the 2 to the tens' position, and the 3 to the units' position. Thus, 100 plus 20 plus 3 equals 123.

Most digital computers operate with a binary code—that is, a numbering system which can have only two values to a digit rather than the ten values a digit has in the decimal system. The two values in a binary representation are 0 or 1. The presence of a 1 in a digit position signifies that digit has a value of 1. The presence of a 0 in that digit's location represents a value of 0.

The most common digital code is the binary code, which has a weighting for the digits which increases by a factor of 2; so the least significant first digit would have a weight of 1, the second digit would have a weight of 2, the third digit a weight of 4, the fourth digit a weight of 8, and so on. Thus, if the four digits of a binary number each have the value of 1, the total value of that four-digit combination is 1111, which is the highest value that can be represented by a four-digit binary number. The decimal equivalent of the binary number is the sum of the weights of the digits containing a 1. As all four contain 1s, the decimal value is $8 + 4 + 2 + 1$ or 15, which is equal to $2^n - 1 = 2^4 - 1 = 16 - 1 = 15$.

To represent the values of decimal numbers, a binary-coded decimal system is frequently utilized. To be able to provide a representation as high as 9 for a decimal number, it is necessary to have 4-bit positions associated for each binary-coded decimal digit. If the decimal value of 1 is to be shown, the least significant bit is 1; the others are 0. If a decimal value of 8 is to be represented, the fourth bit with its weight of 8 is a 1, and the other 3 bits of lesser significance are 0. A representation of 9 would have the least significant bit, and the most significant bit of the 4 bits contains 1s and the two intermediate bits contain 0s, thus giving a decimal value of $8 + 0 + 0 + 1$, or 9, to the 4-bit representation for the decimal digit.

It is apparent from the previous analysis that, if the weights of all the 4 bits are added together, the result will be a value of 15 decimal. However, this would be the maximum decimal value of those 4 binary bits. For decimal representation of 0 to 9 by 4 bits, the bit combinations from 10 through 15 are forbidden and are not used when the 4 binary bits are used to represent a decimal digit. However, some instrument manufacturers do use the codes beyond 9, attaching their own significance to the forbidden combinations to depict such symbols as decimal points, plus, blank, minus, etc.

If two decimal digits are to be represented, it requires two 4-bit increments, or a total of 8 bits, to represent a value from 0 to 99 decimal. However, those same 8 bits can represent a decimal valuation of from 0 to 255, if all the bit weights are permitted to be used in representing the value of the number in binary form. Thus, the most efficient use of the available number of bits in a particular binary group is accomplished when the representation is in true binary, rather than in binary-coded decimal form. Figure 17 shows the comparison of these two conditions.

Codes used in digital data representation can be thought of as being of two types, those which represent only numerical elements and those which can represent both alphabetical and numerical characters. There are many types of numerical-only codes. The binary and 8-4-2-1 binary-coded decimal have been discussed. Others are octal, hexadecimal, excess-three, 2-4-2-1 binary-coded decimal, 4-2-2-1 binary-coded decimal, and gray or reflected code. It is important for the user to be aware of the fact that different types of binary numerical codes exist. The user must be certain the interfacing between the various devices in his system follows a single convention and will be compatible at the code level. If compatibility does not exist, code conversion or translation is required to ensure that the information is exchanged correctly. Code conversion should be avoided whenever possible, because it results in increased system costs and can slow down system operations. While code conversion can be done quickly in a hardware translater, it is more commonly handled by a computer software program, which is substantially slower. As a rule, the software program requires a large number of computer cycles and is thus wasteful of computer time and results in what is known as high "computer overhead"—that is, computer operating time not directly available to a problem solution or system operation.

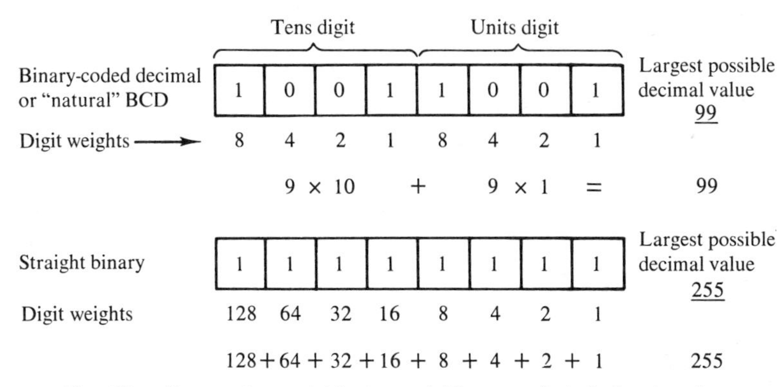

Fig. 17. Comparison of binary and binary-coded decimal codes.

All the above-mentioned numerical codes can express a decimal quantity of 0 through 9 in a binary character of 4 bits. Some of these codes can require as many as 8 bits to represent decimal quantities from 0 through 15 properly. These codes are the 8-4-2-1 or natural binary-coded decimal, the 4-2-2-1 code, the excess-three code, and the 2-4-2-1 code. A comparison of the various codes is shown in Fig. 18.

Several codes are capable of representing alphanumeric characters. A common consideration of all of them is that to provide for a complete set of uppercase alphabetical characters for the English alphabet and the numerical characters 0 through 9 requires a minimum of 36 distinct or unique codes. With the addition of special characters—that is, periods, commas, question marks, asterisks, slashes, parentheses, etc.—the minimum number of digital bits which can possibly be used to define an alphanumeric character would be six. Six bits provide the capability of defining 64 unique characters. For many applications, 64 possibilities for describing characters are not sufficient because of the need for many special control and nontyping functions, such as carriage return and line feed. There has been a trend, therefore, to change from a 6-level to a 7-level code for this purpose. Seven-level code provides the opportunity for 128 possible character combinations and control and function codes.

The most commonly used and widely accepted code is a 7-level code called the ASCII code. ASCII is the acronym for American Standard Code for Information Interchange. This is the code used in "Teletype" communication systems today in the United States. It is also used with virtually every small computer system and in many computerless digital systems where alphanumeric characters are utilized. It is expected that the ASCII code will eventually become the standard information-exchange code for virtually all computer applications and for all digital-system applications in the United States. Figure 19 shows the bit patterns as presently assigned in the 7-level ASCII code. An eighth level is available in paper-tape punches and paper-tape readers for ASCII code. This is often used today for parity checking on a character basis.* The eighth paper-tape level may be used in the future to expand the ASCII code to 8 levels and 256 possible character combinations.

Decimal value	Binary	Octal	Hexa-decimal	Gray code	Excess-3 code	8-4-2-1 BCD	4-2-2-1 BCD	2-4-2-1 BCD
0	0	0	0	0000	0011	0000	0000	0000
1	1	1	1	0001	0100	0001	0001	0001
2	10	2	2	0011	0101	0010	0010	0010
3	11	3	3	0010	0110	0011	0011	0011
4	100	4	4	0110	0111	0100	0110	0100
5	101	5	5	0111	1000	0101	0111	0101
6	110	6	6	0101	1001	0110	1100	0110
7	111	7	7	0100	1010	0111	1101	0111
8	1000	10	8	1100	1011	1000	1110	1110
9	1001	11	9	1101	1100	1001	1111	1111
10	1010	12	A	1111	0100 0011	0001 0000	0001 0000	0001 0000
11	1011	13	B	1110	0100 0100	0001 0001	0001 0001	0001 0001
12	1100	14	C	1010	0100 0101	0001 0010	0001 0010	0001 0010
13	1101	15	D	1011	0100 0110	0001 0011	0001 0011	0001 0011
14	1110	16	E	1001	0100 0111	0001 0100	0001 0110	0001 0100
15	1111	17	F	1000	0100 1000	0001 0101	0001 0111	0001 0101

Fig. 18. Comparison of numerical codes.

DIGITAL-SYSTEM ORGANIZATION

To manipulate or move data in digital form in a digital system, it is necessary for the digital system to have a defined structure or organization, so that an orderly movement of the data in the digital equipment can be accomplished. The digital-system designer can frequently be quite arbitrary, though logical, in the establishment of the organization or the architecture for the system. However, as a result of continuing refinement over the years, certain general standards of organization have been established and recognized by digital-system designers. The first and most important standard organizational element of a digital system is the definition of its word structure. It is the word structure which influences the amount and, to some extent, the precision and ease with which information may be handled in the digital system. Word structure is usually defined in terms of digital bits, each word consisting of a specified number of bits. Thus, it is possible for digital operations to be conducted with digital words formatted to have 8-bit, 12-bit, 16-bit, 24-bit, 32-bit, or larger word structures. This grouping of bits into standard-length words, or quantum of data, is a very important element of the organization of any digital system.

Practice has developed another standard concept, which is the concept of "byte" orientation for digital information. Bytes, as presently defined, are 8 bits in length. Words in a digital system can consist of one or more bytes. The information is transferred around in the system in either bytes or words of the specified length.

* For a discussion of "parity," the reader is referred to Robert Steven Ledley, "Digital Computer and Control Engineering," McGraw-Hill Book Company, New York, 1960.

Char	Code								Char	Code								Char	Code								Char	Code							
@		●							SPACE			●						NULL									↑		●	●					
A		●						●	!			●					●	SOM								●			●	●					●
B		●					●		"			●				●		EOA							●				●	●				●	
C		●					●	●	#			●				●	●	EOM							●	●			●	●				●	●
D		●				●			$			●			●			EOT						●					●	●			●		
E		●				●		●	%			●			●		●	WRD						●		●			●	●			●		●
F		●				●	●		&			●			●	●		RU						●	●				●	●			●	●	
G		●				●	●	●	'			●			●	●	●	BELL						●	●	●			●	●			●	●	●
H		●			●				(			●		●				FE_0					●						●	●		●			
I		●			●			●	)			●		●			●	H. TAB.					●			●			●	●		●			●
J		●			●		●		*			●		●		●		LINE FEED					●		●				●	●		●		●	
K		●			●		●	●	+			●		●		●	●	V. TAB					●		●	●			●	●		●		●	●
L		●			●	●			,			●		●	●			FORM					●	●					●	●		●	●		
M		●			●	●		●	—			●		●	●		●	RETURN					●	●		●			●	●		●	●		●
N		●			●	●	●		.			●		●	●	●		S_0					●	●	●		NOT		●	●		●	●	●	
O		●			●	●	●	●	/			●		●	●	●	●	S_1					●	●	●	●	ASSIGNED		●	●		●	●	●	●
P		●		●					0			●	●					DC_0				●							●	●	●				
Q		●		●				●	1			●	●				●	X-ON				●				●			●	●	●				●
R		●		●			●		2			●	●			●		TAPE ON				●			●				●	●	●			●	
S		●		●			●	●	3			●	●			●	●	X-OFF				●			●	●			●	●	●			●	●
T		●		●		●			4			●	●		●			TAPE OFF				●		●					●	●	●		●		
U		●		●		●		●	5			●	●		●		●	ERROR				●		●		●			●	●	●		●		●
V		●		●		●	●		6			●	●		●	●		SYNC				●		●	●				●	●	●		●	●	
W		●		●		●	●	●	7			●	●		●	●	●	LEM				●		●	●	●			●	●	●		●	●	●
X		●		●	●				8			●	●	●				S_0				●	●						●	●	●	●			
Y		●		●	●			●	9			●	●	●			●	S_1				●	●			●			●	●	●	●			●
Z		●		●	●		●		:			●	●	●		●		S_2				●	●		●				●	●	●	●		●	
[		●		●	●		●	●	;			●	●	●		●	●	S_3				●	●		●	●			●	●	●	●		●	●
\		●		●	●	●			<			●	●	●	●			S_4				●	●	●					●	●	●	●	●		
]		●		●	●	●		●	=			●	●	●	●		●	S_5				●	●	●		●			●	●	●	●	●		●
↑		●		●	●	●	●		>			●	●	●	●	●		S_6				●	●	●	●		↓		●	●	●	●	●	●	
←		●		●	●	●	●	●	?			●	●	●	●	●	●	S_7				●	●	●	●	●	RUB OUT		●	●	●	●	●	●	●
Level ⟶	8	7	6	5	4	3	2	1		8	7	6	5	4	3	2	1		8	7	6	5	4	3	2	1		8	7	6	5	4	3	2	1

Fig. 19. ASCII code bit patterns—7 level. (NOTE: Eighth level presently used for parity-parity bits not shown.)

Whether the data are handled in words, bytes, or groups of bytes is not really of great significance to the instrument-system user, as long as all the hardware is structured to accommodate the bit grouping used, and the user is aware of the method used. Registers which are required for manipulation or storage of the data, memory cells, and recording media are all organized, matched, and sized within a digital system to handle the digital information in this manner. "Register" or "accumulator" are the names for the circuit function in a digital system, used for temporary storage and manipulation of a pattern of bits.

Within the word or byte structure of the digital system, various codes, as noted earlier in this discussion, are utilized for the representation of data. Within the individual bit positions in each byte or word, it was noted the individual bit can have one of two values, a 0 or a 1. The method by which the 0 or 1 is represented electronically in a register can be entirely arbitrary. It is almost a function of designer's choice, although many choices are defined as "standards."

DIGITAL-LOGIC LEVELS

One representation would be to let zero volts signify zero value in one condition or state of the bit position in the register, while +5 V present at the output of a bit position would denote a 1 value or another condition or state of the bit position.

However, practical logic-circuit design considerations and other constraints seldom permit such a straightforward and simple representation. The user is more apt to find that a 0 state is rarely represented with a complete absence of voltage in a system, in order to provide some fail-safe indication as to whether the system is operating or not. If the power were off on a device and, as a consequence, all bit positions in the register of the device contained 0 V and 0 were defined as an absence of voltage, a digital system interfaced to the device would not really know there was a problem from the condition of the register. If the bit positions all contain 0, they could be in that state either because of containing legitimate data or because no power was applied to the device. As a rule, practical logic-circuit design considerations result in voltages being present in differing magnitudes to represent the two possible logic states. Usually, other means are also employed to validate that data are really present in the register.

It is also arbitrary as to which voltage level or logic state is defined as true or false. If the digital system is defined to have positive true and ground false logic levels, the ground being false, or zero level, could with today's diode-transistor logic (DTL) integrated-ciruit logic elements have a voltage range of from 0 to, say, +½ V, with +¼ V being typical for the 0 or false condition. A voltage range of from +2½ to +5 V would be the true or one-level position, with +4 V being typical. If the logic in the system is defined as being ground true and positive false, exactly the opposite would be true over that of the previous example—that is, a voltage range of 0 to +½ V with +¼ V as typical would be considered true, and a voltage range of +2½ to +5 V with +4 V as typical would be considered false.

It becomes immediately apparent that, if one is going to interface digital devices, the logic levels and defined states of the logic, whether positive true-ground false or ground true-positive false, must follow a single convention for the two devices to effect the correct transfer of information from one device to the other. In addition to the ground true-positive false or positive true-ground false logic levels, it is also possible to have ground true-negative false or ground false-negative true, as well as ground true current-sinking logic. The user must also be aware that a variety of voltage and current requirements exists for various types of logic. These can be very incompatible with each other when he is attempting to interface equipment. The timing constraints of the logic are not usually specified by the manufacturer in the equipment data sheets. The logic levels and states may look compatible, but the timing may not allow proper interface operation. It is frequently not possible for the user to control or select the particular logic situations that will match each other directly from instrument to computer, or computer to recorder. Under these circumstances, designing a match between the two instruments is a necessary part of interfacing design.

INVERSION AND LEVEL CHANGING

A match of logic levels and states is usually achievable by using either inversion amplifiers or level-changing amplifiers or a combination of the two in some cases. In addition, voltage levels for either true or false signals may vary over a rather wide range, requiring either amplification of signals in order to effect a match

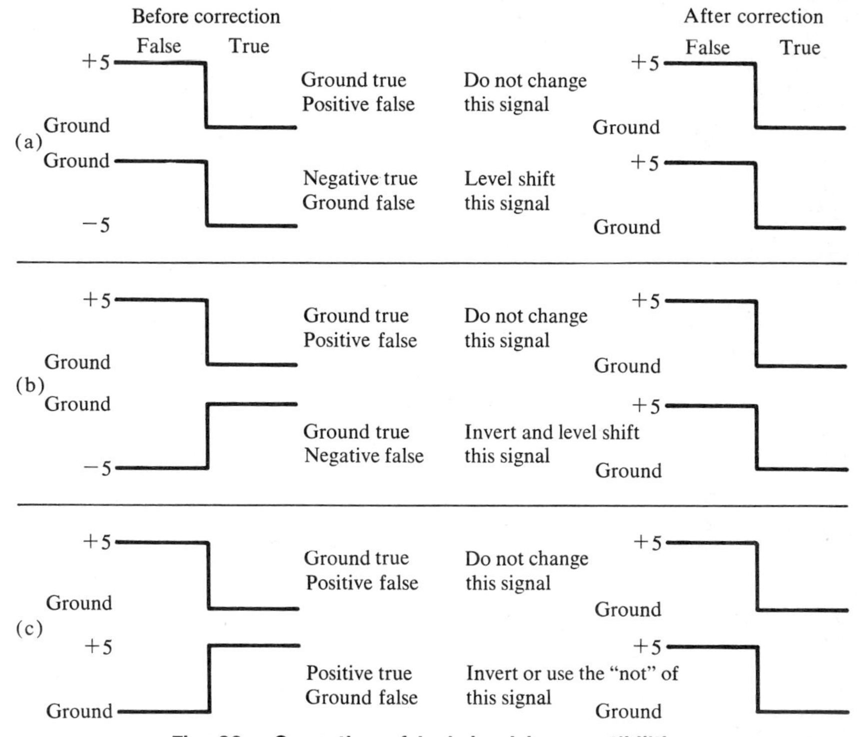

Fig. 20. Correction of logic-level incompatibilities.

or attenuation if an adequate signal level is available that can be reduced to a lower value, to effect an appropriate match.

Figure 20 shows three simple examples of logic-level incompatibilities and the indicated solutions. For simplicity of presentation and to convey the idea of matching, the logic levels are shown as 0 V and ±5 V. Figure 20*a* shows a ground true-positive false level interfaced to a negative true-ground false level. A level shifter, which shifts the level of the negative true-ground false signal more positive by the amount of the negative voltage, will result in establishing a compatible interface. Figure 20*b* shows a ground true-positive false level interfaced with a ground true-negative false level. In this case, both inversion and level shift of one or the other of the logic signals will result in establishing compatibility. The last example (Fig. 20*c*) shows a ground true-positive false signal being matched to a positive true-ground false signal. In this case, inversion is required unless a "not" output is available from the device outputting the data. The "not" condition is represented by a bar placed over the logic symbol. Thus $\overline{\text{true}}$ = not true, or the complement or inverse of True. If true and $\overline{\text{true}}$ signals are available, the user will apply the $\overline{\text{true}}$ signal output of the data source to the input of the other device, which will result in a compatible match.

In addition to the examples of digital-logic interfacing problems noted previously, appropriate attention must be paid to the types of logic which are being interfaced—whether the logic uses discrete components and transistors, or whether the logic is based on integrated circuits. This is important because various logic levels and supply voltages are applied and used in the different types of logic, raising the possibilities of applying excessive voltages, or inadequate signals, to the components being interfaced. Attention must be paid to switching thresholds and noise margins as well in order to have a reliable, consistent, and properly operating interface.*

Attention must also be given to whether the data being transferred appear in the form of short or long pulses, or whether they appear as a level change that remains in a given state until the next state is switched in, or until the state is cleared. The treatment of these conditions varies with the application, and so the user must be aware of what is happening in the system in order to realize a reliable interface. Control functions—such as programming commands, acknowledgment commands, encode or reset commands, or flag-setting commands—may operate on level shifts, state changes, or either the positive-going edge or the negative-going edge of a pulse.

It is therefore important to be aware of the detailed control requirements and, for example, to know whether the pulse is positive true or negative true or positive false or negative false in order to be certain that the proper edge of the pulse will be responded to by the control function being programmed. It is obvious that, if a particular control function is looking for the positive-going edge of a positive pulse in order to initiate a strobe command which would strobe data out of the system and, if instead, a negative-going pulse were used to trigger the strobe command and the positive-going edge did not appear until after the strobe was to appear, the data could be lost. The system design should also be such that the circuitry will be insensitive to noise pulses, but responsive to the desired pulses. This is done by causing the "legal" or desired pulses to have a high enough energy content so the receiving circuit can favor them against noise pulses which have low energy content.

The line and circuit impedances involved in the transfer of digital-logic signals in an interface are usually under 1,500 Ω and more generally in the range between 500 and 1,000 Ω. In cases where coaxial cables are being used for transmitting the information through the interface, the impedances will be set up to match the coaxial-cable impedances, which can vary from about 50 to 90 Ω.

TIMING CONSIDERATIONS

Another very important aspect of interfacing in the digital domain is the element of timing. All digital systems, regardless of their type or use, are always very critically dependent upon the timing relationships between the activities that are going on in the system. Virtually all digital systems require or contain some form of clock. This means that a train of timing pulses is generated within the system which controls the operation of all the elements of the system. The timing relationships within the system are very important because, typically, digital operations are sequential in nature—that is, 16-bit word transfers, for example, may take place with the 16 bits of one word transferred in parallel on 16 lines at once, followed by another 16-bit word transferred in parallel; or they may take place with the 16 bits transferred serially over one line, one bit at a time. In either case, the timing situation is

* The reader is referred to any of the semiconductor and integrated-circuit product catalogs and handbooks issued by the manufacturers of these products for comprehensive treatment and exhaustive information on the proper application, design, and use of the products.

very important because, if the bits do not appear on the lines at the exact time or within the stated time frame that they are supposed to be there, they are usually irrevocably lost and will not be transferred to the next step of the operation. All digital-logic elements require a finite period of time to respond to a switching command or stimulus. A change of state may be delayed from a few nanoseconds to several microseconds, depending on logic-switching speed and the number of logic elements in the switching sequence. This is known as the propagation delay of the circuit and must be allowed for in setting up system timing relationships.

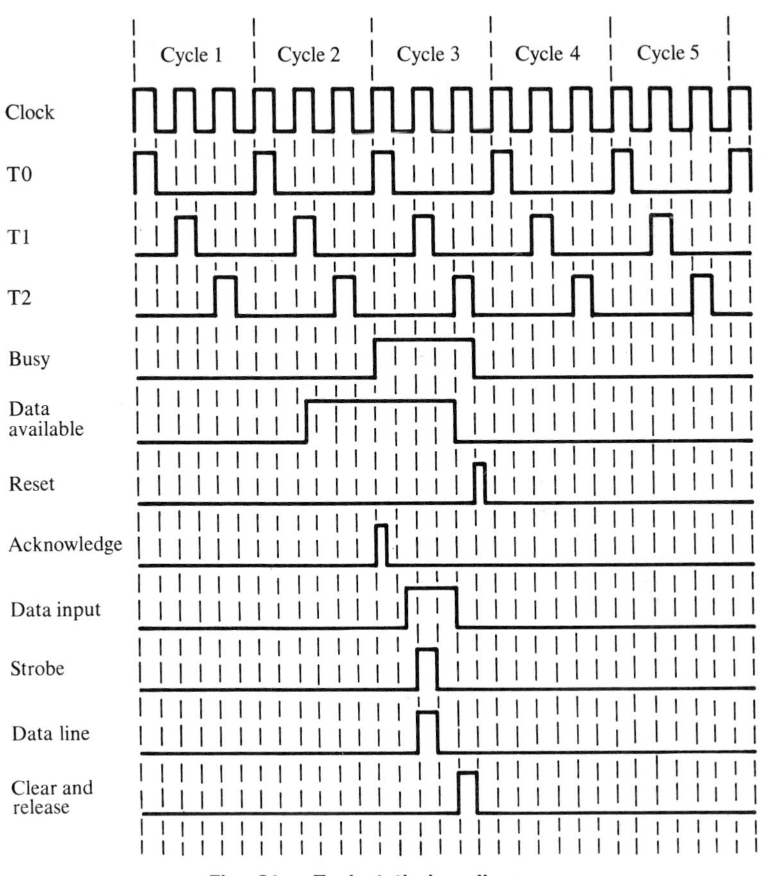

Fig. 21. Typical timing diagram.

18. Timing Diagram A timing diagram of the relationships as they might exist in a simple system is shown in Fig. 21. For purposes of clarity, allowances are not shown in the timing diagram for propagation delay. Instantaneous response is depicted. The timing relationships for 12 different functions are shown in this diagram. The first trace is the CLOCK trace, which shows the clock pulses generated by a clock generator. These are divided into cycles of three clock pulses each, with a total of five cycles shown. The operation of this system depends upon three different time phases which are derived from the train of clock pulses. These time phases are shown as T0, T1, and T2. Each time phase is associated with particular operations in the system.

The BUSY line and the ACKNOWLEDGE line are always caused to go high during time T0, if the DATA AVAILABLE line is high and the BUSY line is not already high because of some other activity in the system. Strobing of the data from the DATA INPUT to the DATA LINE takes place during time T1. When data from the DATA INPUT line have been strobed onto the DATA LINE during time T1, the CLEAR and RELEASE signal is generated during time T2 and the BUSY line goes down during the negative-going edge of time T2. The RESET signal is also initiated during the negative-going edge of time T2 and goes high for a short time and then low before the end of the cycle.

A typical data flow in this timing situation can be represented as follows: During cycle 2, the DATA AVAILABLE line goes high, indicating that data are available to the system. As responses to the DATA AVAILABLE line can occur only during time T0, the system waits until time T0 appears again in cycle 3. The system responds by making the BUSY line go high and issuing an ACKNOWLEDGE pulse during time T0. The ACKNOWLEDGE pulse goes out to the data source, letting the data source know that the system is now ready to accept the data. The data source puts the data on the DATA INPUT line prior to the beginning of time T1. The STROBE pulse is generated during time T1 to strobe the DATA INPUT from the device onto the DATA LINE of the digital system. Upon the completion of this strobing, a CLEAR and RELEASE pulse is generated during time T2. The DATA AVAILABLE line is cleared and the BUSY line goes down at the end of T2. A RESET signal is generated during the negative-going part of pulse T2, and the system is ready for the next operation, whatever it may be. This sort of timing diagram and the time relationships shown are representative of both computer-controlled and computerless digital systems.

It is important to note that the time intervals typical in a computer-controlled system can be quite short. The clock pulses, for example, can be in the order of fractions of a microsecond, which means that the total cycle time might be 1 or 2 μs. Under these conditions, it is easy to recognize the need for stringently observing the timing constraints, in order that the operations which must be performed by the system are, in fact, completed properly. Any unusual time delays or missed operations in the system can result in the data's not being properly transferred and, thus lost, resulting in improper operation of the system. The system needs to drop only one bit to cause utter chaos. In actual practice, the timing diagrams and relationships for typical computer systems are much more complex than the one just reviewed. However, the diagram shown here does serve to indicate the nature of the problem, in order to help the user understand the implications of correct timing in digital systems.

19. Synchronous, Asynchronous, and Paced Operations The system timing diagram shown is clock-controlled and thus considered to be a "synchronous" type of system. This means all internal system operations are carried out in strict reliance on, and in accord with, the timing requirements of the system and must be appropriately meshed together, or synchronized, to operate successfully. The data sources that may be connected to the system, however, can function "asynchronously," or not in synchronism, as long as the digital system provides a means for recognizing that the external device (such as an analog-to-digital converter or a digital voltmeter) needs service. Under these conditions, the user must be sure that the asynchronous operation of the device to be tied to the synchronous system has timing characteristics or buffering capabilities which are compatible with the time periods involved in the operation of the basic digital system. If the data source cannot respond in a way that can be meshed into the system operation, the device may require very costly interfacing circuitry and software, or may not be capable of being economically or satisfactorily interfaced.

Certain types of devices, such as analog-to-digital converters which may contain their own clock, are set up for free running operation. In other words, they will operate independently at their maximum rate of speed if permitted to do so. If the maximum repetitive, self-clocked, operating rate of the device is much higher than needed by the user or the system, time coherence of the data with respect to system timing can be achieved using other possibilities for operating control. The operation of the device may be paced either on a command basis manually by the user, or by a small pulse generator or pacer external to the system, or by command pulses from the system controlled by software. Any of these means will permit the user to operate the measuring instrument at lower speeds, but at regular sampling intervals.

PROGRAMMING OR SYSTEM CONTROL

The design and assembly of digitally controlled instrumentation systems yield one very desirable and valuable capability. This is that the system can usually be programmed. This is true whether the system is under computer control or under the control of a coupler/controller or an independent programming device.

A coupler/controller is a programmable modular device that enables communication and control, and provides means for coordinating and controlling the operation of a variety of digitally interfaceable instruments and equipment. Communication is accomplished with the use of a digital code and can be either unidirectional for just transferring data out to a peripheral, or bidirectional. The latter permits two-way transfers of data and program commands between instruments and peripherals.

The most flexible and thus useful coupler/controller permits bidirectional transfer of data and commands in the ASCII code. It can therefore be utilized as a remote terminal for a computer system with communications between coupler/controller and computer taking place in the standard ASCII code. Modular construction permits plugging in a wide variety of interface cards to configure a system. This is a valuable feature that makes the user's life easy.

20. Computerless Digital Systems In the case of computerless digitally controlled systems, it is possible to program the systems through a coupler/controller or simple programmer to perform desired functions by use of pinboard programming, "read only memory" programming, punched paper tape, punched cards, or magnetic-tape recording. With any of these media, the programming steps are usually very simple. There is a one-for-one correspondence between the programming steps and the operations which are to be performed. Every operation which the system must perform must be accounted for by a specific program step provided to command the system to perform the particular function.

The computerless digital system is of greatest value where calculation, computation, or manipulation of the data at the time that data are being taken are not required. The programming or control of the system is usually easily accomplished, and the output of the system can be recorded or printed or otherwise handled at the discretion of the user. Data from computerless systems are frequently recorded on computer-compatible digital magnetic tape for subsequent processing at a central computer facility. Computerless systems are generally, though not necessarily, slower than computer systems, and this must therefore be taken into consideration when the decision is being made as to the type of system to be acquired.

21. Computer-controlled Systems When a computer-controlled system is to be used, the programming to operate the system can usually be handled in any of the languages available for use with the particular computer. The lower-level language would be the binary 1s and 0s of the machine's own instruction codes. This is a programming means that is seldom used. The user may also program in assembly-level language, where one instruction or code word yields one machine instruction, or through any of the higher-level languages, such as FORTRAN, BASIC, or ALGOL, where one instruction statement or code word yields many machine instructions. The availability of special instrumentation programs for specific applications also makes the job of data acquisition or instrumentation, through the use of a computer-controlled system, very easy for the user.

Computer-controlled systems are used where very high speed operation is required, or where on-line acquisition and manipulation of the data are necessary. "On-line" manipulation means conversion to engineering units of raw data, such as that taken from thermocouples or the conversion of measurement units to engineering units or the calculation of performance, utilizing the acquired engineering data to yield a final desired result *while* the test is in operation.

An example of the latter might be the results derived from testing an internal-combustion engine. The operating temperatures, pressures, shaft speed, and torque output of the engine are all instrumented and connected to a computer-controlled data-acquisition system. The data are taken in typical measurement units, such as volts, and converted to engineering units, such as psi, rpm, degrees, or ft-lb, and then these engineering-unit figures are utilized in the computations which are performed during the test run or "on-line." These on-line calculations yield the final horsepower output and the efficiency of operation of the engine. Various types of laboratory processes or industrial processes also lend themselves well to the acquisition of data and their manipulation on-line in computer-controlled instrument-system applications.

Another application is automatic testing of electronic instruments and devices of various types, such as the characterization of microwave components. Calibration and computation of the performance capabilities of various other types of products are also well within the scope of a computer-controlled instrument system.

SEPARATION DISTANCES

In assembling digital instrumentation systems, one item which is frequently overlooked by the user is the factor of separation distances between the items of equipment which are going to be used and the effect of these distances on system operation. Generally speaking, most digital circuitry is operating at very high speeds; the pulses have fast rise and fall times, and so under ordinary conditions of use, the separation distance between various elements of equipment is kept quite short, usually under 20 ft. Most standard interfaces available from manufacturers of instruments and computers are designed for approximately this amount of separation distance.

If it is necessary to operate a digital device at some distance away from the computer, such as a few hundred to a few thousand feet, it becomes necessary to take special measures to assure that the pulse shapes are preserved and will be transmitted correctly, and in the correct time relationships to allow the system to function properly. Specially designed line drivers and receivers with special cables are usually required to transmit the digital information around at computer-system internal speeds.

If information is to be transmitted digitally at slower rates, it is possible to use standard alphanumeric communication codes. These can be handled with modem (modulator-demodulator) devices which are designed to transmit data at a variety of speeds (but rarely at computer-system internal speeds) over the common-carrier or private-line telephone networks. The requirements of each installation will affect the manner in which the problem is solved. The user should be aware that this type of problem and a variety of solutions for it do exist.

RECORDING REQUIREMENTS

An important consideration which must not be overlooked is the method by which the data to be acquired by the system will be recorded. The methods should be consistent with the type of system. If the system is all analog, then an analog recording technique should be used. If the system ends up with a digital output, there are several types of digital-data-recording devices which can be considered.

22. Analog Recording The most common type of analog recorder used in industry and in the laboratory is the strip-chart recorder, also known as a graphic recorder, potentiometric recorder, or servo-type recorder. In this recorder, a chart-transport mechanism moves paper over a platen on which a pen is in turn moved to record the analog information. The pen movement is controlled by a servo-driven system, usually utilizing a null-balance principle for the operation of the servo-drive. Recorders of this type may typically be expected to yield recorded representations of slowly time-varying dc data accurate to between a tenth and a quarter of 1 percent of the full-scale range of the recorder.

Another type of analog recorder frequently found in the laboratory is the *X-Y* recorder. The paper usually remains fixed in this recorder, and the pen is moved in two dimensions to trace out the data being recorded. As in the first recorder discussed, a pen movement is controlled by servosystems; in this case, one for each axis of motion. The servos usually utilize the null-balance principle of operation and yield accuracies similar to the strip-chart recorder just discussed. Variations of this type of recorder are available, in which the pen and the paper are both moved under servocontrol to plot complicated data patterns.

Another is the ink oscillographic recorder. Again, a chart drive is used to drive paper past a given point, and a pen mounted on a d'Arsonval type of moving-coil pen-drive motor writes the information on the surface of the paper. These types of recorders are available with pen-motor operation in both open-loop and closed-loop servo configurations. Because the chart width in these recorders is usually rather narrow, as opposed to the previous recorders mentioned, the accuracy is limited by the width of the inked line as well as the characteristics of the galvanometer drive motor. The accuracies of representations for this type of recorder are in the range of 1 to 2 percent of the full-scale range. A variation of this type of recorder replaces the pen with a heated stylus and special heat-sensitive paper. Still another variation uses an electrical-contact stylus on electrosensitive paper.

The optical oscillographic recorder is another instrument for recording values of analog voltages. In this device, a photosensitive or light-sensitive paper is again driven by a paper drive past a zone where light beams reflected from mirrors mounted on small galvanometer motors trace out the data information on the paper. The paper is then "developed" in the photographic sense or, in the case of ultraviolet-light-sensitive paper, by intensification. Oscillographs can come in a variety of paper widths and channel capacities. Generally speaking, they are most useful when many channels of data other than dc levels are to be recorded in time correlation. In these instances, the user wants to see the ac representation or the waveform or variation of dc data being derived from an instrument. Accuracies of these types of recorders can range from 2 to 5 percent of full-scale sensitivity.

Each of these four basic recorders provides the user with a line trace whose amplitude can be measured in order to determine the value of the data recorded thereon. Numerous variations of these four types of recording instruments can be encountered in instrumentation applications.

It is frequently desirable, and in many cases necessary, to be able to record analog data in such a way that they can be retrieved or reproduced in electrical form again. The most common and useful way of achieving this is through the use of magnetic recording. There are basically two methods of magnetic recording available for analog applications.

The first is known as direct recording, where only information of an ac nature will be used or is needed, and where dc values are not important. Where the dc value or the base-line value of the data must be recovered, it is necessary to employ the second method of recording, which will permit the recovery of the dc data. This is the so-called FM type of recording system.*

In the case of the direct recording method, the ac data are recorded directly on the tape track and retrieved directly by playback. The accuracy of the amplitude information contained in direct recording is a function of the frequency response of the recorder and can vary over a considerable range because of many effects. Typical variations in response of the recorded information are 1 to 3 dB. The decibel is a poor unit of measure for instrumentation accuracy and is usually utilized only in audio or video recording. A rough translation would be that 1 dB represents approximately a 10 percent variation. It can therefore be seen that for recording

* For a comprehensive review of analog magnetic recording technology, the reader is referred to Skipwith W. Athey, "Magnetic Tape Recording," National Aeronautics and Space Administration Publication, NASA SP-5038, Government Printing Office, Washington, D.C., 1966.

audio-frequency data signals by direct recording, precision much better than 10 to 30 percent is not too likely.

In the FM system of magnetic recording, a frequency-modulated carrier is recorded on the tape at some high frequency within the frequency-response band of the recorder, and that carrier is frequency-modulated by the information that it is desired to record. As a result of the frequency modulation, it is possible to recover the dc component of the data as well as the dynamic, or ac, component. Well-constructed and properly maintained FM magnetic instrumentation recorders are capable of accuracies of data reproduction in the range of 1 to 2 percent.

23. Digital Recording There are many ways of recording information in a digital format. The most commonly used of these are the punched card and punched paper tape. The most commonly used punched card has a 12-level code known as the Hollerith code. Eighty columns or 80 characters of alphanumeric information can be recorded by punching coded hole patterns in the punched card.

Punched paper tape is very commonly used, and today the most common is the 8-level ASCII coded punched paper tape. The paper tape that the user gets from a Teletype machine is punched in ASCII code. The 8-level punched paper tape provides recording capability for a full alphanumeric character set, as well as a parity bit, thus occupying all 8 levels of the tape. In certain types of recording where only numeric and certain special characters must be handled, it is possible to have 7-, 6-, and 5-level punched paper tape. Either the punched card or the punched paper tape may be read in a reader, thus permitting full automatic retrieval of the data from the record without the necessity for any human intervention other than the loading of the recording media into the appropriate reader.

Another type of digital readout or digital recording is data characters printed on paper. This is of greatest value if the user does not intend to process the information after it is recorded in printed form. The variety of printers available is quite large—ranging from small, 10-column, numeric-only printers, typical of adding-machine-tape output, through variations going up to 132-column full alphanumeric character-set printers spewing out paper at the rate of hundreds of lines per minute.

Other commonly used media for the recording of digital data involve the use of magnetic recording techniques on digitally formatted magnetic tape, magnetic cards, and magnetic disks. In all these methods, the digital signals are converted to electrical signals in an appropriate format. These are then recorded as bits of information in the magnetic domain on the magnetic medium such as tape, card, or disk. The tapes, cards, or disks can then be read using conventional magnetic recording techniques and the output can be played back into a digital system for further processing of the data. Magnetic tape and disk are the most commonly used media in instrumentation digital data recording.

Magnetic-tape recording of digital data probably provides the best long-term file capability with the greatest number of bits of storage per unit of cost (approximately 200 million bits on a 2,400-ft roll of 9-track tape recorded at an 800 bit per inch density). However, a magnetic tape is not easily searched for information, particularly in terms of quick retrieval. If a piece of data is located in the middle of a roll of tape, it is necessary to read that tape in the magnetic playback device until the portion of the tape is reached that contains the data (access time, approximately 3 min at 75 in./s). A magnetic disk, on the other hand, typically does not have as much data-storage capacity as tape (12 to 24 million bits for a large single disk to 150 million bits on a removable disk file) but usually offers a much faster retrieval time (17 to 100 ms on average), thus permitting the user to gain access to his data in about the amount of time it takes for a disk to turn one revolution and a particular track to be selected.

READOUTS AND DISPLAYS

While the data are being recorded on a medium in either analog or digital form, it is frequently necessary for the instrument-system user to have a readout or a display of the data, either as they are being recorded, or after they have been processed in the computer to yield a desired answer. In the analog domain, the graphic recorders discussed earlier usually contain a calibrated scale and a pointer to indicate the magnitude of the reading that is being recorded on the strip chart. A simple meter indicator can frequently be used, depending upon the application. In the case of systems reading analog data and converting them to digital form, the digital voltmeter with its typical numerical display provides information about the magnitude of the signal. However, in the latter case, if the data are being taken rapidly—say, 10, 20, 30, or 40 readings per second—the voltmeter display will, in all probability, be changing so rapidly that the operator will not be able to get a useful reading.

Digital displays include the use of illuminated or projection-type display devices. These switch on lamps behind the character to be displayed. Gaseous-discharge tubes are also used—in which electrodes inside the tube, formed in the shape of the numerals to be presented, are energized as required, thus causing the selected numeral to glow. Solid-state electroluminescent alphanumeric-character displays are also used. The cathode-ray tube terminal is becoming popular in the area of real-time displays, particularly in digital systems, where substantial interaction is necessary between the operator and the system.

Other much simpler and less sophisticated displays will frequently suffice to indicate the extent of a particular control requirement. Annunciators, for example, operated by signals from the computer, alarm bells, or other similar means, can signal off-normal operation. In addition, the experienced user can frequently derive significant information from the bit patterns present on the register displays of the digital system. As he works with the system, he becomes familiar with particular operating modes and particular patterns and rhythms in the displays of registers, and these can reflect the operational status of the system.

Chapter 19

Instrument System Design

EUGENE L. MLECZKO

Hewlett-Packard Company, Palo Alto, California

DEFINING SYSTEM NEEDS

1. Operating Requirements for System Assuming the user has a full and complete understanding of the instrumentation problem that is confronting him and the measurements he needs, the first step in defining a system is to specify the operating requirements for that system. These should encompass the types of measurements to be made, the quantity of these measurements—or the number of instrumentation channels needed—the measurement precision, the speed of data acquisition, and the operating environment (temperature, humidity, vibration, shock, altitude, or any other anticipated parameters), which could adversely affect the operation of the instrument system. It is also necessary to specify how the data are to be manipulated within the system, whether they are going to be operated on directly in a computer or be recorded on some intervening medium, which

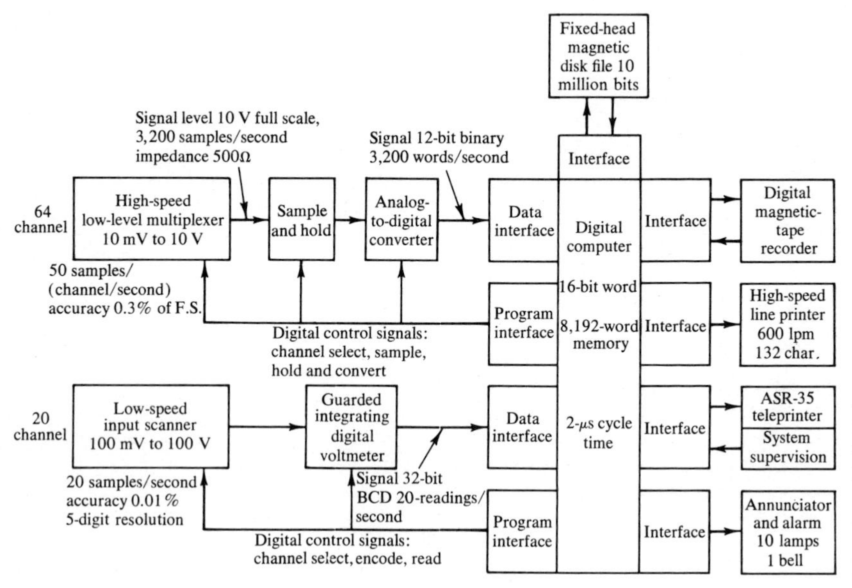

Fig. 1. System block diagram.

will then be removed and sent on to a central data-processing facility for further processing.

The various types of signal-conditioning equipment needed to achieve the required level of system operation, as well as the computer equipment if a computer system is to be put together, and all the required computer peripherals—such as line printers, tape punches, tape readers, card readers, magnetic-tape readers, and disks—all these things should be set forth as part of a written operating requirement for the system.

2. Block Diagram With the operating requirements defined, the next step is the preparation of the system block diagram. Block diagrams can be simple in scope or complex, depending upon their use. The usual block diagram will identify the various functional items required in the instrument system, usually with one block per function. It may also show the signal levels, the line quantities, and the many special interfacing considerations which must be kept in mind when putting all the items of the system together.

A typical block diagram for a small system is shown in Fig. 1. This block diagram provides a representation for all the major functional pieces of equipment. First, it will be noted on the left-hand side of the block diagram that a block of 64 channels of data will be handled, with a voltage range from 10 mV to 10 V full scale on the input. It is required that each channel be sampled fifty times per second and that the accuracy of the data acquisition should be better than three-tenths of 1 percent. The signals are expected to be very slowly varying dc levels. Another 20 channels of input data requiring 5-digit resolution and 0.01 percent accuracy over a range of 100 mV to 100 V, with a sampling rate of 20 channels per second, are also needed. The data are to be primarily dc.

The block diagram shows one low-level multiplexer, one sample and hold unit, and one analog-to-digital converter set up to handle the 64 channels of relatively high speed data. This group of equipment with the associated computer interfaces constitutes one subsystem. One low-speed input scanner and an integrating guarded digital voltmeter will be used for the 20 channels of 5-digit resolution data. These items with their associated computer interfaces constitute the other data-acquisition subsystem. The total required input capacity is for 84 channels of data.

Each of the data-acquisition subsystems requires a data interface to transfer the data that are acquired from the instruments to the computer and a program interface for control of the instruments by the computer.

Typically in the high-speed case, the computer would send out a control word telling the low-level multiplexer (LLMPX) to switch to a particular channel. After the low-level multiplexer complies, the sample and hold unit would be switched on, and the sample taken. After switching to hold, the analog-to-digital converter would be given the command to convert the information from analog to digital and then transmit it to the computer through the data-transfer interface. The LLMPX would then be switched to the next channel and the process repeated.

Similarly, the program interface control would select a particular channel in the low-speed input scanner. Upon arriving at that channel, it would feed the voltage to the integrating digital voltmeter, which would, in turn, take a reading and output it through the data-transfer interface to the computer.

The computer would then operate on the data in accordance with the user's program. This might utilize the magnetic-disk file for temporary data storage—and also perhaps for some subroutine-program storage. It could utilize the magnetic-tape digital recorder to record the data coming in from the data-acquisition subsystems. The high-speed line printer could print out computed results on a selected basis, and the annunciator and alarm panel would serve to indicate any off-limit conditions. The teleprinter would be used primarily for supervisory control of the system and for supervisory messages being typed out by the computer to the system operator. No test data would have to appear on the Teletype unless the operator so requested.

If computational capability were not required by the user in this particular case, it would be possible to substitute a coupler/controller for the computer and to eliminate some of the computer-related peripherals. The data would probably be recorded on the magnetic-tape digital recorder for subsequent processing in a central data processing location elsewhere.

3. System-component Specifications At this point, the user is ready to set down, in appropriate detail, the required specifications for the various components of the system. Assuming that all the requirements have been firmed up, the user can then decide what particular parameters or functional specifications each item of hardware requires. The ensuing list demonstrates some representative specifications. The criteria used to decide on the specific performance characteristics listed are beyond the scope of this book and are very dependent on the user's specific problem.

Beginning with the computer, the following might be typical specifications: memory size—8,192 words, expandable in the main frame to 32,768 words; word size—16 bits; memory-cycle time—2 μs; instruction-execution speed—store a word 4 μs; add—4 μs; multiply—25 μs; divide—25 μs. The computer should have multilevel indirect addressing. Direct memory access should be available at a maximum transfer rate of 500,000 words per channel per second. At least 16 levels of priority interrupt should be provided. The computer should be able to withstand environmental conditions of +10 to +40°C with relative humidity of up to 80 percent at +40°C. Available software should include FORTRAN, BASIC, and ALGOL compilers, as well as an assembler and a real-time executive operating system.

The low-level multiplexer for the system should accept up to 64 channels of information over a signal range of 10 mV to 10 V full scale. The sampling speed should permit looking at the 64 channels at least fifty times for each channel per second. This is a minimum overall sampling rate of 3,200 samples per second. The accuracy of measurements of the data to be handled by the low-level multiplexer should not be degraded beyond 0.3 percent of full scale. The data to be measured will be a very slowly varying dc voltage. The low-level multiplexer should be capable of being programmed by the computer for channel and gain selection to handle the incoming signal properly.

The sample and hold unit should be controllable by the computer and should have an aperture time no greater than 50 ns and a hold time of 5 ms for less than 0.02 percent droop. The analog-to-digital converter should also be controlled from the computer, should have a resolution of 12 bits including sign, and should be capable of accepting bipolar signals. Its accuracy of conversion should be better than 0.1 percent. A data-transfer interface and a program interface for control of the analog-to-digital converter, sample and hold, and low-level multiplexer that are compatible with the measuring components and the computer should be provided.

The low-speed input scanner should accept up to 100 channels of data. Full-scale input-signal-handling capability should be 100 mV to 100 V, with any degradation due to thermal effects limited to less than 1.0 μV at 25°C. It should be capable of operating at sampling rates up to 40 channels per second. The scanner should have a guard connection which will permit the carrying through of a guarded input from the input circuitry of the scanner to the guarded input of the integrating digital voltmeter. The scanner should be capable of being programmed by the computer for channel selection.

The integrating guarded digital voltmeter will have input ranges of 0.1, 1, 10, and 100 V, with a precision of five full digits with a rollover sixth digit. Overranging capability should be to at least 120 percent of full scale. Resolution of the voltmeter should be to 1 μV on the 100-mV range. The accuracy of the voltmeter should be at least 0.01 percent of reading ±0.005 percent of full scale on any range. Its common-mode rejection will be at least 160 dB at dc and 120 dB at 60 Hz with a 1,000-Ω unbalance. It should be capable of a measuring speed of at least 40 measurements per second on any range at the specified resolution and accuracy. The voltmeter should operate over a temperature range of +10 to +40°C with a relative humidity up to 90 percent at +40°C. The voltmeter should be digitally programmable in binary and should have a binary-coded decimal output for transferring data to the computer. A data-transfer interface and a program interface for control of the voltmeter-scanner combination that are compatible with both the voltmeter-scanner and the computer should be provided.

The computer should have available as standard peripherals a magnetic-disk-file for high-speed transfer of information with a storage capability of up to 10 million bits and an access time less than 50 ms; a magnetic-tape digital recorder with a tape capacity of 2,400-ft rolls and with tape speeds up to 75 in./s, and packing densities up to 800 bits per inch; a high-speed line printer capable of handling fan-fold paper at 600 lines per minute with up to 132 characters per line; and a standard ASR 35 heavy-duty teleprinter. An annunciator and alarm panel with 10 lamps and one bell—for indicating out-of-limit conditions on the system—are required along with an appropriate interface.

All the specifications outlined above for the items of the block diagram are ostensibly the most important to the proper operation of the system. The user must be careful not to overspecify his requirements, as this can lead to as many difficulties as underspecifying. In some cases it can be more difficult, because it also results in unnecessary costs. In setting up the specifications, the system components should be specified as clearly and concisely as possible.

Successful operation of the system will hinge on the adequacy of the capabilities of the computer and measurement components. Stimulus components—such as signal sources, audio-frequency generators, radio-frequency generators, signal generators, sweepers, and power supplies—should all be specified. Response components and their modes of operation—voltmeters, receivers, detectors, analog-to-digital converters—also require complete definition. Control components such as contact closures, contact sensors, alarm outputs, and annunciator outputs also are subject to specification, as are readouts and displays of various types. The data-recorder specifications outline the method in which the recorder will be expected to function to meet the requirements of the user's system.

4. Component Availability When the user has determined the basic system block diagram, the operating requirements, and the basic specifications for the system components, he is ready to determine the availability of components to do his particular job. The user is primarily concerned with hardware and software elements for the system. It is here that the user should start contacting component manufacturers to determine if standard components are available for the various defined functions. Software requirements also enter the picture when a computer or a programmable coupler/controller is in the system. With a complete file of manufacturer's data sheets, catalog sheets, information bulletins, and application notes, the user is ready for the next step.

5. Engineering Considerations The user can now begin the engineering consideration of the assembled information (not an easy task). He must evaluate the performance specifications of the pieces of hardware available from the various vendors. He must evaluate the interface requirements between hardware pieces and determine which items of equipment are compatible. He may find that some of his specifications are impractical; he must make compromises to assemble a viable working system within the overall system concept. Perhaps he may have to rethink the concept, to be sure nothing has been overlooked and nothing extraneous has been required of the system. It may be necessary for the user to define certain custom-built interfaces that will allow different items of equipment to work together. This is particularly true if the instrument of one manufacturer is going to be used with the computer of another and, perhaps, with the scanner of a third, and so on. At this point, the user is doing his own system-design work. When he has all the information assembled, the drawings prepared, and a working system completely defined, with all the design data needed to assure successful system function, he is ready to consider the manufacturing and assembly requirements.

6. Manufacturing/Assembly Considerations The manufacturing and assembly of a system is no small task. If the user happens to be an electronic engineer or has an electronic-engineering facility available to him elsewhere in his company, it is possible that he can put the system together "in house." To do this, however, it is necessary to recognize that particular engineering talents and software talents are needed "in house," and if they are not available, they must be developed. People must either be hired to do the job, or individuals already in the organization may require some training and additional experience in order to accomplish the work that needs to be done. A part of the manufacturing and assembling considerations is involved in establishing how the function of system integration and testing gets accomplished. To do these things "in house" usually necessitates establishing internal documentation, drawing, software, and technical-manual standards for accomplishing and recording the work in an orderly, retrievable, and reproducible manner.

7. System Integration and Testing When all the elements of the system are built, and various interfaces constructed and checked out, it is necessary to assemble or integrate the entire system into a working whole—to utilize the hardware and the software together and test the system to see that it does, in fact, perform in the way intended. In this situation, the user is frequently confronted with testing unknown or newly designed hardware interfaces, with unknown or newly written and probably undebugged software. When a problem appears, it is not always easy to isolate whether the problem is in the hardware or in the software. Human nature enters the picture: The programmer will invariably assert that the problem is in the hardware, while the hardware designer will claim that the software programmer did not write the program properly. The result is a difficult, time-consuming, and costly conflict. If this situation appears possible in the user's working environment where the system will be assembled and tested, it might be prudent to consider a possible alternative.

8. The Packaged-system Concept Many instrument and system manufacturers offer what are known as "data-sheeted standard systems" or "packaged systems," which may very closely approximate what the user needs in the system he has defined. The user would thus be well advised to consider seriously the merits of buying a standard system essentially off the shelf, from a supplier who either has the system available as a standard design or may be willing to put together certain modifications of standard systems components into a custom or semicustom system. There is much to be said for this approach. It saves the user a lot of trouble. The engineering effort expended by the manufacturer in defining the standard system is usually quite comprehensive, because the costs can be amortized over a quantity of systems. The engineering package is usually more complete, and probably better than could be done by the user, if he is not experienced or skilled in this kind of work.

If instruments from a number of different manufacturers are needed in the user's original system configuration, there is a lot of merit to purchasing a system from a single supplier. One vendor then has the complete responsibility. Where divided responsibility exists for a system, human nature again enters the picture. One supplier points at the other and says, "Well, my equipment is all right, so it has to be his component that is not working properly" or some such helpful comment. The inexperienced user thus gets a wonderful opportunity to get a lot of instant, on-the-job experience. Once the user has considered all these possibilities, engineering and otherwise, he is ready to start thinking in terms of the economic factors.

SYSTEM ECONOMICS

9. Cost Estimates So far, we have discussed the technical aspects of assembling an instrument system. But what about the costs, the economics? This is a very important element, not to be overlooked. Usually, the user's management will require some form of cost estimate—some indication of how much money it is going to take to put together the system that the user needs. Management will want this information to evaluate if the function performed will indeed be useful to the organization and if the investment in the system will result in a suitable return. Questions such as whether it will also provide a cost savings or an increased profit or will yield lower manufacturing costs must be answered.

In preparing the cost estimate, it is good practice to establish a format for the orderly listing of all the elements of cost. It should allow for extension of unit prices for the purchased hardware, for the purchased software, for any options, for special engineering, for special modifications of standard hardware, for special component costs, for system-integration costs, and finally for the installation charges. Figure 2 presents a suggested labor-cost-estimating format, and Fig. 3 a suggested material-cost-estimating format.

10. Standard Component Costs Component costs can usually be obtained from the vendor's catalog of equipment and price lists usually supplied by the vendor's salesmen. Standard options to catalog equipment are usually also priced. Their costs are added to the basic component costs when the option is included. An option installed in the factory prior to delivery of the basic equipment may cost substantially less than when it is ordered after delivery of the basic equipment and installed on site. Therefore, required options on standard-equipment items should be planned well in advance.

11. Special Component Costs Any component costs involving special features or modifications of standard components or special functions, such as special interfaces to operate between two pieces of equipment built by different manufacturers, usually must be derived on a request for bid and quote basis, if the work is to be done outside the user's organization. It can be a risky undertaking for the user to attempt to estimate these himself, particularly if he is inexperienced. Special engineering costs associated with the development of specials or components should be included in the cost of the special components.

12. Engineering Costs The engineering costs associated with assembling a system of standard and/or nonstandard components can vary widely, dependent upon the complexity of the components, interfaces, and required system functions. In estimating engineering costs, it is best to identify in detail every engineering effort that must be performed in defining, designing, manufacturing, assembling, and testing the system. Some of the functions related to this effort include administration of the systems project; documentation of design in drawings, material lists, process specifications, test procedures, and manuals; design and manufacturing costs of special jigs, fixtures, and test equipment; purchasing; and incoming and in-process inspection procedures. When the total number of man-hours is determined and man-hour costs (including overhead and other related charges) are extended, the user will have the total engineering cost for the system.

Typical engineering costs expressed as a percentage of purchased hardware cost can range from 10 percent to as much as 35 percent, with an average engineering cost in the vicinity of 20 to 25 percent. Extremes have ranged as high as 200 percent. The cost of integration and testing of all the hardware involved in the system is in addition to the engineering costs.

13. Software Costs Software costs are difficult to estimate at best. The cost depends upon the amount of software to be written for the system, the nature of the operations to be performed, and the amount of standard operating software that is available from the computer manufacturer. This latter point is quite important, as standard debugged and vendor-supported software can be worth its weight in gold to the instrument-system user. Many a man has chosen a low-cost computer, only to find that the money he saved was on the software he did not get. It is not unusual for the software investment to equal 50 to 100 percent of the basic cost of the system hardware, including the hardware engineering. The cost can go much higher if standard operating software is not available. This is a cost factor that is not often recognized by novice users of computer-controlled instrument systems. The awakening to this fact can be a traumatic and dismal experience.

There are some estimating guidelines which can be applied to software costs. However, the user must determine how many lines of code or how many machine-language or assembly-language instructions will be needed in the program. If the user can successfully define the size of the program that must be written, he can then apply the guideline that an experienced programmer of average capability can generate from five to seven lines of flow-charted, documented, debugged, and operating code per day.

It is important that this guideline be properly interpreted. In writing a program, the programmer must first familiarize himself with the computer for which the program is to be written, as well as all the standard software available for that computer. He must consider the alternative methods of attack available for solution of the programming problem. He must then select what appears to be the most promising approach and prepare an external reference specification for the program. He then begins flow-charting the program. (Flow charts are to a software programmer what a state road map is to a driver. It points the general direction and gives the big picture of the program.) When the flow charting is complete, the programmer commences actually writing the program in the selected language. When this writing or coding is completed, the programmer is ready to put the

Instrument system—Cost estimating form—Labor					Date:
System name:			Est. By:		Est. No.
Labor cost element	Hours	Rate	Subtotals	Totals	
Engineering Administration Definition Design Drafting Material lists Process specifications Test procedures Manuals					
Software Flow charting Coding Debugging Documentation Manuals					
Purchasing Specifications Quotations Bid evaluation Vendor evaluation Expediting					
Manufacturing Staging Prefabrication Assembly Jigs and fixtures In-process inspection					
Integration and testing Interface testing Verification tests Software tests System tests					
Installation Building modifications Utilities Signal circuits System equipment					
Miscellaneous					
Total direct labor dollars				$	
Overhead rate percent × direct labor dollars				$	
Grand total labor cost—direct labor + overhead =				$	

Fig. 2. Cost-estimating format—labor.

Instrument system—Cost estimating form—Material				Date:
System name:		Est. By:		Est. No.
Material cost element	Quantity	Unit cost	Extension	Totals
Response instruments Amplifiers Scanners multiplexers A/D converters Voltmeters Counters Analyzers				
Stimulus instruments Power supplies Signal generators Pulse generators Synthesizers				
Conditioning equipment Excitation sources Calibrate units Balance units Filters				
Digital programmers Coupler/controllers Computers Interfaces for either				
Peripherals Graphic recorders Analog magnetic tape Teleprinters Strip or line printers Digital magnetic tape Paper-tape punch Paper-tape reader Magnetic disk files				
Displays Digital-alphanumeric Cathode-ray tube				
Instrumentation and control cable Paired-single and multi-nonpaired				
Modifications and specials				
Miscellaneous				
Total direct material dollars				$
Overhead rate percent × direct material dollars				$
Grand total material cost—direct material + overhead =				$

Fig. 3. Cost-estimating format—material.

program into the computer to begin checking and debugging it. If his choice of approach to the solution of the programming problem was correct, he will successfully debug his program and get it running. If not successful, he starts over.

If successful, the programmer will turn the program over to another programmer to verify correct operation and quality of the program. The originating programmer is responsible for writing full documentation, correct listings (the listing is to a programmer what a city map is to a driver; it provides the specific details of what is called for in the program), and an operation manual for the program. When this is all completed, the final number of lines of code in the program are divided by the total number of man-days of effort expended in performing the tasks noted earlier. The result is the figure of lines of flow-charted, documented, debugged, and operating code generated per day by the programmer.

The debugging, flow charting, and documenting of software are all very important requirements. The user should never permit a program to be written without receiving the flow charts for that program, along with all the information relative to the program fully documented. It is also useful to have some record of the history of the debugging procedures that were gone through by the programmer in getting his program to work.

The five to seven lines of code per working day mentioned earlier are for an average programmer of average capability. There are programmers who can generate 10 to 15 lines of code per day, and there are some who may not even reach 5 lines of code per day. Applying the user's man-day cost for programming according to these guidelines will give some idea of what can be expected when it comes to determining the costs of software. A line of code is defined as a statement in BASIC, FORTRAN, or ALGOL (or a single assembly-language instruction), including comments for each line of code as appropriate for documentation.

14. System-integration Costs Systems integration encompasses all the activity needed to verify performance of the various components of the system, their interaction with each other, and the ultimate performance of the system as a single problem-solving or applications unit. System integration and assembly costs are not usually of very large magnitude. Depending upon the complexity of the system and the amount of work allocated to the manufacturing function, the amount of work required for system integration will range from 5 to 10 percent of the value of the hardware in the system. This does not include engineering or software costs previously discussed.

15. Installation Costs Finally, the installation needs to be considered, particularly if the system requires special utility runs, special physical installation such as a raised floor, or large amounts of floor space.

Floor Space. The floor space required by a system, frequently overlooked as a cost item, can represent a substantial related expense. Construction costs for industrial-plant floor space can range from \$25 to \$50 per square foot, depending upon the type of construction and the general use of the facility. If the instrument system is going to be installed in a new plant, that plant must be built sufficiently large to accommodate it. If the system requires 1,000 ft.^{2} of floor space at \$50 per square foot, the cost of the floor space is \$50,000. This is not an insignificant sum to be overlooked when reviewing the requirements and the costs for the overall facility. A typical instrument-system floor plan is shown in Fig. 4.

Utilities. Both power and air conditioning represent substantial expenditures if required in large quantities. Small instrument systems may not require any special utility runs. If the system is going to be large, utilities can represent a substantial cost. Power-service requirements in excess of 10 kW are not uncommon.

Signal Runs. Where the data to be recorded are being run long distances (500 to 1,000 ft), the costs of cable, cable trays, junction boxes, and perhaps a cable tunnel or duct bank can add up to a very large sum of money. This situation would exist with a test stand isolated from its data-acquisition equipment and operators because of the hazardous tests performed.

Installation. The physical installation of all this equipment, the cable, the instrumentation system itself, and any other related items requires the utilization of craft labor—a costly item.

When the user has completed his consideration of all these elements of cost, he may find that the total installed cost of a checked-out operating system can be 2 to 2½ times the basic cost of the system hardware. Under these conditions, and with these kinds of cost factors, the user is well advised to consider the system "make or buy" decision.

16. To Make or To Buy The user may decide that the costs identified here are so high that he can save money by doing the system "in house." It is possible but not probable that he will save money. If the user has skilled people on hand who know how to do this sort of work, who can write software, who are familiar with interfacing and computer technology, and who do not have anything

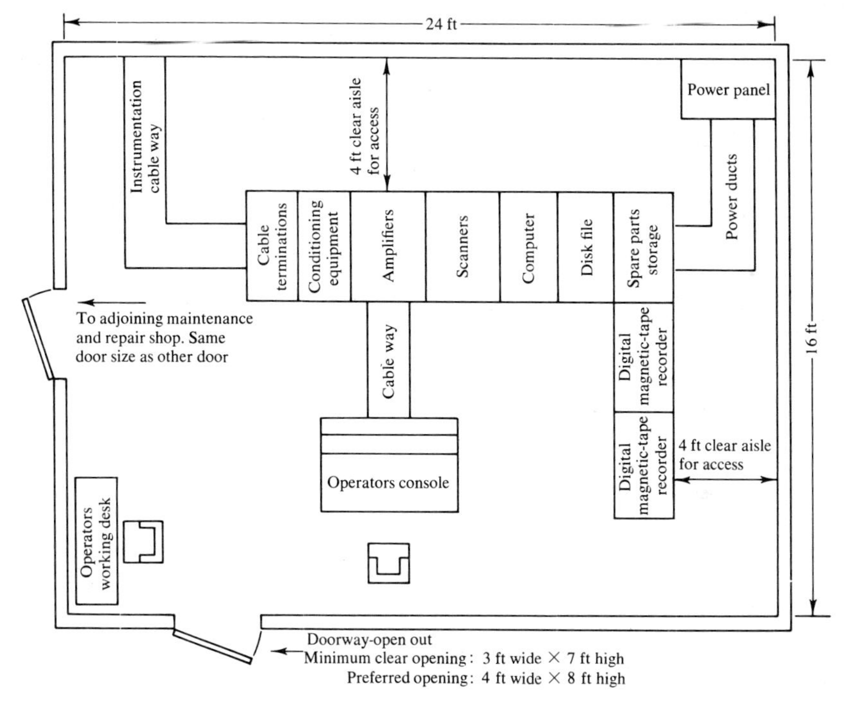

Fig. 4. Typical instrument-system floor plan.

to do anyway, then it is possible. However, the value of a warranty from a reputable manufacturer of systems will not be available to the "in-house" system builder. Or, it may be that the user wishes to develop a capability and a cadre of people with systems expertise, allowing a part of the system investment to be written off to training. Again, the advantage of a vendor's warranty on the system is missing. Any one of these factors can provide reasonable justification to a user to go ahead and make the system himself; however, the cost of overhead, and other indirect costs, including loss of use of people for potentially more profitable pursuits, and diversion of management attention from day-to-day business—which may not be directly associated with the development of the system—should not be overlooked. When all the hidden costs are added together, it is probably more expensive to make a system than it is to buy.

17. Make When the user has decided that he wants to make his own system, he should be no less severe in meeting his own specifications whether the decision has been to build "in house" or not. He must of necessity pay attention to every detail and be completely thorough in his effort. Considerable patience is needed, as the possible combinations for causing trouble are great. It is virtually impossible for the novice instrument-system designer to foresee every pitfall, until the system is actually in operation and the experience is behind him.

18. Buy After consideration of all the factors and alternatives has led the user to the decision to buy the system rather than to make it, several factors need to be considered and actions taken in order to achieve a successful buy.

Specifications. The user should prepare a complete and comprehensive set of specifications for the system requirements. These should be based upon what a vendor can supply. Having gone through the engineering evaluation of data sheets on all available types of hardware, the user should be able to prepare a specification for a system which can be met by a vendor without unusual or unnecessary difficulty. The user should be careful not to overspecify any particular system function. It is certainly acceptable and even desirable to specify growth capability or expansion into the system where it is possible to project such a future need. Certainly, operating characteristics which are not really required should not be requested, since they could add to the cost of the system.

A very common mistake, to be avoided at all costs, is the combination of the best features from a number of vendor's specifications into the user's specifications, in an attempt to get the best possible component, such as a computer, for example. This invariably results in a specification with an inherent fatal flaw. It cannot be met by any vendor. Every equipment manufacturer makes "tradeoffs" in deciding the type of product he will offer and the features the product will have. It is often just not possible to incorporate all the good features of all the best available products in one single product. As a matter of fact, some features can be mutually incompatible and thus not permit such a combination to be provided. When that kind of situation appears in a specification, most vendors quickly recognize it and interpret it as a sign that the purchaser is not qualified to evaluate the specification, and particularly to evaluate what he has requested. Under these conditions, the user can find himself at the mercy of the suppliers when they offer nonresponsive alternative proposals, which must be thoroughly evaluated and which may contain promises that may not or cannot be met.

"Qualified" Vendors. To avoid the possibility of promises that cannot be met, the user should very carefully screen and qualify his vendors. It is usually wise to go to a select group of known suppliers—maybe three or four, perhaps five at most—instead of inviting the whole world to bid on a particular requirement. The qualified vendor should be well known to the user and of good reputation, should have good service and support capabilities, be competent, and have knowledgeable and helpful salesmen and as complete an applicable product line as is practical under the circumstances.

Fit Need to "Standard" System. At this point in time, now that the decision to buy has been made and a specification is in the process of being defined to be issued to a number of qualified vendors, the user should not overlook the possibility of fitting his system requirement to a standard system, possibly offered by one of the qualified vendors. This can result in the optimum use of the user's money and will certainly get the greatest amount of value for his investment. He will receive the benefit of extensive engineering and production utilization, on a system which might cost substantially more if supplied as a custom design.

Acceptance Tests and Verification of Performance. Regardless of the type of system to be purchased, whether a custom one built to exact specifications or a standard one, or possibly a standard one with modifications, acceptance tests and verification of performance are important to the user. They should be specified by the user in the specification, and agreed upon by the vendor, prior to the time that a purchase order is issued to the successful vendor. Again, the user must be careful not to overspecify the acceptance tests and not to overspecify the verification of performance, as it will then result in a typically expensive added-cost item included in the price.

A reliable vendor will generally have certain types of acceptance tests that he would put the system through in his factory before shipping it to the customer. In most cases, this level of acceptance testing should be more than adequate, and the user will not have to pay a premium. If, however, a special test procedure and verification of performance are required, the user should expect to have to pay a premium for this service.

There is often a tendency on the part of the user to want to witness acceptance tests and verification of performance at the vendor's factory, and then again on site after delivery and installation. This approach is valid, but again the user must expect to pay for performing tests in both locations. All the vendor's test equipment and personnel may have to be transported to carry out the tests at the user's plant. Extra costs are even involved in witnessing a factory-acceptance test, because of shipping delays caused by customer coordination and scheduling problems, time required to instruct and convince the customer of test validity, and escort requirements.

SERVICE AND MAINTENANCE

When the system has been purchased, delivered, installed, and checked out and is now doing its job, the task is not entirely completed. The user must still give consideration to the service and maintenance aspects of keeping his system in the best working order.

19. Continued Verification of Performance If diagnostic or verification software is available for the system, it would be wise to run it through the system on a scheduled periodic basis to determine that the system is performing as it should in all respects.

20. Calibration Certain of the instruments in the system will require periodic calibration. This calibration can generally be done by the user's metrology laboratory; or where the user does not have it available, such service can usually be performed by the vendor of the equipment for a nominal fee.

21. Preventive Maintenance Both the continued verification of performance and calibration of those instruments requiring it should be included in a regular schedule of service and preventive maintenance. This preventive maintenance may be scheduled and performed by the user, or the user may choose to award a service contract to the system's supplier to provide this service on a regularly scheduled basis. Even though the user may be a competent, sophisticated electronic-instrument man and know the system, it is still generally worthwhile to consider the possibility of a service contract from the supplier. With this kind of arrangement, preventive maintenance is carried out by service technicians who are probably working regularly with many such systems and components. The chances are that they are more intimately familiar with the operation, the quirks, the inconsistencies, the possible failure modes, than the user. It is entirely possible that this type of service contract can save the user from unnecessary failure, shutdowns, or requirements for unusual maintenance procedures, which he would have to carry out himself. In addition, with a service contract from a supplier, spare parts will usually be carried by the supplier in his inventory, rather than maintained in stock by the user—thus allowing some economic advantage for the user.

Depending upon the critical nature of the user's system application and service needs, service contracts can be set up to provide service on call, plus preventive maintenance any time during normal business hours, 5 days a week. Alternatively, the contract may call for response on a 24-hour basis, 7 days a week, or can be set up to operate on first, second, or third shifts, depending upon the nature of the work load being applied to the system by the user.

CONCLUSION

In conclusion, it should be reaffirmed here that instrument systems are a very useful and powerful tool, if properly conceived, appropriately applied, and operated within a framework defined in a commonsense manner.

It has not been possible in the limited space allocated in this handbook to provide the sort of exhaustive treatment that many of the subjects covered in this chapter may well deserve. However, the intent of the author has been to identify and expose the prospective instrument-system user to a variety of applicable subjects. The emphasis varied with the author's assessment of the needs of the typical non-engineering-oriented instrument-system user. The object of this section is to help a user identify and better understand the many considerations affecting instrument systems. If that understanding helps him to avoid or overcome some of the pitfalls and problems with which he may be confronted when he starts connecting more than one instrument together, this effort can be said to have been worthwhile.

Section Six

Current- and Voltage-measurement Devices

The most common quantity measured by electronic instruments is the magnitude of current flowing in a circuit or induced by a voltage across an element in a circuit. The instruments used to do this have many elements in common. Those instrument elements are discussed in detail in Section Two.

In this section the specific devices which have been designed to perform particular voltage and current measurements will be discussed in detail. Although they have a great deal in common, their differences are also great and both must be well understood in order to facilitate the choice of devices or to ensure the proper use of the instrument at hand. Because of the similarities of devices, there is some cross-referencing to tables in related chapters to avoid repeating identical material. Therefore, a general review of all chapters is recommended as well as a detailed analysis of the material on a particular device.

It should be remembered that almost every measurement problem involves one of these devices and therefore the importance of periodic review of this material cannot be overstated.

The oscilloscope is perhaps the single most used, and abused, instrument in electronic measurement. It not only measures voltage and current but also displays this measurement, as it changes, for visual interpretation. The danger is in taking what the eyes are seeing too literally as the real circuit situation. The instrument may introduce a geat many varied errors, but the viewer's tendency is to believe what the picture shows. Without understanding that the oscilloscope is basically a voltmeter with a time dimension and a pictorial presentation with all the associated problems and considerations of a voltmeter, plus those unique to itself, the user can be seriously misled.

Chapter 20

AC Voltmeters

LEE THOMPSON

Hewlett-Packard Company, Loveland, Colorado

INTRODUCTION

The ac voltmeter is an ac-to-dc converter which accepts an ac-voltage input and produces a dc voltage at its output that is proportional to the input voltage. This dc voltage is then used directly to deflect a meter calibrated to indicate the rms (root-mean-square), or effective, value of the input voltage or is used as the input to any of the dc voltmeters described in Chapter 22.

Generally speaking, whether they have analog or digital displays, ac voltmeters can be classified into four broad categories: rms-responding, quasi-rms-responding, average-responding, and peak-responding. Table 1 tabulates the salient points of each classification.

AC-VOLTMETER DISPLAYS

The terms analog voltmeter and digital voltmeter are used extensively in the field of electronic instrumentation. These terms refer to the type display, or readout, used in the voltmeter. Neither of these terms implies a particular type of ac-to-dc conversion technique. Both analog and digital voltmeters are available using any of the four types of ac-to-dc conversion techniques listed above.

1. Analog Displays The term analog display is used to indicate an output assembly which takes the results of a measurement and gives some kind of visual indication over a continuous range. Typically, this is done with a meter movement whose indicator is a needle which moves across the face of a calibrated scale as shown in Fig. 1.

2. Digital Displays The term digital display is used to indicate an output assembly which takes the results of a measurement and gives a visual indication

TABLE 1 Salient Points of Each Type of AC Voltmeter

Type of ac voltmeter	Distortion	Accuracy, %	Frequency	Response time, s	Measuring signal in noise
Rms-responding voltmeter	Measures waveforms with distortion	0.04–5	1 Hz to 10 MHz	1–2	Measures noise directly
Quasi-rms-responding voltmeter	Measures waveforms with less than about 5% distortion	0.1–5	1 Hz to 10 MHz	1	Measures noise directly
Average-responding voltmeter	Sine waves only	0.1–10.0	1 Hz to 10 MHz	0.5–1	Must use correction factor when measuring
Peak-responding voltmeter	Sine waves only	0.1–10.0	1 Hz to 1,000 MHz	0.5–1	Unsatisfactory unless noise is well defined

Fig. 1. Analog voltmeter.

Fig. 2. Digital voltmeter.

in discrete numbers. The most common method of doing this is to use a gas-filled tube with filaments shaped to look like numbers. Each tube typically contains a filament for each number (zero through nine) and a decimal point. If several of these tubes are placed side by side, the filaments can be controlled to give any numerical reading desired. Figure 2 shows a typical digital readout using this technique. Another technique is to use light-emitting diodes arranged in a pattern to give a numerical indication. The digital display minimizes the human error which is quite common in interpreting the analog display.

RMS VOLTAGE

The rms value of a waveform usually is the quantity of interest in ac-voltage measurements. The rms value (effective value) of an ac voltage is equivalent to the dc voltage which generates the same amount of heat in a resistive load as the ac voltage. For a dc voltage, this heat is directly proportional to the amount of power dissipated in the resistive load. The power in a resistive load due to a dc voltage is

$$P = \frac{V_{dc}^2}{R} \tag{1}$$

where P = power, W
R = resistance, Ω
V_{dc} = dc voltage dropped across the resistor, V

Note that the power is proportional to the square of the dc voltage. For an ac voltage, the heat in a resistive load is proportional to the average power dissipated in the resistive load. The average power in a resistive load due to an ac voltage is

$$P_{av} = \frac{V_{rms}^2}{R} \tag{2}$$

Also, the average power due to an ac voltage is the average, over an integer number of cycles of the voltage waveform, of the instantaneous power in a resistive load. Noting that integration is in fact summing:

$$P_{av} = \frac{1}{T}\int_0^T \frac{V_i^2}{R}\,dt = \frac{(1/T)\int_0^T V_i^2\,dt}{R} \tag{3}$$

where T = period of the waveform
V_i^2/R = square of the instantaneous voltage divided by the value of the resistive load, or the instantaneous power

Equating Eqs. (2) and (3) for average power gives

$$V_{rms}^2 = \frac{1}{T}\int_0^T V_i^2\,dt$$

from which

$$V_{rms} = \sqrt{\frac{1}{T}\int_0^T V_i^2\,dt} \tag{4}$$

This means that the rms value of an ac voltage is equivalent to the square root of the sum of the squares of the instantaneous voltages averaged over the period of the ac-voltage waveform. The first thing to observe from this definition is that the rms value of an ac voltage has no meaning except for periodic-voltage waveforms.

Basically, the rms value of a periodic-voltage waveform can be obtained by measuring the dc voltage at each point along one complete cycle of the waveform, squaring the voltage at each point, finding the average value of the squared terms, and taking the square root of the average value. Regardless of the shape of the waveform, this technique leads to the rms value of the voltage. This technique could be approximated in practice by sampling the waveform at a speed which is high in comparison with the frequency of the waveform, converting the sampled information to digital information, and using a digital computer to calculate the rms value of the voltage waveform.

Another more intuitive way to look at rms voltage is to look at the graphs of an ac-voltage and a dc-voltage waveform. It is a well-known fact that the rms value of a sine wave is 0.707 times its peak value. Looking at the graphs in Fig. 3 and recalling the definition of rms voltage, the basic ac-voltage waveform in Fig. 3*a* should produce exactly the same power (heat) in a resistor as does the basic dc waveform in Fig. 3*b*. If the voltage at each point in time is squared and another pair of graphs is plotted using these values, the squared-waveform graphs in Fig. 3 result. It follows from the mathematical definition of rms voltage that the area under the squared curves (crosshatched area) in Fig. 3 must be equal. That is, the area under a curve of the square of an ac voltage (over an integer number of cycles) is equal to the area under a curve of the square of its dc-voltage equivalent for the same period of time.

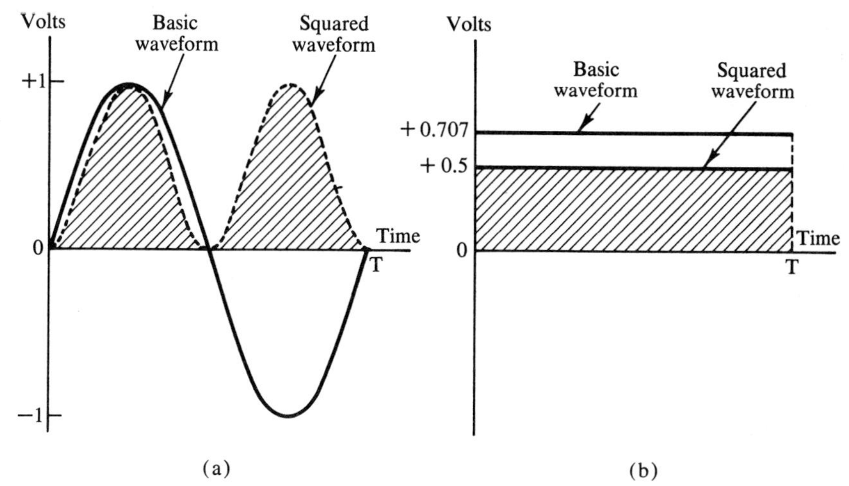

Fig. 3. (*a*) Ac-voltage waveform (sine wave). (*b*) Dc-voltage waveform.

RMS-RESPONDING VOLTMETERS

Since the rms value of an ac voltage is defined in terms of the heat it generates in a resistive load, the most straightforward way to measure the rms value of an ac voltage is to sense the heat it generates in a load and compare it with the heat from a known dc voltage in an equivalent load. A device called a thermocouple[1] can be used to perform this task.

When two dissimilar metals are joined together, a dc voltage is generated at the junction which is proportional to the temperature of the junction. This junction is called a thermocouple. The dissimilar-metal junction is usually packaged in an evacuated or gas-filled package along with a resistive heater element. In the electronics industry, this entire package is often referred to as a thermocouple. Figure 4*a* and *b* shows a typical thermocouple package and its schematic drawing, respectively.

At this point it should be noted that any device which responds to the square of the input voltage (called a square-law device) could be used, instead of a thermocouple, to make an rms measurement. However, except when a thermocouple is used, the response of the "square-law device" is usually an approximation of the square of the input voltage and should be categorized as a quasi-rms-responding voltmeter.

The block diagram in Fig. 5 is that of a typical rms-responding voltmeter. Here, two thermocouples are mounted in the same thermal environment. Nonlinear effects in the measuring thermocouple due to environmental conditions are canceled by similar nonlinear operation of the second thermocouple. The amplified input signal is applied to the resistive heater of the measuring thermocouple while a direct feedback current is fed to the heater of the balancing thermocouple. The direct feedback current is derived from the amplified voltage difference between the thermocouples. The circuitry may be regarded as a feedback control system which matches

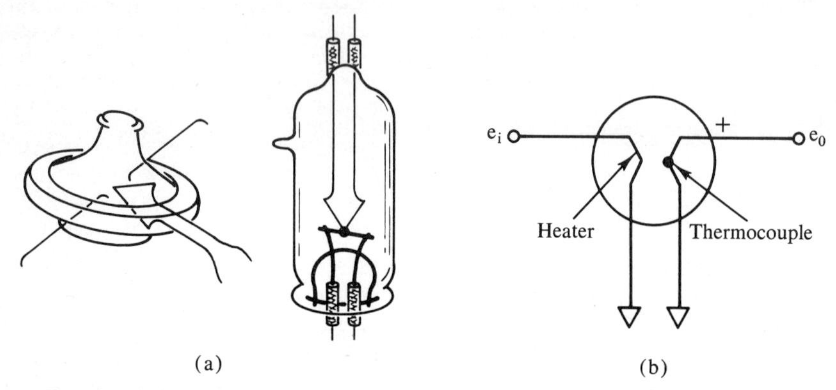

Fig. 4. (*a*) Typical packaged thermocouple. (*b*) Thermocouple schematic.

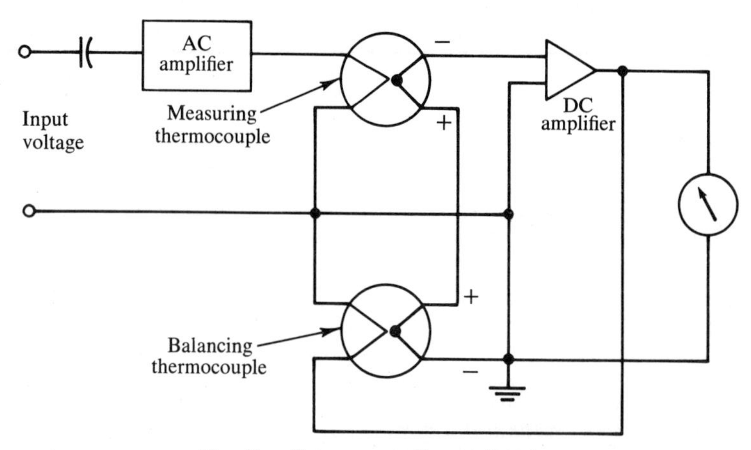

Fig. 5. Rms-responding voltmeter.

the heating power of the dc feedback voltage to the input waveform's heating power. Meter deflection is proportional to the dc feedback voltage, which, in turn, is proportional to the rms value of the input signal. The meter indication, therefore, is linear and not subject to the nonlinearities of the thermocouples.

QUASI-RMS-RESPONDING VOLTMETERS

The object of an ac-voltage measurement is to generate a dc voltage that is proportional to the rms value of the input signal. One way to make this measurement is to use a square-law device as discussed in the previous section. Another way to make the measurement is to design a circuit which will approximate a square-law response. Ac voltmeters which employ the latter technique are called quasi-rms-responding voltmeters.

Figure 6 shows the block diagram of a quasi-rms-responding voltmeter. For true rms response of this voltmeter, the detector should have the response shown in Fig. 7*a*. That is, its output voltage should be proportional to the square of its input voltage.

The most common approach for an approximation of the square-law response is to take advantage of the nonlinear characteristics of diodes which, in the region below 1, have an ampere/volt characteristic which approximates the curve of $I = KV^2$ as shown in Fig. 7*b*.

Figure 8 shows the schematic of a very simple "square-law detector." The circuit is biased so that CR_2 is off and the current through Q_1 and CR_1 is very small for e_i (the input voltage) equal to zero. As e_i is increased, the voltage on the emitter of Q_1 increases by the same amount. This increase in voltage must be dropped across CR_1 and R_2. The voltage change across CR_1 depends on the exact shape of the characteristic curve shown in Fig. 7*b* and the value of R_2. This change in voltage is proportional to the change in e_i. As e_i is increased, the voltage across CR_1 increases and the operating point in Fig. 7*b* moves from position ① toward position ②. This causes a current through Q_1 which is proportional to the square of the voltage change across CR_1. A voltage is developed across R_1 which is proportional to this current, which is, in turn, proportional to the square of the voltage change across CR_1, which is, in turn, proportional to the change in e_i. Thus e_o is proportional to the square of e_i. CR_2 is biased so that it starts to conduct current when CR_1 reaches position ② on its characteristic curve. Thus any additional increase in e_i will not significantly increase the current through CR_1. However, an increase in e_i will cause the operating point of CR_2 to move toward position ② in exactly the same manner as described above for CR_1. More diodes can be added in the same way that CR_2 was added to give more dynamic range. The circuit in Fig. 8 takes care of only the positive portion of the input signal. The complement of this circuit must be combined with it to complete the "square-law detector."

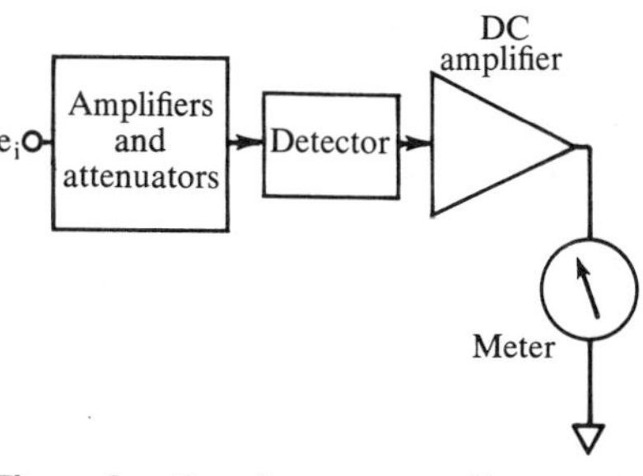

Fig. 6. Quasi-rms-responding voltmeter.

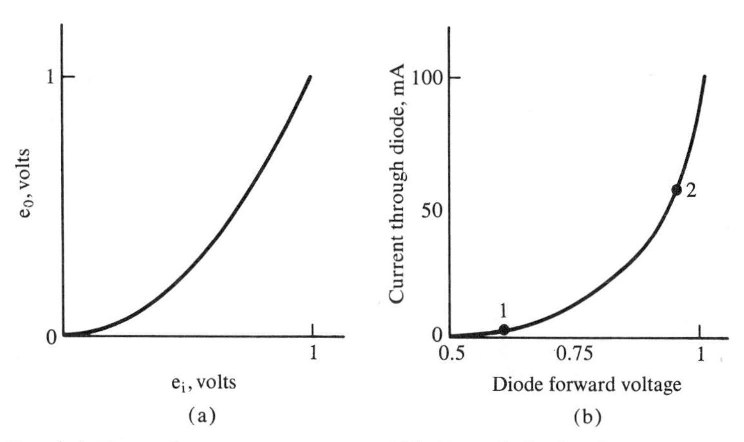

Fig. 7. (*a*) Square-law-response curve. (*b*) Typical diode characteristic curve.

There are numerous ways in which a square-law detector can be approximated. As discussed in a previous section, once a dc voltage proportional to the square of the signal to be measured has been generated, this dc voltage is proportional to a dc voltage which will generate an equivalent amount of heat in a resistive load as the input signal. Thus, the input signal's rms value is known and can be displayed.

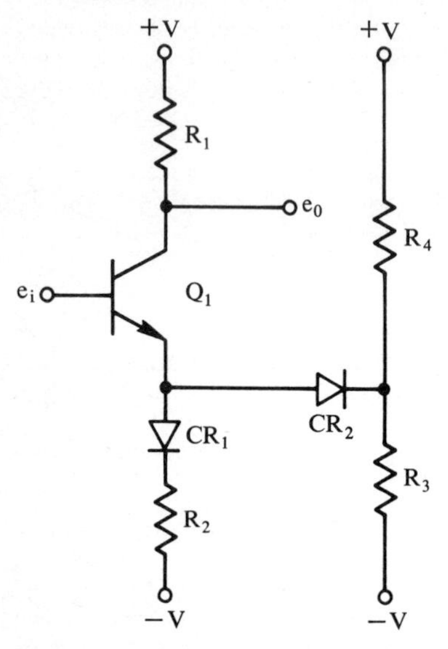

Fig. 8. Simplified square-law detector.

AVERAGE-RESPONDING VOLTMETERS

The average value of an ac-voltage waveform is simply the average of the instantaneous voltage measured over one complete cycle. Mathematically, this is

$$V_{av} = \frac{1}{T} \int_0^T V_i \, dt \qquad (5)$$

Graphically, this is the area under the curve divided by the length of the time axis. Figure 9 shows one cycle of a sine wave. The average value of this waveform is the area of the crosshatched portion divided by T (the period of the waveform).

In most cases, the average value of the input voltage is not the desired quantity. The equivalent dc or rms value of the waveform is usually the quantity of interest. For sine waves, the average value is zero since the waveform has equal positive and negative half cycles. Since, as has been stated, the quantity of interest is the heating capacity of the waveform, the average value of a sine wave is taken to mean the average of the full-wave rectified waveform.

For sine waves *only*, the average value is different from the true rms value of the waveform by the constant 0.91. If, then, the average value can be measured, it is an easy matter to calibrate the voltmeter to reflect the rms value of the

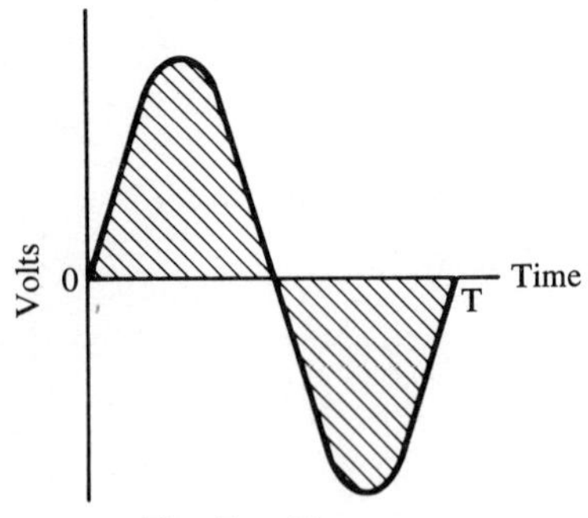

Fig. 9. Sine wave.

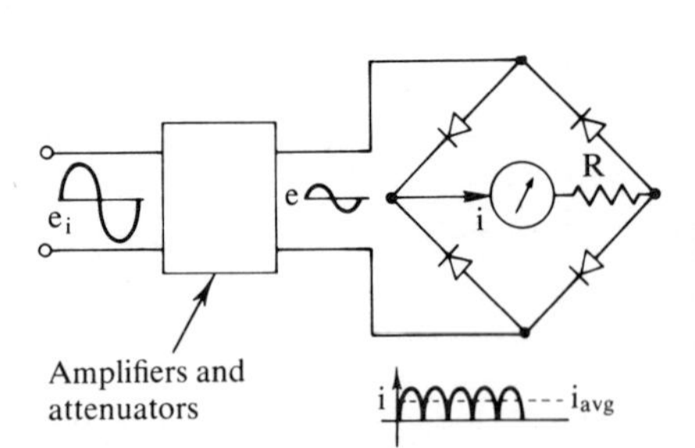

Fig. 10. Average-responding voltmeter.

waveform. This is exactly what is done in an average-responding voltmeter. The input waveform is first rectified, then a voltage is generated which is proportional to the average value of the rectified waveform, and then the constant is introduced to give a reading in rms volts. Once again, the result is exactly equal to the rms value of the input voltage for sine waves only.

Figure 10 shows a simple average-responding voltmeter. The amplifiers are used primarily for impedance matching. As discussed later, it is very important that the input impedance be very high if accurate measurements are desired. The attenuators are used to give the correct output level for different ranges of the voltmeter. The output from the amplifiers and attenuators e is a scaled reproduction of the input waveform. The rectification is performed by the diode bridge, resulting in current i through the meter as shown in Fig. 10. The meter response time is quite slow compared with the period of the input waveform; thus the averaging is done by the meter itself. The resistor R is chosen to give proper full-scale deflection.

There are many variations to the average-responding voltmeter. The averaging done by the meter in Fig. 10 could be accomplished with a capacitor, and the resulting voltage across the capacitor could be used as the input to any of the dc voltmeters discussed in Chapter 22.

PEAK-RESPONDING VOLTMETERS

For sine waves, the peak value of the voltage is different from the true rms value by the constant 0.707. Since the rms value of the waveform is the quantity usually desired, a peak-responding voltmeter measures the peak value of the waveform and adjusts this value by the constant 0.707 to give an rms indication for the input waveform. The rms value obtained is exactly correct for sine waves *only*.

Figure 11*a* shows a simple block diagram of a peak-responding voltmeter. The peak detector can be as simple as a diode and capacitor, and the constant can be introduced with passive elements or calibrated directly into a meter movement. The circuit becomes more complicated if more accuracy is required, but the principle of operation remains the same. Figure 11*b* shows a very simple peak-responding voltmeter. The capacitor is charged to the peak value of the input voltage through the diode. Its only discharge path is through the high-impedance input of the amplifier so that a negligibly small amount of current supplied by the circuit under test keeps the capacitor charged to the ac peak voltage. The dc amplifier is used in the peak-responding voltmeter to develop the necessary meter current.

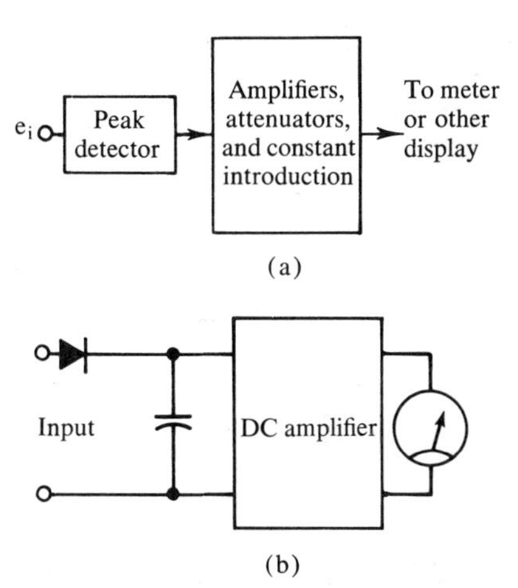

Fig. 11. (*a*) Block diagram of a peak-responding voltmeter. (*b*) Simple peak-responding voltmeter.

ADVANTAGES AND LIMITATIONS OF DIFFERENT TYPES OF AC VOLTMETERS

The kind of ac voltmeter selected for a measurement depends primarily on the kind of waveform to be measured. Each type is superior to the other types in at least one of the areas discussed below.

3. Distortion Basically, in the field of ac-voltage measurement, distortion is the deviation of the voltage to be measured from a sine wave. Another way to look at distortion is in terms of the harmonic content of the waveform.[5] Any waveform is made up of the sum of its fundamental frequency and multiples of this fundamental frequency called harmonics. A sine wave, for example, has no harmonics (it contains a fundamental frequency only) while a square wave theoretically contains an infinite number of harmonics. In general, the faster the rise or fall time of a waveform, the higher are the harmonics contained in that waveform. Figure 12 graphically shows how a fundamental and its second harmonic are added point by point to give the waveform shown by the solid line. If this waveform were being viewed on an oscilloscope, the viewer would see only the waveform represented by the solid line. Second and third harmonics are usually the largest contributors to errors in ac voltmeters because the amplitude of the higher harmonics is usually small enough so that they do not cause significant errors.

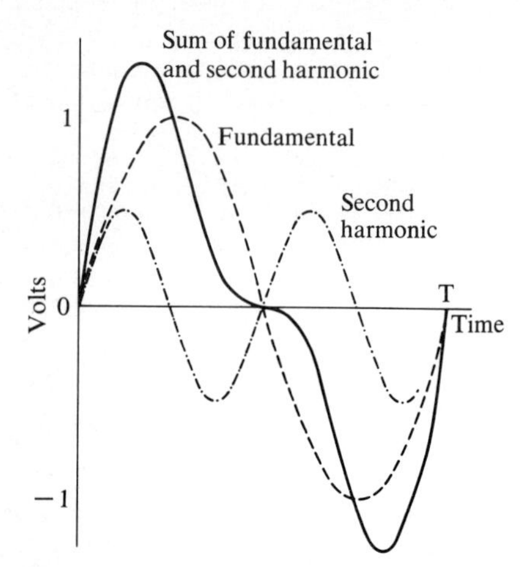

Fig. 12. Second-harmonic distortion.

The rms-responding voltmeter is by far the most accurate instrument if voltages with more than about 5 percent distortion are being measured. Since the rms voltmeter responds to the actual power in the waveform (i.e., responds to all harmonics within its bandwidth), no errors are encountered due to distortion for harmonics which are within the bandwidth of the instrument being used.

The quasi-rms-responding voltmeter represents a reasonable compromise between the rms- and average- or peak-responding voltmeters when voltages with distortion less than about 5 percent are to be measured. The limitation of the quasi-rms voltmeter is in the square-law approximation. The amount of distortion which can be tolerated varies, depending on the technique used to obtain the square-law approximation; but in general, so long as it is known that the distortion is no more than a few percent, the quasi-rms-responding voltmeter performs adequately.

Both the average-responding and the peak-responding voltmeters are extremely susceptible to distortion. In spite of this, both types have found wide acceptance in the field of electronic measurement, primarily because of the wide use of sine waves in the field. There are so many ways that a sine wave can be distorted that it is impossible to enumerate all the possibilities. Figure 13 shows one case of third-harmonic distortion. Figure 13 also points out that the phase of the harmonic with respect to its fundamental affects the peak value and average value of the waveform. The input waveform shown in Fig. 13*a* would cause a higher

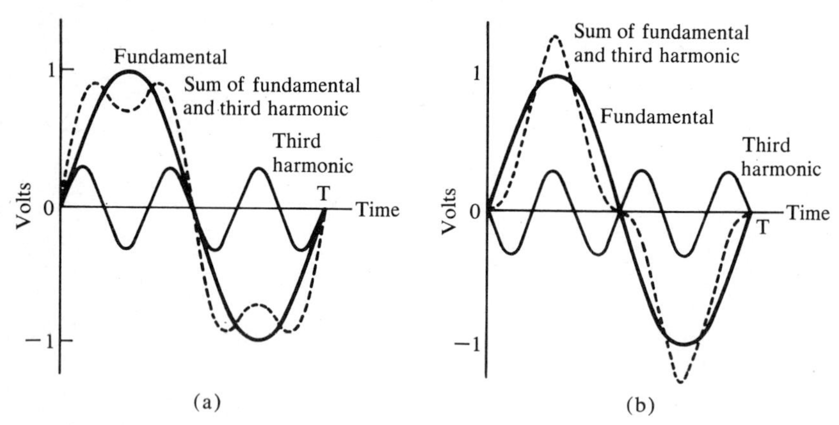

Fig. 13. (*a*) In-phase third harmonic. (*b*) Out-of-phase third harmonic.

than rms reading on an average-responding voltmeter and a lower than rms reading on a peak-responding voltmeter. The input waveform shown in Fig. 13*b* would cause a lower than rms reading on an average-responding voltmeter and a higher than rms reading on a peak-responding voltmeter. Table 2 gives some measurement errors for different amounts of second- and third-harmonic content when using an average- or peak-responding voltmeter. The phase of the harmonic with respect to the fundamental significantly affects the amount of error; this is indicated in the table by a range of the error. In general, if waveforms other than sine waves are to be measured, neither the average-responding nor the peak-responding voltmeter should be used.

4. Accuracy In the field of ac-voltage measurement, the accuracy of an ac voltmeter is the deviation of the indication of the voltmeter from the rms value of the waveform being measured. The unit of measurement is percent error.

When the accuracies of the four types of ac voltmeters are to be compared, the shape of the input waveform must be considered. If waveforms other than sine waves are to be measured, the dominant error will more than likely be due to distortion. These errors are discussed in some detail above.

TABLE 2 Measurement Errors from Harmonic Voltages

Harmonic content	True rms value	Average-responding meter	Peak-responding meter
0	100	100	100
10% second	100.5	100	90–110
20% second	102	100–102	80–120
50% second	112	100–110	75–150
10% third	100.5	96–104	90–110
20% third	102	94–108	88–120
50% third	112	90–116	108–150

Typical errors encountered by the different types of ac voltmeters are: (1) from about 0.04 to 5 percent for rms-responding voltmeters, (2) from about 0.1 to 5 percent for quasi-rms-responding voltmeters, and (3) from about 0.1 to 10 percent for average- and peak-responding voltmeters. The point that must be kept in mind is that the accuracies above hold for each harmonic within its bandwidth for an rms-responding voltmeter and hold for waveforms with less than about 5 percent distortion for quasi-rms-responding voltmeters, but do not hold for any waveform other than sine waves for average- or peak-responding voltmeters.

5. Frequency Except for the peak-responding voltmeter, ac voltmeters are usually limited in high-frequency response to between about 1 and 10 MHz. This is usually caused by limitations in the amplifiers, since they must be broadband. If frequencies outside the bandwidth of the amplifiers are being measured, they will be attenuated and large errors will be encountered. This is not the case in peak-responding voltmeters. Note in Fig. 11*b* that the peak detector can be placed at the input of the voltmeter. This means that all the amplifiers in the voltmeter are dc amplifiers, thus eliminating the amplifier limitation encountered in the other types of dc voltmeters. Peak-responding voltmeters are available which measure frequencies up to several hundred megahertz. However, it must be emphasized that the correct reading will be obtained for sine-wave inputs only, since the voltmeter is calibrated to give an exact rms indication with a sine-wave input.

6. Response Time Response time is the amount of elapsed time from the time the voltage to be measured is applied to the input of the voltmeter until the voltmeter gives an indication that is within its specified accuracy.

The response times of both average-responding and peak-responding voltmeters are typically less than 1 s. Typical quasi-rms-responding voltmeters have response times of 0.5 to 1 s, and typical rms-responding voltmeters are about twice that amount. The primary limitation on response time of the true rms-responding voltmeter is the detector (thermocouple). This time lag is primarily associated with the time required for the thermocouple heater to reach thermal equilibrium after a signal has been applied.

7. Noise If the noise at the output of an ac voltmeter when measuring a noise-free signal is considered, all four types of ac voltmeters should be comparable. Internally generated noise is more a function of the bandwidth of the voltmeter (the more bandwidth the more noise) than of the type of voltmeter used.

If, however, the measurement of a signal in noise is considered, the type of voltmeter to be used is of concern. The peak-responding ac voltmeter is unacceptable for this task, since the peak value of noise is unpredictable. A later section of this chapter shows how to make such a measurement using the other types of ac voltmeters. If the procedure outlined is followed, the average-responding voltmeter can be used to measure a signal in noise. If accurate measurements are to be made, without using correction factors, either the rms- or quasi-rms-responding voltmeter should be used, keeping in mind that the rms-responding voltmeter generally gives more accurate results.

SPECIFICATIONS

8. Input Impedance The input impedance is usually specified as an input resistance shunted by some maximum capacitance. A typical specification is 2 MΩ shunted by less than 50 pF. This specification must be considered in determining errors due to source impedance, as described in a later section of this chapter.

9. Bandwidth The bandwidth specification is the lower and upper frequency limit beyond which accurate measurements cannot be made. Sometimes a useful measurement can be made beyond these limits even though the manufacturer does not guarantee the results. This is something the user must determine through experimentation. Typical ac voltmeters have bandwidths ranging from a lower limit of about 1 Hz to an upper limit of about 10 MHz.

10. Volt-Hertz Rating The volt-hertz rating is a statement of the maximum of the product of the input rms voltage and the frequency, consistent with the bandwidth and range specification, that can be measured. The limitation on this specification is usually the slew rate of the amplifiers. Typical ac voltmeters range from 10^5 to 10^8 V-Hz. If this specification is exceeded, the amplifiers will pass a distorted version of the input wave, which will result in an erroneous reading on the voltmeter.

11. Range The range specification is a statement of the number of ranges and how many rms volts are required for full-scale deflection on each range. Some ac voltmeters have as many as 15 different ranges. The voltage required for full-scale deflection varies from about 3 μV to about 1,000 V.

12. Overrange Capability The overrange capability is a statement of how far above full scale a measurement may be made on any range. Typical ac voltmeters have an overrange capability of from 5 to 50 percent of the full-scale voltage.

13. Response Time The response time is a statement of how long it takes the voltmeter to give an indication that is within its specified accuracy from the time an input signal is applied. Typical response times are about 1 s for all but the rms-responding voltmeter, which has about twice the response time of the other types.

14. Speed Speed is primarily of importance in digital (numerical-display) voltmeters. It is a statement of the number of indications per unit of time that the voltmeter is capable of displaying. This ranges from about one reading every 2 s to about 1,000 readings per second.

15. Sensitivity Sensitivity is the smallest voltage level to which the voltmeter can respond and normally is specified as the voltage level represented by the least detectable change on the lowest range. Some ac voltmeters may have a sensitivity as low as 1μV.

16. Resolution Resolution is the degree to which incremental changes in a measurement or signal level can be discerned. It is expressed as the maximum degree of resolution at full scale plus overranging. Resolution may be expressed in parts per million (ppm). The resolution of an ac voltmeter is closely related to its sensitivity. For instance, the voltmeter which has a sensitivity of 1μV should be able to resolve 0.1 μV (0.1 ppm) easily.

17. Crest Factor Crest factor is defined as the ratio of peak voltage to rms voltage of a periodic waveform. This term applies to rms-responding voltmeters only. It is a statement of the maximum ratio which the signal to be measured may have. Crest factor is of primary importance when measurement of low-duty-cycle pulsed waves is desired. It essentially limits the pulsed energy to which the rms voltmeter can respond.[8] Typical crest-factor specifications range from 5:1 to 10:1.

18. Stability Stability is the freedom from undesirable variations in a measurement with time. This time starts with the calibration of the voltmeter and can usually be reset by recalibrating. Stability may be expressed as a percent change in accuracy per unit time, as a voltage change per unit time, or as accuracy for an extended time (longer than that in the basic accuracy specification). The temperature and relative-humidity range in which the stability specification is valid should be stated.

19. Common-mode Rejection Common-mode rejection is the ability of the voltmeter to reject voltages introduced between the chassis ground of the voltmeter and the ground of the source. Common-mode rejection is usually specified as the ratio of the peak common-mode voltage to the resultant peak normal-mode voltage with 1,000 Ω unbalance in either input lead. It is typically expressed in decibels. The resultant peak normal-mode voltage is the voltage that would have to be injected between the high and low input terminals to give the same output the common-mode signal gives. A typical common-mode rejection specification is 120 dB down at 60 Hz.

20. Noise Noise is usually specified for digital voltmeters. This is the internally generated noise and normally is specified in counts at a fixed frequency of the input wave at full scale. For example, if the specification is ±5 counts at 1 kHz, a four-digit voltmeter with an overrange digit could read 1.0005 or 0.9995 because of internally generated noise alone.

21. Temperature Coefficient Temperature coefficient is the amount of change in accuracy per degree change in temperature from the specified ambient. This is usually expressed as a percent of reading plus a percent of full scale per degree Celsius over a temperature range for the more accurate digital voltmeters, while most analog voltmeters typically just give a temperature range over which the basic accuracy specification is valid, such as 0 to 50°C. A typical specification for a digital ac voltmeter is ±(0.02 percent of reading + 0.002 percent of range) per °C. The errors caused by changes in temperature are additive to the basic accuracy when the temperature is outside the range called out in the basic accuracy specification.

22. Accuracy Determination of the accuracy to expect in a measurement from the specification sheet of most ac voltmeters is no easy task. Specification sheets are usually written in a way to emphasize the strong points of the particular ac voltmeter. For this reason specification sheets should be studied in some detail before an ac voltmeter is purchased.

Before starting to calculate the expected error of a measurement from the accuracy specification, some basic properties of the voltage waveform to be measured must be known. It must be periodic with its fundamental frequency within the specified bandwidth of the voltmeter. For rms responding voltmeters, the input waveform must not exceed the volt-hertz rating or the crest-factor rating of the voltmeter. The voltage level to be measured must be within the specified capability of the voltmeter. The ambient-temperature and relative-humidity specifications must not be exceeded. The length of time since the voltmeter was last calibrated, which is spelled out in the stability specification, must not have been exceeded.

If all the conditions above, plus any other conditions called for in the accuracy specification, are met, the expected error can be calculated from the accuracy specification. First, consider sine waves for the average-responding or peak-responding voltmeters. The accuracy specification is normally given as a percent of full scale and a percent of reading error for different frequency bands. The percent of reading error is a direct error in the indication of the voltmeter; however, the percent of range (full-scale) specification must be adjusted if a voltage different from full scale is being measured. The following equation may be used to adjust the percent of range specification:

$$\text{Adjusted percent of range specification} = \frac{(\text{percent of range specification})(\text{full-scale voltage})}{\text{input voltage}} \tag{6}$$

Example: Measuring 100 mV (0.1 V) on the 1-V range.
Error specification:

0.1 percent of range
0.1 percent of reading

$$\text{Adjusted percent of range specification} = \frac{(0.1\ \text{percent})(1\ \text{V})}{(0.1\ \text{V})} = 1.0\ \text{percent}$$

Total error could be

$$1.0 + 0.1 = 1.1\ \text{percent of reading}$$

The voltmeter would give an indication equal to 0.1 ±1.1 percent due to the percent of range and the percent of reading specification.

Any additional error calculated from the temperature coefficient, stability, or noise specifications must be added directly to the error calculated above.

Another source of error which must be added directly is error due to loading of the source impedance. This error is discussed later in this chapter.

When measuring waveforms other than sine waves with the rms- or quasi-rms voltmeters, the calculation of accuracy is even more complex. Waveforms with distortion which exceeds the distortion specification of the quasi-rms-responding voltmeter (usually less than 5 percent) must be measured with an rms-responding voltmeter if accurate results are required. The accuracy for rms- and quasi-rms-responding voltmeters is normally specified for sine waves only. Therefore, in order to calculate the expected accuracy of a measurement, a knowledge of the Fourier expansion of the input-voltage waveform is required.[5] The procedure outlined above for sine waves must be followed for each component of frequency which is within the bandwidth of the voltmeter. The indication the user can expect is then equal to the square root of the sum of the squares of the indication expected for each frequency component.

$$\text{Expected indication} = [(\text{fundamental} \pm \text{error voltage})^2 + (\text{first harmonic} \pm \text{error voltage})^2 + \cdots + (N\text{th harmonic} \pm \text{error voltage})^2]^{1/2} \tag{7}$$

where N is the highest-order harmonic that is within the bandwidth of the voltmeter. All the signs for the error voltage should be the same in order to avoid error cancellation.

CALIBRATION

Most instruments specify a length of time after which they must be recalibrated in order to achieve optimum performance from the voltmeter. This is primarily due to the time stability of components. Most instrument instruction manuals contain a detailed step-by-step procedure for this recalibration. Typically, they require an accurate source of sine waves and a controlled environment in which the recalibration must be done. The amount of control required is usually directly proportional to the accuracy to which the voltmeter is capable of making a measurement.

FRONT-PANEL CONTROLS

23. Function The function control is applicable when the ac voltmeter is one function of a multimeter. This control is used to select the ac-voltage mode of operation of the multimeter.

24. Calibration Some ac voltmeters (particularly when included in a multimeter) have an external calibration control. Calibration is usually accomplished by connecting the input to an internal reference and adjusting the reading to some desired value.

25. Filter The filter control usually switches a filter in series with the input. This filter can be used to advantage to filter a low-frequency noise out of the input signal when the high-frequency component is the voltage to be measured.

26. Ranging The ranging control selects either manual or automatic ranging. This control appears only on voltmeters which have the ability to select the proper range automatically after sampling the input voltage.

27. Range The range control is used to select the proper range on manual ranging voltmeters and when an auto-ranging voltmeter is set to the manual ranging mode.

28. Overrange Indicator The overrange indicator appears only on digital (numerical-display) voltmeters, since it is obvious when a meter has exceeded its usable range. The overrange indicator is usually a light marked "overrange" or is part of the readout. In either case it signifies that the voltage that can be measured on the range being used has been exceeded.

29. Sample Rate The sample rate of most digital voltmeters can be adjusted from the front panel. This control either increases or decreases the number of times per second that the output of the ac voltmeter is sampled and displayed on the front panel. This control in no way affects the response time specified for the voltmeter.

30. Trigger The external trigger control, combined with some kind of hold-off on the sample rate, allows the user to force the display unit to take one sample and display it each time the trigger is applied.

RF VOLTMETERS

Rf voltmeters are ac voltmeters which respond to frequencies above the range (typically about 10 MHz) of conventional ac voltmeters. Conventional voltmeters responding to the absolute average or the rms value of an ac waveform are limited in sensitivity and bandwidth by the input-impedance converter, amplifier, and detector. These restrictions may be relieved by sampling the signal prior to amplification and detection. This technique constructs low-frequency equivalents of high-frequency signals and permits voltmeters to make measurements over wide frequency and voltage ranges.

A favorite technique is to use the peak-responding voltmeter shown in Fig. 11 and place the peak detector in a probe. The probe delivers a dc voltage proportional to the high-frequency signal being measured to the amplifier, which is easily measured and displayed.

Diode nonlinearities limit the sensitivity of the peak-responding voltmeter described above. An rf voltmeter which eliminates the nonlinearity limitation is shown in Fig. 14. This instrument uses a balanced circuit with one input receiving the peak value of the voltage being measured. The balanced differential amplifier, acting as a null detector, controls the amplitude of an internally generated ac signal which is fed to a second diode in the probe. The peak voltage (dc) from this diode serves as the other amplifier input. The null circuitry ensures that the signal at the second diode has the same amplitude as the input signal.

The internally generated alternating current has a constant frequency (100 kHz)

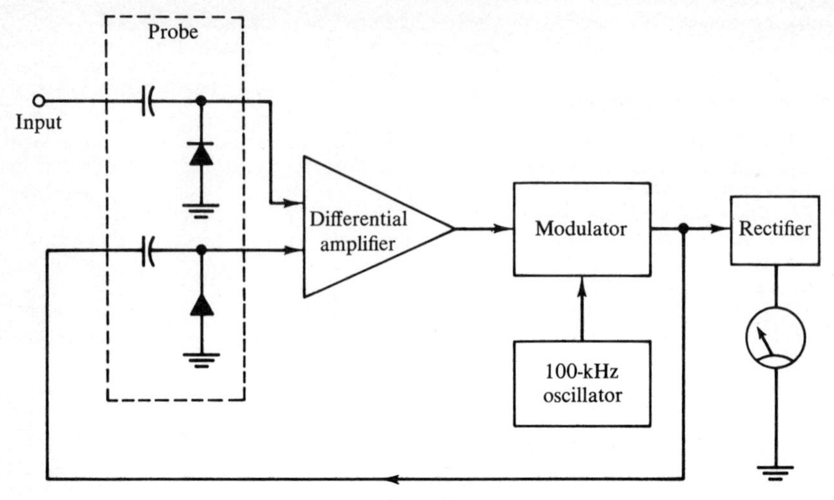

Fig. 14. Rf millivoltmeter.

and is easily measured. It serves as the indication of the unknown input. All that is required is that the two signals be identical in amplitude, so that diode nonlinearities do not enter into the measurement. The most sensitive range on this instrument is 0.010 V (10 mV).

Rf voltmeters using the above techniques are available which have an upper frequency limit in excess of 1,000 MHz. Other techniques are used in rf voltmeters; however, most just construct a low-frequency equivalent of the high-frequency input signal in a different way.

USING AN AC VOLTMETER

31. Effects of AC and DC Coupling The ac and dc coupling covered in this section is restricted to a blocking capacitor at the input of the voltmeter. If an input voltage is being measured with an average value different from zero, whether or not a blocking capacitor is used has a direct effect on the indication of the voltmeter. By far the largest percentage of ac voltmeters are ac-coupled. Dc coupling is primarily restricted to use in ac voltmeters which measure low frequencies (less than 50 Hz) to eliminate the large capacitor that would be required to pass these frequencies. Rms-responding voltmeters are available which measure a waveform with an average value different from zero. However, except for this voltmeter, if the rms value of the ac and dc component of the input voltage is desired, they must be measured separately, and the following equation must be used to calculate the correct rms value of the waveform:

$$V_{rms}(\text{total}) = [V_{dc}^2 + V_{rms}{}^2{}_{(\text{ac component})}]^{1/2} \tag{8}$$

32. A Typical Gain Measurement Using an AC Voltmeter Many times the frequency response of an amplifier must be measured in order to characterize the amplifier. One way to do this is to use an ac voltmeter and an oscillator. The amplitude of the oscillator does not have to be flat with frequency or settable to an accurate value. Its only requirement is that it is stable for a short period of time and has low output impedance.

Figure 15 shows how to connect the oscillator, amplifier, and ac voltmeter to make the measurement. The procedure is first to set the oscillator voltage to some value that does not saturate the amplifier and allows the voltmeter to make a measurement near full scale. Next, a frequency is selected. The oscillator voltage is measured with the ac voltmeter and recorded. Next, the output of the amplifier is measured. These two values are subtracted and divided by the attenuation factor $R_2/(R_1 + R_2)$ at the input of the amplifier to obtain the gain at the frequency selected. The procedure is repeated for as many frequencies as desired.

If the oscillator output impedance and the amplifier output impedance are low enough so that no loading occurs, an accurate measurement can be made with a relatively inaccurate ac voltmeter. This technique assumes that the attenuation factor will be near the reciprocal of the gain of the amplifier so that the voltmeter will make both measurements very near the same level. This measurement is possible because the errors in the voltmeter are usually repeatable at a fixed frequency and voltage level.

33. Using a Guarded Instrument Common-mode error voltages are voltages caused by current flow in the ground lead between the ground of the voltmeter and the ground of the voltage being measured. One major source of this ground current is in the form of externally injected noise. This effect can be greatly reduced by the use of a guard. Guarded voltmeters usually have the voltmeter encased in a conducting shield with a terminal on the front panel electrically connected to the shield or guard. Noise currents are injected into the guard and

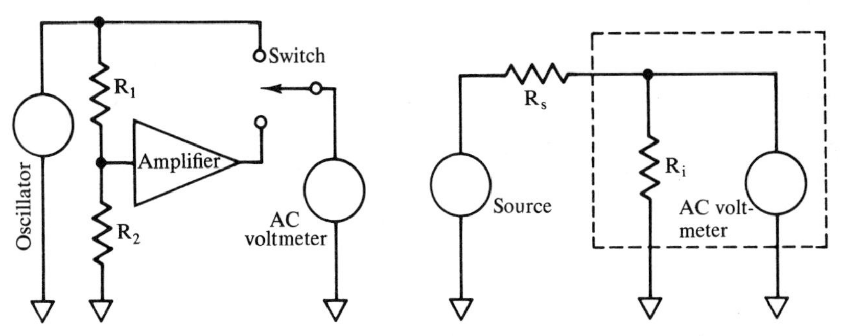

Fig. 15. Measuring frequency response of an amplifier.

Fig. 16. Effects of loading the source.

not into the measurement circuitry. This guard terminal should be electrically connected to the ground of the voltage being measured, thus returning the common-mode current through a connection other than the voltmeter ground lead.[4]

34. Input-lead Precautions The voltage being measured should always be connected to the voltmeter with leads as short as possible. This prevents errors due to current flow in the input leads. If a calibration source is being used which has a remote sense capability, it should be utilized.[2]

Another source of error due to input leads is either electrostatic or magnetic coupling of unwanted signals into the input leads. If the source can supply the additional current required to drive the added shunt capacitance, either shielded cable or a twisted pair of leads can greatly reduce this effect.

35. Grounding Ground leads between the source of the input voltage and the voltmeter should be as short and as low in resistance as possible in order to minimize errors due to current flow in these leads. Sometimes, unexpected results can be obtained when a ground loop back through the power line exists between the source and the voltmeter. This problem can be verified by using either a battery-operated voltmeter or a voltmeter capable of making a floating measurement.

36. Errors Caused by Voltmeter Input Impedance Figure 16 shows an ac-voltage source with some output resistance R_s being measured by a voltmeter with some input resistance R_i. The voltage measured by the voltmeter is

$$\frac{V_{\text{source}} R_i}{R_s + R_i} \tag{9}$$

Therefore, the measurement is in error by the factor $R_i/(R_s + R_i)$. For complex impedances, the error would be determined by $Z_i/(Z_s + Z_i)$. This error can be minimized by either increasing R_i or decreasing R_s. Sometimes an impedance converter must be used if an accurate measurement is to be made.

37. Measuring a Signal in Noise If a signal in noise is to be measured, the best approach is to use an rms-responding voltmeter. First, measure the signal plus noise; then measure the noise alone. The rms value obtained in the first measurement is

$$V_{rms(\text{total})} = [V_{rms}{}^2{}_{(\text{noise})} + V_{rms}{}^2{}_{(\text{signal})}]^{1/2} \tag{10}$$

Solving the previous equation for the rms value of the signal alone gives

$$V_{rms(\text{signal})} = [V_{rms}{}^2{}_{(\text{total})} - V_{rms}{}^2{}_{(\text{noise})}]^{1/2} \tag{11}$$

Most quasi-rms voltmeters will do a reasonable job if the same approach is used. Armed with the fact that the average value of random noise (rectified) is 0.8862 times its rms value, the same approach with a slightly different calculation yields the result for sine wave in noise, using an average-responding voltmeter. The relationship is

$$V_{rms(\text{signal})} = \left\{ V_{rms}{}^2{}_{(\text{total})} - \left[V_{rms(\text{noise})} \frac{0.8862}{0.91} \right]^2 \right\}^{1/2} \tag{12}$$

since a sine wave has average value equal to 0.91 times its rms value. The peak-responding voltmeter is unsatisfactory for this kind of measurement, since the peak value of the noise is unpredictable.

38. Selection of Range Since, as discussed above, the accuracy of the reading gets worse on the lower part of any range, it is to the user's advantage to utilize the range which will give a reading nearest full scale. This is typical of all types of ac voltmeters.

REFERENCES

1. Calhoun, Richard E.: UHF Thermoelements, *Meas. Data,* November–December, 1968, pp. 67–73.
2. Hanson, Fred L.: High-accuracy AC Voltage Calibration, *Hewlett-Packard J.,* June, 1968.
3. Jessen, Kenneth: Taking the Mystery Out of DVM Specs, *Electron. Eng.,* October, 1969, pp. 46–52.
4. McCullough, William: How to Reduce Common-mode Effects, *EEE,* February, 1967.
5. Skilling, Hugh H.: "Electrical Engineering Circuits," John Wiley & Sons, Inc., New York, 1957.
6. Wind, Moe: "Handbook of Electronic Measurements," vol. 1, Polytechnic Press of the Polytechnic Institute of Brooklyn, distributed by Interscience Publishers, Inc., New York, 1956.
7. Which AC Voltmeter, *Hewlett-Packard Application Note* 60.
8. An RMS Responding Voltmeter with High Crest Factor, *Hewlett-Packard J.,* January, 1964.

Chapter **21**

Ammeters

LARRY L. CARLSON

Hewlett-Packard Company, Loveland, Colorado

INTRODUCTION

Ammeters are required to make many different types of current measurements. For example, one ammeter may be required to measure a few microamperes of direct current and another a small 50-MHz alternating current. Generally, an ammeter has special features which allow it to make a special type of measurement. This is the reason there are so many different types of ammeters.

Ammeters can be classified into two main types. The first, the direct-reading type, consists of popular panel meters such as the d'Arsonval movement and the moving-iron movement. The direct-reading ammeter responds directly to the current being measured. For example, a direct current passing through the pivoting coil of the d'Arsonval movement is converted directly into a torque which gives the coil an angular displacement proportional to the current. A pointer attached to the coil rotates in front of a precalibrated scale from which the value of current may be read.

The moving-iron movement, like the d'Arsonval movement, is also direct-reading. Its indications, however, unlike the d'Arsonval movement, are proportional to the root mean square, or rms, of an alternating current which passes through its coil.

The second type of ammeter is the system type. This type encompasses a broad range of ammeters, from those which are passive instruments to those which are electronic. The electronic types usually include a transducer which converts the signal to one which the system can process, a signal-processing unit, and a readout such as the commonly used d'Arsonval movement.

PANEL-METER TYPES

The electromechanical current-indicating devices mentioned in this section have in common a mechanism in which a torque is created as a result of magnetic-field interactions when a current is passed through a coil associated with the mechanism. The position of a lightweight pointer attached to the mechanism indicates the magnitude of the current passing through the coil. The entire mechanism is mounted in a glass-faced enclosure to protect it from dust, and to display the pointer indications.

The rectifier and thermocouple types of ammeters contain signal processors along with a basic d'Arsonval mechanism. The rectifier type converts an ac signal to a pulsating dc signal which drives a d'Arsonval movement, which responds to the average value. The thermocouple type converts an ac or dc (usually ac) signal to an rms-equivalent dc voltage by heating a junction of dissimilar metals. A dc voltage proportional to the temperature difference across the junction appears, and the resulting current flow is used to drive a sensitive d'Arsonval mechanism.

The instruments considered are single-range mechanisms. It is important for the user to understand the capabilities and limitations of these mechanisms, as they can be used in a number of current-indicating applications. More importantly, however, these mechanisms are used in many passive multirange voltage- and current-measuring multimeters where overall specifications are usually determined by the type of movement used. Also a large percentage of the electronic ammeters and voltmeters use the basic d'Arsonval movement as a readout device, and to a certain extent the limitations of the movement are reflected in specification limitations of the instrument itself.

1. DC d'Arsonval Types

Operation. Figure 1 shows an internal view of an instrument called a d'Arsonval galvanometer, named after its inventor. This sensitive moving-coil meter consists of an armature upon which a number of turns of fine wire are wound. The armature, which encloses a soft-iron core, is precisely pivoted upon one of two common suspension systems.

The pivot-and-jewel suspension system, one of the more commonly used and less expensive systems, compares with the pivot-and-jewel system in a watch. Special hardened, polished, alloy-steel pivots attached to each end of the armature ride in the V of a sapphire bearing, as shown in Fig. 2.

More expensive and higher-performance meters use the suspension systems commonly referred to as "taut bands," shown in Fig. 3. Like the delicate classic galvanometer still used in schools and laboratories, the armature of the meter is suspended on a metal band rather than a pivot and jewel. Anchor springs at the end of each taut band pull the suspension bands very tight.

Fig. 1. d'Arsonval movement. (*Hewlett-Packard Company, Loveland, Colo.*)

The taut band serves also as a suspension and a restoring-torque spring. The pivot-and-jewel system requires a pair of spiral control springs at each end of the armature to provide restoring torque.

The most common galvanometer uses an external horseshoe permanent magnet. At the poles of the magnet soft-metal pole pieces are attached which concentrate the magnetic field in a radial manner to give a uniform torque regardless of coil position. Connections from the coil are brought out through the control springs or taut band with wires, and the entire mechanism is mounted in some type of glass-faced enclosure to protect it from dust.

The movement rotates because a current in a magnetic field experiences a force F, and the net effect on the coil is a rotational torque T which acts against the restoring spring as shown in Fig. 4. The amount of angular displacement is proportional to the current flow in the coil.

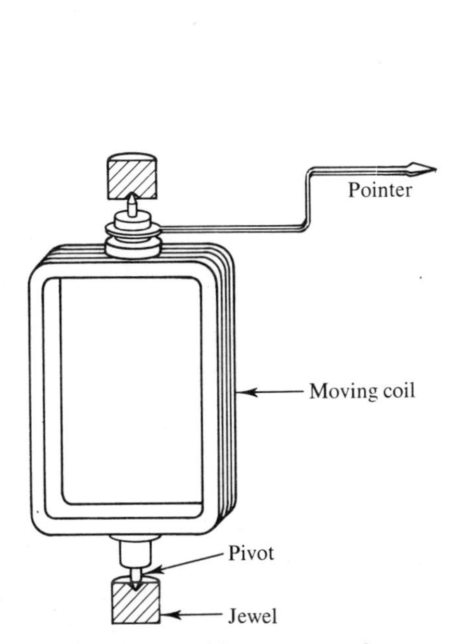

Fig. 2. Pivot-and-jewel suspension system for a d'Arsonval movement.

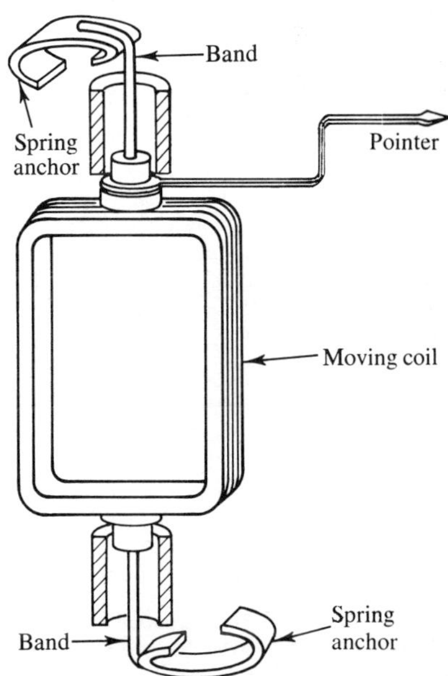

Fig. 3. Taut-band suspension system for a d'Arsonval movement.

The amount of angular rotation is commonly about a quarter of a turn. The coil in some meters is made to rotate clockwise only. That is, zero is at the counterclockwise position. Electron current must enter the terminal marked "negative" to produce "upscale" or clockwise deflection. Some meters referred to as "center zero" meters can be deflected either clockwise or counterclockwise about a center rest position. Electron current, for example, entering the terminal marked "negative" will cause a clockwise deflection, while electron current entering the terminal marked "positive" will produce a counterclockwise rotation.

Current Sensitivity. The maximum amount of current required to cause full-scale deflection is referred to as the current sensitivity. Sensitivity is determined by the number of turns in the coil, the strength of the magnet, and the restoring torque of the control springs or the taut band. Moving-coil mechanisms are designed to operate at no more than a few milliamperes.

Meters with sensitivities as small as 10 μA have been built using the best of permanent-magnet materials. Coil resistances for the more sensitive meters can be quite high. For many meters the coil resistance may be approximated by 50 mV divided by full-scale current sensitivity. This is a crude rule of thumb, since manufacturers can make a number of movements whose resistance is different for a given full-scale current sensitivity.

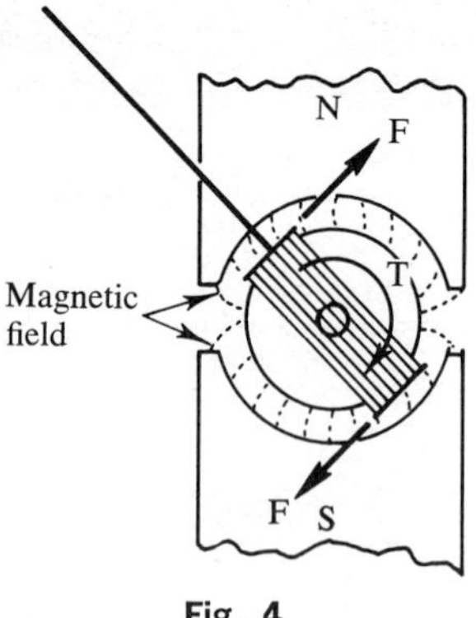

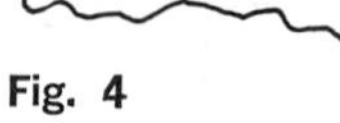

Fig. 4

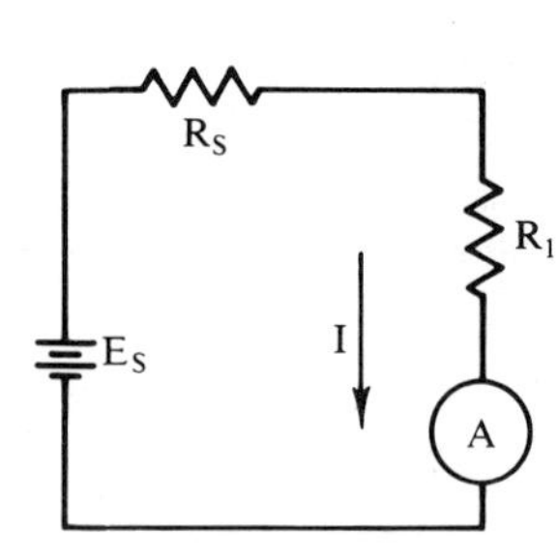

Fig. 5

Insertion Errors. The basic d'Arsonval movement is limited in its use. Generally, the coil resistance of a movement can be as high as several thousand ohms. If employed in a low-impedance network, considerable error may be realized. For example, the current flow through the network in Fig. 5 is related by

$$I = \frac{E_s}{R_s + R_a + R_1}$$

where R_s = source resistance
R_1 = network resistance
R_a = coil resistance of ammeter

If $E_s = 10$ V, $R_s = 0.25\ \Omega$, $R_1 = 2{,}000\ \Omega$, and $R_a = 5\ \Omega$, then

$$I = \frac{10}{0.25 + 2{,}000 + 5} = 4.997 \text{ mA}$$

With the ammeter removed from the circuit, the current I would be exactly 5.00 mA. This current is approximately 0.25 percent higher than with the ammeter. This error does not appear to be significant, since a 0.25 percent error is not discernable on the face of the meter. But suppose, in the example, that $E_s = 1$ V and $R_l = 200\ \Omega$. Then a significant error of approximately 2.5 percent would exist.

This insertion error is difficult to evaluate in a more complicated network, but if network resistance is larger by at least two orders of magnitude (100 times), insertion errors can be limited to less than 1 percent. The ideal case, of course, is to drive the meter with a current source.

Friction Errors. Certain limitations are inherent in the movement. Pivot friction is present in the pivot-and-jewel suspensions. The rolling action of the pivot on the side of the jewel causes a "pivot-roll error," which is referred to as frictional error. These errors can be controlled by two things. First, the pivots and bearings can be designed with a very small contour radius. However, there is a size limitation, as very small jewel units are susceptible to damage by minor impacts or knocks.

Second, the effects of friction are negligible in high torque-to-weight ratio movements. This kind of meter is limited to higher current sensitivities. In the best pivot-and-jewel meters, frictional error can be approximately 0.1 to 0.2 percent of full-scale current.

In the taut-band movement friction is caused by molecular friction in the band under torque. Errors caused by these small frictional forces are negligible for all practical purposes. Higher sensitivities are available using the taut-band system than with the pivot-and-jewel combinations without the disadvantages of frictional errors.

Temperature Errors. When the temperature rises, the basic movement increases in sensitivity. This increase is caused by the reduction of control torque due to the increased temperature. The temperature coefficient of current sensitivity of the majority of pivot-and-jewel types of instruments is in the vicinity of from 0.02 to 0.025 percent per degree Celsius. In most taut-band-type units this error is less than 0.01 percent per degree Celsius.

While the movement current sensitivity is increasing with rising temperature, the resistance of the coil and control springs is increasing at a rate of approximately 0.4 percent per degree Celsius. Therefore, when the coil and spring resistance are an appreciable portion of the total network resistance, these changes must be taken into account.

Temperature compensation can be provided internally in the form of either shunts or multipliers. The temperature coefficients of these compensators are chosen such that their resistance changes with temperature are exactly equal and opposite to the changes in the movement's resistance.

Maximum Current. The maximum current flow through the delicate moving coil must not exceed the rated current of the meter. If the amount of current is not large enough to burn out the fine wire in the coil, the excess torque produced may be great enough to damage the pointer. The user must exercise extreme caution when using the more sensitive ammeters. The meter must not be inserted into a circuit in which the short-circuit current exceeds the full-scale range of the ammeter.

Calibration. The current sensitivity of a basic movement is controlled by the following parameters: (1) the number of turns in the coil, (2) magnet strength, and (3) control-spring torque. The values of these parameters are established during the design and manufacture of the movement.

Generally, during manufacture, the full-scale sensitivity is calibrated by adjusting the strength of the magnet with equipment which can "charge" and "discharge" the magnet. Unless the user has access to such calibration equipment, it is nearly impossible to change the basic current sensitivity of a movement. Occasionally a movement may have a "magnetic shunt" adjustment which allows one to set full-scale sensitivity with the meter in its case.

The general practice in manufacturing the less expensive jewel movements is the use of the same scale for all meters of a given type. Of course, there are subtle differences in each meter mechanism which make it deviate in its ability to track the scale marks. Scales for taut-band movements with greater precision are sometimes individually calibrated by a system which automatically tracks the movement under calibration and photographically exposes a scale which precisely matches its characteristics. The photograph in Fig. 6 shows a double-exposed faceplate for two like movements. Small differences between the two movements are apparent.

Pivot-and-jewel tracking errors are typically 0.5 percent of full scale. Precision taut-band movement without individually calibrated scales typically hold 0.25 percent full-scale tracking, while those with individually calibrated scales are known to hold 0.10 percent full-scale tracking.

The problem of combining instruments into a standard test setup exists in any calibration situation. Many possibilities exist, but one fact cannot be ignored. A standard or reference instrument, be it a standard voltmeter or a standard ammeter, is needed. A typical test setup is shown in Fig. 7, in which a standard voltmeter monitors the voltage across a standard resistor. Potentiometer R_p is adjusted until a precise voltage across R_s is obtained. Hence, a precise current flows through the ammeter, and indicated accuracy may be checked.

Fig. 6. Double-exposed faceplate for two like taut-band movements. *(Hewlett-Packard Company, Loveland, Colo.)*

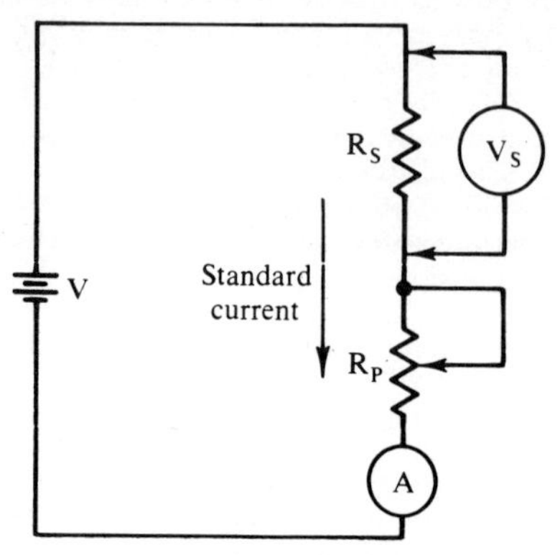

Fig. 7. Calibration network.

2. AC Moving-iron Types In 1820, Arago and Davy discovered that a coil of wire with a current passing through it would magnetize an iron rod placed near the coil and the resulting magnetic forces would draw the rod into the coil. This effect gave rise to a class of indicating instruments called "moving-iron" instruments. This widely adopted class of instruments is capable of indicating an alternating as well as a direct current. Most applications, however, are ac measurements at power-line frequencies.

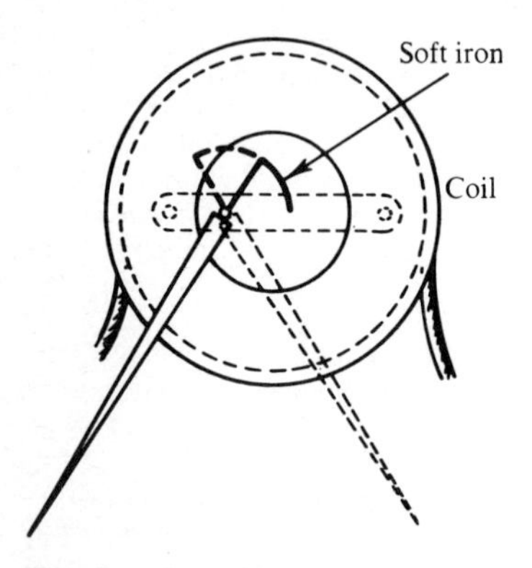

Fig. 8. Attraction-type moving-iron ammeter.

Hundreds of moving-iron ammeters have been designed since 1820. Each has been a little different in its mechanical structure. Two basic types have evolved. They are the "attraction" and "repulsion" types. Since the modern-day moving-iron ammeters employ mostly the repulsion type, only a scant mention of the attraction type will be made.

An attraction-type moving-iron ammeter is illustrated in Fig. 8. This instrument has a single soft iron and pointer assembly suspended off center in a coil. When a current passes through the coil, the soft iron is attracted toward the inner edge of the coil where the magnetic field is stronger. This early instrument was designed to operate in one physical position such that the nonenergized position of the soft-iron mass was below the pivot. This was zero position. Usually, an adjustable counterbalance was attached near the soft-iron piece for the purpose of calibration.

A repulsion-type moving-iron instrument is shown in Fig. 9. Two pieces of iron lying side by side in the same coil are magnetized in the same manner and repel one another. At zero current these two irons are close together, but when current circulates in the coil the two pieces of iron become similarly magnetized and the moving iron is repelled.

Since the irons repel irrespective of the polarity, the instrument will indicate on alternating current. Attraction- and repulsion-type meters indicate rms values, and their response in indication follows a square law.

The repulsion principle has been adopted mostly for soft-iron instruments because of its ability to indicate smaller currents than most other types. A certain amount of adjustment of the scale form can be accomplished by shaping the repulsion iron. Scales for the attraction-type ammeters tend to be compressed at the lower end while scales for the repulsion types are compressed at the upper end. Therefore, combined use of the attraction and repulsion techniques in one instrument allows longer and more reasonably uniform scales.

The instruments mentioned thus far represent some of the inventions by early inventors. Since these developments, many similar improved soft-iron instruments have been developed. From the heavy gravity-type movements with knife-edge suspension evolved the more recent and reliable lightweight movements with jewel suspension and spring return.

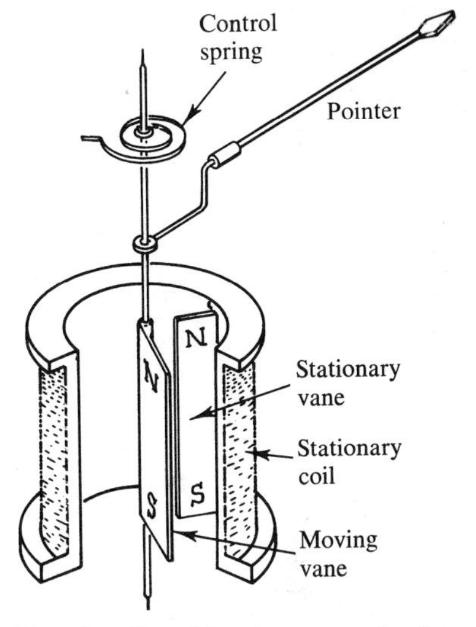

Fig. 9. Repulsion-type moving-iron ammeter.

Current Sensitivity. The amount of current required to cause full-scale deflection is referred to as the movement's current sensitivity. In general, the torque of moving-iron instruments is small compared with that usually obtained in moving-coil instruments. Consequently soft-iron instruments are made with current sensitivities on the order of several milliamperes or greater. More sensitive meters would require coils with larger ampere-turns at the expense of more series inductance, which would limit frequency response.

Limitations. The errors which occur in soft-iron ammeters are similar to those mentioned for a moving-coil ammeter. One other source of error worth mentioning, however, is frequency error caused by inductance and eddy currents. The total inductance is made up of the inductance due to the coil and the iron of the movement.

For a given current flow through the ammeter, changes in inductance will not change the indication of the meter. A change in inductance, however, will change the impedance of the meter. Therefore, if the meter is used as an ammeter in a network, a change in impedance will change the impedance ratio between network and ammeter, and hence a change in insertion error will result.

The effect of an alternating magnetic field on an iron part results in eddy currents which have a demagnetizing effect. Under most circumstances, these eddy currents will cause errors in the indication of the meter.

The soft iron meter is frequency limited, and most applications are found in the power field where low-frequency and large-magnitude currents must be measured.

The maximum current flow through the coil must not exceed the rated current of the meter. If the amount of current is not large enough to burn out the wire in the coil, the excess torque produced may be great enough to damage the pointer.

Care must be taken to use the instrument in the position in which it was calibrated. The gravity types work in one position only. Other nongravity types may work in a number of positions, but errors of several percent may be realized in any position other than the specified calibrated position.

3. Rectifier Types The rectifier ammeter is useful for measuring radio-frequency alternating currents. Its indication is directly proportional to the average value of the current. The rectifier-type panel meter basically consists of a full-wave bridge rectifier and a d'Arsonval movement as shown in Fig. 10. The bridge rectifier converts the alternating current to a pulsating direct current. The d'Arsonval movement then responds to the average value of the pulsating direct current.

Since the average value of a sine-wave signal is directly proportional to its rms value, the faceplates are often calibrated to read rms current. Therefore, such a reading is accurate for a sine wave only. Readings resulting from other waveform shapes are in error. For sine-wave signals with known amounts of distortion, the error in the reading may be determined from Table 2 in Chapter 20.

Current Sensitivity. Current sensitivity or full-scale current at low frequencies is dependent upon the parameters of the d'Arsonval movement. Any change in one of its basic three parameters, number of coil turns, magnet strength, and spring torque, will change the sensitivity of the rectifier-type panel meter.

Limitations. Many shortcomings of this type of meter may be attributed to the d'Arsonval movement. However, other limitations are unique to a rectifier and d'Arsonval meter combination when they are required to measure high-frequency alternating currents.

Input
A

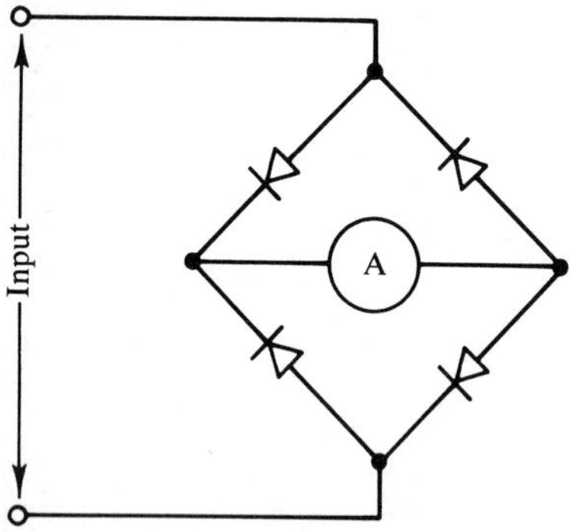

Fig. 10. Rectifier ammeter.

The quality of the rectifying diode usually determines the upper frequency limit of the rectifier-type ammeter. Standard units using low-frequency germanium rectifiers are often specified to read within ±3 percent of full scale at 10 kHz or below. Useful indications for this ammeter to several megahertz are possible. Significant error can be introduced into a measurement if the forward voltage across the germanium rectifying element drops below 0.1 V. At this voltage the resistance of the rectifiers becomes significantly large. Consequently, if the meter is connected to a low-impedance network, considerable error can be introduced.

Special high-frequency diodes such as hot-carrier diodes used as rectifying elements can extend the range of useful indications to several hundred megahertz. Measurements can be made with accuracies of less than 5 percent of frequencies of several tens of megahertz.

Waveform. The rectifier-type meter is calibrated for sine wave. Readings obtained from other types of waveforms will be in error. Sine waves containing known amounts of distortion will introduce error into the reading also. If the distortion is known, the error may be determined from Table 2 in Chapter 20. For example, if 20 percent of second-harmonic distortion is present, the reading will be in error at most by approximately 2 percent.

Calibration. The manufacturer calibrates the rectifier-type panel meter very much like the single d'Arsonval movement. A standard current generated at some low-frequency value such as 1 kHz is passed through the rectifier panel meter. A current amplitude is chosen to give full-scale deflection. Standard procedure is then used in calibrating the full-scale sensitivity of the d'Arsonval movement.

4. Thermocouple Types The thermocouple ammeter is useful for ac measurements, as its indication depends upon the heat developed by the passage of current through a conductor and is thus dependent on the root mean square (the effective value) of the current.

The thermocouple ammeter's indication is proportional to the voltage produced by a thermojunction heated by thermal conduction or radiation from the current-carrying conductor.

A thermocouple is formed when two dissimilar metals are joined together. When heated, this junction generates a small voltage which is proportional to a temperature gradient across the junction. For example, a junction formed with iron and constantan will generate approximately 52 μV/°C temperature difference across the junction.

The thermocouple shown in Fig. 11 is usually connected to a sensitive moving-coil ammeter to indicate the magnitude of the junction voltage. The thermocouple consists of a resistance wire of a few ohms directly coupled to the thermocouple junction. Heat transfer from the wire to the junction is largely by conduction. In the more sensitive type of this meter, the junction and heater wire are placed in an evacuated chamber where isolation from draft and convection air currents is possible. In the more sensitive thermocouple meters, the mass of the metal is kept minimal by using very small component wires. The larger-current thermocouples require larger wires, and consequently the time required to make a measurement is greater because of the greater mass of metal which must be heated.

Current Range. The maximum current required for full-scale deflection for a simple thermocouple ammeter is quite high (typically 10 mA) because considerable power is required to heat the thermojunction and the thermojunction generates only a few microvolts per degree Celsius of temperature difference.

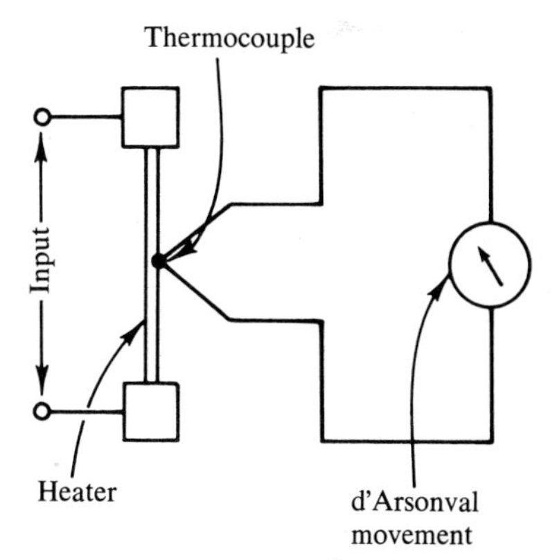

Fig. 11. Thermocouple ammeter.

The more expensive meters using vacuum thermocouples and very sensitive d'Arsonval movements can attain full-scale deflections on the order of 1 mA. Large current thermojunctions may have full-scale deflections on the order of 20 A.

Limitations. The thermojunction ammeter is an excellent rms-responding ac ammeter capable of adequately measuring alternating currents in the range of 20 Hz to 1 MHz with an accuracy of ± 1 percent deviation from some low-frequency current such as 60 Hz. Current indications above 1 to several megahertz, although not accurate, may be useful for comparative measurements.

More expensive high-frequency thermojunction meters can be built which extend the range to MHz at accuracies of ± 2 percent of low-frequency values.

Response times for the larger-current meters tend to be much slower, usually several seconds compared with less than a second for the smaller-current devices.

Ambient-temperature changes affect the reading of most thermojunctions by significant amounts. For example, one manufacturer specifies a temperature coefficient of approximately 0.2 percent per degree Celsius for his standard line of meters, while a more expensive one with a temperature coefficient of less than 0.2 percent per degree Celsius could be built upon request.

Many other limitations of the thermojunction ammeter can be attributed to the d'Arsonval movement. Basic limitations such as accuracy and friction are discussed in the section on the d'Arsonval movement.

SYSTEM AMMETER TYPES

5. AC-transformer Types The ac transformer is usually an accessory component in a current-measuring system. It is a converter whose resistance-terminated output is fed into an ordinary ac voltmeter or oscilloscope for measurement.

The transformer acts to couple a signal inductively to the measuring instrument without a direct electrical connection. The transformer, whose schematic is shown in Fig. 12, consists of a secondary winding of N_s turns of wire wound on a core of magnetic material. The conductor of a network carrying the current in question forms a one-turn primary winding.

From basic transformer theory, the ratio of primary to secondary current is inversely proportional to the turns ratio as given by

$$\frac{I_p}{I_s} = \frac{N_s}{N_p}$$

where I_p and I_s are primary and secondary currents, respectively, and N_p and N_s are the number of turns in the primary and secondary windings, respectively.

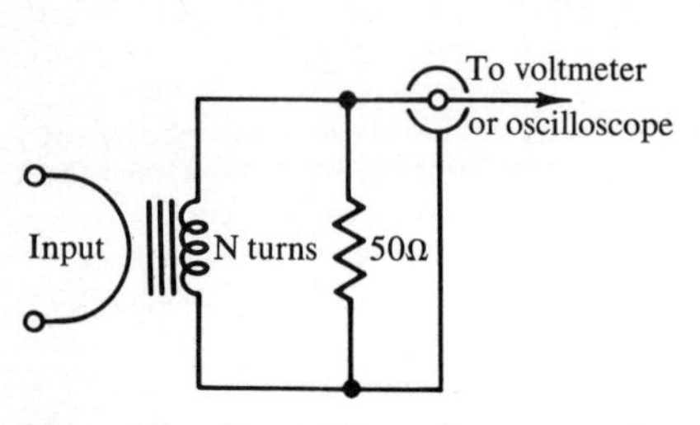

Fig. 12. Current-transformer schematic.

Two types of cores are commonly used. One of these, the split-core transformer, is constructed as shown in Fig. 13. Part of the core may be split away from the main core material to allow one to loop the current-carrying conductor through the center. This type of core is convenient because the conductor in question does not need to be broken. The split-core transformer is usually mounted in a probe body of some type with a hand-actuated mechanism for opening and closing the transformer core.

The other type, the closed-core transformer, is shown in Fig. 14. This type is not as convenient as the split-core type because the wire carrying the current in question must be broken and inserted through a small hole in the side of the enclosure which houses the transformer.

Sensitivity. It is not uncommon for a transformer to have 25 turns in the secondary and to be terminated with a 50-Ω load. Since the terminated output often feeds a 50-Ω shielded cable, the effective load is the parallel sum of the load

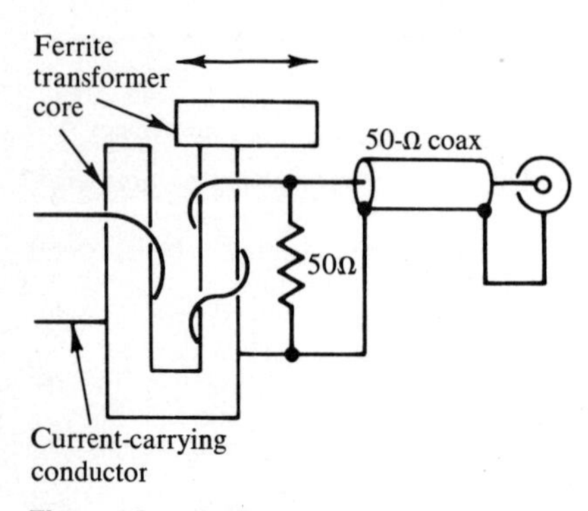

Fig. 13. Split-core current transformer.

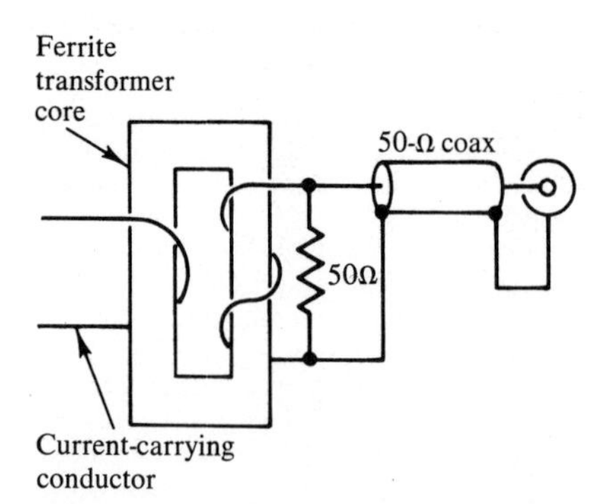

Fig. 14. Closed-core current transformer.

and cable, or 25 Ω. If a current of 50 mA flows in the primary, the secondary current I_s is found to be

$$I_s = \frac{50}{25} = 2 \text{ mA}$$

Hence 2 mA flows through the 25-Ω load, thus developing a 50-mV signal. In this example, the transformer has a sensitivity of 50 mA per 50 mV, or 1 mA/mV.

Frequency Limits. The midfrequency transfer characteristic (1 mA/mV) has been calculated in the example above. The transformer is a frequency-sensitive device, however. Since the secondary current is dependent on the rate of change of input current, one would expect the output at dc to be zero. As the frequency of the input current increases near dc, the output increases also. A point is reached where the output levels off. This breaking point is often referred to as the 30 percent down point or, more simply, the frequency at which the output is down 30 percent from the midfrequency value.

This 30 percent down point is easy to determine. It is the point at which the inductive reactance of the secondary inductor is equal to the load resistance. The frequency at which the inductive reactance equals R_s, in this case 25 Ω, is

$$f = \frac{25}{2\pi L} = 35 \text{ kHz}$$

with $L = 125\ \mu$H.

Unfortunately, the midband response does not hold up forever. As the frequency is increased, a point (a second 30 percent down point) is reached where the output begins to drop off. This output loss is due to a component called leakage inductance.

Leakage inductance may be described as the primary magnetic flux that does not link the secondary windings. At low frequencies the leakage inductance is negligible. In the midband area, an increase occurs in current rate of change and the secondary voltage is constant. Above the second 30 percent down point, the leakage inductance increases more rapidly than the current rate of change and the secondary current output goes toward zero.

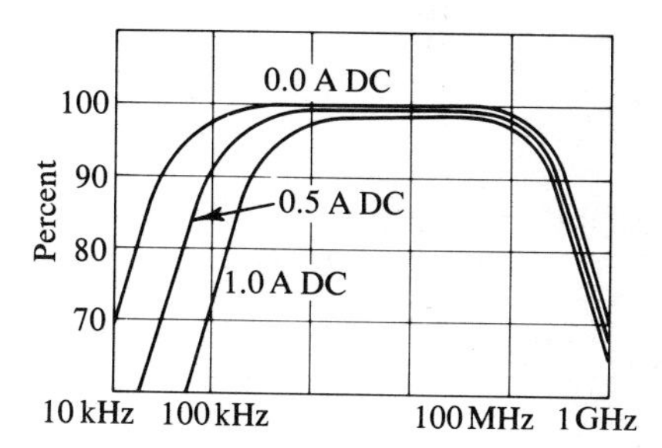

Fig. 15. Frequency response vs. direct current for a current transformer.

The frequency response of a current transformer often specifies the range between the 30 percent down points. It is not common for a good transformer design to cover nearly six decades of frequency between these points. Upper 30 percent down points typically range from 50 to 200 MHz. A few are available up to 1 GHz. Typically, the low break point is a few kilohertz.

Active terminations are available which present a very low termination resistance to the transformer. These are useful in lowering the low-frequency break point to several tens of hertz. The output of the active termination is then fed to an ac voltmeter or oscilloscope for measurement.

Effects of Direct Current. The effects of a direct current on the frequency response of a typical core may be seen in Fig. 15. The presence of a dc signal does not improve the lower-frequency response.

Insertion Impedance. The insertion impedance reflected into the network under test is usually quite small. From basic transformer theory, the resistance and inductance reflected into the primary winding are given by

$$R_i = \frac{R_s N_p^2}{N_s^2} \qquad \text{and} \qquad L_i = \frac{L_s N_p^2}{N_s^2}$$

where R_i and L_i are insertion resistance and inductance, respectively. Hence, for the equations above,

$$R_i = \frac{25\Omega}{25^2} = 40 \text{ m}\Omega$$

$$L_i = \frac{3.125 \text{ mH}}{25^2} = 5\ \mu\text{H}$$

where $R_s = 25\ \Omega$
$L_s = 3.125$ mH

Thus the current probe inserts 40 mΩ shunted by 5 μH in series with the wire in the network under test.

Calibration. The transformer-sensitivity specifications are established during the design and manufacture of the unit. The number of turns and the load resistance which determine sensitivity are fixed and cannot be changed. Sensitivities are typically specified to be better than ±3 percent at some midfrequency.

6. Flux-gate-magnetometer Types The flux-gate-magnetometer-type ammeter, a dc-measuring instrument, employs a special current transformer. Like the ac transformer, the current-carrying conductor functions as a one-turn primary winding. But unlike ac-transformer operation, the current in the primary, a direct current, does not induce a voltage in the sense winding without help.

Since the magnetic flux in the core is caused by a direct current, it will be steady. An ac signal can be induced into the sense windings by switching the flux from a minimum to a maximum. This minimum-to-maximum switching of

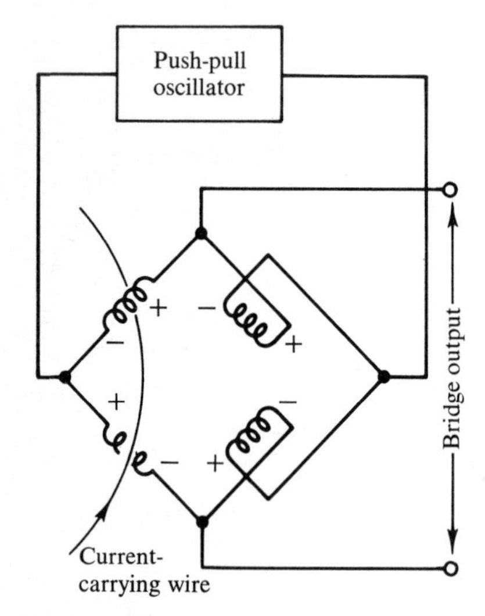

Fig. 16. Flux-gate magnetometer transformer bridge network.

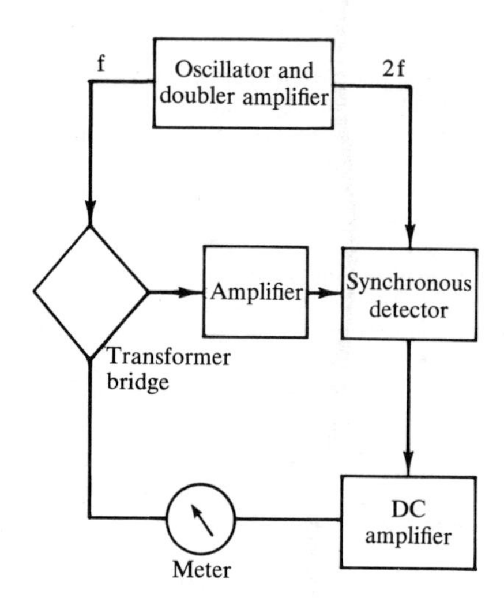

Fig. 17. Simple block diagram of the transformer bridge and metering circuit for a flux-gate-magnetometer-type ammeter.

the flux is referred to as flux gating. Gating is achieved by saturable magnetic cores which are driven into and out of saturation by a large ac drive signal. When the core is saturated, its permeability is greatly reduced, which results in few flux linkages between the sensing coils and the current in the measured wire. When the cores are out of saturation, permeability is high and the flux linkages are greatly increased. The resulting ac signal in the sense windings is proportional to the direct current which flows in the conductor.

A simplified circuit is shown in Fig. 16. The drive coils and sensing coils are combined by use of a bridge configuration. The bridge is balanced as far as the drive signal is concerned so that drive signal is suppressed in the output. The connections for two of the coils are reversed, though, so voltages induced by the gated flux from the measured wire generate an output.

A simplified block diagram of the transformer bridge and metering circuit is shown in Fig. 17. A push-pull oscillator supplies a drive frequency of several kilohertz. The frequency is high enough to drive the small size of the cores and coils somewhere in their midfrequency range.

Flux gating occurs at twice the rate of the push-pull oscillator, since the core saturates twice during each cycle, once during the positive-going part of the drive waveform and once during the negative-going part. Because of this, the magnetometer is often referred to as a "second-harmonic flux-gate magnetometer." The bridge output is therefore a signal which is double the drive signal.

The bridge output is amplified in a tuned amplifier and then rectified in a synchronous detector. The synchronous detector preserves the polarity of the bridge signal so that if the signal polarity were reversed the detector's output would be reversed also. The voltage at the output of the detector is proportional to the current being measured. The output is amplified by a dc amplifier which drives the indicating meter.

Accuracy is affected by the nonlinear behavior of the magnetic circuits as well as by nonlinearities and changes of gain in the amplifier. To ensure that the meter indicates accurately what the measured current is, negative feedback is used to reduce the system's nonlinearities.

Current Sensitivity. Current required for full-scale current readings typically ranges from 1 mA full scale to 10 A. Currents as small as 50 μA can be resolved on a 1-mA full-scale range. The sensitivity can be increased several times by looping the wire through the transformer several times.

Limitations. The transformer is virtually burnout-proof, being able to withstand overloads of hundreds of amperes. However, mechanical damage could occur if it was subjected to any severe mechanical shocks which could fracture the cores and introduce air gaps in the magnetic circuits. Air gaps would reduce magnetic coupling, which would affect the performance. On a split-core type each half must electrically connect to the other when the core is closed so that no air gap exists. Therefore, the core halves should be kept clean.

The instrument readings are little affected by the presence of alternating current with the measured direct current, provided that the ac peak value is less than full scale.

Residual magnetism in ferrous conductors can cause the instrument to read several milliamperes. If ferrous conductors cannot be avoided, the instrument may be rezeroed with the circuit turned off. The reading from the residual magnetism will be zeroed out.

A degausser is built into most instruments to demagnetize the transformer in the event that it has been exposed to heavy direct currents or high magnetic fields.

Calibration. With proper care, a flux-gate magnetometer retains its calibration for long periods, and the instrument may never need to be calibrated. Of course, if calibration is found to be necessary, a standard current can be established with a standard voltmeter, standard resistor, variable potentiometer, and voltage source as shown in Fig. 7. Usually there is one adjustment for full scale which can be set on one arbitrary range. Ranging, which may never need calibration, is usually fixed by a set of precision nonadjustable resistors. The instrument's operating and service manual should be consulted before any adjustments are attempted.

7. Hall-effect Types Ammeters which employ a Hall generator are capable of measuring currents from dc to several hundred megahertz. The Hall generator operates on an interesting phenomenon called the "Hall effect."

Imagine a bar of semiconductor or conductor material whose dimensions are x, y, and z. If a direct current is passed along the x axis and a magnetic field is impressed along the y axis, a potential along the z axis will exist. The operation is basically simple. One can think of the direct current as a uniform distribution of positively and negatively charged particles moving along the x axis. When an external magnetic field is applied along the y axis, the charged particles are displaced along the z axis. The positive particles are displaced one direction and the negative (electron) particles are displaced the opposite. Thus a difference in potential exists along the z axis. This potential is called the Hall voltage. The amplitude of the Hall voltage is a function of the charge concentration (magnitude of the current) in the conducting element, the strength of the magnetic field, the type of material, and the dimensions of the element. The Hall generator is polarity-sensitive also. If the direction of the current or the direction of the magnetic field is reversed, the Hall voltage polarity will also be reversed.

One manufacturer cleverly uses the Hall generator with an ac transformer to extend its frequency range effectively to dc. The Hall generator is mounted in the transformer's core, where it will sense the flux produced by the current in the conductor under test. A block diagram is shown in Fig. 18. The output of the Hall generator is coupled through the secondary winding to a load resistor R_L via a low-frequency amplifier A_1. The signal developed across R_L is amplified by the dc-to-high-frequency amplifier A_2.

The output of amplifier A_1 introduces a dc signal into the secondary winding. The direction of the direct current is such that the magnetic flux produced by the secondary winding is nearly equal and opposite to the dc flux produced in the primary. Thus the Hall generator, amplifier, secondary winding, and transformer core form a feedback system. Because the gain of the amplifier is high, only a very small dc flux remains in the core to maintain the secondary ampere-turns nearly equal to the primary ampere-turns. Consequently, several amperes of direct current can

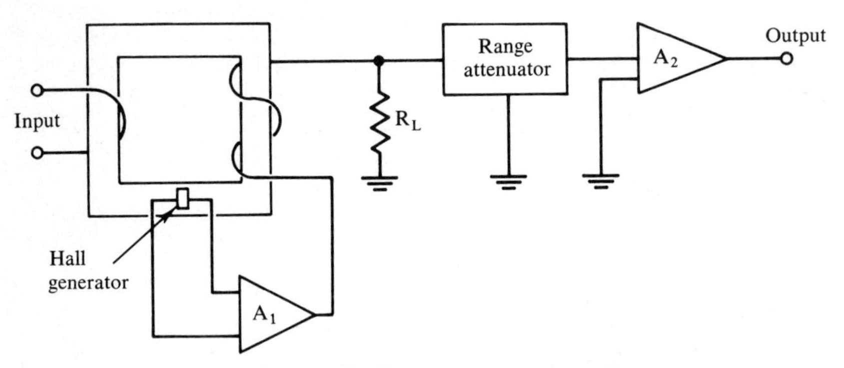

Fig. 18. Hall-effect ammeter schematic.

be measured without saturating the core. The maximum current, naturally, depends on the output capability of amplifier A_1.

The Hall generator, being a very broadband active device (dc to several gigahertz), generates random noise like all other active devices. To make a more sensitive instrument, this random noise is reduced by limiting the bandwidth of A_1 to several hundred kilohertz. The bandwidth of the transformer is made to complement the bandwidth of A_1. That is, the upper 3-dB frequency of A_1 is made to coincide with the lower 3-dB frequency of the transformer. This results in a flat response from dc to the upper-bandwidth limits of the transformer.

The output of amplifier A_2 is available for external measurement by a broadband ac voltmeter or oscilloscope. The latter is preferred because components of direct and alternating current can be observed simultaneously.

Current Sensitivity. The instrument's transfer of current at the input to a voltage output is expressed in terms of millivolts per milliampere. This ratio is known as the current sensitivity. Current sensitivities for a typical instrument may range from 50 mV/mA to 50 mV/mA.

Limitations. The Hall generator, like other semiconductors, is temperature-sensitive. A change in temperature results in a change at both outputs of the Hall generator in the same direction and of equal magnitude. This is a common-mode signal which can cause errors in the balanced input to amplifier A_1. Special compensation networks are provided to minimize this temperature effect.

There is a maximum safe voltage which the transformer insulation is capable of withstanding. The voltage referred to is the potential of the current-carrying conductor with respect to ground. Transformers typically can handle 500 V.

Residual flux in the core can be caused by subjecting the transformer to a large direct current. Residual flux remains when the dc signal is removed. As a result, the Hall generator will process this residual flux as an input signal. A degaussing control is usually included in the instrument to remove the residual flux. Generally an opening at the front panel of the instrument is available for degaussing. The transformer is inserted into this opening, where upon activation of a degauss switch, a series of damped sinusoidal magnetic fields are impressed upon the core.

Calibration. Hall instruments seldom need calibration. However, over long periods of time changes in component values realistically affect the accuracy performance. The calibration procedure for the system described in Fig. 18 is complicated. For example, the response at the frequency where the amplifier A_1 and the transformer complement each other must be adjusted for flatness. Bandwidth and gain adjustments control this response.

The wideband amplifier A_2 requires two important adjustments. The gain adjustment establishes the current sensitivity at some low reference frequency such as 1 kHz. If a precision ac voltmeter with meter readout is used as a reference, it is best to choose a range such that sensitivity calibration is made at full-scale deflection of the meter. High-frequency response can be adjusted by a compensation control. To make the adjustment, the system is pulse-tested, and the shape of the pulse is set for maximum flatness as seen on the face of a high-frequency oscilloscope.

Accuracy. Sensitivity accuracy for Hall ammeters is typically ± 3 percent over a frequency range from dc to 50 MHz. Actual full-scale measurement error, however, depends also on the type of instrument used to measure the output voltage from the Hall ammeter. Measurements within ± 5 percent can be made with a good ac voltmeter, while measurements within ± 10 percent may be made with an oscilloscope.

8. DC-voltmeter Types An ordinary amplifier-type dc voltmeter may be used as an ammeter. The discussion of voltmeter-type ammeters which follows will be restricted to the two types in which current-measurement provisions are designed into the instrument. The first instrument type is one with current-mode and current-range controls available at the front panel, while the second type has no special current-function front-panel control.

To measure a current, the two imput terminals of a floating dc-voltmeter-type ammeter must be connected to two ends of a broken current-carrying conductor. That is, the input is connected in series with the broken ends of a current-carrying conductor. The current in question flows through the voltmeter's input attenuator or shunt and causes a voltage drop which is measured by the amplifier and indicator portion of the voltmeter.

There are basically two voltmeter-system designs which have current-measuring capabilities. One of these systems, shown in Fig. 19, uses an input attenuator to change the full-scale sensitivity of the voltmeter. The gain or sensitivity of the chopper-stabilized dc and d'Arsonval meter combination is fixed as established by the feedback around the amplifier.*

The other type of voltmeter system with current-measuring capability is shown in Fig. 20. This is a low-level voltage-measuring system capable of indicating a few microvolts to approximately 1 V full scale. The ability to read small voltages depends on the gain of the amplifier. For example, if the meter requires 1 V for full-scale deflection, an amplifier gain of 100,000 would be required to indicate 10 μV full scale. To change range to 100 μV, it would be necessary to switch the feedback to change the amplifier gain to 10,000.

Naturally, the shunt resistor shown in Fig. 20 at the input of the voltmeter is required when the voltmeter is used as an ammeter. This shunt resistor, like the range attenuator, is usually quite large (100 kΩ or greater). This sensitive voltmeter type is capable of measuring the few microvolts generated by the few

* The operation of the chopper amplifier and feedback system is discussed in more detail in Chapter 22.

picoamperes of current flowing through the shunt resistor. A current-function switch is often used to switch in the shunt resistor.

Often a voltmeter may use a combination of the two types of systems because of the wide range of voltage inputs it will accept. In either case, the value of

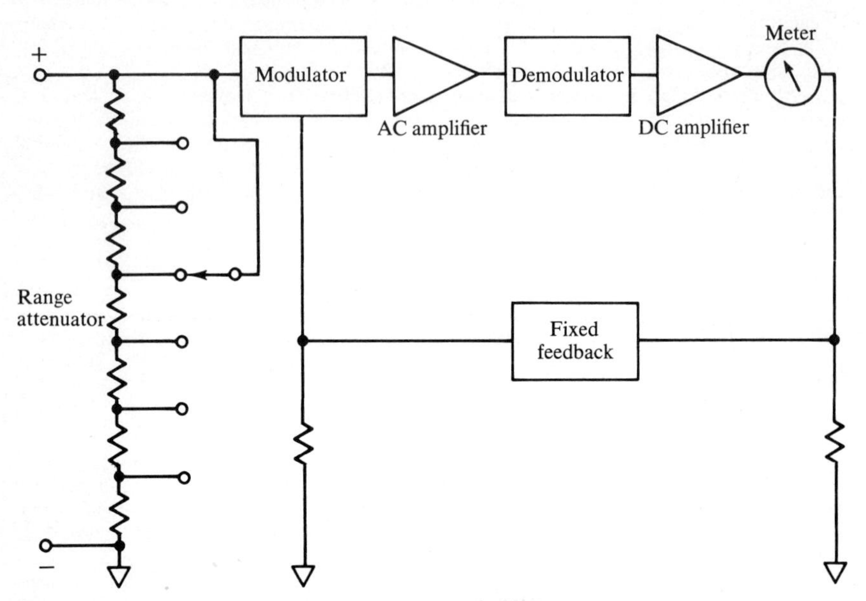

Fig. 19. High-voltage dc voltmeter with input attenuator used as an ammeter. The voltage across the attenuator as measured by the voltmeter is proportional to the current flow through the attenuator.

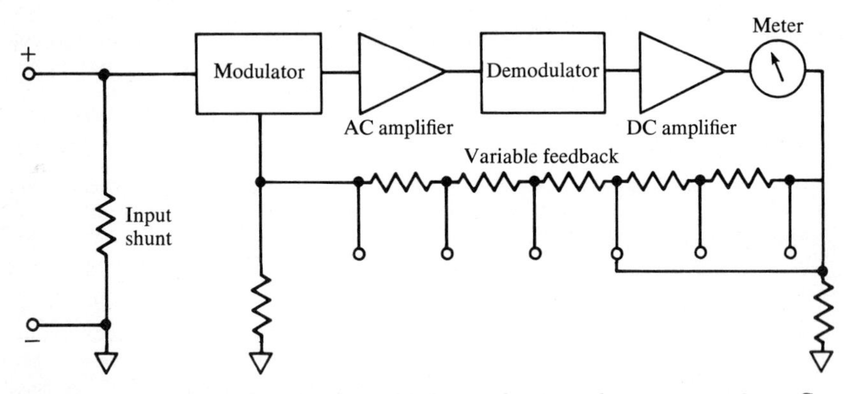

Fig. 20. Low-voltage dc voltmeter with input shunt used as an ammeter. Current flow through the shunt develops a voltage which is measured by the voltmeter.

the range attenuator or shunt must be decreased to approximately 100 kΩ for the lower voltage ranges where the amplifier gain is large. The reason is to minimize noise. Noise generated in large-input-range or shunt resistors would appear as a nervous disturbance on the face of the meter when read on the 10-μV range, for example.

Current Sensitivity. The amount of current required to cause full-scale deflection is referred to as the ammeter's current sensitivity. The current sensitivities for dc-voltmeter-type ammeters are usually very small. For example, a voltmeter whose full-scale ranges are 3 μV to 3 mV may typically measure 30 pA (30×10^{-12}A) to 30 nA (30×10^{-10}A) on the same ranges. Current sensitivity may range from 10 pA to 10 nA on many voltmeters. Ranges covering to 10 mA must be covered by switching in of special low-value shunts. This is done in instruments which have a current-function switch.

It is possible to increase the upper range of current sensitivities to several amperes if desired, however, at the expense of performance of the instrument's use as a voltmeter. For a basic 1-V voltmeter a shunt resistance of 1 Ω would be required to measure 1 A. There is nothing to say that this capability could not be designed into a voltmeter instrument by switching in different shunt resistors as required. However, instrument manufacturers apparently have not chosen to do so. The user is left with the task of supplying his own shunt, which may be paralleled with the input terminals of the instrument.

Input Resistance. As already mentioned, the input resistance of the ammeter is determined by the attenuator of the voltmeter. It is not uncommon for the input resistance to be as small as 100 kΩ and as large as 1 MΩ. In instruments which provide a separate current function, input resistance may be as low as 1 Ω for 1 mA of full-scale current and as high as 100 kΩ on the lower current ranges.

Accuracy. Voltmeters using a d'Arsonval meter may be specified to read ±2 percent of full scale. Typically the accuracy of the instrument used as an ammeter is slightly worse (typically ±3 percent).

Calibration. The instrument's accuracy is likely to suffer over large periods of time as the d'Arsonval meter and components age.

Full-scale sensitivity is likely to suffer most. The voltmeter without separate current function may be calibrated directly from a voltage standard in accordance with the operating and service manual. Usually one full-scale adjustment is available. Adjustment is made on one arbitrary range.

The voltmeter with a separate current function must be calibrated in a test setup similar to the one shown in Fig. 7.

After full scale has been set on the arbitrary range, readings on each other range are expected to be within their rated specifications. No adjustment is available if range accuracy is out of tolerance. Attenuator or range resistors are usually nonadjustable and would require replacement.

SPECIFICATIONS

It is not within the scope of this chapter to mention all the numerous types of specifications which describe the performance characteristics of each of the ammeter types. Since most ammeter types use a d'Arsonval movement, a few of its specifications along with others are discussed. Table 1 lists the ammeter types and a few of their salient features.

9. Accuracy Accuracy is the measure of an ammeter's ability to indicate the absolute value of the current applied. Accuracy is usually expressed as a percentage of full-scale value. Consider, for example, a 10-mA panel meter whose accuracy is specified as ±2 percent of full scale. The manufacturer claims that, for an absolute 10 mA of current applied, the reading will be within ±2 percent of 10 mA, or ±0.2 mA. Note the ±0.2 mA uncertainty exists anywhere on the scale. If one-tenth of full scale, or 1 mA, is applied to the same panel meter, the uncertainty is still ±0.2 mA. But this uncertainty at 1 mA is now ±20 percent uncertainty in reading. It is therefore recommended that measurements be made on ranges where nearly full-scale deflection is obtained for best accuracy.

The standard accuracy tolerance for most d'Arsonval movements is ±2 percent of full scale. Top-grade movements are capable of 0.25 percent of full scale, and 0.5 percent is the practical limit.

10. Tracking Accuracy The ability of a d'Arsonval movement to indicate at a division line in question when energized by a current which is proportional to the actual end-scale current is a measure of its tracking accuracy. This accuracy is expressed as a percentage of actual end-scale value.

The tracking-error test is performed by initially setting zero, then applying sufficient current to produce end-scale deflection precisely. It does not matter what the accuracy of the movement is at this point. It may be 2 percent low at full- or end-scale deflection. In this case a 10-mA movement would require 10.2 mA for a precise end-scale indication. The 10.2-mA current is then reduced proportionally to produce deflection to previously selected scale markings. The difference between the actual value of current required to produce the selected deflection and the value of corresponding current proportional to the actual end-scale current divided by the actual end-scale current results in the tracking error.

Tracking accuracy for standard d'Arsonval movements is often specified at 1½ to 2 times the rated full-scale accuracy of the movement. Therefore, a 2 percent movement may have as much as a 4 percent tracking error at a point on the scale. The more expensive taut-band meter with individually calibrated scales is capable of tracking better than ¼ percent. When these high-performance taut-band meters are specified for equipment with a calibration adjustment, tracking accuracy may be specified instead of full-scale accuracy.

TABLE 1 Ammeter Characteristics

Types of ammeters	Frequency range	Full-scale current range	Typical full-scale accuracy, %
Dc d'Arsonval types	Dc	>10 μA	0.1–5
Ac moving-iron types	Dc to 100 Hz	>100 mA	>3
Rectifier types	10 kHz to 500 MHz	>10 μA	>3
Thermocouple types	Dc and 20 Hz to 50 MHz	>1 mA	1–5
Ac-transformer types	50 Hz to 1 GHz	<1.5 A	>1
Flux-gate-magnetometer types	Dc	1 mA to 10 A	>3
Hall-effect types	Dc to 50 MHz	<10 A	>3
Dc-voltmeter types	Dc	>10 pA	>1

11. Repeatability Repeatability is a measure of a d'Arsonval movement's ability to provide repeat readings with the application of a given current. Repeatability is usually expressed as a percentage of full-scale deflection. Repeatability at a given point is usually measured by increasing the applied current to a specified value at a sufficiently slow rate so that no overshoot occurs. The meter deflection is then noted. The current is increased to a value of at least 10 percent above the specified current and then slowly reduced until the specified current is reached again. The difference in meter deflection divided by full-scale deflection is the repeatability error.

Repeatability is a function of the type of suspension, the friction in the pivots, weight of the movement, and the restoring forces present. One-half percent repeatability in a 1-mA unit in either pivot-and-jewel or taut-band construction poses very little problem. In this case the power input and restoring forces are relatively high. But a 10-μA meter with pivot-and-jewel construction would be hard-pressed to achieve ½ percent repeatability, because power input and restoring forces are low. The more expensive taut-band meter is a natural choice for 10-μA sensitivity with less than ½ percent repeatability.

12. Sensitivity Sensitivity or range is the current required for end-scale deflection. This is a broad specification which applies to most of the ammeter types discussed in this chapter. This specification, however, means something different for current transformers. Sensitivity is expressed as a ratio of the output voltage to input current. For example, a high-frequency transformer may have a sensitivity of 5 mV/mA.

13. Insertion Impedance Impedance is an apparent opposition offered by a circuit to the passage of an alternating current. Impedance, usually expressed in ohms, is the relationship between voltage and current associated with an ac ammeter. Ideally, an ammeter which does not develop an ac voltage across its terminals when inserted into a network under test has zero insertion impedance. Thus no insertion error would be introduced. However, there is no such ideal ammeter.

For broadband ac ammeters it is not a simple matter of specifying an impedance of X Ω, because impedance changes as frequency of the ac signal changes. Therefore, the electronics industry has adopted the custom of specifying impedance in terms of an equivalent network consisting of a resistor, inductor, and capacitor. A typical network is seen in Fig. 21. One manufacturer of a 35 kHz to 1 GHz current transformer, for example, specifies the insertion impedance by listing values for the inductance L, resistance R, and capacitance C. Typical values are $R = 1$ Ω, $L = 5$ mH, and $C = 1.5$ pF.

Instruments designed for use at one frequency such as the moving-iron ammeter are specified differently. For example, one manufacturer lists a 0- to 10-mA movement as having 2,000 Ω at 60 Hz.

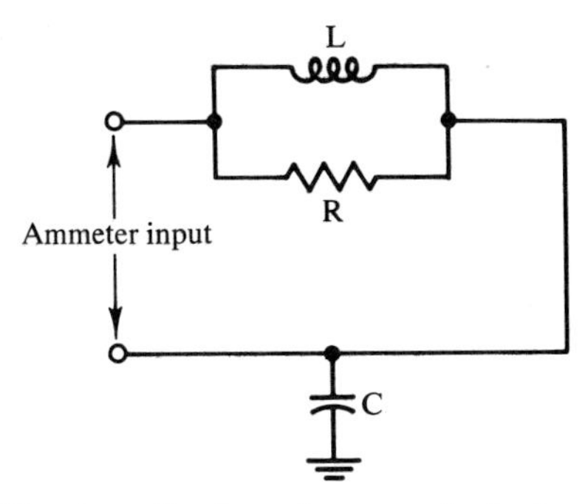

Fig. 21. Insertion-impedance equivalent network.

14. Insertion Resistance Like impedance, the insertion resistance, expressed in ohms, is the apparent opposition offered by a circuit to the passage of direct current. In the strict sense, resistance opposes alternating current as well, but the general practice is to specify the real part of the input impedance (resistance) for any dc ammeter.

Insertion or input resistance is specified for d'Arsonval and dc-voltmeter types of ammeters. It is not uncommon for d'Arsonval input resistances to range from 0.05 to 2,000 Ω for 1-A and 50-mA movements, respectively. Electronic ammeters, too, have a wide range. It is common for resistances to range from 1 MΩ to 1 Ω on 10-pA to 1-mA ranges, respectively.

15. Frequency Influence Measurements made by ac ammeters naturally are affected by the frequency of the current. Above or below some upper or lower respective frequency the ammeter's indication decreases.

There are two ways in which frequency influence is specified. First the change in indication due solely to a frequency change of the applied current from a specified frequency may be stated. For example, an expensive thermocouple-type ammeter may be specified to be with ±2 percent of its low-frequency value at 50 MHz. The change is expressed as a percentage change of full-scale value for a specified frequency change.

The second method of expressing frequency influence is to specify the bandwidth of the instrument. The bandwidth is represented by the range of frequencies between the lower and the upper 3-dB frequencies. The lower and upper 3-dB frequency points are defined as those at which an instrument's indications are approximately 30 percent below the actual value of the current being measured. The bandwidth of a current transformer typically specifies the 3-dB frequencies as 35 kHz and 1 GHz.

16. Waveform Influence The change in indication of an ac ammeter caused entirely by a change in waveform from a specified waveform, usually a sine wave, is a specification of waveform influence. It is generally expressed as a percentage change of full scale. This specification pertains to the average-responding rectifier panel meter; the rms-responding thermocouple panel meter; and the ac transformer with an average-, peak-, and rms-responding ac voltmeter connected to its ouptut. Often waveform influence is not specified. It is usually assumed that the user understands the effects of waveform on average-responding instruments.

Consider, as an example, a 1-kHz sine wave which contains a second-harmonic component, i.e., a 2-kHz signal. If the amplitude of the 2-kHz signal is 20 percent of the fundamental, or 1-kHz signal, the maximum introduced error will be 2 percent of full scale. Table 3 in Chapter 23 is useful in evaluating the error when the harmonic content of the signal is known.

BIBLIOGRAPHY

Calhoun, Richard E.: UHF Thermoelements, *Meas. Data,* November–December, 1968, pp. 67–73.

Drysdale, C. V., and A. C. Jolley: "Electrical Measuring Instruments," Part 1, "General Principles and Electrical Indicating Instruments," 2d ed., rev. by G. F. Tagg, John Wiley & Sons, Inc., New York, 1952.

McAbel, Walter E.: "Probe Measurements," Tektronix., Inc., October, 1969.

Terman, Frederick E., and J. M. Pettit: "Electronic Measurements," 2d ed., McGraw-Hill Book Company, New York, 1952.

Weber, Joe: "Oscilloscope Probe Circuits," Tektronix, Inc., November, 1969.

Chapter 22

DC Voltmeters

LARRY L. CARLSON

Hewlett-Packard Company, Loveland, Colorado

INTRODUCTION

The dc (direct-current) voltmeter is an instrument used for measuring a constant voltage between two points. It is expected to make many different types of dc measurements. Among a few of these measurements are network biasing where the user seldom cares for accurate answers better than several percent; standard measurements requiring accuracies better than 0.01 percent; and high-speed measurements where several hundred or several thousand measurements per second are taken for high-speed data-acquisition systems. The list of the different types of measurements is a long one. This is the reason there are so many different kinds of dc voltmeters.

There are basically two main classifications of dc voltmeters. The first, the analog dc voltmeter, uses a d'Arsonval meter to indicate the result of a measurement. A pointer fixed to the movement of the meter is deflected to a position which is proportional to the quantity of the voltage being measured. The user is left with the task of interpreting the indication of the pointer.

The second main classification of dc voltmeters is the automatic digital type usually referred to as a digital voltmeter (DVM). The DVM displays measurements as discrete numerals rather than as a pointer deflection on a scale.

A brief description of the dc voltmeter types which make up the two main analog- and digital-voltmeter classifications is given below. Specification and front-panel terms are used throughout these descriptions without definition. The reader is encouraged to refer to later sections in this chapter for definitions of these terms.

TYPES OF ANALOG DC VOLTMETERS

1. d'Arsonval Type The d'Arsonval voltmeter, the most simple of all types, is a passive voltmeter which requires no power of its own for operation. The power required to operate it is taken from the network under test.

The d'Arsonval voltmeter consists of a d'Arsonval meter* and a resistor (see Fig. 1*a*). Since the d'Arsonval meter is a dc-responding instrument whose indication is proportional to the amount of current flowing through its coil, the value of the resistor R can be selected to give full-scale deflection for any desired input voltage. If, for example, it takes 1 mA to cause full-scale deflection, then 1,000 Ω, including the resistance of the meter, will be required for full-scale deflection when the input is 1 V. The sensitivity of this voltmeter would be 1,000 Ω/V. Sensitivity for the simple d'Arsonval voltmeter commonly ranges from 100 to 20,000 Ω/V.

* More information on the d'Arsonval meter may be found in Chapter 21.

A versatile multirange voltmeter may be made of several resistors which can be switched, one at a time, in series with the meter. Full-scale deflection for different values of voltage can therefore be obtained as shown in Fig. 1*b*.

Low input resistance is the simple voltmeter's greatest disadvantage. For example, suppose that a voltmeter of 1,000 Ω/V sensitivity is used to measure a 1-V battery with output resistance as shown in Fig. 2*a*. With no current flowing, the open-circuit voltage V_{oc} is equal to the battery voltage of 1 V. When the meter is connected to the network as shown in Fig. 2*b*, the circuit is closed and a current of $I_m = 0.00091$ A flows. This causes a 0.09-V drop across the 100-Ω resistor and causes the meter to indicate an "open-circuit" voltage which is 9 percent low. A 10,000 Ω/V meter would cause a 0.9 percent error. A similar example for a complete circuit is shown in Fig. 3. The meter creates a parallel current path that becomes a new circuit and alters the current through the original circuit.

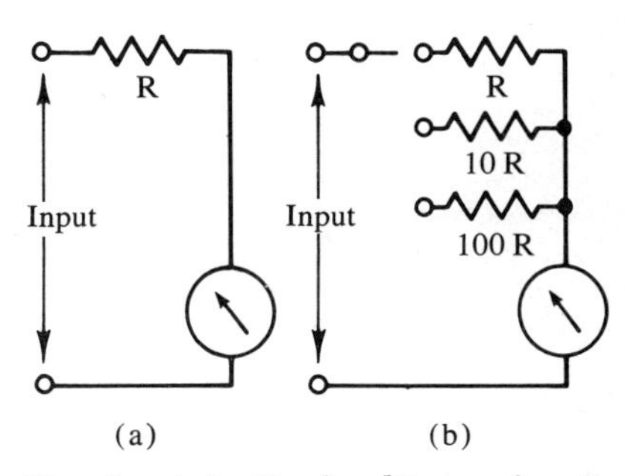

Fig. 1. (*a*) Simple d'Arsonval voltmeter. (*b*) Simple three-range d'Arsonval voltmeter.

The simple d'Arsanval dc voltmeter is manufactured in two forms. In a panel meter, one of the forms, the movement and a multiplier resistor are housed in a small plastic case appropriate for mounting in a panel. The second form, a

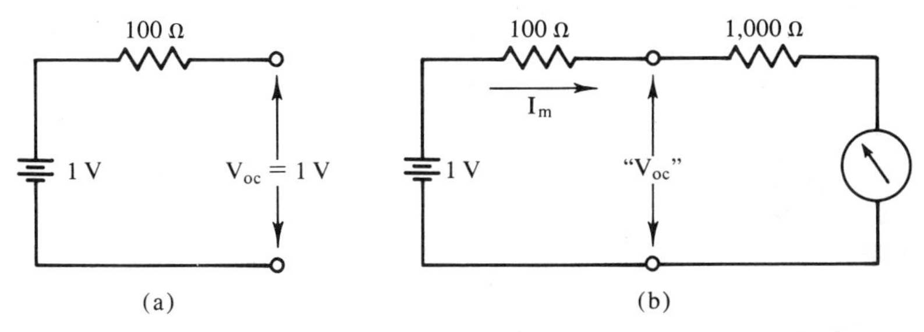

Fig. 2. (*a*) Open-circuit network to be tested. (*b*) 1,000 Ω/V simple d'Arsonval voltmeter connected to the open-circuit network of part *a* causes current to flow.

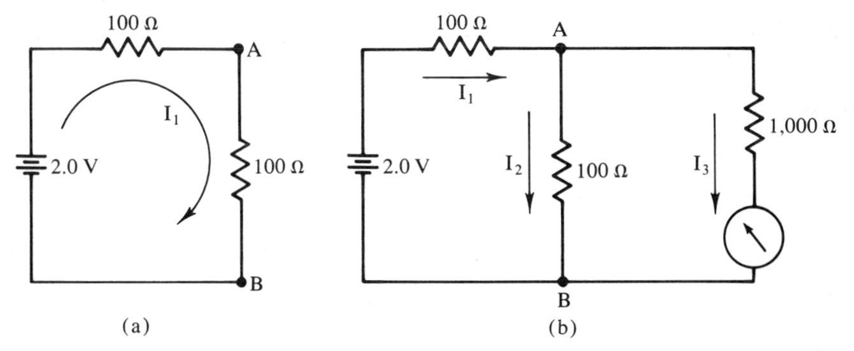

Fig. 3. (*a*) Closed-circuit network to be tested. $I_1 = 0.01$ A, $V_{AB} = 1$ V. (*b*) 1,000 Ω/V simple d'Arsonval voltmeter connected to the closed-circuit network of part *a* changes the current flow through resistor *AB*. $I_1 = 0.0104$ A; $I_2 = 0.0095$ A; $I_3 = 0.00095$ A; $V_{AB} = 0.95$ V; error in reading = −5 percent.

more expensive one, is a multirange instrument which contains the movement, several multiplier resistors, and a range switch housed in a slightly larger box.

The basic d'Arsonval meter is responsible for a number of limitations which affect the performance of the simple d'Arsonval voltmeters. Generally, the sensitivity of the movement increases when temperature increases. Also, the resistance of the coil increases at a rate of approximately +0.4 percent per degree Celsius. Compensation can be provided internally in the form of either shunts or series resistors whose temperature coefficients are chosen such that their resistance changes with temperature are exactly equal and opposite to the changes in the movement's resistance.

In the pivot-and-jewel movement, variations in pivot friction and spring characteristics cause noticeable repeatability errors.* The more expensive taut-band movement, however, is far superior to the pivot-and-jewel because repeatability errors are negligible.†

The general practice in manufacturing the less expensive meter is to use the same scale or a limited number of scales for all meters of a given type. Of course, there are subtle differences between meter mechanisms which make them deviate somewhat in ability to track scale marks. Tracking accuracy‡ is a specification which asserts the movement's ability to track the scale marks.

Accuracy of the simple voltmeter is dependent upon the accuracy of the current sensitivity of the d'Arsonval movement and the accuracy of the multiplier or range resistor. Accuracies for less expensive voltmeters typically are ±3 percent of full scale, while the more expensive ones can boast ±1 percent of full scale.

2. Amplifier-driven d'Arsonval Type A significant improvement in performance can be realized when a meter is driven by an amplifier. The amplifier offers more sensitive ranges and higher input resistance than can be obtained with a simple meter and range-multiplier resistors. The input resistance of an electronic amplifier is usually high enough that correction for loading effect upon the network under test is not required. Typical accuracies range from 0.5 to several percent.

With the amplifier types, other convenient features are possible. For example, a recorder output available on many electronic voltmeters will deliver a dc voltage proportional to the meter indication. While power-line operation is common, battery operation is sometimes provided where portable operation is desired.

Two basic types of amplifiers commonly used are (1) direct-coupled types and (2) chopper types. The direct-coupled amplifier is usually found in lower-cost electronic voltmeters. A block diagram of a direct-coupled type is shown in Fig. 4*a*. As in any multirange voltmeter, an input attenuator is included for the purpose of changing the full-scale sensitivity of the voltmeter. For example, the basic sensitivity may be 100 mV without attenuator. Then, to measure 1,000 V the input attenuator must be set to attenuate 10,000:1. The dc filter eliminates any ac signal which may be superimposed on the input. The dc amplifier shown in Fig. 4*b* amplifies the dc input to drive the meter. Feedback is provided to stabilize the transfer characteristics of the amplifier.

Although the direct-coupled amplifier offers high input resistance, its lowest range, usually 0.1 to 1 V, is limited by the dc stability of the amplifier. The dc stability is a measure of an amplifier's ability to maintain a constant reading for a given input. Dc drift is usually caused by a change in the input field-effect transistor's operating point as the temperature is changed. This shift in operating point is equivalent to several millivolts of change at the input. Hence, several millivolts on ranges less than 100 mV would be a sizable disturbance.

The chopper amplifier is found in higher-priced electronic voltmeters where ranges are provided to cover a few millivolts or microvolts full scale. The basic concept is simple. The input direct current is converted (modulated) to a proportional alternating current, amplified by an ac amplifier, and then converted (demodulated)

* Repeatability is defined in Chapter 21.
† The taut-band and pivot-and-jewel movement types are discussed in Chapter 21.
‡ Tracking accuracy is defined in Chapter 21.

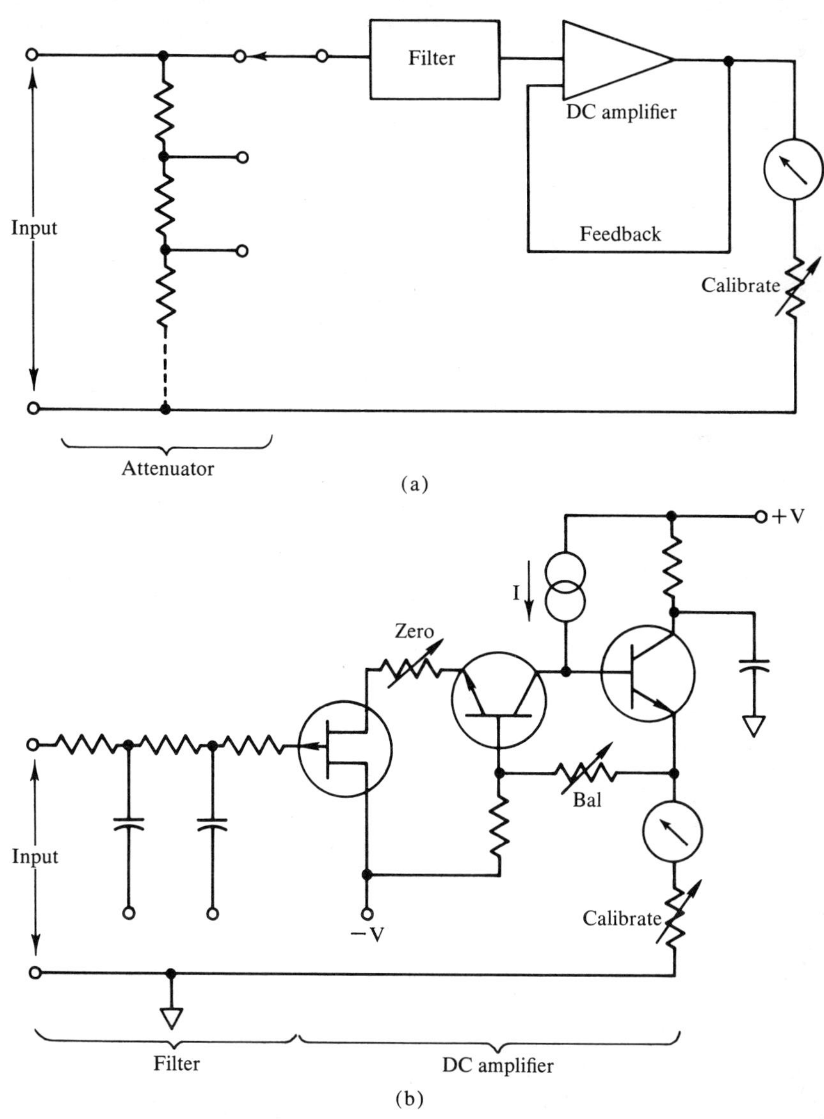

Fig. 4. (*a*) Block diagram of a direct-coupled amplifier-driven d'Arsonval voltmeter. (*b*) A solid-state direct-coupled amplifier-driven d'Arsonval voltmeter.

back to a direct current. Any dc drift at the input of the ac amplifier will not be passed to the output. Therefore, zero offsets of a few microvolts or less are possible.

A schematic of a chopper amplifier is shown in Fig. 5*a*. The manufacturer of this particular chopper amplifier uses a photocell chopper and demodulator. A photocell has many megohms of resistance when unilluminated, and a few hundred ohms when illuminated with a neon or incandescent bulb. The transition time between these two conditions limits the maximum chopping rate to a few hundred

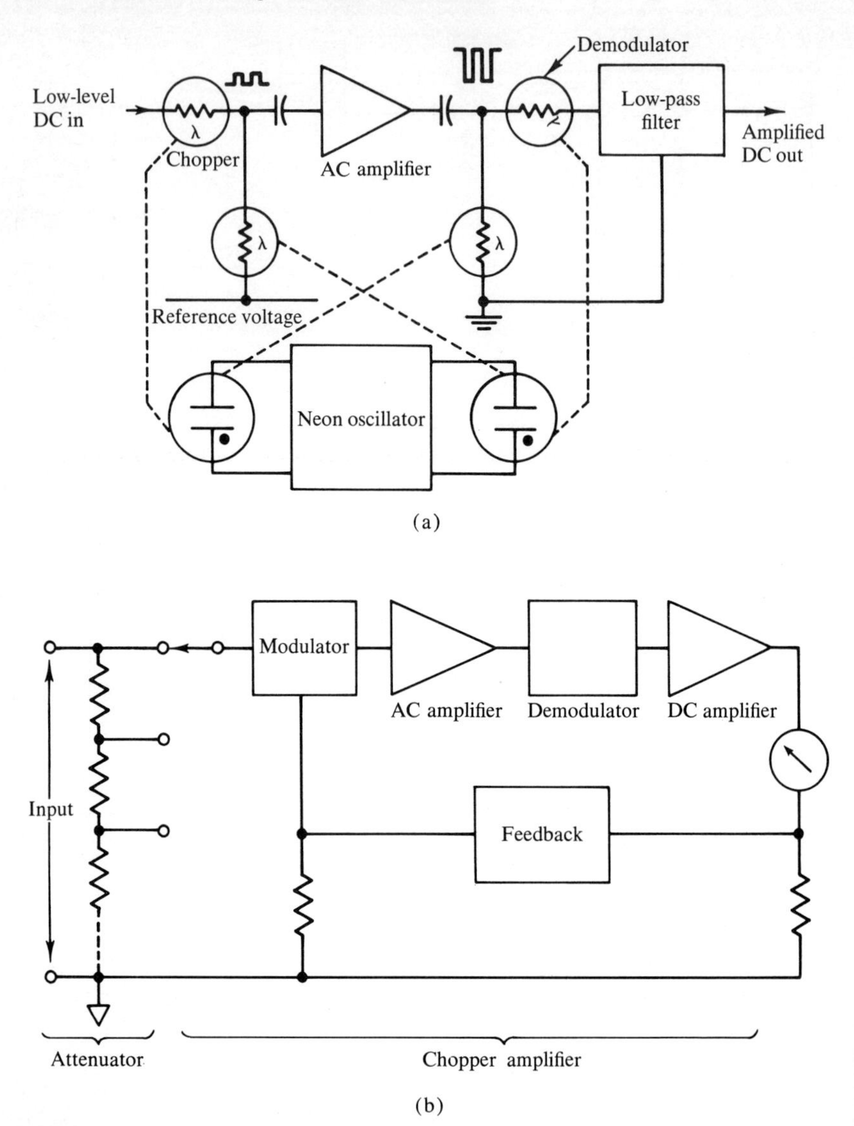

Fig. 5. (*a*) Photoconductive chopper amplifier. (*b*) Block diagram of a chopper-amplifier-driven d'Arsonval voltmeter.

hertz. Usually four photocells are mounted in one assembly with a simple neon oscillator. This provides a synchronous demodulator as well as a series-shunt half-wave modulator.

The electronic-voltmeter system which employs the chopper amplifier is shown in Fig. 5*b*. In many respects the system is similar to the direct-coupled amplifier system. An input attenuator selects the range, and overall feedback stabilizes the amplifier transfer characteristics. This feedback also develops a high dc input resistance on the order of 1,000 MΩ or more. The input resistance presented to the voltmeter terminals is determined by the input attenuator.

3. Manual Potentiometric Type The potentiometric type voltmeter is usually equipped with manual digital and analog readouts. Measurement time is slow and tedious, but high resolution and accuracy are its main advantages.

The basic potentiometric method of measuring an unknown voltage is illustrated in Fig. 6. A stable internal voltage reference is divided into parts by a potentiometric divider and subtracted from the unknown input. The difference is measured by a sensitive null meter.

In electronic manual-balance voltmeters (often referred to as differential voltmeters), the null meter is a chopper-stabilized dc null meter whose full-scale sensitivity often covers 1 μV to 1 V. The reference is commonly a stable voltage derived from a temperature-controlled zener diode. A set of precision resistors and n number of switches make up the divider. The switches allow the reference voltage V_{ref} to be manually subdivided into a voltage whose resolution at the divider output is n digits.

The operation of the differential voltmeter, for example, is basically one of setting the null meter on its least sensitive range and extracting the most significant digit manually without reversing the polarity of the null meter. The process is repeated by increasing the sensitivity of the null detector by a factor of 10 and extracting

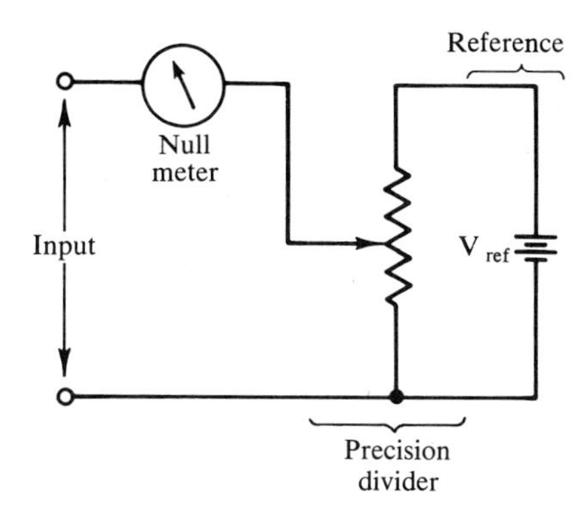

Fig. 6. Simple potentiometric voltmeter.

the next most significant digit. This process is continued until all n digits are resolved.

The simple potentiometric method of measuring unknown voltage illustrated in Fig. 6 is limited to one range determined by the reference voltage. The reference voltage is usually restricted to 10 V or less. Near infinite input resistance is obtained at null only. Lower off-null input resistance can be detrimental in a standards laboratory where loading of standard voltage cells is often undesirable. To extend the range of the simple potentiometric voltmeter, often an input attenuator is switched in on the higher (100 to 1,000 V) voltage ranges. Input resistance then is limited to the resistance of the attenuator. A 10-MΩ input resistance on these higher ranges is common.

To overcome the input-resistance limitation, one manufacturer builds an expensive differential voltmeter whose input stage develops an input resistance exceeding 10^9 Ω. This high resistance, usually a good approximation of an open circuit, is maintained independent of null condition. The block diagram is illustrated in Fig. 7. A special high-gain high-voltage (1,000 V) amplifier with overall feedback isolates the input from the divider and null meter. The overall feedback around the high-gain amplifier assures gain accuracy and produces the high input resistance. On the higher ranges (10 to 1,000 V) it is necessary to attenuate the output to the level of the reference. This is done by the output attenuator.

Differential voltmeters are capable of measurements better than 0.005 percent

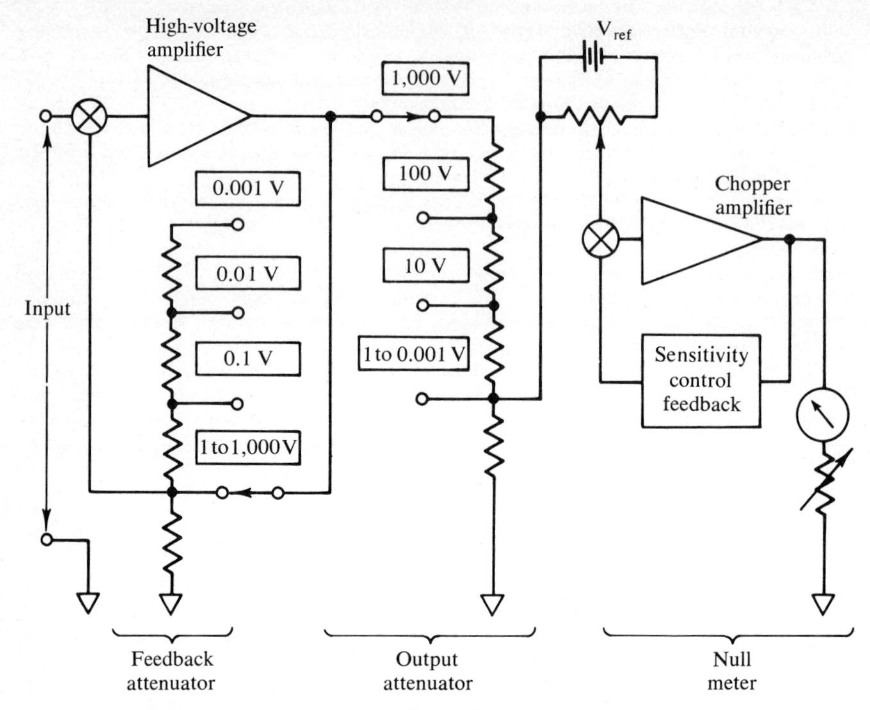

Fig. 7. Electronic potentiometric (differential) voltmeter.

absolute accuracy. This is made possible by extremely well matched divider resistors and stable references whose stabilities are often quoted at better than 0.0015 percent per month. To assure these kinds of accuracies, the calibration period for such instruments may be as often as once per month.

TYPES OF AUTOMATIC DIGITAL-READOUT DC VOLTMETERS

Digital voltmeters (DVMs) display measurements as discrete numerals rather than as a pointer deflection on a scale commonly used in analog voltmeters.

Several advantages in DVM characteristics sometimes lead to selection of a DVM in preference to analog measurement methods. Direct numerical readout in DVMs reduces human error and tedium, and increases reading speed. Automatic polarity and range-changing features also reduce operator error. Many also have outputs to make permanent records of measurements with printers, card and tape punches, and magnetic-tape equipment. Data in digital form may be processed by computer with no loss of accuracy.

Digital instruments are available to measure, in addition to dc voltages, ac voltages, direct currents, and resistance. However, all these functions require additional signal processing, after which they can be measured by the basic dc DVM considered here.

4. Voltage-to-Time Ramp Type The operating principle of the ramp voltage-to-time digital voltmeter is the measurement of time for a linear ramp to change from input level to zero or ground. This interval of time is proportional to the unknown voltage at the input.

The timing diagram in Fig. 8 illustrates the conversion technique. The ramp is compared continuously with the unknown voltage being measured. At the instant the ramp and unknown become coincident, a comparator circuit generates a pulse which opens a gate. The ramp continues until a second comparator senses that the ramp has reached zero volts and a pulse is generated which closes the gate.

The time interval between the gate's opening and closing is proportional to the unknown voltage. When the gate is open, clock pulses from an oscillator are allowed to enter the counter. The total number of pulses counted during the time interval is a measure of the input voltage. Proper choice of ramp speed and oscillator frequency will scale the readout to read conveniently in millivolts. Suppose, for example, that 100 V/s ramp slope and 100 kHz oscillator frequency are chosen. If an input voltage of 1,000 mV is applied to the input to the basic converter, it will take exactly 0.01 s from the time the first coincidence is detected to the time of the second coincidence. During this 0.01-s interval, 1,000 pulses (100 kHz times 0.01 s) will have been counted. Hence, indicating devices connected to the counter will display the contents of the counter as 1,000 mV.

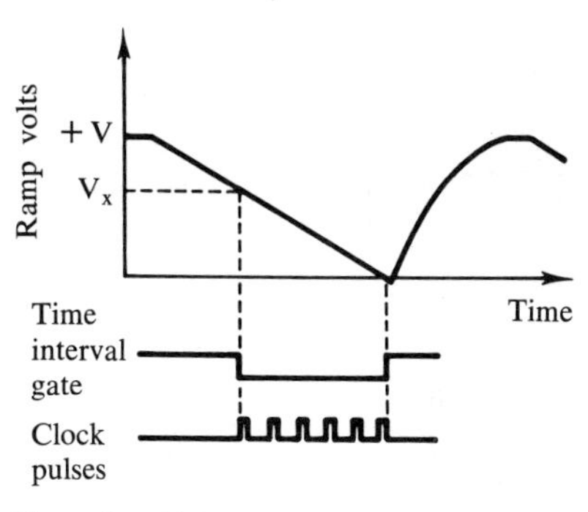

Fig. 8. Voltage-to-time conversion.

The block diagram in Fig. 9 illustrates the basic components of a voltage-to-time ramp-type digital-voltmeter system. The unknown voltage to be measured is applied to the input comparator. When the internal ramp and the input coincide, the input comparator generates a start pulse which allows pulses to enter the counter. A stop pulse is generated by the ground comparator when the ramp coincides with zero volts. At this time, no more pulses are entered into the counter. The contents of the counter are transferred to the visual readout with the results of the measurement. At the end of the period the counter is reset to zero and the linear ramp is regenerated, thus starting a new measurement cycle.

The accuracy of this type of system depends on the linearity of the ramp and the sensitivities of the comparators. Ramp and comparator systems are not uncommon which will allow conversion accuracy on the order of 0.01 percent of full

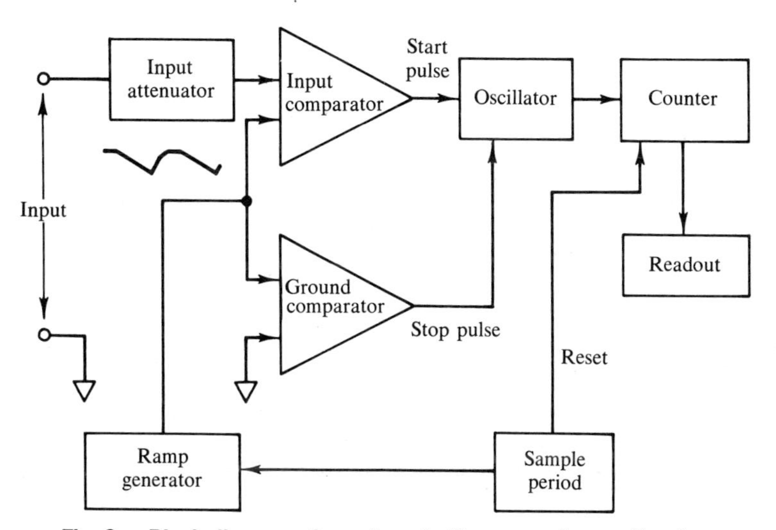

Fig. 9. Block diagram of a voltage-to-time ramp-type voltmeter.

scale with a resolution of 10 μV. Reading rates can be as high as several per second.

Unfortunately, this technique is not noise-immune. For example, suppose a conversion is about to start, i.e., the ramp is nearing the input level, and a burst of noise superimposed on the input causes premature triggering of the input comparator. Consequently, the conversion time will be in error and a measurement error will result.

5. Staircase-ramp Type The basic staircase-ramp-type converter system generates a precise voltage staircase whose step corresponds to the least significant digit of the measurement.

The basic technique is illustrated in Fig. 10. At the start of a measurement, a start pulse opens a gate to allow clock pulses to enter a counter and be counted. The outputs of the counter are connected to a digital-to-analog converter whose voltage-level output is proportional to its digital input. As each pulse is entered into the counter, one is added to the least significant digit, and correspondingly

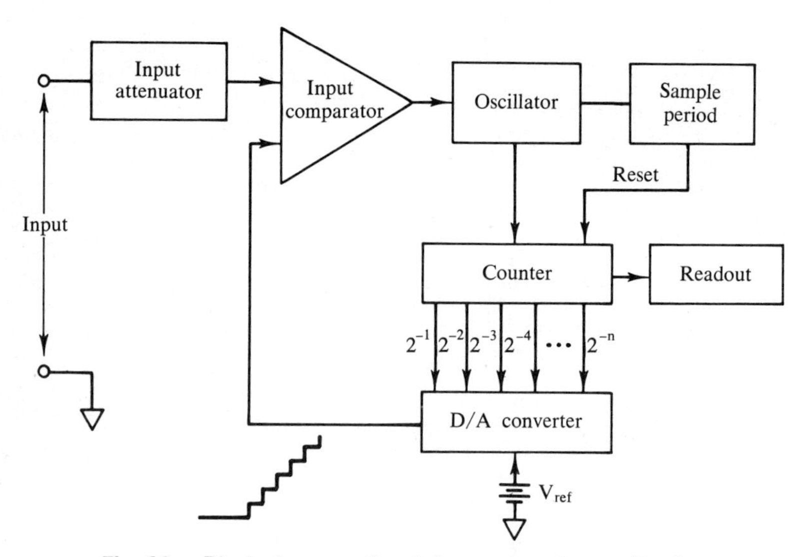

Fig. 10. Block diagram of a staircase-ramp-type voltmeter.

the output of the digital-to-analog converter is incremented by one least significant step in the staircase ramp. The input is compared with this internally generated ramp. When the comparator detects coincidence, the counter is stopped and its contents are transferred to a visual-readout device. The contents of the counter are proportional to the unknown input voltage.

The performance of the staircase-ramp-type voltmeter is very much like that of the voltage-to-time-type voltmeter. Bursts of superimposed noise, too, will cause erroneous readings. Accuracy will depend on the conversion accuracy of the digital-to-analog converter and the stability of the internal reference voltage.

6. Successive-approximation Type The successive-approximation DVM, like the staircase-ramp DVM, is a parallel-feedback type of analog-to-digital converter. It incorporates a feedback path containing a digital-to-analog converter. Its operation is based on making n successive comparisons between the input voltage V_x and a feedback voltage V_f from the output of the digital-to-analog converter. The number n represents the number of digits in a binary number which resolves the unknown to within a certain prescribed accuracy.

The block diagram in Fig. 11 is a simplified version of a successive-approximation

DVM. Its operation can best be described by example. Suppose that the voltmeter has a basic reference voltage $V_{ref} = 10$ V. An unknown voltage $V_x = 3.4$ V is to be converted to a decimal equivalent of V_x to within ± 0.2 V. A 6-bit converter will be necessary to make this conversion within the prescribed limits. The sixth bit will resolve the feedback voltage V_f in steps of 2^{-6} or $\frac{1}{64}$ of V_{ref}, or approximately 0.156 V. The operation goes as follows:

1. During the first timing interval the most significant bit 2^{-1} is set to a logical ONE, thus making $V_f = \frac{1}{2} V_{ref} = 5.000$ V. The difference $V_x - V_f$ is amplified, and the error voltage V_e is negative. The most significant bit hence is reset to a logical ZERO.

2. The next most significant bit 2^{-2} is set to a logical ONE, thus making $V_f = (0 + \frac{1}{4})\, V_{ref} = 2.500$ V during the second timing interval. V_e is positive; so bit 2^{-2} remains a logical ONE.

3. Bit 2^{-3} is set to a logical ONE. $V_f = (0 + \frac{1}{4} + \frac{1}{8})\, V_{ref} = 3.750$ V. V_e is negative; so bit 2^{-3} is reset to a logical ZERO.

4. Bit 2^{-4} is set to a logical ONE. $V_f = (0 + \frac{1}{4} + 0 + \frac{1}{16})\, V_{ref} = 3.125$ V. V_e is positive; so bit 2^{-4} remains a logical ONE.

5. Bit 2^{-5} is set to a logical ONE. $V_f = 3.437$ V. V_e is negative; so bit 2^{-5} is reset to a logical ZERO.

6. Bit 2^{-6} is set to a logical ONE. $V_f = 3.281$ V. V_e is positive; so bit 2^{-6} remains a logical ONE.

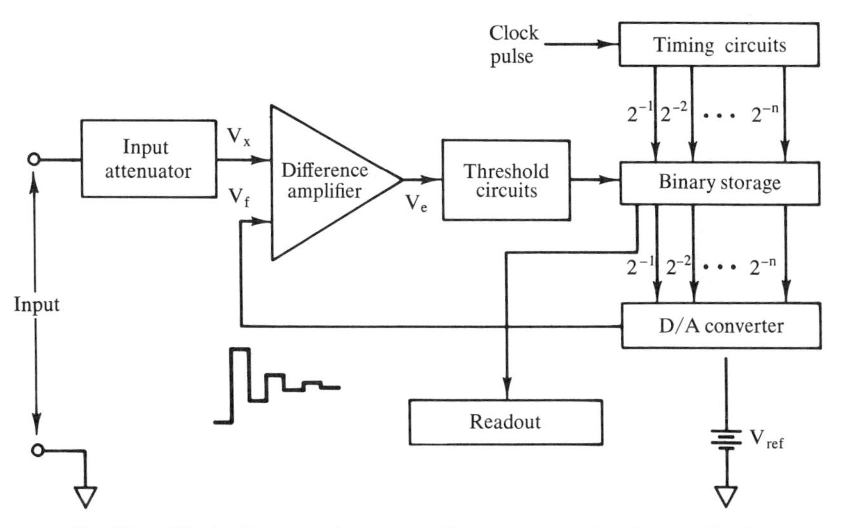

Fig. 11. Block diagram of a successive-approximation-type voltmeter.

The result contained in the binary storage unit is 010101 or 3.281, its decimal equivalent. The result, low by 0.149 V, is within the prescribed limit of ± 0.2 V.

The accuracy of the successive-approximation technique is dependent on the stability of the reference and the accuracy of the digital-to-analog converter and differencing amplifier. Total conversion accuracy is dependent, however, on the conversion rate. The higher the conversion speed is set, the lower will be the accuracy of conversion. Voltmeters with 12-bit successive-approximation converters have been built which provide an accuracy of ± 0.05 percent of full scale at a rate of several thousand readings per second. The successive-approximation technique, like the ramp-type technique, is not noise-immune. Bursts of noise superimposed on the input occurring at critical comparison times will result in erroneous readings.

7. Continuous-balance Type The continuous-balance-type DVM employs a parallel-feedback-type digital-to-analog converter similar in some respects to the successive-approximation technique. The continuous-balance type behaves like a servosystem in that a change in the unknown V_x corresponds to an immediate reaction by the feedback system in such a direction as to reduce the error.

The block diagram in Fig. 12 shows the essential parts in the continuous-balance system. The operation is basically simple. If a positive difference between V_x and V_f exists, the differencing and threshold amplifier will generate a $+V_t$ (threshold voltage) which will set the up/down counter in the "up-count" mode. As each clock pulse occurs, a count is entered into the least significant bit of the counter. The bit outputs feed the parallel inputs of the digital-to-analog converter. As each bit is added, the output of the digital-to-analog converter is incremented by one least significant part of V_{ref} or $\frac{1}{2}^n$ times V_{ref}. As the feedback voltage V_f approaches the value of V_x, the output of the threshold circuit is less than $+V_t$ and greater than $-V_t$. Null or balance is reached in this condition, and the up/down counter operation stops.

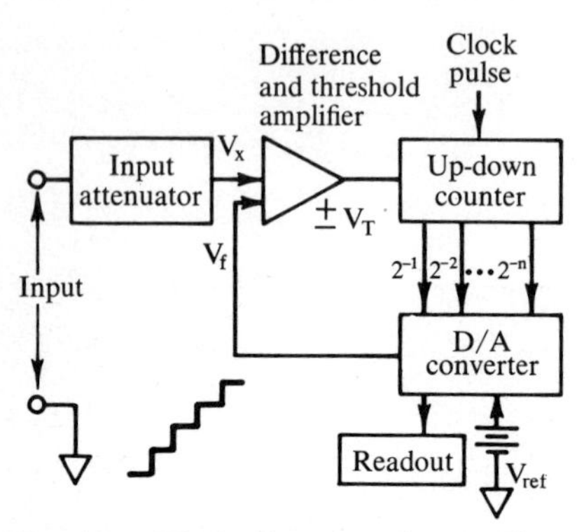

Fig. 12. Block diagram of a continuous-balance-type voltmeter.

Conversion time for the continuous-balance type can be extremely long if V_x is shifted from zero to full scale. However, for small changes in V_x, new conversions are ready in a very short period of time. Like the successive-approximation type, the accuracy is dependent upon the reference-voltage stability and accuracies of the digital-to-analog converter and differencing and threshold circuits. Again there is a tradeoff between conversion speed and accuracy. As the clock speed is increased, conversion accuracy decreases.

Superimposed noise on the input of the continuous-balance system tends to cause an annoying problem of "searching." A final stable answer is never found.

8. Integrating Type The integrating technique is often referred to as a voltage-to-frequency conversion.

The operation is basically as shown in Fig. 13. A positive voltage at the input causes a negative-going ramp at the output of the integrator. When the ramp

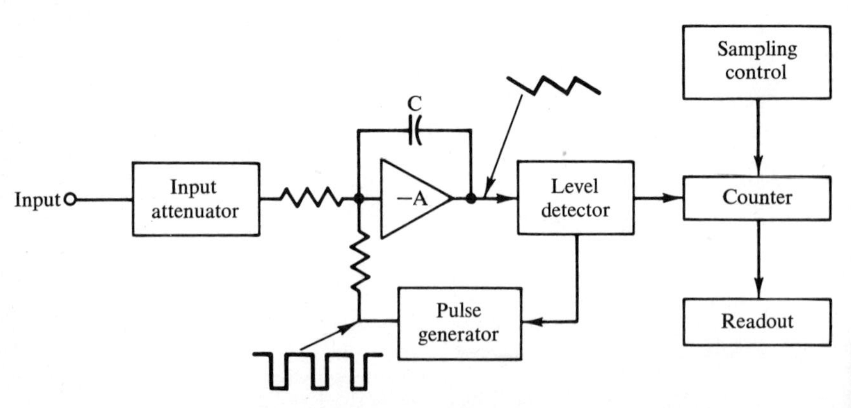

Fig. 13. Block diagram of an integrating-type voltmeter.

reaches a certain prescribed voltage level, a level detector fires, which in turn triggers a pulse generator. The pulse generator produces a rectangular pulse with closely controlled width and amplitude just sufficient to draw enough charge from the capacitor C to bring the input of the integrator back to the starting point. The cycle then repeats.

The ramp slope is proportional to the input voltage. A higher voltage at the input would result in a steeper slope, allowing a shorter time duration for the ramp. Consequently, the pulse-repetition rate or frequency would be higher. Since the pulse frequency is proportional to the input voltage, the pulses can be counted for a known time interval to derive a digital measure of the input.

The accuracy of the integrating type of digital-to-analog converter is primarily dependent upon the stability of the level detector, the amplifier, and the capacitor. Instruments using the integrating technique can typically read fifty times a second with a conversion accuracy of better than 0.01 percent of full scale.

The major advantage of the integrating voltmeter is its ability to "integrate" the input over the sampling interval. The reading represents a true average of the input voltage. The pulse-repetition frequency "tracks" a slowly varying input voltage so closely that changes in the input voltage are accurately reflected as changes in pulse-repetition rate. The total pulse count during a sampling interval therefore represents the average frequency, and thus the average voltage. The noise is thereby averaged out during the measurement without requiring input filters that would slow the voltmeter response time. The voltmeter, furthermore, achieves essentially infinite rejection of power-line hum when the measurement interval is an exact multiple of the hum waveform period; this is the most prevalent source of signal noise.

ANALOG- AND DIGITAL-VOLTMETER SPECIFICATIONS

Specifications are a written description of the quality, capabilities, size, and features of an instrument. Instrument specifications are found to vary in simplicity depending upon the complexity and cost of the instrument. For example, the performance rating of a basic inexpensive dc analog voltmeter may include a simple accuracy specification such as ± 1 percent of full scale on any range over a 10 to 40°C temperature range. On the other hand, the performance rating of a complex, expensive differential voltmeter may include a more detailed accuracy specification such as $\pm$ (0.005 percent of reading + 0.0004 percent of range + 1 μV) at 23°C $\pm$ 1°C, less than 70 percent relative humidity. In addition to accuracy, a stability and temperature coefficient may be specified.

This section will define some of the common specification terms and relate them to the voltmeter types. In Table 1 a tabulation of several of the more important features is found for each of the dc-voltmeter types discussed in this chapter. The feature specified for each type is based on the state of the art and does not necessarily mean that less capable instruments do not exist. Ultimately, the degree of capability of any instrument must be determined from the manufacturer's specifications.

9. Range The range specification lists the range of full-scale voltages over which a dc voltmeter may be operated. For example, a range specification may state that for some given voltmeter there are eight ranges covering 100 mV to 1,000 V. Methods of range selection (manual, automatic, remote, etc.) may also be stated in this section.

10. Overrange Some instruments have overrange capabilities. This feature allows an instrument to measure voltages several percent over any selected full-scale range. A specified overrange of 10 percent, for example, means that as much as 1.1 V may be read on the 1-V range.

11. Sensitivity Sensitivity is defined as the smallest voltage level to which the voltmeter can respond and normally is specified as the voltage level represented by the least detectable change on the lowest range. Some dc voltmeters may have a sensitivity as low as 0.1 μV.

12. Resolution Resolution is the degree to which small changes in a dc voltage level can be identified. This specification may be stated in several ways depending upon the voltmeter type. The resolution of a basic dc analog voltmeter is normally quoted as one minor scale division.

Resolution for a dc differential voltmeter, on the other hand, is expressed as a percentage of full scale or parts per million at full scale. For example, a typical specification might list resolution as follows: null meter gives full-scale indication of ±0.01 percent of range; maximum resolution 1 ppm at full scale. The latter statement refers to the smallest discernible quantity on the scale of the meter.

The resolution of a dc digital voltmeter is usually expressed as the number of significant digits available in the readout.

13. Accuracy Accuracy is a statement of the largest allowable error expressed as a percentage or an absolute value. It can be a difficult specification to interpret, because from four different accuracy statements which exist, as many as three may be combined together to express the accuracy.

TABLE 1 Salient Features of Different Types of DC Voltmeters

Dc-voltmeter type	Ranges	Accuracy, %	Input resistance	Speed (readings per sec)	Resolution
Analog d'Arsonval....	50 mV to 5,000 V	≧1	100 Ω to 1 MΩ/V	.....	0.5 mV
Analog dc amplifier...	0.1 to 1,000 V	≧1	>100 kΩ	.....	1.0 mV
Analog chopper amplifier	3 μV to 1,000 V	≧1	>100 kΩ	.....	0.1 μV
Manual potentio-metric	1 mV to 1,000 V	≧0.005	$>10^{10}$ Ω	.....	1 ppm of range
Voltage-to-time ramp..	0.1 to 1,000 V	≧0.05	>10 MΩ	5	10 μV
Staircase ramp.......	0.1 to 1,000 V	≧0.02	>10 MΩ	100	1 μV
Successive approxima-tion	0.1 to 1,000 V	≧0.02	>10 MΩ	1,000	1 μV
Continuous balance...	0.1 to 1,000 V	≧0.02	>10 MΩ	100	1 μV
Integrating..........	0.1 to 1,000 V	≧0.005	>10 MΩ	50	1 ppm of range

The four types of accuracy statements normally used are

(*a*) $$\text{Percent of reading} \geqq \frac{100\,(\text{indicated value} - \text{true value})}{\text{true value}}$$

(*b*) $$\text{Percent of full scale or of range} \geqq \frac{100\,(\text{indicated value} - \text{true value})}{\text{full-scale value}}$$

(*c*) x units of the smallest readout division expressed in counts ≧ (indicated value − true value)

(*d*) $$x \text{ volts} \geqq \text{indicated value} - \text{true value}$$

The use of these accuracy specifications depends upon the type and complexity of the dc voltmeter. Regardless of which specification or specifications are used (*a, b, c,* or *d*) the user will, in the final analysis, want to know what the maximum error is in percent of reading. It is easy to determine what the maximum error is in percent of reading from specification *a*, but what about the others? The other three represent a constant quantity which must be applied anywhere across the scale on a given range. It is important to note, for instance, that at 0.1 scale the absolute quantity is ten times larger in percentage than at full scale. To be more specific, suppose the accuracy of a basic dc analog voltmeter is specified as ±2 percent of full scale. This represents a ±20-mV uncertainty on the 1-V range. At 0.1 scale (100 mV), a ±20-mV uncertainty represents ±20 percent error in reading. Another example is the accuracy specification for a three-digit DVM. The specification is expressed as the sum of specification *a* and *c* such as ±0.2 percent of reading ±2 counts. Here ±2 counts is a constant quantity of ±2 mV on the 1-V range. This also represents larger measurement errors at readings less than full scale. These examples are illustrated in Fig. 14, where the error in percent of reading is plotted vs. voltmeter indication in percent of full scale.

It is not uncommon for the accuracy of an expensive, highly accurate differential voltmeter to be specified using the sum of specifications *a*, *b*, and *d*. A typical specification may read ±(0.005 percent of reading + 0.0004 percent of range + 1 μV). The maximum percent of error at any voltmeter indication can be evaluated in a manner similar to the example cited above for the three-digit DVM.

It is clear from Fig. 14 that more accurate measurements are made at or near full scale. Accuracy ratings generally apply for a zero-impedance source.

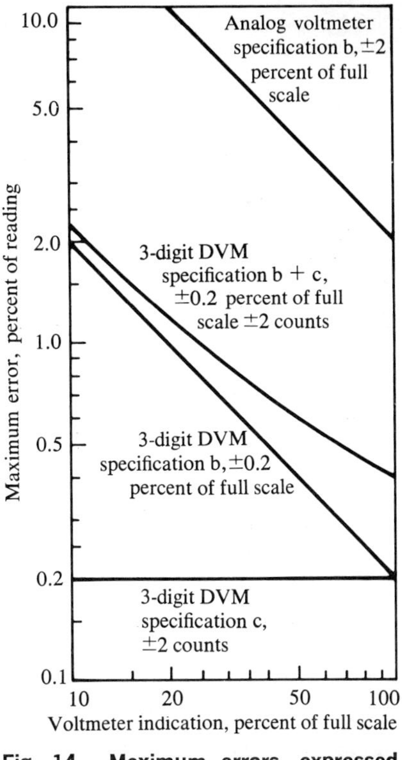

Fig. 14. Maximum errors, expressed as a percent of reading, as a function of input level for an analog voltmeter and three-digit DVM.

14. Stability Stability is a measure of an instrument's ability to remain within its rated accuracy for some specified period of time. Stability may be specified in two parts, long-term stability and short-term stability. For a specified period of time, stability is often stated as an accuracy specification. For example, the long-term stability for a highly accurate DVM may be stated as ±(0.04 percent of reading + 0.0002 percent of range) over a 90-day calibration period while the short-term stability is stated as ±(0.002 percent of reading + 0.001 percent of range) per day. Another way short-term stability may be stated is in terms of a change in percent or ppm of reading over a given time period. Examples are 1 ppm per hour and 5 ppm per day.

The stability specification is used only for the highly accurate dc differential and digital voltmeters.

15. Response Time The response-time specification is a statement of the time from the application of a full-scale step input to the time the instrument settles within its rated accuracy. For autoranging digital voltmeters, response time would include the maximum time required for polarity and range changes. Response time is not applicable to manual differential voltmeters. Time required to obtain a reading is dependent upon the response time of the operator.

16. Input Impedance The input-impedance specification is a statement of the complex loading a given voltmeter may present to a network under test. A dc resistance and shunt capacitance are often listed.

The user may be interested in the input impedance for determining measurement accuracy. He must also be aware of network-stability problems which might be encountered when the network under test is presented the complex loading of a voltmeter.

17. Normal-mode Rejection The normal-mode rejection (NMR) specification is an expression of an instrument's ability to reject a superimposed ac signal at the input. A normal-mode source e_n is shown in Fig. 15. There are two ways in which normal-mode rejection is typically specified.

First, it may be specified as the ratio of the normal-mode voltage to the resulting error in reading at a particular frequency. This ratio should apply at all signal levels from zero to full scale. Normal-mode rejection ratio (NMRR in decibels) is

$$\text{NMRR} = 20 \log_{10} \frac{e_n \text{ (peak volts)}}{\text{voltmeter error (peak volts)}} \quad \text{dB}$$

An example of a normal-mode rejection ratio specification is 60 dB at 100 Hz.

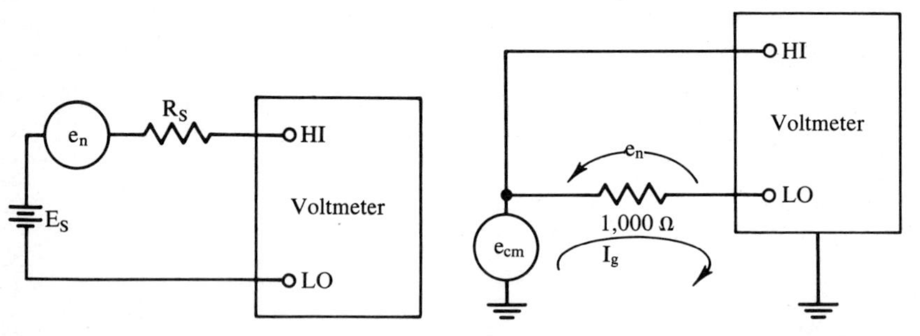

Fig. 15. Dc voltmeter with normal-mode generator.

Fig. 16. Dc voltmeter with common-mode generator.

Second, normal-mode rejection may be specified as a peak value of e_n which restricts the voltmeter error to be less than specified. A typical example for a basic *dc* analog voltmeter is as follows: ac voltages 60 Hz and above which are 80 dB (10,000 times) greater than end scale will affect readings less than 2 percent.

18. Common-mode Rejection Common-mode voltage sources which exist between the chassis ground of a voltmeter and the ground of the source tend to introduce normal-mode voltages in the measurement loop connected to the HI and LO terminals of the voltmeter. A common-mode source e_{cm} shown in Fig. 16 develops a ground current I_g which flows through the 1,000-Ω resistor in the line connected to the LO terminal. A normal-mode voltage e_n is developed across the 1,000-Ω resistor which is measured by the voltmeter. The ability of the voltmeter to reject or minimize the current I_g is referred to as common-mode rejection (CMR).

Common-mode rejection is usually specified as the ratio of the peak common-mode voltage to the resultant error in the reading caused by the normal-mode voltage generated across a 1,000-Ω unbalance in either input lead. This ratio (CMRR) is usually expressed (in decibels) as

$$\text{CMRR} = 20 \log_{10} \frac{e_{cm} \text{ (peak volts)}}{\text{voltmeter error (peak volts)}} \quad \text{dB}$$

Expensive differential and digital voltmeters have a special guarding feature which is designed to reduce common-mode signal interference. A typical specification is 120 dB at 100 Hz.

A second method of specifying common-mode rejection is to list the peak value of e_{cm} which restricts voltmeter error to be less than specified. The frequency at which the specification applies must be listed along with a given unbalanced resistance in the input.

19. Noise Noise is an internally generated disturbance which appears as a nervous meter indication on the most sensitive ranges of a sensitive analog voltmeter. Digital voltmeters are similarly affected by noise, but the disturbance may appear as a jitter in the least significant digit of the readout. A noise specification for a sensitive analog voltmeter may read <0.3 μV peak to peak.

20. Environmental Operating Conditions Environmental conditions usually limit the usefulness of a voltmeter. Most laboratory-type instruments are not designed to operate in extreme hot, cold, or humid environments. Consequently, the performance rating, especially accuracy, must be qualified for a given range of environmental operating conditions. Most often an operating temperature and humidity range is specified. In special cases, where high-accuracy voltmeters are concerned, a temperature coefficient of accuracy for a specified range of temperatures is given. An example of an accuracy and temperature-coefficient specification for a high-accuracy differential voltmeter will best illustrate the environmental operating conditions.

Accuracy: $\pm$(0.005 percent of reading + 0.0004 percent of range + 1 μV) at 23°C $\pm$1°C, less than 70 percent relative humidity

Temperature coefficient: less than $\pm$(2 ppm of reading + 1 μV) per °C, 10°C to 40°C

21. Operational Features A number of special features may be listed, such as manual or automatic ranging, manual or automatic polarity selection, type of readout, and any other modes of operation not covered in the specifications.

22. Input-Output Features For an analog voltmeter with a recorder output, range, accuracy, and output impedance for the recorder output must be specified.

Certain automatic digital voltmeters are able to take measurements at the command of an external data-acquisition system and, at another command, output its measurement to the same system. For such a voltmeter the command inputs for reading and for outputting must be specified. In addition, the digital outputs must be specified as to codes, logic levels, and other pertinent information.

FRONT-PANEL TERMS

Many commercial dc voltmeters have additional functions such as ac voltage, resistance, and ratio. Consequently, there are many types of front-panel terms other than those necessary for basic dc-voltmeter operation. The controls and panel terms discussed here will be applicable to a basic dc voltmeter of any type discussed in this chapter. Some controls unique to a particular class will be pointed out.

23. Range Control The range control allows the operator to set the full-scale sensitivity of the voltmeter. The 1-V range, for example, requires 1 V at the input for full-scale indication. This control usually operates the taps on an input attenuator and programs the range indicator on a digital voltmeter's readout.

24. Zero Control The zero control allows the operator to set a zero indication on a meter indicator when the input is known to be zero volts. An adjustable internal voltage source in series with the input and controlled by the zero control serves as the bucking voltage to offset any dc inbalances present in the system.

25. Mechanical Zero The mechanical zero is found on the face of a d'Arsonval meter. It is a screwdriver adjustment which sets the position of the indicator to zero when the instrument is "off," i.e., no current in the coil.

26. Potentiometric Readout Control The position of a readout control is usually indicated on the face of a mechanically attached dial with numerals from 1 to 9 printed on its face. On some instruments the position is indicated on an electrical readout device.

The indicated position of all readout controls is the answer to the measurement of an unknown source. To adjust the first readout control, first set the null meter on its least sensitive range. Adjust the first readout control to the largest digit which does not reverse the null meter. The adjustment of the most significant readout control extracts the most significant digit in the measurement. Other digits in the measurement may be found by adjusting each lesser significant readout control in succession, each time increasing the sensitivity of the null meter.

27. Null-sensitivity Control The null-sensitivity control on a manual potentiometric voltmeter may be a set of push switches associated with the readout controls or a separate rotary control. The push switches may be labeled X1, X10, etc., while the rotary control may be labeled null range. These controls set the full-scale range of the null meter.

28. Sample-rate Control The sample-rate control allows the operator to change the number of times per second that the input of a dc digital voltmeter is sampled and displayed on the front panel.

29. Trigger Control The trigger control allows the user to select the internal or external triggering of a reading cycle for a dc digital voltmeter. The internal trigger position is the normal operating condition where start-a-reading cycle signals are generated internally. In the external trigger position, the user must supply start-a-reading signals.

SOURCES OF ERROR IN USE

Knowing the capabilities of a given dc voltmeter is extremely important in making meaningful measurements. However, equally important, the operator must be aware of sources of error external to the instrument in a particular measurement situation. The concern for error is especially important when accurate measurements on the order of ±0.005 percent of full scale are being made with instruments capable of resolutions of five or six digits and tenths of microvolts.

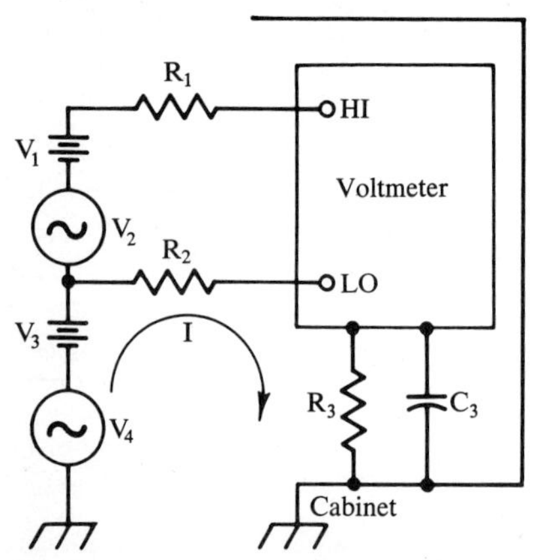

Fig. 17. Equivalent circuit of normal-mode and common-mode signals present in a measurement situation.

30. Normal-mode Noise Extraneous noise, which includes all dc and ac voltages other than the dc voltage being measured, is the greatest contributor of external error. This noise can be caused by electromagnetic pickup in the input leads, or it may be an inherent component of the unknown dc voltage such as ripple at the output of a power supply. This type of noise is referred to as normal-mode or superimposed noise.

The equivalent network of normal-mode (NM) and common-mode (CM) signals in a dc voltmeter is shown in Fig. 17. V_1 is the signal to be measured and V_2 is the undesired normal-mode signal.

One source of NM signal is thermal voltages. Thermal voltages of a few microvolts are commonly generated at the junctions of dissimilar metals. A list of magnitudes for different junctions is given in Table 2. As far as the dc voltmeter is concerned, these thermal voltages are indistinguishable from the dc signal to be measured. If dissimilar junctions are unavoidable in the user's circuit, temperature equalization can be accomplished by close physical spacing or by using an isothermal (insulated) box. The isothermal box will protect the circuit from air drafts which cause slow thermal fluctuations and, thus, low-frequency voltages. If the voltmeter has a zero control, it is advantageous to adjust zero when the voltmeter is connected

TABLE 2 Thermoelectric Effect in Metals

Metal	*μV/°C against platinum at 0°C*
Aluminum	3.8
Antimony	47.0
Bismuth	−65.0
Copper	7.4
Iron	16.0
Palladium	− 5.6
Silver	7.1
Constantan	−34.4

to some variable source which has been set to zero. This operation will compensate for any thermal voltages present in the "hookup." If the source is not variable, which often it is not, then it should be removed and replaced with a short-circuiting bar made of the same material as the terminals of the source.

Galvanic voltages, like electrochemical batteries, are another easily generated NM voltage. For example, a voltage of several millivolts can be generated across two adjacent terminals of a "dirty" or contaminated glass epoxy circuit board when warm, moist air is blown across it. A dry environment, cleanliness, and good-quality insulators help minimize galvanic voltages.

31. Common-mode Noise. Most dc voltmeters are designed to allow the user to make floating measurements. That is to say, the negative input terminal of a voltmeter is isolated internally from ground, thus making it possible to measure voltages in a circuit which are not referenced to ground. Therefore, it is common for a voltage as large as several hundred volts to exist between the negative terminal and instrument ground.

The extent to which a measurement is floating is represented by dc and ac noise signals V_3 and V_4, respectively, in Fig. 17. V_4 is usually caused by ground currents when the source and instrument are located some distance apart. However, V_4 can be generated by electrostatic coupling in the power transformer of a power-line-operated instrument. Proper double shielding of the power transformer can eliminate the internal generator.

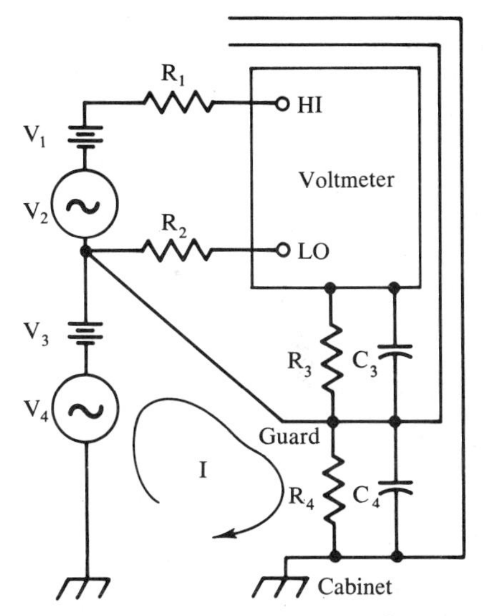

Fig. 18. Application of guarding to the system shown in Fig. 17.

The effects common-mode generators have on a measurement can be understood by referring to Fig. 17. R_3 is the insulation resistance between instrument common and cabinet, and C_3 is the capacitance between instrument common and cabinet. R_1 and R_2 represent resistances resulting from long input leads or unbalanced source resistances. Measurable currents can flow around the loop from V_3 and V_4 through R_2, R_3, and C_3. A voltage develops across R_2 which superimposes a direct or alternating current or both on the input of the voltmeter, thus resulting in a measurable error.

Most precision power-line-operated voltmeters provide a shield called a guard which can minimize common-mode errors. For example (see Fig. 18), the guard shield effectively reduces the value of C_3 by many orders of magnitude and also increases the value of R_3. The most obvious path for current due to V_3 and V_4

is through R_4 and C_4. This path avoids the main measurement circuit and generally causes no measurement problems.

Another method for eliminating common-mode errors is to use a battery-operated instrument. In this mode of operation two advantages are gained. Since V_4 is often internally generated on power-line-operated instruments, this source will be eliminated. Second, the instrument chassis can be floated; therefore, R_3 will effectively be increased.

32. Source Resistance The user must be aware of a possible error which might exist if the source resistance is sufficiently large relative to the input resistance of the voltmeter. If the source resistance is R_s (see Fig. 19) and the input resistance is

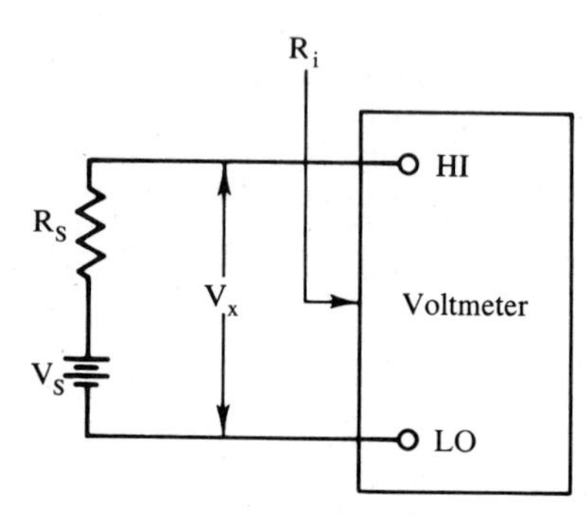

Fig. 19. Voltmeter loading causes error in measurement.

R_i, the V_x will be equal to V_s reduced by $R_s/R_s + R_i$. If, for example, R_i = 10 MΩ and R_s = 100 Ω, a measurement error of approximately −0.01 percent will result.

BIBLIOGRAPHY

Which D.C. Voltmeter? *Hewlett-Packard Co. Application Note* 69, Aug. 15, 1965.

Precision D.C. Voltage Measurements, *Hewlett-Packard Co. Application Note* 70, July 20, 1965.

Jessen, Kenneth: Taking the Mystery Out of DVM Specs, *Electron. Eng.*, October, 1969, pp. 46–52.

McCullough, William: The Effects of Superimposed Noise on DVM Measurement, *EEE*, July, 1967.

McCullough, William: How to Reduce Common-mode Effects, *EEE*, February, 1967.

Chapter **23**

Multimeters

LEE THOMPSON

Hewlett-Packard Company, Loveland, Colorado

INTRODUCTION

The term multimeter in the strict sense refers to any instrument which makes more than one kind of measurement. However, the vast majority of multimeters, as multimeters are known in the electronic-measurement industry, make two or more of the following basic measurements: dc voltage, ac voltage, dc resistance, and direct current. This chapter will deal with this common form of multimeter only.

MULTIMETER DISPLAYS

The terms analog multimeter and digital multimeter are used extensively in the field of electronic instrumentation. These terms refer to the type display, or readout, used in the multimeter.

Fig. 1. Analog multimeter.

Fig. 2. Digital multimeter.

1. Analog Displays The term analog display is used to indicate an output assembly which takes the result of a measurement and gives some kind of visual indication over a continuous range. Typically, this is done with a meter movement whose indicator is a needle which moves across the face of a calibrated scale as shown in Fig. 1. The meter face may have a different scale for each function. Each scale will be marked to indicate under what conditions it should be used.

2. Digital Displays The term digital display is used to indicate an output assembly which takes the results of a measurement and gives a visual indication in discrete numbers. The most common method of doing this is to use a gas-filled tube with filaments shaped to look like numbers. Each tube typically contains a filament for each number (zero through nine) and a decimal point. If several of these tubes are placed side by side, the filaments can be controlled to give any numerical reading desired. Figure 2 shows a typical digital readout using this technique. Another technique is to use light-emitting diodes arranged in a pattern to give a numerical indication. Along with the numerical readout, digital multimeters typically give a visual indication of the function (type of measurement being performed) and the sign when appropriate. This is usually done with either a special tube with filaments shaped to give the desired indication or with a back-lighted panel. The digital display is very easy to read and as a result minimizes the human error which is quite common in interpreting the analog display.

MULTIMETER MEASUREMENTS

3. Dc-voltage Measurement The one function which is always included in a multimeter is the ability to measure dc-voltage potentials. All other measurements are typically made by either generating a dc voltage proportional to the unknown (whether it is ac voltage, direct current, or dc resistance) and measuring this generated voltage with the dc-voltage-measuring portion of the multimeter or by using a meter movement such as the moving-iron type which will respond to both ac and dc voltages.

The dc-voltage measurement can be made in one of several ways. The inexpensive multimeters use a simple d'Arsonval meter movement with different resistor taps for different full-scale voltages. A slightly more expensive multimeter may have an amplifier driving the d'Arsonval movement for better impedance isolation between the source and meter movement. This impedance isolation minimizes errors due to source impedance which are so common in less expensive multimeters. Both these types are analog multimeters.

A more accurate and more expensive type of dc voltmeter is the manual potentiometric type. This type of dc measurement scheme would not ordinarily be used in a multimeter since it is a very slow special-purpose dc voltmeter.

The more expensive digital multimeters typically use more sophisticated techniques to measure dc voltage. Both the voltage-to-time-ramp type and the staircase-ramp type are quite common in digital multimeters. However, both types are susceptible to errors due to noise superimposed on the dc voltage to be measured.

The successive-approximation technique is another very popular dc-voltage-measuring scheme used in digital multimeters. They can be made to take several thousand readings per second and are relatively simple to build. They are, however, subject to errors due to noise similar to the two ramp types mentioned earlier.

The integrating-type dc voltmeter is used in digital multimeters primarily because of its ability to average out the superimposed noise.

Table 1 tabulates the salient features of different types of dc voltmeters. Each of the types of dc-voltage-measuring techniques mentioned above is discussed at length in Chapter 22.

4. Ac-voltage Measurement In ac-voltage measurements, the rms (root-mean-square) value of a waveform is usually the quantity of interest. The rms value of an ac-voltage waveform is equivalent to the dc voltage which generates the same amount of heat in a resistive load as the ac voltage.

Ac voltage is measured in a multimeter by first generating a dc voltage which is proportional to the rms value of the ac voltage and then measuring the dc voltage with the dc-measuring portion of the multimeter or by measuring it directly with a meter movement such as a moving-iron type which responds to both ac and dc voltage. When the first technique is used, the portion of the multimeter which generates the dc voltage is known as an ac converter since it in essence converts an ac voltage to a dc voltage.

Generally speaking, ac converters can be classified into four broad categories: rms-responding, quasi-rms-responding, average-responding, and peak-responding. Table 1 (p. 20-5) tabulates the salient points of each classification.

RMS-responding ac converters employ a thermal-sensing device called a thermocouple. These voltmeters respond directly to the rms (ability to supply heat to a resistive load) value of the waveform being measured. Quasi-rms-responding ac converters do not sense the heat directly but use electronic circuits to approximate the rms value of the waveform being measured. The two classifications of ac converters above are typically more sophisticated than the average- or peak-responding voltmeters and are used in the more expensive multimeters.

In multimeters, the most widely used technique to measure ac voltage is either the average- or the peak-responding converter. These converters respond to the average value and the peak value of the waveform being measured, as the names imply. For any periodic waveform, there is a constant scale factor which relates the rms value of the waveform to either its peak or average value. For sine waves only, the rms value is equal to 0.707 times the peak value or 1.1 times the average value. If either the average value or the peak value of the waveform is measured and the proper scale factor is introduced, the indication will be in rms volts, which is the desired result. Note there is a different scale factor for every type of waveform. Therefore, average- and peak-responding ac converters are accurate for sine waves only. Table 2 (p. 20-13) gives some measurement errors for different amounts of second- and third-harmonic distortion when using an average- or peak-responding voltmeter. The phase of the harmonic with respect to the fundamental significantly affects the amount of error; this is indicated in the table by a range of the error.

Rms voltage and each category of ac converters are discussed at length in Chapter 20.

5. Dc-resistance Measurement DC resistance is defined as the voltage dropped across a resistor divided by the current through the resistor. There are several ways to make a dc-resistance measurement; however, in multimeters, by far the most common technique is either to drive the unknown resistor with a known voltage and measure the current or to drive it with a known current and measure the voltage. If these two terms are known, the multimeter can be calibrated to give an indication in ohms.

There are two variations of the dc-resistance portion of a multimeter which are quite common. They are called the two-terminal and the four-terminal resistance (or ohm) meters. In the two-terminal measurement technique, the current through the unknown and the voltage-sense leads is the same. Therefore, any voltage drop in the leads will be sensed by the voltmeter, and an error will result.

The four-terminal measurement technique uses two wires to deliver current to the unknown and two different wires to sense the voltage drop across the resistor. Using the four-terminal technique eliminates errors due to the resistance of the input leads. Most inexpensive multimeters use the two-terminal technique, while more expensive multimeters are more likely to use the four-terminal technique. Table 1 shows typical range and accuracy that are specified in multimeters capable of ohms measurement. Dc-resistance measurement is covered in detail in Chapter 27.

TABLE 1 Typical Accuracy and Ranges for Multimeter Ohms Measurement

Technique	Range of resistances measured	Range of accuracy specifications, %
Two-terminal..........	1 Ω to 10 MΩ	±0.3 to ±10
Four-terminal..........	1 Ω to 10 MΩ	±0.01 to ±1

6. Dc Measurement Techniques for measuring current are numerous. Different techniques are employed for alternating and direct current and for different magnitudes of current. Table 1 (p. 21-18) tabulates some of the more significant features of the different current-measuring techniques. All these techniques are discussed at length in Chapter 21.

In multimeters measuring direct current, two techniques are commonly employed. The first is to allow the current to flow directly through the coil of a d'Arsonval or moving-iron meter movement. By varying the shunt resistor around the coil, full-scale indication can be obtained for any desired input current. This is by far the most common technique used in multimeters.

Another technique which is used in multimeters is to allow the current to flow through a known resistor and measure the voltage with the dc-voltmeter portion of the multimeter. Full-scale indication can be obtained for different levels of input current by varying the resistor. This technique is often used in the more expensive multimeters which have an input buffer amplifier.

SPECIFICATIONS

The specifications of multimeters are itemized for each manufacturer's multimeter in what is commonly called the "spec sheet." This spec sheet usually consists of a different section for each measurement that the multimeter is capable of performing. For example, a multimeter capable of measuring dc voltage, ac voltage, dc resistance, and direct current would have four different sections, one for each function, in the spec sheet.

Each section of the spec sheet should be independent of the other sections. For example, the user should not be required to add the dc-voltmeter accuracy specification to the ac-voltmeter accuracy specification in order to obtain the accuracy of an ac-voltage measurement, even though both measurements are made in a typical ac-voltage measurement. The ac-voltage portion of the specifications should specify accuracy of the reading obtained from the meter or digital readout.

Each section of the spec sheet would contain the same information that would be contained in a spec sheet for an instrument which performed that function only. A detailed explanation of the specifications, along with typical values, is contained in Chapters 20 to 22 and 27.

FRONT-PANEL CONTROLS

The only front-panel control that is unique to multimeters is the function control. This control selects the kind of measurement (dc volts, ac volts, ohms, or current) to be performed by the multimeter. All other front-panel controls are identical to those described in Chapters 20 to 22 and 27.

CALIBRATION

Most instruments specify a length of time after which they must be recalibrated in order to achieve optimum performance from the multimeter. This is primarily due to the time stability of components. Most instrument instruction manuals contain a detailed step-by-step procedure for this recalibration. Typically, they require an accurate dc-voltage source, an accurate source of sine waves, some known resistors, and an accurate source of direct current to calibrate the dc voltmeter, ac voltmeter, ohmmeter, and ammeter section of the multimeter, respectively. For more accurate multimeters, the manufacturer may require a controlled environment in which the recalibration must be performed.

TRADEOFFS BETWEEN A MULTIMETER AND UNIQUE-FUNCTION INSTRUMENTS

The most significant advantages of a multimeter over two or more unique-function instruments are cost and space saved. For example, a multimeter which would perform dc-voltage, ac-voltage, resistance, and current measurements would cost considerably less and require considerably less bench space than four instruments with comparable specifications to perform the same tasks. However, the user can use only one function at a time on a multimeter, while he can make all four measurements noted above simultaneously with four unique-function instruments.

Another factor the user must consider in purchasing a multimeter is the availability of the combination of measurement techniques he needs. For example, if he needs a successive-approximation dc voltmeter, a peak-responding ac voltmeter, four-terminal ohms measurement, and dc current sensing, this particular combination may not be available.

Another factor, if accurate high-frequency ac-voltage measurements or accurate low-resistance measurements must be made, is the wiring from the input terminals to the different sections of the multimeter. This wiring is typically longer in a multimeter than in unique-function meters because of the need to connect several functional sections to the input. The longer wires typically have more stray capacitance to ground, which restricts the high-frequency measurement capability of the ac voltmeter. Also, the resistance of the longer leads contributes an error in the two-terminal technique when low-resistance measurements must be made.

USING A MULTIMETER

7. Using a Guarded Instrument Common-mode error voltages are voltages caused by current flow in the ground lead between the ground of the multimeter and the ground of the unknown signal. One major source of this ground current is in the form of externally injected noise. This effect can be greatly reduced by the use of a guard. Guarded multimeters usually have the measurement portion of the multimeter (excludes circuitry associated with the display) encased in a conducting shield with a terminal on the front panel electrically connected to the shield or guard. Noise currents are injected into the guard and not into the measurement circuitry. This guard terminal should be electrically connected to the ground of the unknown signal being measured, thus returning the common-mode current through a connection other than the multimeter ground lead.*

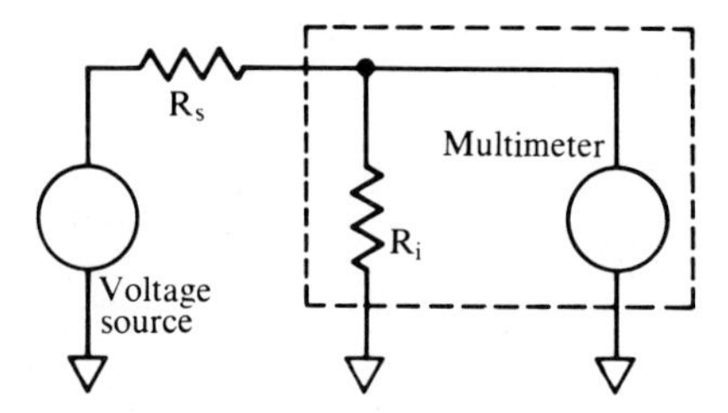

Fig. 3. Effect of loading the source.

8. Input-lead Precautions The voltage being measured should always be connected to the voltmeter with leads as short as possible. This prevents errors due to current flow in the input leads. If a calibration source is being used which has a remote sense capability, it should be utilized.

Another source of error due to input leads is either electrostatic or magnetic coupling of unwanted signals into the input leads. If the source can supply the additional current required to drive the added shunt capacitance, either shielded cable or a twisted pair of leads can greatly reduce this effect.

9. Grounding Ground leads between the source of the input signal and the multimeter should be as short and as low in resistance as possible in order to minimize errors due to current flow in these leads. Sometimes, unexpected results can be obtained when a ground loop back through the power line exists between the source and the multimeter. This problem can be verified by using either a battery-operated instrument or an instrument capable of making a floating measurement.

10. Errors Caused by Input Impedance In ac- and dc-voltage measurements, the input impedance of the multimeter can contribute errors. Figure 3 shows a voltage source with some output resistance R_s being measured by a multimeter

* William McCullough, How to Reduce Common-mode Effects, *EEE*, February, 1967.

with some input resistance R_i. The voltage measured by the multimeter is

$$\frac{V_{source} R_i}{R_s + R_i} \tag{1}$$

Therefore, the measurement is in error by the factor $R_i/(R_s + R_i)$. For complex impedances, the error would be determined by $Z_i/(Z_s + Z_i)$. This error can be minimized by either increasing R_i or decreasing R_s. Sometimes an impedance converter must be used if an accurate measurement is to be made.

11. Selection of Range Typically, multimeters give more accurate results near full scale than on the lower portion of the scale. Therefore, it is to the user's advantage to utilize the range which will give a reading nearest full scale. The one instance where the above statement is untrue is in the case of an analog ohms scale which indicates ohms from near zero to near infinity. In this case multipliers are selected for the numbers on the scale. A multiplier should be selected which gives a reading near midscale in order to obtain the most accurate result.

BIBLIOGRAPHY

McCullough, William: How to Reduce Common-mode Effects, *EEE,* February, 1967.

Wirtz, Barton A.: Digital Multimeters—Types, Techniques, and Tradeoffs, *Electron. Instr. Dig.,* August, 1969, pp. 34–42.

Digital Multimeters—Who Makes What Types? *Electron. Instr. Dig.,* August, 1969, pp. 45–47.

Chapter 24

Oscilloscopes

JACK E. DAY*

Oregon Museum of Science and Industry, Portland, Oregon

* At the time of preparation of this chapter, the author was employed by Tektronix Inc., Beaverton, Oregon.

INTRODUCTION

1. Basic Description The oscilloscope draws (or plots) a graph on a cathode-ray-tube screen such as one finds on a television set. This graph may be plotted continuously in a smooth line or point by point as one plots a graph on a piece of paper. The *information* which is graphed is of vibrations or changes which normally cannot be seen, heard, or otherwise perceived by our unaided senses. Consequently, by means of the oscilloscope, we are able to "see" the behavior of processes of which we would normally be unaware (Fig. 1).

More formally, the oscilloscope is a device which displays in graphical form the "instantaneous" magnitude of some phenomenon as it changes with respect to some independent variable such as time. The graph is an analog of some aspect of the phenomenon which helps us to understand it better. The phenomenon can be uniformly repetitive, arbitrary, or unitary. Because the display is visual, it can be studied, measured, and analyzed at leisure—either directly or by means of photographs (Fig. 2).

2. Applications Quantities which change over substantial periods of time, such as population, the weight of individuals, or traffic loads on highways, can be measured merely by counting the units of interest within or in relation to certain arbitrarily selected intervals (Fig. 3). However, many events* occur too rapidly to permit counting or are of a nature which does not lend itself to counting.

* It is useful here to introduce the concept of event, since it simplifies discussion of what the oscilloscope displays. An event, as used here, simply means some kind of change or changes that can be translated into a corresponding change of electric current or voltage. In this context, a single, simple pulse or step function would be a single event, whereas a sine wave would be a uniformly repetitive succession of uniform events (see Fig. 4).

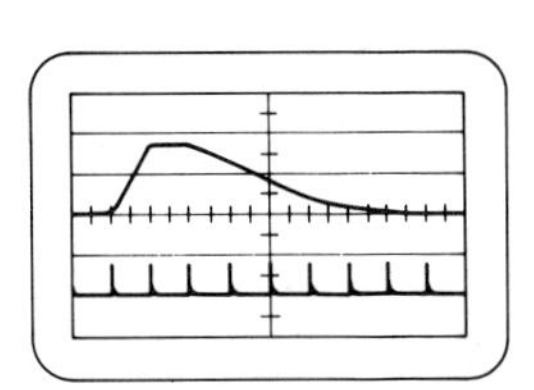

Fig. 1. Idealized oscilloscope display with waveform of interest above and timing pulses below.

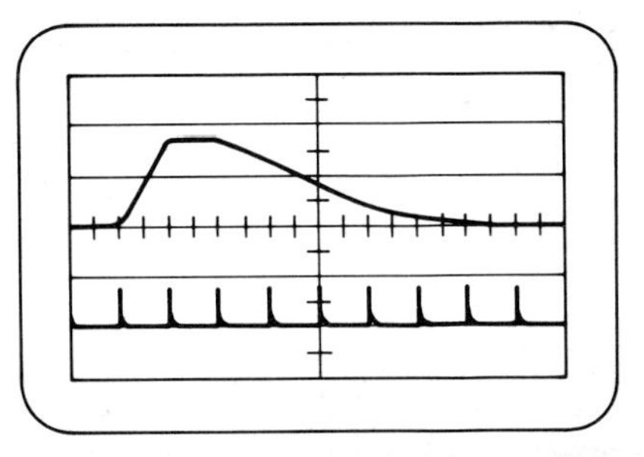

Fig. 2. Enlarged idealized oscilloscope display. It can be seen that many things about a waveform can be measured, including amplitude, time of rise, duration of the flat top, time of decay, etc.

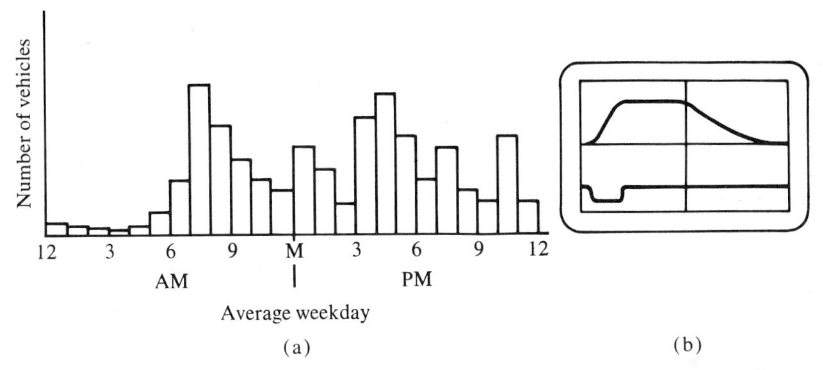

Fig. 3. (*a*) Graph of average weekday vehicle load on a certain street between a suburb and an urban center. Notice the peaks in the morning and late afternoon caused by commuters going to and from their work and in the late evening caused by entertainment traffic. (*b*) Oscillogram of the turnoff characteristics of a high-speed transistor. The turnoff pulse is at the bottom (12 ns wide); the transistor response is the upper trace. It turns on in 1.5 ns (1.5×10^{-9} s). (Light travels about 1 ft in a nanosecond.)

Basically, an oscilloscope will display any change in *electric* current or voltage, or in anything which can be converted into electric current or voltage. The characteristics of present-day instruments can display changes which occur over a range from hundredths of nanoseconds (less than 10^{-10} s) to several minutes. (At the latter end of the range there are other instruments which may do the job as well as or better than the oscilloscope, e.g., strip recorders.) Consequently, any variation of any kind whatever can be displayed on an oscilloscope if it can be converted into an analogous variation of electric voltage or current. The devices which make such conversions are known as transducers.

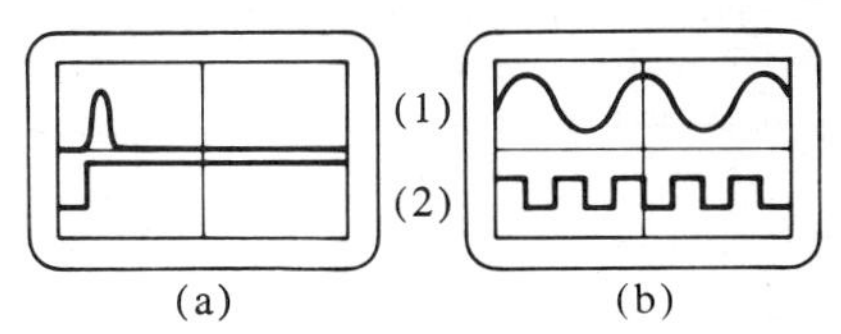

Fig. 4. (*a*) Single events: (1) positive unipolar pulse, (2) positive step function. (*b*) Repetitive events: (1) sine wave, (2) square wave.

Well-known transducers include such examples as the cartridge in the tone arm of a record player, which converts physical displacement (the squiggly character of the record groove) into analogous electrical fluctuations; the microphone, which converts variations in air pressure into variations in electric current; and in a more limited sense, the common thermostat, which changes sawtooth variations in temperature into square waves of electric current.

Less common examples to the layman are such things as strain gages, which transduce variations in length; certain speedometer systems, which operate on variations in angular velocity; electrical stethoscopes, which actually are microphones; "electric-eye" cameras, which adjust the lens opening to compensate for the amount of light on the scene to be photographed; television-camera tubes, which produce an electric current corresponding to the amount of light present at a given point; and tiny thermocouples for responding to minute and rapid variations in temperature.

Present-day scientific, technological, and industrial efforts require devices to convert change in almost any phenomenon to electrical changes. It should not be inferred that a transducer gives only an electrical output. Strictly speaking, a transducer is any device which, upon being the recipient of one form of energy which varies in an arbitrary way, gives an output in another form of energy which varies correspondingly. As an example, a loudspeaker is a transducer that converts variations in electric current into variations in air pressure by means of the piston action of the speaker cone. We are concerned here with transducers which give electrical outputs because that is the type of input required by present-day oscilloscopes.

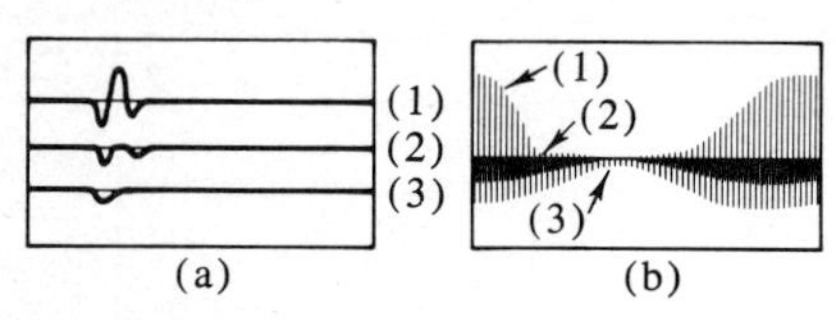

Fig. 5. (*a*) Response of a hypothetical nerve cell to a drug: (1) normal response without drug, (2) after 30 s, (3) after 1 min. (*b*) Gross response of cell over a period of several minutes as the drug takes effect, reaches maximum effect, and assimilates.

Naturally many oscilloscopes, perhaps most, are used to measure changes which occur in equipment that depends upon electrical impulses to operate them. This includes such equipment as computers; radars; and various kinds of communication equipment where the intelligence is transmitted by pulses which vary in amplitude, duration, timing, occurrence, or various combinations of these. It also includes information-display systems (including television) and other electrical, electronic, and electromagnetically controlled devices, etc.

The computer industry illustrates the range of use of the oscilloscope. Oscilloscopes are used in:

Basic research into the properties of materials
The development of new devices using those materials
The design of new circuit configurations using those new devices
The development of new computers using such circuits
The testing and calibration of the new computers in production
The maintenance and repair of such computers when in the hands of users
And in many cases as a part of the computer itself to monitor the performance of the various units

The diversity of use of the oscilloscope is very great. It can be used to observe the effect of a drug on the response of a single nerve cell. By first observing the response of the cell to a standardized stimulus (electrical, light flash, etc.), it can be determined whether the drug enhances, moderates, eliminates, delays, accelerates, or otherwise modifies the action of the cell. A suitably rapid sweep will permit investigation of the individual components of cell response (the onset, the continuation, the decay or termination), and it can be observed how each of these changes over a period of time. A suitable slow sweep rate will permit observations of the gross response of the cell as the drug begins to take effect, as it reaches maximum effect, and as it becomes finally assimilated by the system (Fig. 5).

A radically different use of the oscilloscope is in the field of mining. The removal of large amounts of ore from the ore body requires enormous amounts of explosive.

The oscilloscope can be used to time the detonation of a given charge to coincide with the arrival of the shock wave from an adjacent, previously detonated, charge so that the effect of the blast is multiplied. In a large operation where substantial quantities of ore are to be moved, a substantial reduction in the amount of explosive required can be achieved. In addition, significant economies can be realized in eliminating further handling of the ore since the size and timing of the charges will significantly affect the size of the ore chunks (Fig. 6).

It will be seen that the use of the oscilloscope is limited primarily by the imagination of those who seek to use it.

3. Operating Principles The goal sought by the use of the oscilloscope is to obtain knowledge about events which occur too rapidly to be observed and/or are not accessible to direct observation by the unaided senses. These events include, but are not restricted to, matters in the electrical, chemical, biological, and mechanical realms.

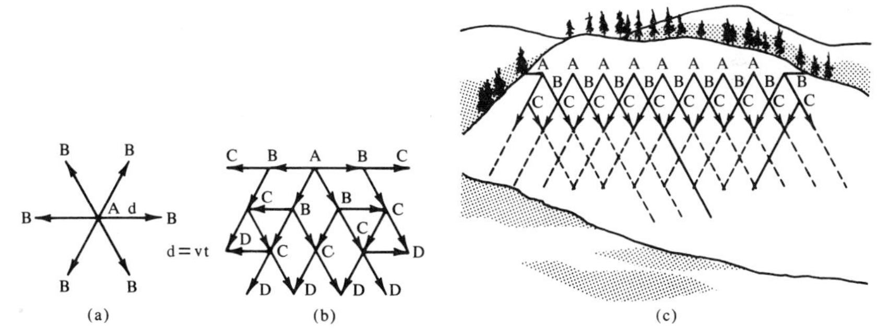

Fig. 6. (*a*) Whenever a sudden disturbance occurs in a rigid structure, such as an ore body, a shock wave proceeds through the material at a rate determined by the elasticity of the material. When an explosion occurs at point *A*, a shock wave will proceed outward radially and arrive at points *B* after a time *t*. (*b*) If explosive charges are planted at points *B* and timed to explode coincidentally with the arrival of the shock wave from *A*, the shock waves from explosions *B* reinforce that from *A*. In addition, the shock waves from two *B*'s will arrive coincidentally at any one *C*, giving a further reinforcement. (*c*) A pattern of explosives, arranged as shown on an exposed ore body, will drop a pile of rubble at the base of the cliff, with very little energy dissipated outward into the air.

The problem, therefore, is to extract from some nonelectrical event, say a mechanical vibration or a chemical reaction, the capability of developing a corresponding change in an electrical or magnetic field which can be used to deflect the beam of electrons in a cathode-ray tube. It must then be intensified from the few microvolts available or modified from the several thousands or million amperes involved in certain kinds of electrical discharges to the proper electrical intensity to deflect a minute electron beam.

These signals must then be "charted" in time so that they can be examined adequately to determine what information they contain.

The oscilloscope is designed around the cathode-ray tube,* which embodies two fundamental phenomena:

* The term "cathode ray" is the name given to the "rays" which emanated from the cathode of a glow-discharge tube in the early days of electric-discharge experimentation. K. F. Braun in Germany (hence the name "Braun tube") and J. J. Thomson in England were the first ones to form the cathode rays into a beam and to deflect them by electric and magnetic fields, Braun to display an alternating current (thus building the first oscilloscope) and Thomson to prove that cathode rays would respond to electric fields as well as magnetic and were indeed electrified particles (electrons, we now call them).

1. When a moving electron is injected into an electric or magnetic field, it will be deflected from its initial path in a direction and by an amount that depends upon the velocity of the electron, the strength of the field, and the direction of the field with respect to the direction of electron motion (Fig. 7).

2. When a moving electron collides with an atom or molecule of some substance, one or more electrons of the substance will be excited temporarily to high-energy states and will emit energy when they revert to their former level. Depending upon the energy of the incident electron, and the substance involved (called a phosphor) the emitted energy can be in the form of visible light (Fig. 8).

The cathode-ray tube exploits these phenomena to:

Form a beam of electrons which can be sharply focused, and then pass it through two sets of electric or magnetic fields at right angles to each other and to the electron beam.

This beam is then impinged upon a surface composed of phosphor particles to form a visible spot which can be moved by the direction and strength of the fields.

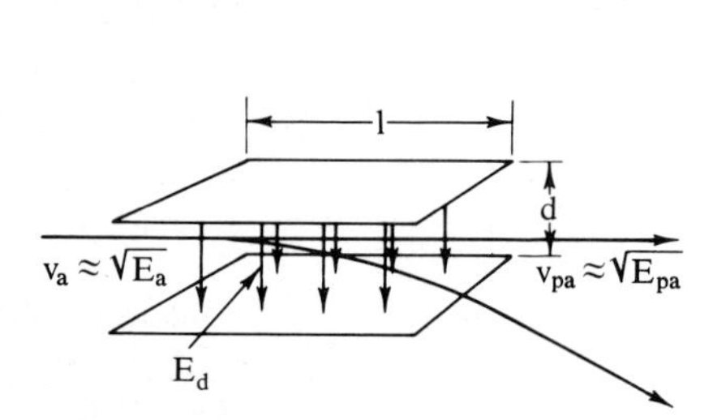

Fig. 7. The deflection is determined by the velocity v_a of the electron beam, the length l of the plates, the spacing d of the plates, and the deflection potential E_d.

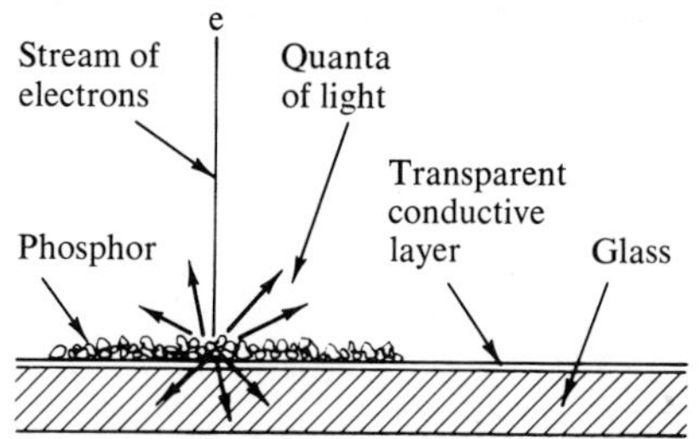

Fig. 8. Quanta of light energy are given off when a moving electron strikes a phosphor particle.

The versatility of the oscilloscope rests on the deflection of the electron to trace the waveform of interest. Since the electron is the least massive of the stable particles and has the highest charge-to-mass ratio, it has the least inertia and is the easiest to move around under given conditions. Consequently, it can respond to changes which take place in a very short time.

Even so, limitations imposed by the inertia and the velocity of the electron have required the development of increasingly sophisticated ways of displacing the electron so that the oscilloscope can be used to investigate changes of greater and greater rapidity or shorter and shorter duration. At the present time, single events that occur in the order of tenths of nanoseconds (less than 0.1×10^{-9} s) or with a frequency of a few gigahertz (more than 10^{10} Hz) can be recorded directly, and repetitive events that change in the orders of hundredths of nanoseconds (less than 0.01×10^{-9} s) or a few tens of gigahertz (less than 10×10^{10} Hz) can be recorded indirectly, that is, by sampling methods.

DESIGN PHILOSOPHIES

The two basic philosophies embodied in oscilloscopes depend upon the character of the signals to be viewed:

One philosophy is based upon the assumption that the signal to be observed is uniformly repetitive at least during the time of observation and of a character that does not depart significantly from a 50 percent duty cycle; that is, the ratio of negative-going to positive-going portions of the signal is somewhere in the range of roughly 20 to 80 percent. Instruments designed according to this philosophy are usually called "synchronized oscilloscopes."

The other design philosophy assumes that the signal to be observed may occur only once or, if more than once, in an arbitrary and unpredictable manner. Instruments designed according to this philosophy are often called "triggered oscilloscopes."

The two philosophies produce instruments that are totally different in capability, nomenclature, and usefulness. While the triggered oscilloscope can be used to observe uniform signals, the synchronized oscilloscope cannot be used to observe arbitrary signals (Fig. 9).

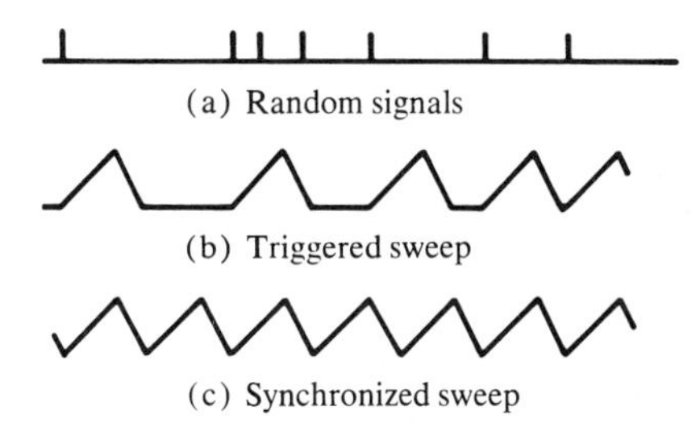

Fig. 9. If a random signal is presented to a synchronized oscilloscope, the sweep generator is unable to synchronize except when the signal occurs immediately prior to the beginning of the sweep. On the other hand, in the triggered oscilloscope, the sweep occurs with each signal except during the period of the sweep and hold-off.

4. Synchronized Oscilloscopes. The synchronized oscilloscope has roots that reach deep in recent scientific history. Over 100 years ago, Jules Antoine Lissajous, a French physicist, discovered that designs of beauty and elegance would be traced out by sand streaming from a container mounted on the lower of two pendulums whose lengths bore a simple relation to one another and which were oscillating at right angles to one another. These figures (Fig. 10) have become known as Lissajous figures, and most students have encountered them in freshman courses in physics or mathematics. This technique translated to the oscilloscope was used very early, perhaps by Braun in 1897, to determine the frequency of an unknown simple signal on the vertical axis of an oscilloscope, by comparing it with a known frequency on the horizontal axis, and it is used even

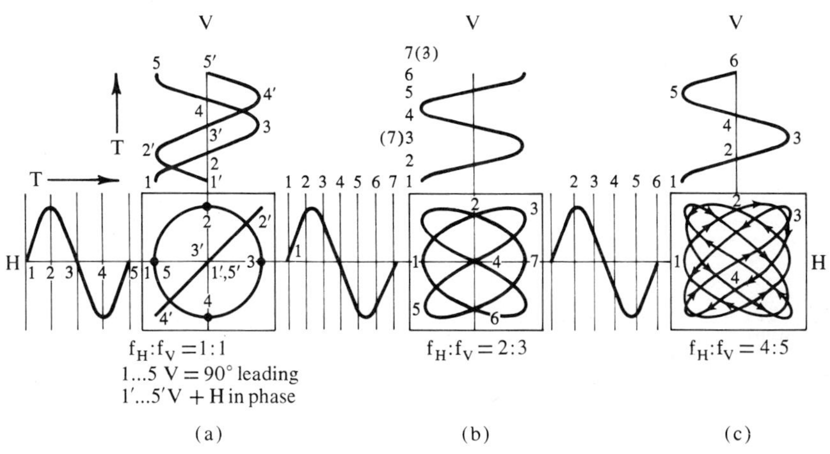

Fig. 10. Examples of Lissajous figures using standard sine waves. (*a*) Circle 1, 2, 3, 4, 5 is composed of a sine wave on the vertical plates leading the sine wave on the horizontal plates by 90°; the slant line is composed of two sine waves in phase. (*b*) Vertical, 90° leading, 1.5 × horizontal *f*. (*c*) f_v, 90° leading, 1.25 × f_H.

today in simple applications, such as comparing the frequency of secondary frequency standards with the primary standard.

The philosophy of the synchronized oscilloscope results in a display which is a special case of a Lissajous figure. That is, the horizontal signal is a sawtooth waveform whose frequency is a precise submultiple of the vertical-signal frequency. A sawtooth waveform is one that starts from a given voltage level and progresses *uniformly* to a second voltage level in a given period of time, after which it returns in some fashion to the original level from whence it recurs repetitively. The important feature is the uniformity of change. Whenever such a waveform (Fig. 11) is combined with a waveform of arbitrary waveshape, the resulting Lissajous figure will be simply the "shape" of the arbitrary signal (Fig. 12) displayed in

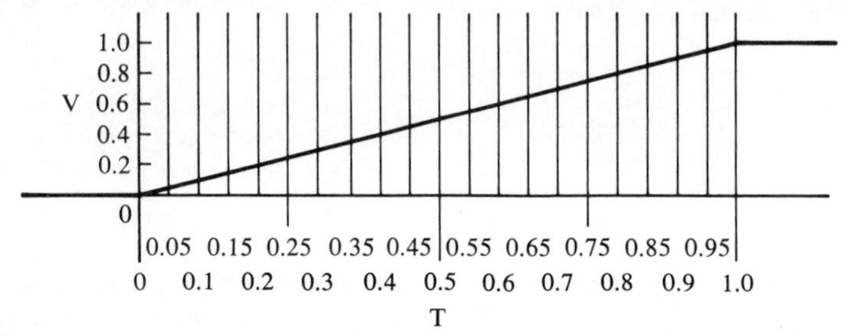

Fig. 11. A sawtooth waveform is one which changes uniformly in voltage each unit of time.

time (the time involved being the period of the sawtooth signal). In essence, the sawtooth signal "disappears" visually, and only the shape of the arbitrary signal is perceived.

5. Triggered Oscilloscopes The triggered instrument was called into being by the need to observe events which occurred only once or in an arbitrary and unpredictable manner or where the portion of interest was so small compared with the period between signals that a uniformly repetitive sweep could not provide

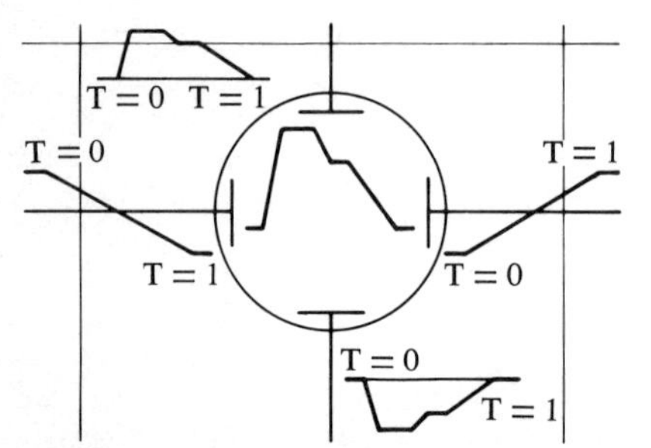

Fig. 12. When a sawtooth voltage is combined with an arbitrary signal the arbitrary signal is displayed, the sawtooth being manifested merely as a uniform displacement from one side to the other.

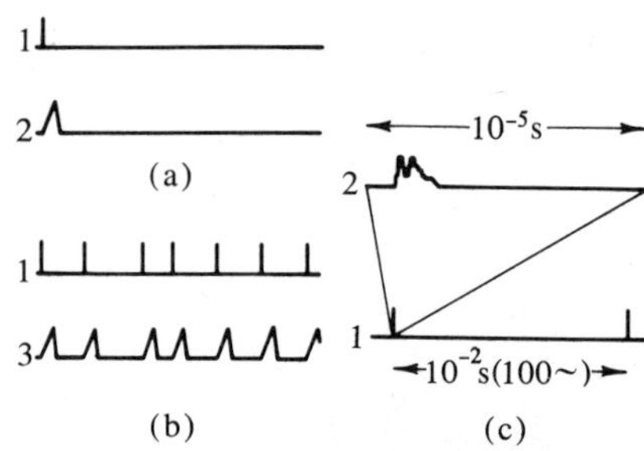

Fig. 13. (*a*) A single event requires a time base which will start when the event occurs. (*b*) Random events require a time base which occurs only when an event occurs. (*c*) A repetitive event which proves to have fine detail that simply cannot be shown by an ordinary repetitive sweep.

a magnification adequate to examine closely the portion of the signal of interest (Fig. 13).

The electric-power industry very early found it desirable to know both the waveshape and amplitude of transients which occurred on their lines because of lightning strikes, broken conductors, switches opening unexpectedly, etc. Since adequate oscilloscopes were not available commercially, they solved their problem by the construction of special instruments. The early work in atomic energy required an instrument which would respond to a single event or to a random succession of events. The development of television and radar, where many signals of interest occupy only a fraction of a percent of the period of the repetition rate, or frequency of operation, made it necessary to have an instrument which would give a sweep waveform of the desired duration only when it was needed and not in a uniformly repetitive manner. From these demands developed the so-called triggered oscilloscope.

The basic structure used by the early oscilloscope designers to solve these problems used the transient of interest to activate a switch (usually a bistable multivibrator) which would initiate the generation of a single sawtooth waveform of appropriate duration and shape (not necessarily linear; some sweeps were and are parabolic, exponential, or logarithmic to give an expansion of the early portion of the transient to enable it to be studied in detail). At the same time, the cathode-ray-tube indicator would be unblanked, and the transient itself was then delayed for a short period of time* before being applied to the vertical deflection plates to enable the sweep waveform to be started and operating linearly.

6. Comparison of Synchronized and Triggered Oscilloscopes A comparison of the elements of the triggered instrument with those of the synchronized instrument will show that the types of circuits, operation, nomenclature, and units of measurement are different, and that these differences stem from the differences in the character of the signal viewed.

Synchronized Instrument	*Triggered Oscilloscope*
HORIZONTAL AXIS (Fig. 14)	
An astable sawtooth oscillator is synchronized at some submultiple of the displayed signal, and the unit of measurement is usually in hertz	A monostable or bistable sawtooth function generator is initiated by the event of interest, and the unit of measurement is usually in time/division
VERTICAL AXIS (Fig. 15)	
An ac-coupled circuit amplifies or attenuates the signal and is calibrated in terms of gain or amplification (×0.1, ×10, ×100) or in rms volts/full-scale deflection	A dc-coupled circuit amplifies or attenuates the signal, and is calibrated in terms of dc volts/division, permitting measurements of dc level as well as deflection

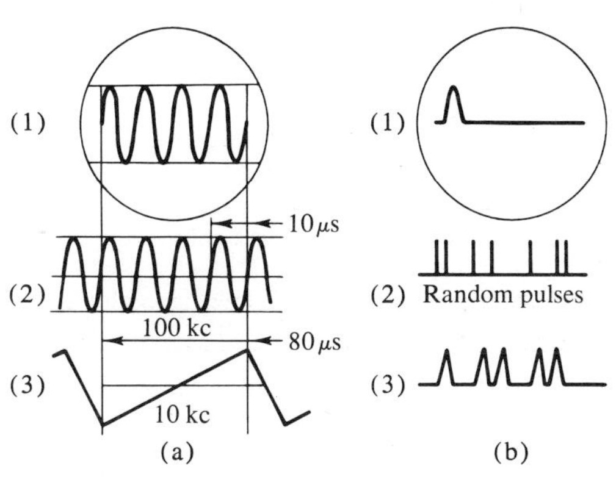

Fig. 14. (*a*) Synchronized oscilloscope. (*b*) Triggered oscilloscope. (1) Display, (2) signal to be displayed, (3) shape of sweep waveform.

* It is the author's understanding that a device to observe the effects of lightning strikes on the radio-transmitting antennas on the Empire State Building used a delay network consisting of a pair of telephone lines between New York City and Buffalo. This delay gave the sweep generator time to get started and the cathode-ray tube unblanked before the signal deflected the trace vertically. The multivibrator had to be reset after a suitable delay, either manually or automatically.

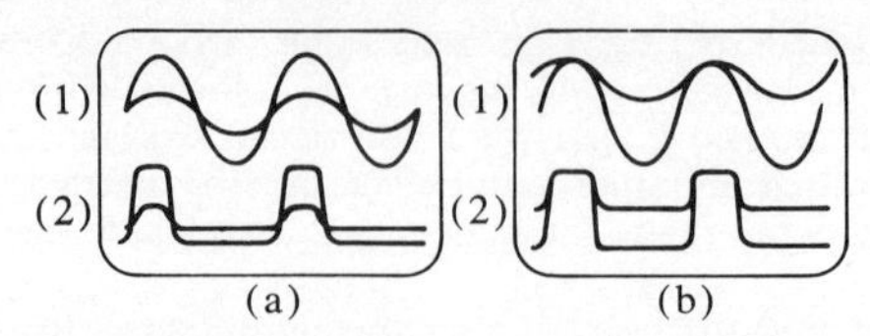

Fig. 15. Vertical amplifier performance. (*a*) AC circuit. (*b*) DC circuit. (1) Display as sine wave signal amplitude is varied, (2) display as pulse amplitude is varied. From the dc display we find that the sine wave goes negatively from Ov and the pulse does also, being, in fact, a negative gate whose ON time is greater than the OFF time. From the ac display, we would completely misconstrue these two signals.

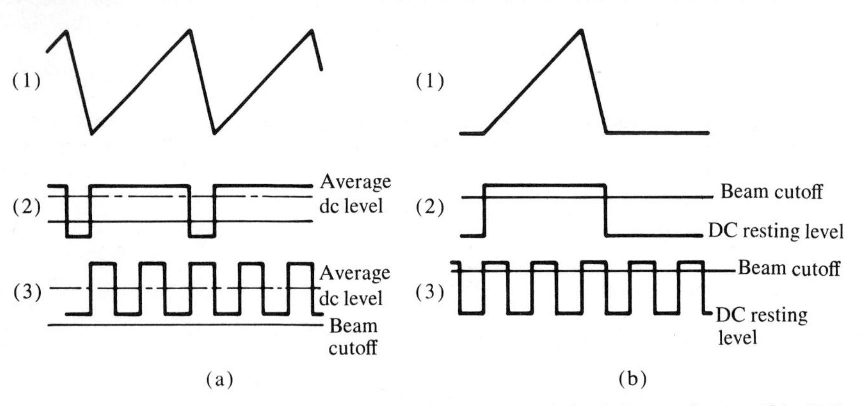

Fig. 16. Comparison of blanking performance. (*a*) AC coupling. (*b*) DC coupling. (1) Shape of sweep waveform, (2) shape of blanking waveform, (3) behavior when sweep length is shortened and the duty cycle of the blanking waveform changes. Notice how the ac-coupled circuit "rides up" as the duty cycle increases so that the beam does not cut off in condition. (3) The dc circuit does not have this problem.

Synchronized Instrument	*Triggered Oscilloscope*
Z AXIS (Fig. 16)	
A negative pulse is ac-coupled to the grid of the cathode-ray tube during the flyback period of the synchronized instrument, blanking the return trace between sweeps	A positive dc voltage is dc-coupled to the grid of the cathode-ray tube during sweep duration, unblanking the trace when a sawtooth is generated

The synchronized instrument was the first available commercially, especially prior to World War II and for a few years thereafter. Even now a few low-priced instruments are of this type.

The triggered instrument began to make its appearance during World War II in response to the needs of radar, television, and other new technologies. It became commercially available following the war and during the intervening decades has become the indispensable instrument in laboratories and design centers working with modern-day technology. The remainder of this chapter will be concerned only with the triggered instrument and its characteristics unless specifically stated otherwise.

One point concerning terminology needs to be made. The terminology describing oscilloscope capability developed during the time that the synchronized instrument was the principal type in use. It was natural that vertical-amplifier capability was specified in terms of bandwidth. This usage still persists today, although the concept of rise time has become much more useful to describe the potential signal-handling capability of the amplifier. Consequently, although the terms bandwidth and rise time may be used interchangeably here, the concept of bandwidth is the foundation on which the usage of these terms rests. Therefore, the term bandwidth in this article, unless otherwise stated, will be used in a specific sense, namely, from dc to the 70.7 percent amplitude point in an amplifier rolloff characteristic which decreases at 6 dB/octave (the so-called gaussian rolloff, Fig. 17). This topic will be dealt with at greater length in the section on the vertical amplifier, as it is of utmost importance to the subject of observed signal fidelity.

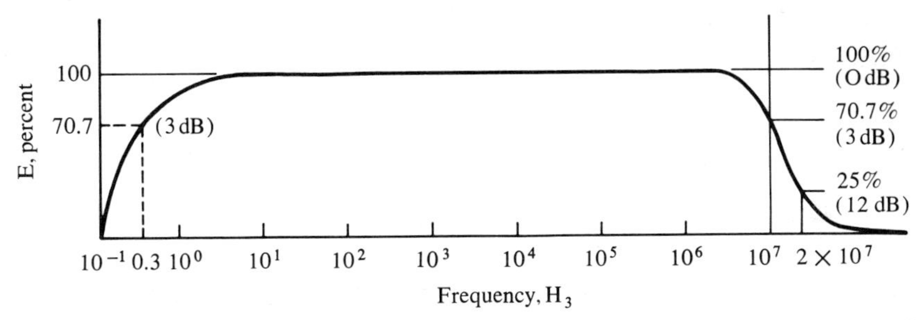

Fig. 17. Frequency response characteristic of a typical amplifier which is capable of operating in the ac or dc mode. In either case, the upper frequency limit (the 3-dB point) is 10 Hz. The lower 3-dB point in ac coupling is 0.3 Hz.

BASIC STRUCTURE OF AN OSCILLOSCOPE

An oscilloscope consists primarily of four sections or elements. These are:

1. The display element or cathode-ray tube
2. The signal-amplification element or vertical amplifier
3. The horizontal element or time-base generator
4. The energy source of power supply

THE CATHODE-RAY TUBE

The cathode-ray tube normally consists of three principal sections:

1. The display surface
2. The deflection elements
3. The beam-forming structure

A "storage" tube may have one or more additional elements, including

4. Flood gun
5. The storage target and structure

7. The Luminescent Screen The display surface—the phosphor screen—is the "chart" on which the "graph" of the event of interest to the observer is "drawn." Phosphor type, spot size, intensity, and tube size are factors which determine what can be seen, the amount of detail which can be discerned, and the accuracy with which measurements can be made.

The phosphor screen emits light when impacted by a moving electron or electron beam. There are two characteristics of this emitted light which determine its usefulness in the oscilloscope. One, called fluorescence, is the light emitted immediately (less than 10^{-8} s) following the impact by the moving electrons. It is probably the result of electrons (which have been elevated to higher energy levels by the impact) reverting to their ground state and emitting light quanta in the process. The other characteristic, called phosphorescence, is the light emitted subsequently (more than 10^{-8} s) to the impact and may be emitted some seconds or even minutes later. This is apparently due to an electron-trapping process. The two terms originally were used to distinguish between visible emissions with afterglows which were short compared with the persistence of the eye (0.1 s) and those which were longer. They are still so used loosely, but such use should be discouraged (see Fig. 18).

Both fluorescence and phosphorescence are present in the phosphor. Consequently, the potential of the phosphor screen compared with the cathode determines the energy with which the electron impacts the phosphor. The accelerating potential, as it is called, can appear within the electron gun, or it can be divided between the gun and the screen. Having all the acceleration take place in the gun has the disadvantage that the velocity of the electrons through the deflection plates is very great, giving a very "stiff" beam. On the other hand, placing a part of the total potential following deflection decreases the "stiffness" of the beam but also decreases the rise time of the deflection plates (Fig. 19). Many oscilloscopes use a compromise ratio of "postdeflection" acceleration to "predeflection" acceleration of about 5:1.

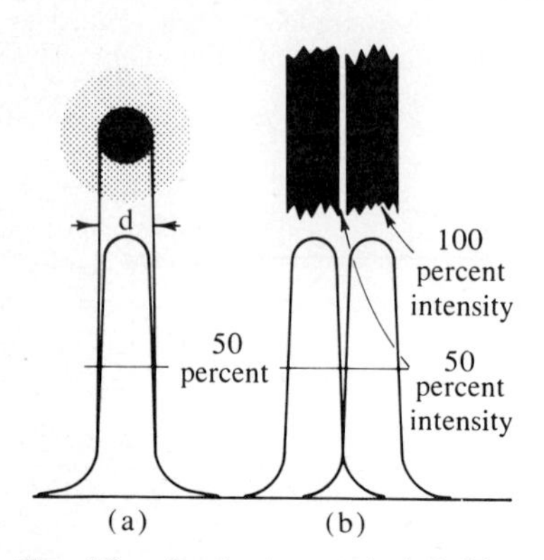

Fig. 18. Spot size and definition. (*a*) The spot size is measured at the 50 percent intensity level. (*b*) The definition is determined by the distance between two adjacent lines when the intensity ratio is 50 percent.

A too high intensity may result in burning the phosphor screen because of the heat generated by the electron beam. On the other hand, very fine detail may be missed if the intensity is set too low.

The size and aspect ratio of display on the screen vary from 1:1 (very seldom) to 1:4 (also very seldom), with the most usual range being from 4:10 to 8:10. The size ranges from less than 3 in. in diameter to 7 or over (Fig. 20).

8. The Deflection System The electron beam (which is the "pencil" by means of which the "graph" is "drawn" on the phosphor screen) is deflected by passing it through either an electrostatic or an electromagnetic field whose strength and direction can be varied as desired. Nearly all oscilloscopes except those large-screen models used as lecture demonstration units, use electrostatic deflection, and the discussion will be directed toward that method unless otherwise stated.

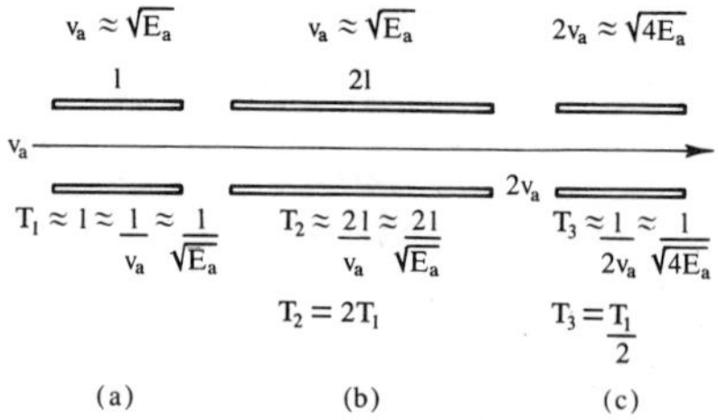

Fig. 19. Problem encountered when beam velocity is increased, or plate length is increased. (*a*) At a given beam velocity, it takes a time τ_1 for the beam to traverse the deflection plates; lengthening the plates doubles the sensitivity, but halves the frequency response of the deflection system. (*b*) Doubling the beam velocity doubles the frequency response and improves the intensity of the spot, but also halves the deflection sensitivity, since the beam only spends half the time between the plates that it did at the lower beam velocity.

The electrostatic field is obtained by developing a potential difference between two shaped metal electrodes called deflection plates. The spacing, shape, size, and location of these plates determine the deflection sensitivity and size of display as seen on the screen (Fig. 21).

Usually the vertical deflection plates are located farther from the faceplate than the horizontal plates, since the greater distance of travel after deflection gives a larger physical displacement on the screen.

The horizontal plates are therefore required to deflect the beam over a greater distance at a lower sensitivity, which may seem contradictory, as it obviously requires a much larger voltage swing from the horizontal amplifiers than from the vertical.

However, the choice is deliberate and is not perverse; it is the result of the fact that we *know* the range and character of the signal to be handled by the horizontal system and can therefore allow for it in the design, whereas we do *not* know the range and character of the vertical signals and therefore must have the benefit of every design advantage that can be obtained.

The horizontal system normally handles a fixed-amplitude signal of given character with only the frequency of occurrence being changed. The vertical system, if the oscilloscope is to be useful, must be prepared to handle a range of signal amplitudes without distortion of at least 20:1 and as much as 100:1 during the same trace. (Obviously, with preamplifiers and attenuators, signal-handling capabilities will be much greater, as explained in the next section.)

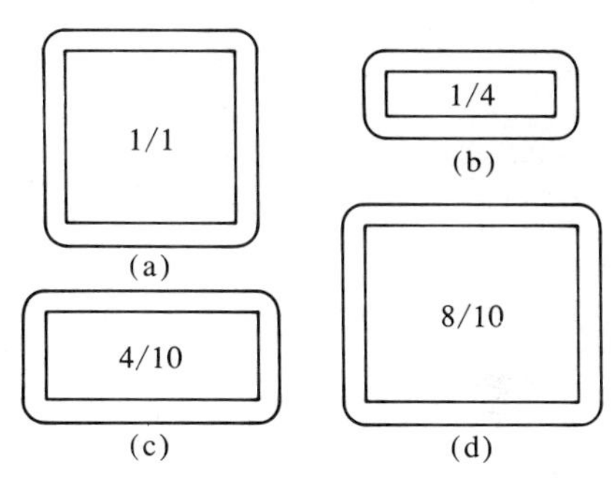

Fig. 20. Typical cathode-ray tube aspect ratios. (*a*) and (*b*) The extremes: (*a*) normally used in lower frequency instruments and (*b*) appears only in very high frequency (i.e., gigahartz) instruments. (*c*) and (*d*) The more normal ratios encountered.

The vertical deflection plates are usually much more sophisticated than the horizontal plates, because of the need to handle unknown signals of as low a level and short a period as possible. The two requirements tend to be mutually exclusive. Increased sensitivity can be obtained by (1) increasing the length of the deflection plates (Fig. 14), which increases the period of time the electron is influenced by the field and increases the capacitance of the plates, both of which decrease the frequency response and increase the rise time; or (2) decreasing the spacing between the plates, which also increases the capacitance unless the area of the plates is decreased proportionately.

This problem has been partially solved by dividing the plates into small segments in the direction of electron travel, and connecting the segments to each other by small, precise amounts of inductance. The resulting structure is a pair of delay networks with the electron beam traversing the space between the plates of the common capacitors (Fig. 22). Properly designed, a substantial reduction in rise time can be obtained by such a structure, and a number of commercial oscilloscopes now use such deflection systems.

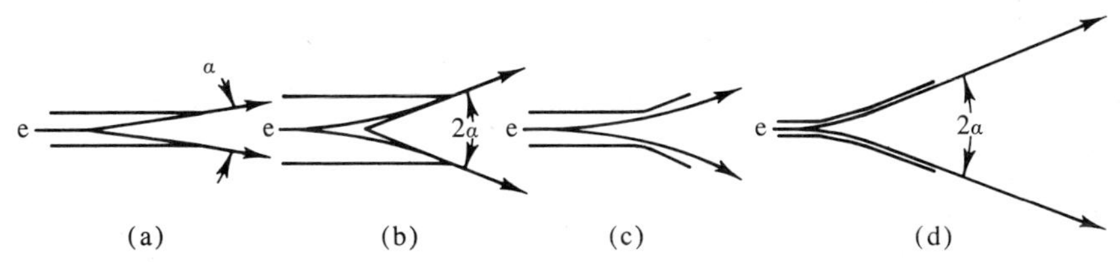

Fig. 21. Effect of deflection plate shape on scan and sensitivity. (*a*) Plates of a given spacing and length will permit a given scan and will have a given sensitivity. (*b*) Doubling the spacing will double the scan, but halve the sensitivity. (*c*) Flaring the exit tips of the plates will improve the scan without significantly reducing the sensitivity. (*d*) Reducing the spacing and giving a more elaborate shape to the plates will improve the sensitivity and give greater scan. An added benefit is that by such shaping the plates will also shape the deflection field so that the electron beam is always traveling normal to it, reducing distortion significantly as the beam traverses the limits of scan.

9. The Beam-forming Structure The electron beam is obtained from some kind of cathode and is formed by one of several methods. The whole structure is called an electron gun.

Most cathode-ray tubes use a standard oxide cathode in a fairly standard triode structure. Experiments have been made with field emitters (point emitters) which offer certain real advantages as a cathode for a cathode-ray tube, but there are disadvantages of even greater significance, and these are not in general use.

Spot size is determined by the minimum diameter that the electron beam attains from the time it leaves the cathode. In most tubes, the electrons are emitted from the cathode over a fairly wide area (Fig. 23); but under the influence of the grid cup and the anode, their paths cross over just beyond the grid, creating a cross section of minimum area. The electron lens system then focuses an image of this crossover section on the phosphor screen, giving a spot diameter which, while small, nevertheless cannot be smaller than the crossover area.

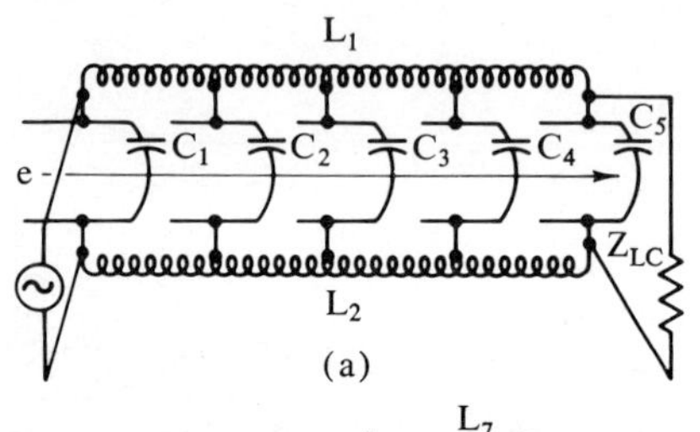

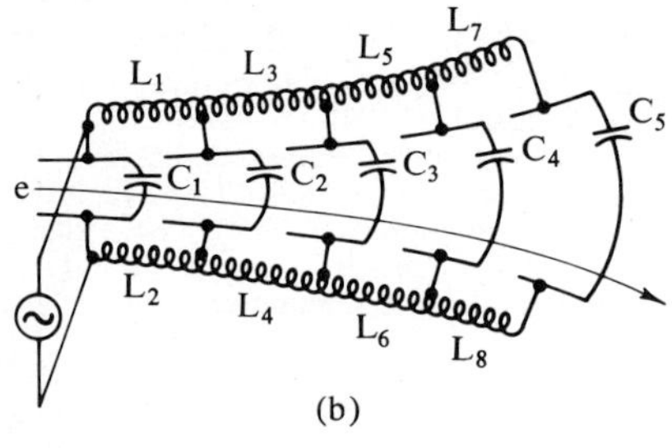

Fig. 22

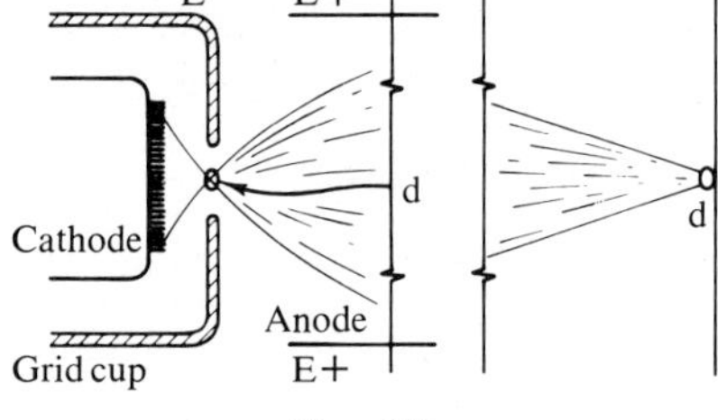

Fig. 23

Fig. 22. Distributed deflection plates. (*a*) An electron beam *e* entering the system with velocity *v* is subjected to the deflecting field between the first two plates. As it travels down the system, it encounters the same field between the second pair of plates, etc. The values of *L* and *C* are chosen so that the deflecting signal velocity is equal to *v*. Consequently, the beam encounters the same deflecting field over and over again, increasing the sensitivity substantially. (*b*) By shaping the plates, the advantages discussed in Fig. 21 are obtained in this type of deflecting system. Obviously, the values of *L* and *C* have to be modified so that the signal velocity is uniform and equal to the beam velocity.

Fig. 23. Determination of spot size. Although the electrons are emitted from a fairly large area of the cathode, because of the influence of the grid cup and the anode field, their trajectories cross somewhere in the vicinity of the grid hole. The diameter of the crossover point is determined by the effect of the emission vectors of the individual electrons and, in turn, it determines the minimum diameter of the spot on the screen which is simply a focussed image of the crossover.

Point emitters (Fig. 24) would make an ideal cathode for cathode-ray tubes, since the lens systems could focus the emitter image on the screen, giving a spot much smaller than that obtainable by conventional methods. Unfortunately such tubes, while giving very high definition, have other problems, including reliability and reproducibility.

Another promising cathode is the so-called Pierce cathode (as a part of a Pierce gun), which does not have a crossover point but does have a very small crossover section which makes possible a small spot diameter. This gun (Fig. 25) has not proved too satisfactory in cathode-ray tubes, as it is better adapted for higher beam current than is normally required.

The "electron gun" is composed of a series of electrodes (cylindrical or planar) with selected voltages between each element, and so disposed that a series of electric fields are formed which act as lenses for the electron beam, permitting it to be focused into a fine spot on the phosphor.

10. Storage Systems Some cathode-ray tubes differ from the standard tube described above. For example, some have multiple guns, permitting several traces to be obtained on the screen. They may all share a common horizontal deflection system, in which case multiple unknown signals can be compared on a common

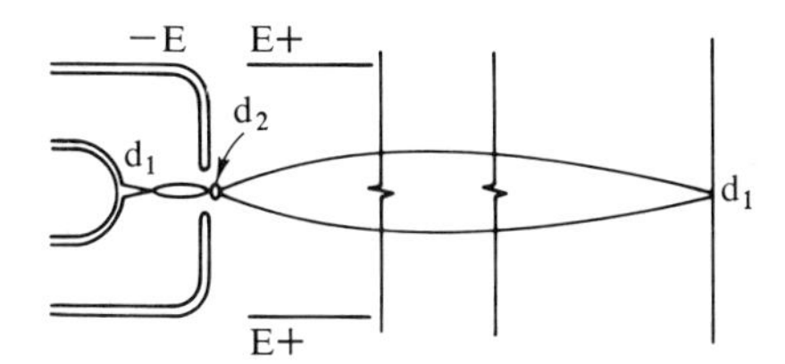

Fig. 24. Effect on spot size of field-emission cathode. Since these points are extremely small, on the order of a few microns radius, the imaged spot can be very small. Unfortunately, no satisfactory cathodes have yet been produced for cathode-ray tubes using this technique.

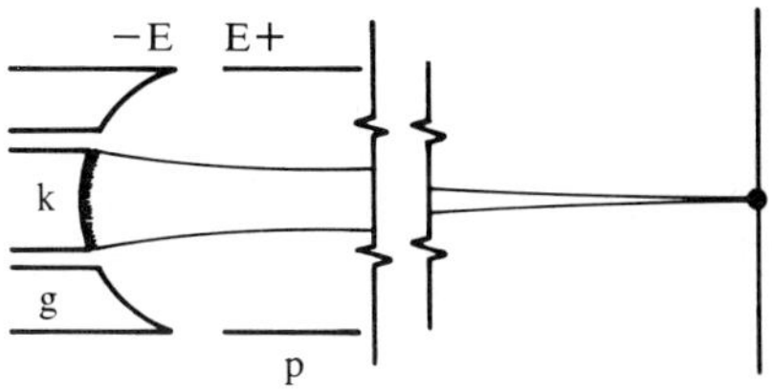

Fig. 25. Pierce gun. The shape of the cathode *k*, the electrode *g* and the anode *p* is such that the electron beam is "compressed" to an ever-narrowing cone, coming to a focus at the phosphor surface.

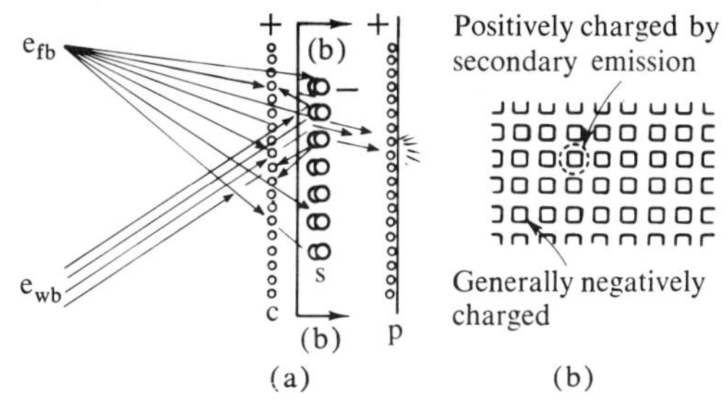

e_{wb} = high-energy writing beam
e_{fb} = low-energy flood beam
c = collector mesh for secondaries
s = storage mesh, insulator deposited on permeable mesh
p = phosphor screen

Fig. 26. Conventional storage structure. (*a*) As the writing beam e_{wb} strikes the (slightly) negatively charged insulating storage target deposited on the target screen S, secondary electrons are emitted, creating a region which is slightly positive, relative to the potential of the flood beam e_{fb}, permitting the electrons to pass through the "hole" created, in the storage screen and, being accelerated by the highly positive charge on the viewing screen *p*, duplicates visually the pattern written on the storage screen by the writing beam. The secondaries are collected by the collector *c*, as are the flood electrons which are repelled by the charge on the unwritten portion of the storage screen, which normally is slightly negative to the potential of the flood beam. (*b*) The appearance of the surface of the storage surface, normally an insulator with a high secondary-emission ratio, deposited on a metallic permeable mesh.

time base, or they may be complete electron guns, sharing only a common screen, in which case each trace can be independently deflected on both vertical and horizontal axes.

Other cathode-ray tubes permit a written trace to be stored. One method stores on an insulator deposited on a fine-mesh screen spaced toward the electron gun from the faceplate. The regular high-energy electron beam "writes" on the insulator, creating a positively charged pattern by secondary emission (Fig. 26). A low-energy electron gun, whose cathode is only a few volts negative to the unwritten storage screen, floods the screen with low-energy electrons, some of which impact the positively charged written area with sufficient energy to maintain secondary emission (but not to initiate it), while other electrons pass through the "holes" created by the high-energy beam, accelerate to the phosphor screen, and cause it to luminesce in the written pattern.

Another type of storage target is a layer of phosphor material which is deposited in such a way that it is electrically an insulator. When such a target is "written" by a high-energy electron beam, sufficient secondary electrons are emitted from the written areas so as to charge that portion positive, and this condition is maintained by the low-energy electrons from the flood gun. Because of the insulating qualities of the target, the charge does not spread and because the target is also a phosphor, the written portions continue to luminesce until erased (see Fig. 27).

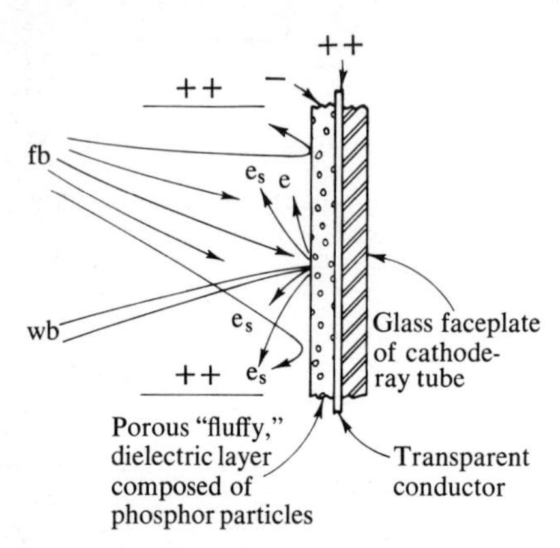

Fig. 27. Anderson storage target. The complex structure of a conventional storage target is eliminated by depositing a standard phosphor in such a way that a charged area, created by secondary emission from the energy of the writing beam, will not spread or creep. In other words, the display element is the storage element and a much tougher tube is the result.

THE VERTICAL AMPLIFIER

In most oscilloscopes the signal of interest is placed on the vertical axis of the display. As the signal is seldom the proper amplitude to give a convenient size of display on the screen, some means is necessary to amplify or attenuate the signal to give the proper voltage swing at the deflection plates.

It is of the utmost importance that this amplification or attenuation be without distortion or, if distortion is present, that it be measurable.

This requirement of signal fidelity is extremely important, since the user instinctively interprets what he sees on the screen as being what is happening in the device under test. Consequently, while expected by the user, the concept and its implications are not well understood by those who are not intimately associated with oscilloscope design.

Normally, good signal fidelity means wide bandwidth when compared with the frequency of the signal being handled. This is a useful enough concept for most uses. Bandwidth normally refers to the points on the frequency-response curve where the amplification is 70.7 percent of the amplification in the midrange (spoken of as being 3 dB down or the 3-dB points). Sometimes statements are made which include the terms "sharp cutoff" or "slow rolloff" to indicate the capabilities of the amplifier or the character of the response curve on either side of the 3-dB points (see Fig. 17).

However, the concept of bandwidth, while useful to indicate roughly the amplifier capability of the oscilloscope, is not very useful to describe its performance when dealing with an arbitrary signal. In fact, there is no simple way to predict the response, to an arbitrary signal, of an amplifier with a given response curve.

What is wanted and expected in an oscilloscope amplifier is one which will "translate"—or convey—a given fluctuation of some kind—electrical, mechanical, chemical, etc., without change to the fluorescent screen of the cathode-ray tube. That is, no matter what the character or amplitude of the electrical signal presented at the input to the oscilloscope, each element of the signal as displayed on the screen must bear the same relationship in amplitude, timing, etc., to all the other elements as it did in the original signal. The signal path, including probe switches, attenuator, amplifiers, and cathode-ray tubes, should not insert signal elements not in the original or remove those which are present.

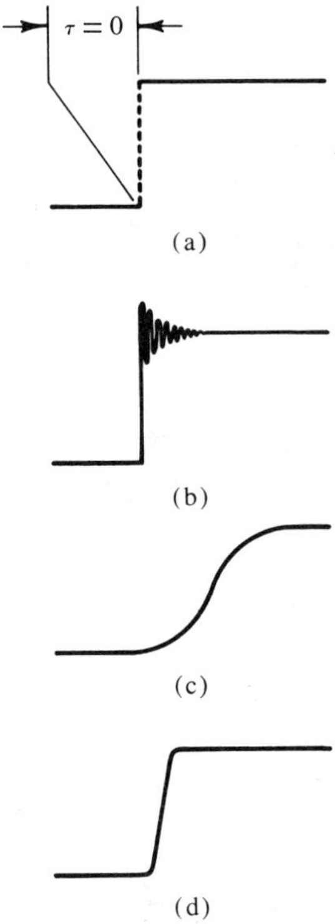

Briefly, the signal should suffer no distortion as it is amplified or attenuated by the oscilloscope.

Obviously this is realizable only within limits, especially as the upper limitation of frequency capability is approached. The character of the decreasing amplifier response can cause all kinds of distortion to appear—both additive and subtractive—and an inspection of the amplifier response curve can give only a very rough idea of what the distortion will be even to an experienced person. It is nearly impossible to adjust a complex amplifier for the desired response by measuring the response curve between adjustments.

11. Rise Time However, a concept which is very simple, and yet which is very elegant and powerful when determining the response of an amplifier to an arbitrary signal, is the concept of rise time. This is the time required for the output voltage to move between the 10 and 90 percent points of its final value when a step function is applied to the input. This concept simply relies upon the character of the response of an amplifier or attenuator to a step function —an instantaneous or "no time" transition between two levels (Fig. 28*a*). Here "instantaneous" means just that, since it is precisely the function of an oscilloscope to permit the display and examination of waveforms which change between two voltage levels in an arbitrary period.

The reason that this concept is so powerful in testing the performance of amplifiers, attenuators, and other devices is that any departure from the step function can be easily detected and evaluated.

A circuit will give one of four responses to a step function:

1. Resonances of various frequencies will be stimulated in a circuit, causing oscillations of one kind or another to appear in the displayed signal (Fig. 28*b*).

2. Stray capacitances or lumped inductances will cause certain portions of the signal to be lost or not to be accepted, and consequently substantial portions of the signal will be missing, causing the sharp corners, etc., to be omitted (Fig. 28*c*).

3. Some combination of the preceding responses will appear.

4. An "optimum" response will be given to the signal. This is a response in which the two dc levels are joined by a ramp, with the points of joining the dc levels exhibiting a slight rounding instead of being discontinuous (Fig. 28*d*). Overshoot and ringing represent the *addition* of signal elements which were not present in the original signal. *Severely rounded portions* represent the *absence* of a substantial amount of signal formerly present. Consequently, these conditions represent unacceptable signal distortion. The ramp response is the optimum response, since it represents the minimum of lost signal elements and the addition of no spurious elements. Such a response also represents a gaussian shape for the frequency-response curve, that is, one which falls at 6 dB/octave of frequency beyond the 3-dB point (see Fig. 17).

$\tau = 0$

(a)

(b)

(c)

(d)

Fig. 28. A step function and various circuit responses to it. (*a*) A step function. The time τ ideally is 0 and in practice is as short as present electronic devices can generate. (*b*) Resonances can be stimulated at various points in an improperly designed or adjusted circuit or (*c*) portions of the signal can be lost by stray capacitances or inductances. (*d*) An ideal response of an achievable circuit to a step function.

Although we do not have perfect step-function generators, we do have devices which are as close to it as is physically possible to approach with available materials and techniques, which for most purposes are fast enough (shorter than 10^{-10} s). When such a device is used as a source of a step function to test a properly adjusted amplifier, the response of the amplifier defines the "rise time" of the amplifier. Rise time is related to bandwidth by the relationship $T = 0.35$ to $0.45B$, where T = time in seconds between the 10 and 90 percent points of voltage change

B = bandwidth in hertz

With modern technology and circuit design the 0.35 factor can be realized consistently (the gain-bandwidth product as a figure of merit for amplifier performance then becomes a gain–rise time quotient).

Rise times add together as the square root of the sum of the squares of the rise times of the individual components involved, i.e., $\sqrt{R_{T1}^2 + R_{T2}^2 + R_{T3}^2}$. For example, a test signal with a given rise time injected into a properly adjusted amplifier of the same rise time will give a signal on the screen of the cathode-ray tube which is 1.4 times the rise time of the signal. Such a relationship means that meaningful information can be extracted from a display containing signal elements which have a rise time one-half to one-third that of the rise time of the amplifier (that is, where the observed rise time is degraded about 5 to 10 percent).

As indicated earlier, although rise time and bandwidth are sometimes used interchangeably when referring in a general way to amplifier capabilities, the rise-time figure is a better measure of the capability of the amplifier to follow the fluctuations of an arbitrary signal.

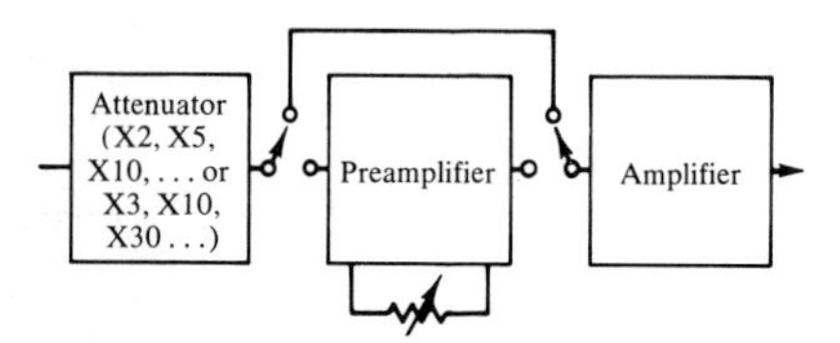

Fig. 29. Basic amplifier-attenuator configuration. Various combinations of attenuator and preamplifier interconnections permit a range of signal of 10^4 to be accepted.

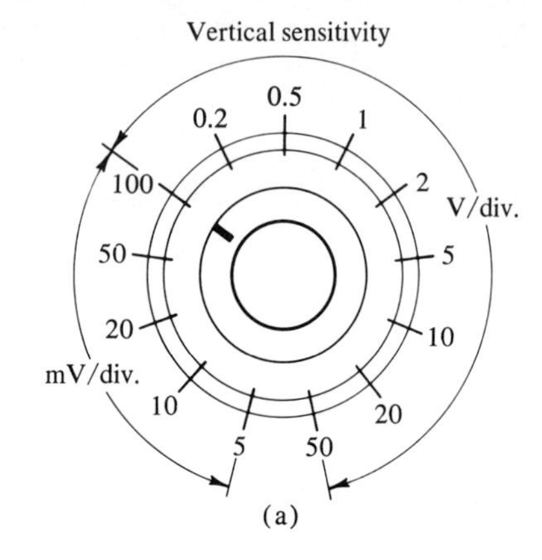

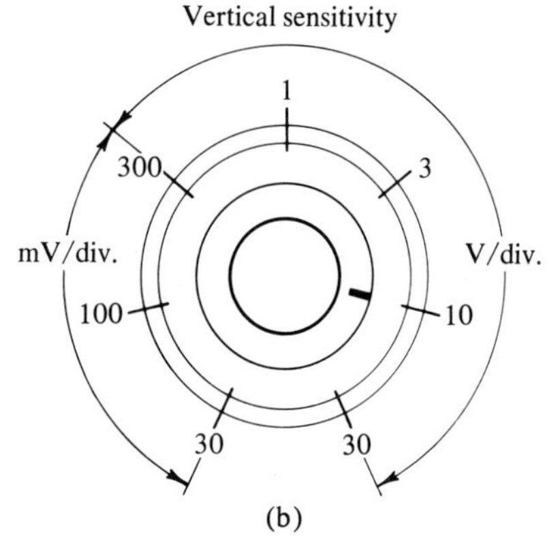

Fig. 30. Appearance of sensitivity controls of vertical amplifier. (*a*) Wide-range amplifier. (*b*) Lesser range amplifier.

It cannot be emphasized too strongly that no displayed signal will change voltage levels faster than the amplifier rise time, no matter how short the rise time of the input signal.

A signal with an infinitesimal rise time will be displayed as a signal with the rise time of the amplifier. Bluntly, the amplifier simply cannot respond any faster.

12. Vertical-amplifier Sections Most vertical amplifiers in modern oscilloscopes are constructed in three or four sections—an attenuator section, a preamplifier, a deflection amplifier, and a delay line or network. The attenuator section normally precedes the preamplifier (Fig. 29), since this restricts the range of signal the amplifier is called upon to handle to a reasonable range. The attenuators may be wholly external to the amplifiers or partly external. If the proper combination of attenuators, preamplifier, and deflection amplifier is selected, most instruments can display a dynamic range of signals of more than 1,000:1 or greater. Almost all modern amplifiers are calibrated in terms of sensitivity rather than gain, and the sensitivity ranges usually change by factors of 1, 2, 5, 10, . . . or 1, 3, 10, . . . so that there will be some overlap between adjacent ranges (Fig. 30). It is obvious that within the limits of the eye to detect, the response of the amplifier on any two adjoining ranges should be identical to a given signal.

The signal delay line or delay network can be a specially designed and constructed cable or an actual network composed of lumped inductances and capacitances, with some of the capacitances being adjustable. These networks are normally in parallel and are usually inserted between the deflection amplifiers and the deflection plates of the cathode-ray tube (Fig. 31).

Several oscilloscopes have a substantial amount of delay built into the vertical deflection structure, as described earlier. However, these instruments still require delay between the cathode-ray tube and the input so that the sweep generator

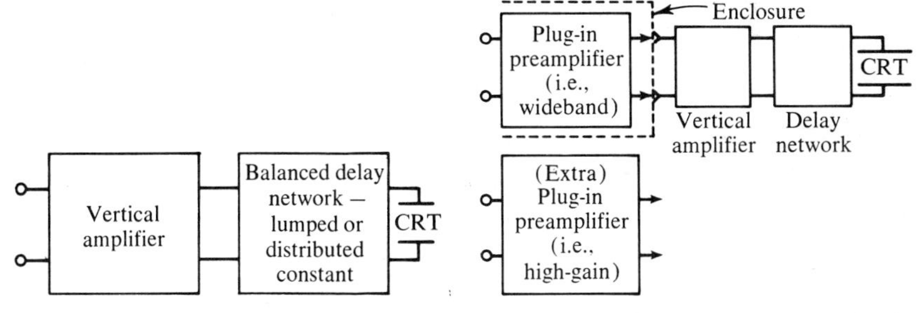

Fig. 31. The normal configuration of the amplifier, delay network, and cathode-ray tube. Some new, high-frequency oscilloscopes have the deflection amplifier located physically at the deflection plates to minimize stray capacity and the subsequent loss of high-frequency signal components.

Fig. 32. Block diagram of a plug-in oscilloscope. The output of the plug-in amplifiers is standardized both in impedance and voltage capabilities so that no adjustment has to be made when changing from one to the other.

has time to start and the cathode-ray tube is unblanked before the vertical signal appears on the deflection structure (see Fig. 22).

One instrument with an elegantly designed distributed deflection system has the delay line preceding the vertical amplifier, which is an integrated circuit mounted on a single monolithic chip and driving the deflection system directly. This cathode-ray tube reportedly has a deflection factor of 3 V/cm, and the oscilloscope has an overall sensitivity of 10 mV/cm at 250 MHz.

Most oscilloscopes have been constructed so that the attenuators and the preamplifier are in a separate unit which can be changed to give different characteristics to the total instrument performance. Such units, usually of the plug-in type (Fig. 32), can give a wide range of capabilities of the total instrument. For example, wideband, high sensitivity, multiple trace, spectrum analysis, sampling, digital readout, programmable, differential, etc., are a few of the various types of vertical-amplifier performance that can be obtained with a plug-in system. Each of these gives added areas of usefulness to the oscilloscope.

THE HORIZONTAL SECTION

The time base of an oscilloscope usually appears on the horizontal axis of the display. Normally it is linear, although for certain purposes logarithmic, hyperbolic, parabolic, or other types may be useful in presenting certain specialized information

(Fig. 33). Most general-purpose instruments, however, do not contain such nonlinear time bases. It also needs to be accurate, fast-starting, accurate-ending, and wide-range (it should cover the whole range of phenomena that the vertical amplifier is capable of handling).

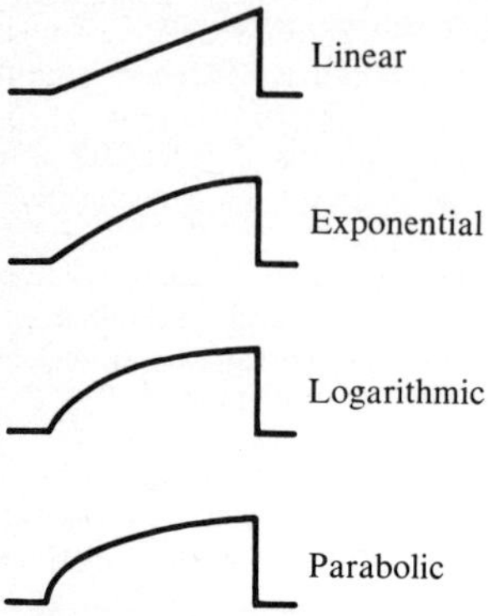

Fig. 33. Various types of time-base waveforms. The linear is normal. The others are used when it is desired to expand the early portion of the display because the phenomenon of interest contains high-frequency components during that time.

The horizontal section of a modern oscilloscope usually consists of at least three sections (and sometimes more depending upon the mode of use) (see Fig. 34):

1. A trigger generator
2. The time-base generator proper
3. The horizontal amplifier

If the instrument includes a "delayed-sweep" mode of operation, it will also have

4. A delay generator
5. Trigger pickoff circuits inserted between the trigger generator and the time-base generator

13. The Trigger Generator The function of the trigger generator is to provide a standardized fast pulse output whenever the input voltage to the generator reaches a given level from a given direction. This change in input voltage can occur slowly or rapidly. The important considerations are as follows:

1. The trigger output pulse should be of a standard shape and amplitude so that the multivibrator switch which controls the time-base generator is required only to respond to a trigger pulse which is unvarying in all respects except time, which can be arbitrary (Fig. 35).

2. The trigger pulse should occur at the same voltage level on the input signal, so that the sweep will start at the same point on each repetition of the signal and produce a jitter-free display (Fig. 36).

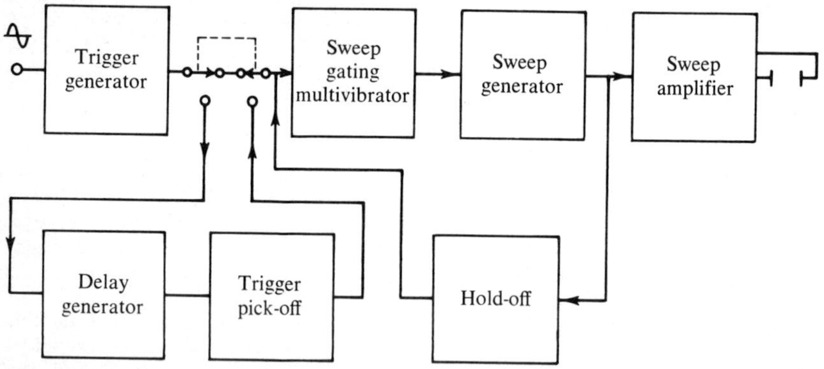

Fig. 34. The horizontal section of a modern oscilloscope. The trigger generator, by providing standardized triggers whatever the input signal, permits stable operation of the sweep generator by limiting the variable parameter to which it has to respond to that of time only. The sweep gating multivibrator provides a sharply defined initiating and terminating control voltage to the sweep generator. The sweep generator generates a sawtooth voltage of precisely defined starting point, shape, and ending point and also provides a protective voltage to the gating multivibrator input to make it unresponsive to triggers which might occur during the period of the sawtooth. The delay generator and trigger pick-off provide a means of precisely delaying the start of the sweep generator until a predetermined instant. They also permit other, more complex modes of operation, also.

14. The Time-base Generator The time-base generator must meet several requirements, each of which is rather stringent:

1. The generated waveform should occur when and only when desired.
2. Nothing should interfere with it once it has been initiated or for a sufficient period after termination to permit the various circuit components to reach quiescence to eliminate instabilities of starting level and time, termination, etc.
3. The waveform should be linear.
4. It should start immediately.
5. It should terminate when no longer needed (when the trace reaches the right side of the screen).
6. It should be available again for initiation as soon as the holdoff period is passed.
7. Each waveform must be precisely like every other waveform, whether they occur regularly, randomly, or singly.

Fig. 35. Idealized trigger waveform. Actually, it can be nearly any simple shape as long as it is precisely reproduced each time it is generated.

Most oscilloscopes also permit the sweep to be initiated when one of the following occurs:

1. A desired precise delay after the occurrence of a given event (i.e., the sweep is initiated by the delay generator itself)
2. The first event following a given delay after an earlier event (i.e., the sweep is initiated by the first event after the desired delay has occurred)
3. Once, by an event occurring after the instrument has been armed (i.e., the sweep is prevented from triggering after having been initiated by some desired event which occurred after the instrument has been set for the purpose)

15. The Horizontal Amplifier The horizontal amplifier has three functions:

1. To amplify the time-base waveform properly to deflect the electron beam the desired distance on the cathode-ray-tube screen

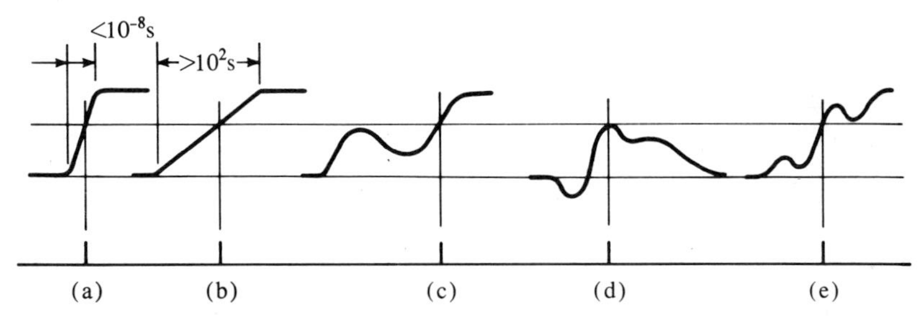

Fig. 36. Desired performance of trigger circuit to various waveforms. In each case, the trigger is generated at precisely the same voltage level, no matter what the shape or rise time of the signal. In addition the character of the incoming signal does not affect the trigger shape.

2. To give a calibrated magnification to a desired portion of the displayed waveform (some oscilloscopes do not contain this feature)
3. To accept external signals for the generation of other types of displays if desired by the operator

The horizontal amplifier should give no detectable distortion to the time-base waveform throughout the range of time-base generation designed in the oscilloscope. Although the horizontal amplifier normally does not have the bandwidth capabilities of the vertical amplifier, it is required to give a much greater undistorted voltage swing, since the horizontal dimension of the display on the face of the cathode-ray tube usually is greater than the vertical (see Fig. 20*c* and *d*), while the sensitivity of the horizontal deflection plates of the cathode-ray tube is less than that of the vertical plates, as explained earlier.

Some oscilloscopes offer the plug-in feature in the horizontal channel as well as in the vertical. This gives great versatility within the limits imposed by the writing rate of the cathode-ray tube and the rise time/gain capabilities of the deflection amplifiers, and it offers the potential of permitting nearly the complete range of capabilities one could desire in a cathode-ray-tube display, depending only upon the plug-in design.

THE POWER-SUPPLY SECTION

It is the function of the power supply of an oscilloscope to provide stable voltages and currents, at the proper levels, to the other circuits of the oscilloscope to permit them to operate normally and accurately. When it is considered that in most oscilloscopes the power supply comprises from one-fifth to one-third the components of the instrument, it will be realized that this requirement is more rigorous than first seems apparent. There is good reason for it. Many modern oscilloscopes guarantee measurement accuracies of less than 3 to 5 percent and when in good condition will actually permit measurement to be made within 1 percent. Such performance is not obtained without cost. Although the development of transistors and more recently integrated circuits has permitted the design engineer to be less concerned about such matters as heat, aging, mechanical vibration, space, and complexity, it still remains true that most circuits are designed to give their specified performance at a given operating level. However, the energy source itself—the electrical mains—may not remain stable, and the load placed on the power supply may vary (different-sized plug-ins, for example). For reasons of engineering, aesthetics, and economy, the capabilities of the rectifier circuits which convert the ac energy of the mains to the dc energy required to operate the circuits are optimized to supply the maximum energy which it is envisaged the oscilloscope will require in *regular* operation. As this is usually not appreciably greater than the average energy which will be required, normal fluctuations in energy supply or load requirements could cause the voltage and/or current available from an unregulated power supply to fluctuate substantially. Consequently, the power supply of most modern high-performance oscilloscopes contains a number of powerful regulator circuits to stabilize the voltages and/or currents available, in the face of substantial fluctuations of energy supply and/or load requirement, i.e., plus or minus 10 percent. A chart illustrating filter and regulation follows:

	Minimum	Design center	Maximum	Transients
Voltage:				
Best case	95	117	135	≈3.5 μs
Worst case	105	117	129	≈35 μs
Regulation:				
Best case	<0.001 %	<<0.001 %	<0.001 %	
Worst case	0.01 %	0.005 %	0.01 %	
Ripple:				
Best case	<1 mV	<<1 mV	<1 mV	
Worst case	20 mV	10 mV	20 mV	

VERTICAL PLUG-IN CAPABILITIES

The oscilloscope with a plug-in feature offers the possibility of modifying the types of information presented by the cathode-ray-tube display in certain respects. The plug-in feature can be in the vertical or horizontal channels, or both. Although not exhaustive, the following list will give some idea of the range of performance available merely by changing plug-ins.

16. Real-time Performance The basic real-time performance is that permitted by the vertical deflection amplifiers of the main frame.

Plug-in Type	*Description of Operation*
Basic	The basic plug-in would permit the maximum sensitivity at that rise time. The usual group of controls permits: 1. Selection of one or more inputs (with ac or dc coupling) 2. Calibrated attenuators to permit viewing signals in a dynamic range of several hundred (with continuously variable gain adjust between ranges) 3. Positioning of the trace An additional 10× sensitivity with somewhat degraded bandwidth is sometimes available by means of an extra internal preamplifier
High sensitivity	The most obvious variation is to alter the sensitivity. Plug-ins giving sensitivities of 100 to 1,000 times the basic sensitivity carry the signal capability well into the 10 μV/cm region.
Multiple channel	Another variation is to include several signal channels in one plug-in. Depending upon the complexity (and cost), the channels can be viewed in various combinations such as separately, sequentially (each channel triggering the time base), chopped (each channel sampled at some convenient arbitrary rate, with the sweep triggered at some time common to all signals), combined (added or subtracted), and each channel can be positioned, attenuated, identified, etc. (Fig. 37)
Differential biological	Yet another variation gives the difference between two related signals. Any signal component which is common to both signals (the "common-mode" signal) is suppressed to a value substantially below the value of the difference signal, typically $1:10^2$ to $1:10^5$ (Fig. 38)

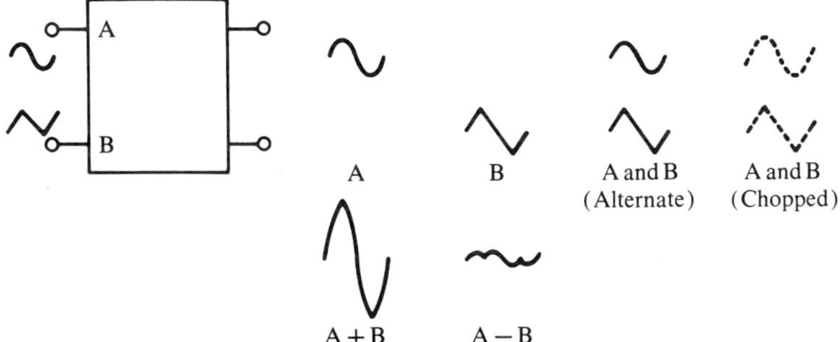

Fig. 37. Types of operation available from some dual trace amplifiers. Some units permit *A* and *B* displays to be inverted. Alternate trace operation displays each signal on alternate sweeps which can be displaced from one another or brought together for comparison. The chopped display switches between each signal at some desirable rate, displaying a short segment of one before switching to the other. $A + B$ simply adds the signals together and displays the sum. $A - B$ displays the difference.

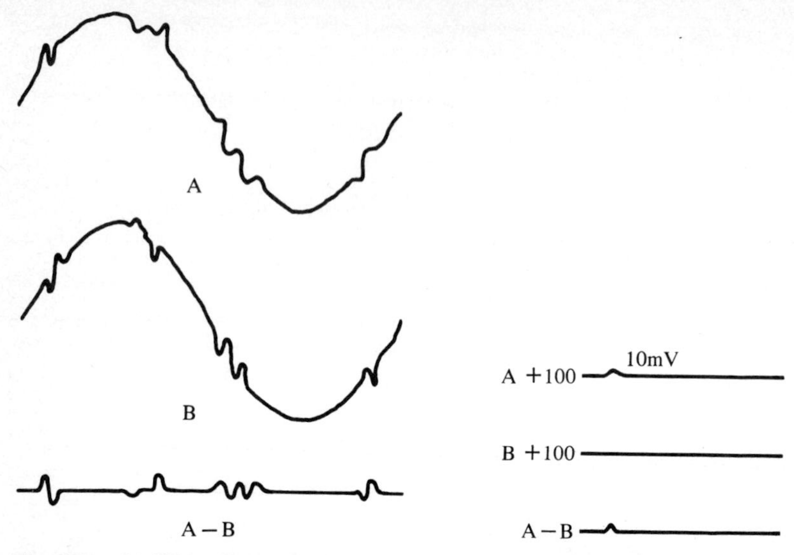

Fig. 38. A differential amplifier subtracts two signals (one of which may be 60-Hz hum, for example) and only the difference is displayed, the common signal canceling out.

Fig. 39. Sometimes a low-level signal (power supply ripple, for example) will occur at a high dc level. Some plug-ins permit a dc voltage of like potential to be subtracted from the dc component of the sought for signal and only the low-level portion will be displayed.

Plug-in Type	*Description of Operation*
Comparator	A variation of the differential amplifier permits low-level dc difference voltages to be measured at high dc levels and in the presence of large common-mode signals (Fig. 39)
Current measure	An additional variation permits current measurements to be made with an appropriate current probe (Fig. 40)
Bandpass	Some differential amplifiers permit choice of upper and lower 3-dB points, enabling specific components to be seen that would otherwise be masked by harmonics or fundamentals (Fig. 41)

17. Sampling Performance The rise-time capabilities of an oscilloscope can be improved significantly by sampling techniques if repetitive signals are involved. For example, a given oscilloscope with 35 ns minimum rise time at 5 mV/cm sensitivity using a conventional amplifier will display 350 ps rise time at 2 mV/cm sensitivity, using sampling techniques. This represents an improvement of 250 times in a figure of merit represented by the reciprocal of the rise time–sensitivity product. Such an improvemet is bought at a price, in that it takes more than 250 times as long to generate the sampled display as it does to generate the regular display. (It also costs more in money. The sampling system is much more complex.) This may not be much of a factor when observing signals that occur at repetition rates above tens or hundreds of kilohertz, but it would have a noticeable impact at repetition rates of a few hertz.

Basic sampling amplifiers: The performance available from sampling amplifiers is somewhat more limited in type than that from real-time amplifiers. Most sampling plug-ins will give high sensitivity at wide bandwidth perhaps on two channels, and some will permit time-domain reflectometry measurements to be made. How-

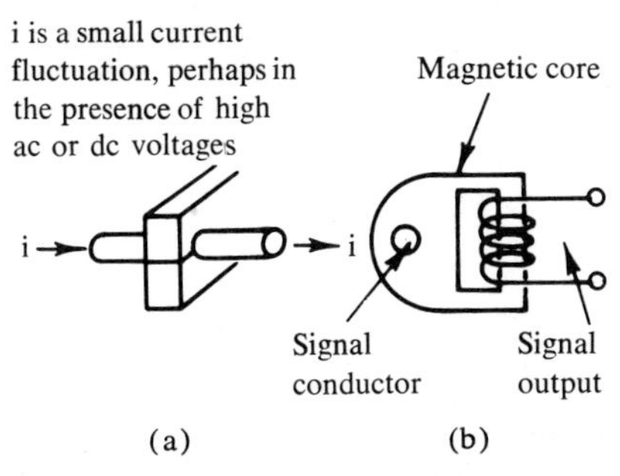

Fig. 40. A current probe is usually constructed of magnetic material shaped (perhaps by a sintering process) to intimately clasp the current-carrying conductor. The magnetic circuit will be closed by a similarly shaped piece coming together in opposition or by a bar of magnetic materials slid or otherwise placed across the conductor gap. The current fluctuation in the conductor causes flux lines in the magnetic material to cause a similar fluctuation in the signal pickup loop.

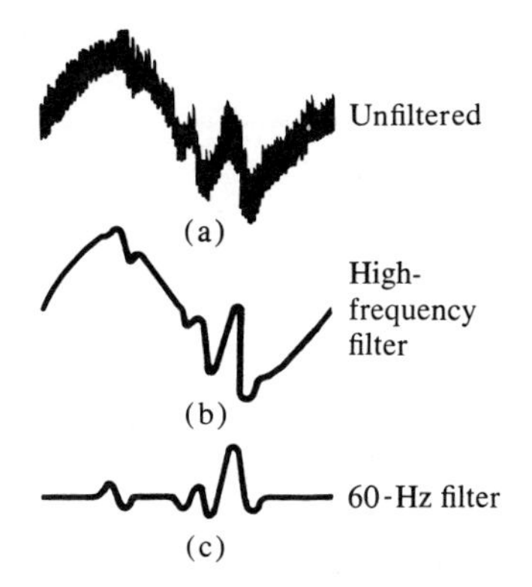

Fig. 41. Use of filters in differential amplifiers to permit masking of all frequencies but those of interest. (*a*) Signal as amplified, unfiltered. (*b*) High frequencies (neon lamp interference, for example) filtered out. (*c*) Power-line radiation filtered out.

ever, differential, comparator, and current-measurement units are seldom, if ever, encountered. The complexity of a sampling system determines that it will be primarily designed for areas of broad, general-purpose use, since the cost of engineering a system is difficult to justify for a sale of only a few units. Consequently, there is less selection in sampling-amplifier plug-ins than in normal-amplifier plug-ins. Sampling-amplifier plug-ins for oscilloscopes which have the plug-in feature in the vertical channel alone will have a special sampling sweep included in it, since sampling with real-time sweeps will work only below about 0.1 ms/div. Most oscilloscopes which offer sampling plug-ins have the plug-in feature in the horizontal channel also, permitting the use of a special sampling-sweep plug-in (Fig. 42).

Multiple trace: Although two-channel sampling plug-ins are available, more than two channels are confined to automated, programmable systems for production-testing complex devices, such as thin-film and integrated-circuit devices. These may have as many as 16 channels, whose outputs may be monitored by an oscilloscope. However, these devices are not *oscilloscopes* but *systems,* of which the display oscilloscope is simply one unit (Fig. 43).

Time-domain reflectometry and fault location: This plug-in permits measurements to be made of the quality of transmission in a signal path such as a cable, by sending a very fast pulse into the cable and measuring the timing and character of any reflections. The timing of the reflected signal permits location of any discontinuities in path impedance, and the character of the reflection permits analysis of the type of discontinuity. Fault location is a variation of this and enables the location of a fault to be pinpointed to within a few feet before a party is sent to repair it (Fig. 44).

18. Spectrum Analysis For some time, plug-in units have been available which permit an oscilloscope, which is basically an instrument for time-domain analysis, to display the relative amplitudes of the various frequency components of a signal, permitting frequency-domain analysis of that signal. By concentrating the specialized circuits needed for this type of measurement in a relatively inexpensive plug-in

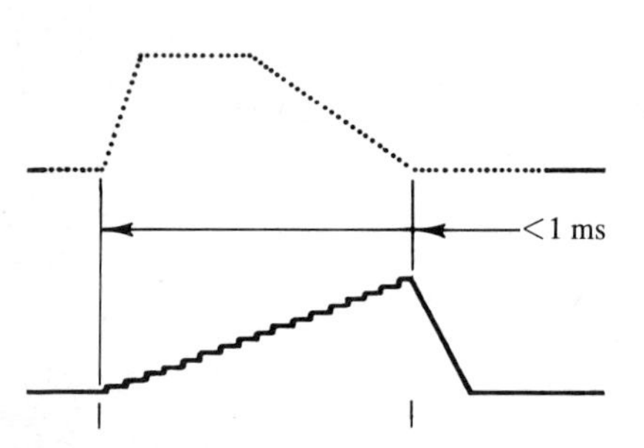

Fig. 42. Sampling with real-time sweeps is only effective for sweep rates longer than about 0.1 ms/div because of jitter introduced by system instability. Where the signal to be sampled requires a shorter equivalent display time, a "stairstep" sweep waveform is generated with the sweep voltage "stepping" a given amount each time the signal is sampled whether on a cyclical or random basis. The display is then a series of dots delineating the signal.

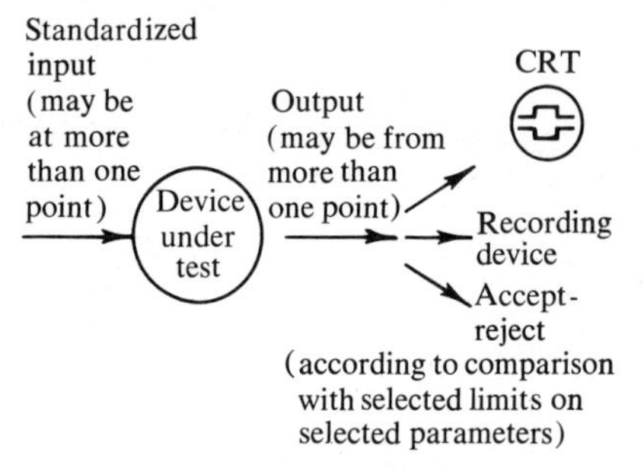

Fig. 43. Multiple channels are used to test complex devices such as thin-film and integrated-circuit devices. Standardized signals can be injected into any desired part of the device, and the output can be tested by sampling methods, with those not falling within certain limits being rejected or by-passed in subsequent circuit interconnections. In these operations the oscilloscope becomes merely a device by which the system is set up and calibrated, and which may be used occasionally to observe the system performance.

(Fig. 45) the benefits of such analysis have been extended greatly, since the cost of the balance of the circuitry, including the power supplies, cathode-ray-tube circuits, sweep and trigger circuits, etc., can be shared with normal oscilloscope usage.

19. Digital Readout Some plug-ins are available which not only permit readings to be made from the display on the cathode-ray tube but also give certain values from digital indicators. From such instruments it is a short step to voltage outputs which will drive some type of printing device to give a printed output for a permanent record of certain readings (Fig. 46).

20. Automatic Gain Setting Once the digital information is available, it is a short step to design plug-in amplifiers which, by means of analog-to-digital converters, sample the amplitude of the received signal and automatically adjust the preamplifier, attenuator, and amplifier configuration so that the observed display will always fit within certain minimum and maximum limits on the screen. This performance can be had merely upon receipt of the signal or upon being activated by the operator (Fig. 47).

21. Programmable Plug-ins With the advent of integrated-circuit technology, it has become feasible to providc the extra circuitry in plug-ins to permit the various modes of performance available from a plug-in amplifier by manual manipula-

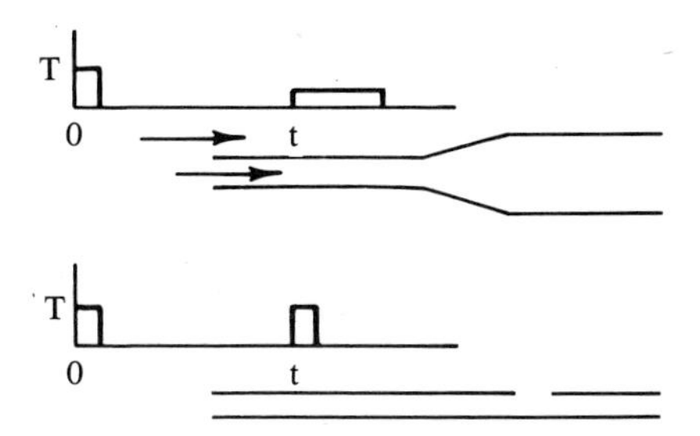

Fig. 44. Time-domain reflectrometry uses the principle of reflection to pinpoint breaks, changes in impedance or, in some cases, shorts in a transmission line. A short pulse is sent into the line and the time until the reflection is received can be measured. From the character of the reflection, the nature of the discontinuity can often be ascertained and the distance measured to a very accurate degree.

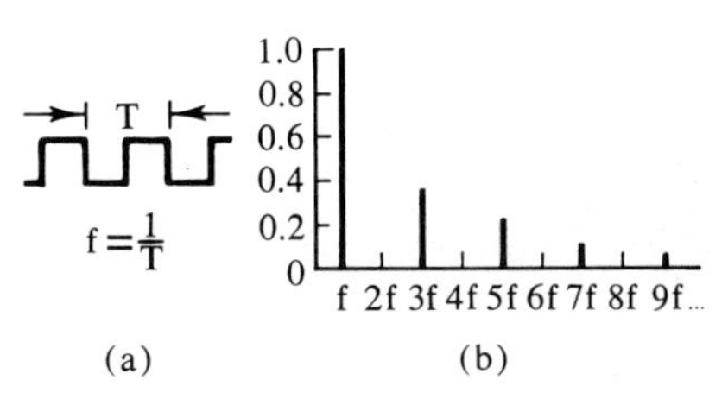

Fig. 45. Spectrum analysis permits the frequency components of a repetitive signal to be displayed and analyzed. Some signals have a distinctive character (for instance, a person's voice), and frequency analysis can be used to identify such signals. It can also be used in some instances to determine whether or not a signal is merely a stray, randomly generated signal or whether it contains intelligence of some kind. (*a*) Basic waveform. (*b*) Frequency component-spectrum.

tion of the various controls to be obtained by electronic switching. Once this point has been reached, it is a relatively simple matter conceptually to provide a programming section so that the various settings needed to perform a series of measurements can be made automatically. From this concept, it is again a

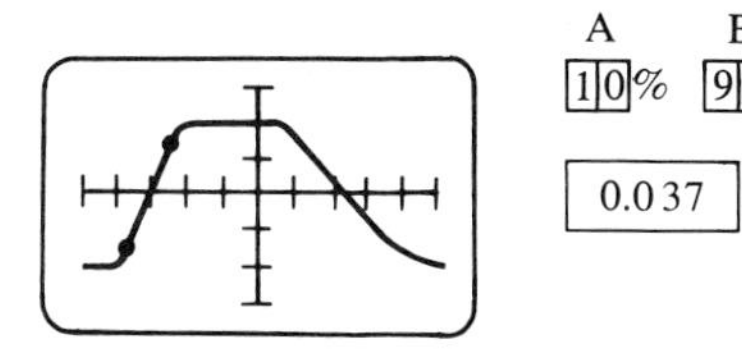

Fig. 46. Oscilloscope display with digital readout. In this case the two dots are located at the 10 and 90 percent points on the rise time. The digital readout indicators show this as well as the time in whatever units are appropriate. The indicators can be mechanical counters connected to a dial or any one of the several types of electronic devices.

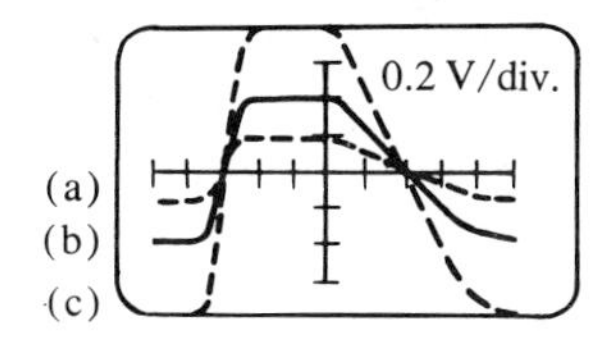

Fig. 47. An automatic gain-setting amplifier operates by determining whether the signal will occupy less or more than certain given limits on the screen. Depending upon the results of the measurement, a servo loop will change the attenuators so that the signal will be displayed within certain predetermined limits. (*a*) 0.5 V/div less than 2 div. (*b*) 0.2 V/div less than full scale and more than 2 div deflection. (*c*) 0.1 V/div more than full-scale deflection.

short step conceptually to an instrument which monitors the results of the measurements in a "go no-go" setting and, whenever an unacceptable reading is obtained, either rejects that particular unit and passes on to the next or stores the information so that when interconnections are to be made, the defective section is bypassed.

Such programmable plug-ins can be real-time or sampling amplifiers and, in the latter case, can work on a random basis or a clock cycle.

Once this point has been reached, the plug-in moves from the oscilloscope into a larger unit and the oscilloscope itself becomes a component in a larger, more complex system.

22. Special-purpose Vertical Plug-ins In addition to the types of plug-in performance described in the foregoing, a number of specialized types are also available. These include:

1. Operational amplifiers for performing desired mathematical operations on signals of interest.

2. Transducer/strain gage plug-ins permit strain gages and other types of transducers to be connected directly to the oscilloscope without intermediate adapters, and permit measurements to be made directly in pertinent units on the oscilloscope, i.e., microstrain/div, pF/div, etc.

3. Optical-signal-detector plug-ins permit analysis of laser signals.

4. Polarigraph plug-ins permit chemical analysis of certains types of unknown chemical compounds.

5. Core-analysis plug-ins permit evaluation and analysis of various magnetic core materials.

HORIZONTAL-CHANNEL PLUG-INS

Most oscilloscopes which provide for horizontal-channel plug-ins will accept the same type of plug-in for both horizontal and vertical channels. This gives a great versatility, permitting such types of display as *X-Y* and raster presentations.

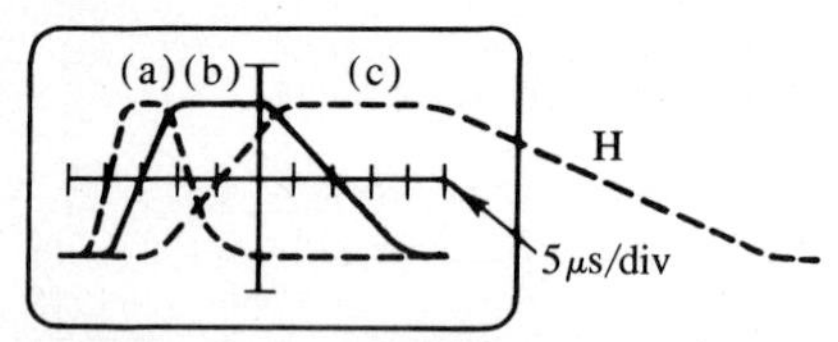

Fig. 48. The automatic adjustment also can be incorporated into the sweep time circuitry. The positive and negative going portions of the signal are used for the "gage" points, by means of which the circuits judge whether the signal will occupy an appropriate portion of the screen and, if not, in which direction the sweep generator should be adjusted. (*a*) 20 μs/div less than 5 div display. (*b*) 10 μs/div full signal contained on screen. (*c*) 5 μs/div more than full-scale display.

However, since most users are interested in time-dependent displays, most horizontal plug-ins are time-base units.

23. Basic Real-time Units The basic real-time performance is that which would be expected in a non-plug-in oscilloscope:

1. Sweep time range from seconds to microseconds, with magnification on all ranges

2. Convenient selection of trigger modes to accommodate a wide range of signal types

Some plug-ins include extra high gain magnification of good accuracy.

Others include a second time base, with a delay-time control and complete trigger controls, permitting a delayed-sweep type of operation.

Programmable time bases permit automatic selection of various desired sweep rates, where a particular sequence must be used repetitively in a production testing situation.

Some plug-ins provide automatic selection of a time base that is appropriate to the signal being observed, by operation of the circuits on the signal itself, and that is available to initiate the selection process either when the unknown signal is received or upon receipt of an initiating pulse from the operator (Fig. 48).

24. Sampling-sweep Plug-ins Sampling requires special time-base generators that produce "stair-step" time-base waveforms rather than the familiar ramp or sawtooth waveform. The latter waveform will "smear out" the sampled dot into a bar or teardrop, so that the regular sweep can be used for real-time sampling only at sweep rates longer than about 0.1ms. Sweep times much less than that require a stairstep waveform with a fixed voltage step at each sampling pulse, and the sampled voltage is displayed as a dot on the screen spaced a fixed amount from the foregoing and following dots (see Fig. 42).

The selection of sampling-sweep plug-ins is limited to only a few types:

Basic Sampling Sweep. Various plug-ins offer equivalent time sweeps from about 10 ps/div to about 100 μs/div. Modes of operation include repetitive and single sweeps, manually initiated and externally swept.

Random-sampling Sweep. This type of plug-in is necessary where the signal of interest is uniform in shape and therefore accessible in principle to sampling techniques but cannot be examined by a sampling pulse which is uniformly repetitive (Fig. 49).

Programmable Sampling Sweep. This type of plug-in offers the benefits of sampling techniques for production-line environments where several different sweep rates may be desired in specific sequence. Sample rates, sweep rates, and delay times are programmable or can be manually set.

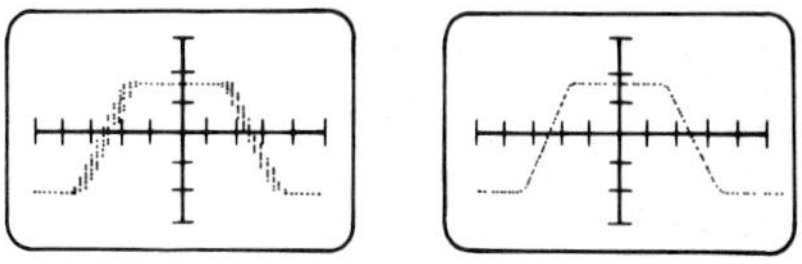

(a) (b)

Fig. 49. (*a*) Appearance of display of signal sampled by sequential method where signal has a slight jitter of random nature. Note that dots are evenly spaced but rise and fall are blurred, i.e., ill-defined. (*b*) Appearance of display of signal sampled by random nature. Note that dots are randomly spaced but rise and fall are sharply defined.

SIGNAL-DETECTION TECHNIQUES

An indispensable condition for securing valid information from the cathode-ray oscilloscope is that the signal to be displayed must be obtained from its source. We have already discussed the use of transducers. Since the transducers themselves are nearly always supplied separately from the oscilloscopes, adequate instructions for proper use will usually be supplied with them. Naturally, the transducer output must be properly matched to the oscilloscope input, and it may be necessary to insert some kind of stage between the two to avoid the distortion possible because of mismatch.

Obtaining a signal from an electronic device is at the same time both simpler *and* more likely to be a source of error than when seeking to obtain a signal from a nerve, a chemical reaction, or some kind of mechanical vibration. We *know* there are problems involved in converting the signal from these sources into an electrical fluctuation, and we make our plans accordingly. It is not so obvious that there may be analogous problems in obtaining a signal from a source of electrical energy.

25. Oscilloscope Probes All electric circuits will have associated with them in greater or lesser degree the characteristics of inductance, capacitance, and resistance in addition to the currents and potentials involved. The degree to which one or the other of these characteristics predominates determines in large part the performance of the circuit. In a large proportion of the circuits of interest the amounts of these electrical characteristics would be very small. When we introduce an electrical probe into such a circuit for the purpose of obtaining the signal the oscilloscope is to display, we may find that the characteristics of resistance, capacitance, and inductance associated with the probe substantially alter the amounts and/or proportions of these characteristics in the circuit of interest and therefore will substantially alter the performance of the circuit and the signal obtainable from it.

The act of measuring can change the very performance of the circuit we wish to measure.

It is of great importance to be aware of this possibility and select the proper probe to minimize or avoid it. Oscilloscope probes are normally designed to give an input-impedance characteristic to the oscilloscope comprised of a large resistive component, a small capacitive component, and an extremely small, nearly nonexistent, inductive component. These may range from 0.7 pF and 500 Ω for a 0.1 ns rise-time probe to 13.5 pF and 10 MΩ for a probe with 17 ns rise time. The inductance will be in nanohenrys and can be ignored. The wideband instrument referred to earlier has a probe with an input impedance of 3 pF and 100 kΩ with a rise time of about 0.75 ns. Unfortunately, such a design normally involves a substantial attenuation of the amplitude of the signal. If, because of the original amplitude of the signals, attenuation cannot be tolerated, other approaches may have to be substituted, such as using cathode- or emitter-follower probes or other devices with exceedingly small input-impedance characteristics.

Modern semiconductor devices and techniques permit such favorable gain-bandwidth products that, in most applications, the attenuation of the signal introduced by the probe is not significant. The influence of the probe on the signal, which does matter, can thus be minimized by proper probe design, and whatever amplitude is lost in the process can be recovered by the oscilloscope amplifier. Of course, this capability does not hold if one is dealing with "state-of-the-art" signals or closely approaching them. However, for many measurements, 20 dB or more of attenuation can be tolerated in the interest of avoiding deterioration of the signal waveform because of the presence of the signal probe.

Certain signal characteristics require exceptional care to prevent the measurement process from introducing distortions of its own. For instance, a signal with an exceedingly fast rise time can be modified beyond recognition if the user does not pay close attention to changes in impedance which occur in the signal path between the signal source and the oscilloscope. Each abrupt change of impedance will cause a reflection of the signal, causing unrecognized resonances which severely distort the observed signal. Solutions for the situation may require cables, connectors, and termination impedances of special design, or the use of a coaxial cable in which the center conductor is actually a low-resistance wire designed to absorb any stray reflections which might occur. The physical length of cables can represent a significant fraction of the electrical wavelength of certain frequency components in a fast waveform and cause distorting reflections, resonances, and other reactive effects.

On the other hand, signal generation involving large currents will create substantial magnetic fields (for example, switching devices for keying high-powered radar pulses). These fields can in turn generate large circulating currents through grounding conductors, chassis, and other supposedly inert elements, causing spurious elements to be introduced into the displayed signal. The cure for this type of distortion is largely empirical but generally will be found to consist of returning the ground connections of all units involved in the measurement to a common point, so that each one will be subject to the same generated magnetic field. The same spurious signals will be developed in each conductor, and they will cancel one another out.

In some situations, the circuit to be examined will have an operating condition so critical that the addition of the probe characteristics may cause it to become unstable or cease operating altogether. Where these conditions exist, it usually will be found that the circuit in question is buffered—has circuits to isolate the circuit from changes which may cause improper operation—at both the input and output. Consequently, the desired waveform can be secured from a point that is inert. Much modern equipment has test points designed into its critical circuits specifically intended to permit examination of the waveforms of such circuits without interfering with their operation. Such points should always be looked for.

UNDERSTANDING THE DISPLAY

The primary purpose of the modern cathode-ray oscilloscope is to permit measurements to be made of unknown signals. The graphical form of the display permits direct measurement to be made of certain quantities but requires others to be computed by an analysis of the waveform.

The two primary axes of the display will normally represent time horizontally ("real" time in a regular oscilloscope and "equivalent" time in a sampling oscilloscope) and some quantity measured in units of convenience in the vertical, which may be simple voltage or current. On the other hand, it may be distance, temperature, force, or some other quantity of interest to the observer.

In any case, the display will have been adjusted automatically or manually to occupy a convenient portion of the screen to permit easy inspection and measurement.

At this point the operator will want to know what each horizontal and vertical division of the graticule scale represents, since his analysis of the waveform will depend to some extent upon the magnitude and duration or time of occurrence of some event of interest. The time figures on the sweep-range switch will tell him what amount of time is represented by each horizontal division, and the sensitivity figures on the vertical-amplifier-range switch will tell him how much voltage is represented by each vertical division. It may, of course, be necessary to convert the volts/div to units of force (of rotation *or* temperature), light intensity, or any other unit which represents the magnitude of the phenomenon of interest.

For example, the display shown in Fig. 50 will illustrate the technique. Two traces are shown for convenience in illustrating a stimulus/response phenomenon in a hypothetical biological organism.

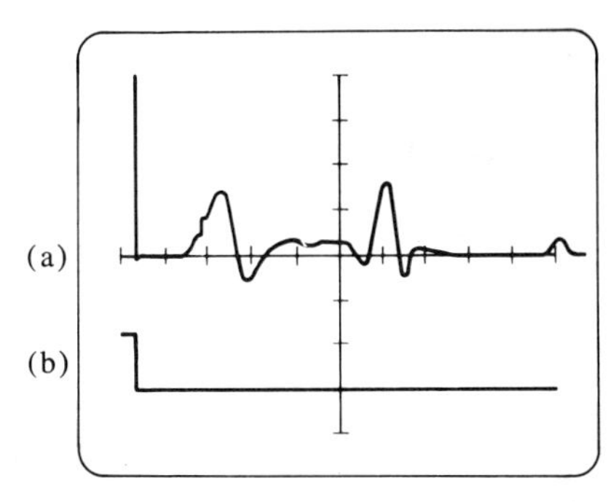

Fig. 50. Waveforms to illustrate the method of analyzing a waveform.

Trace *B* shows the voltage or current delivered to the organism. In this case, the sweep rate (which will be the same for both traces) is 1 ms/div (10^{-3} s for each principal horizontal division). The vertical sensitivity is 1 V/div (1 V per division of vertical deflection). The stimulating pulse is essentially square in shape, approximately 0.35 ms in duration, and approximately 1.25 V in amplitude.

Trace *A* shows the response. (Although the figures will be given as absolute measurements, they must be read as approximate, with an accuracy of about 2 percent.) The sensitivity is 0.1mV/div (10^{-4} V per division of vertical deflection).

The stimulating pulse feeds through and causes the initial deflection, which we are not concerned with. However, at 1.4 ms after the onset of the stimulus, the organism starts to respond, and the response rises until 2.3 ms to a level of +145 μV with an anomalous interruption between 1.8 and 1.9 ms at a level of +70 μV. The response then drops to a level of −60 μV by 2.9 ms, recovers to +30 μV by 3.6 ms, goes through a sine-wave fluctuation of 1 ms period and ±10 μV variation until 4.6 ms, continues at a level of +30 μV until 5.1 ms, and then falls to −25 μV by 5.6 ms, rises to 160 μV by 6.1 ms, falling to −50 μV by 6.6 ms, recovering to +15 μV by 6.8 ms, and decaying slowly to or by 8.7 ms. About 9.8 ms, a +35-μV triangular pulse commences, decaying again to 0V by 10.3 ms.

Some oscilloscopes present the sweep rate and vertical sensitivity figures immediately adjacent to the oscilloscope screen. This can be done in several ways. The simplest, and little used, method is to have figures from some kind of rotating dial connected to the front panel show through windows immediately adjacent to the cathode-ray-tube screen. Another method is to have some kind of readout device, such as glow-discharge tubes or fiber-optic devices, which gives an appropriate indication for each position of the horizontal and vertical controls. A third method is to use the electron beam of the cathode-ray tube, to trace out the appropriate figures on the cathode-ray-tube screen itself, on a time-shared basis with the signals.

Obviously, reciting time and amplitude figures about a waveform does not mean that we understand it. However, by examining both the waveform and the associated figures, we may be able to ask some questions which may lead to further measurements, tests, and analyses, which may eventually lead to an understanding. Why the anomolous fluctuation in the middle of the initial rise? Why the further "blip" after the organism has apparently settled to quiescence? These and other questions may lead to some understanding of the biological mechanism involved.

The ability to analyze comes only with familiarity gained by use. To most users, the oscilloscope is simply a tool, and time spent learning to use it is time subtracted from the task for which it was obtained, and therefore is resented. However, it will be found that such time will generally be repaid many times over, when the manipulation of the oscilloscope becomes so routine that it does not get in the way of the progress of the experiment. The investigation of complex and subtle phenomena is seldom possible without the use of complex and subtle equipment. It is not reasonable to expect such equipment to be used without some time spent in learning what it can do, how it operates, and how to operate it.

FRONT PANELS

Of course, the dominant feature of the appearance of any oscilloscope is the cathode-ray tube, which by virtue of its size will occupy a substantial portion of the front-panel space. The tube is usually positioned in the upper portion of the panel space and may be at the upper left or in the center. Panel-mounted instruments for use in racks of coordinated equipment usually have the cathode-ray tube mounted close to the center of the panel, occupying most of the vertical distance of the panel (Fig. 51).

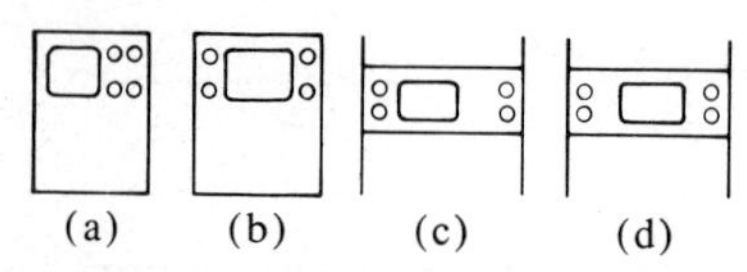

Fig. 51. Appearance of the most common front panel configurations. (*a*, *b*) In those instruments which have a vertical aspect ratio, the cathode-ray tube is usually in the upper center or left-hand corner as for those with a horizontal aspect ratio. (*c*, *d*) Panel-mounted instruments usually have their tube near the center of the panel.

Front-panel controls are used to modify the operation of the circuits of the oscilloscope in order to obtain desired modes of operation. For example, a control may change a voltage level to adjust the point at which a multivibrator circuit will change state, permitting changes in the sensitivity of a trigger circuit. Another control may select different combinations of precision capacitors and resistors to modify the rate of voltage change in the sawtooth generator. Another control may modify the interrelationship of several different circuits, permitting the various types of sweep operation described earlier.

Generally, each control will be labeled according to its observed result, rather than its circuit function, permitting the operator to anticipate the effect of his adjustment on the display. For example, the control to adjust the bias level of the cathode-ray-tube grid is labeled "intensity," not "CRT bias adjust," and the switch to select the sensitivity range is labeled "volts/cm," not "amplifier attenuator selector."

Obviously, with several dozen controls on the front panel, one cannot simply snap the power switch to "on" and expect to obtain a recognizable display. The phosphor screen can be permanently damaged by such an incautious action. Most oscilloscopes are provided with instruction manuals which give complete instructions for placing the instrument in condition to turn on, and these manuals should be studied carefully prior to such an act. Many instruments have small lamps to indicate the condition of various controls, and some instruments have lighted controls to indicate which are being used and in some cases which ranges are being used.

Normally, related controls are grouped together in distinctly marked areas of the front panel. Consequently, the focus, intensity, astigmatism, and graticule-intensity controls, all concerned with the appearance of the display, will usually be found grouped. The controls relating to the vertical amplifier (Fig. 52) will normally be grouped, including the vertical positioning, the vertical sensitivity-range

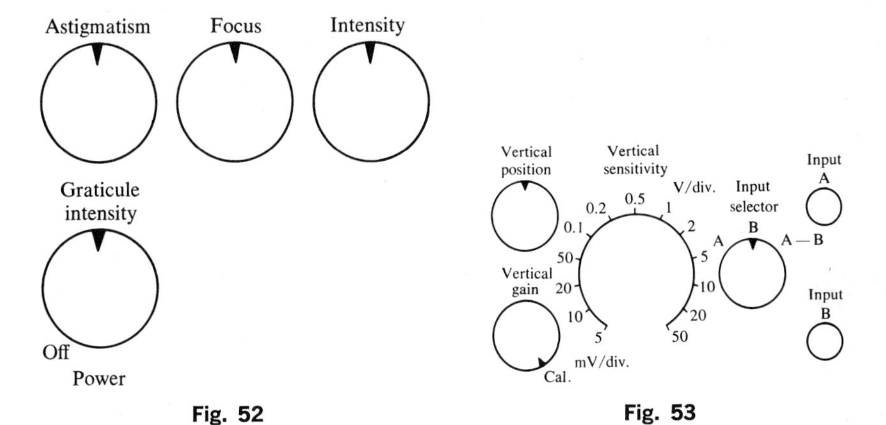

Fig. 52. One arrangement of the controls associated with the cathode-ray tube. The graticule intensity control may or may not have the power switch on it, and it may be calibrated for reproducibility in setting.

Fig. 53. The vertical controls are arranged differently according to whether they are on a plug-in or on the front panel of the oscilloscope itself. When on the oscilloscope they are often found in the upper right-hand corner since this is a convenient spot for a right-handed person when he is looking into a viewing hood or otherwise not able to directly observe what he is manipulating.

switch, and the variable sensitivity control. In addition, for those instruments which have more than one input, an input-selector switch and any other controls which may relate to the vertical portion of the instrument will be included in this grouping (Fig. 53).

The horizontal section of the instrument will have many controls, since one or more are associated with each circuit portion. The trigger generator will have several controls designed to facilitate triggering from negative- or positive-going slopes, slow or fast rise times, automatic synchronization, etc. Also included are controls to vary the level at which the display will be initiated by an incoming waveform. The sweep generator, in addition to having a control for adjusting the stability of the multivibrator, will also incorporate the sweep-range switch. If the instrument contains facilities for delayed sweep operation, in addition to duplicate controls for triggering range and stability for the delaying sweep generator, there will be control for setting the delay. Finally, the horizontal amplifier will have controls permitting magnification, coarse and fine positioning adjustments, and switches to permit amplification of external signals as well as the time base (Fig. 54).

Horizontal Deflection System Function Controls

Trigger	Sweep	Amplifier	Other
Source	Range	Magnifier	Delaying
Internal	Stability	On	sweep
External	Triggered	Off	Same
Polarity	Astable	Position	controls
Positive	Mode	Coarse	as main
Negative	Single sweep	Fine	delay time
Rise time	Delayed	Source	multiplier
Fast	Delayed-	Internal	
Slow	triggered	External	
DC		sensitivity	
Coupling			
AC			
DC			
Sensitivity			
Calibrated			
Uncalibrated			
Mode			
Triggered			
Synchronized			

Fig. 54. Basic controls and settings usually available or required for the horizontal section of the oscilloscope. Because of the complexity and space problem, many of these are ganged on coaxial shafts.

In addition, every instrument contains a number of terminals at which various internal waveforms, which would be of use to gate, trigger, or delay external equipment, are available. Instruments may incorporate the plug-in feature to gain versatility in the vertical channel only or in both vertical and horizontal channels, therefore permitting a wide and diverse variety of operation to be obtained.

SOURCES OF ERROR

Other than outright mistakes in reading and those due to actual instrument malfunction (which will usually be detected in other ways), there are generally two sources of error in an oscilloscope; inherent and functional.

26. Inherent Errors Certain errors are inherent in measurement, and this is especially true of oscilloscope measurement. Some of these are obvious, such as those relating to accuracy of performance, while others are not so obvious. The latter will be treated first.

1. The act of measurement can introduce errors. In order to display a signal, we must first detect it, and detection can alter it. In many electronic circuits, the stray capacitance will be substantially increased by the capacitance of the probe used to convey the signal from the source to the oscilloscope. Consequently, the signal as observed, other things remaining equal, will be different—of longer rise time—than the signal that occurs normally. The difference will be undetectable, except insofar as a lower-capacity probe would indicate a change in performance which would point toward the undisturbed performance. This kind of error becomes especially possible with the greater prevalence of integrated and thin-film circuits.

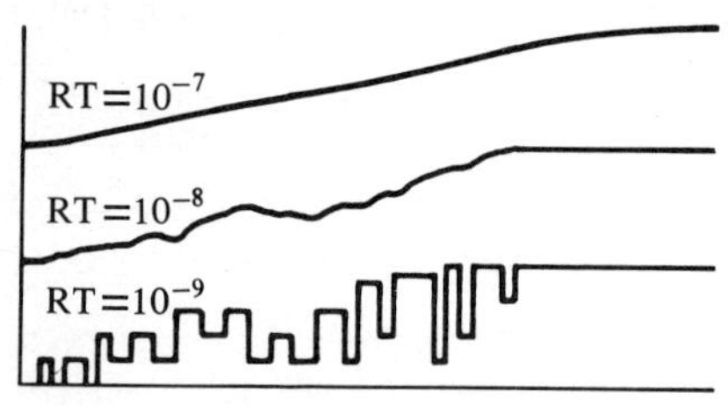

Fig. 55. A given signal can have a drastically different appearance depending upon the bandwidth with which it is observed.

2. The error introduced by rise-time limitations has already been introduced implicitly. This kind of error is due simply to the fundamental performance limitations of the instrument and can be easily overlooked. There is a tendency on the part of oscilloscope users to accept what they see on the screen as the very thing that is happening in the device under investigation. This can be very misleading where the phenomenon involved has a switching time very much greater than the amplifier rise time. The waveforms in Fig. 55 illustrate the problem. It must be kept in mind that when the measured rise time on the screen is within a few percent of the performance rise time of the instrument, there is a distinct possibility that there is a great deal of missing information which can be seen only with an instrument of substantially greater bandwidth.

3. A somewhat analogous error will be encountered if a probe designed for use below about 15 MHz is used with an oscilloscope designed for use above about 25 MHz. It will be recalled that an improperly terminated transmission line—including standard coaxial cable—will "ring" when signals are transmitted through it which contain frequency components whose wavelengths are an odd multiple of the electrical length of the cable. Most instrument probes are approximately a meter in physical length, which means that their electrical length is appreciably longer. Consequently, if a conventional coaxial probe is used to view signals containing frequency components much above about 25 mH, spurious frequency components will distort the presentation. Special measures, such as using resistive-conductor coaxial cable, must be taken to avoid these results. Some of these measures have been discussed in other parts of this book.

4. Most modern instruments will have horizontal and vertical amplifiers with different bandwidth/rise time and gain characteristics. If a signal other than that from the internal time-base generator is used on the horizontal axis, differences in phase and amplitude response between the horizontal and vertical channels can cause undetected errors in measurement.

5. Other examples of errors which could be classified as inherent include parallax

errors in making measurements by means of graticule markings which are not coplanar with the phosphor screens and errors due to the limitations of precision of component values and limitations on measuring the fine detail of waveforms because of the granular nature of the phosphor.

Recognizing inherent errors is mainly a matter of experience and is the result of knowing the performance limitations of the various portions of the instrument and recognizing when they begin to affect the measured characteristics of the observed signals.

27. Functional Errors Certain errors are due to the functioning of the instrument and are caused by many things, including operator errors, malfunction of components, etc. Malfunctions will be dealt with in the next section.

One classification of errors to be discussed should probably be entitled "operator blunders." Incredible as it seems, power cords are not connected, mains switches on the workbench are not thrown, instrument switches are not turned on, the intensity control is turned off, etc. That these types of errors occur and that they occur with operators who are technically qualified can only be considered as proof that scientists and engineers sometimes have their minds on other things. Probably the best protection against this kind of error is to have a checklist mounted on the side of the instrument case which can be referred to whenever the oscilloscope does not work.

The next category of errors might be called errors of misadjustment. Even an experienced oscilloscope operator can be thrown into panic if all his controls are turned clockwise or counterclockwise when his back is turned. Placing the vertical or horizontal position control at one or the other extreme of its range (especially if the magnifier is on) will make it difficult to locate the trace if one is not prepared for such a misadjustment. On the other hand, even if a trace is present, the magnifier can give an erroneous measurement if the operator does not know that it is on. Most oscilloscopes have inside screwdriver adjustments, etc., which somehow can become misadjusted.

Perhaps one of the most common misadjustments which can occur is that the probe is not properly compensated. For whatever reason (and there are many) a probe can become uncompensated and if used will accentuate or attenuate certain frequency components and cause errors in the display which will be undetected unless a standard waveform is observed. For this reason, the following two suggestions are offered:

1. Check the probe compensation each work period (every morning).
2. *Always check the compensation whenever a probe is connected to an oscilloscope.*

Never assume that the probe being connected is the one which was removed or that the oscilloscope or plug-in to which the probe is being connected is the one from which it was removed.

28. Calibration Requirements—Preuse, Periodic, and Postrepair It has been commented earlier that a hazard in the use of oscilloscopes is the tendency on the part of the user to accept the display at face value unless something is obviously wrong. Unfortunately, a number of things can be wrong which will *not* be obvious unless the user knows what the display is supposed to look like.

The only way this hazard can be minimized is for the instrument to be calibrated on a periodic basis by qualified persons. The duration of the period depends upon the type of oscilloscope, the operating environment, and to some extent, its age. A good average period in a normal environment would be the lesser of 1,000 hours of operation or 6 months for solid-state instruments, and the lesser of 500 hours or 6 months for vacuum-tube instruments.

Use in unusual conditions of heat, moisture, dust, or mechanical abuse would reduce these periods proportionately. Experience will indicate if the chosen period can or should be modified. It may be found that new instruments have a noticeable aging period and that extremely old instruments begin to have catastrophic failures.

In addition, the instrument should be recalibrated each time it is repaired.

An important caution must be restated here:

Always check the probe compensation whenever it is connected to an oscilloscope, and preferably at the beginning of each workday. It is painful, and sometimes embarrassing, to learn this the hard way.

29. Typical Operating Problems Most modern oscilloscopes are fairly complex and sophisticated instruments, and their repair and maintenance can best be handled by persons specially qualified for such work. Much time, effort, and trouble can be saved by such a procedure, especially when it is considered that each hour spent working on the instrument by the user is an hour subtracted from his primary research, development, or other project.

Often, a telephone conversation with someone at the local sales office or repair center either will bring someone to restore the instrument or will give the operator several specific suggestions to enable him to repair it himself. It should be remembered that both the maintenance engineers and the field engineers have had the benefit of experience with hundreds of instruments and their problems. The probability is very high that a specific trouble has been encountered before, and it simply makes good economic sense to take advantage of that experience.

However, it may be that a user will not have access to a qualified maintenance person and must rely on his own ingenuity to restore the oscilloscope to proper operation. When this is the case, certain steps applicable to any oscilloscope can be used to isolate the defect most quickly. These steps rely upon keeping the basic structure of the oscilloscope clearly in mind [that is, it consists of the cathode-ray tube, the vertical amplifier, the time base (including amplifier), and the power supply] and systematically approaching the malfunction through the interrelationship of the separate sections.

The first step:

Consult the instruction manual provided with the oscilloscope to determine if a malfunction is present. Nearly all instrument manufacturers provide instruction manuals which deal extensively with every aspect of instrument performance and operation.

Next, make certain that the operator errors discussed earlier are not present. They each generally occur only once in an individual operator's career, but they *do* occur.

Finally, what is the nature of the malfunction? Most will result in some sort of measurement error. The type of error can be extremely helpful in diagnosing the malfunction, many of which can be localized by observing the character of the defective display:

1. Power-supply trouble will generally affect the performance of both the horizontal and vertical circuits, as will cathode-ray-tube problems.
2. Troubles common to all sensitivity ranges of the vertical amplifier will usually be found beyond the point where the preamplifier and attenuators are located. Troubles appearing only on certain ranges will generally be in the preamplifier or attenuator sections.
3. Troubles common to all sweep ranges will also usually be found in the horizontal amplifier section, whereas those appearing only on certain ranges indicate resistor, capacitor, or switch problems.
4. Several modes of triggering and sweeping are usually available. The trouble can often be localized by observing whether it occurs in all such modes or not.
5. Some instruments have multiple-signal channels and time bases. If the trouble is in one only, a built-in oscilloscope is available to troubleshoot the defective portion.
6. The sweep-generator circuitry in most oscilloscopes is composed almost completely of bistable circuits. If the trouble has been localized to that portion of the instrument, the vertical amplifier, set to suitable dc sensitivity ranges, can be used as a convenient voltmeter to locate the trouble, in conjunction with the circuit diagram. The range of adjustment of the various controls can be measured easily and conveniently by observing the movement of the spot, and the resting potentials of the various circuits can be evaluated against the indicated values of the schematics. *Do not burn the phosphor screen* with a too high intensity trace.

Only a few suggestions have been given here to indicate the approach to the isolation of a malfunctioning circuit. Each instrument type is unique, and each malfunction is unique. The user with a defective instrument must analyze the various resources at his disposal and determine which course of action will be most likely to restore it promptly to full use.

UNDERSTANDING THE SPECIFICATIONS

An oscilloscope represents a large number of compromises. These affect every aspect of the instrument design and determine, in the final analysis, what can be done with it.

The intended end use establishes the oscilloscope specifications. One intended for general-purpose bench use in laboratory or design engineering may be available in several versions primarily differing in basic bandwidth with perhaps an optional extra sweep generator to provide a timed-delay performance. Such a family of products is often designed around a 5-in. cathode-ray tube, as this offers a convenient compromise between size of display and size of product.

Certain end-use requirements will impose limitations which influence nearly all other characteristics. For example, a requirement for extreme portability means batteries for the principal source of electric power, which limits both the voltage and current available. These limitations influence the minimum rise time, the maximum voltage swing in both horizontal and vertical axis, the maximum voltage available for trace intensification, the auxiliary capabilities, etc.

On the other hand, an instrument for investigating aspects of some of the subatomic particles will require extremely wideband capabilities, very fast sweeps, and very high intensity traces for single-sweep photography. These specifications require high current, high voltage, or both, as well as complex circuitry and components. The result is an instrument that is called portable only in the sense that it may be on wheels and that normally will be used in a fixed installation associated with some kind of a particle generator.

However, outside of extreme requirements for one particular feature, which will require compromises on *all* other characteristics, the general-purpose instrument represents compromises on each of the characteristics.

The cathode-ray tube itself represents a compromise. The maximum frequency response (or minimum rise time) which is sought to be observed will determine the accelerating potential necessary to display adequately a single transient delineating the response of the amplifier to a step function at the fastest sweep speed. The accelerating potential, on the other hand, influences the deflection sensitivity, total deflection, and maximum frequency response, which are determined by the geometry of the deflection system. Greater deflection sensitivity means a lower-frequency response, smaller total deflection and vice versa.

The total deflection permitted by the cathode-ray tube determines the total voltage swing required from the horizontal and vertical amplifiers for undistorted deflection. This must be compatible with the bandwidth (or rise time) desired from the instrument. Since the product of the amplifier gain and bandwidth is a constant, the gain determined by whatever bandwidth is chosen determines the minimum signal which the amplifier can usefully handle, *at that bandwidth.*

The minimum sweep time desired (or the maximum sweep speed) is determined primarily by the design rise time of the vertical amplifier. The minimum sweep time is usually chosen to display the rise time of the amplifier over a sufficiently expanded distance that any fine detail (which of course will be limited by the amplifier rise time) can be easily examined. Although this sweep rate does not compare with the rise time of the vertical amplifier, it must be remembered that the sweep voltage must be extremely linear over a voltage swing sufficient to deflect the electron beam nearly the full horizontal diameter of the screen. Also, the voltage swing required is increased by the fact that the deflection sensitivity of the horizontal plates is substantially lower than that of the vertical plates, since this pair of plates is closer to the screen than the vertical plates and is curved apart to a greater degree to obtain the greater deflection on the horizontal axis.

The power supply must furnish sufficient current at adequate voltage levels to permit the various functions to take place in an undistorted manner. It is desirable to have these quantities and levels be undisturbed in spite of changes in the supply voltage or the current loads. Further, it is desirable that very fast transients not be connected, via the power supply, to other sections of the instrument. Otherwise, unexpected signal components may be found to have originated in the sweep-gating multivibrator, or nonlinearities of the sweep may be found to come from the response of the amplifier to a very large, fast transient. These requirements mean a heavily regulated supply which requires space and added power; adds complexity, expense, and weight; and reduces reliability.

It will be seen that each instrument is a fabric of compromises. Bandwidth must be traded for gain. Intensity must be traded for deflection sensitivity and scan. Size affects power-supply capacity, which affects bandwidth and scan. Extreme high performance affects size, versatility, and above all, cost (which, of course, is influenced by, and influences, all characteristics and any significant departures from normal of any of them).

Consequently, when any given instrument is used—particularly if it is a high-performance model using the latest developments of design technology—it will usually represent a subtle balance of performance characteristics, size, and cost. Modifying any of the characteristics to obtain better performance will almost inevitably result in a deterioration in one or more other characteristics of greater magnitude than the improvement obtained, and will probably increase the cost.

This is not to say that improvements cannot be made. They can. However, they usually come about as the result of a new development in component technology or a complete redesign of the product.

30. How to Buy an Oscilloscope When confronted with the question of whether to buy an oscilloscope or not, several important points should be considered:

1. Does the measurement need require it, or will it in the near future?
2. The user should consult with the people who sell the model he is interested in and ask for a demonstration. He should consult competitive makes. Field engineers love to give demonstrations, especially comparative demonstrations.
3. The oscilloscope should be tried out on a familiar problem, so that it can be evaluated for the particular requirements.

First, be sure that an oscilloscope is really required.* Catalogs may be obtained from the various manufacturers. These will contain specifications of the various instruments. Many contain comparative charts of all oscilloscope types manufactured by that firm.

What is the significant or controlling characteristic of the application? Rise time? Low-level signals? Portability? Adverse environment? Flexibility? Whatever it is, various oscilloscopes meeting that requirement can be compared as to their other characteristics to see which will most nearly satisfy the measurement need.

As an example, the requirement may call for a general-purpose oscilloscope with laboratory capabilities, but the location is atop Mt. Fuji in Japan, and the instrument will service radar, microwave communication gear, and other electronic equipment in several buildings located on the crater rim. Obviously, portability will be a prime need, with environmentalized display running a close second.

* It is surprising how many users do not actually need the instruments they buy. This author has seen $1,000 oscilloscopes performing functions normally satisfied quite well by a $50 volt-ohm-meter. He has also seen $2,000 oscilloscopes where a $1,000 oscilloscope would work equally well. Apparently, there are status symbols in instrumentation as in automobiles. On the other hand, he has seen engineers limp along with an inadequate oscilloscope rather than buy a particular brand because of prejudice.

These situations are unreasonable and serve neither the users nor the instrument manufacturers. Oscilloscopes and other instruments should be bought on the basis of present need, with a sharp eye cocked for anticipated needs within a reasonable future. The price to be paid should be balanced with the reputation of the manufacturer for providing products and services upon which the customer can rely.

Examining the "portable" instruments of several manufacturers, we may find the following situation:

Instrument	*A*	*B*	*C*	*D*	*E*	*F*	*G*	*H*	*I*	*J*
Weight, lb	23½	33	17½	7	30	32	31¼	37	28	41
Ruggedness	No	No	Yes	Yes	Yes	Yes	Yes	No	Yes	No
Risetime, ns	100	35	58	90	24	7	2.4	7	7	1.5
Cost	$795	$1,050	$1,045	$960	$1,850	$2,050	$2,925	$2,065	$3,100	$3,150
Other	.....	......	Battery	Battery	Battery	......	......	Plug-in	Plug-in	Plug-in

Sweep ranges and other performance characteristics are generally compatible with rise time.

Obviously, portability, environmentalization, and performance each cost money, and when combined, they cost more.

Instrument *D* is attractive because it is environmentalized and battery-operated at a reasonably low price, but the 90 ns rise time is probably inadequate to service the equipment properly.

Instrument *J* is attractive because the plug-in feature permits a broad performance range, but the weight and price are high and the instrument is not environmentalized.

Instruments *F*, *G*, or *I* appear to offer reasonable compromises between cost and performance while meeting the requirements of portability and environmentalization.

While fictitious, the foregoing example illustrates the types of choices that have to be made by the prospective buyer.

Most catalogs will list the oscilloscopes in some kind of chart, permitting easy comparison and quick selection of instruments. However, when the buyer turns to the individual instrument descriptions, he must evaluate the detailed specifications. How is this done and what do they mean?

Illustrated below is a typical specification sheet for a newly announced oscilloscope that is representative of good design and construction.

For ease of discussion, the headings of each section will be repeated, with explanatory material following.

31. Summary of Typical Oscilloscope Specifications

I. VERTICAL AMPLIFIERS (*Y*-AXIS)

Two identical amplifiers (channel A and B)

A. Modes of operation:

1. Channel A only
2. ± Channel B only (polarity control over display of signal on B channel)
3. A and ± B chopped at 600 kHz (both channels displayed)
4. A and ± B alternate
5. (A − B) only
6. (A − B) and ± B chopped*
7. (A − B) and ± B alternate*

B. Amplifiers

Drift-compensated, dc amplifiers

1. Bandwidth
   - *a*. Dc: 0 to 50 MHz
   - *b*. Ac: 3 Hz to 50 MHz
2. Rise time
   - *a*. 7 ns
3. Deflection coefficient
   - *a*. 13 calibrated positions from 2 mV/div to 20 V/div
   - *b*. Tolerance ± 3 percent
   - *c*. Continuous control: 1:2.5 (not calibrated)

* In these positions both (A − B) and B are displayed; so it is possible to display simultaneously the differential signal on channel B.

4. Magnification
   a. 10× magnification of gain (result 200 μV/div at reduced bandwidth of 0 to 5 MHz)
5. Overshoot
   a. Less than 2 percent at maximum sensitivity
6. Visible-signal delay
   a. 20 ns, total line delay 65 ns
7. Input
   a. Asymmetrical, choice of ac/o/dc. In position 0 the amplifier is decoupled from the input and connected to earth.
   b. Connectors, BNC
   c. Input impedance 1 MΩ/20 pF
   d. Maximum input voltage 400 V (dc + ac peak)
   e. Input *RC* time 50 ms
8. Positioning range
   a. 3× useful screen height (24 divisions)
   b. At 10× gain it increases to 160 divisions
9. Beam finder
   a. The deflection sensitivity can be reduced by means of a pushbutton switch

C. Calibration
1. Calibration voltage 600 mV ± 1 percent
2. Frequency 2 kHz ± 1 percent
3. Calibration current 6 mA (short circuit), tolerance ± 2 percent

II. HORIZONTAL AMPLIFIER AND TIME-BASE GENERATOR (*X*-AXIS)

One dc-coupled amplifier

A. Deflection by:
1. Main time base
2. Delayed time base
3. External voltage via channel Y_B with a bandwidth of dc to 5 MHz and maximum sensitivity 2 mV/div

B. Main time base
1. Sweep speeds
   a. 1 s/div up to 50 ns/div in 23 calibration steps
   b. Tolerance ± 3 percent
   c. Continuous control 1:2.5 (not calibrated)
2. Magnification
   a. 5× (so maximum sweep speed is 10 ns/div)
   b. Tolerance ± 5 percent
3. Positioning range
   a. With 5× magnification the complete trace can be brought on the screen
4. Mode
   a. Auto, triggered, single shot
5. Triggering
   a. SOURCE: i. Internal channel A
      ii. Internal channel B or
      iii. External
   b. SLOPE: + or −
   c. COUPLING: i. LF: 3 Hz to 1 MHz
      ii. HF: 2 kHz to 50 MHz
      iii. Dc: dc to 50 MHz
   d. Minimum trigger signal up to 50 MHz
      i. Internal 1 div
      ii. External 1 V
6. External input
   a. BNC connector

b. Input impedance: 1 MΩ/20 pF (same as for vertical inputs)
c. Maximum input voltage: 300 V (dc + ac peak)
7. Level
a. POTENTIOMETER CONTROL. ×5 range increase with the aid of a pull switch
b. INTERNAL: i. In position 5× continuously adjustable over 40 div
ii. In position 1× continuously adjustable over 8 div
c. EXTERNAL: i. In position 5× continuously adjustable over 25 V
ii. In position 1× continuously adjustable over 7 V
8. Time-base signal output
a. BNC connector on rear side
b. Open circuit 0 to 8 V
c. Short circuit 0 to 1.7 mA
C. Delayed time base
1. Sweep speeds
a. 0.5 s/div up to 50 ns/div (22 calibrated steps)
b. Tolerance: ±3 percent
c. Continuous control 1:2.5 (not calibrated)
d. In position "off" the time base is switched off
2. Magnification
a. 5× (so maximum sweep is 10 ns/div)
b. Tolerance: ±5 percent
3. Mode
a. Triggered immediately after delay interval by main sweep
b. Triggered after delay interval by measuring signal (for jitter-free measurements)
4. Triggering
a. See main time base
5. Delayed gate output
a. BNC connector on rear side
b. Open circuit 0 to 2 V
c. Short circuit 0 to 3 mA
III. Z AXIS (Electron-beam Control and Display System)
A. Cathode-ray tube
1. Type
a. With internal graticule
b. Useful screen area 8 × 10 cm
c. Phosphor (P31)
d. Total accumulated voltage 10 kV
e. Continuous control of graticule illumination
B. Z modulation
1. Source
a. Internal. External
i. Internal
(*a*) Brightness control by main time base
(*b*) Brightness control by main time base intensified by the delayed time base
(*c*) Brightness control by delayed time base
(*d*) In position "chopped," suppression of the beam during switching
ii. External
(*a*) Dc-coupled
(1) Required voltage 1 V (for visible marking)
(2) Input impedance: 1 MΩ/20 pF
(3) Bandwidth dc to 5 MHz
(*b*) Ac-coupled
(1) Required voltage 1 V (for visible marking)
(2) Input impedance 50 Ω
(3) Bandwidth 3 kHz to 50 MHz

IV. Supply Voltage

A. By means of voltage selector adjustable to main voltages of 110-125-145-220-245 V

1. Voltage variations ± 10 percent variations can be tolerated with negligible effect

V. Temperature Range

Operating within specifications: 0 to +45°C
Operating: −10 to +55°C
Storage: −40 to +70°C
These temperature ranges are in conformity with IEC standard 68.

VI. Dimensions Overall and Weight

Height: 24.4 cm (9.61 in.)
Width: 34.06 cm (13.41 in.)
Depth: 53.4 cm (21.02 in.)
Weight: 18.8 kg (41.4 lb)

32. How to Read a Specification Sheet

I. Y Axis

Two identical amplifiers (channel A and B)

This oscilloscope has two vertical amplifiers of identical characteristics, called channels A and B for ease of identification and discussion. How can they be used?

A. Modes of operation

1. Channel A only

The signal amplified by channel A can be displayed alone.

2. ± Channel B only

The signal amplified by channel B can also be displayed alone, normally or inverted (±). By implication, channel A *cannot* be inverted.

3. A and ± B chopped at 600 kHz

Both signals can be displayed at the same time, with channel B normal or inverted. "Chopped at 600 kHz" indicates that each channel is displayed alternately for approximately 0.83 μs, at a 600-kHz rate. A 100-μs sweep would contain 60 elements.

4. A and ± B alternate

Both signals can be displayed at the same time, with B normal or inverted but on alternate sweeps, of whatever rate.

5. (A − B) only

The signal displayed is the difference of the signal on B channel subtracted from the signal on A channel.

6. (A − B) and ± B chopped

Two traces are displayed, in a chopped mode. One trace is the (A − B) signal and the other is ± B.

7. (A − B) and ± B alternate

Two traces are displayed alternately, (A − B) and ± B.

B. Amplifiers

Drift-compensated, dc amplifiers

Both Y-axis amplifiers in this oscilloscope are direct-coupled; that is, they can amplify dc voltages due to temperature changes, aging, etc. The catalog description will usually discuss what is done in greater detail.

1. Bandwidth

a. Dc: 0 to 50 MHz

In the direct-coupled state, the upper 3-dB limit is 50 MHz.

b. Ac: 3 Hz to 50 MHz

In the capacitively coupled state, the upper 3-dB limit remains the same, but the lower 3-dB limit is 3 Hz.

2. Rise time

a. 7 ns

The fastest (or shortest) transient which this instrument will display is 7 ns (7×10^{-9} s). That would be so for a signal with 0 rise time.

A signal with 7 ns rise time would display as a signal with 10 ns rise time. The rise-time bandwidth product is 0.35, which shows good design.

3. Deflection coefficient
   a. 13 calibrated positions from 2 mV/div to 20 V/div.
   The range of deflection sensitivities evidently runs on a 2, 5, 10 basis, for a range of at least 10,000:1 in signal amplitudes which can be handled.
   b. Tolerances ± 3 percent
   The accuracy of display deflection will be within ± 3 percent.
   c. Continuous control: 1:2.5 (not calibrated)
   In addition to the calibrated steps of the sensitivity range, a gain control gives a range of 1:2.5, giving a continuous sensitivity range from 2 to about 50 mV/div, a range of 25,000:1.
4. Magnification
   a. 10× magnification of gain (result 200 μV/div at reduced bandwidth of 0 to 5 MHz)
   Evidently, this instrument has the capability of 10× magnification on the *Y axis*, which would be very useful for study of detailed signals. When this feature is used, the bandwidth drops to dc to 5 MHz.
5. Overshoot
   a. Less than 2 percent at maximum sensitivity
   This amplifier is designed for a rise time–bandwidth product between 0.35 and 0.40.
6. Visible-signal delay
   a. 20 ns, total line delay 65 ns
   A signal which triggers the sweep will appear in the display as though it occurs 20 ns after the sweep starts. By implication, the sweep generator starts and the cathode-ray tube is unblanked, within 45 ns after a portion of the signal is diverted from the vertical amplifier to the trigger circuitry.
7. Input
   a. Asymmetrical, choice of ac or dc. In position 0 the amplifier is decoupled from the input and connected to earth.
   This amplifier is asymmetrical, that is, the signal is introduced between the input and ground, rather than differentially. There are three positions on the input switch, ac, 0, and dc. In ac, a capacitor would be inserted into the circuit to prevent any dc component of the signal from being amplified. This is very useful when it is wished to observe very small signals at a large dc-voltage level.
   In the 0 position, the input to the amplifier is grounded, discharging any stored charge before switching to dc amplification, which is a desirable function.
   In dc, not only can the signal itself be observed and measured, but also the dc level at which it occurs.
   b. Connectors, BNC
   The input connectors are the convenient bayonet-type BNC connectors, permitting fast connect and disconnect, with good electrical conductivity and signal-transmission characteristics.
   c. Input impedance, 1 MΩ/20 pF
   The signal source, looking directly at the oscilloscope input, will see 1 MΩ bypassed by 20 pF. If the frequency components of the input signal are above 1 khz, the capacitive reactance will begin to reduce the input impedance substantially and perhaps affect the signal source, in which case a probe would be desirable.
   d. Maximum input voltage 400 V (dc + ac peak)
   The various input components, such as the BNC connector, the switch mechanism, and the input capacitor in the ac position have a safe toler-

ance of 400 V, which should not be exceeded by the algebraic sum of the ac and dc components of the signal.

e. Input *RC* time, 50 ms

The time required to discharge the input circuit substantially when it has been charged to any particular potential will be 0.23 s (4.6 *RC*). This is *not* the rise time of the input circuit, but the time determined by the value of the ac input capacitor and the value of the input resistance.

8. Positioning range

a. 3× useful screen height (24 divisions)

The positioning control has a range which, when centered, will permit the portion of the signal at the lower graticule limit to be positioned to the top limit and vice versa. Since the graticule is 8 div in vertical extent, this gives in effect 24 divisions of range.

b. At 10× gain it increases to 160 divisions

In effect, the position control, even in 10× magnifier position, will position for 160 divisions of the potential 240-division range.

9. Beam finder

a. The deflection sensitivity can be reduced by means of a pushbutton switch

If the beam is off screen, a push of this button reduces the gain (presumably of both the horizontal and vertical amplifiers) so that the spot is on the screen, permitting the operator to know how he should adjust the position controls to restore it in the normal operation.

C. Calibration

1. Calibration voltage 600 mV ± 1 percent

The calibration voltage is usually a square wave, although these specifications do not say so. (The body of the description must be consulted.) Only one range is available, with 1 percent accuracy.

2. Frequency 2 kHz ± 1 percent

Whatever the waveshape of the calibrator voltage, its frequency is 2 kHz and, with an accuracy of 1 percent, it can be used as a rough frequency standard for checking sweep timing.

3. Calibration current 6 mA (short circuit), tolerance ± 2 percent

If the output of the calibrator is short-circuited to ground, 6-mA pulses of current will be available, presumably to calibrate a current probe. The accuracy of current level under these conditions is ± 2 percent. (Again, check the detailed description to see whether further information is given.)

II. *X*-Axis

One dc-coupled amplifier

How can it be used?

A. Deflection by:

1. Main time base

The sawtooth waveform from the main time base will be the usual mode of display.

2. Delayed time base

An extra mode of display uses a sawtooth whose operation can be delayed from a given time.

3. External voltage via channel Y_B, with a bandwidth of dc to 5 MHz and maximum sensitivity 2 mV/div.

The horizontal amplifier can also be used independently, evidently using the Y_B amplifier, but with a bandwidth limitation of dc to 5 MHz. The maximum sensitivity available is 2 mV/div, which is very respectable, requiring only a 20-mV signal for full-screen deflection.

B. Main time base

1. Sweep speeds

a. 1 s/div up to 50 ns/div in 23 calibration steps

b. Tolerance ±3 percent

This sweep generator is a very wide range circuit, giving a total calibrated sweep time of 10 s to 0.5 μs in steps of 1, 2, 5, etc. (This last is by implication, as the specification does not tell us. The body of the description would have to be consulted.) The accuracy timing is ± 3 percent.

c. Continuous control 1:2.5

A sweep-time-adjustment control gives a range of 2.5 times, permitting a continuously variable sweep from 50 ns/div to 2.5 s/div (uncalibrated except at the fastest position).

2. Magnification

a. 5× (so maximum sweep speed is 10 ns/div)

b. Tolerance ± 5 percent

A magnifier permits examining any part of the sweep at a 5× magnification, giving a sweep rate (not speed) of 10 ns/div for the fastest range. The accuracy of timing with the magnifier on is ± 5 percent.

3. Positioning range

a. With 5× magnification the complete trace can be brought on the screen

The range of position with the magnifier on is equal to 50 divisions.

4. Mode

a. Auto, triggered, single shot

The sweep-generator circuit will operate in one of several different ways, including:

AUTO: This implies that the time base will trigger automatically from any signal falling within certain voltage and frequency limits. Depending upon the design, the sweep may be quiescent or free-running until a signal is present.

TRIGGERED: The time base will initiate from any signal within the capabilities of the circuitry, *whenever one occurs.* This can be random, repetitive, or a single occurrence.

SINGLE SHOT: This mode of operation is the result of a circuitry arrangement which triggers the sweep at the first signal which occurs after the controls have been set, *but will operate no more until they have been reset.*

5. Triggering

a. SOURCE

i. Internal channel A

ii. Internal channel B or

iii. External

The sweep generator can be initiated by the signal on channel A, channel B, or from an external source. This last would be for use in the chopped mode of presentation, where the switching transients of the chopper might make it difficult for the trigger circuitry to "see" the signal of interest on which to trigger.

b. SLOPE: + or −

The controls can be set to initiate the sweep on positive- or negative-going slopes. The circuitry is evidently of the type which has a hysteresis effect, permitting triggering at a given level on a given slope.

c. COUPLING

i. LF: 3 Hz to 1 MHz

This circuit would permit triggering from a signal within the stated frequency limits riding a dc level, for example, which would trigger the instrument if not eliminated. This would indicate a capacitively coupled low-pass filter.

ii. HF: 2 kHz to 50 MHz

This circuit (evidently a capacitively coupled high-pass filter) would permit triggering the time base from a signal which would be riding on a changing voltage at a frequency below the lower limit, 60 or 400 Hz ac, for example.

iii. Dc: dc to 50 MHz

In this position, the sweep circuits will respond to any signal within the stated range, which means that even a slow change of dc level will initiate the time base when it reaches a given level.

d. Minimum trigger signal up to 0.50 MHz

i. Internal 1 div

A signal within the range of dc to 50 MHz with a change in amplitude represented by 1 division on the screen will be sufficient to trigger the time base.

ii. External 1 V

When triggering from an external signal, a change of 1 V within the stated frequency range will be sufficient to initiate the time base.

6. External input

a. BNC connector

b. Input impedance: 1 MΩ/20 pF (same as for vertical inputs)

c. Maximum input voltage: 300 V (dc + ac peak)

The input characteristics for the horizontal amplifier are the same as for the vertical channels except that the maximum input voltage is limited to 300 V, which should not be exceeded by the algebraic sum of the dc voltages.

7. Level

This title is ambiguous but evidently refers to the trigger-level control on many oscilloscopes which helps to adjust the trigger sensitivity of the time base. The body of the description would have to be consulted.

a. POTENTIOMETER CONTROL. 5× range increase with the aid of a pull switch

This control has the attractive feature of increasing the range of triggering level (presumably by decreasing the sensitivity) by a factor of 5×.

b. INTERNAL

i. In position 5×, continuously adjustable over 40 divisions

Although ambiguous, apparently this control can adjust the triggering position of the time base over a range equivalent to 40 divisions of deflection on the screen.

ii. In position 1×, continuously adjustable over 8 divisions

The triggering level control in normal position can adjust to trigger at any point on a signal that fills the screen vertically.

c. EXTERNAL

i. In position 5×, continuously adjustable over 25 V

ii. In position 1×, continuously adjustable over 7 V

When triggering on external signals, the control will permit the time base to be triggered within a 7-V range on the 1× position and within a 25-V range on the 5× position (that perhaps should be 35-V range).

8. Time-base signal output

a. BNC connector on rear side

b. Open circuit 0 to 8 V

c. Short circuit 0 to 1.7 mA

The sawtooth waveform from the main-time-base generator is available for external use from a front-panel BNC-type connector. This can be used to drive a slave monitor, or it can be used as a means of linearly varying a dc level in synchronism with the time base.

C. Delayed time base

The characteristics of this time base are approximately the same as those of the main time base, except that the 1 s/div range is absent and the circuit is designed to work in modes different from the main circuit. The principal use of this time base is to give a calibrated magnification to a particular portion of a waveform viewed by the main time base. For example, if the main time base is set at a rate which would display a complete television frame (two complete fields, 16,666.7 μs), the delayed sweep could be set at 10 μs/div and each line of each field could be examined minutely and individually, or the delayed sweep could be set to 1 μs/div and each portion of each line could be examined.

This time base can be initiated immediately upon the completion of a given interval of time determined by the main time base and (presumably) a delay control of some kind. In essence, it is triggered by the main-time-base sawtooth when it reaches a given level. This mode of operation will show the time jitter of signal until the inherent system jitter of the oscilloscope begins to be a substantial portion of the signal jitter (more than 10 percent).

It can also be initiated by the first signal to occur after a delay set by the main time base and delay control. In this case, the main time base merely resets the holdoff circuit, while the next signal triggers the time base. This gives a very stable picture of the signal of interest, even though it may occur at substantially different times (for example, the modulated pulse in a PTM system, where the intelligence is carried in the *time* of occurrence before or after a standard time.

One principal difference is that the continuous control on the delayed sweep rate has an "off" position which disables the sweep circuit.

An additional difference is that the sawtooth waveform of the delayed time base is not available externally but the gating waveform from the sweep-gating multivibrator is. This can be used to trigger or gate external equipment during the duration of the delayed time-base waveform. This gate is 2 v in amplitude for an open circuit and 3 mA of current for a short circuit.

III. Z Axis

A. Cathode-ray tube

1. Type

a. With internal graticule

b. Useful screen area 8 × 10 cm

c. Phosphor (P31)

d. Total accumulated voltage 10 kV

e. Continuous control of graticule illumination

Most high-performance oscilloscopes now use cathode-ray tubes designed especially for the instrument so that the optimum performance can be obtained. Consequently, the type number is ordinarily meaningless, since that type is seldom used in other oscilloscopes or for sale commercially.

This cathode-ray tube has a generous display area, especially for the bandwidth and sweep rates listed and, with the 10 kV accelerating potential and P31 phosphor, has the capability of permitting single-shot photography at the fastest sweep rate and shortest rise time.

The graticule is located on the phosphor side of the screen, which permits measurements to be made without parallax error. The graticule can be illuminated, and this is variable continuously from no illumination to the maximum.

B. Z modulation

1. Source

a. Internal. External

The intensity of the trace can be varied either by internal signal (from sweep unblanking, etc.) or by external signal.

i. Internal

(*a*) Brightness control by main time base

This is the ordinary unblanking controlled by the gating waveform from the sweep-gating multivibrator.

(*b*) Brightness control by main time base intensified by the delayed time base

When it is desired to examine a particular portion of the displayed signal at a faster sweep rate as described in Part II C3d (above), it is necessary to identify which part will be displayed. The sweep-gating waveform voltage of the delayed sweep-gating multivibrator is added to the regular unblanking voltage of (*a*) above, and the portion to be displayed on delayed sweep will appear as an intensified portion of the trace.

(*c*) Brightness control by delayed time base

This is the same type of function as in (*a*) above.

(*d*) In position "chopped," suppression of the beam during switching

In the "chopped" position, switching transients from the multivibrator which switches the deflection amplifier between signal channels can cause an undesirable distortion of the signal under certain conditions. An equally undesirable bright "haze" can also appear as a background to the displayed signals if the sweep time is long compared with the switching period. This instrument has the very desirable feature which "blanks" the trace during the switching time, eliminating these objectionable characteristics.

ii. External

(*a*) Dc-coupled

(1) Required voltage 1 V (for visible marking)

(2) Input impedance 1 MΩ/20 pF

(3) Bandwidth dc to 5 MHz

This instrument apparently has a wideband dc amplifier designed for amplifying small signals for intensity-modulating the trace. The characteristics of this circuit would permit a television video signal from the second detector to be used to modulate the intensity.

(*b*) Ac-coupled

(1) Required voltage 1 V (for visible marking)

(2) Input impedance 50Ω

(3) Bandwidth 3 kHz to 50 MHz

The ac input may or may not make use of the amplifier, but the implication is that it does, since a 1-V signal will visibly affect the brightness. The low-impedance input ensures that the wideband capabilities can be realized, permitting 7-ns rise time signals to be used for blanking and unblanking. At the highest sweep rate (10 ns/div with the 5× magnifier on), even the unblanking would occupy a good fraction of a graticule division.

IV. SUPPLY VOLTAGE

A. By means of voltage selector adjustable to main voltages of 110-125-145-220-245 V.

This instrument can be used at a number of ac line voltages, permitting its use in a number of countries.

1. Voltage variations: ±10 percent variations can be tolerated with negligible effect.

This instrument will operate at its advertised characteristics over most of the voltage fluctuations that will be encountered on the average power line.

V. TEMPERATURE RANGE

Operating within specifications: 0 to +45°C

Operating: −10 to +55°C

Storage: −40 to +70°C

These temperature ranges are in conformity with IEC standard 68.

This instrument can operate within a range of temperatures that would be uncomfortable for the operator. Within specifications, it will operate between 32 and 113°F. Within the range 14 to 131°F, the performance, while degraded, will still permit useful measurements to be made. It should be realized that different environmental conditions may have different effects at the same temperature reading.

VI. DIMENSIONS OVERALL AND WEIGHT

Height: 24.4 cm (9.61 in.)

Width: 34.06 cm (13.41 in.)

Depth: 53.4 cm (21.02 in.)

Weight: 18.8 kg (41.4 lb)

This oscilloscope is a moderately compact instrument. Nevertheless, it is small enough that it will be able to handle a wide range of tasks in many places that bench-type instruments simply could not tolerate. With it, most of the electronic signals to be encountered in ordinary industrial environments can be measured with ease.

This somewhat lengthy evaluation of a specific set of oscilloscope specifications is for the purpose of illustrating what a person should look for when evaluating several such products. The catalogs of most manufacturers have a rather complete discussion of the characteristics of their oscilloscopes, in addition to the brief summary analyzed above.

Several important points have been omitted. For example, no mention is made of a probe or probe characteristics. No mention is made of the energy requirements or the line frequency within which the instrument will operate. Another omission is whether forced-air cooling or convection cooling is used. This would determine the kind of environment it could be used in.

33. Placing the Instument in Operation Once the instrument has been purchased and it is unpacked and sitting on the bench:

1. Forcibly restrain yourself from plugging in the line cord until you
2. *Read the instruction manual!*
3. Identify the various controls and their positions and functions.
4. Open it up and look inside. See what you got for your money.
5. *Read the instruction manual.*
6. Go to the section entitled "Turning It On" or whatever it says, and set the controls the way it directs.
7. *Turn the intensity control off.*
8. Retrieve the power cord from the company safe and plug it in.
9. Turn on the switch.
10. *Wait a minute.*
11. Turn the intensity up to a moderate level.

You should have a picture of a calibrator waveform or some other display signal, which will enable you to adjust the various controls and evaluate the effects on the display.

Chapter **25**

Power Meters

EDWARD W. ERNST

Department of Electrical Engineering,
University of Illinois, Urbana, Illinois

INTRODUCTION

A power meter may be used to measure the electrical power delivered by a source of electrical energy or to measure the electrical power furnished to a load. The selection of a power meter for a particular measurement requirement must be based on several items, including the frequency of the electrical signal, the expected magnitude of power, the waveform of the signal to be measured, the accuracy that is believed to be necessary, and whether the measurement is of power delivered by a source or furnished to a load. This broad set of requirements has given rise to a variety of instruments for the measurement of electrical power.

1. Power Power is the rate at which energy is transferred between systems or units. A given unit may either absorb energy (power is delivered to the unit) or supply energy (power is furnished from the unit). This suggests at least two categories of power meters: (1) those meters which absorb the power that is measured (absorption-type), (2) those meters which measure the power *transmitted* through the meter from a source to a load (transmission-type).

The definition of power suggests the relations

$$\text{Power} = \frac{d(\text{energy})}{dt} \qquad \text{and} \qquad \text{Energy} = \int (\text{power})\, dt \tag{1}$$

as the basis for power measurement. Power meters of the heat-sensing type make use of these relationships and extensions of them. Another approach is suggested from the relationship

$$\text{Power} = \text{voltage} \times \text{current} \tag{2}$$

where the values of the quantities in the equation are the *instantaneous* values which exist at a given time. The value of power given is known as the *instantaneous power* and is a function of time. The *average power* P is the quantity usually measured. It is related to the instantaneous power by

$$P = \frac{1}{T} \int_0^T p\, dt \tag{3}$$

That is, the average power P is the average value of the instantaneous power p. If the voltage and current may be represented as sinusoidal signals, the expression for P may be written as

$$P = VI \cos \theta \tag{4}$$

where V = rms value of voltage, V
I = rms value of current, A
θ = phase between the voltage and current waveforms

The unit of power is the watt.

If the load which absorbs the power to be measured is resistive, then $\theta = 0$ and $P = VI$. Further simplification is possible if the load is a resistance of constant, known value, as $V = IR$. Thus

$$P = \frac{V^2}{R} \tag{5}$$

or

$$P = I^2 R \tag{6}$$

and P may be determined by measuring either V or I. However, if the load is not constant and known and/or if it is not resistive, the measurement is more complex and the power meter will, necessarily, be a more complex instrument. Those power meters which absorb the power to be measured must provide the load for dissipation of the energy, and the use of a known, constant, resistive load contributes much to simplification of the power meter.

The problems encountered in measuring power are somewhat dependent on the frequency of the signal to be measured. Thus a given power meter is useful only over a limited range of frequencies. Power meters suitable for one frequency range may be quite different from those suitable for another frequency range for similar reasons.

LOW-FREQUENCY POWER METERS

Direct and low-frequency power can be measured by calorimeters (heat sensing) or the measurement of voltage or current at a known load. However, the most frequently used meter for these frequency ranges is the electrodynamometer meter shown in Fig. 1.

2. Electrodynamometer The electrodynamometer movement has two coils, one (movable) suspended in the magnetic field of the other (fixed). The torque on the movable coil is proportional to the product of the currents in the two coils. A

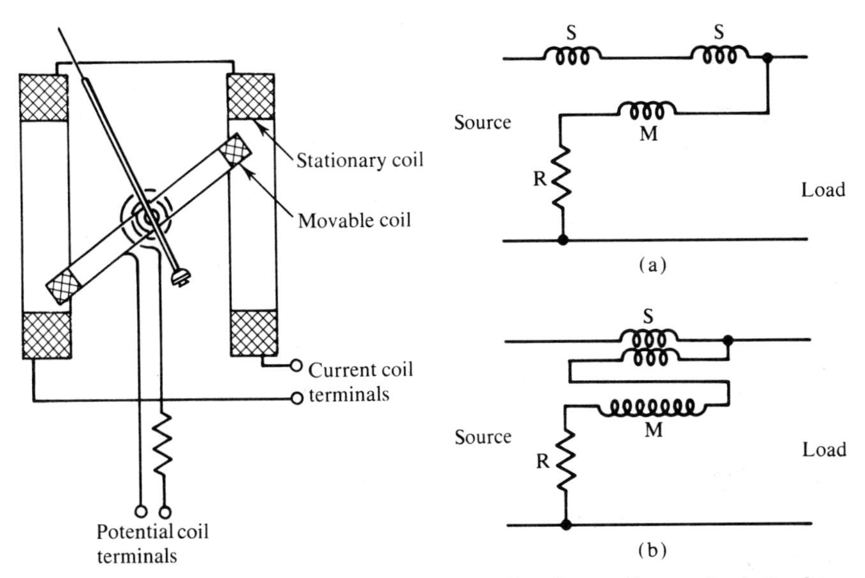

Fig. 1. Electrodynamometer wattmeter movement.

Fig. 2. Connections of electrodynamometer wattmeter. (*a*) Uncompensated wattmeter. (*b*) Compensated wattmeter. *S*, (stationary) current coil; *M*, (movable) voltage coil.

spring opposes the rotation of the coil. The amount of rotation of the coil—shown by the position of the pointer affixed to the coil—indicates the *average value* of the *product* of the two currents. The current in one coil (usually the fixed coil) is proportional to the current to the load, and the current in the other coil (the movable coil, usually) is proportional to the voltage to the load. Thus the dynamometer indicates the average value of the instantaneous voltage-current product—the average power. The two sets of terminals on the meter—the current to the load is passed through one set, the voltage across the load is connected to the other—are connected to the two coils of the meter. From the diagram of Fig. 2*a*, it can be seen that the meter will indicate the power delivered to the potential coil plus the power delivered to the load. If the potential coil were connected at the other terminal of the current coil, the meter would indicate the power delivered to the current coil plus the power delivered to the load. Although the error introduced by measuring some of the power consumed by the meter may be small, the compensated wattmeter, shown schematically in Fig. 2*b*, may be used when this error cannot be tolerated.

The electrodynamometer wattmeter is used for dc signals and frequencies up to several hundred hertz. Measurement of power at dc and 60 Hz represents the most widespread use of these meters. Although a given instrument has a useful range of power levels of about 1:5 (for each scale), power meters of this type are available to measure power levels from a few watts to several kilowatts. The long period of development and use has lead to a rugged instrument with an available accuracy that ranges from 0.5 to 3 percent of full scale.

ABSORPTION POWER METERS FOR HIGH FREQUENCY

An absorption-type power meter absorbs or uses the power that is measured and has three basic parts:

1. A load to dissipate the electrical energy
2. A means of sensing the level of power dissipated in the load
3. A means for indicating the level of power

It is necessary that the electrical characteristics of the load be known and remain constant for the frequency, power, and temperature range over which the instrument is to operate. Note that the load terminates the transmission line which delivers

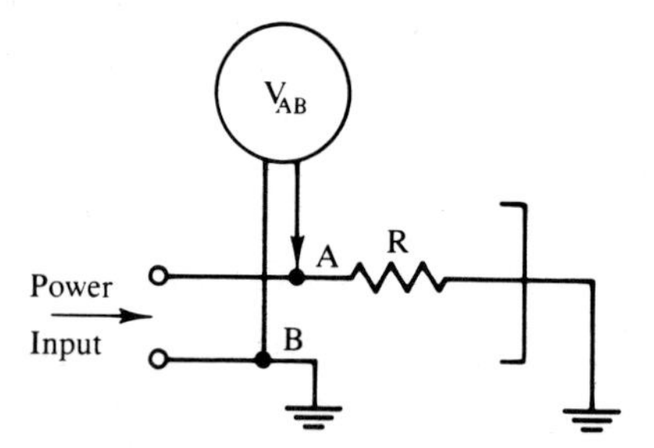

Fig. 3. Voltage-sensing absorption power meter.

the power to be measured. Thus the connector provided must be appropriate for the range of frequency and power to be measured. Detection of the heating effect of the electrical power provides a direct means of sensing the power to be measured. An alternate method is to sense the voltage or current to the load and calculate the power from this information. In some instruments, the first two parts are combined, as it is necessary to utilize all the power available for sensing the level.

3. Voltage-sensing Meter A diagram of a typical voltage-sensing absorption power meter is shown in Fig. 3. The load resistance is designed to offer a resistive load of constant value for the frequencies of interest. The value of resistance is chosen as that needed to terminate the transmission line properly. Thus a voltage probe may be applied to the transmission line at any point ahead of the load resistor. The measured voltage may be converted to power by $P = V^2/R$ (25-5). The power meter is calibrated to read directly in watts by calibrating the indicating scale directly in terms of power. Thus, if the voltage-measuring device is linear, power will be shown on a square-law scale, as in the plot of Fig. 4*a*. Note that even if the deflection of the indicator is not a linear function of the measured voltage, a power calibration is appropriate. Figure 4*b* shows a scale in which two sets of markings corresponding to two ranges of the power meter have been placed on the same scale. The deflection is proportional to voltage; the power is proportional to the square of the voltage.

The limitations on frequency are the limits of the load resistance and the voltage-measuring device. Load resistances are available which exhibit constant characteristics for frequency ranges from dc to 4.0 GHz. Typical frequency ranges for voltage-measuring devices are from a low frequency, such as several megahertz (10^6 Hz) to 1 or 2 GHz (10 Hz). Smaller portions of the frequency range, including higher frequencies, may be covered by the voltmeter, for example, the frequency range 2,500 to 3,500 MHz. At frequencies outside the frequency range for which the power meter is to be used, a reading will usually be obtained. This reading may be either higher or lower than the correct reading; at frequencies close to the design range, the error is usually smaller than for frequencies farther from the design range. At frequencies outside the design range, the power meter may not present a satisfactory load to a transmitter or other power source.

The power-dissipation limit of the load resistance and the maximum voltage capability of the voltmeter impose limitations on the maximum power which can be measured. The power limitation imposed by the load resistance is simply the maximum temperature at which the resistance is designed to operate. As the power

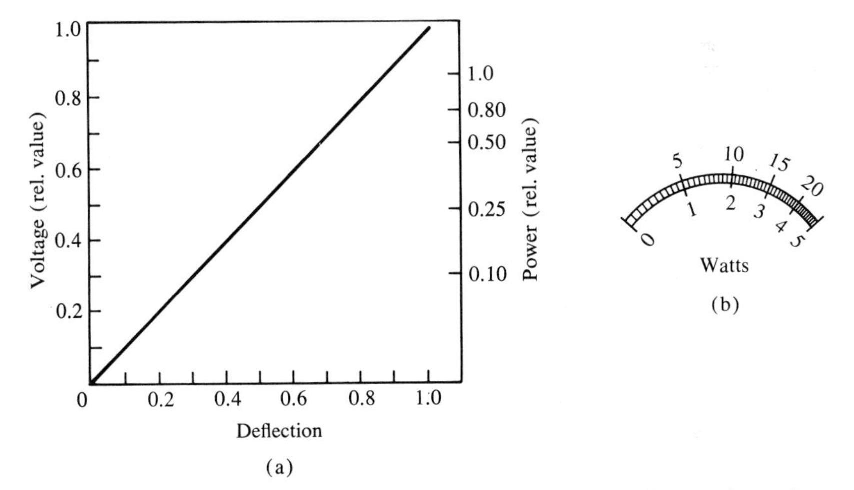

Fig. 4. Voltage-sensing power-meter scales. (a) Scale relations for voltage-sensing power meter (all quantities are given as fractions of the full-scale value). (b) Scale for voltage-sensing power meter. (*Bird Electronic Corp., 1968 catalog.*)

is increased, the temperature which the load resistor will assume in order to dissipate the power will increase. The voltmeter not only imposes a maximum power as determined by the maximum voltage but also gives rise to a minimum power corresponding to the minimum voltage which can be indicated with the desired accuracy. For most instruments, this will be approximately 10 percent of the lowest full-scale reading.

In general, these meters are calibrated in terms of their response to a continuous-wave (cw) signal, and they indicate the average power for such a signal. The voltage indicated is the average voltage of the amplitude. If the amplitude varies with time (as in an amplitude-modulated signal, for example), the power meter will indicate the power level determined from the square of the average voltage. However, average power is determined from the average of the voltage squared [refer to Eq. (5)], and it can be seen that these are not the same [i.e., $\overline{(v^2)} \neq (\bar{v})^2$]. Thus for waveforms other than cw, instruments calibrated on this basis will not be correct, as shown in Table 1. For example, if an amplitude-modulated signal with 100 percent modulation is measured, the power level indicated will be approximately two-thirds of the true average power. There is a variation of this instrument designed to meet some of the above difficulties. This is a power meter in which the voltmeter indicates not the average value but rather the peak value of the signal amplitude. Thus the level of power indicated is proportional to the square of the peak voltage and is known as peak power. Thus a peak-power meter indicates the average value of power present during a burst or peak of signal energy.

Typically, the accuracy of a voltage-sensing absorption power meter is ±5 percent of the full-scale reading. A part of this uncertainty can be attributed to the in-

TABLE 1 Waveform Effects with Power Meters (Watts)

Waveform	True avg power	Voltage sensing avg power	Peak power
CW (100 V)	100	100	100
AM 100% mod. (200 V)	150	100	400
SSB 2 tone (100 V)	50	40.5	100
Pulse (100 V; 10% → ← 90% →)	10	1.0	100

R_0 assumed as 50 Ω

$$\text{Peak power} = \left(\frac{\text{peak volts}}{2\,R_0}\right)^2$$

NOTE: Peak volts = $\sqrt{2}$ (volts) rms

accuracy of the indicating instrument used as an output device. A more accurate output device (such as a digital voltmeter) would improve the accuracy. A larger portion of the uncertainty is due to the rectifier which converts the high-frequency signal to direct current and the uncertainty of the relation between the voltage sample and the voltage at the load.

HEAT-SENSING METERS (CALORIMETRIC)

A second type of absorption power meter is that which senses directly the electrical power dissipated in the load. As shown in Fig. 5, the manner of sensing the power dissipated is to determine the effect of heating the load in which the power is dissipated. The most fundamental method of measuring electrical power is to dissipate it as heat and measure the resulting temperature rise. True calorimetric power meters involve the dissipation of a certain amount of energy in an isolated calorimetric body so that no heat escapes and a measurement of the resulting temperature rise. The calorimetric power meter provides for the dissipation of electrical power by a resistance which terminates the transmission line (a constant level of power is a constant flow of energy), provides for controlling the flow of heat through predetermined thermal paths, and measures the temperature rise established by this heat flow. If the calorimetric body in the basic calorimeter of Fig. 5 is thermally isolated from the environment, the rate of temperature rise will be proportional to the power dissipated in the load.

4. Substitution Calorimeter The need to know the thermal mass of the calorimetric body as well as the difficulty in obtaining complete isolation from the environment greatly restricts the usage of the basic calorimeter power meter. Some of these problems are avoided by using a direct or low-frequency electrical power source to calibrate the temperature-measuring device, resulting in a substitution calorimeter (Fig. 6). The direct or low-frequency power required to achieve a

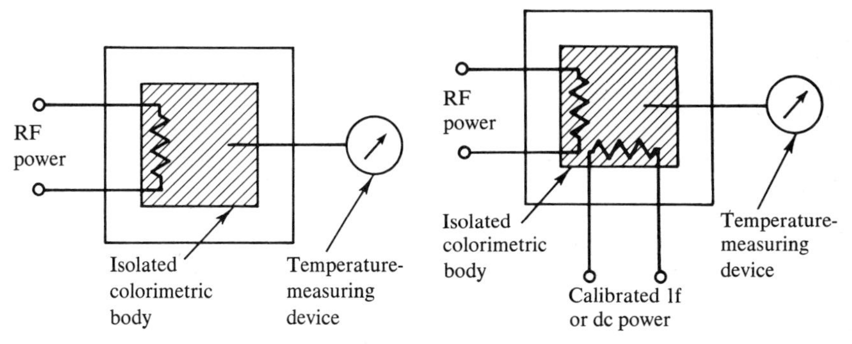

Fig. 5. Power-sensing absorption power meter. (*Proc. IEEE, June, 1967.*)

Fig. 6. Substitution calorimeter. (*Proc. IEEE, June, 1967.*)

particular temperature in the calorimeter can be measured by another means (voltage sensing or electrodynamometer, for example) that is more accurate. A meter of this type is operated in one of two ways.

Method 1. The temperature to which the unknown power will bring the calorimetric body is noted. Then, with the unknown power removed, the calibration power is increased until the calorimetric body again assumes the same temperature. It is then assumed that the amount of power from the unknown source is equal to the amount of power from the calibrated or known source.

Method 2. Calibrated power is applied to bring the device to some predetermined temperature prior to the application of the unknown power. When the unknown power is applied, the amount of calibrated power is reduced so that the temperature of the body remains constant. As a constant temperature is indicative of a constant total electrical-power dissipation in the body, it is assumed that the reduction in calibrated power (which can be determined readily) is equal to the amount of unknown power applied.

In both cases, the assumption that equal quantities of dc power and unknown radio-frequency power cause equal heating must be evaluated.

5. Basic Flow Calorimeter The basic flow calorimeter consists of the load for converting the electrical energy into heat in a liquid, a system for circulating the liquid, and a means for measuring temperature differences within the circulating liquid which are caused by the dissipation of the electrical power. The thermal mass of the liquid and the rate at which it flows past the dissipating elements must be known in addition to the temperature difference which is caused by the added heat. As with the static calorimeter, the problems of determining some

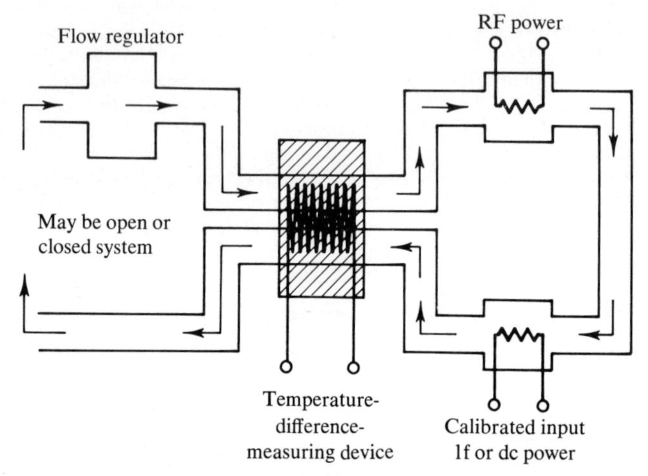

Fig. 7. Substitution flow calorimeter. (*Proc. IEEE, June, 1967.*)

of these quantities can be eliminated by using substitution methods as shown in Fig. 7. The substitution flow calorimeter consists of the same components as the basic flow calorimeter with an additional load for introducing the calibration power.

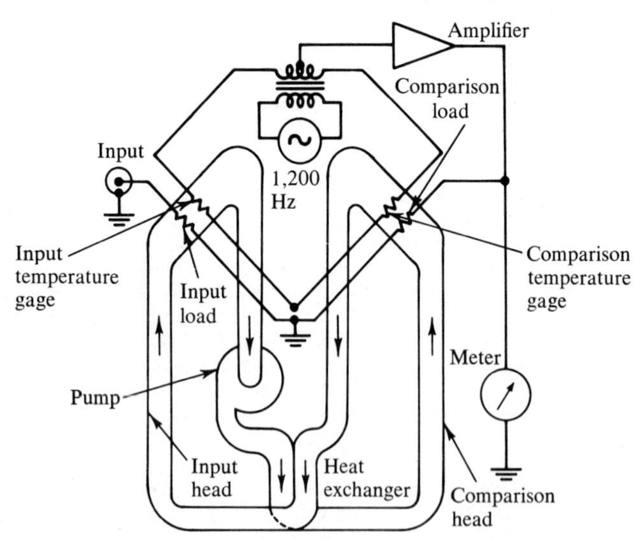

Fig. 8. Comparison flow calorimeter. (*Hewlett-Packard, AN 64.*)

6. Comparison Flow Calorimeter A variation of the substitution flow calorimeter is the comparison flow calorimeter shown in Fig. 8. In this instrument, the fluid is passed in separate streams by the input load and the comparison load. The comparison power is adjusted so that the temperature difference detected at the comparison load is the same as the temperature difference detected at the input load. As the flow rate and the temperature of the fluid incident upon both the comparison load and the input load are the same, equal temperature differences are assumed to indicate equal power dissipated at the input load and the comparison load. Thus the unknown input power is then equal to the calibrated comparison power.

7. Bolometer Bridge One of the frequently used instruments for measuring rf power is the bolometer bridge. A bolometer is a temperature-sensitive resistance element. Its resistance is changed as a consequence of the heating produced by the absorbed radio-frequency power. This change in resistance is measured with

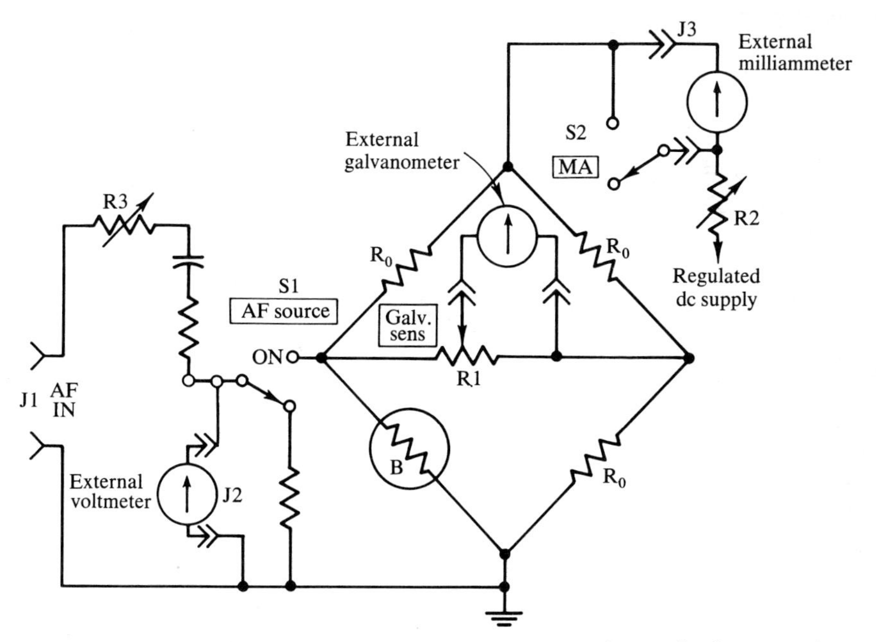

Fig. 9. Manually balanced bolometer bridge. (*Hewlett-Packard, AN 64.*)

a bridge circuit. In nearly all bolometer-bridge instruments, some means is devised to maintain the resistance of the element constant during the measurement process by substitution of direct current or low-frequency power. As the bolometer element terminates the transmission line, any change in the resistance allows the termination offered by the bolometer to vary with variation in the level of power being measured.

A manually balanced bolometer bridge is shown schematically in Fig. 9. Initial balance is obtained by adjusting R_2 to control the direct voltage applied to the bridge. The bolometer resistance changes with changes in the applied voltage, and the bridge is balanced when the bolometer resistance equals R_0. The addition of an unknown amount of rf power unbalances the bridge, and the direct voltage must be reduced to restore balance. As the total power dissipated in the bolometer is the same under the two conditions, the rf power is

$$P_{rf} = \frac{V_1^2 - V_2^2}{4R_0} \tag{7}$$

when V_1 = direct voltage to bridge at initial balance
V_2 = direct voltage to bridge with rf power applied

An alternate method is to balance the bridge initially *with* the rf power applied and then *substitute* a low-frequency signal to the bolometer to restore balance. If the low-frequency voltage applied across R_0 is V_3, then

$$P_{rf} = \frac{V_3^2}{R_0} \tag{8}$$

The diagram for a self-balancing bridge is shown in Fig. 10. The bridge-amplifier combination forms a feedback oscillator that is stable at an amplitude which very nearly balances the bridge. At the initial balance (no rf power applied), the dc bias is adjusted so that the voltmeter indicates a specified level from the oscillator. Although this adjustment sets the voltmeter pointer to 0 on the scale, this is actually the full-scale reading of the voltmeter. As rf power is applied to the bolometer, the oscillation level necessary to maintain balance will decrease by the

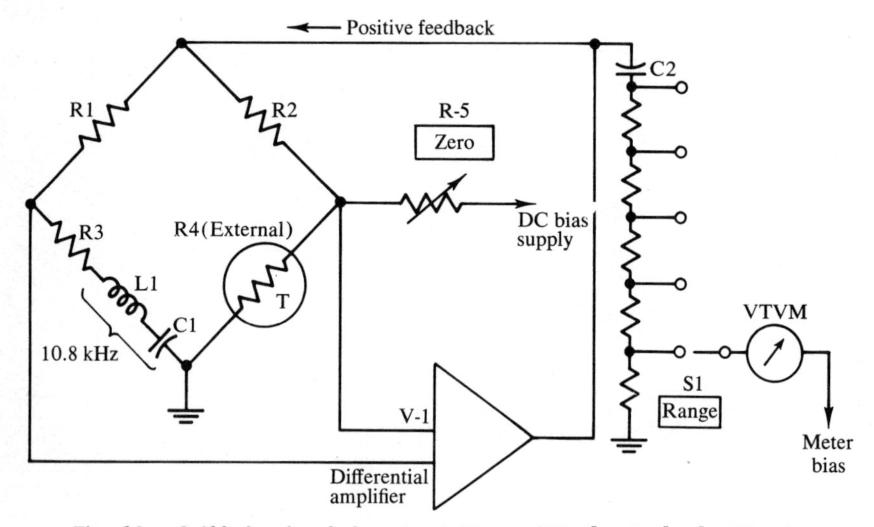

Fig. 10. Self-balancing bolometer bridge. (*Hewlett-Packard, AN 64.*)

amount of applied rf power, and the voltmeter indication will depart from zero. The deflection from zero can be calibrated directly in rf power:

$$P_{rf} = \frac{1}{4R}(V_1^2 - V_2^2) = \text{const} - \frac{V_2^2}{4R} \tag{9}$$

Figure 11 indicates the panel and controls of a typical bolometer bridge.

Bolometer bridges are most frequently used to measure power in the range from 0.1 mW (thousandths of a watt) to 10 mW. Bolometers and the associated bridges may be specifically designed to extend these ranges by an order of magnitude in either direction (i.e., 0.01 to 100 mW).

A bolometer-bridge power meter responds to the average power applied. Thus the indicated power will be the average power over a time interval related to the time constant of the bolometer. If the time constant of the bolometer is less than the period of variation of the signal, interpretations of the reading may be difficult. The accuracy that can be realized with these instruments is determined by the accuracy of the bridge and how well the bolometer/mount combination meets the requirements noted. Presently available instruments are capable of accuracy in the 0.5 to 10 percent range, with 2 to 5 percent frequently achieved.

8. Temperature-compensated Bolometer Bridge The bolometer bridge is sensitive to changes in ambient temperature; this sets a limit to the minimum power level to be measured with a bolometer bridge. *Temperature-compensated* bolometer-bridge power meters reduce this problem and permit accurate measurements at lower power levels. Temperature compensation is achieved by several methods, all utilizing a second identical bolometer exposed to the same temperature environment but not the radio-frequency power.

9. Bolometer Elements The bolometer is the only component of the bolometer-bridge power meter to which the rf signal is applied; thus the range of frequencies over which the power meter can be used is determined completely by the bolometer/mount combination. Bolometer elements are usually mounted in either coaxial or waveguide structures so that they are compatible with common transmission-line systems used at rf and microwave frequencies. Several are shown in

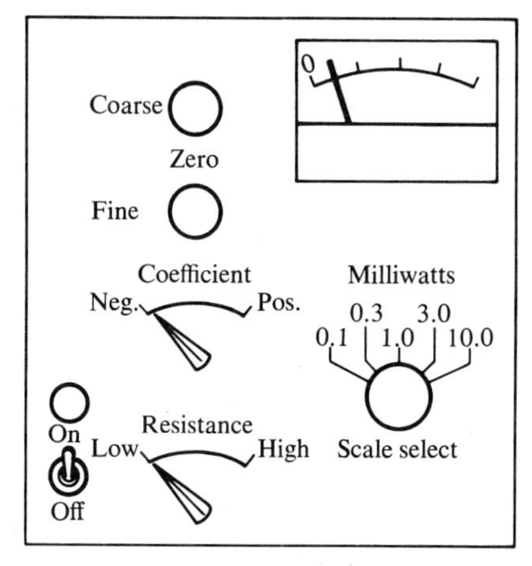

Fig. 11. Panel layout for self-balancing bolometer bridge.

Fig. 12. The bolometer/mount combination must be designed to satisfy six important requirements:

1. Present a good impedance match to the source over the frequencies of interest
2. Minimize I^2R and dielectric losses within the structure so that power is dissipated in the bolometer and not in other parts of the structure
3. Provide isolation from thermal and physical shock
4. Keep leakage in and out of the mount small
5. Minimize the effects of ambient-temperature variation
6. Provide electrical separation between the rf circuit and the bolometer bridge circuit

If the bolometer/mount is not matched to the source, not all the incident power will be absorbed, but some will be reflected. Thus, although the power meter will indicate the power dissipated in the bolometer, it will not indicate the power available to a properly matched load. Figure 13 shows this mismatch loss in terms of the percent of the measured power as a function of the standing-wave ratio (SWR) of the load. This chart is applicable to any power-sensing absorption meter.

Figures 9 and 10 show the bolometer element as a part of the bolometer-bridge circuit. It is important to recognize that the bolometer element is also a part of the rf circuit. The diagrams of Fig. 12 show the capacitance which has a low impedance (nearly zero) at radio frequency and a very high impedance at the low frequencies used in the bolometer bridge.

The frequency range over which a single mount may be used varies considerably. Some coaxial mounts are rated for use over a 10 MHz to 10 GHz range

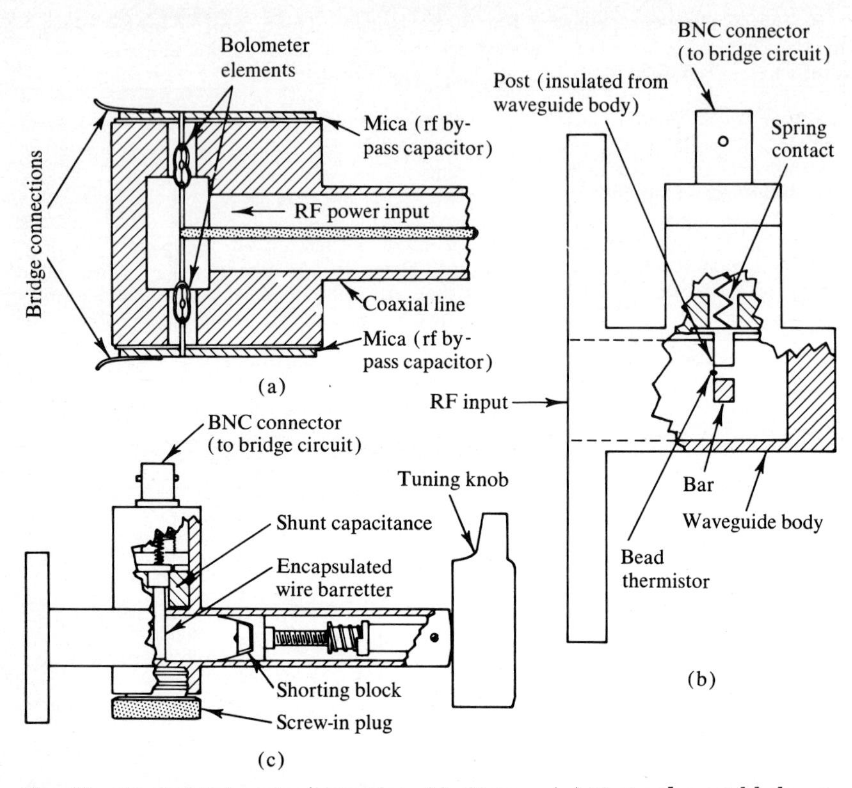

Fig. 12. Typical bolometer/mount combinations. (*a*) Untuned coaxial bolometer mount. (*Terman and Pettit, "Electronic Measurements," McGraw-Hill Book Company.*) (*b*) Untuned-waveguide thermistor mount. (*Hewlett-Packard, AN 64.*) (*c*) Tuned-waveguide bolometer mount. (*Hewlett-Packard, AN 64.*)

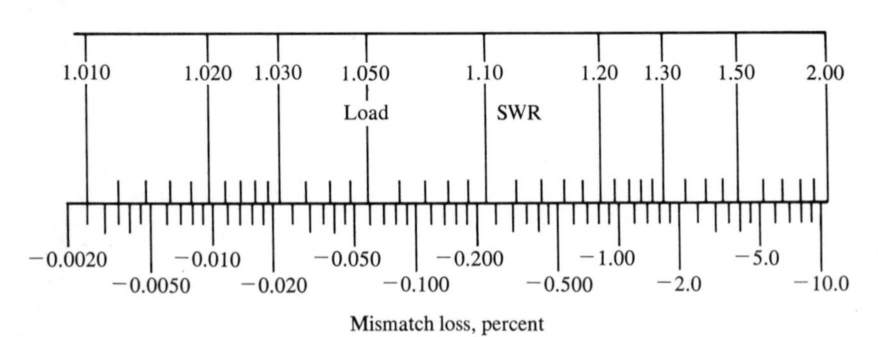

Fig. 13. Mismatch loss as a function of SWR. (*Hewlett-Packard, AN 64.*)

with a maximum SWR of 1.5:1. If, however, a maximum SWR of 1.3:1 is chosen, the frequency range may be limited from about 50 MHz to 4.0 GHz. The untuned-waveguide mounts may exhibit an SWR as high as 2:1 for some frequencies in the bands. A tuned-waveguide mount permits the mount to be adjusted for a lower SWR (1.25:1 or less) at any frequency in the band.

10. Barretters and Thermistors The term bolometer is used to designate a temperature-sensitive resistance. The barretter, the thermistor, the thin-film bolometer, and the load lamp are a few of the elements used as bolometers. The thermistor has a negative temperature coefficient; the other three have a positive temperature coefficient. The barretter and the thermistor are the most commonly used.

By proper construction of the bolometer element, the heating effect of low-frequency (dc or audio) and microwave power will be nearly the same. The barretter

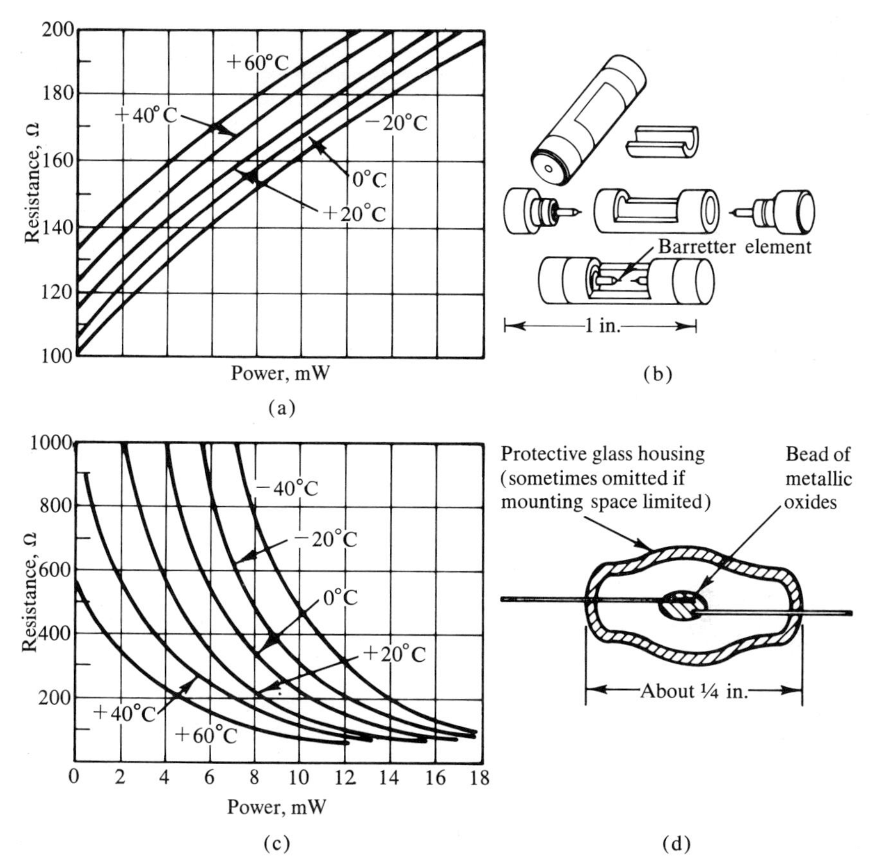

Fig. 14. Characteristics of bolometer elements. (*a*) Temperature characteristics of a barretter. (*Hewlett-Packard, AN 64.*) (*b*) Barretter construction. (*Hewlett-Packard, AN 64.*) (*c*) Temperature characteristics of a bead thermistor. (*Hewlett-Packard, AN 64.*) (*d*) Bead-thermistor construction. (*Hewlett-Packard, AN 64.*)

consists of a short length of fine wire suitably encapsulated so that it can be mounted in the bolometer/mount or a thin metallic film deposited on a base of glass or mica which can be mounted in the bolometer/mount. The small dimensions of the barretter and the relatively high conductivity of the metal used combine to require extremely thin wires or films. For example, the platinum wire used in a barretter is approximately 0.0025 cm in diameter, less than 1 cm in length, and with resistance between 100 and 200 Ω. Thermistors are made of a compound of metallic oxides and are frequently in the form of a small bead (approximately 1 mm in diameter) with wire terminals affixed to the bead. Figure 14 shows the resistance of a typical wire barretter and a typical bead thermistor as a function of the *total* power dissipated in the element.

TRANSMISSION POWER METERS FOR HIGH FREQUENCY

11. Directional Couplers and Absorption Power Meters Although the meters used for measuring direct and low-frequency power are transmission-type meters and measure the power transmitted through the meter and delivered to an undesignated load, most power meters available for use at radio frequency and microwave frequencies are absorption power meters and measure the power available from a source. The use of a directional coupler allows an absorption meter, such as the bolometer-bridge power meter, to be used for measuring transmitted power. The directional coupler provides two output ports in addition to the input-output line through which the power is coupled to the load. These are the incident power port and the reflected power port. As the names suggest, the signals available at these ports are a fixed fraction (coupling value = sampler power/main-line

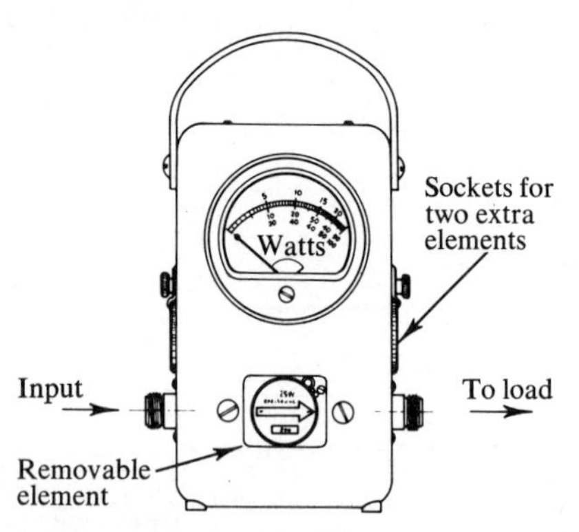

Fig. 15. Voltage-sensing transmission power meter. (*Bird Electronic Corp., 1968 catalog.*)

power) of the power incident upon or reflected from the load. Thus, by measuring the power available at each port, it is possible to determine the power delivered to the load. As the power delivered to the load is the difference between the incident power and the reflected power, this may be determined as

$$P_{\text{delivered}} = \frac{P_{\text{incident sample}} - P_{\text{reflected sample}}}{\text{coupling (numeric)}} \tag{10}$$

For example, if an incident sample and a reflected sample of 8 and 3 mW, respectively, were measured and the coupling (in decibels) of the directional coupler were −30 dB, the power delivered to the load would be 5 W. The error to be expected with this method of power measurement is the error of the absorption power meter used to measure the sampled power plus the error contributed by the directional coupler. The latter error includes the inaccuracy of the coupling plus the error resulting from imperfect separation of incident and reflected power.

12. Directional Couplers and Voltage-sensing Meters Several transmission-type power meters are available for radio frequency which combine a directional coupler and a voltage-sensing absorption power meter. One of these is shown in Fig. 15. The coupling element is removable to allow both incident and reflected power, different frequency bands, and different levels of power to be measured. The limits on frequency and power as well as the accuracy appear to be similar to those for voltage-sensing absorption power meters.

SPECIFICATIONS AND CALIBRATION

13. Specifications Specifications for power meters usually include:

1. The frequency range
2. The power level
3. The accuracy
4. The effect the meter will have on the system (SWR for an absorption meter, SWR and/or transmission loss for a transmission meter)

For a bolometer-bridge meter, separate specifications are usually given for the bridge and the bolometer/mount. If other bolometer/mounts are to be used with a bolometer bridge, it is necessary that the bridge be able to operate at the resistance level and with the temperature coefficient of the bolometer/mount. When signals other than cw are to be measured, it is often necessary to convert the indicated

TABLE 2 Specifications for Power Meters

Item	*Comment*
Frequency range	Wide frequency ranges are preferred for general use; for work in a given range of frequencies the capability of operating at other frequencies is relatively unimportant
Power level	Must be matched to the power level to be measured. Power measurement at low power (0.1–10 mW) is more difficult than at higher levels
Accuracy	Usually stated in terms of *achievable* accuracy under particularly favorable conditions. Under other conditions (other frequencies within the band, other power levels, modulated signals, etc.) the *available* accuracy is degraded
SWR	SWR from 1.00 to 1.25 causes less than 1 % mismatch loss (an error). Higher SWR causes increased mismatch loss (see Fig. 13)
Transmission loss (for transmission-type meters)	Ideally, zero. May be expected to be a smaller fraction (dB value smaller) for higher power levels
Temperature coefficient and resistance (for bolometer bridges and mounts)	The bolometer bridge and bolometer/mount must be compatible in both items. A bridge which will accept mounts with either positive or negative temperature coefficient, and with a range of resistance values, is useful
Quantity to which the meter responds	Most power meters indicate the average power. A voltage-sensing power meter may indicate power proportional to the square of the average voltage. Peak-power meters can be particularly useful for some requirements

reading to that desired. For this, additional information is required. The availability of power meters that respond to peak power levels is a partial answer to the problems of measuring the power of modulated signals. Table 2 summarizes information related to the specifications of power meters.

14. Calibration A persistent question that must be resolved for any measuring instrument is whether or not the indication of the instrument corresponds to the value of the quantity to be measured; that is, how can the instrument be calibrated? Power-sensing power meters may be much more readily calibrated than their voltage-sensing counterparts. If dc or low-frequency power is substituted for the rf power, the determination of the amount of substituted power by careful measurement of the voltage can be used to check the calibration. The assumption of equal heating effects representing equal power to the measuring load is unlikely to change with use or time for a given unit. An rf source with known output at the frequency for which calibration is desired is needed to calibrate a voltage-sensing power meter. For all power meters, particularly those of the absorption variety, the ability to offer low SWR at the frequencies of interest should be measured whenever the calibration of the instrument is checked. A transmission-type power meter and an absorption-type power meter may be readily compared. The electrodynamometer power meter used at dc and low frequency may be calibrated with a known resistance load and a suitable voltmeter or ammeter.

Power meters are susceptible to damage by the application of power greatly in excess of the rated value. Possible damage ranges from destruction of the power-handling elements and the resultant failure to operate to a deterioration of the calibration, including a change in the SWR.

BIBLIOGRAPHY

Harris, Forrest K.: "Electrical Measurements," chaps. 11 and 12, John Wiley & Sons, Inc., New York, 1952.

Barlow, H. M., J. C. Beal, and H. G. Effemey: Experimental Applications of Hall-effect Wattmeters at 50 Hz, *IEEE Trans. Instr. Meas.*, vol. IM-14, no. 4, pp. 238–247, December, 1965.

Microwave Power Measurement, *Hewelett-Packard Co., Application Note* 64.

Rumfelt, Anne Y., and Lyman B. Elwell: Radio Frequency Power Measurements, *Proc. IEEE*, vol. 55, no. 6, pp. 837–850, June, 1967.

Section Seven

Circuit-element Measuring Instruments

All instruments are composed of smaller building elements, either passive such as resistors or active such as transistors. The operation of the instrument and the reliability of its meaurement or signal generation depend upon the proper stability or function of these smaller elements.

Instruments designed to measure circuit elements are used to help locate malfunctions in other instruments by measuring the value of a passive element or operation of an active device. They also are used in the design of new circuits where the parameters must be measured accurately. In either case these instruments are an important tool for anyone using electronic instrumentation. The understanding of their operation is important because there are distinct limitations on the amount of information available. This is crucial and should be kept in mind when using these instruments.

These chapters explain the instruments and what they measure so that the reader is informed about what can and cannot be done. The risks of the measurement are brought to the reader's attention as well as how to get the most informaion from the instrument in use.

Chapter **26**

Active-element Measurement Instruments

CHARLES HOUSE

Hewlett-Packard Company, Colorado Springs, Colorado

INTRODUCTION

Active devices or components—vacuum tubes, transistors and other semiconductors, and integrated circuits—are probably the most important elements in today's electronic hardware. Since these components are more complex in operation than passive components such as resistors, capacitors, and inductors, it has become both necessary and common to find test equipment built specifically for active-component testing in design and service applications. Because device parameters are the test function of interest, they are included in the discussion of each tester category.

Instruments designed to test active components vary considerably. One way to categorize them is by the type of device to be tested; this results in *vacuum-tube testers, semiconductor testers,* and *integrated-circuit testers.* Within each category, further subdivision may be made between the number of parameters tested, or between *static* (dc), *dynamic,* and *functional* (ac) tests.

VACUUM-TUBE TESTERS

1. Vacuum Tubes Vacuum tubes have been, until recently, the component mainstay of the electronics industry; indeed, they are still favored in many specialized applications (e.g., high frequency, high power, optoelectronics). Today, a large percentage of all radios and television sets in the country still use vacuum-tube circuitry. Consequently, vacuum-tube testers are and will continue to be valuable test instruments.

The kinds of tubes most likely to be encountered for service are *diodes, triodes,* and *pentodes,* plus combinations such as *dual triodes.* The names refer to the number of electrodes, not counting the filament (*di* = two, *tri* = three, *pent* = five).

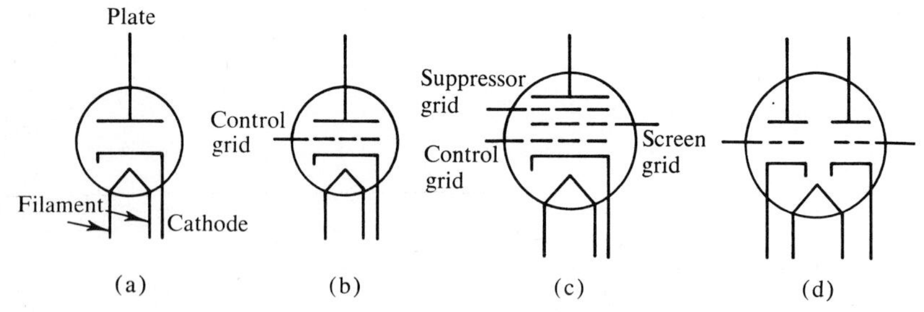

Fig. 1. (*a*) Diode. (*b*) Triode. (*c*) Pentode. (*d*) Dual triode.

Figure 1 illustrates the schematic of these several types. More specialized tubes, such as the picture tube or cathode-ray tube (CRT) of a television set, are best left to the service specialist, since most tube testers are not adapted for such testing.

Vacuum tubes are usually numbered in a system which describes the filament (heater) voltage of the tube by the first number, the principal use of the tube (amplifier, rectifier, modulator, detector, or power) by appropriate letters, and the number of total elements in the bottle by the last number. Thus a 6-V filament, dual-triode rf detector tube is described by the number 6DJ8; the similar tube with a 12-V filament is a 12DJ8. A 6D6 is a 6-V filament pentode for a more restricted detector task; a 6AU6 is conversely a 6-V filament pentode intended for audio or rf amplification. The meaning of these numbers, while helpful, is not necessary to the tester, but it is important that the tube number be matched to the socket and test conditions on the tube tester.

2. Common Failure Modes Two common failure modes of tubes are *reduced emission* (not enough electrons emitted to maintain the desired current flow) and *shorted electrodes.* Very simple tube checkers, such as the models found in many drugstores and supermarkets, test only for these two conditions. While it is true that a tube reading "doubtful" or "bad" on such a checker is probably ruined, it is not certain that the tube is good even if these tests say so, because other parameters are quite significant for correct tube operation.

Multielectrode (≥ 3) tubes have three related parameters of much more importance to the actual circuit performance that a simple "short-circuit" or "emission" tester cannot evaluate. These are g_m, the grid-to-plate transconductance; μ, the amplification factor; and r_p, the plate resistance. These are related by the equation

$$g_m = \frac{\mu}{r_p} \tag{1}$$

At any given operating point, these parameters vary in a fashion most easily shown on graphs of plate voltage and current as a function of control-grid variations. These graphs are termed "characteristic curves." Typical curves for a triode and a pentode are shown in Fig. 2. Characteristic curves are especially valuable for choosing the optimum biasing for a tube design (e.g., the point where μ is maximum and most linear).

3. Vacuum-tube-tester Operation Tube testers are usually categorized into *static, dynamic,* and *curve-tracer* testers.

Static Testers. Static testers measure dc conditions only, namely, the short-circuit and emission qualities of the tube. Both these tests, and indeed virtually all vacuum-tube test situations, require that the test operator plug the tube into the

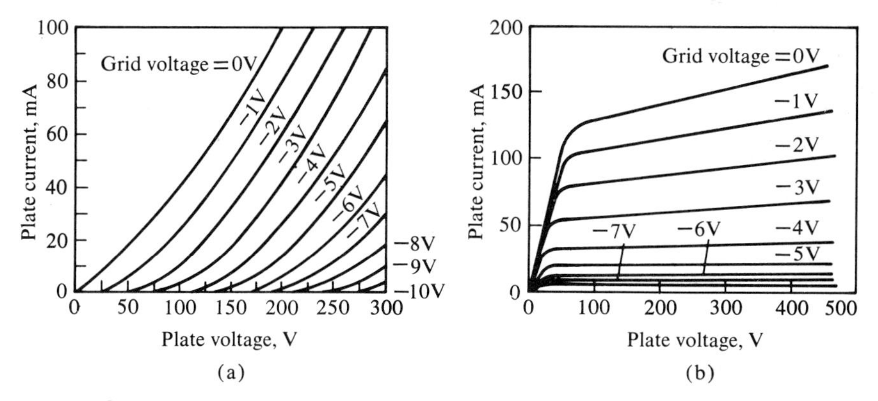

Fig. 2. Typical plate characteristic curves for (a) triode and (b) pentode.

correct socket on the tube tester (Fig. 3). Note that there are many shapes and sizes of sockets in which the tube will fit. In such cases, the sockets are numbered and a chart with the machine will specify which tubes are intended for a given socket. These must be followed correctly for proper testing. After the tube is mounted, a switch or button will be found for testing short circuits and another for emission. The test schematics typically found in such testers are shown in Fig. 4.

Dynamic Testers. Dynamic testers use ac signals to test one or more parameters of the tube under operating conditions. Typically transconductance, an ac parameter, is tested along with the dc checks of short circuits and emission. Some testers simply use the same meter indication for g_m that they do for emission or short-circuit tests. If this is true, the meter reading will be only "good," "doubtful," or "bad." About all that can be ascertained on such a tester is relative readings of g_m between different tubes; in general, a higher g_m indicates a better tube. The more expensive dynamic testers provide a direct reading of g_m in micromhos (a mho is the inverse—both spelling- and unit-wise—of an ohm; thus 1 μmho = 1/1,000,000 ohm = 10^{-6} mho). Charts of acceptable values of g_m are tabulated in manufacturers' handbooks for all tube varieties; these are sometimes posted with the chart specifying tube types for a given socket.

Operation of a dynamic tube tester is not difficult once it is understood what each knob is intended to do. Because the g_m test is dynamic, it is necessary

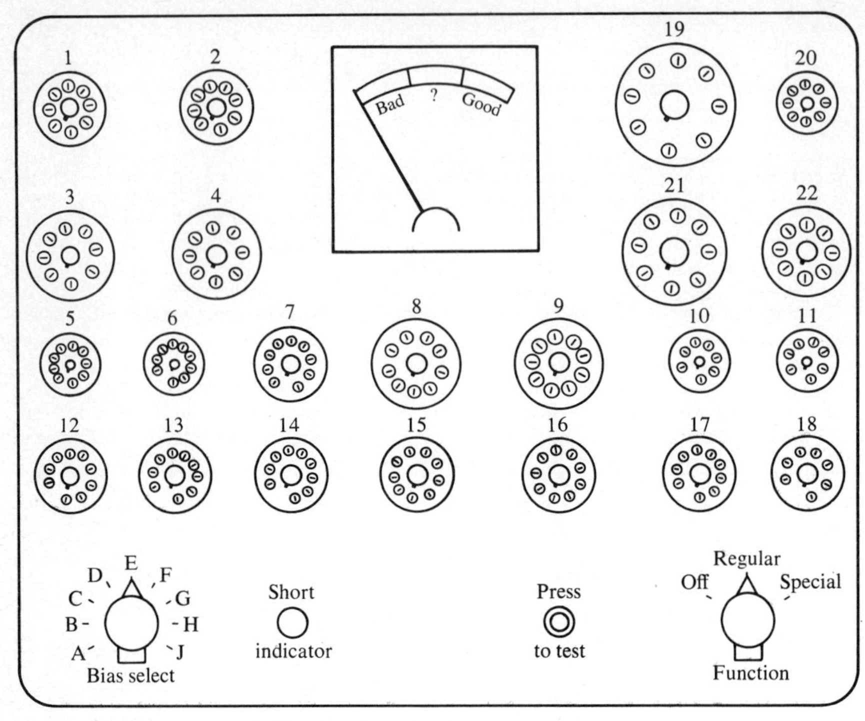

Fig. 3. Static tube-tester panel.

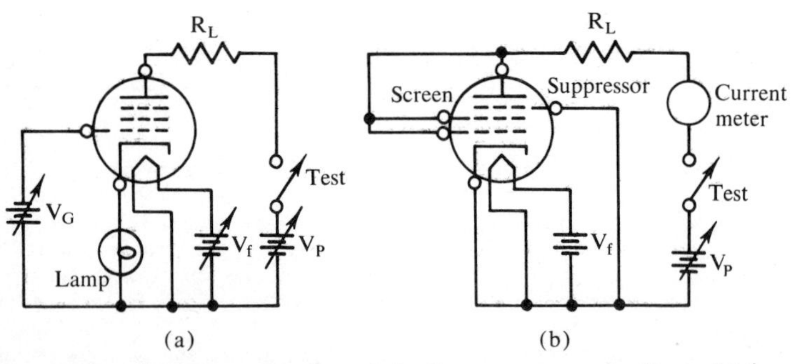

Fig. 4. Static-tube-tester circuits. (*a*) Short-circuit test. V_G is high, so that tube should be "cut off." If lamp is lighted, a short exists between cathode and one of plate, control grid, or filament. (*b*) Emission test.

that all electrodes of the tube be biased (correct operating voltage impressed) correctly. This requires adjustment of (1) the filament voltage, (2) the voltage at every grid, (3) the plate-load resistor, and (4) the signal at the control grid (Fig. 5). The chart with the machine or the manufacturer's data on the tube will indicate the proper settings or the range of settings which may be used on each control. One standard circuit for g_m testing is shown in Fig. 6. It is important to note that the simpler tester indicating "good" or "bad" is not likely to allow selection of different test conditions. For example, plate-load selections will be lettered knob positions (e.g., *A, B, C,* or *D*) rather than numbered to allow choosing a specific resistance (e.g., 500, 1,000, or 2,000 Ω). Other capabilities occasionally found in dynamic tube testers are specific tests for noise (with a headphone) or gaseous leakage. It is worth noting that the tests performed by any tube checker may occasionally be insufficient to determine whether a given tube is "good" in a given circuit, because there are some special conditions in which a tube may be required to operate that are not tested by most tube testers. Perhaps the most common such situation is very-high-frequency performance where interelectrode capacitance matters (e.g., in vhf oscillator requirements) and in which the exact placement of elements within the tube is important. Other cases might include saturation characteristics or operation in the "square-law" region, but these are relatively uncommon design situations.

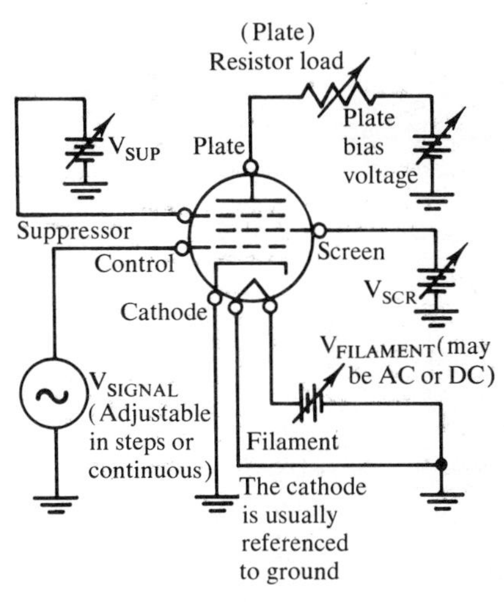

Fig. 5. Adjustments for g_m test.

Curve-tracer Testers. A vacuum-tube curve-tracer tester is an instrument very similar to an oscilloscope which traces a picture corresponding to the tube's "characteristic curves" as shown in Fig. 2. In a sense, this type of instrument is more "dynamic" than even the dynamic tester described above, for it checks continuously a wide variety of operating points and control-signal sizes, and then displays a picture of the instantaneous values of g_m and r_p at each point. Thus all related parameters of the tube may be accurately calculated at any operating point desired, a capability hardly possible with the best dynamic tester. Figure 7 illustrates the calculation of these parameters for two different bias conditions on a triode characteristic curve.

The controls on the curve-tracer tube tester are quite similar to those on the dynamic tester, but important differences exist. Figure 8 shows the instrument front panel. The first connections, as before, are selection of filament and grid voltages. For plate voltage, though, a scale is selected for the abscissa, or X dimension, of the display (say, 50 V/div). The same is true for plate current, which is the ordinate, or Y dimension (5 mA/div). Then, a plate-load resistor value can be chosen (10 kΩ), to present a load line as shown in Fig. 9. The next step is to select a control-grid signal increment, for example, 2 V/increment. This means that the first curve drawn will be the plate voltage–current relationship with the control-grid voltage = 0 V (with respect to the cathode voltage), the second will be −2 V, the third −4 V, and so on. The only procedure remaining (unless the number of curves is controlled) is to apply bias to the tube, via the knob labeled "sweep voltage." Progressive rotation of the knob will give pictures as shown in Fig. 9. Variations due to changing any grid voltage, plate load, or other parameter can be readily discerned. For example, the voltage input steps may be changed to draw more compacted or wider curves, representing smaller or larger input signals; the plate voltage or current may be varied along with the plate-load resistor to see the effects of changing power supply or load situations. The major advantage of the curve-tracer tester is in design where changes in

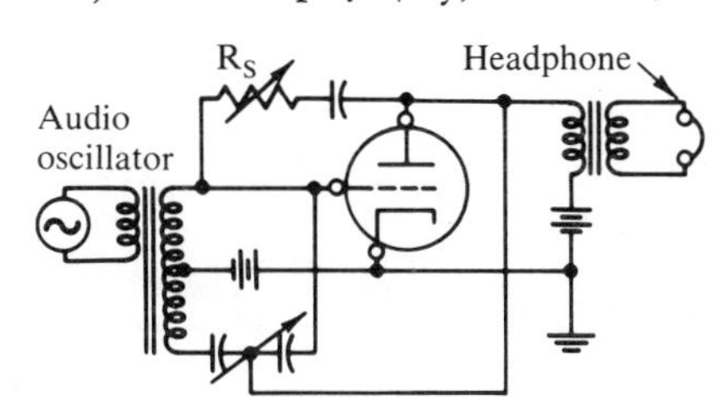

Fig. 6. Transconductance measurement. R_s is adjusted for a headphone null; then $g_m = 1/R_s$.

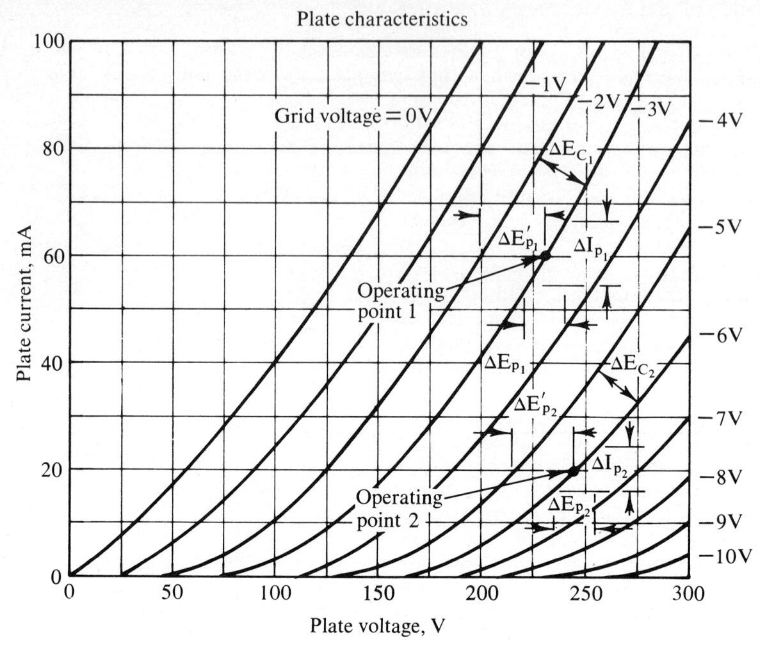

Fig. 7. Calculation of tube parameters from characteristics.

$$\mu = \frac{\Delta E_p'}{\Delta E_c} \qquad r_p = \frac{\Delta E_p}{\Delta I_p} \qquad g_m = \frac{\mu}{r_p}$$

Example 1

$$\mu_1 = \frac{230 - 200}{1} = 30$$

$$r_{p1} = \frac{240 - 220}{(66 - 54) \times 10^{-3}} = 1.66 \times 10^{+3}\ \Omega$$

$$g_{m1} = \frac{30}{1.66 \times 10^{+3}} = 18 \text{ mmhos or } 18{,}000\ \mu\text{mhos}$$

Example 2

$$\mu_2 = \frac{245 - 215}{1} = 30$$

$$r_{p2} = \frac{255 - 235}{(24 - 16) \times 10^{-3}} = 2.5 \times 10^{3}\ \Omega$$

$$g_{m2} = \frac{30}{2.5 \times 10^{+3}} = 12 \text{ mmhos or } 12{,}000\ \mu\text{mhos}$$

tube performance for optimization are important, or in service where a tube exhibits erratic behavior which is undetected by static or dynamic testers.

SEMICONDUCTOR TESTERS

4. Semiconductors Just as with vacuum tubes, there are numerous semiconductor components intended for specific jobs. *Diodes, bipolar transistors* (both *p-n-p* and *n-p-n*), and *field-effect transistors* (FETs) are commonly found. A physical representation and schematic of several devices is shown in Fig. 10. Since its invention in 1947, the transistor has made large inroads on vacuum tubes in electronic circuitry. Although the semiconductor phenomenon has been known longer than the vacuum-tube concept (the original galena crystal of "crystal set" radios was a naturally occurring point-contact semiconductor diode), the real impact of semiconductor design did not occur in commercial equipment until the middle 1960s. This trend has placed heavy reliance in subsequent years upon semiconductor testers, of which today a great variety exist.

Numbering systems in semiconductors never achieved a comprehensive nature as in vacuum tubes, largely because the advances, when they finally came, were too rapid to allow much more than mere assignment of numbers in sequence. The numbering systems thus indicate with the first digit only how many *p-n* junctions are in the device (one less than the number of leads in general). Thus all diodes are 1Nxxx, all transistors including FETs are 2Nxxx, and all four-layer devices are 3Nxxx. The differences between transistors 2N2216, 2N2217, and 2N2218 cannot be told from the numbering, however. In fact, 2N2216 and 2N2217 are quite different, while 2N2217 and 2N2218 are very similar. Consequently, a manufacturer's list of specifications must be consulted to find out what a given transistor is supposed to do.

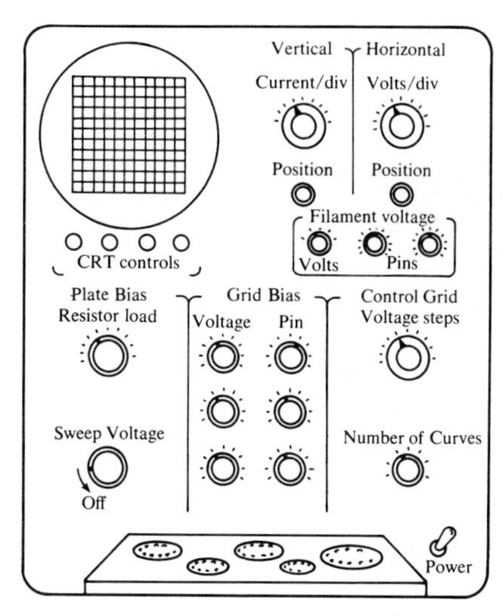

Fig. 8. Curve-tracer tester.

Transistors exhibit quite as much variety as tubes in package size and shape, but lead variations are not as great (since there are fewer connections) and thus testers do not have the bewildering array of sockets for transistors. The major problem for the operator is that of correctly connecting the leads of the tester

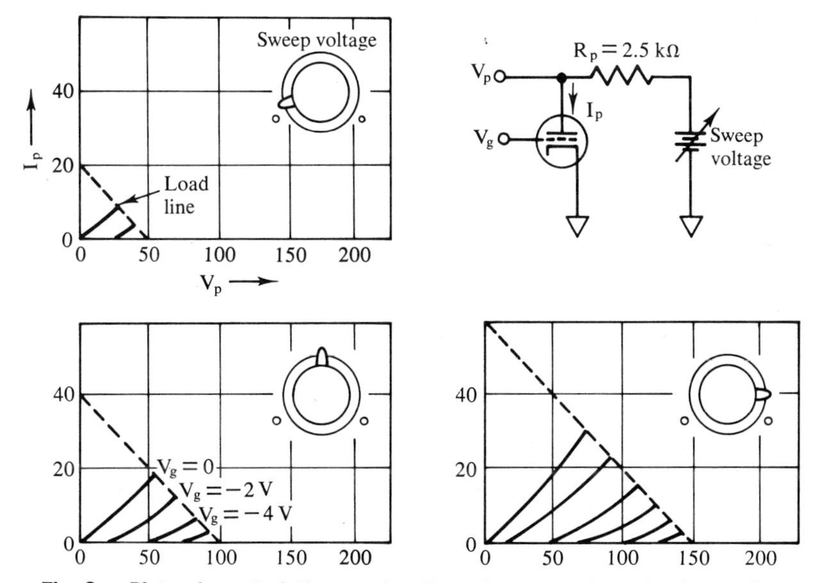

Fig. 9. Plate characteristic as a function of sweep voltage knob rotation.

(usually labeled "base," "emitter," and "collector") to the proper leads of the device for a given test (Fig. 11).

Table 1 lists several of the major parameters of interest in transistor testing. Short-circuit and open-circuit tests are clearly important to the user. Reverse collector-to-base leakage current I_{CBO} is an important test because it indicates the quality of rectification of the device. Tests for beta (β or h_{fe}), the amplification

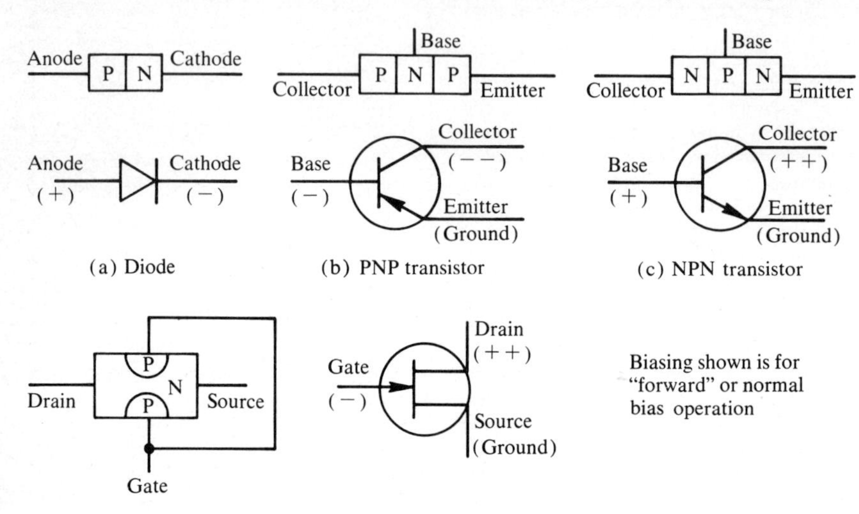

Fig. 10. Semiconductor symbols.

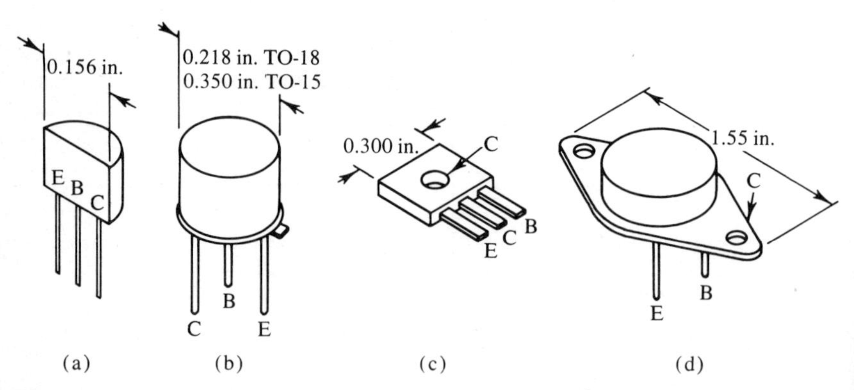

Fig. 11. Representative transistor case styles and lead configurations. (*a*) Plastic case TO-92 (low power). (NOTE: Some devices of this style reverse the base and emitter leads.) (*b*) Metal case TO-5 or TO-18 (low power). (*c*) Plastic case 77 (medium power). (*d*) Metal case TO-3 (high power).

capability, are also quite valuable. Occasionally, tests are included for input resistance, output resistance, voltage breakdown, and saturation voltage. Figures 12 and 13 illustrate how some of these parameters appear on typical diode and transistor characteristic curves.

5. AC vs. DC Semiconductor Specifications It is worth noting that a parameter written in capital-letter subscript, such as h_{FE}, is a static or dc measurement test, while a small-letter subscript, such as h_{fe}, indicates dynamic or ac test data.

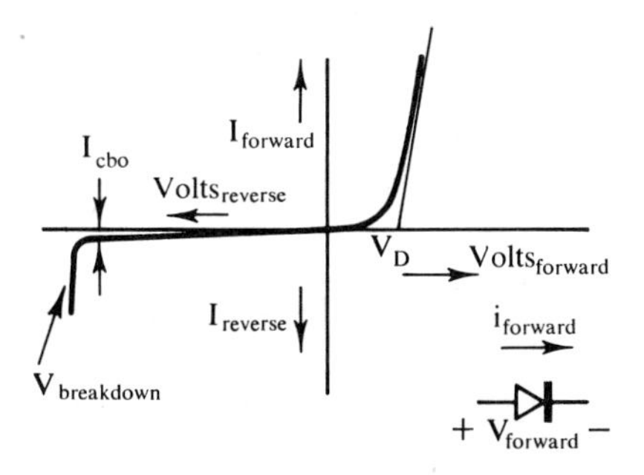

Fig. 12. Diode characteristics. Forward characteristics: V_{BE} of transistors or V_{diode} appear the same. V_D 0.3V for germanium devices, V_D 0.7V for silicon devices.

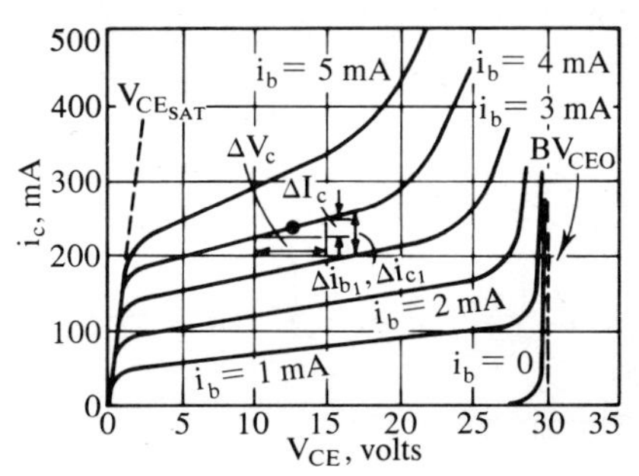

Fig. 13. Transistor parameters.

$$\beta = h_{fe} = \frac{\Delta i_{c1}}{\Delta i_{b1}} = \frac{260 - 200}{1} = 60$$

$$r_{\text{out}} = \frac{\Delta V_c}{\Delta I_c} = \frac{15 - 10}{250 - 225 \text{ mA}} = 200\ \Omega$$

6. Semiconductor-tester Operation Transistor testers may be considered in categories similar to those for tube testers—*static, dynamic,* and *curve-tracer* types.

Static Testers. Static testers measure short-circuit and open-circuit conditions, and dc leakage current I_{CBO} as shown in Fig. 14. Usually dc beta h_{FE} is also tested as shown. Such testers require (1) selection, through a panel control, between *p-n-p* and *n-p-n* types of transistor (manufacturer's data sheets will help here if it is not known), (2) connecting all three leads correctly (be sure that none touch), and (3) choosing a power range (low, medium, or power). Some testers require instead of power that the base and collector current settings and collector voltage be made by knobs according to values on a chart for transistor types.

TABLE 1 Semiconductor Test Parameters

Parameter	Description
Dc tests:	
Open circuit	Between any two leads
Short circuit	Between any two leads
h_{FE}	Amplification, base-to-collector
I_{CBO}	Reverse leakage current, collector-to-base
V_{CBO}	Breakdown voltage, collector-to-base, with emitter open
V_{CEO}	Breakdown voltage, collector-to-emitter, with base open
V_{CES}	Breakdown voltage, collector-to-emitter, with base shorted to emitter
V_{CER}	Breakdown voltage, collector-to-emitter, with a specified base resistance
$V_{CE_{sat}}$	Saturation voltage, collector-to-emitter
V_{BE}	Base-to-emitter voltage (forward)
Ac tests:	
h_{fe}	Amplification, base-to-collector
R_{in}	Input resistance
R_{out}	Output resistance
t_r	Rise time (10 to 90 percent)
t_s	Saturation time
C_{ob}	Collector capacitance, base open
f_t	Gain-bandwidth product, common-emitter biasing

Generally if a transistor case is type TO-18 or TO-5 metal or TO-92 plastic (Fig. 15), it is small-power ($\leq$500 mW maximum dissipation). Larger packages or solid-header TO-5 cases are medium-power (to ~5 W at 25°C or 77°F). Very large styles are truly power transistors ranging up to 100 or more watts capability. It

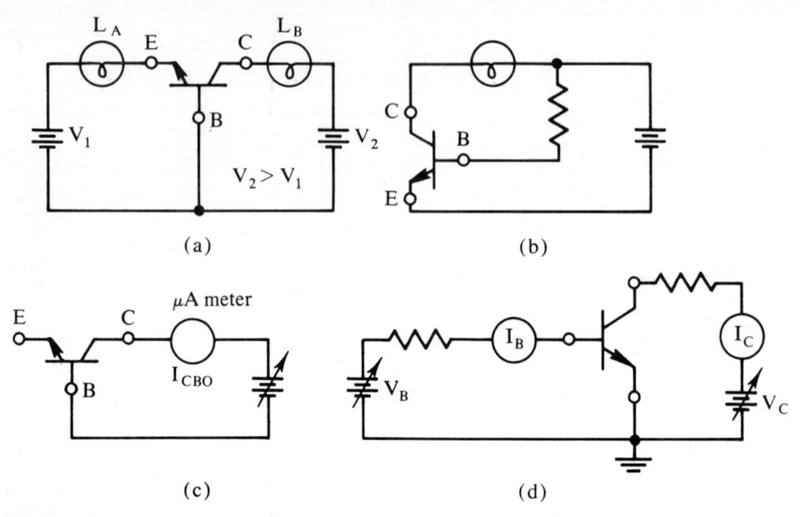

Fig. 14. Static tester circuits. *n-p-n* devices shown—biasing reversed for *p-n-p*. (*a*) Short-circuit test. If base emitter is shorted, lamp *A* lights; if base collector is shorted, lamp *B* lights; if collector emitter is shorted, both lamps light. (*b*) Open-circuit test. If lamp is lighted, device is OK. If lamp is not lighted, one of the junctions is open. (*c*) I_{CBO} test. (*d*) h_{FE} test. $h_{FE} = I_C/I_B$. (Usually the same meter is used for I_B and I_C, and a switch changes its location.)

is important to select the right power range, and it is additionally necessary to keep the test time relatively short on a given device, since I_{CBO} and h_{FE} are both affected by temperature. Applying power for extended periods (minutes or more) raises the temperature in the device, thus giving erroneous readings (usually high for both I_{CBO} and h_{FE}). Readings obtained must be compared with manufacturer's specifications; typically a device is still usable even if I_{CBO} is five to ten times nominal ratings, but beta should meet the minimum specification.

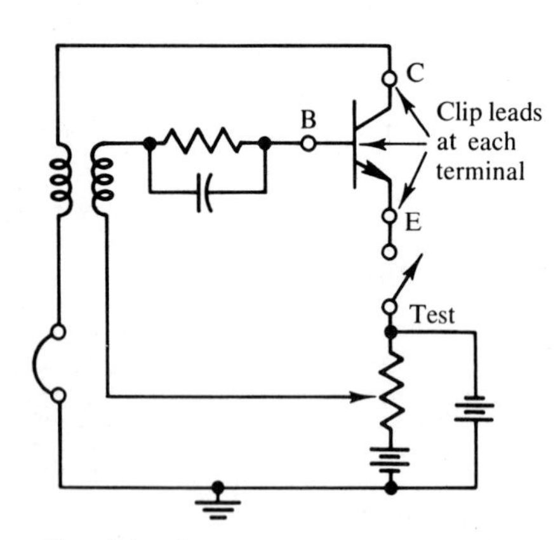

Fig. 15. h_{fe} **tester—oscillator type.**

Dynamic Testers. Two types of dynamic testers are commonly encountered. The simpler type, an *oscillator tester,* provides an "in-circuit" test of whether a transistor is amplifying (i.e., if h_{fe} is adequate for oscillation). The second, a *transistor analyzer,* measures some parameters, such as r_{in} and h_{fe}, in-circuit, and additionally measures i_{cbo}, r_{in}, and h_{fe} of a test device (not in a circuit) with quantitative numbers.

The circuit of the oscillator tester is shown in Fig. 15. The operator connects the clip leads to the transistor in the circuit and presses the "TEST" button. A signal tone will be heard from the loudspeaker (or earphone) only if the transistor is good. The advantage of such a tester for quick troubleshooting is obvious—no leads need to be unsoldered. By the same token, little of the relative quality of the device is learned since no data numbers are obtained.

The transistor analyzer, while more difficult to use, gives better total information about the device being tested. A typical panel is shown in Fig. 16 along with simplified schematics of the three major tests—I_{cbo}, h_{fe}, and r_{in}. The operator selects a knob for *n-p-n* or *p-n-p* type and then measures I_{cbo}. A knob is available for selecting full-scale value of the meter ($\times 1 = 50\ \mu$A, $\times 10 = 500\ \mu$A, and $\times 100 =$ 5 mA). R_{in} is measured by using an ac bridge network; the meter is now used in an ac voltmeter mode, and the R_{in} knob is rotated until a null is obtained on the meter. Then the setting of the R_{in} dial equals the R_{in} of the transistor or circuit under test.

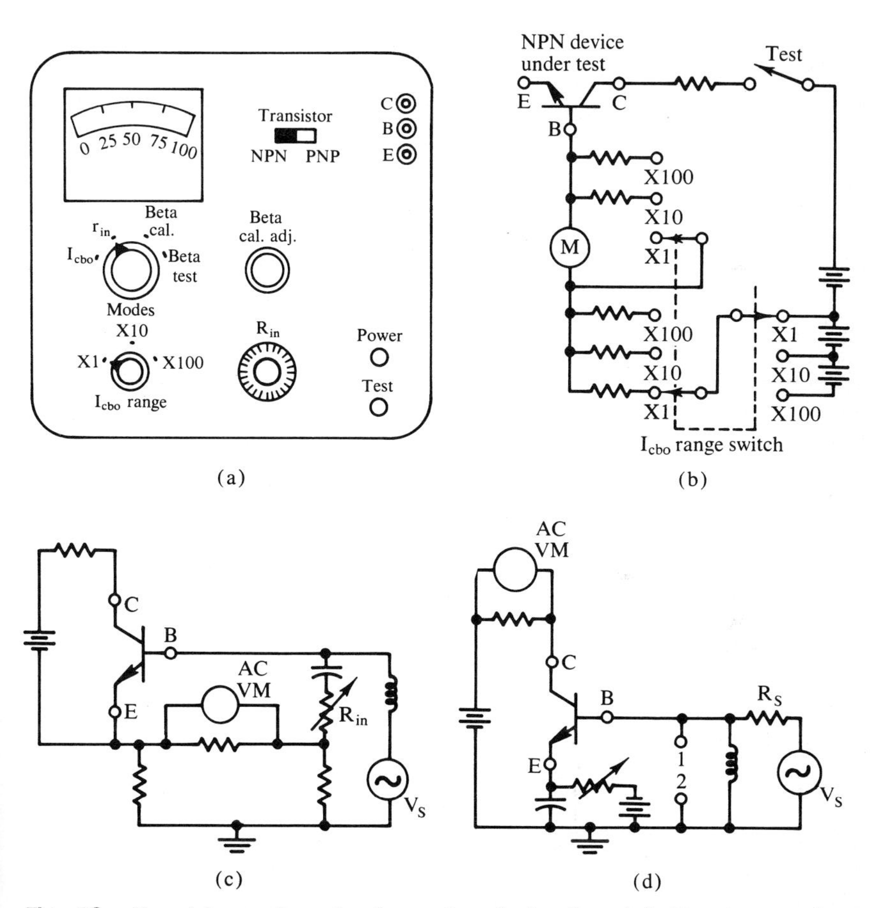

Fig. 16. Transistor-analyzer front panel and circuits. (*a*) Transistor analyzer panel. (*b*) I_{cbo} test circuit. (*c*) r_{in} test circuit (using ac voltmeters as null). (*d*) h_{fe} or beta test circuit (a voltmeter between points 1 and 2 will measure r_{in} if $R_s \gg R_{in}$). "Beta cal" mode puts ac voltmeter across V_s and adjusts for full scale.

Beta is read out also with the ac voltmeter scale. An input ac signal is fed to the base of the transistor, and the meter is calibrated to "1" against that signal by switching to "beta cal" on the "mode" switch and adjusting the "cal adj" knob. Then the "mode" switch is turned to "beta test" and h_{fe} is read directly, since it is expressed by the ratio

$$h_{fe} = \frac{\Delta i_c}{\Delta i_b} \tag{2}$$

Curve Tracers. Much like the vacuum-tube curve tracer, the transistor curve tracer displays the characteristic curves of semiconductors. Especially with transistors this often can be the only effective test method of pinpointing problems. Figure 17 illustrates some typical transistor problems which can be told at a glance with a curve tracer that would be hard to discover any other way.

Figure 18 illustrates the front panel of a curve tracer. First, make certain that the "peak volts" or "sweep voltage" knob is turned down; then connect the device to the socket (often test jigs are provided for standard pin configurations such as TO-3, TO-5, and TO-18 cases along with the usual three connector inputs

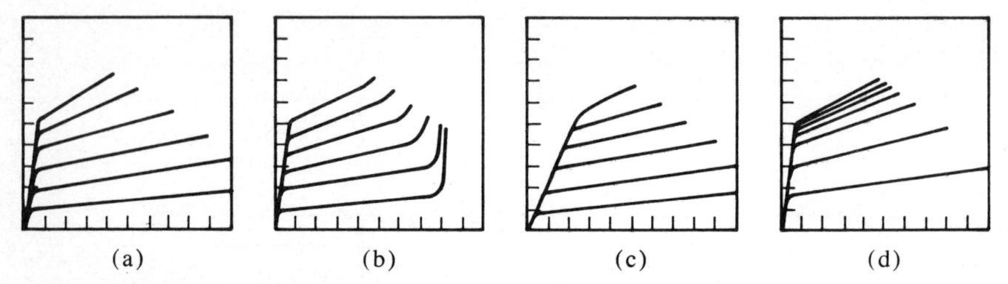

Fig. 17. Transistor parameter variations. (*a*) Good transistor. (*b*) Low V_{CEO}. (*c*) High $V_{CE_{SAT}}$. (*d*) Nonlinear h_{fe}.

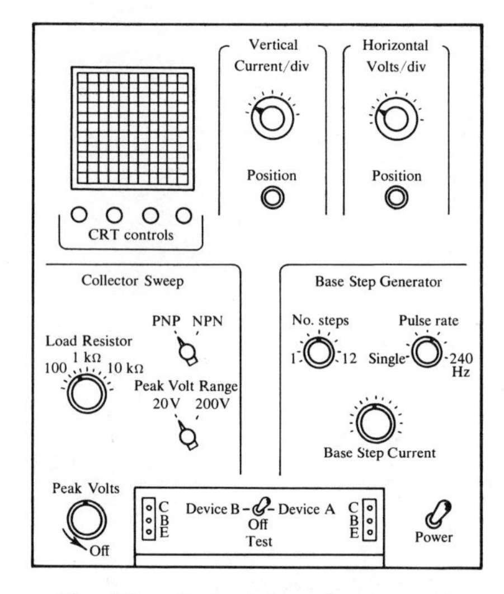

Fig. 18. Curve-tracer front panel.

labeled "base," "emitter," and "collector"). Transistors are more easily destroyed than tubes by overvoltage or power applications; so care must be exercised not to misapply voltage or power to the device while adjusting the tester.

Notice that there are four main areas on the panel besides the cathode-ray tube controls (intensity, focus, etc.). These are *collector voltage, vertical, horizontal,* and *base step generator.*

Turning first to collector voltage (where we found the "peak volts" knob), there is a *p-n-p*/*n-p-n* choice, a "peak volts range" choice, and a "load resistor" choice. Adjusting these selects the schematic of Fig. 19*a* or *b* plus values for $V_{P\ \max}$ and R_L.

If the device is *p-n-p*, the "position" knobs of the horizontal and vertical areas should be used to position the dot on the cathode-ray tube (turn up the intensity if necessary) to the upper right-hand corner of the 10×10 division scale, or graticule. If the device is *n-p-n*, position instead to the lower left-hand corner. Then set the horizontal "volts/div" scale knob and the vertical "current/div" scale

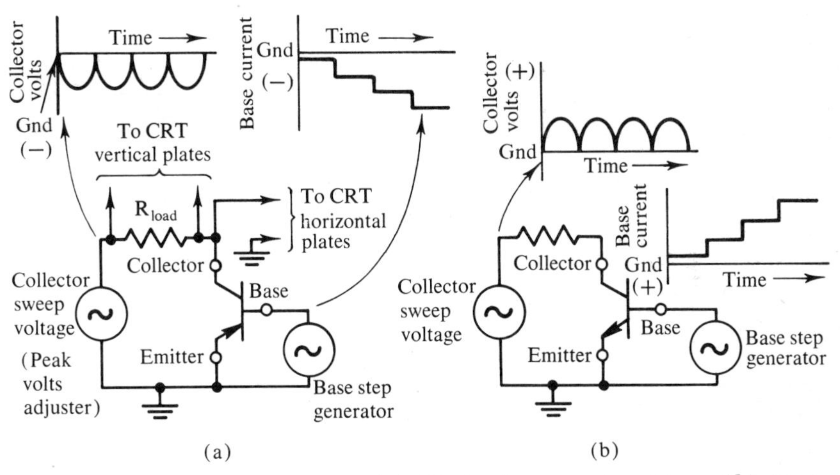

Fig. 19. Curve-tracer operation. (*a*) Biasing for *p-n-p* transistor. (*b*) Biasing for *n-p-n* transistor.

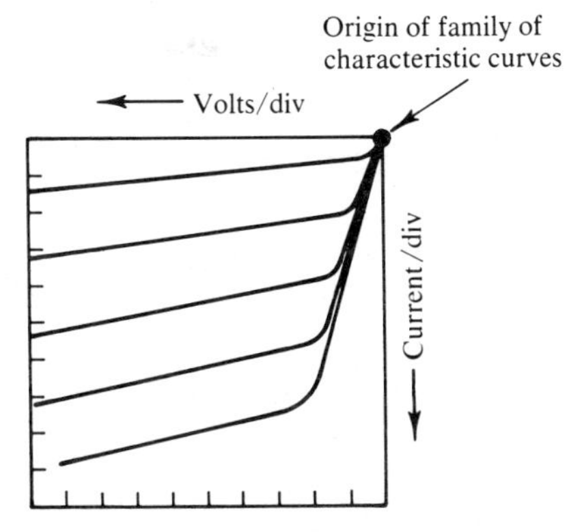

Fig. 20. Cathode-ray-tube display selections for *p-n-p* transistor (analogous to *n-p-n* of Fig. 17*a*).

knob. Figure 20 shows the choices which now have been made for the cathode-ray tube display.

The base step generator controls the family display that will be shown. The number of steps to be displayed (from 1 to 12), the incremental base current between steps, and the rate of pulsing the transistor with these steps (ranging from once only to a 240-Hz repetition rate) is selected here. For devices where power dissipation is a big problem, a single family display is required. This mode requires a camera to store the family display for analysis. For practical device testing, the repetitive display works best.

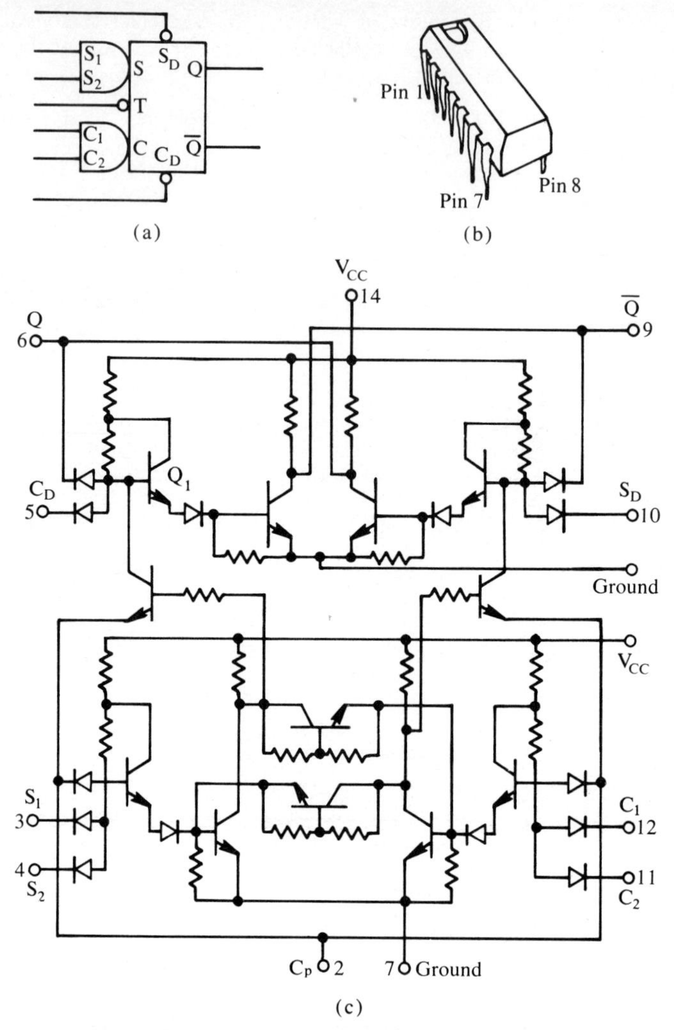

Fig. 21. Diode-transistor logic clocked flip-flop. (*a*) Block diagram. (*b*) Package. (*c*) Schematic.

Synchronous Truth Table

t_n				t_{n+1}
S_1	S_2	C_1	C_2	O
0	x	0	x	O_n
0	x	x	0	O_n
x	0	0	x	O_n
x	0	x	0	O_n
0	x	1	1	0
x	0	1	1	0
1	1	0	x	1
1	1	x	0	1
1	1	1	1	u

The curve tracer is now ready for application of "peak volts." Just as in the tube tester, curves will expand as the knob is rotated (Fig. 9), and each region of interest may be examined in detail. Changes in load line, horizontal or vertical scale, or base are possible while operating to see a localized region better.

In addition to the above standard characteristic curves, many specialized tests may be made on transistor curve tracers, for which the respective operating and instruction manuals should be consulted.

INTEGRATED-CIRCUIT TESTERS

7. Integrated Circuits The most recent active-device components to appear in quantity in electronics hardware are called *integrated circuits* (ICs). These may be combinations of many transistors and diodes on one substrate, or they may include passive elements as well (resistors, capacitors, and occasionally inductors). Commonly, an integrated circuit contains enough components that it performs a total circuit function, such as a gate, an operational amplifier, or a waveshaping filter. Testing and use of integrated circuits is consequently a different problem from that of tubes and transistors. If an integrated-circuit flip-flop (bistable multivibrator) contains, for example, the circuit of Fig. 21, we cannot test for transistor Q_1 since we cannot connect to any of the base, emitter, or collector leads. Moreover, we could not replace that transistor even if we knew it was bad. Thus, we usually test only to see if the total package works, which means testing *circuit function* rather than *device characteristics*.

One useful way to categorize integrated circuits is by application—thus there are *digital* integrated circuits, *linear* (or analog) integrated circuits, and *complex arrays*. Table 2 lists a variety of common circuits included within each category.

TABLE 2 Integrated-circuit Design Applications

Digital	Linear	Complex arrays
Gate (multiple input, AND, OR, NAND, NOR)	Operational amplifier	Stereo preamplifier
Inverter	Rf-if amplifier	Multiplexer
Flip-flop	Video amplifier	Voltage regulator
Counter	Sense amplifier	Read-only memory
Adder	Differential amplifier	Random-access memory
Subtractor	Comparator	Analog-to-digital converter
Expander		Character generator
Translator		
Shift register		

Digital techniques, because they use binary language (1 or 0), are not as concerned with rise time or amplitude as analog techniques; so it has been possible to standardize voltage and power levels to a high degree. This has led to integrated-circuit testers which can readily test for some digital circuit functions, since biasing and operation are essentially common. Testers for analog-function or complex-array circuits are, by contrast, usually restricted to simpler tests because of the diversity of functions that would have to be accommodated.

Two types of common digital integrated-circuit packages are available—*bipolar transistor logic* and *field-effect transistor logic*. The former is offered commercially in four styles from most manufacturers—resistor-transistor logic (RTL), diode-transistor logic (DTL), transistor-transistor logic (TTL), and emitter-coupled logic (ECL). Field-effect logic is most often available as metal-oxide semiconductor (MOS) logic; it is restricted in speed by comparison with bipolar logic, but it offers economy for certain circuit functions such as nonaddressable computer memory. The various standard circuit configurations are shown in Fig. 22; standard power-supply voltages and speed-of-operation capabilities of these integrated-circuit families are summarized in Table 3.

No consistent numbering system exists for integrated circuits; so manufacturer's data sheets must be consulted in every test situation.

8. Integrated-circuit-tester Operation Just as with transistor and tube testers, integrated-circuit testers are classified as *static* or *dynamic* depending upon whether the parameters are tested as part of a dc or ac circuit. Instead of curve tracers

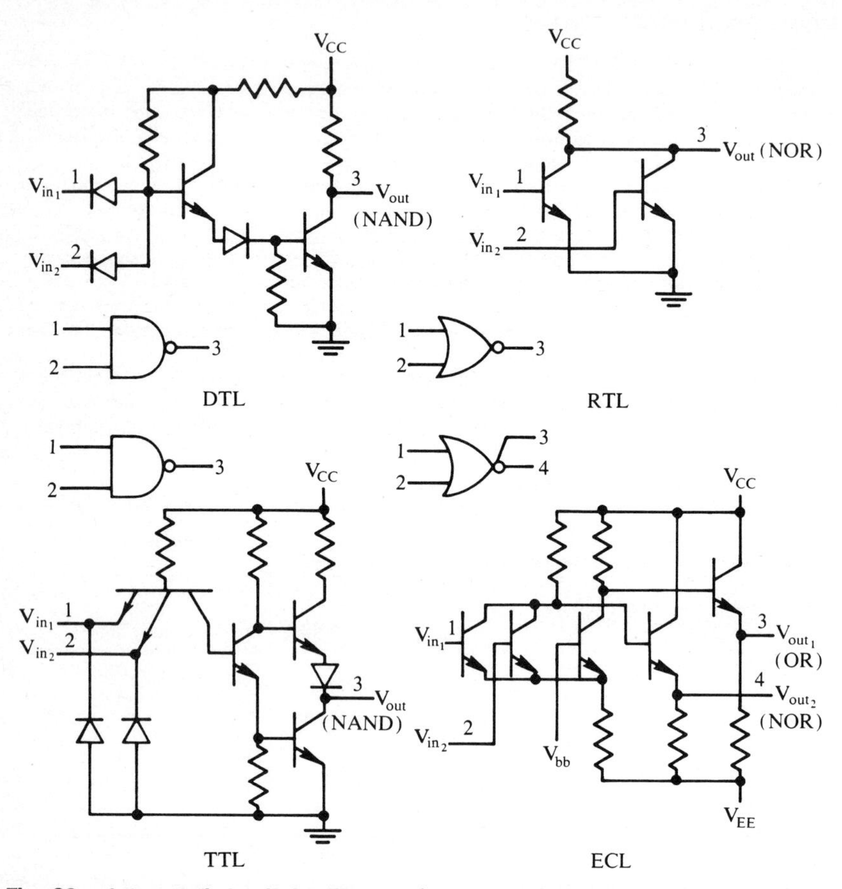

Fig. 22. Integrated-circuit families. Schematics and function blocks of two-input gates.

drawing characteristic curves, however, the sophisticated class of integrated-circuit tester is considered a *functional* tester, as it is able to stimulate the circuit inputs and test for proper dynamic functional response.

Static Testers. Static integrated-circuit testers typically measure the same dc parameters as static transistor testers—open-circuit, short-circuit, and leakage current I_{CBO}. Since integrated circuits, however, have typically 14 to 16 pins in even the simple circuits, such tests are both more valuable and necessary. Usually, static integrated-circuit testers require (1) a program card or knobs to identify the circuit class (such as digital RTL flip-flop), (2) plugging the integrated circuit into a standard 16-pin socket (for 14-pin and 16-pin devices be sure to insert pin 1

TABLE 3 Typical Integrated-circuit Family Characteristics

Integrated-circuit family	Bias voltage	Max toggle (switching) rate	Dual J-K flip-flop power consumption	Logic 1 voltage	Logic 0 voltage
RTL..........	+3.6 V, gnd	1–10 MHz	120 mW	+1.2 V	+0.2 V
DTL..........	+5.0 V, gnd	10–40 MHz	140 mW	+3.5 V	+0.2 V
TTL..........	+5.0 V, gnd	20–50 MHz	100 mW	+3.5 V	+0.2 V
ECL..........	gnd, −5.2 V	50–120 MHz	250–500 mW	−0.75 V	−1.55 V
MOS..........	gnd, −30 V	1 MHz	75 mW	−1 V	−10 V

of the device into pin 1 of the socket), and (3) pressing a "TEST" button. The tester will give a readout, on lights or a meter, of "GO" (which means "good") or "NO GO" (which is "no good").

Dynamic Testers. Dynamic testers include two types of machines—one aimed at digital integrated-circuit testing, another at linear integrated-circuit testing. Some testers may include both capabilities. Most testers in the latter class will be programmed from computer cards for the integrated-circuit type to be tested. This section illustrates a unit with full operator switch control, as it is common in

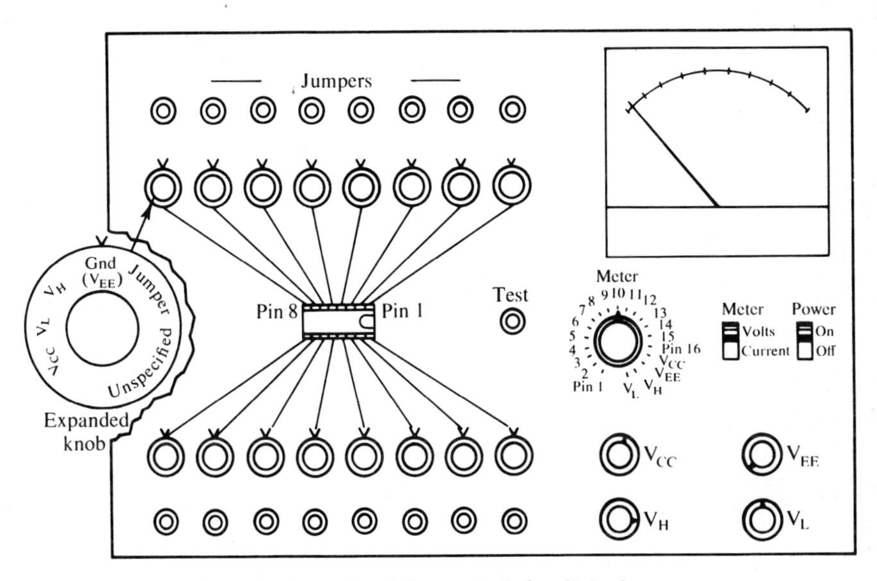

Fig. 23. Digital integrated-circuit tester.

concept and explains generally how the testing is accomplished. Figure 23 shows a simplified panel of a digital dynamic integrated-circuit tester with logic switches for the operator to assign to the various pins of his test integrated-circuit socket.

The first assignment is power biasing: V_{cc} and ground (or V_{ee} for ECL) are assigned to the appropriate socket pins (see Table 4 for digital bipolar pin biasing). V_{cc} is chosen, and all input pins of the device not to be used are connected to ground. Power may now be applied, and total current drain monitored on the meter, for comparison with the manufacturer's specifications.

TABLE 4 Digital Bipolar Pin Biasing

	V_{cc}		Ground or V_{ee}		Switching levels, volts	
Family	Pin	Volts	Pin	Volts	V_{low} = 0 state	V_{high} = 1 state
RTL........	14	3.6	7	0	+0.2	+1.2
DTL........	14	5.0	7	0	+0.2	+3.5
TTL........	14, 4	5.0	7, 10	0	+0.2	+3.5
ECL........	3	0	2	−5.2	−1.55	−0.75

Pin numbers refer to typical styles of dual-in-line or flat-pack integrated circuits.

Next, there are input-voltage selections available to develop desired output functions. On the panel shown, connections may be made to any pin from any voltage. Some testers use patch-cord connections instead of internal switch assignments as shown. In any event, the voltmeter may then be connected to any output pin to monitor the output voltage. Figure 24 shows a digital integrated-circuit flip-flop under test and the several choices of input voltages with the desired output voltages.

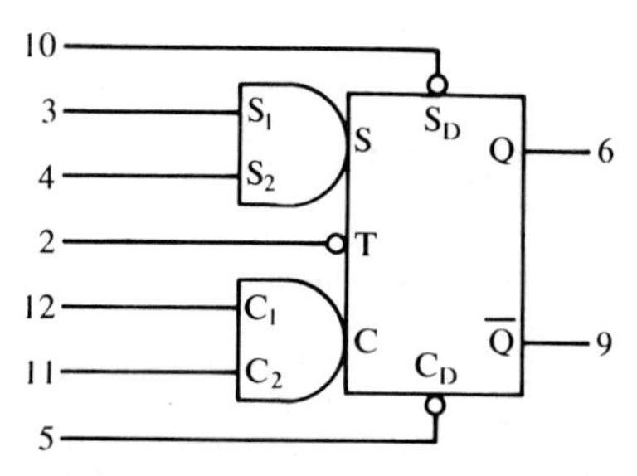

Fig. 24. Voltage-level testing. Digital integrated circuits. Preliminary conditions: V_{cc} (pin 14) = 5.0 V; gnd (pin 7) = 0 V; pins 4,9 connected and pins 6,11 connected to give a JK-flip-flop mode.

Logic voltages	Test 1	Test 2	Test 3	Test 4
Apply to pin 3..	0 (0.2 V)	1 (3.5 V)	0 (0.2 V)	1 (3.5 V)
Apply to pin 12.	0 (0.2 V)	0 (0.2 V)	1 (3.5 V)	1 (3.5 V)
Test for on pin 6	Unchanged when "TEST" button is used	1 (3.5 V)	0 (0.2 V)	Changes state when "TEST" button is hit

A variation on the tester described above would provide a switch to choose the logic family (RTL, DTL, TTL, or ECL), and then logical 1s and 0s are assigned to inputs and monitored at the output terminals. Readouts on such a machine would be lights for 1 and 0 rather than a meter. Linear dynamic testers are sometimes capable of applying a stimulus pulse, and reading both ac gain and an output slew rate ($\Delta V/\Delta t$). Dynamic testers usually give go no-go results as well as values; however, some read only in go no-go form. Some testers test saturation time, switching time, and dynamic voltage output among other parameters, but typically such testers are very special-purpose machines seldom encountered in a service, calibration, or production department.

Functional Testers. Functional testers do essentially the same tests as dynamic testers, with the exception of ac linear-circuit stimulus. Additionally, they are normally automated to a high degree and thus make many tests very rapidly. Moreover, they are simplified in panel appearance (Fig. 25) significantly, in order that special skill in testing parameters is not necessary. Thus, test results are nearly always in go no-go form.

The device designation and specifications are programmed into the tester (often by tape for these relatively expensive testers), and the device is installed in the test socket (sometimes this loading is even done automatically). On a typical tester, pushbutton testing (or even automatic advance) is conducted in quick succession for device orientation, power, function, dynamic noise, and toggle.

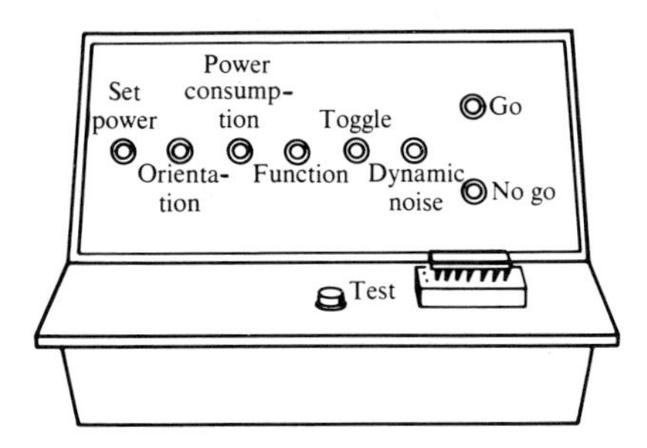

Fig. 25. Integrated-circuit functional tester.

The measurements being made under orientation simply assure that the device has pin 1 oriented with pin 1 of the test socket. The power range is known for any function in any family, and this number is the $|V_{cc} - V_{ee}| \times I_{\text{total}}$ reading of the dynamic tester. The function test is simply a check of whether an AND gate really gives a signal output for only the case of all inputs being positive (or any other function under test) without regard to speed. Thus the test is analogous to setting the switches on the dynamic machine for functional test. The toggle test is the same functional test conducted with ac signal inputs, checking for the fastest frequency at which the time-varying outputs occur in proper order. Dynamic noise tests are ac noise signals injected to ascertain whether noise immunity of the device meets specifications. This means that the device function will not change in the presence of switching noise.

Note that any or all of these tests could be found on a dynamic tester as defined above. There are no solid definitions of what a given tester will be called, and different manufacturers label their equipment variously. The most consistent definition between functional and dynamic testers relates to the readout and the required setup skill for the operator rather than the measurements made.

Chapter 27

Impedance Measurement Instruments

HENRY P. HALL

General Radio Company, Concord, Massachusetts

INTRODUCTION

Impedance is the basic passive electrical quantity, the only inherent electrical property of all materials or components. While it is defined as the ratio of two active, variable quantities, voltage and current, it is more fundamental in that its unit can be more accurately determined and more easily maintained.

To measure impedance, one must apply and measure voltage and current, for indicating instruments require some finite power to produce a finite deflection or reading. There are a variety of ways to do this; the simplest, most basic, and most useful methods are described in this chapter. The choice of measurement method depends on many factors: accuracy, speed, cost, form of result required, test conditions, and equipment available. The following discussion should help in making this choice.

This discussion also should help in understanding the principles of the instruments described and in their use. However, a more detailed description of the basic principles can be found in any of the general references, and the operating instructions for specific instruments should be consulted, particularly in case of difficulty.

1. Basic Definitions When a voltage is applied between two points on a "material," current will flow. How much will flow depends on the *resistance* of the material. A high resistance limits the flow of current just as high friction hinders the motion of an object.

The mathematical definition of resistance R is the ratio of voltage E to current I. This is Ohm's law:

$$R = \frac{E}{I} \tag{1}$$

The energy dissipated in the resistor is I^2R, which is also equal to the product EI or E^2/R from the relationship of Ohm's law.

Another measure of how easily material will pass a current is *conductance* G. This is the reciprocal of resistance, $G = 1/R = I/E$, so that a high conductance might be thought of as "electrical slipperiness" for a high slipperiness means a low friction and vice versa.

Mechanical motion can be impeded by other things besides friction. For example, it takes force to extend a spring or lift a weight. The energy used to extend a spring or lift a weight is not lost, for once the force is removed or reversed in direction, the energy stored in these devices is returned. The electrical analogs to these mechanical energy-storage devices are capacitance C and inductance L. In order for these storage devices to return their energy, the applied voltage or current must change.

An alternating or ac voltage is one that regularly reverses its direction or *polarity*. If an ac voltage is applied to a circuit containing only resistance, the alternating current that flows is still determined by the circuit resistance ($I = E/R$ from Ohm's law). However, if capacitance or inductance are present, they also affect the flow of current. Therefore, Ohm's law must be modified by substituting *impedance* Z for resistance so that

$$Z = \frac{E}{I} \tag{2}$$

Impedance includes the effects of capacitance and inductance as well as resistance.

In a mechanical system with only friction present, the motion will stop when the force stops. However, if a spring or mass is present, there will be motion when the force is removed. Thus the force and the resulting motion are out of step or out of phase. Likewise if a voltage is applied to a network containing capacitance or inductance, the resulting current will be out of phase with the voltage. If the voltage has a sinusoidal waveshape (Fig. 1), the current will be sinusoidal also (if the impedance is linear) but will be ahead (lead) or behind (lag) the voltage. The phase angle between them in degrees is the time difference between corresponding points divided by the time *period* ($1/f$, see Fig. 1) multiplied by 360°.

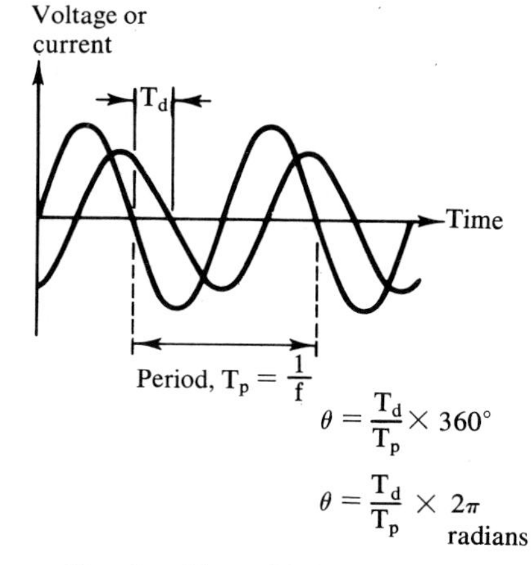

Fig. 1. Sinusoidal waveforms.

A sinusoidal or sine wave can be generated by taking the projection of a line or *vector* which is rotating at an angular rate of $2\pi f = \omega$ radian per second (Fig. 2, 1 radian $= 360/2\pi$ degrees). At any time t the angle rotated is ωt radians,

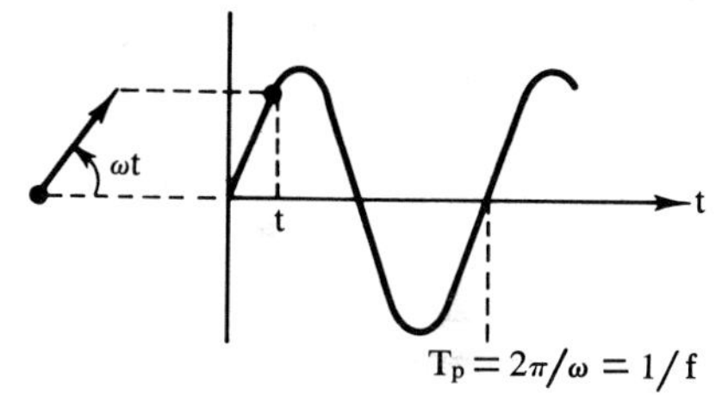

Fig. 2. Vector generation of a sinusoidal wave.

and at that time the magnitude of the sine wave is sine (ωt) multiplied by the length of the vector. The two signals of Fig. 1 could be generated by two vectors rotating on the same axis but with different lengths and separated by a constant angle θ. The relationships between the vectors can be diagramed with either one shown with zero phase angle, even though they are both rotating in time. These are shown in Fig. 3, with the current assumed to be real (i.e., in the horizontal direction).

The voltage vector in Fig. 3*a* leads the current vector by an angle θ. From the ac version of Ohm's law [Eq. (2)], this voltage E is equal to IZ. This vector can be broken up into two components, or separate vectors, one in phase with the current IR and one at 90° to the current IjX. (Here j is $\sqrt{-1}$ and indicates vectors at right angles to the reference.) The voltage IZ is the sum of the two vectors $IZ = IR + IjX$. By dividing both sides of this equation by I, we get $Z = R + jX$, which is diagramed in Fig. 3*b*. A quantity in this form is called a *complex* number. The first term is called the real part, the second, with the j factor, the imaginary part. The real part of an impedance R is the *ac resistance,* and the imaginary part X is the *reactance.*

The length of the impedance vector Z is called the *magnitude,* written $|Z|$. From the Pythagorean theorem, $|Z| = \sqrt{R^2 + X^2}$. The tangent of the angle is X/R, and is called the Q (quality or storage factor) of the impedance. A high-Q component has low energy loss. The cotangent of θ is R/X and is called the dissipation factor D. Note $D = 1/Q$.

For an inductance $X = \omega L = 2\pi f L$ and $Q = \omega L/R$. Note that the voltage vector will lead the current vector for an inductor. A capacitance has a negative reactance $X = -1/\omega C$, giving a lagging voltage. D is used as a measure of the phase angle of capacitors where $D = \omega RC$.

The relationship between the voltage and current vectors can also be drawn using the voltage as the reference (or real) vector as in Fig. 4. Here the current is equal to E/Z or EY, where Y is *admittance* ($Y = 1/Z$) and is also a complex quantity. The current EY can be divided into two components: $EY = EG + jEB$. Removing the voltage from this equation gives a vector diagram of the admittance (Fig. 4*b*). Here G is the *ac conductance* and B the *susceptance*. From the diagram, the magnitude of admittance is $|Y| = \sqrt{G^2 + B^2}$. It is important to note that the complex quantities Z and Y are reciprocals and the magnitudes $|Z|$ and

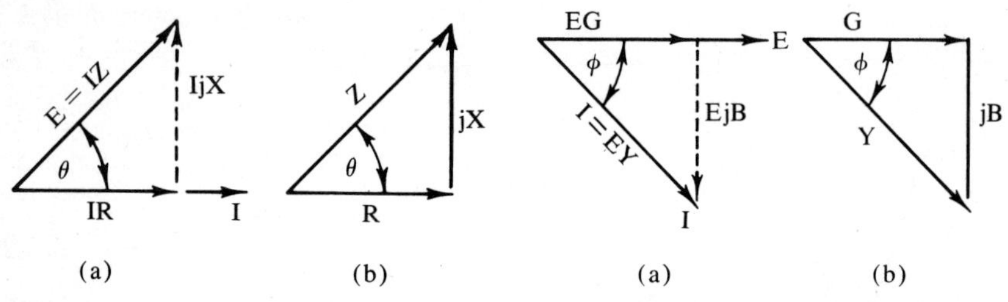

Fig. 3. Voltage and impedance vector diagrams.

Fig. 4. Current and admittance vector diagrams.

$|Y|$ are reciprocals, but R is not equal to $1/G$ (unless $B = 0$) and X is not equal to $1/B$ (unless $G = 0$).

$$Z = R + jX = \frac{1}{Y} = \frac{1}{G + jB} = \frac{G - jB}{G^2 + B^2} \tag{3}$$

$$|Z| = \sqrt{R^2 + X^2} = \frac{1}{|Y|} = \frac{1}{\sqrt{G^2 + B^2}} \tag{4}$$

Also note that the angle between the vectors is the same ($\phi = -\theta$, see Table 1).

Vectors may also be expressed in polar form, as for example, $Z = |Z|e^{j\theta}$. The relationships between the polar and cartesian forms are given in Table 1.

TABLE 1 Symbols, Units, and Formulas

Quantity	Unit	Formulas
R Resistance	ohm, Ω	$R_{dc} = \dfrac{E}{I}$; $R_{ac} = \lvert Z\rvert \cos\theta$
G Conductance	mho, ℧*	$G_{dc} = \dfrac{I}{E}$; $G_{ac} = \lvert Y\rvert \cos\phi$

TABLE 1 Symbols, Units, and Formulas (Continued)

	Quantity	Unit	Formulas
C	Capacitance	farad, F	$C = \dfrac{1}{\omega X}$
L	Inductance	henry, H	$L = \dfrac{X}{\omega}$
X	Reactance	ohm, Ω	$X = \omega L = \dfrac{1}{\omega C} = \lvert Z\rvert \sin \theta$
B	Susceptance	mho, ℧*	$B = \omega C = \dfrac{1}{\omega L} = \lvert Y\rvert \sin \phi$
Z	Complex impedance	ohm, Ω	$Z = \dfrac{E}{I} = R + jX = \lvert Z\rvert e^{j\theta}$
$\lvert Z\rvert$	Impedance magnitude	ohm, Ω	$\lvert Z\rvert = \sqrt{R^2 + X^2} = \dfrac{\lvert E\rvert}{\lvert I\rvert}$
Y	Complex admittance	mho, ℧*	$Y = \dfrac{I}{E} = G + jB = \lvert Y\rvert e^{j\phi}$
$\lvert Y\rvert$	Admittance magnitude	mho, ℧*	$\lvert Y\rvert = \sqrt{G^2 + B^2} = \dfrac{\lvert I\rvert}{\lvert E\rvert} = \dfrac{1}{\lvert Z\rvert}$
θ	Impedance phase angle	radian	$\theta = \tan^{-1} \dfrac{X}{R} = -\phi$
ϕ	Admittance phase angle	radian	$\phi = \tan^{-1} \dfrac{B}{G} = -\theta$
t	Time	second, s	
f	Frequency	hertz, Hz†	$f = 1/\text{period}$
ω	Angular frequency	radian/s	$\omega = 2\pi f$
D	Dissipation factor		$D = \dfrac{R}{X} = \dfrac{G}{B} = \dfrac{1}{Q} = \cot \phi$
Q	Quality or storage factor		$Q = \dfrac{X}{R} = \dfrac{1}{D} = \tan \theta$
PF	Power factor		$\text{PF} = \dfrac{R}{\lvert Z\rvert} = \dfrac{D}{\sqrt{1 + D^2}} = \cos \theta$

Prefixes

a	atto	10^{-18}	m	milli	10^{-3}
f	femto	10^{-15}	k	kilo	10^{3}
p	pico	10^{-12}	M	mega	10^{6}
n	nano	10^{-9}	G	giga	10^{9}
μ	micro	10^{-6}	T	tera	10^{12}

Example: 1 μF (microfarad) = 10^{-6} F = 10^{6} pF = 10^{3} nF.

* or siemens, S.
† or cycles per second, cps, or c.

If an impedance is *linear,* it has a constant value independent of the voltage or current applied. While most components are linear over a wide range, all become nonlinear when their power or voltage ratings are widely exceeded. For these components, measurements at various levels, all well below ratings, will give satisfactory agreement. However, some components, such as diodes, thermistors, iron-cored inductors, and some ceramic and electrolytic capacitors, are nonlinear in various degrees. For these components, good agreement between measurements can be obtained only if equal signal levels are used. Nonlinear components will also change in ac value if a dc voltage or current bias is applied, and this must be specified if the measurements are to be meaningful.

2. Basic Types of Impedance Measurement Impedance measurements are made on various devices for a variety of reasons. The devices measured fall into five general categories.

Component Measurements. Separate resistors, capacitors, and inductors are measured by the manufacturers of these devices and by users who want to ensure that the components received are of proper value. They are also measured in engineering laboratories to determine their value and to see how this value changes under different environmental and electrical conditions.

Production and inspection tests must be fast and inexpensive. Generally the deviation from the true value is checked to be within prescribed tolerances on a "go no-go" basis so that the actual value is never read or recorded. However, high-reliability components are measured many times, with careful records made of their values to determine components that change. Engineering measurements are of greater variety. For example, a designer of electronic equipment often must know the value of a component at high frequencies or under certain voltage or load conditions. Generally this measurement device is more flexible but slower. Often he will require several instruments to get the information he needs.

Usually components are specified as to value, and for inductors and capacitors some measure of their phase angle Q or D. Resistors are usually measured at dc, but in most cases an ac measurement will do just as well and also give phase-angle information, which is sometimes important. Small capacitors, below 1,000 pF, are often measured at 1 MHz because of industry and military standards. Larger values, to 1 μF, are measured at 1 kHz and even larger values at 120 Hz for the same reason. While D is usually specified, for very large values the equivalent series resistance is sometimes used (see Sec. 16).

Inductors change more with frequency and test conditions. Small "air-cored" inductors are often measured at specified test frequencies in the rf range or at some frequency well below their resonant frequency. The inductance of iron-cored chokes and transformers must be measured at specified signal levels because they are nonlinear; i.e., their value changes with level.

For almost all components, the effective series values are used (see Sec. 16). Parallel values are used for some high-frequency measurements and sometimes for measurements on iron-cored chokes and transformers.

Network Measurements. Impedance measurements on electronic networks, both passive and active, are made in great variety. The input and output impedance of passive filters and packaged networks is often specified and may vary widely with frequency. These data may be presented as plots of the real and imaginary parts of impedance or admittance or plots of magnitude and phase. Active networks and integrated circuits have input and output impedance specifications which generally must be made under specific test conditions.

The definitions of impedance and admittances can be extended to include the ratio of voltage at one pair of terminals to current at another or vice versa. These quantities are called *transfer* impedances or admittances. Examples are the transconductance of vacuum tubes and the transfer z and y parameters often used for transistors and passive networks. If these measurements are to be independent of input and output impedances, they are made by applying a low-impedance voltage source or high-impedance current source and measuring the resulting short-circuit current or open-circuit voltage, respectively (see Fig. 5).

Often it is desirable to measure the impedance of a component while it is connected in a circuit, or "in situ." This presents two problems. First the measuring device must not damage other components; transistors are particularly susceptible. Second, to get an accurate measurement, the effects of the rest of the circuit must be removed. In situ measurements may be made accurately by connecting points in all other conducting paths shunting the unknown together to form a common terminal (see Fig. 6). If a voltage source is connected from this common point to one side of the component under test and the short-circuit current from the other end of the component to the common point is measured, their ratio E/I is the impedance of the component.

Precision Measurements. To ensure that the impedance-measuring devices used to measure electrical components are as accurate as they should be, it is necessary that they be checked by measuring standards of impedance of even higher accuracy. Likewise these standards must be checked by even more accurate measuring instruments which, in turn, are checked by even more accurate standards. In the United States, the eventual end of this chain is the National Bureau of Standards, which gives calibrations with tolerances of as little as 1 ppm (0.0001 percent) for certain resistors (1 Ω and 10 kΩ) and 5 ppm for certain capacitors. In order to keep this chain of measurements operating properly, a large number of measurements are made at various levels of accuracy. The phrase "traceability to NBS" is used by the military to describe a procedure in which documented proof is available to show that all measurements in this chain have been properly and periodically made (see Chapters 2 and 3).

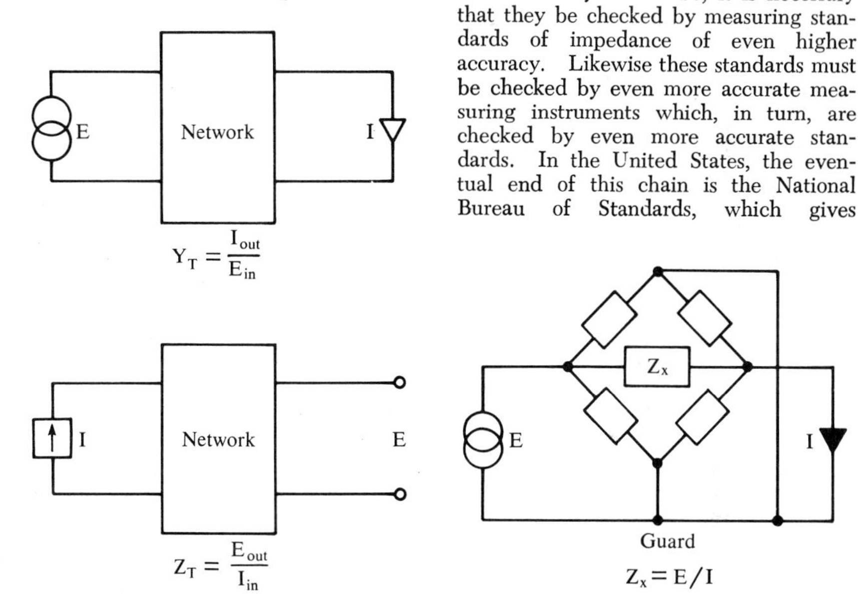

Fig. 5. Transfer admittance and impedance.

Fig. 6. Measurement of an impedance in a network.

Generally these precision measurements are made on impedance bridges similar in principle to those described later in this chapter but of more sophisticated design. Several techniques are widely used in precision measurements but can be very useful even for lower accuracy.

Direct Substitution. To compare two impedances of nearly equal value most accurately, first one is measured on a high-resolution bridge and then the other. If only the last digits of the bridge are readjusted between the two measurements, the measured difference is independent of the actual accuracy of the bridge. The bridge need only have adequate stability for the time it takes to make the two measurements.

Four-terminal Measurements. If a relatively low-valued resistor is measured, the connecting leads and actual contacts will make a significant error. Moreover the leads or terminals of the resistor may have sufficient resistance so that the position of the connection to them may make a difference. For these reasons, low impedances are often measured with four leads, and low-impedance standards are constructed with four terminals (see Fig. 7). Some technique is used (such as a Kelvin bridge, Sec. 14) that makes this four-terminal measurement with adequate immunity to the impedance of the leads. In principle, this is done by applying

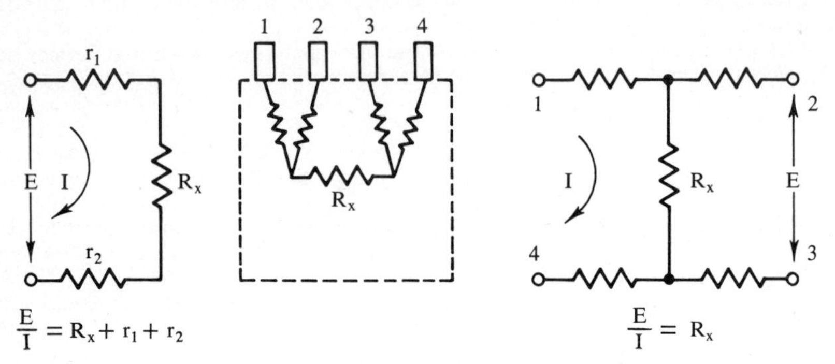

Fig. 7. Two-terminal and four-terminal resistors.

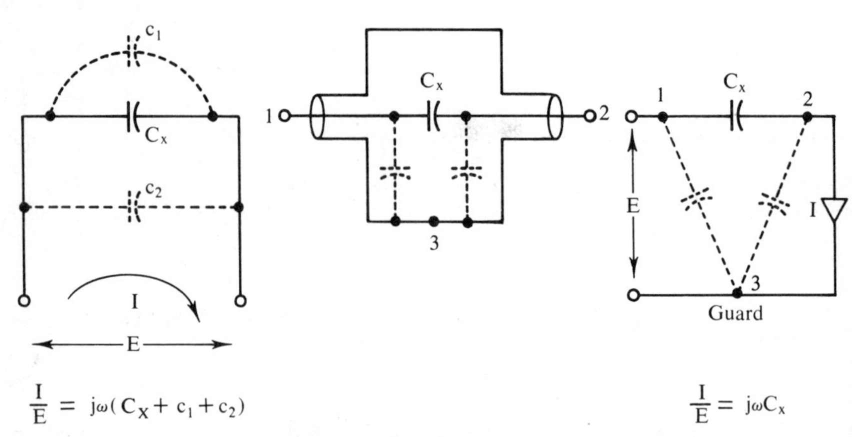

Fig. 8. Two-terminal and three-terminal capacitors.

the current to one pair of leads and measuring the voltage at the other (see Fig. 7), which is actually a *transfer* impedance measurement (see above).

Three-terminal Measurements. When measuring a high-valued impedance, such as a small capacitance, capacitance or conductance between the two connecting leads causes a large error. For this reason, shielded leads are used to make a "guarded" measurement (Fig. 8). In principle, this measurement is a transfer admittance measurement (see above). It is most easily made by transformer-ratio-arm bridges which are little affected by capacitance to the shield or "third terminal" (see Sec. 23).

Transducer Measurements. Many nonelectrical physical quantities are measured by means of suitable transducers which convert them into impedance changes. Some quantities measured this way are mechanical strain, liquid level, pressure, temperature, relative humidity, length, and angular position. Impedance measurements are used because of their accuracy. The overall accuracy is usually limited by the transducer calibration and stability, and because electrical measurements may be made at some distance from the device being measured. Three-terminal and four-terminal techniques allow high accuracy even at several hundred feet. This is particularly important when the device under test must be in an extreme environment or is otherwise inaccessible.

Impedance measurements are used to specify a variety of electromechanical devices such as motors, loudspeakers, and solenoid switches. The designer of a system using these devices, such as a servomotor control system, must know their electrical characteristics in order to obtain optimum performance.

Measurements on Materials. Extensive research is carried out on the electrical and magnetic behavior of materials. Reference books are filled with data on a tremendous variety of compounds, and materials manufacturers usually give extensive specifications. The rapid growth of semiconductor technology and synthetic insulating materials has increased the importance of these measurements in the last few years. While many other measurements are made, the three most common are the measurement of resistivity or conductivity of sheet materials and solutions, dielectric constant K and loss D measurements on both solid and liquid insulating materials, and permeability μ and loss of magnetic materials.

The main problem of resistivity or conductivity measurements on solid materials is to convert the measured resistance to resistivity with good accuracy. This conversion depends on the dimensions and geometry of the electrode structure. Standard, guarded electrode structures are used for both volume and surface resistivity.[1] The four-point-probe[2] method is an adaptation of the four-terminal measurement principle used to avoid errors due to contact resistance and high current density at the contact point. The resistivity of insulating materials is referred to as *insulation resistance* and can be extremely high. It is usually measured at relatively high dc voltages (see Sec. 8).

Liquids are measured using appropriate electrode structures.[3] For electrolytic solutions, there is danger of error due to chemical decomposition at the electrodes. For this reason, a low-frequency ac test signal is often used. One method[4] avoids any electrodes whatsoever by having the liquid form a loop which couples two toroidal transformers effectively, making one turn on each. A transformer ratio-arm bridge is formed by connecting a known and variable impedance between windings on the two cores in such a manner as to balance the flux induced by the current in the solution.

Dielectric properties are measured by forming a capacitor of known dimensions with an appropriate test fixture.[5] The dielectric constant K is the ratio of the capacitance with the material in place to the capacitance of the same structure with dry air as the dielectric. Again, the dimensions and geometry must be accurately known, and guarded sample holders are usually used. Several modern synthetic materials have extremely low loss and require precise bridges to measure their low dissipation factors. Dielectric properties are often specified from below power frequencies up through the microwave range.

Many measurements are required on magnetic materials to give adequate design data because of their nonlinearity and frequency dependence.[6] Accurate loss measurements are particularly important for the materials to be used in power equipment to ensure their efficiency. These measurements are made with both wattmeter methods and special inductance bridges. Magnetic cores for rf use usually are studied from Q-meter measurements on coils wound on them.

3. Basic Types of Impedance-measuring Instruments Impedance-measuring instruments are usually classified as either meter-type or null-type devices, although there are many instruments which are combinations of these two basic techniques. Basically, a meter-type device is one which measures voltages and currents from which impedance is determined. A null device compares the unknown impedance against a known adjustable impedance in a network having a known relationship between its elements when it is adjusted to give zero output signal. Meter methods are generally faster because they require no balance but are less accurate because they depend on meter calibrations.

The basic meter circuit is that of the ammeter-voltmeter method in which the current and voltage are measured separately (Fig. 9). Both dc and ac measurements can be made with appropriate meters. For ac, the quantity measured is the impedance magnitude. Adding a wattmeter to the circuit gives additional information from which phase angle or resistance and reactance can be calculated.

There are three drawbacks to this method. First, there is a small error from either the ammeter impedance (Fig. 9*a*) or the voltmeter impedance (Fig. 9*b*) because they are not zero or infinite, respectively. The difficulty can usually be

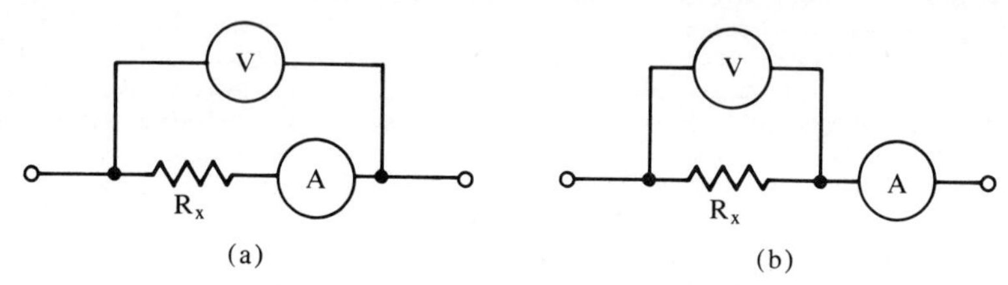

Fig. 9. Ammeter-voltmeter methods.

overcome by the use of electronic meters. Second, a calculation is required which is inconvenient. Several instruments supply a constant current or a constant voltage so that the meter can be calibrated directly in impedance or admittance. The third drawback is the meter accuracy and the difficulty in reading the meter accurately. Digital meters have greatly improved this shortcoming.

Better accuracy may be obtained by placing a known impedance of comparable value in series with the unknown (Fig. 10) and measuring the voltage across

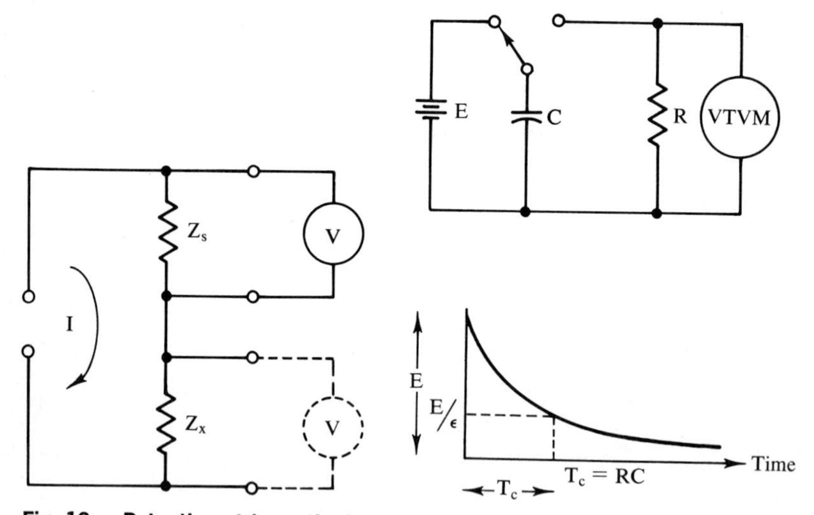

Fig. 10. Potentiometric method. **Fig. 11. Time-constant measurement.**

this standard and the unknown component with the same meter. If the two meter readings are nearly the same, the meter-calibration errors are largely avoided. This method is very useful at all frequencies and particularly good for low impedances, for if the voltmeter impedance is high, the connecting leads have little effect (see four-terminal measurements above).

Either resistance or reactance may be measured by combining one of each and measuring the resulting time constant. For example, in Fig. 11, the time taken for the voltage to drop to 0.368 of its initial value after the switch is thrown is the time constant of the network *RC*, from which either quantity may be calculated if the other is known. Often periodic pulse is applied and an oscilloscope is used as a detector, forming various pulse-technique impedance-measuring devices. These transient methods became less accurate if either component has an appreciable phase angle or has a frequency-dependent value.

Meters are combined with *LC* resonant circuits both to indicate the condition of resonance and to measure the amount of resonant rise, as in a *Q* meter (see Sec. 19). While the *Q* measurement is made on the meter, the inductance is obtained by the known relationship between *LC* and frequency at the resonant condition. In this respect, resonant-circuit measurements are similar to null measurements because they depend on component relationships at some repeatable circuit condition.

The most common null-type impedance-measuring circuit is the bridge network of Fig. 12. This can be considered as two voltage dividers with a common input and a sensitive indicating amplifier, or *null detector,* connected between their outputs. If one impedance is adjusted until there is no output signal, the voltage-division ratio of the two dividers is equal:

$$\frac{Z_2}{Z_1 + Z_2} = \frac{Z_4}{Z_3 + Z_4} \qquad (5)$$

from which one can get

$$Z_3 Z_2 = Z_1 Z_4 \qquad \text{or} \qquad Z_1 = \frac{Z_2 Z_3}{Z_4} \qquad (6)$$

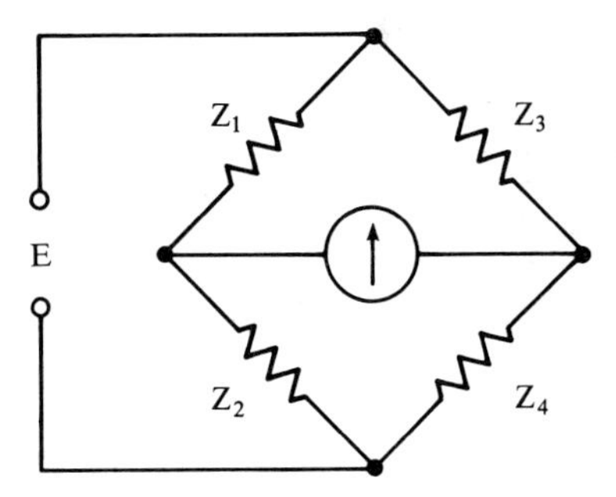

Fig. 12. Basic bridge circuit.

so that if three impedances are known, the fourth can be accurately determined. (Note that this circuit has a resistor in series with the unknown, which can be thought of as measuring current, and a voltage divider in parallel with it, which can be thought of as measuring voltage, thus relating it back to the ammeter-voltmeter method.) The dc version of this bridge used for resistance measurements is called the Wheatstone bridge (see Sec. 10). A variety of ac bridges are used for measuring ac impedances and reactive components. Two adjustments are necessary in an ac bridge to balance both real and imaginary parts of a complex unknown. The most common commercial instruments of this type are general-purpose impedance and "universal" bridges that combine several bridge circuits to measure *R*, *C*, and *L* (see Sec. 21).

Since it compares the unknown with stable known impedances, instead of relying on meter calibrations, the bridge has the inherent advantage that the null condition is independent of the detector gain or input-signal level (if all bridge components are linear). Moreover, the null condition can be determined extremely closely, limited only by detector gain and noise. Repeatable measurements to 1 part in 10^8 are not uncommon in precision-measurement systems.

Many other networks that will give a null output have been used for impedance measurements, including T networks which have one terminal common to input and output circuits, which simplifies grounding.[7] Generally these networks are frequency-dependent and therefore less attractive for commercial impedance-measuring instruments.

Commercial bridges are available that make the bridge balance automatically using servosystems with digitally switched bridge components to obtain balance.[8] These can make measurements very rapidly for production and inspection and also give output data in digital form for record or further processing.

Another way bridges are used to make rapid measurements is not to balance them at all but to use the unbalance voltage on a measure of deviation from the nominal value (see Secs. 15 and 24). While these could be classified as deviation meters, the accuracy of the meter is not important to overall accuracy if the deviation is small.

4. Instruments and Specifications There is a tremendous variety of impedance-measuring instruments designed for a wide variety of measurement jobs. Table 2 lists the more common types with typical specifications. There are many more special types for particular applications.

TABLE 2 Impedance-measuring Instruments

Instrument	Typical range	Typical accuracy	Uses and comments
Resistance:			
Ohmmeter	1 Ω–1 MΩ	5–20 %	Quick circuit checks, continuity
Milliohmmeter	0.1 μΩ–1 kΩ	2–5 %	Wire and switch measurements
Megohmmeter	10 kΩ–100 TΩ	3–10 %	Insulation resistance
Digital ohmmeter	0.01 Ω–10 MΩ	0.01–1 %	Rapid measurements, digital output data
Wheatstone bridge	0.1 Ω–10 MΩ	0.01–1 %	Many types, wide price range
Kelvin bridge	0.1 μΩ–100 Ω	0.01–1 %	Four-terminal measurements
Megohm bridge	10 kΩ–1,000 TΩ	0.1–1 %	Guarded, 3-terminal measurements of high resistance
Ratio set	1 μΩ–1 MΩ	0.2–10 ppm	Comparing resistance standards
Comparator	0.1 Ω–100 MΩ	0.01–0.1 %	Production sorting
Capacitance:			
Capacitance meter (1 MHz)	0.01–1,000 pF	0.5–1 %	Rapid measurements
Universal bridge (1 kHz)	0.1 pF–1,000 μF	0.1–1 %	General-purpose, wide range
120-Hz capacitance bridge	10 pF–1 F	1 %	Testing electrolytic capacitors
1-MHz capacitance bridge	0.01 pF–1,000 pF	0.1–1 %	Testing small capacitors
Precision capacitance bridge	10 af–10 μF	0.01 %	Comparisons to 1 ppm
Automatic capacitance bridge	0.01 pF–1,000 μF	0.1 %	Rapid production measurements
Inductance:			
Inductance meter (1 MHz)	0.01 μH–mH	0.5–1 %	Rapid measurements
Q meter	0.1 μH–100 mH	3–5 %	High-Q accuracy, rf
Universal bridge (1 kHz)	1 μH–1,000 H	0.1–1 %	General-purpose
Precision L bridge	1 nH–1,000 H	0.1 %	Low-frequency comparisons to 1 ppm
Complex impedance:			
Impedance meter	1 Ω–10 MΩ	3–6 %	Reads magnitude and phase 5 to 500 kHz
Impedance comparator	1 Ω–1 MΩ	0.01–0.1 %	Magnitude and phase difference
Vhf bridges	1–5,000 Ω	1–3 %	Many different types
Uhf admittance bridge	0.1–1,000 m℧	2–5 %	50-Ω coaxial system

Most instruments are cataloged with much more complete specifications than are shown. In most cases, these specifications are guaranteed by the manufacturer for a reasonable period of time. Therefore, the specifications indicate the poorest behavior to be expected from a fairly new instrument. It is understandable that manufacturers want their instrument specifications to look good. When comparing specifications, all the "fine print" should therefore be studied. Manufacturers also want their specifications simple for ease of use. Unfortunately some instruments, particularly ac bridges, have inherent sources of error which are reflected in complicated error terms which should be included in the specifications if their behavior is to be accurately described. A few general comments about various specifications may be helpful.

Range. Usually the range given is the complete range and not the range over which the basic accuracy applies. For example, a resistance bridge may have a specified range of 1 mΩ to 1 MΩ and a specified accuracy of 1 percent. However, this does not necessarily mean that 1 mΩ can be measured to 1 percent. More likely 1 mΩ is the smallest division or last digit in the lowest range so that 1 percent accuracy can be achieved only down to 100 mΩ. If the resolution or the number of ranges is given, it is usually possible to interpret the specifications properly.

Accuracy. Accuracy of a measurement is its closeness to the true value.* Usually accuracy is given as a percent, although for precision measurements it is often given in parts per million (1 ppm = 0.0001 percent). The term "limit of error" is coming into use as being more correct, for it is argued that an instrument with an error of 1 percent is really 99 percent accurate. This phrase also indicates that it is the *limit* of the error and not the typical error.

Accuracy, or limit of error, is given either as a percent of reading or as a percent of full scale or as a combination of both. It must be remembered that 1 percent of full scale is 10 percent of the reading at one-tenth of full scale. The accuracy of digital instruments is usually specified as a percent plus a number of counts. The latter can be converted into a percent of full scale.

The accuracy of deviation measurements has caused some confusion, because it is often given as a percent of a percent. For example, if the *difference* between two impedances, a standard and an unknown, is measured with 3 percent accuracy, but that difference is only 1 percent of their value, the accuracy in determining the impedance of the unknown is $0.03 \times 0.01 = 0.0003 = 0.03$ percent plus the accuracy of the standard.

Precision. Precision is the repeatability of a measurement.* Generally, an instrument is more precise than accurate. Precision depends on resolution, which is the fineness or "readability" of the adjustment or indication; on sensitivity, which is the ability to see the effect of a small change; and on stability with time and environmental changes.

DC RESISTANCE MEASUREMENTS

Because resistance is defined as the ratio of voltage to current by Ohm's law (see Sec. 1), an obvious way to measure it is to measure the voltage across it and the current through it and calculate the resistance. This ammeter-voltmeter method (see Fig. 9) is often used in the laboratory but is rarely incorporated in resistance-measuring instruments because of the required calculations. However, this method is the basis for all meter-type instruments, and even bridge-type instruments can be thought of as using this principle (see Sec. 3).

5. The Ohmmeter If the current through a resistor is held at some constant value, the voltage across it is proportional to the resistance, and a voltmeter indicating this voltage may be calibrated in resistance. Alternatively, if the voltage applied to a resistor is held constant, the current through it is proportional to conductance, the reciprocal of resistance: $G = 1/R = I/E$. The scale of the ammeter indicating this current could be calibrated in conductance. It could also be calibrated in terms of resistance, even though the scale would be nonlinear and would go to infinity when the current was zero (see Fig. 16). A battery will give a rather constant voltage, so that the simplest ohmmeter consists of a battery and an ammeter.

Basic Ohmmeter Circuit. The basic ohmmeter circuit is shown in Fig. 13. Here R_x is the resistor to be measured (the "unknown"), R_s is a meter shunt used to change range, R_z is the zeroing adjustment, and R_m is the resistance of the indicating meter. If R_z is adjusted to give a meter current I_{max} that will produce a full-scale

* These are simple definitions. Many more sophisticated definitions have been proposed. See Chapter 4.

deflection when R_x is shorted, then, when R_x is inserted, the meter current will be

$$I = I_{\max} \frac{1}{1 + (I_{\max}/ER_s)R_x(R_s + R_m)} \tag{7}$$

The meter scale will extend from a reading of zero when $R_x = 0$ and $I = I_{\max}$ to a reading of ∞ when $R_x = \infty$ and $I = 0$ (see Fig. 14).

While any value of E, R_s, and R_m will give an on-scale indication for any value of R_x, it is very difficult to read the scale accurately at either end. Therefore, ohmmeters have several ranges which multiply the readings by 10, 100, 1,000, etc. In the simple circuit above, R_s can be selected with a switch to provide this multiplier. In most actual commercial ohmmeters the switching is usually more complicated, with resistors both in series and in shunt with the meter being switched together. In some cases, the voltage E is increased to give adequate sensitivity for high-resistance ranges.

6. Use of the Ohmmeter The use of the ohmmeter is very simple. First set the resistance multiplier to that nearest the expected value of the resistance to be measured. Next clip or touch the test leads together and set the "zero" or "ohm adj" control for a meter reading of zero. Then connect the leads to either

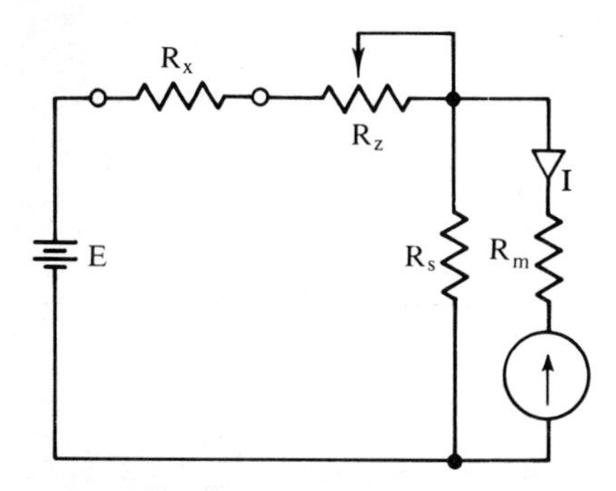

Fig. 13. Basic ohmmeter circuit.

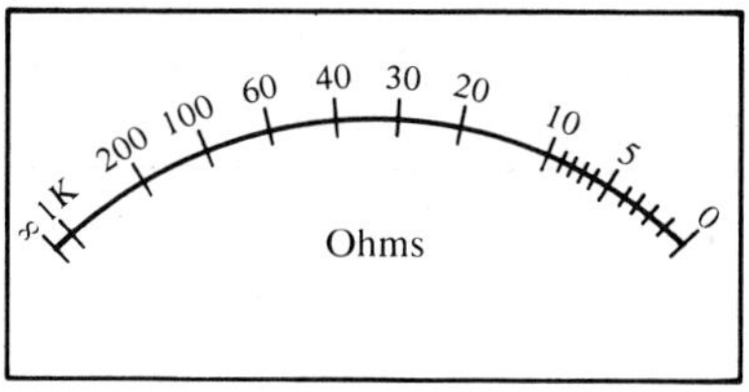

Fig. 14. Ohmmeter scale.

end of the resistor under test, and read the meter indication and multiply it by the range multiplier used. For best accuracy, the meter reading should be in the middle portion of the scale. If it is necessary to change the multiplier scale to avoid readings at either end, it is preferable to recheck the zero setting.

In use, it is important to remember that the ohmmeter measures the net resistance between the probes. Therefore, if the resistor to be measured is connected in a circuit, the ohmmeter will indicate the parallel combination of the resistor and all other dc conducting paths shunting it. Parallel paths blocked by a low-leakage capacitor will not affect the steady-state reading but will cause meter transient. Note that on the highest ranges, touching both probe tips with your hands will produce an error because of the shunting resistance of the human body.

Remember also that the ohmmeter supplies a dc voltage and the polarity of this voltage differs on different instruments. Therefore, some care should be used in making measurements on semiconductors or circuits containing them, particularly when using the highest ranges, which may apply voltages of 30 or 45 V.

Care and Maintenance. The calibration can be checked by measuring resistors of known value: a decade resistor is especially convenient. The most usual cause for error is low battery voltage, and this usually is first noticed when the zero adjustment can no longer be set correctly. The batteries should be changed when this happens.

Needless to say, the meter should be treated carefully, avoiding mechanical shock or electrical overload. Damage from overload can occur if the ohmmeter is connected to circuits which have other sources of voltage applied. Be particularly careful when using multimeters that the selector switch is not accidentally set to an ohmmeter position when voltage measurements are attempted.

7. The Digital Ohmmeter Ohmmeter accuracy is limited by the accuracy of the applied voltage and the accuracy of reading the meter scale. Electronic ohmmeters overcome the former by using precision-regulated supplies. Digital ohmmeters also overcome the latter limitation by providing a high-resolution easy-to-read display.

Unlike a meter scale a digital readout cannot be made nonlinear (and cannot go to infinity). Therefore, in order to have the readout indicate resistance and not conductance, a constant current is supplied, and the voltage across the unknown is measured, for it is proportional to the resistance. This basic circuit is inherently "four-terminal" (see Sec. 2).

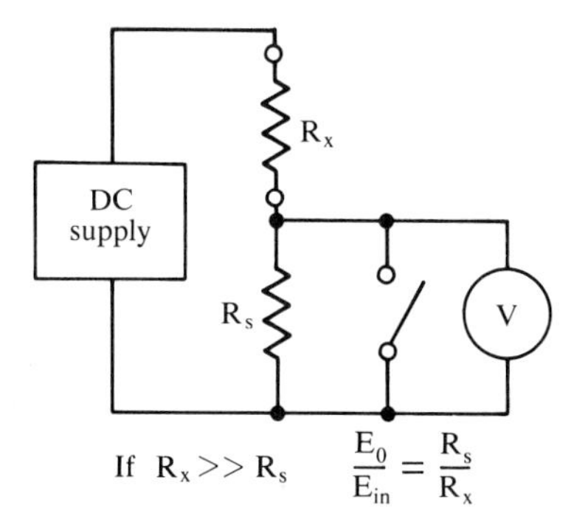

Fig. 15. Basic megohmmeter circuit.

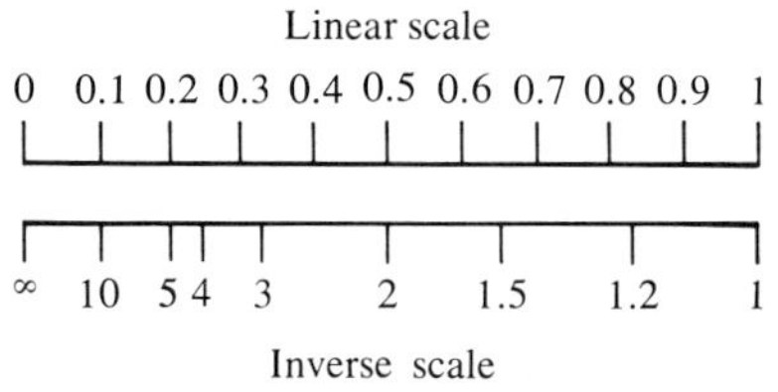

Linear scale

0 0.1 0.2 0.3 0.4 0.5 0.6 0.7 0.8 0.9 1

∞ 10 5 4 3 2 1.5 1.2 1

Inverse scale

Fig. 16. Linear and inverse scales.

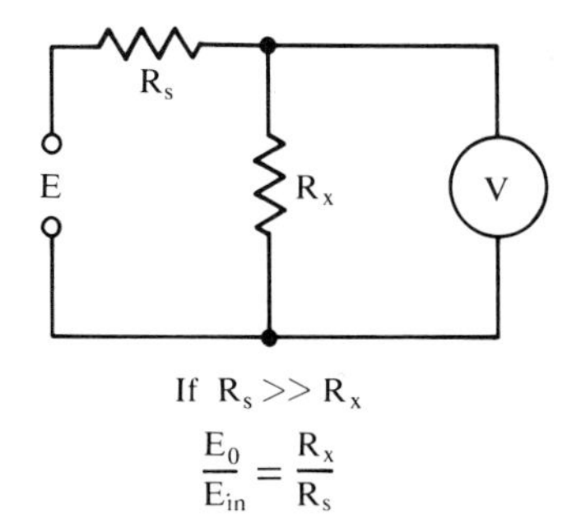

Fig. 17. Basic milliohmmeter circuit.

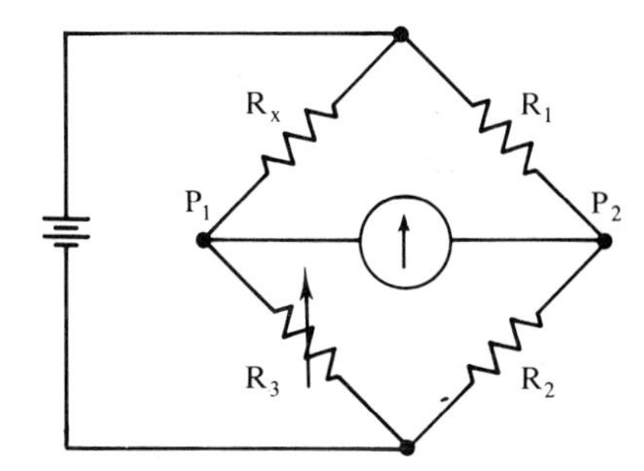

Fig. 18. The Wheatstone bridge.

8. The Megohmmeter This is an ohmmeter for measuring very high resistance, particularly the resistance of insulating materials. It applies a high voltage to the unknown resistance and measures the resulting current by measuring the voltage across a high-resistance standard (R_s in Fig. 15) with a high-impedance voltmeter. An inverse scale (Fig. 16) is used so that such a device is first adjusted to give a correct infinity reading instead of a zero reading. A Megger is a megohmmeter which is powered by a hand-generated crank. Insulation tests are generally made at standard voltages,[9] 500 V being the most common.

9. The Milliohmmeter This instrument supplies rather large currents to low-valued resistors. Usually a four-terminal connection is made which avoids errors due to connecting leads (see Sec. 2). An amplifier is required to make the voltmeter more sensitive, and often low-frequency alternating current is used to avoid dc drift (see Fig. 17).

10. The Wheatstone Bridge The Wheatstone bridge is a circuit for comparing an unknown resistor R_x, in Fig. 18, with other resistors of known value. Because these resistors can be more accurate and stable than a meter calibration, a bridge can be capable of extreme accuracy.

In the circuit shown, the meter is used to detect a voltage between points P_1 and P_2, and one resistor R_3 is adjusted until this voltage is zero. In this condition the bridge is said to be balanced, or *nulled,* and the relationship between the resistance of the four branches or "arms" of the bridge is

$$R_x = \frac{R_1 R_3}{R_2} \tag{8}$$

The adjustment R_3 is proportional to R_x at balance and is calibrated in terms of resistance. Usually another bridge arm is changed in 10:1 steps to change range. Note that the null relationship is independent of the magnitude of the applied voltage (if all resistors are linear) and also independent of the detector sensitivity. However, adequate supply voltage and detector sensitivity are required so that the unbalance can be detected to the degree of precision required. Note also that the same null relationship will hold if the supply and detector connections are interchanged.

11. DC Bridge Sources and Detectors Some dc bridges include built-in sources and detectors while others require external accessory devices. When they are included, the instrument is easier to set up and use, but often these instruments can give better results at very low or very high resistance values if an optimum external source and detector are used.

The higher the applied voltage, the better the sensitivity. However, the applied voltage is limited by the power ratings of the resistor under test and the resistors in the rest of the bridge network. Maximum power to the detector is obtained when the detector impedance is equal to the bridge output impedance. The power sensitivity of a detector must be considered as well as its impedance. For a given detector and a given power in the bridge, reversing the source and detector connections will improve the overall sensitivity if it results in a better impedance match between the bridge and detector.

The source and detector do not have a common ground, and therefore, one must be ungrounded or "floating." Leakage resistance from this floating device to ground will shunt a bridge arm and should be considered as a possible source of error. A battery makes a handy floating supply, but electronic power supplies with good isolation from ground are available. There is a wide choice of detectors from passive galvanometers to electronic voltmeters or special high-sensitivity null detectors designed especially for precision measurements.

12. Use of the Wheatstone Bridge While the suggested operating procedure will differ for various commercial Wheatstone bridges, the basic procedure is similar. First, with the applied test voltage off and the detector sensitivity turned down, connect the resistor to be measured to the "unknown" terminal. Then if the nominal value of the resistor is known, set the multiplier dial and adjustment to this value and apply the test voltage. If not, set the adjustment in the middle of its range, apply the input voltage, and turn the range switch for minimum deflection. Then make the final adjustment of the variable arm to obtain a minimum detector indication while in the meanwhile increasing the detector sensitivity for better resolution.

After a zero output or null is reached, it is generally good practice to remove the bridge input voltage and "zero" the detector if such an adjustment is available. If the zero indication required adjustment, then it is necessary again to apply the input voltage and rebalance the bridge. The measured value of the unknown is then the value of the main reading multiplied by the indicated range multiplier.

When measuring low-valued resistors, particularly if long leads are used, the leads should be clipped together and their resistance measured. This measured lead resistance should be subtracted from the measured value of the resistor under test.

Precautions. Resistance bridges may be damaged by application of too much power. It is preferable to use a current-limited power supply or place a resistor in series with the supply of such value that the power to the bridge is limited to a safe value, such as ½ W (unless very low-power resistors are to be measured, in which case a lower power limit is required). The value of the resistor should be approximately $R = E^2/4P$, where E is the open-circuit supply voltage and P the power limit desired.

Detectors can be damaged by overload and should be set to minimum sensitivity before a voltage is applied to the bridge. Galvanometers are particularly susceptible to mechanical damage and electrical burnout. Initial balance adjustments should always be made with the detector sensitivity turned down. A wise precaution is to shunt a galvanometer null detector with diodes such that the current through it is limited to a safe value.

Calibration. It is not necessary to check every possible resistance setting to assure accuracy. Generally, it is sufficient to check the main settings of the variable bridge arm and then make one measurement on each range to check the range resistors.

The main adjustment is most easily checked by making measurements with a precision decade box in the unknown arm. If this adjustment is a rheostat, usually 10 measurements are adequate; if it is a decade adjustment, each step of each dial should be checked. A decade box or fixed standard resistor can be used to make one check on each range, preferably near the full-scale setting for maximum resolution.

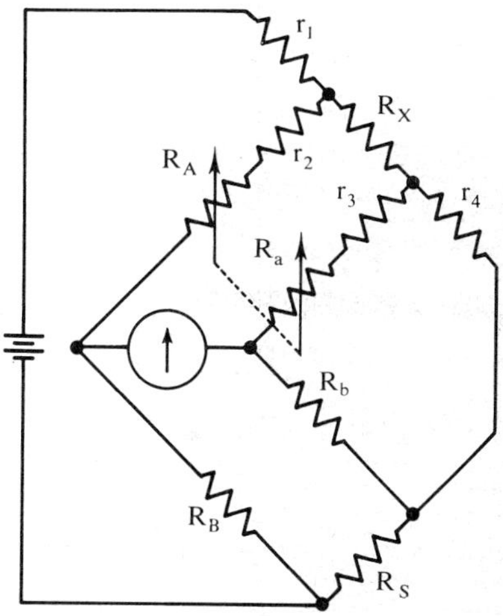

13. The Kelvin Bridge Low-valued resistors are more accurately measured with a four-lead connection, to avoid lead and connection errors (see Sec. 2). The resistance to be measured is defined as the resistance between the points where the leads join, and the measuring circuit should make the effects of the lead resistances negligible.

Fig. 19. The Kelvin bridge.

The Kelvin bridge (Fig. 19) greatly reduces the effects of these leads. Here r_1 is in series with the supply and thus causes no error, and r_2 is placed in series with a relatively high-valued bridge arm R_A, causing little error. The main error would be caused by the voltage drop in r_4, because R_s is usually much smaller than R_A (for better sensitivity), so that substantial current may flow in this side of the bridge. The Kelvin bridge has two additional arms R_a and R_b, which divide the voltage across r_4 (and any additional resistance) proportionately so that it causes negligible error. To do this, the ratio R_a/R_b must equal R_A/R_B, and therefore, R_A and R_a are both adjustable and are ganged.

A direct-reading ratio set is a Kelvin bridge in which R_s is external to the bridge and can also be four-terminal. Such instruments are used for very precise comparisons of low-valued resistance standards. They often have additional adjustments in the R_B and R_b arms to compensate for r_2 and r_3 (called *lead* and *yoke* adjustments, respectively).[10]

14. The Megohm Bridge Very high-valued resistors are measured on special Wheatstone bridges which have high applied voltage and very high resistance detectors to obtain adequate sensitivity. These resistors can be very susceptible to shunt-leakage resistance across their terminals caused by moisture or dirt. Therefore, high-valued standards are shielded and the third terminal is tied to a "guard" point, forming a three-terminal network analogous to a three-terminal capacitor (see Sec. 2). For most applications an opposite corner of the bridge is an adequate guard point, for example, point P_2 in Fig. 18. One leakage resistance would then shunt the detector, causing no error, and the other would shunt the bridge arm R_1, but this would be much lower in value than R_x and therefore would be much less affected.

15. The Resistance-limit Bridge or Comparator This is a bridge which is not nulled, but rather the amount of unbalance voltage is used to indicate the variation between a known and an unknown resistor. Usually two arms are made equal (R in Fig. 20), in which case the open-circuit output voltage is

$$\frac{E_o}{E_{\text{in}}} = \frac{R_x - R_s}{2(R_s + R_x)}$$

The output voltage is measured by a high-impedance voltmeter which has scales indicating the percent difference between the two resistors. These devices are widely used for production sorting or matching but make good general-purpose resistance bridges if an adjustable standard is included in the instrument.

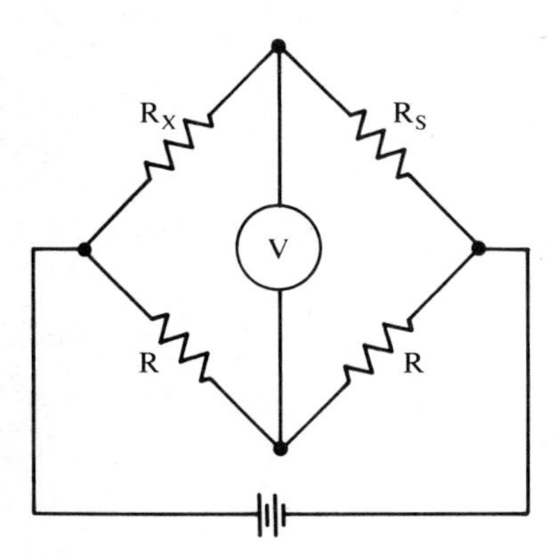

Fig. 20. The resistance comparator.

AC IMPEDANCE MEASUREMENTS

While ac measuring circuits are in many ways similar to those used for dc, they are affected by inductance and capacitance, making them complex in the mathematical sense of having real and imaginary parts, and also more complex in the sense of being more complicated. To specify a (linear) impedance completely at one frequency two indications or balances must be made so that both parts of the impedance can be determined. This requirement generally results in a more complicated instrument, a more complicated measurement procedure, and perhaps most important, a more complicated interpretation of the measurement results. This last difficulty is caused by different ways in which a given impedance may be expressed. To obtain the results in the most useful form, it is necessary to know what form is required and how to convert from one form to another if the measuring instrument does not indicate the impedance in the required form. The various possible forms of expressing impedances are most easily understood by considering their corresponding *equivalent circuits*.

16. Equivalent Circuits Any actual, physical device is actually a complicated electrical network because it has resistance, inductance, and capacitance in each infinitesimal part of its structure. However, at *one frequency* its impedance can be specified by two quantities which may be expressed in two basic forms, each related to a simple *equivalent circuit* which gives the same electrical behavior at that one frequency. These two equivalent circuits are the series or the parallel combination of an ideal resistance and an ideal reactance, which is either an inductance or a capacitance. In general, neither equivalent circuit will be accurate at another frequency. However, for single components, usually one of them will be useful over a reasonable frequency range.

When an impedance is expressed as the sum of its real and imaginary parts (its resistance and reactance), the associated equivalent circuit is the *series* combination of an ideal resistance and an ideal inductance or capacitance depending on its sign:

$$Z = R + jX = R_s + j\omega L_s \tag{9}$$

$$Z = R - jX = R_s + \frac{1}{j\omega C_s} \tag{10}$$

Here the subscript s indicates the equivalent series value as shown in Table 3. This same impedance can be expressed as an *admittance* ($Y = 1/Z$) for which a *parallel* equivalent circuit is applicable:

$$Y = G + jB = G_p + j\omega C_p \tag{11}$$

$$Y = G - jB = G_p + \frac{1}{j\omega L_p} \tag{12}$$

where the subscript p indicates the parallel quantity.

As shown in Sec. 1, R is not equal to $1/G$ and X is not equal to $1/B$ unless the impedance is purely resistive or reactive. Likewise $C_s \neq C_p$, $L_s \neq L_p$, and

TABLE 3

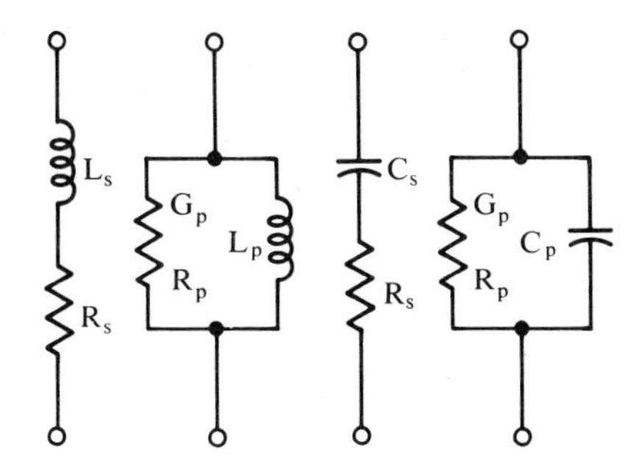

Inductance and resistance:

$$Q = \frac{X}{R} = \frac{G}{B} = \frac{\omega L_s}{R_s} = \frac{R_p}{\omega L_p} = \frac{1}{D}$$

$$L_p = L_s\left(1 + \frac{1}{Q^2}\right) \qquad L_s = L_p\frac{Q^2}{1 + Q^2} = L_p\frac{1}{1 + D^2}$$

$$R_p = R_s(1 + Q^2) \qquad R_s = R_p\frac{1}{1 + Q^2}$$

Capacitance and resistance:

$$D = \frac{R}{X} = \frac{B}{G} = \omega R_s C_s = \frac{1}{\omega R_p C_p} = \frac{1}{Q}$$

$$C_p = C_s\frac{1}{1 + D^2} \qquad C_s = C_p(1 + D^2)$$

$$R_p = R_s\left(1 + \frac{1}{D^2}\right) \qquad R_s = R_p\frac{D^2}{1 + D^2} = R_p\frac{1}{1 + Q^2}$$

$R_s \neq 1/G_p$ unless the impedance is purely capacitive, inductive, or resistive. An example of series and parallel networks that have equal impedances at one frequency is given in Fig. 21. Sometimes the *equivalent parallel resistance* R_p is used, and this is defined as $1/G_p$.

The relationships between the equivalent series and parallel quantities are given in Table 3. These relationships are written in terms of the dissipation factor D and the quality factor Q, defined in Sec. 1 and also in Table 3. Unless specified otherwise, the equivalent series values are usually used in specifying components, even when the parallel equivalent circuit is a closer approximation to the actual behavior.

More complicated equivalent circuits are often used to approximate more closely the behavior of a component or network over a wider frequency range. For example, an equivalent circuit for an inductor is often shown to have both series and parallel resistance, representing winding resistance and core loss, respectively.

Some impedance-measuring instruments indicate impedance or admittance magnitude and phase angle. Impedance readings can be transformed more easily into equivalent series values and admittance more easily into parallel values by the formulas of Table 1.

17. The Vector Impedance Meter[11] If a known and constant current is passed through a complex impedance, the magnitude of the voltage across it is a measure of the impedance magnitude $|Z|$, and the phase angle between the voltage and current is the impedance phase angle θ (see above). A voltmeter and phasemeter will read these quantities directly. The magnitude range may be switched by varying the current or the voltmeter sensitivity in 10:1 steps to give a wide range.

It is difficult to drive an accurate constant current through a high impedance because of shunting impedance. Therefore, on these ranges a constant voltage is applied and the resulting current is proportional to the admittance magnitude. Because $|Y| = 1/|Z|$, the magnitude meter will read $|Z|$ on an inverted scale (see Fig. 16). The phase angle θ is measured by the phase meter in any case.

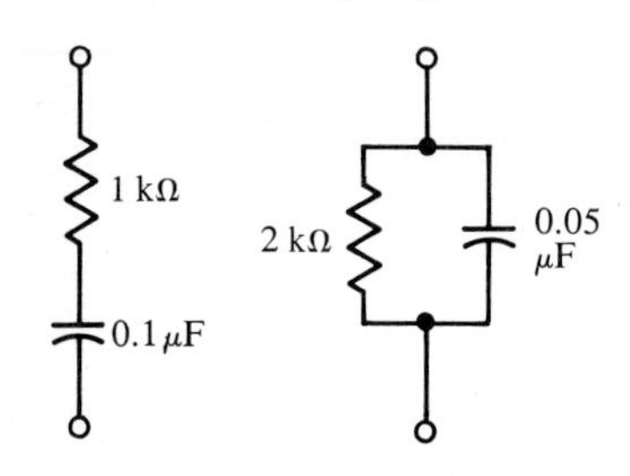

At 1592 Hz, $Z = 1{,}000 - j\,1{,}000\ \Omega$ and $Y = 500 + j\,500\ \mu\mho$ for both networks

Fig. 21. Equal series and parallel impedances (at one frequency).

Impedance meters can also be designed to read R and X instead of $|Z|$ and θ by using phase-sensitive detectors to separate the components which are in phase (real) and in quadrature (imaginary) with respect to the input current. In the constant-voltage mode, these meters must read G and B because inverse meter scales cannot be used to convert to R and X [see Eq. (3)].

Use. These instruments are very easy to use, and indeed, this is one of their main advantages. If the signal frequency is set to the desired value, and the component is attached and the range switch set to give an on-scale reading, the desired $|Z|$ and θ can be read directly off the meters. The only calculation is to apply the impedance multiplier. The accuracy is usually limited to a few percent.

At frequencies which are decade multipliers of $1/(2\pi)$ (i.e., 192 Hz, 1.92 kHz, etc.) the magnitude meter will read the inductance of a pure inductor because $Z = \omega L = 2\pi f L$. If the inductor has loss, the reading will actually be proportional to $L\sqrt{1 + (1/Q)^2}$, but if Q is over 7, the resulting error will be less than 1 percent.

If the meter has an inverse scale (see Fig. 16), it indicates $|Y|$. Therefore, at these same frequencies the magnitude meter will read capacitance (actually $C\sqrt{1 + D^2}$) because $Y = \omega C = 2\pi f C$. The resulting error is 1 percent for a D as high as 0.14. Phase-angle measurements on these impedance meters are generally not very accurate, so that such meters are not recommended for measurements of low D or high Q.

18. The Capacitance Meter This instrument can be considered as a greatly simplified form of the more general impedance meter, but it bears a closer resemblance to the dc megohmmeter in that a voltage divider is formed by the unknown and standard. In the circuit of Fig. 22, if C_T is much larger than C_x,

$$\frac{e_o}{e_{in}} = \frac{C_x}{C_x + C_T} \cong \frac{C_x}{C_T} \tag{13}$$

If e_{in} and C_T are known and constant, the voltmeter scale can be calibrated to read C_x. If C_T is large, stray capacitance from either terminal of C_x to ground

(C_a and C_b) will have negligible effect on the measurement, so that "direct" or "three-terminal" capacitance measurements can be made.

19. The *Q* Meter[12] This device is very similar to the capacitance meter except that it measures resonant voltage rise instead of attenuation. In the circuit shown (Fig. 23), if C is adjusted to give a maximum voltmeter reading, then $E_o/E_{in} = \omega L_x/R_x = Q_x$. Thus if E_{in} is held constant, the meter indicates Q directly (as long as the voltmeter has sufficiently high input impedance). The inductance can be calculated from the resonant condition $L_x = 1/\omega^2 C$. This device is one of the most sensitive circuits for measuring Q, but the accuracy of the inductance reading is usually limited to several percent by the accuracy of C and frequency dial calibrations.

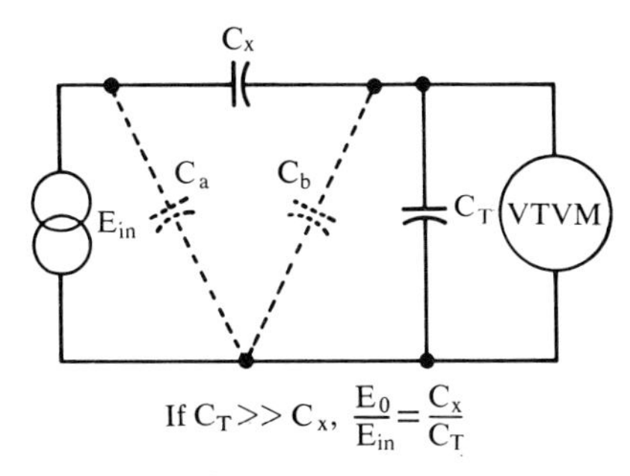

Fig. 22. Capacitance-meter circuit.

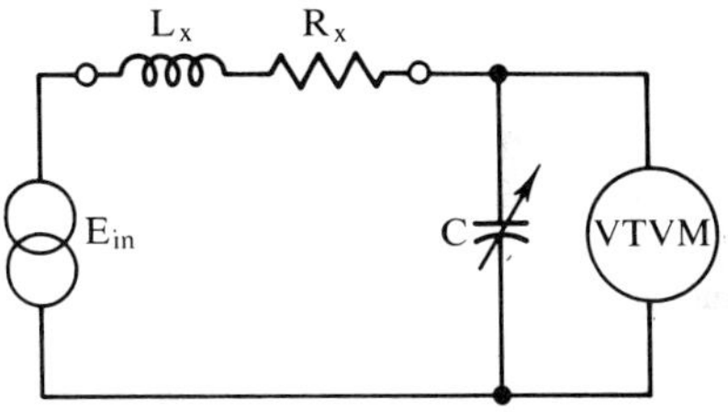

Fig. 23. *Q*-meter circuit.

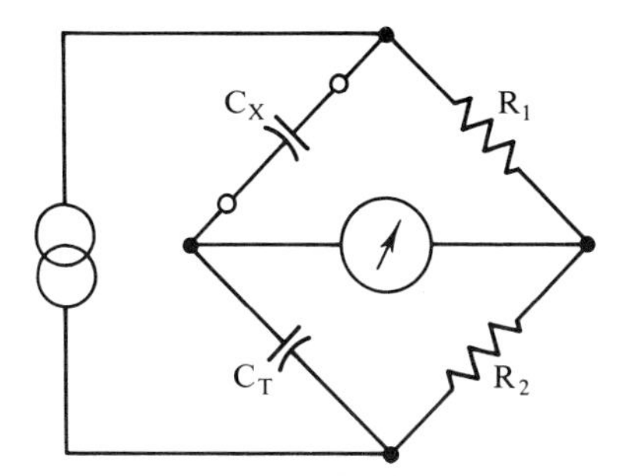

Fig. 24. Basic capacitance bridge.

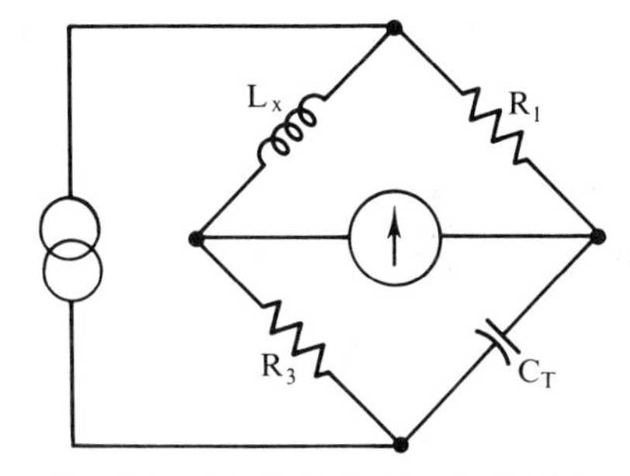

Fig. 25. Basic inductance bridge.

20. Impedance Bridges The basic Wheatstone bridge (Fig. 18) will give a null output for alternating as well as for direct current, if the same balance conditions are met, as long as all arms are pure resistors. However, in general, for alternating current the bridge arms are complex impedances. If impedances are substituted for resistors in the balance equation, we have

$$Z_x = \frac{Z_1 Z_3}{Z_2} = Z_1 Z_3 Y_2 \tag{14}$$

Therefore, if Z_x is complex, having both real and imaginary parts, then at least one of the other bridge arms must be complex, and two adjustments must be made to balance both the real and imaginary parts of the above equation to get a bridge null.

If a pure capacitor is to be measured, it can be balanced by another pure capacitor in an adjacent arm (Fig. 24), giving the balance condition $C_x = C_T(R_2/R_1)$, which can be derived from the general equation above. However, capacitors have loss, and another component must be added to the bridge to balance this out in order to obtain a true null. The position of this additional component determines whether equivalent series or parallel capacitance is measured. A resistor in series with C_T or a capacitor in parallel with R_2 will give the series-impedance values. An opposite connection of these same components will give the parallel components.

While some inductance bridges balance the unknown against a standard inductor, these are rarely used in commercial instruments because of the inherent disadvantages of inductors: high loss, poor frequency response, size, and susceptibility to magnetic pickup. More practical inductance bridges make use of the proportionality between the impedance of one arm and the admittance of the opposite arm [Eq. (14)] and balance an inductor with a capacitor as in Fig. 25, where $L_x = R_1R_3C_T$. Loss

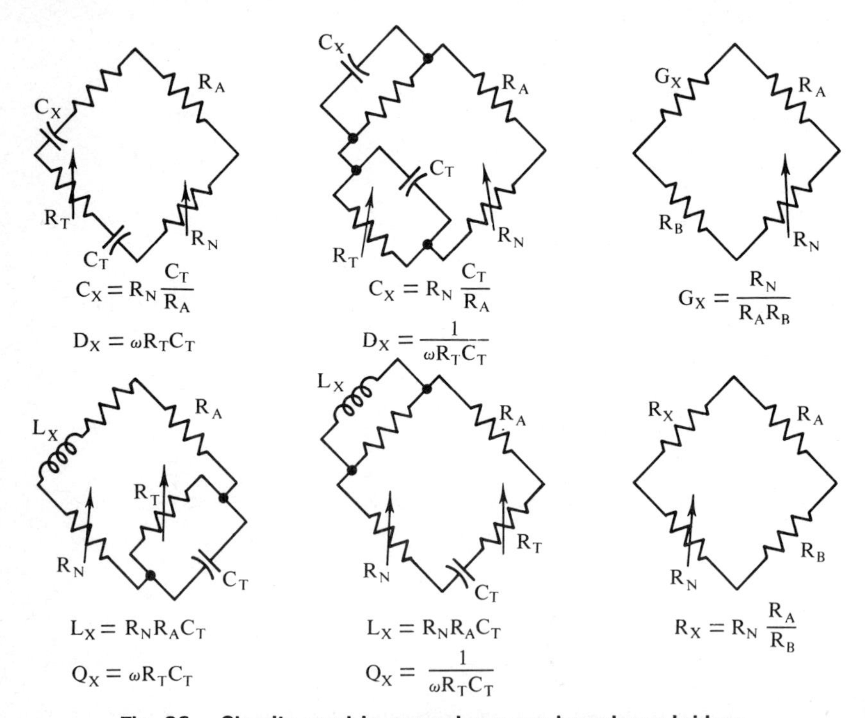

Fig. 26. Circuits used in general-purpose impedance bridges.

in the inductor can be balanced by adding a resistor in parallel with C_T or a capacitor in series with either R_1 or R_3 to give equivalent series-impedance components, or by adding the same components with the opposite connection to give parallel components.

21. The General-purpose Impedance Bridge A great variety of ac bridges have been described[13] but most of those are for specific purposes and only a relatively few are used in commercial instruments. The most common commercial bridges are instruments that contain several bridge circuits for measuring a wide range of capacitance, inductance, and resistance. They are called "CRL" (for capacitance, resistance, and inductance) or "universal" bridges. They usually measure series or parallel capacitance and D, series or parallel inductance and Q, and both ac and dc resistance using the circuits and balance conditions of Fig. 26. The internal ac test signal is usually 1 kHz, but an external oscillator can be used from 20 Hz to 20 kHz or higher. The ac resistance bridge usually requires an external balancing capacitor to get a satisfactory null if the unknown has an appreciable phase angle.

Unless otherwise specified, the equivalent series value is used in the specifications for inductors and capacitors. Usually the D range of the series-capacitance bridge is adequate, but the Q range of the series-inductance bridge usually has a maximum value of 10. However, the parallel-inductance bridge can be used for high-Q measurements, for if Q is greater than 10, the difference between the series and parallel values is less than 1 percent (see Table 3).

Use. The panel legend on most general-purpose bridges is usually sufficient to allow proper operation with internal signals as long as the operator is familiar with basic bridge-balancing procedure. However, it is usually necessary to refer to the operating instructions for measurements requiring an external ac or dc supply or dc bias.

The preferred procedure is to just set the "function" (or "generator-detector") switch to the type of signal required, set the bridge selector to the type of impedance to be measured, and set the range (or multiplier) switch to that position covering the expected value of the unknown. The unknown impedance should then be connected and the main adjustments varied to obtain a null output. Usually it is necessary to turn the detector sensitivity down initially so that the null-detector indication is on scale for the first adjustments. The detector-gain adjustment should be turned up as the null is approached to obtain the sensitivity required for the degree of accuracy desired.

Most ac null detectors indicate the magnitude of the bridge output voltage without regard for the sign of the voltage. Therefore, the indication will be in only one direction whether the adjustments are set too high or too low. For this reason it is necessary to keep the indication on scale so that changes in the indication can be seen and the user can move both adjustments in the direction which will reduce the output.

Such a detector also will not distinguish between a magnitude unbalance (C, R, or L) and phase unbalance (D or Q), and both adjustments should be varied to see their effect. This procedure is usually facilitated if the D (or Q) adjustment is set to low D (or high Q) at the start.

When very lossy components (a D value of ½ or more or Q of 2 or less) are measured, there will be considerable interaction between the two adjustments, resulting in what is referred to as a "sliding balance." A good null can usually be reached if many alternate balances are made, but the process can often be hastened by adjusting the components slightly beyond the setting that produces a minimum deflection. Some instruments have mechanical[14] or electrical[15] means of avoiding this sliding null; their operating instructions should be consulted for proper use.

Precautions. User safety is generally not a problem as long as only internal signal sources are used and no bias is applied. Power sources that are dangerous by themselves are, of course, also dangerous in the system. A more subtle source of danger is the possibility of lethal energy stored in circuit capacitors or inductors even though the supplies themselves are safe. Biased capacitors should always be discharged before they are disconnected from a bridge, and inductors should never be disconnected while appreciable current is flowing in them.

The instrument itself can be damaged by application of too much power, and the ratings for applied signal or bias should be looked up in the operating instructions.

Sources of Error. Aside from the problems of distinguishing between equivalent series and parallel values, the most commonly made errors occur during the measurement of very low and very high impedance components and in the measurement of iron-cored inductors. Any leads connecting the unknown to the bridge will have series resistance and inductance and shunt capacitance. Likewise the bridge itself will have these "residual" parameters, which are often specified. Initial measurements with the connections open-circuited or short-circuited can be used to correct high- and low-impedance measurements, respectively. The corrections are easy if it is only necessary to substract the short-circuit resistance from the measured resistance or the open-circuit capacitance from the measured capacitance. However, correcting a capacitance measurement for a residual inductance is more complicated, and usually correction formulas are supplied in the instructions.

Direct or "three-terminal" measurements on shielded capacitors (see Fig. 8) can usually be made using the case terminal as a guard, because one stray capacitance falls across the detector and the other across the standard, which is quite large. The instructions should be consulted for such measurements and for ac measurements using shielded leads.

Iron-cored inductors are subject to many errors. Not only is the loss apt to be high, making the series and parallel values quite different, but such coils are nonlinear, and the measured value will depend on the excitation level. This level should be specified and correctly set by placing a voltmeter across the inductor but removing it before the final balance if its impedance causes error. The value of such inductors also depends on previous history, and they should be demagnetized before measurement. Transformers and inductors designed for use at power-line frequencies often are capacitive at 1 kHz and therefore will not balance on an inductance bridge.

22. Radio-frequency Bridges Several different types of bridges are available for measurements from low radio frequencies up to the vhf and even uhf range. Generally, these use bridge or T networks in which both adjustments are capacitors because variable capacitors have better high-frequency performance than variable resistors.

These devices often indicate R and X, with the R direct-reading and the X reading requiring a multiplying factor containing the test frequency. Other instruments read C and G directly.

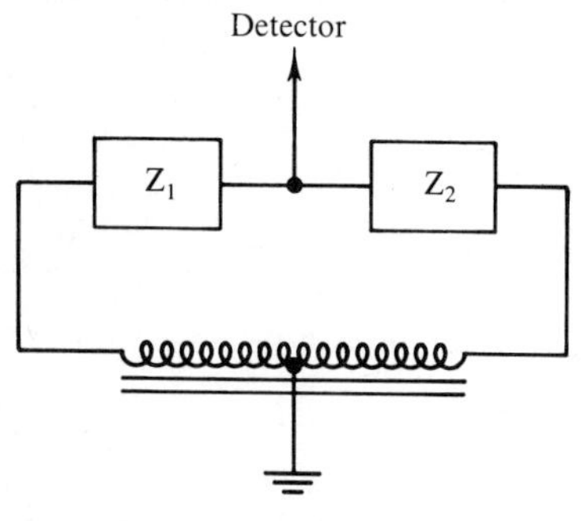

Fig. 27. Impedance comparator circuit.

23. Transformer-ratio-arm Bridges[16] If two adjacent bridge arms are tightly coupled windings on a single high-permeability core, their ratio accuracy can be extremely precise and stable. Moreover, because of their coupling, an impedance shunting of one winding will have very little effect on the ratio. For these reasons, such techniques are used in precision ac bridges, particularly three-terminal capacitance bridges where the rather large stray capacitance to the guard terminal may be placed across an inductive arm with negligible effect. Four-terminal ac resistance bridges, analogous to the Kelvin bridge, have additional transformers and are often used in precision resistance thermometry.

24. Impedance Comparators An ac version of the resistance-limit bridge (Fig. 20) can indicate the impedance difference between two similar impedances of any type. Usually such a bridge uses a transformer to supply the opposite voltages required (see Fig. 27). If phase-sensitive detectors are used to separate the in-phase and quadrature parts of the output voltage with respect to the input, the former will indicate the percent magnitude difference and the latter phase-angle difference. If the components tested are relatively pure, the magnitude difference will closely equal the C, R, or L difference. Such instruments are widely used in production sorting of components.

REFERENCES

1. Metallic Conductors, ASTM Standards, Part 8, Standards B63 and B193; Insulating Materials, ASTM Standards, Part 29, Standard D257.
2. Smits, F. M.: Measurement of Sheet Resistivities with the Four-Point Probe, *Bell System Tech. J.*, vol. 37, p. 711, 1948 (Also ASTM Standards, vol. 8, Standard F84).
3. ASTM Standards, Part 29, Standard D924.
4. Relis, M. J.: U.S. Patent 2,542,057 (also Beckman Instruments catalog).

5. ASTM Standards, Part 29, Standard D150.
6. ASTM Standards, Part 8, Standards A34, A341 to 349, A566, A596, and A598.
7. Tuttle, W. N.: Bridged-T and Parallel-T Null Circuits for Measurements at Radio Frequencies, *Proc. IRE*, January, 1960.
8. Fulks, R. G.: The Automatic Capacitance Bridge, *Gen. Radio Experimenter*, April, 1965.
9. ASTM Standards, Part 29, Standard D257, paragraph A.1.4.2 (lists 100, 250, 500, 1,000, 2,500, 10,000, and 15,000 V, with 100 and 500 V as "most frequently used").
10. Wenner, F.: Methods, Apparatus, and Procedures for the Comparison of Precision Standard Resistors, *J. Res. NBS*, vol. 25, p. 225, August, 1940.
11. Alonzo, G. J., R. H. Blackwell, and H. V. Marantz: Direct Reading, Fully Automatic Vector Impedance Bridge, *Hewlett-Packard J.*, January, 1967.
12. Cook, L. O.: A Versatile Instrument—The Q Meter, *BRC Notebook*, no. 4, winter, 1955.
13. Hague, B.: "Alternating Current Bridge Methods," Sir Isaac Pitman & Sons, Ltd., London.
14. Hall, H. P.: Orthonull—A Mechanical Device to Improve Bridge Balance Convergence, *Gen. Radio Experimenter*, April, 1959.
15. Katsumi, Yoshimoto: A New Universal Bridge with Simplified Semi-automatic Tuning, *Hewlett-Packard J.*, vol. 18, no. 1, August, 1966.
16. Oatley, C. W., and J. G. Yates: Bridges with Coupled Inductive Ratio Arms as Precision Instruments for the Comparison of Laboratory Standards of Resistance or Capacitance, *Proc. IEE*, vol. 101, pp. 91–100, March, 1954.

BIBLIOGRAPHY

Harris, F. K.: "Electrical Measurements," John Wiley & Sons, Inc., New York, 1952.
Terman, F. E., and J. M. Pettit: "Electronic Measurements," 2d ed., McGraw-Hill Book Company, New York, 1952.
Stout, M. B.: "Basic Electrical Measurements," Prentice-Hall, Inc., Englewood Cliffs, N.J., 1950.

Section Eight

Signal-generation Instruments

The ability to analyze the function of a circuit depends upon the ability to stimulate that circuit to perform its designed function. This stimulus usually comes from one of the many forms of signal generation equipment. In order to know the meaning of a measured response, we must first know a great deal about the impressed signal such as its frequency, amplitude, waveshape, stability, modulation, and apparent impedance.

Chapter 28

Function Generators

JAMES D. WAGNER, Ph.D.

Tektronix Inc., Beaverton, Oregon

Function generators are a class of signal sources which produce a wide variety of waveforms. Typical function generators usually produce sine, triangle, and square waveforms and may additionally produce cosine, ramp, or other waveforms.

Function generators find wide use as general-purpose signal sources. Features not commonly available from sine oscillators also make function generators particularly useful in special applications.

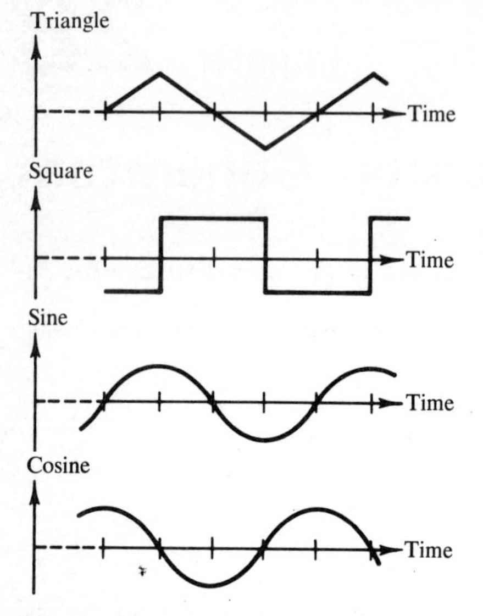

Fig. 1. Basic function generator waveforms.

GENERATION OF FUNCTIONS

The name "function generator" is derived from the type of waveform produced by the generator; the term "function" here refers to the description of how the generator output varies with time. The basic waveforms shown in Fig. 1 can be described in simple mathematical terms or functions.

1. Square and Triangle Functions The foundation for all the function generators is the generation of the square and triangle waveforms. These two waveforms are generated by a combination of two electronic circuits, an integrator and a hysteresis circuit, resulting in a type of multivibrator.

An integrator is a circuit which provides an output voltage having a rate of change proportional to the applied input voltage. The integrator most often found in function generators is the active integrator shown in Fig. 2 with its input-output characteristics.

A hysteresis circuit has input-output characteristics as shown in Fig. 3. The well-known Schmitt trigger is one of the most common hysteresis circuits.

Interconnecting a hysteresis circuit and an active integrator, as in Fig. 4, results in a triangle waveform at the integrator output and a square waveform at the hysteresis output. Circuit operation may be visualized in the following manner: Suppose that the voltage at the output of the integrator is equal to the lower trip level of the hysteresis input and the hysteresis output is in its lower state (Fig. 3, point A). Then the integrator output will increase linearly with time (see Fig. 2). When the output of the integrator (the hysteresis input) reaches the upper trip level of the hysteresis input (Fig. 3, point B), the output of the

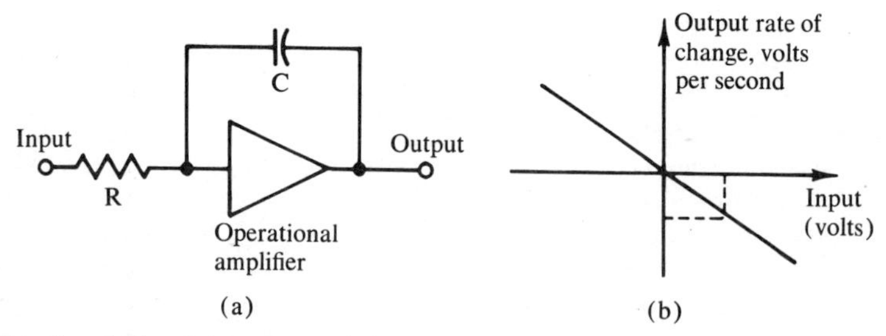

Fig. 2. Active integrator. (*a*) Circuit. (*b*) Input/output characteristics.

hysteresis circuit switches to its upper level (Fig. 3, point C); the output of the integrator then begins to decrease linearly with time (Fig. 2). This action continues until the integrator output reaches the lower trip level of the hysteresis circuit

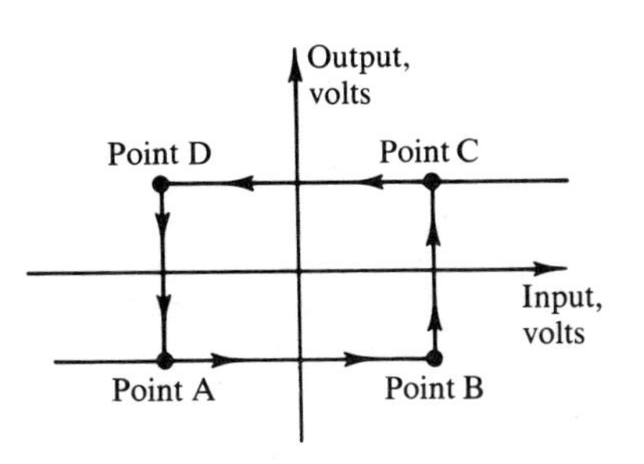

Fig. 3. Hysteresis diagram.

Fig. 4. Square-triangle generator.

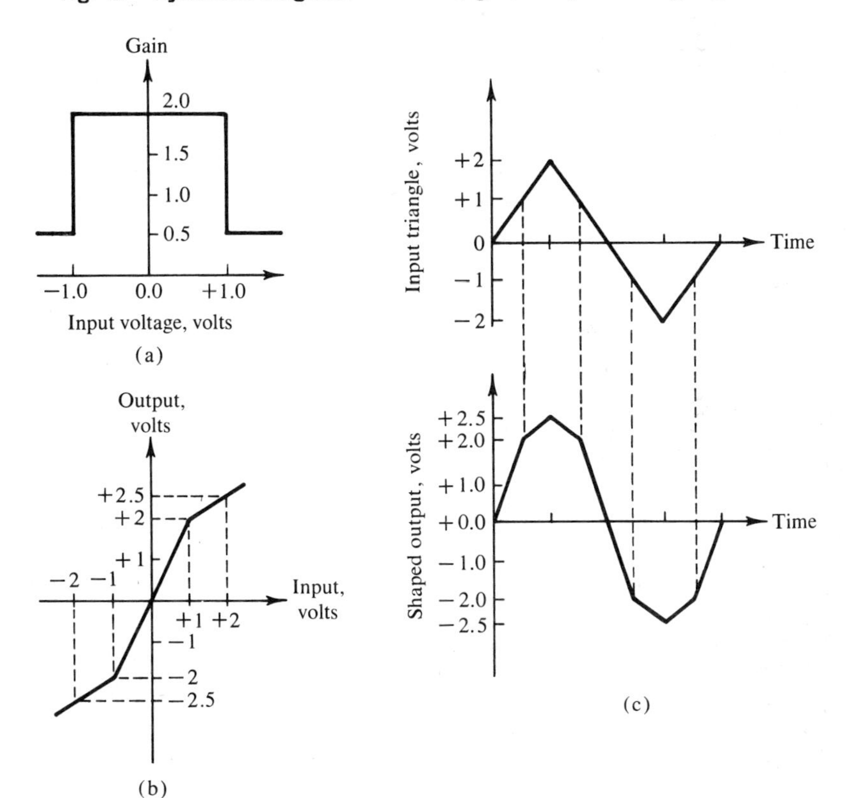

Fig. 5. Simplified sine shaper. (a) Amplifier gain plot. (b) Amplifier transfer characteristics. (c) Shaping process.

(Fig. 3, point D). The output of the hysteresis circuit then switches to its lower state (Fig. 3, point A), and the cycle begins to repeat.

The frequency of operation of the square-triangle generator is determined by the values of the R and C in the integrator and the amplitude of the signal applied to the input of the integrator. The latter is usually changed for continuous frequency variation while the R and C values are used to determine the frequency range.

2. Sine Function The sine in a function generator is produced by shaping the triangle in a nonlinear amplifier. An example of the shaping process, in simplified form, is shown in Fig. 5.

The input to the sine shaper is shown in Fig. 5*c* as a triangle with a peak-to-peak amplitude of 4 V centered at zero volts. The shaping amplifier shown has a gain, or amplification factor, of 2 for inputs between −1 and +1 V, and a gain of ½ for inputs less than −1 V or greater than +1 V. Each point where the amplifier gain changes produces a change in the slope of the output signal. The output shown in the figure, while not a good sine, is a much better approximation than the original triangle. An amplifier having an even larger number of gain changes can produce a good approximation of the sine function.

3. Cosine Function The cosine, which is the sine shifted by 90°, is commonly generated by integrating the sine function. The integration is usually done with an active integrator of the type shown in Fig. 2. Phase-lock techniques, which will be described in detail later, can also be used to generate a cosine.

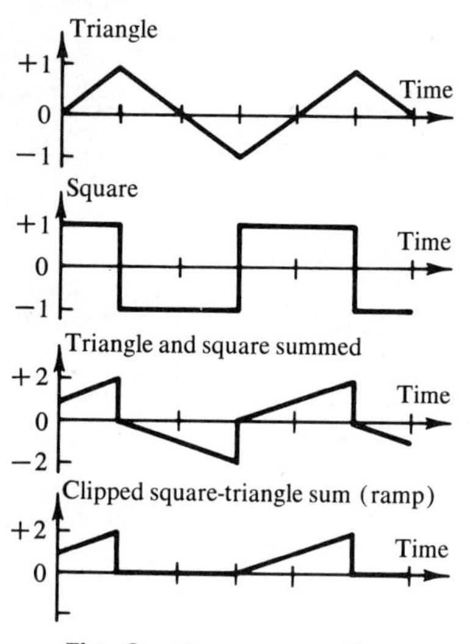

Fig. 6. Ramp generation.

4. Ramp Function The ramp function, also called the sawtooth function, is similar to the triangle. Two methods are in use for producing a ramp. One is essentially the same as that used for the triangle; the difference is that the integrator is designed to produce a triangle with one slope which is much steeper than the other.

The other method adds the square and triangle, then clips the lower half of the resulting waveform as shown in Fig. 6.

The first procedure is normally used to generate a ramp which is independent in timing of the other functions. The second is used when a ramp synchronized to the other functions is desired.

5. Haversine and Sine-squared Functions The haversine is the function $A(1 + \sin X)$ and is produced by shifting the sine so that its negative peak coincides with a zero-volt base line.

The sine-squared function ($\sin^2 X = \frac{1}{2} - \frac{1}{2}\cos 2X$) as produced in a function generator is, in reality, a haversine; the haversine has the same frequency as the sine, while the sine squared has twice the frequency of the sine. Relationships between the sine, haversine, and sine squared are shown in Fig. 7.

6. Control Functions Much of the versatility of function generators is due to the capability for control. Several of the control functions, usually called operating modes, are detailed below.

Voltage control of frequency allows the operating frequency to be controlled by an externally applied voltage in addition to the normal front-panel controls. The process usually alters the signal applied to the integrator. This function is often called VCF (voltage-controlled frequency) or VCG (voltage-controlled generator).

Phase lock controls the function-generator frequency by comparing it with another signal. The comparison takes place in a phase detector which produces an output voltage proportional to the phase difference between the inputs; by applying the detector output to the VCF input of the function generator, any difference between the applied signal and the function-generator frequency is corrected.

By adding a voltage to the detector output, the phase difference between the function generator and the external signal can be adjusted. This can be used to generate a cosine function using the external signal as the sine function.

Free run. It has been assumed to this point that the generator runs continuously. It will be seen that this is not necessarily the case. If not continuous or free-run, operation becomes a specific mode of operation.

Gated operation refers to the ability to stop and start the generating process rapidly. Gating is usually achieved by placing a short circuit across the timing capacitor in the triangle integrator. With the short in place, the integrator output is a fixed value; with the short removed, normal operation occurs.

In gated operation (Fig. 8*a*) applying an external voltage removes the short. Removing the external voltage readies the internal circuitry for reapplication of the short; it is not applied, however, until the triangle reaches the correct level, so that the waveforms are completed if the external voltage is removed before the end of the cycle.

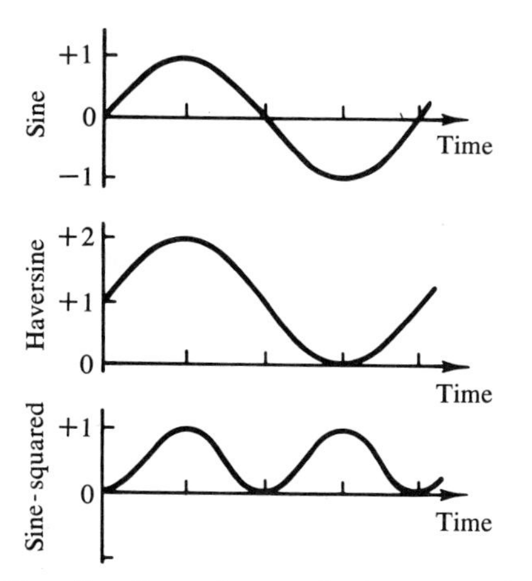

Fig. 7. Haversine and sine-squared functions.

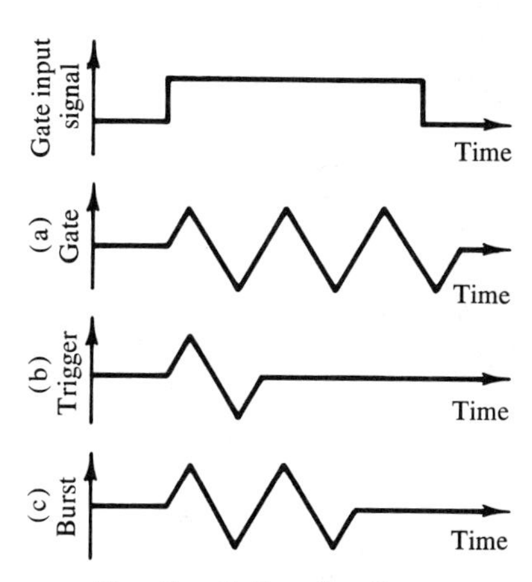

Fig. 8. Gating functions.

Triggered operation is the same as gating, except that only one waveform cycle is produced each time the external voltage is applied, as in Fig. 8*b*.

Burst is also similar to gated operation. But instead of having the external voltage duration determined by the number of cycles produced, it is determined by either counting or internal timing as shown in Fig. 8*c*.

FRONT-PANEL TERMS

Most of the terms used on front panels of function generators are identical to terms used on pulse or sine generators; for a few terms, however, a unique interpretation is applied. Several of those terms are explained in the following section.

7. Output Amplitude Unlike sine generators, amplitudes in function generators are measured peak-to-peak, rather than rms, because of the variety of waveforms provided. The amplitude of a waveform is the voltage difference between the most positive and the most negative points of the waveform, excluding aberrations.

8. Output Level Also called output dc level, output level is the difference between the midpoint of a function and zero volts, except perhaps for haversine and ramp. The midpoint is halfway between the most positive and most negative points of the waveform, exclusive of aberrations. Note that the term "level" does not here carry the meaning of amplitude as it does on some generators.

9. VCF Ratio The VCF ratio indicates the ratio between the output frequency and the frequency indicated on the front-panel controls. It is also called sweep width or, when the VCF input only reduces the frequency, expansion ratio, since the output period is expanded in that case.

BASIC INSTRUMENT SPECIFICATIONS

Since function generators are similar in many respects to both pulse and sine generators, many specifications are similar. Also, since function generators were developed after other generators, most of the specifications used in common with the other generators are consistent. Where there was no precedent, specifications were devised; on these specifications, there are often differences between manufacturers about defining terms.

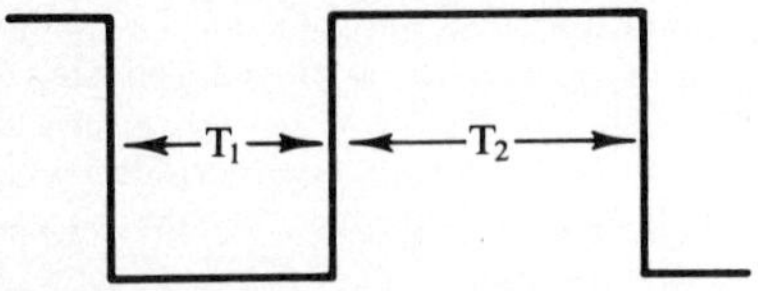

Fig. 9. Square symmetry. With the figure are the following equations: Symmetry error $= |T_1 - T_2/T_1 + T_2| \cdot 100\%$, percent symmetry $= 100\% -$ symmetry error.

10. Specification Definitions The following paragraphs present definitions for many function-generator specifications.

Frequency range is the span of frequencies produced by combinations of the front-panel controls, exclusive of VCF input. Several tuning bands, often in decade steps, are commonly required to cover the entire range.

Frequency accuracy is the maximum difference between the selected and generated frequency. Accuracy includes all possible sources of error, including calibration and stability; it may be expressed as a percentage of indicated frequency or as a percentage of maximum frequency on each band.

Frequency stability includes changes due to temperature, power-source variations, and time. It is often divided into short-term components, such as jitter, and long-term components, such as temperature. Stability is expressed, like accuracy, in percentages.

Square symmetry measures, in percent, the ratio of the durations of the two halves of the square function. When the two halves are of equal duration, symmetry is 100 percent. Another measure of the same parameter is square-symmetry error, which is the difference between actual symmetry and the ideal 10 percent symmetry. Square symmetry is shown in Fig. 9.

Square transient response is a group of quantitative terms describing the shape of the square function. These include rise and fall times, overshoot, droop, and others. See Chapter 3 for more detail.

Triangle symmetry is measured the same way as square symmetry.

Triangle linearity measures the slope of the triangle in comparison with a straight line. The two common linearity definitions, often not distinguished, are diagramed in Fig. 10. The "absolute slope" definition compares the worst instantaneous slope of the triangle with the average slope. The "deviation from straight line" definition compares the difference between the actual triangle and a "best" fitted straight line to the triangle amplitude. There is no simple conversion between the two definitions, but the magnitudes are similar for the same triangle.

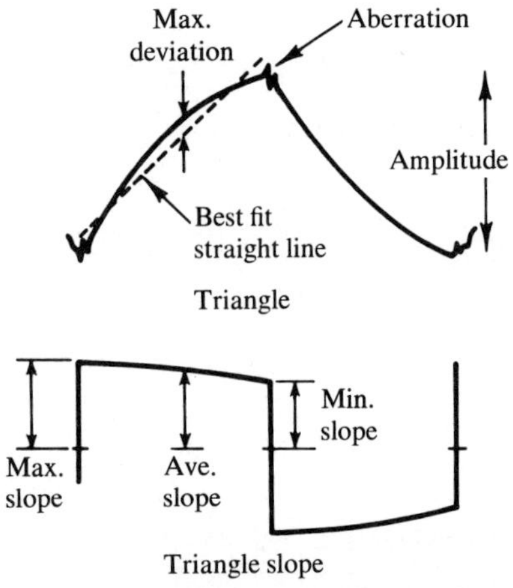

Fig. 10. Triangle linearity. With the upper half (triangle) are the statements: Deviation from straight line percent nonlinearity = max. deviation/amplitude · 100%, percent linearity = 100% − percent nonlinearity. With the lower half (triangle slope) are the statements: Absolute slope percent nonlinearity = max. slope − min. slope/av. slope · 100%, percent linearity = 100% − percent nonlinearity.

Ideal linearity is 100 percent, while triangle nonlinearity or linearity error indicates the difference between the actual linearity and ideal 100 percent linearity.

Triangle aberrations refer to transients which are usually located at triangle peaks. The specification normally compares the peak amplitude of the transient with the triangle amplitude. Occasionally, aberrations are included within the linearity specification.

Ramp linearity is defined the same as triangle linearity.

Ramp fall time is the time required for the ramp to return from its peak level to its base level. It may also be called flyback time and is defined in the same way as square rise or fall time.

Sine distortion measures the deviation of the sine output from an ideal sine.

Output amplitude is the maximum amplitude available at the generator output. Amplitude may differ between functions and may be specified for a particular load.

Output-amplitude stability is usually given as a percentage of the output amplitude at a constant frequency. This specification is usually divided into a short-term (noise) component and a long-term (temperature and power source) component; it may differ between functions.

Output impedance is the equivalent impedance in series with the output terminal of the generator.

Maximum output load is the smallest impedance which can be connected to the generator output before significant distortion or damage occurs.

TABLE 1 Typical Function-generator Specifications

Frequency range	0.001 Hz to 1 MHz
Frequency accuracy	4 % of dial reading
Frequency stability	0.05 % short-term (10 min), 0.3 % long-term (5 h)
Square-symmetry error	Less than 1 %
Square-transient response	Rise and fall time 50 ns
Triangle linearity	Better than 99 % below 100 kHz, better than 95 % 100 kHz to 1 MHz
Sine distortion	1 % or better below 100 kHz, 3 % or better 100 kHz to 1 MHz
Output (all waveforms)	10 V peak to peak into open circuit, 50 Ω output impedance, level adjustable ±5 V, max load 25 Ω, ±1 dB all frequencies
VCF input	50:1 range with at least 10 V input
VCF frequency response	dc to 10 kHz

VCF range is the maximum amount which the frequency can be altered by the VCF input. It may also be called maximum VCF ratio, maximum sweep width, or maximum expansion ratio.

VCF sensitivity is the minimum VCF input which will give the VCF range; sensitivity may also be given in volts input per decade of frequency change.

VCF linearity is the linearity of the frequency-voltage relationship for the VCF operation. As with triangle linearity, there are several ways of defining this specification.

One method compares the actual VCF ratio with the best straight-line fit on a VCF ratio-input voltage graph; the comparison can be expressed as a percentage either of maximum VCF ratio or of the actual ratio at which the error occurs.

The other definition compares the actual frequency generated rather than the VCF ratio.

VCF frequency response specifies the VCF input frequency range for which the linearity specification is valid.

Phase-lock sensitivity specifies the minimum phase-lock input voltage for correct operation. The phase-lock input may also be limited to a specific frequency range.

11. Typical Specifications Table 1 gives a set of specifications for a typical function generator.

FRONT-PANEL CONTROLS

For the following descriptions, refer to Fig. 11.

Frequency range selects the frequency band, usually in decade steps. It is also called a decade or frequency switch.

Frequency multiplier selects the specific frequency; it is not labeled on many generators. The output frequency is determined by multiplying the range and multiplier settings.

Frequency vernier allows a fine adjustment of frequency.

Function selector selects the function available at the output: it is commonly labeled with names or diagrams of the functions.

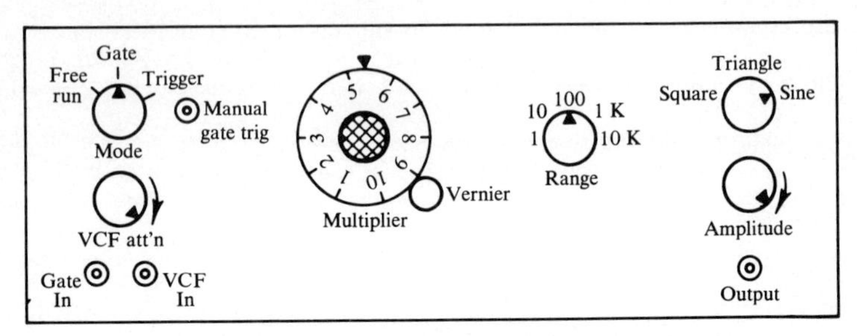

Fig. 11. Typical function generator front panel.

Amplitude, also called attenuator or amplitude attenuator, permits adjustment of the output amplitude.

Mode selector selects free run, gate, trigger, or burst operation; some function generators also switch phase-lock operation with the mode selector.

Manual gate/trigger is for manual operation of the gate, trigger, or burst functions.

VCF attenuator attenuates the VCF input voltage.

Output level, also called dc offset or dc level, adjusts the output level.

Phase angle sets the phase angle between the reference input and function-generator output in phase-lock operation.

SOURCES OF INHERENT ERROR

Function generators, like most instruments, have characteristics which produce inherent sources of error. Most of the errors indicated here occur in all function generators with the specified feature.

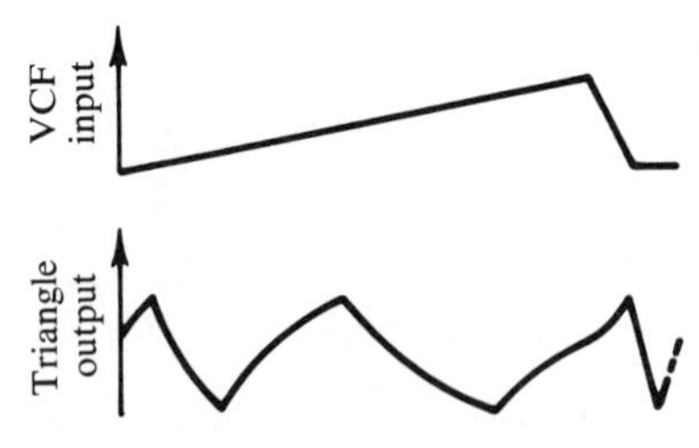

Fig. 12. Effect of rapidly changing VCF input on triangle.

12. Waveform Distortion with VCF Operation When the VCF input is a changing voltage, the frequency of the function generator is continuously changing. As a result, the slope of the triangle changes continuously, and it is meaningless to even consider triangle linearity. The effect is particularly apparent when the frequency of the VCF input is comparable with the output frequency, as in Fig. 12. For the same reason, sine distortion is also meaningless in this case.

13. Phase-lock Multiple Responses The nature of the phase detector used in phase-lock systems allows several relationships between the reference and function-generator frequencies. The relationships are described by the equation $F = nf$, where n is a positive integer, f is the reference frequency, and F is the function-generator frequency.

Normally, it is desired that n be unity; but depending on initial conditions, n can take on other values. If, for example, the function generator is set at 2 kHz when a 1-kHz reference is applied, lock will probably occur with $n = 2$.

ELECTRICAL PROBLEMS AND SOURCES OF ERROR IN USE

The manner in which some of the functions are generated can create problems for the unaware user; some function generators also exhibit unique limitations to their operation.

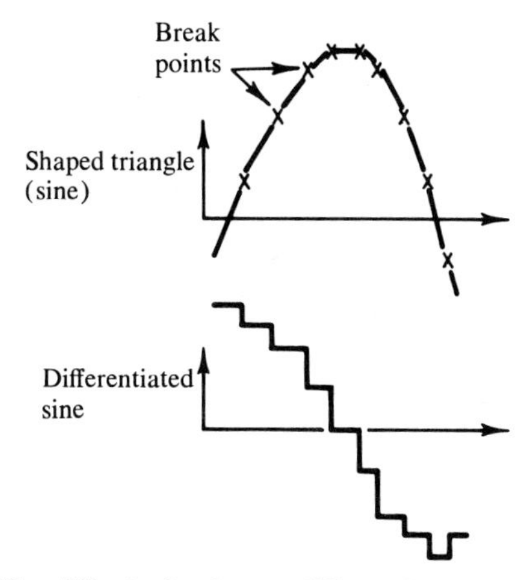

Fig. 13. Effect of extreme differentiation on sine.

14. Sine Differentiation As outlined in the description of the sine function, the sine is actually composed of straight-line segments. If the sine is used in applications where it is highly differentiated, as in phase shifting, the result will bear little resemblance to a sinusoid; it will appear instead as a series of steps, as shown in exaggerated form in Fig. 13. If differentiation must be used, a time constant smaller than one-tenth the output period should be avoided.

15. VCF Range Generators with VCF capability vary greatly in their VCF input characteristics. Some generators allow the frequency to be reduced only from the dial setting. Some other generators allow the frequency to be increased at minimum multiplier settings, decreased at maximum multiplier settings, and increased or decreased by varying amounts at intermediate multiplier settings; this situation often leads to uncertainty about allowed VCF inputs and VCF range.

16. VCF Stability Since the VCF input helps determine the output frequency in VCF operation, instability in the voltage applied to the VCF input will degrade the frequency stability of the generator.

17. Output Impedance Output impedance can lead to varying output amplitudes under varying loads. For example, a generator with a 50-Ω output impedance generating a 5-V triangle into a nearly open circuit, such as an oscilloscope input, will produce only 2.5 V when loaded by 50 Ω. Thus, when output amplitude is important, it is necessary to consider both the load and output impedances.

BIBLIOGRAPHY

"Application Manual for Computing Amplifiers," Philbrick Researches, Inc., Dedham, Mass, 1966.
Ashley, J. Robert: "Introduction to Analog Computation," pp. 57–61, 273–276, John Wiley & Sons, Inc., New York, 1963.
"Electronics for Measurement—Analysis—Computation," pp. 366–368, Hewlett-Packard, Palo Alto, Calif., 1969.
"Generation and Measurement Equipment," pp. 1–13, Wavetek, Inc., San Diego, Calif., 1968.

Chapter 29

Oscillators

CHARLES HOUSE

Hewlett-Packard Company, Colorado Springs, Colorado

INTRODUCTION

An oscillator, an instrument providing sine-wave signal outputs, is traditionally the most valuable stimulus for electronic-system test and design. Depending upon the oscillator design or application, different names, such as oscillator, test oscillator, audio signal generator, or function generator, are applied. These names, while useful, are not always assigned in standard fashion by every manufacturer; so it becomes necessary to check requirements against an instrument's specifications in any application.

TABLE 1 Performance Specifications

Oscillator type	Frequency range	Frequency stability	Power output	Amplitude stability	Distortion	Attenuation	Balanced output	Modulation	Output monitor	Phase control	Residual, spurious AM, FM	Nonsinusoidal output
Oscillator	x	x	x	x	x							
Test oscillator	x	x	x	x	x	x	x		x			
Signal generator	x	x	x	x	x			x			x	
Function generator	x	x	x	x	x					x		x

All oscillators generate sine-wave signals of known frequency and amplitude for signal-source requirements. Typically, a *test oscillator* also includes a calibrated attenuator and output monitor, a *signal generator* designation implies modulation capability, and *function generators* provide nonsinusoidal (pulse, square-wave, triangular wave, etc.) outputs in addition to the sine-wave signal. Typical specifications which are included under each type of oscillator are summarized in Table 1.

This chapter will discuss primarily sine-wave oscillators with frequency ranges to ~100 MHz. Subject topics of further interest include "function generators" for nonsinusoidal waveforms, and "signal generators" for higher-frequency signal generation and modulation.

CATEGORIES

Oscillators may be classified in several ways. Table 2 categorizes several types by *design principle* and by *frequency band*. There are two basic classes of oscillator

TABLE 2

Design Principle	*Frequency Band*
Feedback oscillators:	Audio frequency (af), 20 Hz–20 kHz
RC feedback	Radio frequency (rf), 20 kHz–30 MHz
LC feedback	Video frequency, dc–5 MHz
Crystal oscillators	High frequency (hf), 1.5–30 MHz
	Very high frequency (vhf), 30–300 MHz
Negative-resistance oscillators	

design. The more common type uses an active device as an amplifier, the output of which is fed back in phase to its own input (positive feedback) to cause regeneration. This design is therefore termed a *feedback oscillator.* The second type uses an active device with an inherent negative-resistance characteristic, which provides its own regeneration. This type, accordingly called a *negative-resistance oscillator,* may use negative feedback for bias stability, just as does the feedback oscillator. Such feedback is not considered in the name, which is based upon only the regeneration means.

1. Feedback Oscillators Feedback oscillators are further partitioned into three divisions—*LC feedback networks, RC feedback networks,* and *crystals.* Table 3 lists a number of oscillator designs in each category.

TABLE 3

LC feedback	*RC* feedback	Crystal
Colpitts	Phase shift	Pierce is equivalent to the Colpitts *LC*
Hartley	Wien bridge	Most *LC* configurations are possible, but are not named
Clapp	Twin-T	
Tuned plate or collector	Bridge-T	
Vackar		
Seiler		

LC Oscillators. The first oscillators were of the *LC* variety; the most common ones encountered are the Colpitts and Hartley designs. Figure 1 illustrates the basic nature of an *LC* design block diagram; choice of the elements from among inductors and capacitors determines which of the named varieties are obtained. The schematic representations of several *LC* oscillator circuits are shown in Fig. 2. It is perhaps of interest to note that the Clapp, Seiler, and Vackar circuits are very similar to the Colpitts design; the variations were made in order to obtain greater tuning range or better frequency stability under specific conditions.

Frequency of oscillation for LC oscillators is typically written as

$$f_0 = \frac{1}{2\pi\sqrt{LC}} \tag{1}$$

where L and C are the respective total inductance and capacitance. In most LC circuits, a tuning range of perhaps 2.5:1 is available before the amplitude is significantly affected. Tunable oscillators are often called *variable-frequency oscillators* (VFO), and any of the above designs may be employed in a VFO. The Vacker is probably the most frequency-stable, followed by the Clapp, Seiler, and Colpitts designs, although all are similar in capability. Usually a frequency-stability specification will not indicate which design is used, however, and thus in general these distinctions are ignored. To obtain very-low-frequency oscillations, it is apparent from Eq. (1) that both L and C must become very large. The practical difficulty involved has led to use of LC oscillators for frequencies typically above 1 MHz, and RC oscillators at lower frequencies.

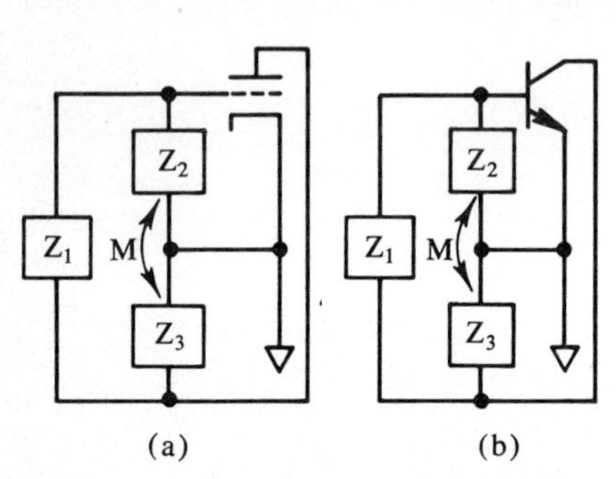

Fig. 1. (*a*) *LC* tube oscillator. (*b*) *LC* transistor oscillator. *Z*'s are impedances (*L*'s, *C*'s, and crystals); *M* is mutual coupling between impedances (as between inductances in a transformer).

Crystal Oscillators. Crystals may be represented as LC circuit equivalents. Figure 3 illustrates both the crystal symbol and its electrical representation. Because of the close analogy to an LC combination, crystal designs are often lumped with LC oscillators. The Pierce crystal design, for example, is a crystal analog of the Colpitts design, as shown in the comparison schematics of Fig. 2. The other designs of Fig. 2 are often found with crystals as well. The basic difference between LC oscillators and crystal oscillators is that the latter have a very limited

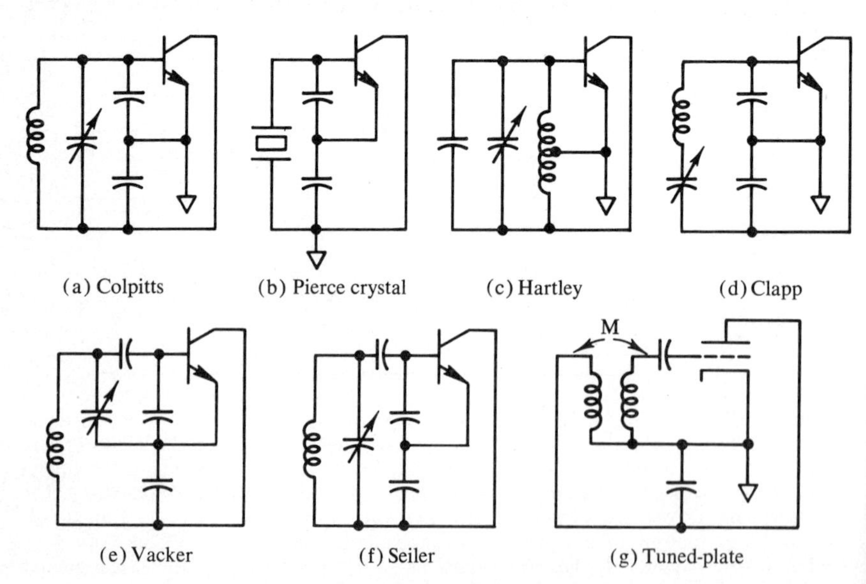

Fig. 2. *LC* **oscillator circuits.**

tuning range (or none at all) but much better frequency stability. The typical frequency range of crystal oscillators is ≥100 kHz.

2. *RC* **Oscillators** *RC* oscillators take one of two basic forms. A *phase-shift oscillator* is shown in Fig. 4 and a *Wien-bridge oscillator* in Fig. 5. The phase-shift oscillator relies upon some phase shift in each *RC* network sufficient to cause 180° of phase shift between input and output of the ganged three-stage *RC* network. This design is capable of providing signals from a few hertz to several hundred kilohertz by varying the *R*'s and *C*'s appropriately. Since variation of any single

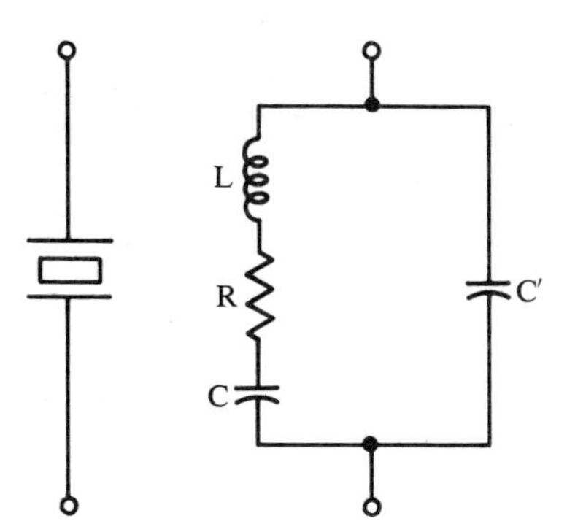

Fig. 3. Crystal. (*a*) Symbol. (*b*) Electrical equivalent circuit.

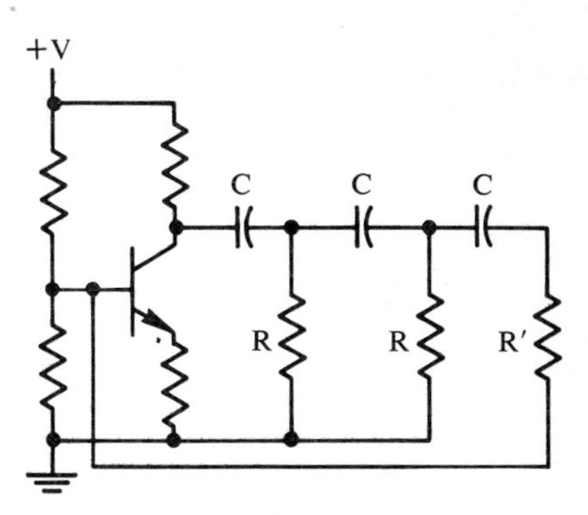

Fig. 4. Phase-shift oscillator. *R'* in parallel with R_{in} of transistor base = *R*.

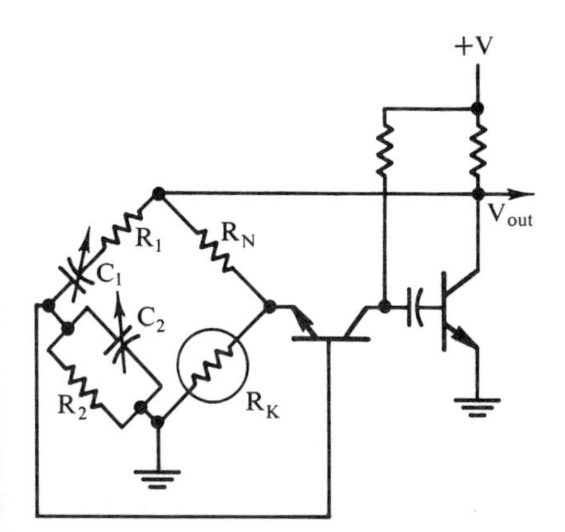

Fig. 5. Wien-bridge oscillator.

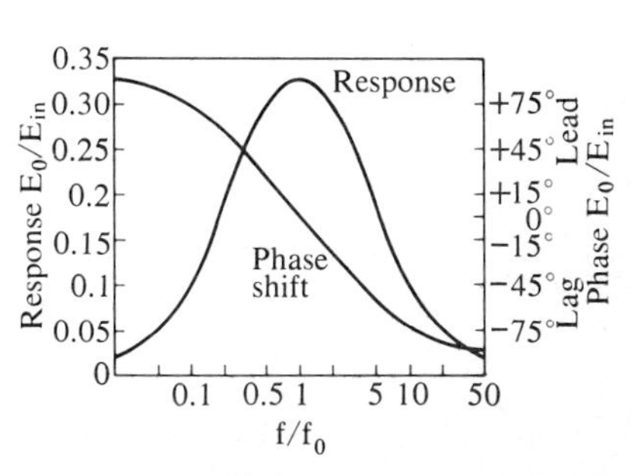

Fig. 6. Response and phase shift for frequency deviation.

element affects the impedance looking into the phase-shift network, this design is not especially suitable for wide frequency variation without variation in output-signal amplitude. The Wien-bridge oscillator, a somewhat later development, overcomes this difficulty well, and has consequently become the more common *RC* oscillator encountered. The twin-T and bridge-T oscillators listed in Table 3 are simple variations of the Wien-bridge design.

The basic Wien-bridge oscillator circuit (Fig. 5) is a two-stage amplifier with both positive- and negative-feedback loops. Positive feedback for regeneration is applied through the adjustable-frequency network R_1C_1–R_2C_2 of the Wien bridge.

The amplitude and phase characteristics of the network, with respect to its driving voltage, are shown in Fig. 6. These curves show the amplitude response to be maximum at the same frequency where the phase shift through the network is zero. Oscillations are therefore sustained at this frequency. The resonant frequency f_0 is thus expressed as

$$ {}_0f = \frac{1}{2\pi RC} \tag{2} $$

where $R = R_1 = R_2$ and $C = C_1 = C_2$. Unlike *LC* circuits, where the resonant frequency varies inversely with the square root of C [Eq. (1)], the frequency of the Wien-bridge oscillator varies inversely with C itself. Thus, frequency variation greater than 10:1 is possible with a single sweep of an air-dielectric tuning capacitor. Moreover, with the negative-feedback loop, we will see presently that the amplitude may be held steady as this wide frequency variation is obtained. Range switching is typically accomplished by switching the resistor values. Practical limits on the size of resistors usually allow *RC* Wien-bridge designs to attain a minimum frequency of ~2 Hz.

The negative-feedback loop involves the other pair of bridge arms R_n and R_k. R_k is often a temperature-sensitive resistor with a positive temperature coefficient, such as an incandescent lamp operated at a temperature level lower than its illumination level. This lamp, being sensitive to the amplitude of the driving signals, adjusts

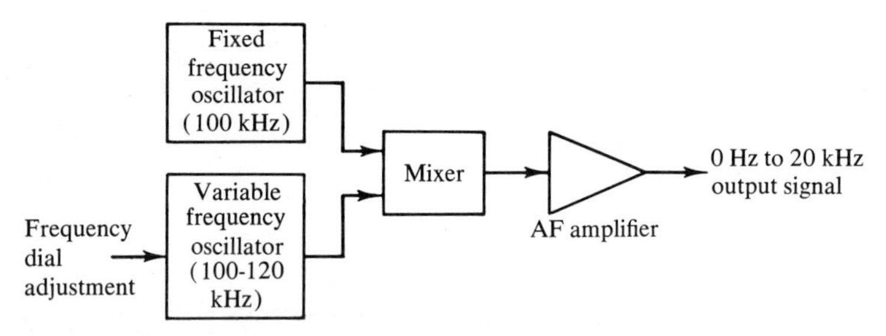

Fig. 7. Beat-frequency oscillator.

the voltage-division ratio of the branch accordingly. Thus, as the amplitude of the oscillations increases, the resistance of R_k increases. The negative feedback also increases, reducing the gain of the amplifier and restoring the amplitude to normal.

The amplitude of oscillations in any oscillator increases because of the positive feedback until some form of limiting occurs. In *LC* oscillators, device saturation controls this limiting, which consequently is not especially stable. A vacuum-tube Wien-bridge oscillator design usually depends upon the temperature-sensitive resistor R_k for amplitude control. This allows operating the amplifier entirely within the linear portion of its transfer characteristic, resulting in a low-distortion sinusoidal output.

Solid-state *RC* designs often use a peak-detector circuit to provide a negative-feedback signal proportional to the output voltage, because the current drawn by an incandescent lamp is incompatible with transistors and battery power sources.

3. Beat-frequency Oscillators Prior to the time that the Wien-bridge oscillator was developed, *beat-frequency oscillators* were the only means of obtaining a wide variation in frequency range with a single dial rotation (corresponding to adjustment of one variable capacitor). The principle was based upon the mixing of two different frequencies to develop a "beat" or difference frequency which could then be used as the signal source. Thus, as illustrated in Fig. 7, a fixed-frequency oscillator of 100 kHz would be mixed with a variable-frequency oscillator with a variable range from 100 to 120 kHz to produce a "beat-frequency" output of 0 Hz to

20 kHz. The complexity of this technique by comparison with the Wien-bridge oscillator has led to its demise for most oscillator applications.

4. Negative-resistance Oscillators Numerous negative-resistance elements are available to the electronics circuit designer, such as tetrodes, tunnel diodes, neon tubes, and unijunction transistors. All have at one time or another been incorporated into oscillator designs for various applications. The basic problem with such oscillators is dependence upon the inherent stability of the negative-resistance region of the device, a rather low stability in most situations. Two types of oscillators are likely to be encountered—the *dynatron,* based upon a tetrode negative-resistance region coupled with an *LC* tank circuit, and a *tunnel-diode oscillator,* the solid-state equivalent of the dynatron with the additional virtue of very high-speed operation, making it especially valuable in vhf and uhf oscillator requirements.

Figure 8 illustrates a tunnel-diode volt-ampere characteristic curve, along with a schematic of a current source and a time-varying waveform measured across

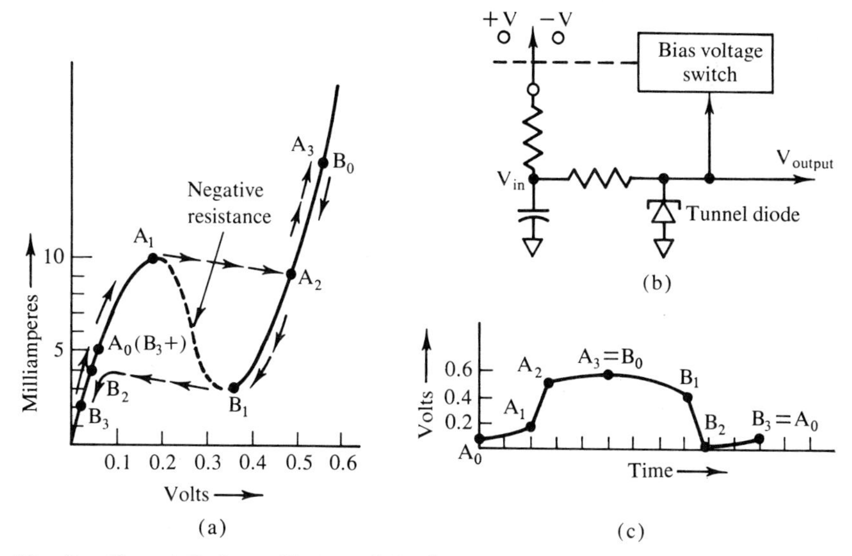

Fig. 8. Tunnel-diode oscillator. (*a*) Characteristic curve. (*b*) Schematic. (*c*) Time plot of V_{output}.

the device. Assume first that the diode is biased at point A_0, whereupon an increase in V_{in} (due to the capacitor charging) causes more current to flow through the diode. The only way to obtain this much current flow in the diode is to move to point A_1, jump to point A_2, and then travel up to A_3. This causes an output waveform as shown in the time plot. Since a tunnel-diode switching time is very fast, the transition time from A_1 to A_2 is very short.

As the higher output voltage is obtained, it provides negative feedback which switches the voltage source on the input bias network. This acts to discharge the capacitor, which decreases the current available for the diode. The current path followed now on the diode characteristic curve is from B_0 (or A_3) to B_1, when it cannot go lower without switching over to B_2, and then up to B_3 (or A_0) to start the cycle again. Note that the output waveform is not sinusoidal, but rather a poor square wave. Shaping is often employed beyond this point, in order to improve the sinusoidal quality, but often the lack of sinusoidal form is of little consequence. Of course, at very high frequencies the switching time becomes a significant portion of the total cycle time and a more sinusoidal output results naturally.

PERFORMANCE SPECIFICATIONS

The basic specifications of interest for any oscillator are five in number. The *frequency range* covered and the *frequency stability* are clearly fundamental properties. The *power output* (or amplitude output) and *amplitude stability* are often quite as important. Lastly, the amount of *distortion* present in the signal is significant for assessing the quality of the oscillator. Secondary specifications exist, of course, and are important in specific applications; those of Table 4 are discussed here.

TABLE 4 Performance Specifications

Primary	*Secondary*
Frequency range	Attenuation and accuracy
Frequency stability	Balanced output
Power or amplitude output	Flatness (of frequency response)
Amplitude stability	Frequency accuracy
Distortion	Modulation
	Output monitor
	Phase control, synchronization
	Pushbutton tuning
	Residual, spurious AM, FM

5. Primary Specifications

Frequency Range. The initial question about any oscillator is what frequency range it covers. Many oscillators are built to correspond to a given frequency band (Table 2). The common *audio oscillator*, for example, is an instrument with a frequency range of (at least) 20 Hz to 20 kHz. Many so-called audio oscillators, though, have a much wider range (e.g., 5 Hz to 500 kHz); so it is better to check the actual specification than to rely upon the name.

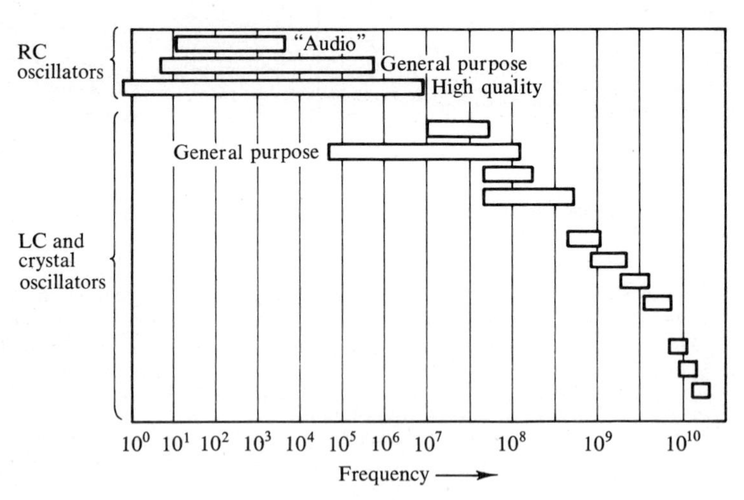

Fig. 9. Band coverage of typical oscillators.

Figure 9 illustrates the typical frequency-range capability of various oscillator designs. Note that *RC* oscillators cover many frequency decades but that they are most common in the 1-Hz to 1-MHz category. Extending frequency range at either end is relatively expensive.

LC oscillators, on the other hand, have many fewer decades but work especially well in bands above 1 MHz. Some instruments provide only a few octaves, while others give broader coverage for proportionately more cost.

Typical specifications for an *RC* oscillator will include the total range, plus the range of one sweep of the dial before a multiplier must be changed. Thus, a specification might read: 10 Hz to 1 MHz in six decade ranges. Since *LC* tuning ranges will not cover a full decade, their specifications differ in listing the frequencies within a given band as well. For example: Range—50 kHz to 65 MHz in 6 bands (50 to 170 kHz, 165 to 560 kHz, 0.53 to 1.8 MHz, 1.76 to 6 MHz, 5.8 to 19.2 MHz, and 19 to 65 MHz).

Frequency Stability. The ability of an oscillator to maintain a selected frequency over a period of time is specified as *frequency stability.* Component aging, power-supply variations, and environmental changes (such as temperature and humidity) all affect stability. In addition, the different types of oscillator designs have widely varying capabilities.

RC oscillators are the least stable oscillators, with Wien-bridge circuits somewhat better than phase-shift designs. Specifications are usually written as a percentage of the set frequency, but occasionally as a particular number of hertz variations. Thus, typically, one encounters wording such as:

Frequency stability = ±0.04 percent

Standard stabilities for *RC* oscillators are from 0.05 to 0.005 percent. If listed in hertz, the variation is usually less than 10 Hz for a generator capable of oscillation from a few hertz to perhaps 20 kHz or more.

Sometimes specifications are more explicit, showing what happens as certain environmental factors change. For example, a specification may read

Frequency stability:

±10 percent line-voltage variation—less than 0.01 percent

Change of frequency with temperature—less than ±100 ppm/°C

Often manufacturers of *RC* oscillators will not specify frequency stability, figuring correctly that it is an inconsequential portion of the frequency-accuracy specification. Obviously in such cases, frequency accuracy becomes the primary specification instead of secondary as treated here.

LC oscillators are usually more stable than their *RC* counterparts. The specifications are written in very similar fashion. A typical wording may read:

Drift: Less than 50 ppm (or 5 Hz, whichever is greater) per 10-min period after 2-h warm-up; less than 10 min to restabilize after changing frequency.

Another typical wording, this one for an oscillator covering the 1- to 110-MHz band, may read as follows:

Frequency drift:

±0.01 percent ± 500 Hz for 10-min periods after 1-h warm-up

±0.1 percent/°C temperature change

±0.001 percent/V line-voltage change

The difference in the above specifications points up the fact that numbers used by different manufacturers must be compared with caution. Some specify a short-term stability (e.g., 10 min) without regard to environment; others specify the temperature or voltage variations separately from a short- or long-term circuit-stability specification; still others may include an option for crystal-clock phasing or automatic frequency control (AFC) to specify a stability that the basic oscillator is incapable of providing.

Crystal oscillators are by far the most frequency-stable oscillators. Specifications of 10 ppm ± 0.05 ppm/°C or 0.01 percent from 0 to +60°C are common. Heated-oven crystal designs may be significantly better yet, consistently attaining, for example, 5×10^{-10} parts/second, and 5×10^{-8} parts/24 h over an external 0 to +60°C environmental range.

Power Output. The amount of deliverable voltage or power from the generator into a load is a primary specification often misunderstood because it is stated in several different ways.

The classical method of defining maximum power output is illustrated in Fig. 10. Note that this method requires specifying $R_L = R_s$, which is often not desirable or possible. A specification for an *RC* oscillator will often be written for $R_s = 600$ Ω, whereas *LC* or crystal oscillators more typically will have 50-Ω source resistances because of the higher-frequency spectrums.

With this method, typical specifications may read:

1. 1 W or 24.5 V into 600-Ω load
2. 3 W or 42.5 V into 600-Ω load
3. 1 W or 7.1 V into 50-Ω load

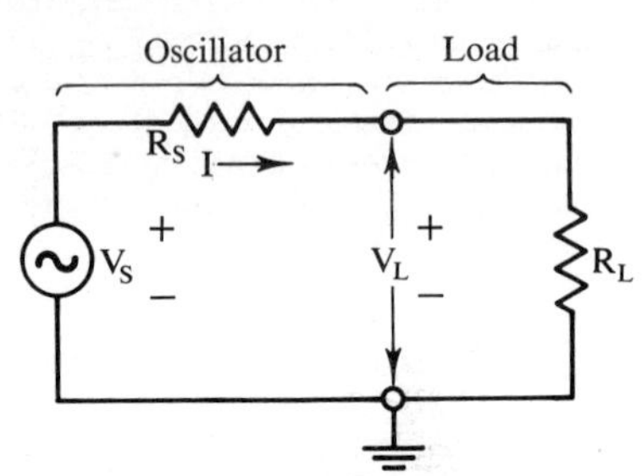

Fig. 10. Defining maximum power output.

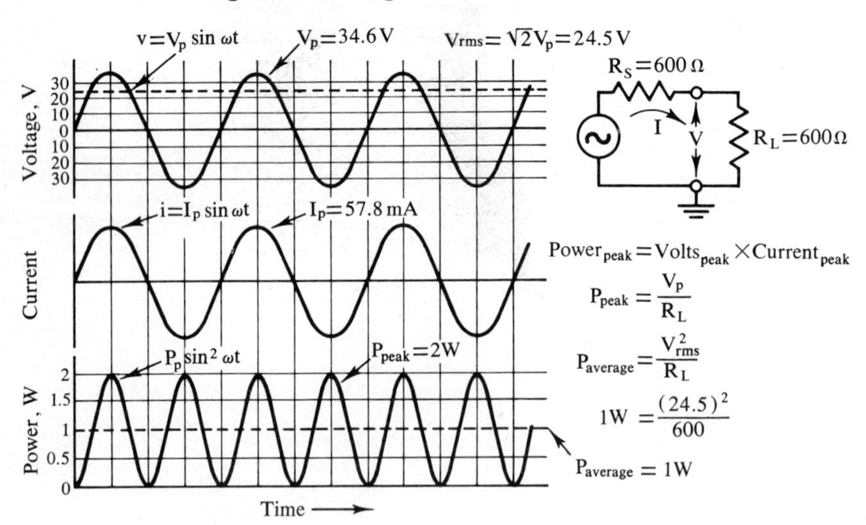

Fig. 11. Waveform plot of voltage and power.

It is important to understand the terms in use for these specifications. Figure 11 shows an oscilloscope waveform plot of the voltage and power in the load resistor as a function of time for specification 1 above. In particular, note that root-mean-square (rms) voltage and average power values are used instead of peak values. The equation for converting an amplitude or power-output specification into the form desired is

$$P_{av} = \frac{V_{rms} I_{rms}}{R_L} = \frac{V_{rms}^{\;2}}{R_L} = I_{rms}^{\;2} R_L \tag{3}$$

A more complete way of stating specification 1 above would be

Output—1 W (average) or 24.5 V (rms) into 600 Ω; 49 V (rms) open circuit

An entirely correct but less well-known specification makes use of the decibel form of power or voltage rating.

$$\text{Power output, dBm} = 10 \log_{10} \text{power in milliwatts} \quad (4)$$
$$\text{Power output, dB} = 10 \log_{10} \text{power in watts} \quad (5)$$
$$\text{Output level, dBV} = 20 \log_{10} \text{output in volts} \quad (6)$$

Again, such a specification presumes that $R_L = R_s$ in order to obtain the maximum average power output. A typical wording for this type of specification (with a range attenuator included) is as follows:

+23 to −70 dBm (50 Ω output) full scale, 10 dBm per step; coarse and fine vernier

TABLE 5

Power (avg)		Voltage (rms)	$R_s = R_L$
Decibels	Watts		
−40 dBm (−70 dB)	0.1 μW	2.24 mV	50 Ω
−30 dBm	1 μW	7.07 mV	50 Ω
−20 dBm	10 μW	22.4 mV	50 Ω
−10 dBm	100 μW	70.7 mV	50 Ω
0 dBm (−30 dB)	1 mW	224 mV	50 Ω
+10 dBm	10 mW	707 mV	50 Ω
11 dBm	12.5 mW	790 mV	50 Ω
13 dBm	20 mW	1.0 V	50 Ω
20 dBm	100 mW	2.24 V	50 Ω
22 dBm	160 mW	2.82 V	50 Ω
23 dBm	200 mW	3.16 V	50 Ω
27 dBm	500 mW	5.0 V	50 Ω
30 dBm (0 dB)	1 W	7.07 V	50 Ω
33 dBm	2 W	10.0 V	50 Ω
40 dBm	10 W	22.4 V	50 Ω
−40 dBm (−70 dB)	0.1 μW	7.74 mV	600 Ω
−38 dBm	.16 μW	10 mV	600 Ω
−30 dBm	1 μW	24.5 mV	600 Ω
−20 dBm	10 μW	77.4 mV	600 Ω
−18 dBm	16 μW	100 mV	600 Ω
−10 dBm	100 μW	245 mV	600 Ω
0 dBm (−30 dB)	1 mW	774 mV	600 Ω
+2 dBm	1.6 mW	1 V	600 Ω
10 dBm	10 mW	2.45 V	600 Ω
18 dBm	60 mW	6 V	600 Ω
20 dBm	100 mW	7.74 V	600 Ω
22 dBm	160 mW	10 V	600 Ω
30 dBm (0 dB)	1 W	24.5 V	600 Ω
35 dBm	3 W	42.4 V	600 Ω
40 dBm	10 W	77.4 V	600 Ω

Table 5 is a correlation chart for several standard power, voltage, and dBm figures, listed for both 50- and 600-Ω resistances.

Some units are also specified for their unique output characteristics when driving a reactive (inductive or capacitive) load; the operating manual for such an instrument should be consulted.

Amplitude Stability. The ability of an amplifier to maintain a constant-amplitude output over a period of time, or during environmental or frequency-range changes, is termed *amplitude stability*. It is often alternatively incorporated either into the *amplitude-accuracy* specification, which also includes attenuator-range inaccuracy, or into the *flatness* specification, which describes amplitude stability only as a function of frequency-range change.

As discussed above under Categories, *RC* Wien-bridge oscillators have a high degree of inherent amplitude stability as a function of frequency range by contrast with *LC* oscillators or *RC* phase-shift oscillators. Even so, many *RC* Wien-bridge oscillators are not specified for amplitude stability, accuracy, or flatness; so the user should not be surprised if this primary specification is missing on the data sheet. Many manufacturers simply consider their instrument "good enough" for quality audio work, and consequently ignore the specification. *LC* oscillators often do not specify this either, but for the rather different reason that there often is essentially no stability.

The best specification that one might find delineates the several contributing factors as follows:

Stability: ±2 percent per month, 20 to 30°C

Flatness: ±2 percent 100 Hz to 1 MHz; ±3 percent 10 to 100 Hz

Accuracy: 1 V range, ±1 percent 20 Hz to 1 MHz, ±2 percent 10 to 20 Hz; 1 mV, 10 mV ranges, ±2 percent 20 Hz to 1 MHz, ±3 percent 10 to 20 Hz

More commonly, a specification for just one or two of the three areas is cited. A

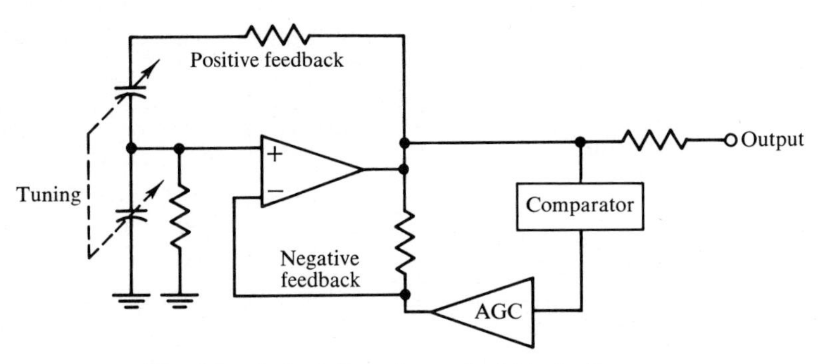

Fig. 12. Automatic gain control block diagram.

specification of that variety for an *LC* oscillator may be labeled "frequency response and output accuracy," with a wording of:

At any output voltage below 1 V, output-level variation with frequency is less than 2 dBm across the entire frequency range; output accuracy is better than ±1 dBm at any frequency.

One technique occasionally cited on a data sheet is automatic gain control (AGC). This is a feedback design which senses any variation in output amplitude as the frequency range or environment changes, and produces a correction signal to restore the original amplitude. Figure 12 illustrates one method. The output resistance of the AGC circuit can be varied slightly to change the divider ratio of the negative-feedback network. An error in output voltage is detected by the peak comparator and sent to the AGC amplifier. This changes the resistance ratio in the negative-feedback loop in the proper direction to bring the output back to a constant level. An oscillator with this type of amplitude stabilization can easily hold the output constant to within ±1 percent between 10 Hz and 1 MHz. Units of this nature may be very descriptive in the amplitude-stability specification:

Amplitude stability vs. time: In any period of 1 h or less, within ±0.02 percent. In any 24-h period or less, within ±0.1 percent

Amplitude stability vs. line: For a 10 percent line-voltage change, less than ±0.01 percent for full frequency range

Amplitude stability vs. temperature: Within ±0.1 percent per degree Celsius
Amplitude stability vs. frequency range: Cycle to cycle, less than 0.1 percent; within ±0.025 dB from 10 Hz to 1 MHz

A similar technique in *LC* oscillators is termed "leveled" output, whereby the output is monitored and attenuated dynamically to maintain a constant output.

Distortion. Presence of signal in the output which occurs at frequencies other than that set on the frequency-range dial is termed *distortion.* Two types exist—*harmonic,* wherein the distortion frequency (or frequencies) is related to the desired output frequency by the equation

$$f_{\text{har}} = \frac{1}{n} f_{\text{out}} \text{ or } n f_{\text{out}} \tag{7}$$

where n = integer, and *noise,* which is unrelated to f_{out}. *Hum* is a special case of noise distortion related to the instrument power-line frequency (e.g., 60 Hz).

Distortion is undesirable, because it reflects an impurity in the oscillator output signal which may be thought to originate in the circuit under test. If an oscillator is used for distortion measurements, as often found in audio and communications work, it should contribute much less distortion than the levels being tested for in the circuits.

Harmonic distortion usually results from nonlinear operation in the oscillator circuit during some portion of the generation process, and as might be anticipated, it increases at higher frequencies. Hum and noise can be introduced at a variety of points in oscillator circuits. When the oscillator is operated at a relatively high level, the amount of hum and noise is usually negligible, since these quantities in output amplifiers are ordinarily independent of output amplitude. Conversely, it may be appreciated that even though the hum and noise signals may be quite small compared with the rated output, they may be significant portions of low-level output signals.

Typically distortion will be specified in the same terms as power output; thus units giving voltage or power in decibels will rate distortion in the same units, and those with voltage or wattage ratings will use percentage-distortion specifications. A typical *RC* oscillator specification might read:

Distortion: Less than 0.1 percent 100 Hz to 100 kHz, to 0.5 percent at 10 Hz, and 1 percent at 1 MHz
Hum and noise: Less than 0.05 percent of full rated output

Some units provide hum and noise compensation, so that it is roughly constant regardless of vernier setting; such a specification will read "Less than 0.05 percent of attenuator or vernier setting."

Wideband *LC* oscillators will label the distortion contributions slightly differently, but the type of specification is the same:

Harmonic output: At least 30 dB below the carrier (f_{out})
Spurious AM: Hum and noise sidebands are 70 dB below carrier down to the thermal level of the 50-Ω output system

6. Secondary Specifications

Attenuation and Accuracy. The inclusion of a calibrated *attenuator* for maximum-output amplitude selection greatly increases the convenience of using an oscillator for certain types of testing. Just as with power-output ratings, attenuators are most often labeled in steps of decibels or volts. Discrete decibel steps are usually in 1 or 10-dB increments for power, and 20 dB for voltage; voltage increments are normally in a 1, 2, 5, 10 sequence. A gain vernier allows continuous adjustment between any two steps.

Accuracy of a calibrated attenuator range will be specified in the form of a percentage (e.g., ±2 percent) or a fractional deviation (e.g., ±0.25 dB). Often this specification includes the long-term (environmental) amplitude stability of the oscillator, a fact not always easy to determine from the data sheet.

Balanced Output. A basic oscillator design has a single-ended output which is time-varying and referenced to ground. A *balanced-output* oscillator has a differential output, wherein one side goes positive and the other negative simultaneously with respect to ground. The load resistance sees the sum of the two sides. This is of value especially because the outputs may be "floated" and placed across any load without regard for ground potential. Thus a balanced-output oscillator may be used to stimulate a resistance in a circuit under test, regardless of the location (bias-wise) of the resistor. Figure 13 shows the waveforms as a function of time for both single-ended and balanced-output systems.

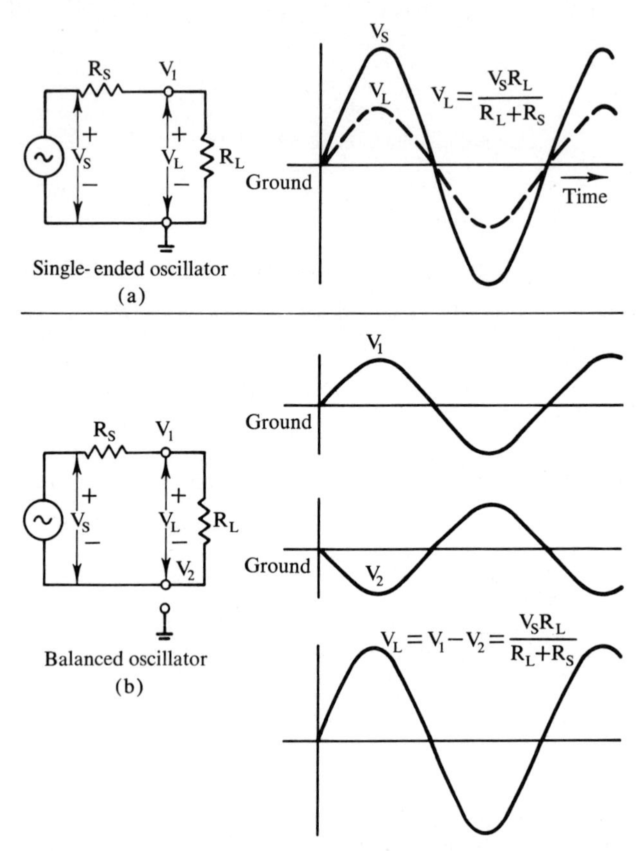

Fig. 13. Oscillator output waveforms.

Some oscillators allow selection of both single-ended and balanced operation, and perhaps two or more source resistances for each case. A typical unit, for example, offers:

Unbalanced output: 50 Ω, 75 Ω

Balanced output: 135 Ω, 150 Ω, 600 Ω

Flatness. Frequency-response flatness is a specification of how flat the output level remains as the frequency range is covered. Flatness varies considerably with different oscillator designs; in many cases, it is considered a component part of the amplitude-stability specification previously discussed.

Typical specifications may either show a curve such as that of Fig. 14 or state a "flatness," or alternatively a "frequency response," specification as:

"Flat within ±3 percent" or "±2 percent 100 Hz to 1 MHz, ±3 percent 10 to 100 Hz"

Frequency Accuracy. The *frequency-accuracy* specification reflects the worst deviation of the actual output frequency from that indicated on the frequency-range dial (or pushbuttons). It is usually all-inclusive, encompassing environmental effects, readout-mechanism parallax, frequency stability, and attenuator-component tolerances and their aging. Consequently, it is rather loosely specified.

Typical numbers for *RC* oscillators are ±2 percent, while *LC* oscillators more commonly are ±1 percent. Frequency accuracy may go under other titles, such as *dial accuracy* or *calibration accuracy.* Some oscillators are designed for accuracy and specified much tighter; for example, one digital unit with a frequency range of 10 Hz to 1 MHz is listed for frequency accuracy of:

±0.2 percent or ±0.1 Hz, whichever is greater (25°C)

Modulation—AM, FM, and Pulse. Signal generators are oscillators incorporating *modulation* capability to simulate communications signals. Three types of modulation capability are found commonly—AM, FM, and pulse.

Amplitude-modulation capability is ordinarily from a 1-kHz internal signal; different units will have varying degrees of modulation-level capability (from <30 to

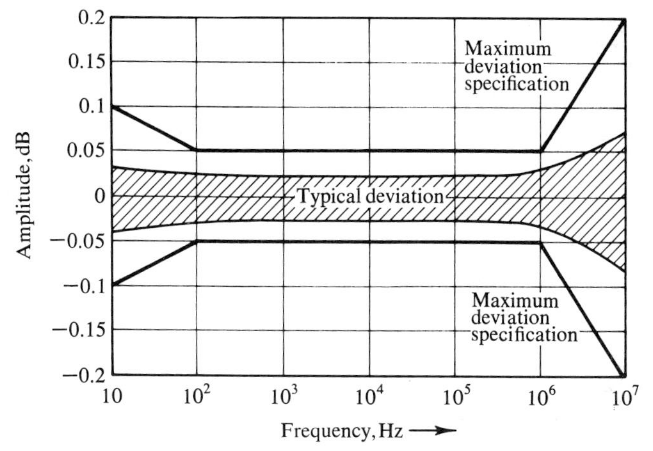

Fig. 14. Frequency-response flatness specification.

>95 percent). External signal modulation is also possible on many, from dc to 20 kHz (the full audio band). Usually distortion and incidental frequency modulation of the carrier signal (the fundamental oscillator output signal) are also specified.

Frequency-modulation capability is very similarly treated. A typical internal modulation capability is 75 kHz, with distortion <1 percent. Better units specify FM distortion range and accuracy, calibration, nonlinearity, and spurious FM. Consult the signal-generator section or the instrument operating manual for further information.

Pulse-modulation capability is usually limited to external sources. Rise-time and fall-time specifications are typically given along with an on-off pulse-amplitude ratio in decibels.

Output Monitor. Numerous oscillators include an analog voltmeter readout which serves as an *output-signal monitor.* Typically the voltmeter measures the actual oscillator output after the amplitude control (or vernier) but prior to a calibrated attenuator (this avoids having to provide a multirange voltmeter). The meter reading is usually in both volts and decibels, but the power indication necessarily assumes that $R_L = R_s$ since a voltmeter cannot read power.

Note that an output monitor may be used in conjunction with the amplitude control to fine-tune for better frequency-response flatness. Some units take full advantage of this, offering an expand-scale voltmeter control for use after the output has been adjusted on the normal scale. The difference in specified flatness with this relatively simple addition for one manufacturer's oscillator is:

Flatness:

Normal scale—±2 percent 100 Hz to 1 MHz, ±3 percent 10 to 100 Hz

Expand scale—±0.25 percent all frequencies on 3-V, 1-V scales (no attenuator)
±0.75 percent on 0.3-V range and below

Phase Control, Lock, or Synchronization. Many times it is desirable to have two different oscillators set at the same frequency, yet because of frequency-stability problems, it is virtually impossible to obtain any true correlation for any period of time. An external *synchronization* capability will permit an oscillator set essentially to the same frequency as another to be "locked" to the other. A typical wording of a synchronization specification is:

A 1.5-V peak-to-peak external signal will lock oscillator over a range of approximately ±0.5 percent with a slight change in distortion and amplitude for a sine-wave synchronizing signal.

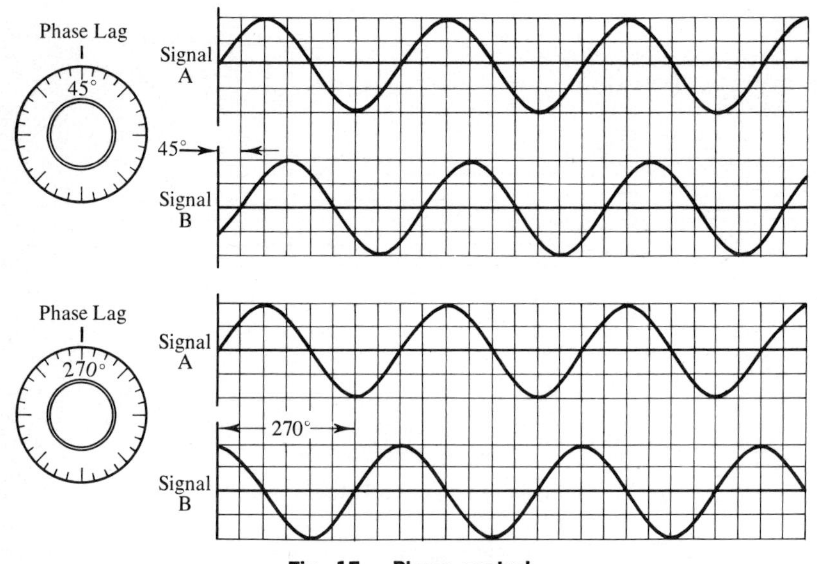

Fig. 15. Phase control.

It is also desirable to have *phase control* between the two sine-wave signals that are synchronized. There are two common methods for achieving this. Units exist which have two outputs, one signal a delayed version of the other. The delay is controlled by a knob labeled "phase lag" marked in degrees. The knob rotation and corresponding pair of output signals as a function of time are shown in Fig. 15. Another type of unit incorporates a *phase-lock loop* to accomplish the same variable-phase capability with respect to its signal and one from another synchronized oscillator.

Pushbutton or Digital Tuning. Wien-bridge oscillators are available with discrete frequency selection by either pushbutton or digital switch selection. The resistive branches of the frequency-selective network (Fig. 5) are made up of parallel combinations of resistors which determine the digits (choice is typically between three and five digits). The frequency range is also pushbutton-selectable, selected by switching the capacitors (Fig. 18).

Pushbutton tuning enables the frequency to be changed by precise increments, and it also permits electronic control for remote programmability in some instruments. The greatest specification change comes in the new capability for resetting a frequency to accuracy much greater than the standard frequency accuracy attainable with dial-adjustable oscillators. A typical specification might be:

Frequency range: 10 Hz to 1 MHz in 4,500 discrete steps; overlapping vernier permits setting to intermediate frequencies

Frequency accuracy: ±1 percent

Frequency resettability: ±0.02 percent

Residual, Incidental, and Spurious AM, FM. Harmonic, hum, and noise distortion were earlier defined as broadband specifications. *Spurious* AM and/or FM specifications are distortion specifications for smaller frequency bands.

Residual AM may be roughly equated in effect to hum modulation, since hum is 60-Hz amplitude modulation superposed on the output signal frequency. The residual AM specification is intended to cover any cw frequency from 20 Hz to 20 kHz. Specifications will read about as follows:

< -50 dB (rms volts) $<$10-kHz bandwidth.

Residual FM is a small frequency modulation analogous to hum amplitude modulation. It is specified either as Δf or as a ratio of $\Delta f/f_{osc}$:

±20-Hz peak, or less than ±1 part in 10^{+6}, whichever is greater

Incidental FM or AM is a modulation equivalent to *residual FM or AM* in effect and mode of specification; its origin, though, is from the AM or FM modulation signal used in signal generation. Specifications are consequently much looser, since a known source of distortion is intimately involved.

FRONT-PANEL CONTROLS

Oscillator front panels are simple in concept but widely varying in appearance. We will concentrate upon the similarities first and then explore some unique controls.

Figures 16, 17, and 18 show the frequency-range dial for three different oscillators.

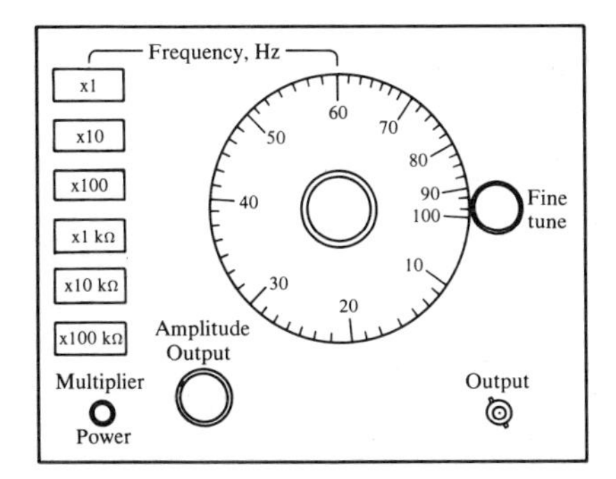

Fig. 16. ***RC*-oscillator front panel.**

Figure 16 is of an *RC* Wien-bridge oscillator with a big rotatable dial spanning one frequency decade. The multiplier switches at the side permit selection of the decade. Note that the dial allows only a single 360° rotation. Sometimes a knob for fine tuning is included which is a control linked by gears to the large dial. Rotation of the fine-tuning knob 360° will adjust perhaps 6° of the large-dial rotation.

Figure 17 illustrates the band tuning of a typical *LC* oscillator. The band-selector knob rotates the drum readout of the various bands, and then the frequency range within a band is selected by rotating the range knob which gear-drives the dial indicator. This type of frequency selection is very similar to that found for one band on FM tuners, or for several bands on radios with AM, FM, and short-wave receiver capability.

A third type of frequency tuning, newer and much less common, is by pushbuttons. The circuitry is usually a Wien-bridge *RC* oscillator modified for large parallel combinations of resistors to give multiple discrete frequencies (Fig. 18). This type of panel allows setting the frequency range to three significant figures on any decade provided. In addition a vernier allows overlap between any two discrete frequencies.

Output amplitudes and terminals vary also. Figure 16 shows a continuous amplitude control and a balanced 600-Ω output (+ and − terminals). Connection between + and − terminals gives a balanced output which may be "floated" off ground as much as several hundred volts typically. Alternatively, connection of the ground terminal to either terminal provides a ground reference if desired.

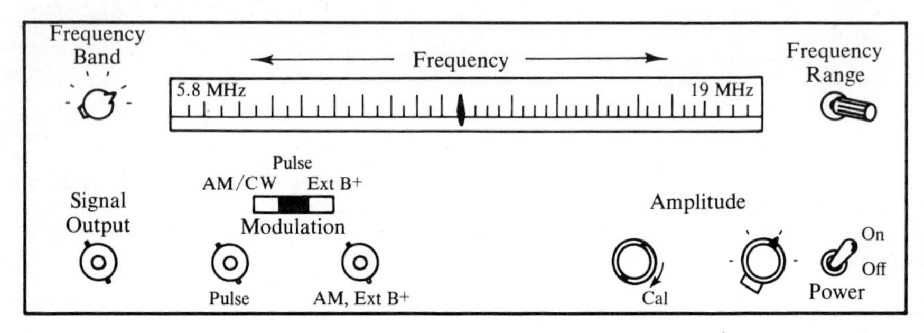

Fig. 17. ***LC*-oscillator front panel.**

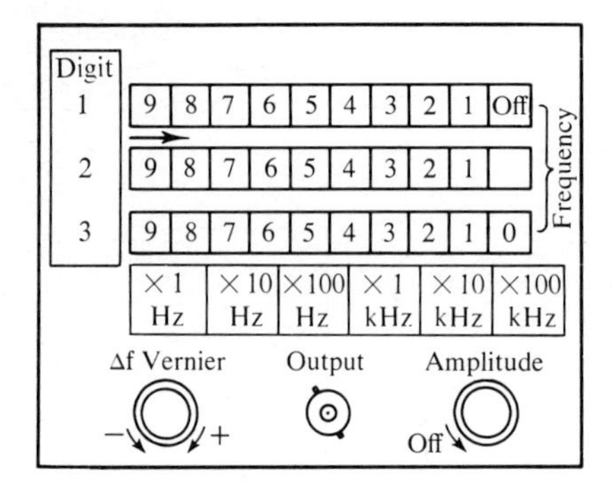

Fig. 18. Pushbutton-oscillator front panel.

Fig. 19. Output monitor meter-face.

Figure 18 shows both 50- and 600-Ω single-ended outputs, while the instrument of Fig. 17 has only a 50-Ω output connection. This instrument contains two amplitude knobs—one is a knob indicating a calibrated power-output level, the other a vernier capable of continuously reducing a level to the next lower level. There is a "cal" position for the vernier, which renders it inoperative.

The instrument of Fig. 17 also contains inputs for pulse, AM, or FM modulation for use as a signal generator.

Use of an output monitor is relatively easy if one is familiar with a voltmeter. Figure 19 shows the meter readout for a standard output monitor. Note that the meter face mentions that it is accurate for power output in dBm only into a 50-Ω load. This is true since power is a function of both voltage and resistance (or current) and a voltmeter cannot tell the full story. For output voltage (rms), it of course is correct regardless of impedance. Since the voltmeter reads the output, it will indicate a full meter-needle swing as the "amplitude" knob is rotated.

SOURCES OF ERROR

7. Resistance and Impedance Matching Since 50- and 600-Ω source resistances are quite common for oscillators, and one is frequently told to "match" impedances carefully, some attention should be given to this "problem." For example, it was stated in the power-output discussion that $R_L = R_s$ is necessary for maximum power output. To illustrate why, consider that maximum voltage V_{max} occurs for $R_L = \infty$ (open circuit), while maximum current I_{max} occurs for $R_L = 0\ \Omega$ (short circuit). For many cases, we see intuitively that $R_L = R_s$ is an improper choice, especially if it is voltage or current rather than power that we seek to maximize.

To define maximum power output, however, it can now be shown that

$$P_{out} = (V_{out})(I_{out}) \tag{8}$$

$$V_{out} = \frac{V_{max} R_L}{R_L + R_s} \tag{9}$$

$$I_{out} = \frac{V_{max}}{R_L + R_s} \tag{10}$$

Thus

$$P_{out} = \frac{V_{max}{}^2 R_L}{(R_L + R_s)^2} \tag{11}$$

This may be differentiated by calculus techniques to show directly that maximum P_{out} occurs when $R_L = R_s$, but we may see the same effect by a simple example:

Let $V_{max} = 10$ V, $R_L = 10\ \Omega$, and $R_s = 10\ \Omega$.
Using Eq. (11) to calculate P_{out}:

$$P_{out} = \frac{(10)^2\,(10)}{(10 + 10)^2} = \frac{1{,}000}{400} = 2.50 \text{ W}$$

Now, let $R_L = 9\ \Omega$.

$$P_{out} = \frac{(10)^2\,(9)}{(9 + 10)^2} = \frac{900}{361} = 2.49 \text{ W}$$

Alternatively, let $R_L = 11\ \Omega$.

$$P_{out} = \frac{(10)^2\,(11)}{(11 + 10)^2} = \frac{1{,}100}{441} = 2.49 \text{ W}$$

Thus, although the differences are slight, it is seen that matching $R_L = R_s$ does result in maximum power transfer. The effects of different ratios of R_L and R_s for voltage, current, and power transfer are shown in Fig. 20.

Cable connections are important for resistance and impedance matching in many cases. If an oscillator has a 50-Ω output, it will perform best with a 50-Ω termination at the far end of a 50-Ω cable. Otherwise, the inductance and capacitance of the cable will cause high-frequency mismatch. If unshielded cable is used, radiation of the output signal may be expected, and distortion or worse could result.

Balanced oscillators in particular require attention to cabling to avoid amplitude and phase-shift distortion. For example, mismatch of input cables, such as a 50-Ω cable on the positive output terminal and a 600-Ω cable on the negative output terminal, is occasionally seen. At dc conditions no noticeable effect will be seen if R_L is much much larger than 600 Ω; if, however, it is of the same magnitude of resistance, amplitude distortion will occur at all frequencies. Moreover, regardless of the load resistance, at high frequencies (≥ 1 MHz) the phase difference in the two signals from the cables alone is far more than most practical test situations are trying to determine.

High-frequency Impedance Matching. In reality, oscillators have a source output impedance Z_s rather than the pure resistance R_s as we have largely assumed in the discussion. To determine the proper load impedance for maximum power transfer, one must take this fact into account.

Since the load impedance Z_L and the source impedance Z_s are in series, the total impedance may be written as

$$Z_T = Z_s + Z_L = (R_s \pm jX_s) + (R_L \pm jX_L) = (R_s + R_L) \pm j(X_s + X_L) \quad (12)$$

The maximum current flow for a given voltage occurs at minimum impedance, which means that $X_S = -X_L$. This case now reduces to the simple one where $R_L = R_S$ is required. Consequently, at maximum power transfer, Z_L has been adjusted to be the *complex conjugate* of Z_S.

$$Z_L = R_L + jX_L = R_s - jX_s = \bar{Z}_s \quad (13)$$

This procedure is termed impedance matching, and is valid at only one frequency (wherever the matching is done). Its value is in obtaining the rated power output where high-frequency reactance would otherwise reduce the oscillator power delivery to the load.

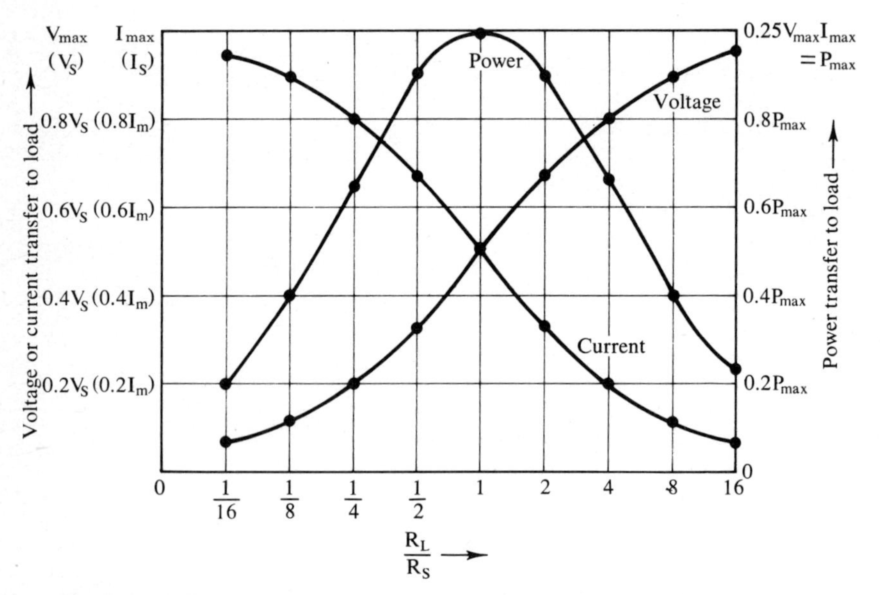

Fig. 20. Voltage, current, and power transfer for varying ratio of R_L to R_S.

8. Leveled Output It is often desirable to obtain a constant output level across the load with changing frequency—this is the purpose of the *flatness* specification, and the reason for AGC and leveled-output designs. When reactive loads rather than pure resistances are encountered, some precautions must be taken. Figure 21 illustrates two methods of leveled-output correction, both of which are employed in different instruments. The first results in an output voltage across the load impedance that is very frequency-dependent if the reactive components of Z_s and Z_L differ. If the reactive load is set to kZ_s, however, the output will not vary with frequency. This is termed a compensated load impedance. Since V_s is leveled, V_{out} is also leveled or constant with frequency change.

The second approach provides V_{out} as a constant, independent of Z_s, Z_L, or frequency. This approach is more convenient as it requires no load compensation; it is usually the method incorporated in output-monitor meter designs.

Note, however, that the first approach does allow determination of the load-impedance frequency characteristics, for the case where $Z_s = R_s$ and Z_L is unknown.

This is done as shown in Fig. 22, and is a capability not possible with the second case of Fig. 21. The operating manual of a given instrument should clarify these high-frequency problems for a particular case.

9. Changing Output Impedance It is unfortunately true that some oscillators with attenuators have varying output impedance at different attenuator settings. This makes impedance matching or a leveled-output requirement much harder to obtain. Figure 23 shows a typical situation where this problem is encountered.

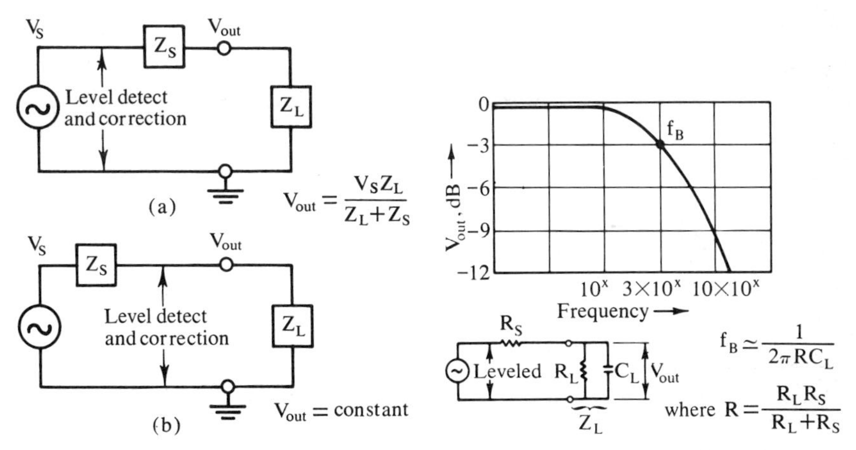

Fig. 21. Two methods of leveled output.

Fig. 22. Determination of Z_L.

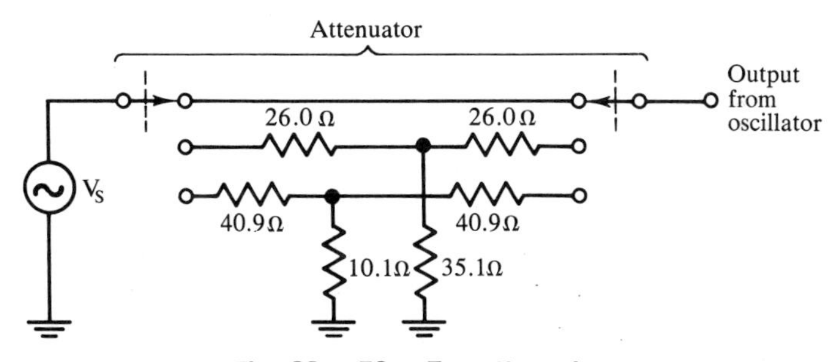

Fig. 23. 50-Ω Tee attenuator.

Note that on the maximum signal-output range, $R_s = 0$ Ω, but on all the other ranges, a tee attenuator is used to give a constant 50-Ω output resistance. If the load resistor is 50 Ω, and the cable connection is 50-Ω coaxial cable, every range will be matched except the top one. Even if an output monitor is used, the cable termination is mismatched and any change in frequency necessitates recalibration. This problem is more serious in *LC* oscillators than in *RC* because of the higher-frequency spectrum at which they operate. The best way to avoid the problem is to check carefully the output-impedance specifications for any high-frequency oscillator with an attenuator.

Chapter 30

Pulse Generators

JEROME L. SHANNON

Tektronix, Inc., Beaverton, Oregon

1. Description The pulse generator is an instrument that can provide a voltage or current output whose waveform may be described as a pulse or series of pulses. Other instruments such as function generators, signal generators, and oscilloscopes may provide such a waveform, but where provided they are nearly always a secondary or alternate mode of operation and offer very limited usage.

A pulse (in the general case) may be defined as a wave (voltage or current) which departs from an initial level for a finite duration and ultimately returns to the original level. This definition is so inclusive that it is common to differentiate between pulse generators and other signal sources by defining the output of a pulse generator as a wave (voltage or current) which changes from an initial level to some other single level for a finite duration, then returns to the initial level for a finite duration. This type of waveform is often referred to as a rectangular pulse which may or may not be repetitive.

Fundamental time and amplitude relationships of common pulse terms are shown, referenced to each other, in an idealized diagram of a series of pulses (see Fig. 1). A pulse generator whose output-pulse parameters are suitably well known may be used to stimulate devices, circuits, or systems. The reactions of the devices, circuits, or systems, when properly measured, can be used to describe or specify many of their characteristics.

In order to achieve meaningful results, the suitability of the measuring device or instrument, along with the method of measurement, is as important as the suitability of the pulse generator.

The oscilloscope, since it can conveniently display, in graphic form, a wide range of voltage or current levels on one axis while representing time on the other axis, is a nearly ideal companion instrument for making amplitude vs. time domain measurements such as switching time, propagation delays, storage times, and recovery times. In addition, frequency response of a device under test may be calculated after the pulse response is measured, using this combination of instruments. Other instruments such as voltmeters, frequency analyzers, and counters may be capable of valid measurement in conjunction with a pulse generator but are usually not as convenient nor are they as versatile. Moreover, the oscilloscope can be used

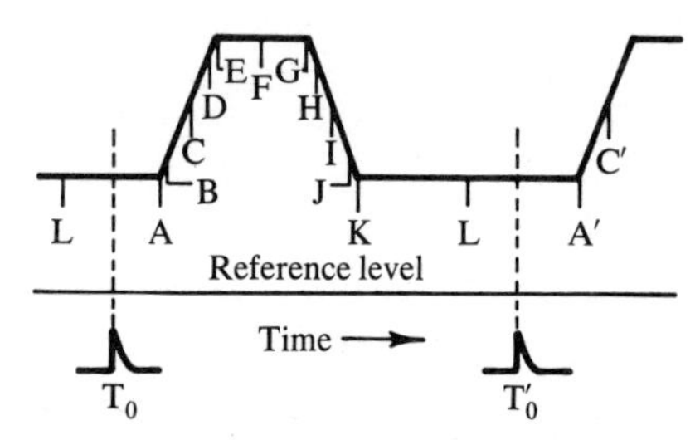

Fig. 1. Reference level: May be expressed in voltage or current (usually system ground).
Base-line offset: L minus reference (in voltage or current)
Pulse amplitude and polarity: F minus L (in voltage or current)
Leading edge: Duration AE
Trailing edge: Duration GK
Rise time: Duration BD (usually 10 to 90 percent of amplitude)
Fall time: Duration HJ (usually 90 to 10 percent of amplitude)
Pulse duration: Duration CI (where C and I are 50 percent of amplitude)
Period: Duration AA' (equals 1/frequency if periodic)
Delay: Duration $T_0 - C$ (T_0 represents a related signal often called pretrigger or sync pulse)
Duty factor: (Duration CI/duration AA') $\times$ 100 (in percent)

to measure most parameters of the pulse generator or vice versa if one of the two instruments is known to be calibrated.

In the design and testing of digital circuits used in computers, communication systems, and other types of digital equipment, pulse generators are widely used to simulate signals or information which may be encountered during the actual usage of such equipment. A special class of pulse generators whose output can simulate the data content of digital words is often required. These are usually called data generators or word generators.

There are many pulse generators which have been designed to emphasize performance in respect to one or more parameters such as amplitude, switching times, minimum pulse duration, maximum repetition rate, or other parameters. However, because of device limitations and cost, every pulse generator must compromise performance of some kind to achieve outstanding performance of another kind. Pulse generators that are able to perform satisfactorily in a wide variety of applications may be thought of as general-purpose generators, but the user must be aware that it is important to know what a particular pulse generator cannot do as well as know what it can do. Only after an examination of its features and an assurance that it is meeting the published performance specifications may the user determine with confidence if a particular pulse generator is suitable for the applications in mind.

2. Operator Controls To the degree that an operator may adjust or select the type of pulse(s) he desires in conjunction with selecting the use of certain features and operating modes, a pulse generator may be said to be general-purpose. Front-panel controls consisting of switches, verniers, and connectors along with appropriate terminology are provided so as to enhance the operator's use of the instrument (see Fig. 2).

A list of common controls and features is shown below, accompanied by either a definition of the parameter or a statement related to usage.

Important pulse parameters often controllable by the operator are:

Amplitude. Expressed as the difference, in volts or amperes, between the reference base line and that portion of the pulse that is described as the "top" or "flat-top."

Polarity. Either positive or negative, referring to amplitude expressed in volts or amperes.

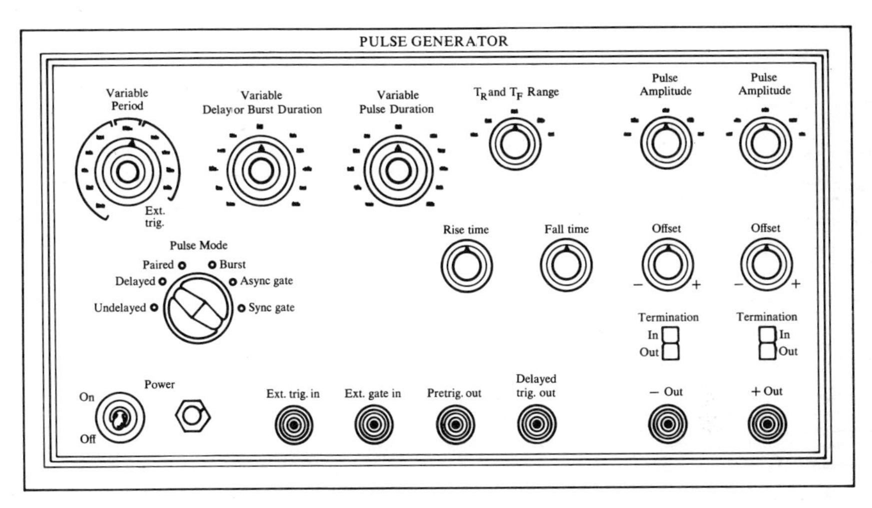

Fig. 2. Typical front panel for pulse generators.

Rise Time. The interval at the *leading edge* of a pulse between two amplitude reference times. Usually 10 and 90 percent of the amplitude unless otherwise specified.

Fall Time. The interval at the *trailing edge* of a pulse between two amplitude reference times. Usually 10 and 90 percent of the amplitude unless otherwise specified.

Duration. The interval between an amplitude reference time on the leading edge and an amplitude reference time on the trailing edge, usually 50 percent of amplitude unless otherwise specified. Duration is frequently referred to as width.

Period. The interval between corresponding reference points on successive cycles of repetitive pulses. Period is frequently referred to as pulse-repetition frequency or pulse-repetition rate if the waveform is periodic.

Delay. The interval separating an amplitude reference time on the leading edge of the pulse (usually 50 percent of the amplitude) from a synchronizing signal. The synchronizing signal is often called "pretrigger" or "sync" but may simply be an undelayed pulse.

Duty Factor. The ratio of the duration to the period. May be limited by output-power capability or by switching and recovery times required by internal circuitry. In some instruments the latter limitation may be overcome by choosing the complement of the normal output (refer to complementary outputs).

Base Line. The level, volts or amperes, expressed in either polarity, from which the pulse starts. The deviation from a reference level (usually 0 V) to the base line is referred to as offset.

In addition to control of major pulse parameters, general-purpose pulse generators provide many additional features to enhance the versatility of the instrument.

Some of the common features are:

External Trigger. Allows the user to disable the period generator and substitute an external signal.

Manual Trigger. Allows the user to disable the period generator and substitute a signal which is generated *once* for each manual operation of a switch (usually a pushbutton).

Pretrigger Output. An auxiliary output ahead of the main pulse(s) useful for triggering other equipment. Often used as a time reference T_0. Sometimes called sync output.

Delayed Trigger Output. An auxiliary output, whose delay after pretrigger output is adjustable, used to trigger other equipment. Often used in conjunction with the pretrigger output or external trigger input to establish an interval of known delay.

Simultaneous Outputs. Usually of opposite polarity, they constitute the main pulse outputs of a pulse generator. Used one at a time, they provide choice of polarity. Used together, they are useful to test certain types of logic functions. Often each output has independent control of amplitude and base-line offset.

Complementary Output(s). Allows the user to exchange the on time and off time of the period without altering the amplitude, base line, or polarity. Especially useful for extending the duty factor to nearly 100 percent when limited by internal circuit switching and recovery times. When using complementary output(s), the user must remember that the duration control determines the off time and that the on time is the difference between the period and the duration.

Output Termination(s). An internal termination(s) that may be switched across the output source to convert from a high-impedance current source to a low-impedance voltage source. Also if the impedance of the termination(s) is nearly equal to the characteristic impedance of the user's output cable(s), any reflections due to impedance mismatch at the far end will be absorbed for the most part, thereby greatly reducing unwanted aberrations caused by external connections. In actual practice the output-termination(s) cable(s) is nearly always 50Ω, and best results are obtained when driving 50-Ω loads. Use of an internal termination will reduce the amplitude by one-half when 50-Ω loads are used.

In addition to setting pulse parameters and selecting the use of desired features, the user may need to operate a pulse generator in one of several possible modes of operation. Common operating modes are:

Undelayed. The beginning of the leading edge of the output pulse is fixed in time with respect to the pretrigger pulse. The amount of delay settable by by the equipment manufacturer and is usually found to be 30 to 50 ns.

Delayed. The beginning of the leading edge of the output pulse is variable in time with respect to the pretrigger pulse. The amount of delay settable by the user may range from a few nanoseconds to tens of seconds.

Paired Pulse. Often called double pulse, this mode provides two successive pulses for each period. The first pulse, which is the same as the undelayed pulse, is followed by the delayed pulse. In this mode the period must be set longer than the sum of both pulse durations plus the delay to allow sufficient time for completion of both pulses.

Gated. In this mode the output pulses are modulated by an external waveform so as to turn off or turn on the output pulses during the duration of the gating waveform. Gating may be synchronous or asynchronous with respect to the leading edge of the first pulse in any one group of pulses. In synchronous operation the period generator is off and turned on by the external gating waveform and continues to run until the removal of the gating waveform. In asynchronous operation the period generator is on but no output is allowed to initiate other functions until a gating waveform is applied. Therefore, the leading edge of the first pulse will be usable in making desired measurements or performing desired functions.

Burst. This is the same as gated except that the gating waveform is generated internally when triggered by an external signal. In some instruments the delay generator is converted to a burst-time generator which determines the duration of the burst while the external trigger rate determines the burst-repetition rate. The period generator continues to determine the repetition rate of the pulses within the burst.

When operating pulse generators, the user should first achieve an understanding of how the functional circuits are interrelated and controlled by the front-panel controls. This is most easily accomplished by a careful reading of the operating manual and by comparing the circuit block diagram with the front-panel controls. A careful comparison of the block diagram (Fig. 3) and the front panel (Fig. 2) illustrated here will help the reader develop a better understanding of pulse generators.

3. Specifications Specifications for instruments are used to describe the major electrical, physical, and environmental characteristics of an instrument type. The

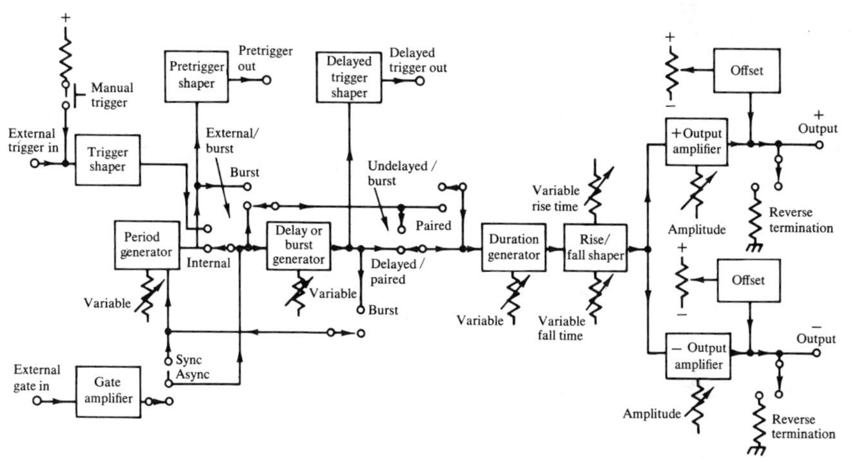

Fig. 3. Block diagram of pulse generator circuit elements.

specifications form the basis of the contract between the purchaser and the seller; that is, they describe in specific detail what performance the buyer may legally expect if he purchases an instrument from the seller.

The potential user of a pulse generator, or any other electronic equipment, should refer to the instrument specifications to help determine if a particular instrument will be usable in making desired measurements or performing desired functions.

When selecting a particular instrument, the user usually is attempting to select the instrument that best suits the applications he has in mind. The specifications, along with terms relating to price, delivery, warranty, and after-sale service, are the primary factors used to make a buy decision. In addition, the reputation of the seller and the seller's instruments is often considered.

Listed below are major electrical characteristics of general-purpose pulse generators accompanied by specifications available in modern instruments. It is important to realize that these specifications are only representative of what is available but that no instrument would offer all of them.

Period:

Time: 10 s or longer and as short as 1 or 2 ns

Accuracy: 3 percent, may be much better if digitally programmed

Jitter: 0.05 percent or better

Delay or burst:
  Time: 1 s or longer and as short as 1 to 2 ns
  Accuracy: 3 percent may be much better if digitally programmed
  Jitter: 0.05 percent or better
Pulse duration:
  Time: Same as delay or burst
  Accuracy: Same as delay or burst
  Jitter: Same as delay or burst
Paired pulse:
  Minimum separation: 1 to 2 ns (defined as time from leading edge of undelayed pulse to the leading edge of the delayed pulse)
  Duty factor: 80 percent or better, typically reduced to 50 percent at a minimum period. Typically much less in high-power output-pulse generators
Rise and fall:
  Time: ½ ns to seconds
  Accuracy: 3 percent, may be much better if digitally programmed
  Linearity: Within 1 percent of ideal ramp on slower ranges
Pulse output:
  Amplitude: Up to 100 V or 2 A (may be much more in special types)
  Accuracy: 3 percent, may be much better if digitally programmed
  Aberrations: 3 percent of pulse amplitude (normally includes preshoot, overshoot, ringing, and flatness of pulse top and pulse base line)
Source resistance: Greater than 500 Ω, if called a current source. Typically 50 Ω ±5 percent if a voltage source.
  Amplitude stability: 2 percent or better
  Coincidence: When dual outputs are available, the leading edges are within 1 ns of each other
Base-line offset:
  Amplitude: Up to ±10 V or ±200 mA
  Accuracy: 0.1 percent or better
  Stability: 0.1 percent or better
Gating and triggering:
  Requirements: Usually compatible with present-day semiconductor-logic levels
  Auxiliary outputs: Usually compatible with present-day semiconductor-logic levels

BASIC GENERAL-PURPOSE PULSE GENERATOR

4. Description of Operation The period generator, or rate generator as it is sometimes called, determines the period of the output pulses. It is usually, but not necessarily, an astable emitter-coupled multivibrator. Control of the period is easily accomplished by changing the timing capacitor value (usually by decades) and varying the current in the emitters, provided some type of clamping is used in the collectors.

Provision is made for shaping the output for proper triggering of the delay or duration generators which follow. Also the period generator is capable of being turned off in such a way that the output from the gating amplifier allows the period generator to operate only during the gate time. Since the start of the period is synchronous with the start of the gate, this operation is known as synchronous gating. When the period generator is free-running but its output is not allowed to trigger the circuits that follow, except when there is a gating pulse to the period generator itself, asynchronous gating occurs.

If it is desired to use an external signal to determine the period, the generator is shut off and properly shaped triggers from the external trigger input replace the output of the period generator. Synchronous gating cannot be provided, however.

An auxiliary output of the period generator usually called the pretrigger is, after shaping, provided at the front panel for purposes of establishing a time reference.

The delay generator determines the time that the output pulses may be delayed with respect to the time reference of the undelayed outputs. It is usually, but not necessarily, an emitter-coupler monostable multivibrator. Control of delay time is accomplished by changing the timing-capacitor value (usually by decades) and varying the current in the timing-capacitor charging path.

Provision is made for shaping the output for properly triggering the duration generator by connecting its input to the output of the external trigger shaper and connecting its output to the synchronous gating line of the period generator whose output, which is turned off as in synchronous gating, is connected to the input of the duration generator. When the external trigger starts the delay generator, it produces an output pulse equal in duration to the settings of the delay controls. This pulse acts as an internally generated gating waveform to gate on the period generator synchronously.

An auxiliary output of the delay generator is, after shaping, provided at the front panel for purposes of establishing a delayed time reference.

The duration generator, sometimes called width generator, determines the duration of the output pulses. The duration generator is nearly always the same type of circuit as the delay generator. The output is not shaped, since the rise/fall shaper which follows requires only a change in levels to initiate its operation.

Usually trigger outputs are not provided from the duration generators; however, some instruments have an auxiliary output which can be used in conjunction with external data generators. The output from the external data generators is then fed back to the pulse-generator outputs via an external connector.

If the input of the duration generator is connected to the output of the period generator only, the operation is called undelayed even though a finite delay may exist between the output pulses and the pretrigger output. If the duration generator is connected to the output of the delay generator, the operation is called delayed, meaning that the output pulses are delayed from where the undelayed pulses would have been by an interval set by the delay-generator controls. If the output of both the period generator and the delay generator is connected to the input of the duration generator, the operation is called paired pulse or double pulse. In this mode, there are two pulses per period, the first being the undelayed pulse and the second the delayed pulse. Both pulses will have the same duration.

The rise/fall shaper determines the switching times of the leading and trailing edges of the output pulses. Usually two complementary transistors whose collectors are common to each other are alternately switched on and off by the output of the duration generator. The current in either collector charges a timing capacitor connected between ground and the junction of the two collectors. The currents during the on states are constant; therefore, the voltage across the capacitor changes linearly with time. If the positive- and negative-going voltage changes are both clamped at appropriate levels, the output will describe a trapezoidal wave. Control of the rise and fall times is accomished by changing the timing-capacitor value (usually by decades) or by varying the value of either or both of the constant-current sources. Since the timing capacitor is common to both the rate of rise and the rate of fall, only the changes in the current sources are independent, restricting the maximum ratio of rise time to fall time or vice versa.

The + and − output amplifiers in conjunction with their offset circuits are used to set the magnitude of the output pulses along with the base-line references for each output. Both amplifiers are usually very similar, the major difference being the use of transistor types, i.e., *npn* or *pnp*.

Since the output amplifiers must amplify the linear ramps from the rise/fall shaper, the transistors involved are operated primarily within their linear regions. Most output stages use one or more transistors in parallel, with their collectors connected to the user's load via the front-panel connector. To obtain variable pulse amplitude, the output state is normally operated near cutoff, and current in the output stage is increased toward saturation during the time the pulse is generated.

Offset is provided by connecting two variable-current sources from + and − supplies to the ouput connector. The algebraic sum of the two current sources determines the base-line offset. Since both the output stage and the offset sources are current sources, the pulse and base-line offset voltages can be known only when the resistance of the load is considered. If the output controls are calibrated in voltage, it is usually into 50 Ω.

Often an internal 50-Ω termination may be switched across the output. This may be used to lower the source impedance of the output amplifier and offset circuits; it is also used to absorb reflections from the load when mismatch occurs.

To protect the output from excessive voltages caused by reflections, inductive "kickback," external voltage, or a load of too many ohms, both positive and negative diode clamps are usually connected to the output. These clamps limit the maximum voltages at the output.

5. Guide to Troubleshooting and Functional Check-out (Using Front-panel Controls and an Oscilloscope) An operator should first recheck his control setup and ascertain that the instrument is set up and connected to the load properly (see Sec. 6).

By keeping in mind the major circuit functions and their relationships to each other, troubles can usually be isolated to these major circuits or to the connections between them. When a circuit is found to be defective, it is a good idea first to check the power supplies carefully, since a power supply that is operating improperly may adversely affect some, but not necessarily all, of the circuits.

The following steps performed in sequence should help to isolate most troubles, but first look carefully for damaged components, hardware, and leads.

1. While monitoring the pretrigger output with a suitable oscilloscope and high-impedance probe, check for proper signal while operating the period generator through its range of operation. Check gating and external triggering functions if deemed necessary.

2. With the oscilloscope externally triggered by the pretrigger output, monitor the delayed trigger output. Check for proper signal and correct amount of delay while operating the delay generator through its range of operation, making sure that period is adjusted so as to prevent scaling. Repeat while operating in delayed and paired pulse modes.

3. With the oscilloscope triggered as in step 2, monitor the auxiliary output of the duration generator if provided; if not, use the instrument manual to help locate the duration-generator output. Check for proper output, remembering to measure dc voltage. For both the on state and the off state, refer to the manual for these levels. Operate the duration generator throughout its range of operation again, adjusting period to prevent scaling. Repeat as deemed necessary for delayed and paired pulse modes.

4. Use the manual to help locate the output of the rise/fall shaper, usually an emitter follower. Again check for proper signal and dc voltages as indicated by the manual while operating rise/fall shaper through its range of operation.

5. With the base-line offsets and internal terminations switched out, monitor the pulse outputs while terminating into 50-Ω external loads. Operate the pulse-amplitude controls through their range. Switch in offsets, and operate the offset controls through their range. Switch in internal terminations. Observe that pulse amplitude and base-line offset voltages are reduced by half. Switch internal terminations out and replace external 50-Ω loads with loads of several hundred ohms; operate the pulse-amplitude controls, and observe that the outputs are limited at the maximum voltage output as stated in the manual.

6. These simple checks should help locate the problem area. If they fail to do so, it probably means the trouble occurs only under some combinations of the operating controls, and it may be necessary to go back to the original setup where the trouble was first noticed. By moving controls one at a time and carefully observing any changes in the nature of the trouble, the problem area may become apparent.

7. Assuming that neither abnormal line voltage nor abnormal ambient temperatures are the cause and the above steps did not help locate the trouble, the next step is probably turning the instrument over to an expert instrument-repair man

or someone more familiar with the instrument and its circuitry. If neither is available, a careful study of the manual and additional checks will have to be made.

6. Sources of Error Inherent errors exist in any pulse generator because design compromises have had to be made in order for the manufacturer to produce and sell an instrument that represents good value to the customer. Most of these errors will be troublesome only when making certain measurements where the desired accuracy of measurement is near or exceeds the manufacturer's specifications. Check the manufacturer's specifications carefully. Some errors inherent in most pulse generators are:

1. *Period Jitter.* Slight variations in period are usually caused by inadequate power-supply regulation or ground-loop problems. Period jitter is usually greatest when the delay time or pulse duration is set at the maximum allowed for a given period. Period jitter can be checked by using a good time-interval meter with a recording output or a good oscilloscope with delaying sweep set to observe time displacements of a pulse several pulses following the pulse that triggers the start of the sweep.

2. *Delay-time Jitter.* Usually caused by inadequate power-supply regulation and by problems associated with triggering the delay generator on, especially when the delay time is set to the maximum allowed for a given period. Delay-time jitter may be measured with a good time-interval meter or a good oscilloscope with delaying sweep. Observe the time differences between the leading edge of the undelayed pulse and the leading edge of the delayed pulse while operating in the paired-pulse mode.

3. *Pulse-duration Jitter.* Causes are similar to those associated with delay-time jitter. Pulse duration may be measured using a good time-interval meter or a good oscilloscope using delaying sweep. Observe the time displacements of the trailing edge of the pulse while triggering the sweep on the leading edge.

4. *Rise/fall Time Variations.* Usually caused by changing pulse amplitude or base-line offset which adversely affects the rise/fall times. Load requirements may also affect the rise/fall times. These variations are best measured with a good oscilloscope whose specified rise time is many times faster than the rise/fall times to be measured.

5. *Pulse Aberrations.* Aberrations are characteristics of a given output stage and may be adversely affected by changes in pulse amplitude or base-line offset. Load requirements may also effect a change in pulse aberrations. These aberrations are best measured with a good oscilloscope whose specified rise time is many times faster than the aberrations.

6. *Pulse-amplitude Variations.* Usually caused by changes in duty factor or base-line offset which change the power dissipated in the output stage, causing localized heating of the output transistors, which can change their gain. Pulse-amplitude variations can be easily measured using a good oscilloscope or voltmeter.

7. *Base-line Drift.* Causes are similar to those affecting pulse-amplitude variations and can be measured in the same way.

8. *Synchronous-gating Errors.* Caused by trigger jitter in the gating circuit or by turn-on jitter in the period generator. Also, if the charge across the period-generator timing capacitor when turned off awaiting the gate waveform is different from that during the off cycle of normal operation, the first period during the gate time will be different from the periods which follow. Gating errors are best measured using a good oscilloscope which is externally triggered by the external gating waveform while observing the start of the first pulse for jitter and comparing its period with those that follow.

9. *Pulse-duration Changes with Changes in Rise/Fall Time Setting.* If the rise time or fall time is varied, it is apparent that more or less time will be utilized for the leading or trailing edges to pass through 50 percent of the pulse amplitude. Since pulse duration is usually defined as the interval from the 50 percent level on the leading edge to the 50 percent level on the trailing edge, the changes in rise time or fall time must change the pulse-duration time. To overcome this difficulty, if required the user should set up the rise and fall times first and then set the de-

sired pulse duration while using an oscilloscope to measure the actual times involved.

Improper techniques and forgetfulness on the part of the user can cause errors which may invalidate measurements being conducted. An understanding of the instrument and the measurement being conducted along with care in setting up the equipment being used will help to eliminate errors of this sort. Some common user errors are:

1. Exceeding maximum allowable duty factor or setting pulse duration greater than period. This causes scaling to occur so that the period will be much longer than anticipated. Also period and duration jitter may exceed the manufacturer's specifications.

2. Setting delay time in excess of maximum allowable percent of period or greater than period. Same problems arise as in 1 above.

3. Setting delay time and pulse duration so that their combination exceeds the period. Same problems arise as in 1 and 2 above. Remember that sufficient time must be allotted for two pulses in the paired-pulse mode.

4. Not setting delay time long enough to maintain minimum separation while operating in paired-pulse mode. This causes the undelayed pulse and the delayed pulse to merge, since the duration generator has insufficient time for recovery between pulses.

5. Setting the rise time longer than the pulse duration. This prevents the output pulse from achieving the desired amplitude, since the ouput of the duration generator will switch the rise/fall shape before it has had time to reach its leading-edge clamp level.

6. Setting the fall time longer than the remainder of the period after the pulse duration. This prevents the output pulse from achieving its desired baseline since the output of the duration generator will switch the rise/fall shaper before it has had time to reach its trailing-edge clamp level. Notice that by setting both rise and fall times to exactly the time available, the pulse generator can be made to generate triangular waveforms!

All the above user errors can be eliminated by sketching on paper or forming a mental picture of the waveform desired, taking care not to set up anything inconsistent with the time(s) allowable.

7. Failure to remember that changes in rise/fall times will change the pulse duration. See number 9 of inherent errors.

8. Impedance mismatches between output connectors, cables, and loads. Mismatching causes reflections which are re-reflected to the load. Reflections can be minimized by switching in the internal termination and/or using external attenuators of the proper impedance. It is necessary to remember that the pulse-amplitude and base-line offset voltages delivered to the load will be reduced by these precautions.

9. Failure to take cable losses into account. Long cable runs or lossy cable attenuate the high-frequency components of fast rise pulses to be delivered to the load. Losses may be determined by comparing the output waveform at the generator with the waveform at the load with a good oscilloscope whose rise time is many times faster than the rise/fall times of interest.

10. Failure to take into account cable-propagation delays. When checking digital circuits, it is often desirable to maintain nearly exact time relationships between signals. Propagation delays of the cables being used must be known and accounted for, or additional cable of the same type may be added between connections so that the signals have the desired time relationships when delivered to the circuit(s) under test.

11. Mistakes in setting pulse-amplitude and base-line offset voltages. Errors are usually caused by failure to remember that the output stage and the offset circuitry are usually constant-current sources with respect to loads of a few tens of ohms. Therefore, the pulse and base-line voltages across the load will change when the load impedance is changed. Actual voltages across the load can be measured and set using a good oscilloscope when necessary.

Chapter 31

Microwave Signal Generators

HARLEY L. HALVERSON

Hewlett-Packard Company, Palo Alto, California

INTRODUCTION

Signal generators are energy sources. In fact, broadly speaking, any energy source from a light bulb to a battery to an oven might be classed as a signal generator. This is much too broad a class to deal with; so for the purpose of this discussion a signal generator is a source of ac electrical energy which has most of the following characteristics:

1. Calibrated and variable-frequency output
2. Calibrated and variable-voltage-level output
3. Modulation capability

The output of a signal generator is said to be *modulated* if its amplitude or frequency is varied as a function of time in response to some modulation signal.

It is this characteristic (modulation capability) which allows the signal generator to *simulate* a transmitted radio signal to test radio receivers of all types. Such characteristics as sensitivity, frequency-calibration accuracy, filter alignment, and distortion can be measured and adjusted.

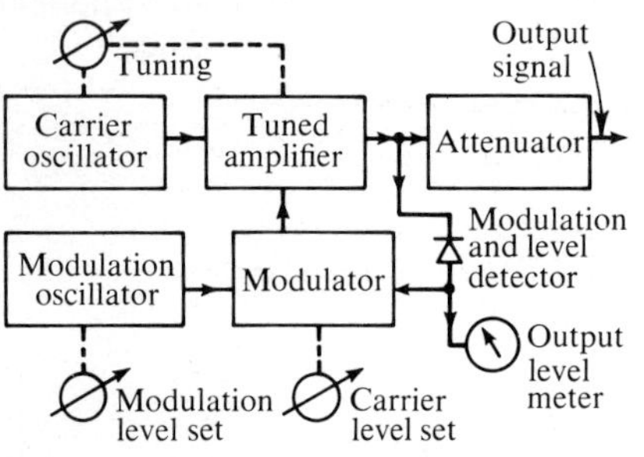

Fig. 1. Amplitude-modulated signal generator.

In another class of applications, the signal generator is used as a *signal source.* In conjunction with a detector it can be used in applications where it is necessary to measure transmission and reflection characteristics. For example, the gain of an amplifier, the frequency response of a filter, or the impedance match of an antenna can be measured. Generally no modulation is required when the generator is used as a signal source.

The basic circuit blocks which are characteristic of a signal generator are shown in Fig. 1. This particular generator is called a *fundamental oscillator amplitude-modulated* signal generator. It is called a fundamental oscillator because only the fundamental output of one oscillator is used to generate the carrier signal. Other generators to be described later use several oscillators mixed together to produce the carrier signal.

THE OSCILLATOR

At the heart of every signal generator is an oscillator which produces the ac signal voltage. In a generator capable of being modulated, this signal is called the *carrier signal.* A second oscillator may be included to produce the *modulation signal.* Oscillators are built in many different ways and may produce many different waveshapes. Among the more common are sine waves, square waves, triangular waves, and pulses. (See Chapters 28 to 30 for a more complete discussion of these oscillators.) In a signal generator the carrier signal is almost always a sine wave. The modulation signal may also be a sine wave, but square waves and pulse waves are also common modulating signals.

Such circuits as the Hartley, Colpitts, emitter-coupled, cross-coupled, and many more can be used in a signal generator to produce the sine-wave carrier signal. The kind of oscillator is not as important to the quality of the generator as is quality of the components used in the design and the care taken in the design itself.

The most important characteristics of an oscillator are its *stability* and its *spectral purity.* A stable oscillator is one whose frequency does not change with temperature, vibration, line-voltage changes, magnetic fields, power-supply ripple, etc. A spectrally pure oscillator is one in which the noise output is far below (smaller than) the signal output.

The stability required to make a measurement depends on the application. In some cases, stability is sacrificed to achieve other wanted characteristics, like broad tunability or sweepability. For this reason there are a great many different types of signal generators with widely varying characteristics (see Table 1). The most common ones will be described later.

To be useful in a general-purpose signal generator the oscillator frequency must be tunable. This may be accomplished by varying the value of a capacitor or inductor or both in the oscillator circuit. In high-frequency (microwave) oscillators tuning may be accomplished by varying the volume of a resonant cavity which forms part of the oscillator circuit. Such oscillators are called *mechanically tuned* oscillators. If well designed, these oscillators have good frequency stability at a reasonable cost. The disadvantages are mechanical complexity, large size, and fairly slow tuning speed.

It is also common to build oscillators which are *electrically tuned;* that is, the frequency is changed by varying a voltage applied to a tuning element in the oscillator circuit. This might be a back-biased diode which acts as a voltage-variable capacitor or specially wound current-variable inductor. It might also be

TABLE 1 Signal-generator Comparison

Signal-generator type	Application	Stability	Freedom from spurious and harmonics	Tunability	Notes
AM	Signal simulation	Fair	Good	Good	Receiver test
FM	Signal simulation	Fair	Good	Good	Receiver test
Sweep	Signal source	Poor	Fair	Good	Wide-sweep-component test
Heterodyne	Signal source and simulation	Poor	Poor	Good	Multidecade sweep
Synthesized	High stability	Very good	Fair	Poor	Digital frequency output very accurate
Synchronized	High stability	Good	Fair	Poor	High stability without accuracy

a magnetically tuned yttrium-iron-garnet (YIG) sphere which behaves like a resonant cavity at frequencies above a few hundred megahertz when placed in a magnetic field.

Electrically tuned oscillators have very fast tuning capability, small size, simple mechanical design, and the ability to be programmed (tuned) with reasonable accuracy by a computer. Since the output frequency is proportional to a voltage and voltages are hard to control, the frequency accuracy and stability are usually not as good as in mechanically tuned oscillators. The frequency accuracy and stability of both types of oscillators can be improved greatly by frequency or phase-locking schemes, which will be discussed later.

THE AMPLIFIER

In the generator shown in Fig. 1, the output of the oscillator is fed to a narrowband amplifier tuned to the same frequency as the oscillator. The oscillator and amplifier are *tracked* so that both tune together as the generator is tuned.

The purpose of the amplifier is not just to obtain more signal power out of the generator. It improves the quality of the instrument in several ways. The amplifier isolates or buffers the load connected to the generator from the oscillator. This keeps the oscillator frequency from being pulled by changes in the reactance of the load. When an amplifier is used, modulation can take place in the amplifier rather than in the oscillator, which also improves stability. The tuned amplifier also filters out unwanted harmonics and noise produced in oscillators.

Some modern solid-state signal generators will use an untuned broadband amplifier in place of the tuned amplifier. This approach eliminates the need for tracking the oscillator and amplifier. An untuned amplifier is most often used with an electrically tuned oscillator, since electrically tuned amplifiers are hard to design. The broadband amplifier does isolate the oscillator, but it does not filter harmonics and noise. In fact, it may well add broadband noise of its own to the output.

Another approach sometime used to provide isolation is to build a high-power oscillator and buffer it from the load by inserting an attenuator or *pad* between the oscillator and the load. This wastes oscillator power, but it saves building an expensive amplifier.

LEVELING AND MODULATION

The signal out of the amplifier is seldom constant as the oscillator and amplifier are tuned across the band. Variations in the gain of the amplifier, variation in the oscillator efficiency, and tracking errors all add up to produce this variation in signal level. Since it is much easier to make measurements when the output voltage is constant as frequency is tuned, a feedback loop is employed to correct for these variations. This feedback loop is called the *leveling loop*, or *ALC* (automatic level control). It adjusts the output voltage by changing the gain of the amplifier.

The leveling diode detects the level of the carrier signal before the output attenuator. It produces a dc voltage proportional to the carrier level which is fed to an output meter calibrated to display this carrier level. The same dc voltage is also fed to the modulator, where it is compared with a *reference voltage*. This forms a feedback loop which keeps the detected carrier voltage equal to the reference voltage. The carrier level can now be varied by varying the reference voltage. If the modulating voltage is superimposed or added to the reference voltage, the feedback loop will force the level of the output signal to follow the modulation signal. Thus the same circuit can be used for both AM modulation and level set.

THE ATTENUATOR

The *attenuation* at the output of the signal generator reduces the voltage output to the desired level for making measurements. The range of attenuation varies from generator to generator but is usually over 120 dB [dB = 10 log (P_2/P_1) where P_1 is a reference power level, normally 1 mW into 50/Ω, and P_2 is the output power]. This wide range is necessary to test the sensitivity of receivers. The actual level of the output signal is the sum of the attenuator setting and the setting indicated by the output-level meter.

There are many different attenuator designs. In quality generators designed for use below about 10 GHz the output attenuator will usually be either a *piston attenuator* or a *step attenuator*. Above 10 GHz these attenuators are more difficult to build, and *waveguide attenuators* are often used. Although the waveguide attenuator produces very good results, it becomes very large at frequencies much below 10 GHz.

The operation of the piston attenuator is shown in Fig. 2. The carrier voltage is fed to a coupling loop at one end of a round tube. The output coupling loop is attached to the end of a piston which slides inside the tube. Attenuation increases as the two coupling loops are separated. A dial is mechanically coupled to vary with separation and is calibrated in volts, decibels relative to some reference level, or both.

The step attenuator uses resistors to dissipate the unwanted power. It is composed of several sections, each attenuating a fixed amount of power. The magnitude of the attenuation varies from section to section according to some code so that the various sections may be added together to achieve any desired attenuations. The level-set control and the output-level meter are used to interpolate between steps. With a reduction in accuracy, step attenuators are available for use up to 18 GHz.

The waveguide attenuator uses a resistive card mounted along the axis in the center of a waveguide to produce the attenuation. The card is slipped into the waveguide through a slot in the waveguide wall. Attenuation is changed by changing the depth the card is inserted into the waveguide.

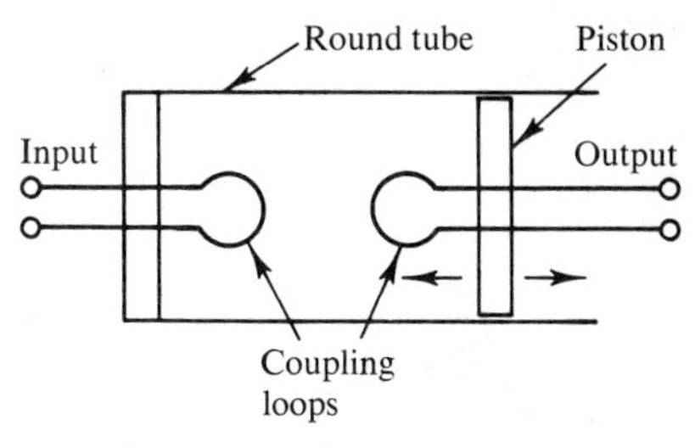

Fig. 2. Piston attenuator.

TYPES OF SIGNAL GENERATORS

Some or all of the functional blocks just described are included in the design of any signal generators. But in spite of much commonality there are still large differences between the various types of signal generators. These differences tailor the generators for best use in specific application, for example, AM radio testing, FM radio testing, radar testing, and filter and amplifier alignment. Thus frequency coverage and modulation capability are dictated as much by market need as by design considerations. No one signal generator, regardless of price, meets the requirements of all applications. Here are the most common types and some of their most important characteristics.

1. AM Signal Generator The basic block diagram for this generator is the one used to discuss the functional blocks (Fig. 1). The oscillator is almost always mechanically tuned. Other variations are often designed to improve the specifications or reduce cost.

The important specifications to consider are those which relate to frequency accuracy and setability, output-level accuracy, signal stability and purity, and modulation distortion.

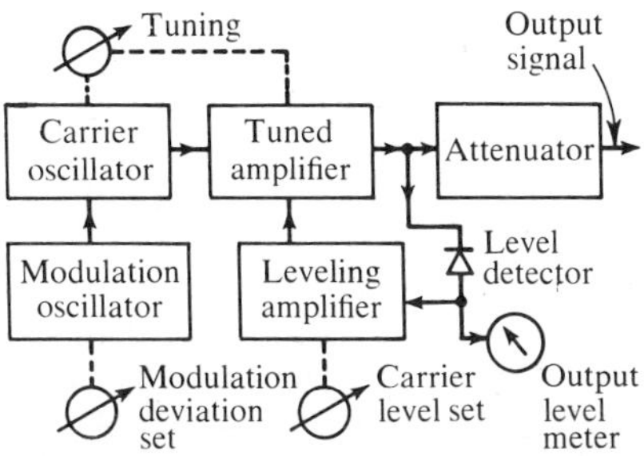

Fig. 3. Frequency-modulated signal generator.

2. FM Signal Generator The FM (frequency-modulation) signal generator is very similar to the AM signal generator. Its typical block diagram is shown in Fig. 3. The principal difference is that the modulation voltage is applied directly to a tuning element in the oscillator circuit rather than to the leveling loop. The tuning element varies the frequency of oscillation in proportion to the modulating signal. A voltage-variable capacitor compensated to change frequency linearly or a current-variable inductor does this job nicely. The amplifier must be broadband enough to pass the modulated oscillator signal, since the amplifier center frequency does not vary with the modulation.

Leveling and attenuation are accomplished in the same way for both generators. The same performance characteristics are important in both. Both these generators are primarily signal simulators and are used for receiver testing.

3. Sweep Generator The sweep generator is an oscillator which can be turned or swept rapidly over a band of frequencies. It is most often used for component testing. The measurement system is shown in Fig. 4. The oscillator in the generator shown is electrically tuned, although mechanically tuned (motor-driven) oscillators are sometimes used. Because it is electrically tuned, the block diagram is very similar to the FM generator. The principal difference is in the magnitude of the frequency deviation. The maximum deviation of the FM signal generator is much smaller than that of the sweep generator. Because of the demands this wide sweep would place on an amplifier, sweep generators are usually designed with

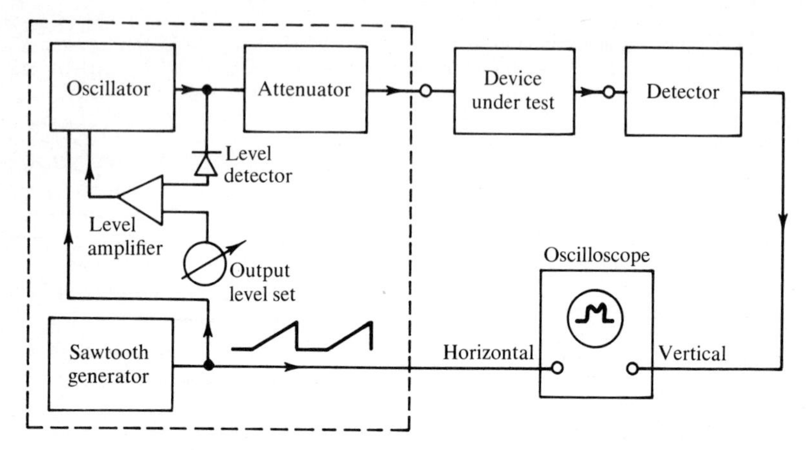

Fig. 4. Sweep generator and measurement system.

just an oscillator. With no amplifier to buffer the output, and because the oscillator is electrically tuned, the frequency stability of the sweeper is not as good as that of the signal generator.

The system in Fig. 4 shows a detector and an oscilloscope used with the sweeper. The system measures the transfer (input to output) response of a device such as an amplifier or a filter as the frequency changes. This is only one of many possible measuring systems but is representative of how the sweep generator is used. The detector converts the output of the sweeper modified by the device under test to a dc voltage which can be recorded on the oscilloscope. Note that the horizontal-deflection voltage is fed directly from the sweep generator to the oscilloscope. If this voltage is proportional to the output frequency of the sweeper, the display is said to be linear. This means that points equally spaced in frequency will be equally spaced in position on the cathode-ray tube (CRT). This linearity is an important characteristic of a good sweeper.

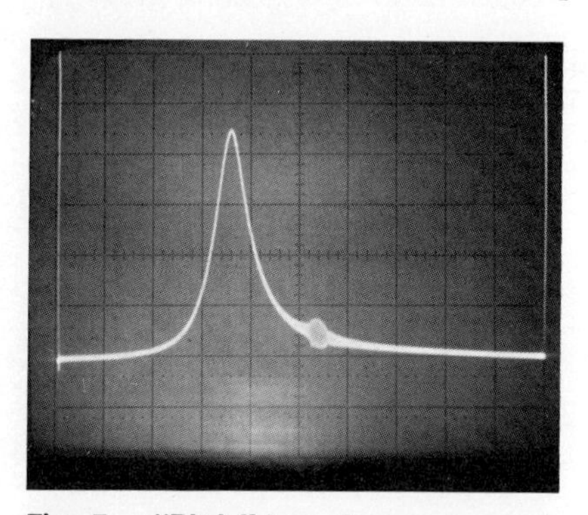

Fig. 5. "Birdy"-type frequency marker. Intermediate-frequency filter response of a receiver. The "birdy" mark calibrates one frequency in the sweep. Additional marks would be necessary for additional frequencies.

Other important characteristics are constant output over the sweep range, calibrated sweep ranges, versatile sweep controls, and good frequency stability.

A feature included in the design of most sweepers is some provision for marking frequency on the CRT. The mark may be a "birdy," an intensified spot, or a blanking (attenuation) of the output power. A "birdy"-type mark is shown in Fig. 5. The display may show a single frequency mark referenced to a stable oscillator or a series of marks referenced to harmonics of a stable oscillator. If the reference oscillator is crystal-controlled, such markers may be quite accurate. This type of marker may be essential when the sweep is nonlinear. With linear and accurately calibrated sweeps, frequencies may be read directly on the CRT and the sweep generator. In this case markers are not essential, but they still may be very helpful for certain kinds of production-line testing. Markers referenced to crystal oscillators are fixed-frequency. It may therefore take several oscillators to obtain all the frequencies of interest.

Some sweep generators have a variable-frequency marker which takes advantage of the linear relationship between the tuning (sweep) voltage and the output frequency. This circuit detects when the tuning voltage reaches a certain level and marks the CRT at that point. A continuous control changes the voltage level at which the mark occurs. This control is connected to a dial which is calibrated to read out frequency. Such a marker is only as accurate as the proportionality between the tuning voltage and the frequency ($\simeq$1 percent).

4. Heterodyne Sweep Generator The voltage-tuned sweep generator described above, when used above 1 GHz, is limited in sweep range to about one octave.

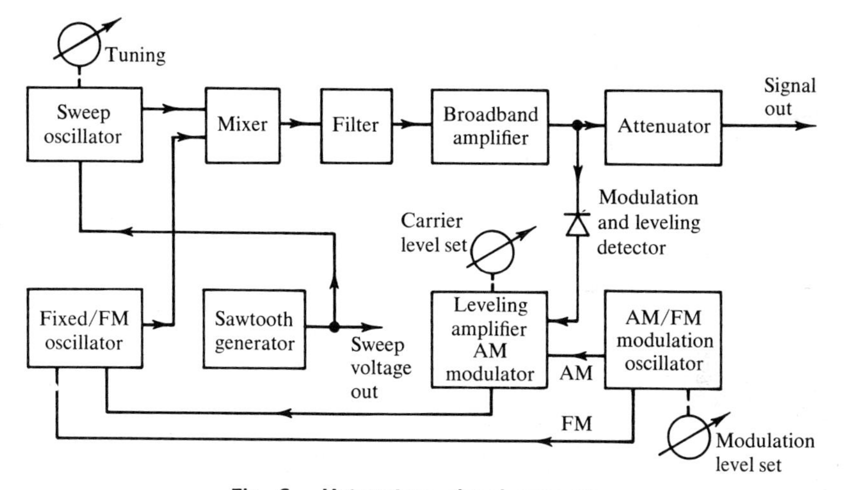

Fig. 6. Heterodyne signal generator.

Many applications requiring a sweep generator below 1 GHz could use much more than octave sweep range. One generator which achieves this is the heterodyne sweep generator (Fig. 6).

A high-frequency voltage-tuned oscillator which may sweep less than an octave is mixed with a second high-frequency fixed oscillator. The output of the mixer is the difference frequency of the two oscillators. If the voltage-tuned oscillator is able to sweep 1 GHz starting at some high frequency, the difference frequency may cover the ranges from zero to 1 GHz in one sweep.

Several other desirable features can also be achieved. The output may be amplitude-modulated by modulating only the fixed oscillator. Narrowband FM may also be applied by this fixed oscillator. Since the oscillator does not have to be tuned, the FM modulation may be linearized and accurately calibrated.

But with these desirable features come some problems. For one, the output of the mixer is not just the difference frequency between the two oscillators. The output also contains the sum and difference frequencies of all the harmonics of the oscillators. These other frequencies do not all tune in the same direction as the desired output. Some will actually cross the desired output as the generator sweeps. To keep these spurious outputs low, the mixer must be designed and operated at a low output level. The output should be filtered and amplified to at least 10 mW to be useful. Broadband amplifiers used in such generators add broadband noise to the output. They are also expensive.

The output of the generator is only as stable as the poorest of the two oscillators. This instability may be high, as a percent of frequency, at low output frequencies. Care should be taken when using heterodyne generators to keep these characteristics from affecting the measurements.

5. Synthesized Signal Generator Regardless of how much care is taken in designing a fundamental signal generator, some applications will require greater frequency stability. One method of achieving this greater stability is by using a frequency synchronizer with the signal generator. This technique will be described under Signal-generator Accessories.

An even more stable signal can be derived by synthesizing the signal from a high-quality single-frequency crystal oscillator. Such a generator is called a *synthesized signal generator.* There are many ways of accomplishing the frequency synthesis, some very complicated. A simple way of conceptualizing the process is to start with a single frequency, say 10 MHz; then by multiplication or division other frequencies are generated, say 100 kHz, 1 MHz. Harmonics of each of these decade frequencies are generated and filtered. For example, 200 to 900 kHz and 2 to 9 MHz. These frequencies are now mixed and filtered as necessary to produce any frequency in 100-kHz steps up to 100 MHz. As finer steps are desired, more dividers, mixers, and filters are included. The output signal has nearly the same stability as the 10-MHz reference signal. Stabilities of parts in 10^9 are common for synthesized signal generators.

The user of the synthesized signal generator sets the output frequency through a keyboard entry or a series of dials. The tuning is digital and not continuous, although a somewhat less stable mode of operation called the *search mode* is often included which does tune continuously. This mode substitutes a variable oscillator for one of the synthesized fixed frequencies. The variable oscillator allows the user to tune continuously over a digit's range. The specific digit which is continuously variable is usually selectable by the user. Since tuning is accomplished by a switching process, the generator is easily adapted to computer control. This synthesis process forms the oscillator for the generator. The rest of the generator is similar to the other generators described with an untuned or no output amplifier.

One limitation of the synthesized signal generator is the spurious signals present in the output. As with the heterodyne signal generator these signals are produced by the mixing process and are very difficult to filter completely. In a well-designed generator, however, they will be 70 to 90 bB below the main signal.

SIGNAL-GENERATOR ACCESSORIES

Signal generators are designed to stand on their own for most applications. When swept measurements are made, a detector and an oscilloscope or *X-Y* recorder may be used, as shown in Fig. 4. Generally only one or two sine-wave modulation frequencies are designed into the signal generator. If other frequencies or waveforms are needed, a separate oscillator may be connected to the external modulation jack.

In some generators which are dc-connected, this same jack may be used to control the output level of the generator (dc modulation). An application for this is described below under External Leveling. A special application for modulation which may not be able to use the internal modulation capability of the generator at all is *pulse modulation.* This too will be discussed under a separate heading.

The dial accuracy of good generators is about 1 percent, with better accuracy possible by using the crystal calibrator. If this accuracy is not sufficient or convenient enough, a *frequency counter* makes an excellent accessory. Usually an unmodulated high-level output is available to connect to the counter. This leaves the normal output free to be modulated or attenuated. If the inherent frequency accuracy of the generator is not adequate, the frequency stability may not be adequate either. For these applications a *frequency synchronizer* may be needed. This instrument can be used only with signal generators that have a dc-coupled external FM input jack. The synchronizer will also be discussed under a separate heading.

EXTERNAL LEVELING

A well-designed modern generator will be leveled at the output. This means that as frequency is charged, the output-signal level remains fixed. Occasionally the output jack of the generator is not the point where the leveled signal is needed. It might be more desirable if the leveled signal were at the end of a cable or the output of a filter. This is accomplished by using an external leveling circuit. A typical circuit is shown in Fig. 7.

At the point where a leveled signal is desired the signal is sampled using a signal splitter and a detector. The splitter might be a hybrid or directional detector or a resistive T. The hybrid or directional detector produces the best source match. This means that waves traveling down the transmission line toward the source are not reflected by the signal splitter or generator mismatch. The resistive T is not as good in this respect but may be much broader-band. The detector should have the right polarity in the output so that the feedback is negative. Thus if a positive-going signal at the leveling jack increases the output level, the dc voltage out of the detector should be negative.

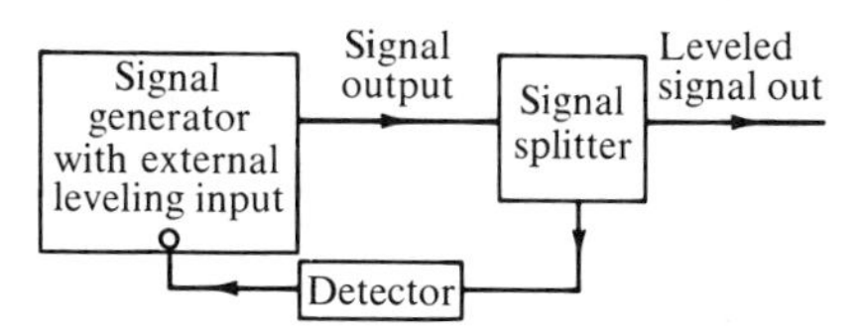

Fig. 7. External leveling.

The leveling feedback loop will work to make the dc voltage out of the detector equal to some fixed reference in the generator. If it does this perfectly, then the output rf voltage will vary only with variation in the flatness of the power splitter and detector.

PULSE MODULATION

All signal generators have provision for internal modulation of the rf output. Usually the highest modulation frequency is limited to the audio range (a few kilohertz).

For pulse applications, the modulator may need to be capable of rise times of less than a nanosecond (10^{-9} s). This is equivalent to modulation frequencies in the gigahertz range. This is far above the capability of most signal generators. To produce these very fast pulses, an external pulse modulator must be used. The signal output of the generator is fed through the modulator, where it is alternately allowed to pass or is switched off to form the pulses. The modulator usually has the pulse circuitry built into it.

A technology of growing importance to communications is pulse-code modulation. The signal generator is modulated in frequency, phase, or amplitude in response to a train of pulses. Megahertz modulation rates are usually adequate to accommodate these pulses. The signal generator may have this capability built into it.

THE FREQUENCY SYNCHRONIZER

If the drift stability or residual FM of a signal generator is not adequate for making some specialized measurements, a frequency synchronizer may be used to stabilize the generator. Only generators with dc-coupled external FM inputs may be used with synchronizers. The synchronizer takes its name from the process it uses for stabilizing the signal generator. It synchronizes or phase-locks the oscillator in the signal generator to a stable reference oscillator in the synchronizer.

Figure 8 shows how the synchronizer is connected to the signal generator. Part of the rf output of the generator is fed to the synchronizer. This signal is converted to an if frequency, and its phase is compared with that of a stable oscillator at the if frequency in a phase detector. A dc voltage proportional to the phase error between the two oscillators is fed back to the signal generator to control its frequency.

When the signal generator is *phase-locked* to the synchronizer reference oscillator, the frequency can be tuned only by tuning the reference oscillator. This tuning range is usually very limited. To tune further, the feedback loop must be opened and the generator locked to another harmonic of the reference oscillator. The result is a very stable signal which is not very convenient to tune.

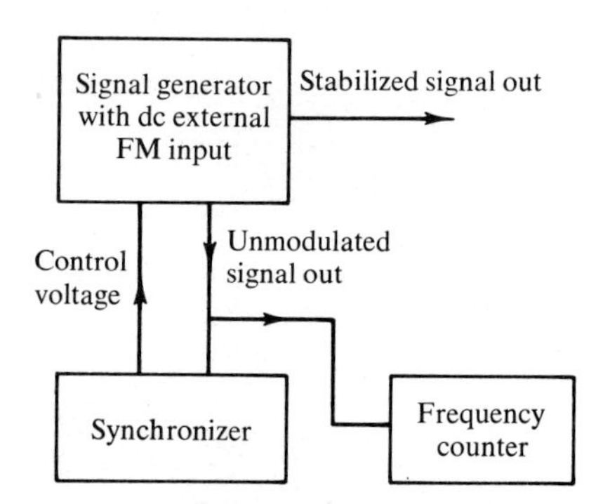

Fig. 8. Synchronized signal generator.

The counter shown in Fig. 8 allows frequency to be set very accurately. The need for accuracy usually goes hand in hand with the need for stability.

BASIC SPECIFICATIONS

The specifications accompanying signal generators vary widely. Signal sources, sweepers, AM, FM, or pulsed signal generators, and heterodyne or synthesized signal generators each have different specifications in both degree and importance. In all cases the specific application determines the specifications needed by the signal generator. The first sections of this chapter point up the differences in the various generators (see Table 1). This section will discuss generator specifications without regard to specific instruments.

6. Basic Oscillator or Carrier

Frequency Range: The range of frequencies over which the generator tunes or sweeps. These frequencies may be covered in one band or several.

Accuracy: This is the accuracy to which the output frequency agrees with the instrument's frequency dial.

Resetability: This indicates the repeatability of a frequency set on the dial.

Drift: The long-term frequency stability of the oscillator. Drift is normally specified after a certain warm-up period. It may be given at a fixed ambient temperature and as a function of ambient-temperature change. A special type of drift is *settling time.* This is the maximum time after a new frequency has been set that the oscillator drift slows down to a specified rate.

Harmonics (Carrier Distortion): The harmonics in the output are specified to be below the carrier a certain number of decibels. Since carrier distortion implies the presence of harmonics, this harmonic content can be specified by specifying a carrier distortion as being below a certain percent. One percent distortion is equivalent to a harmonic's being at least 40 dB below the carrier level.

Residual FM: The frequency instability of the carrier caused by noise and power-line ripple modulating the carrier frequency.

Incidental FM: The frequency or phase modulation which occurs as the generator is amplitude-modulated.

Residual AM: The amplitude instability of the carrier caused by noise and power-line ripple modulating the carrier amplitude.

Incidental AM: The amplitude modulation which occurs as the generator is frequency-modulated.

7. Output Level

Attenuator Range: The range over which the output of the generator can be adjusted. The output is usually calibrated in volts or decibels relative to some reference level—typically 1 mW into 50 Ω.

Output Accuracy: The accuracy to which the output agrees with the calibration of the attenuator and output-level meter.

Output Impedance: The source impedance at the output port looking back into the generator—usually 50, 75, or 600 Ω.

8. Sweep Capability

Linearity: The degree to which the output frequency is linearly related to the horizontal-sweep reference voltage or the degree to which the output frequency changes linearly with time. Linearity is easy to understand but very difficult to specify. It may be specified as the deviation from a straight line connecting the end points, or from the best straight line through the curve.

Sweep Accuracy: The accuracy of the sweep width relative to the calibration.

Sweep Speed: The range and accuracy of sweep speeds incorporated into the instrument design. This is not a critical specification. The instrument should have a slow sweep range for use with *X-Y* recorders and a fast sweep range for use with nonstorage-type oscilloscopes.

9. Modulator

Percent AM: The maximum amplitude-modulation percentage achievable with the generator (see Front-panel Terms). The generator should be capable of at least 30 percent.

Peak Deviation FM: The maximum frequency-modulation deviation achievable with the generator.

Frequency Response: The range of frequencies over which the generator can be modulated.

Modulation Distortion: The distortion which accompanies the modulation process. The distortion will usually be less at lower deviations or percent modulations. Distortion levels of 1 percent or less are desirable.

When the generator is capable of pulse modulation and has an internal pulse generator built in, the following specifications apply.

Rise Time: The time required for the modulated carrier to go from the 10 to the 90 percent level when a step-modulation voltage is applied.

Decay Time: The time required for the modulated carrier to go from the 90 to the 10 percent level when the step-modulation voltage is removed.

Pulse Width: The range of pulse widths available from the pulse generators. Ranges from 1 ms to 10 ns are common.

Repetition Rates: The pulse-repetition rate available from the pulse generator. Ranges from 100 Hz to 10 MHz are common.

FRONT-PANEL TERMS

The front-panel terms are those associated with frequency, time, output level, and modulation.

Frequency: Signal-generator frequency is expressed in hertz. Multipliers are kilo (10^3), mega (10^6), and giga (10^9).

Time: Pulse widths are expressed in seconds. Multipliers are milli (10^{-3}), micro (10^{-6}), and nano (10^{-9}).

Output Level: The output level can be expressed in volts or decibels relative to a reference level of voltage or power. Voltage and power multipliers are milli (10^{-3}) and micro (10^{-6}). The term dBm means dB relative to 1 mW, dBW to 1 W, etc. If the output impedance is 50 Ω, the following conversions apply:

$$1\ \text{mW} = 0.224\ \text{V} = -30\ \text{dBW} - 0\ \text{dBm}$$
$$1\ \text{V} = +13\ \text{dBm} = +120\ \text{dB relative } 1\ \mu\text{V}$$
$$1\ \mu\text{V} = -107\ \text{dBm}$$

A 10× change in voltage is equivalent to a 20-dB change.
A 10× change in power is equivalent to a 10-dB change.

$$\text{dB} = 10 \log \frac{P_2}{P_1} = 20 \log \frac{V_2}{V_1}$$

where P_1 or V_1 is the reference level and P_2 or V_2 is the output level.

Modulation: Figure 9 shows a carrier 50 percent amplitude-modulated. Figure 10 shows a carrier frequency-modulated with an index of modulation equal to 0.5 ($m = 0.5$).

Note that no information about the index of modulation is presented by the

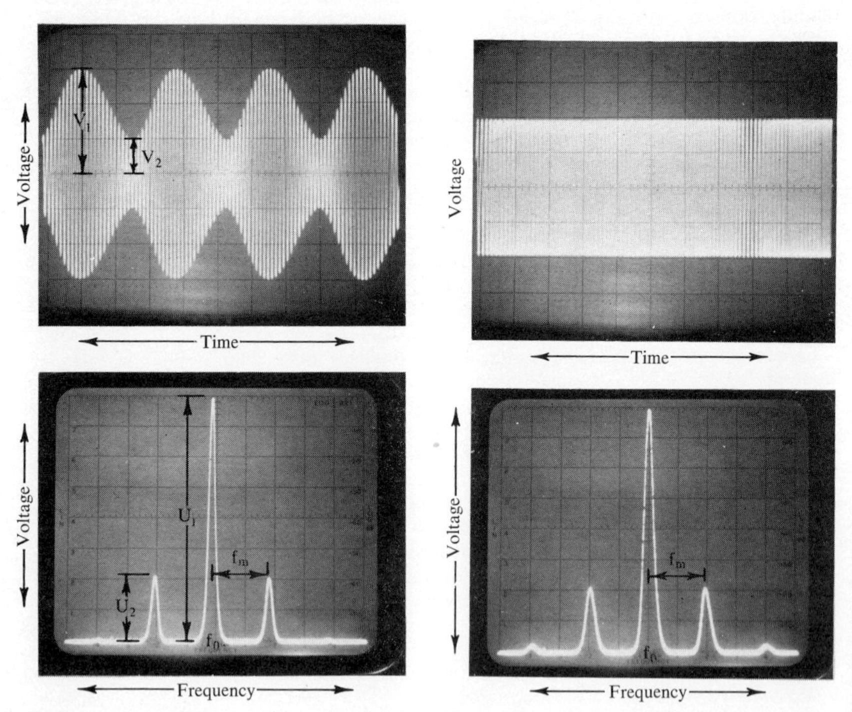

Fig. 9. (*a*) Oscilloscope (time-domain) presentation of 50 percent amplitude modulation. Percent AM (oscilloscope) = $(V_1 - V_2)/(V_1 + V_2) \times 100$. (*b*) Spectrum analyzer (frequency-domain) presentation at 50 percent amplitude modulation. Percent AM (spectrum analyzer) = $(2U_2/U_1) \times 100$.

Fig. 10. (*a*) Oscilloscope (time-domain) presentation of $m = 0.5$ frequency modulation. $m = \Delta F/f_m$, ΔF = peak-to-peak deviation, f_m = modulating frequency. (*b*) Spectrum analyzer (frequency-domain) presentation at $m = 0.5$ frequency modulation.

oscilloscope when the carrier is frequency-modulated. The spectrum-analyzer presentations for amplitude and frequency modulation look the same for small indexes of modulation. As m is increased, the two spectrum-analyzer displays become quite different.

Amplitude modulation greater than 100 percent is not permitted by the definition given. This is more a limitation of the definition than of what is actually possible. From a practical standpoint, modulation greater than 100 percent is almost never used because of the great distortion produced in demodulating the carrier in a receiver. Frequency modulation with $m > 1$ is often used.

FRONT-PANEL CONTROLS

As was true with the signal-generator specifications, the kinds of controls found on signal generators vary with the kind of generator. Some controls like "frequency tuning" are common to all generators. Other controls like modulation are found only on certain generators. The following description will group controls by function. Different generators will have different combinations of functions. None will have all the functions described.

Range Switch: Selects the desired frequency band or range of operation.

Frequency Tuning: The main control for setting frequency.

Frequency Vernier: A fine-tune control of frequency.

Modulation Mode/Level: Sets AM, FM continuous wave, internal or external modulation. It is usually associated with a modulation-level control.

Output Level: Controls output level by setting the attenuator, the reference voltage in the leveling loop, or both. Output level is read as the sum in decibels of the attenuator setting and the output-level meter. If the attenuator is a piston type it will provide continuous control. If the attenuator is a step type, both the attenuator and the reference level must be adjusted for continuous control.

Sweep Controls: The sweep width of a sweep generator is set by a start-stop control or a symmetrical width control. If both are present, the controls will be independent, and a selector switch sets which of the two modes is being used.

Start Sweep: Sets the frequency at which the sweep starts.

Stop Sweep: Sets the frequency at which the sweep stops.

Symmetrical Sweep Width (ΔF): Sets the total width of the sweep around a center frequency control (usually the continuous wave frequency-tuning control).

Sweep Mode: Sets the continuous wave, start-stop or ΔF.

Trigger Mode: Sets the sweep generator to free-run, synchronizes it to the *line* frequency, holds it ready for a *single sweep*, or disables the sweep generator for *manual sweep*.

Manual Sweep: A control for manually tuning the generator over the range set by the sweep controls. It is used primarily for setting up *X-Y* recorder limits.

Sweep Time: Sets the sweeps per second or second per sweep of the sweep generator.

Marker or Calibrator: A control for calibrating or marking the frequency of the output. Many different systems are used. The output level may be reduced sharply at the calibration frequency. A heterodyne beat between the calibration frequency and the output frequency may be used (see Fig. 5).

Pulse Controls

If the generator is capable of pulse-modulating the output, it will have the following controls.

Pulse Width, Pulse Rate: Sets the width and repetition frequency of the pulse generator.

Synchronize, Pulse Delay: Allows the pulse generator to be triggered from an external signal and the pulse delayed relative to that signal.

In addition to these adjustable controls, connectors are usually provided on the front or back panels to bring in modulation and synchronization signals, bring out sweep voltages for recorders or oscilloscopes, allow external leveling, provide an unmodulated sample of the output frequency, etc.

SOURCES OF ERROR

A signal generator is a simple instrument to use. Errors will usually be associated with calibration accuracy or instability in the generator. A generator capable of the accuracy and stability required should always be used. Here are some of the more serious errors to watch out for.

Mismatch Errors: These errors are caused by elements in the transmission system connected to the generator whose characteristic impedance differs from that of the generator. These mismatches cause part of the signal to be reflected. As a result the output-level calibration is disturbed. The reflected signals will cause standing waves to be set up along the transmission line so that the voltages will not be constant.

If signal level is important, mismatches must be checked. Even those caused by good connectors can cause problems in a precise measurement. One technique for correcting the errors caused by mismatch is to level the system using a directional detector at the point of the measurement. This also overcomes losses in the cables connecting the system.

Mismatch can also cause a pulling of the oscillator frequency if it is not properly buffered from the output. A load connected to the generator which is mismatched can look reactive rather than resistive to the generator. If the oscillator sees this reactance, its frequency will be altered.

Harmonics and Spurious Signals: Harmonics of the desired signal are always present in the output of a signal generator. The user should always question how the system being tested will respond to the harmonics. For example, if the transmission characteristics of a high-pass filter are being measured, generator signals will be attenuated in the stop band. If the main signal frequency is in the stop band and one of its harmonics is in the passband, the hormonic may be larger at the detector than in the main signal. This can cause large errors if a broadband detector is used. A good narrowband detector which is not sensitive at the harmonic frequencies can eliminate this problem. Low-pass filters at the output of the generator can be used to attenuate harmonics.

Harmonics can also cause problems when the reflection coefficient of a system is measured. The reflection at the fundamental frequency of the test signal may be very low. But if the harmonics are reflected and a broadband detector is used, the measurement may indicate a poorer match than is actually present. Again a narrowband detector or filter can be used to reduce errors.

If the harmonic distortion of an amplifier is being measured, harmonics from the signal generator will not be distinguishable from those developed in the amplifier. The distortion in the source must always be less than that in the amplifier under test.

Leakage: Signals which are conducted or radiated from a signal generator other than through the output jack are called leakage signals. They cause problems in measuring or detecting very small signals with a sensitive receiver. The test to determine whether a signal indicated by the receiver is a leakage signal or not is to reduce the output level from the signal generator using the output attenuator. The level measured by the receiver should follow the changes in the signal generator. If it does not, part of the indication may be caused by leakage.

To reduce the effects of leakage, be sure that all parts of the system are well grounded. Connectors should be clean and tight. Cables should be double-shielded. If leakage is still a problem, a better-shielded generator or receiver may be required.

Chapter **32**

Frequency Synthesizers

ATHERTON NOYES, Jr., Ph.D.

Ath Noyes and Associates, Concord, Massachusetts

1. Definition A frequency synthesizer is an instrument whose primary function is the generation of any stable precision frequency chosen from a band of frequencies, often many decades in extent. It combines the advantages of a wideband continuously adjustable oscillator with the frequency precision, at any setting, of a crystal-controlled single-frequency oscillator or frequency standard. Such a device is obviously a most important tool, in the laboratory or wherever else frequency precision and agility are both needed.

The term "synthesizer" in this chapter will be used exclusively for a "frequency-coherent" device, which means that any chosen output frequency is exactly proportional to one single driving frequency. The percentage accuracy of any chosen output is thus the same as the percentage accuracy of the standard source (except for transitory "phase-windup" effects).

This definition deliberately excludes other devices (often also called synthesizers) which derive their output from selected combinations of different driving frequencies stored in suitably chosen banks of crystals.

2. Synthesizers Are Arithmetic Manipulators of Frequency Any synthesizer, under our definition, achieves synthesis by using the basic steps of addition, subtraction, division, and multiplication of frequency. Any frequency directly used in the synthesis process is thus either the sum or difference of two other frequencies each derived proportionately from the standard, or related to such an intermediate standard by a simple multiplier or divisor.

Members of the rapidly growing group of commercially available synthesizers differ, basically, in the techniques used to perform these arithmetic steps, and in the mechanical arrangements provided to make the instrument convenient for the intended use.

Let us first consider some of the panel arrangements and available controls typical of modern synthesizers, and proceed from this to an understanding of how these controls operate, with coordination of some of the factors influencing performance, and some ground rules by which performance may be judged.

3. Panel Controls on Modern Synthesizers

Frequency Selection and Display. All modern synthesizers display the output frequency as a multidigit decimal number. Types of control and display are, in general, either a line of rotary dials, each detented at 10 positions from 0 to 9, or a matrix of pushbuttons, with 10-digit positions from 0 to 9 in each column, and as many columns as the number of selectable digit positions (see Fig. 1).

The rotary-dial display is usually easy to read, without error. Changing frequency, manually, is, however, rather slow, since each dial must be manually turned to its new reading.

The pushbutton matrix is much faster for manual selection. A price is paid for this fast operation, however. A large amount of panel area must be allocated to it; so the instrument becomes taller and more wasteful of rack height than is otherwise necessary, and there is substantial chance for error in that the chosen digits are not in line for easy reading but scattered over the rectangular array area.

Search. One of the common uses of a synthesizer is to adjust it to match the center frequency of a sharply selective network, or to agree closely with some external frequency of unknown value.

The high precision of setting inherent in separate, individual-digit controls creates a great inconvenience in such operations. In the absence of further aids it might be necessary to search each low-rank decade digit by digit, at each available setting of the higher-ranking decades—an obviously formidable task.

For this reason most general-purpose synthesizers make available a "search" mode of operation. Three types of search are currently available in commercial instruments:

1. Search, *continuously,* of the whole frequency region controlled by any single 0 to 9 decade. This is achieved by connecting the output of a continuously variable oscillator to replace the discrete digits of any chosen digit rank. When this type of search is used, all the displayed digits, other than the one being searched, have their usual weight (Fig. 2*a*). Reading is therefore ambiguous.

2. Search, *continuously,* of the frequency region *at and below* the selected rank (Fig. 2*b*). Frequency reading of the "search" dial continues logically from the active digits.

3. Search, *continuously,* of a region centered on the *total digital display.* The search excursion available on the manual dial can be varied in decade steps through many decades of sensitivity by pushbutton operation (Fig. 2*c*).

In any of these three types of search, the search deviation factor is chosen by inserting the search-oscillator frequency as a replacement for a synthesized frequency at one of a number of locations in the overall synthesis chain. This selection is commonly done by manual pushbutton or switch, but in some synthesizers the selection can be remotely programmed.

Sweep, FM. Closely related to manual search is obviously a sweep or frequency-modulation function. Most synthesizers have in their circuitry provision for varactor control of the search-oscillator frequency. When, as is common, an external input connection to this varactor is provided, the search function, and therefore sweep or FM, is available in response to an electrical input.

The excellence of this feature varies widely among synthesizers, being dependent

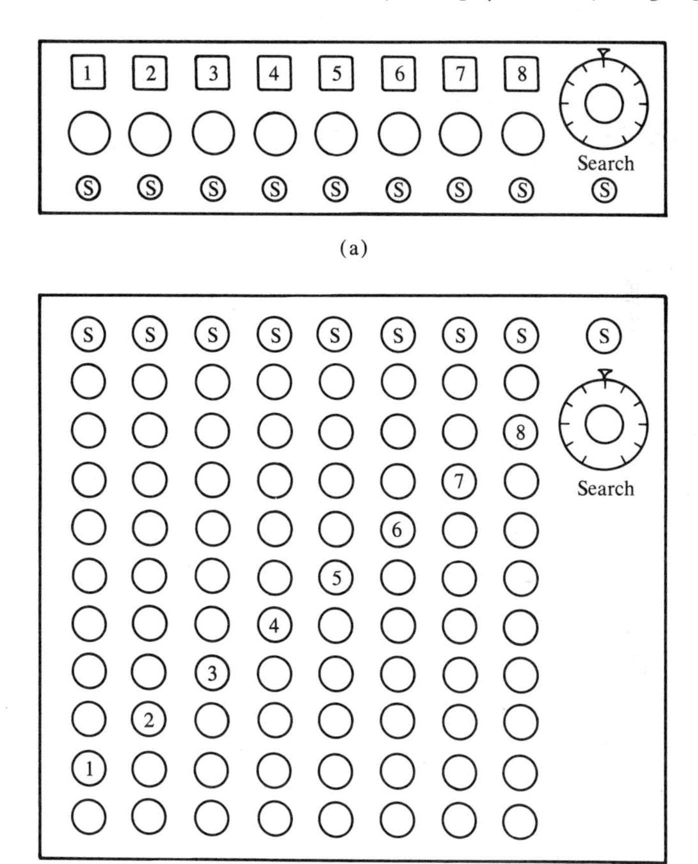

Fig. 1. (*a*) In-line display, easily readable but slow to set manually. (*b*) Push-button matrix, fast-setting manually, but hard to read and wasteful of panel space.

on sweep linearity, available bandwidth, and the like. The specifications for the individual model should be studied if this feature is important.

Some commercial synthesizers provide built-in control signals for sweep or FM; others merely supply an input jack for inserting such signals.

In any case, the synthesizer with its multidigit frequency control and its capability of sweeping at any rank in the synthesis chain is invaluable for achieving closely known narrowband sweeps about precision center frequencies selectable at will. Evidently, electrically controlled search capability with wide range of sensitivity (deviation per volt) available also provides means of phase locking the synthesizer to a varying external signal.

Precise Determination of Search or Sweep Deviation. This may be made using circuits and controls included in some synthesizers. It is usually accomplished by providing means of monitoring the search-oscillator frequency. Since in many synthesizers the total available frequency excursion of the search oscillator is the same no matter what decade is being searched, a direct measurement of the search-oscillator frequency permits easy and highly precise calculation of its effect in modifying the synthesizer output frequency.

As an example, if the search oscillator is being used to sweep the $\times 1$ Hz decade, its total frequency excursion (which might, for instance, be 100 kHz)

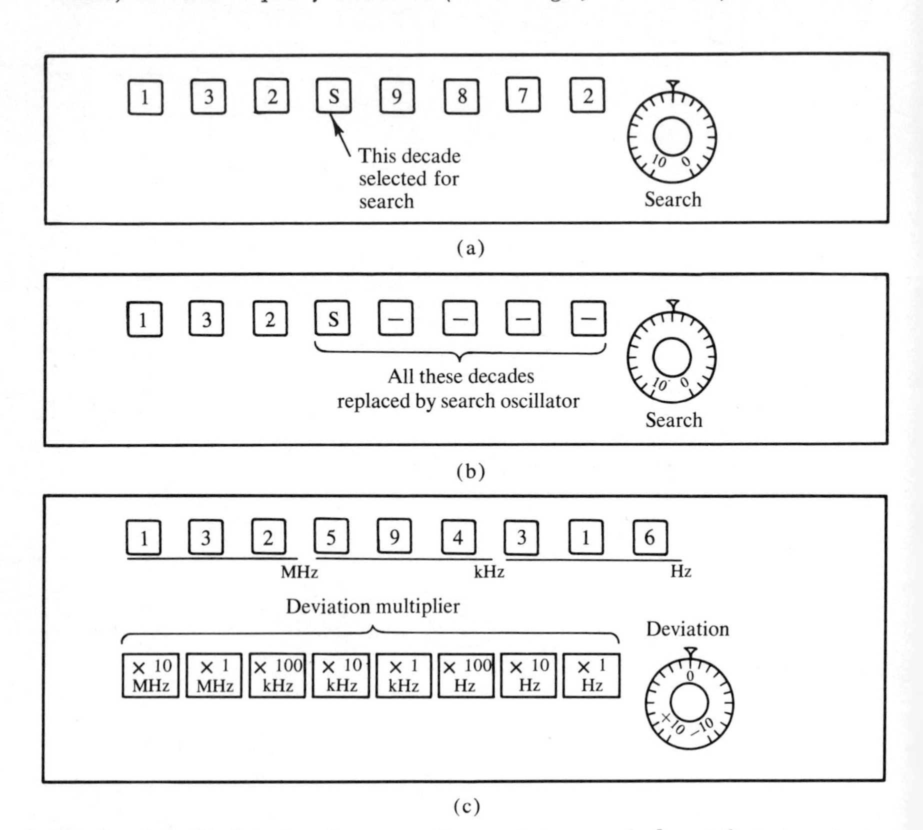

Fig. 2. (*a*) All digit decades except the one being searched contribute to output. (*b*) Search-oscillator-dial reading adds logically to the active digits at left. (*c*) All frequency digits active at all times. Search deviation from dialed frequency selected by multiplier button and continuous zero-center deviation control.

produces only a 10-Hz effect on the output frequency; so this is a magnification effect of 10,000:1. Thus, if the search oscillator in this example is moved 10 Hz, the synthesizer output changes by only 10^{-3} Hz.

If the frequency of the search oscillator is or can be brought out of the instrument, external circuitry can be provided to make use of this effect. Or, more conveniently in some synthesizers, a calibrating mixer circuit is provided internally in which a separately synthesized stable frequency is subtracted from the search oscillator frequency, providing at the "beat" terminal of such synthesizers only the frequency *excursion* from the starting reference. This can be conveniently monitored, or employed to drive a strip-chart recorder.

Such a technique is useful in measuring the very small frequency drift of a precision oscillator, to which the synthesizer has been phase-locked by voltage control of the search oscillator.

Phase Modulation. Some synthesizers provide an electrical input jack through which a signal can shift the phase of the output frequency by a proportional amount. The phase shift per volt is independent of the actual output frequency.

Such phase-modulation circuitry usually will permit phase excursions of up to ±2 or 3 rad at rates from dc to a megahertz or so. With suitable deemphasis such circuitry can also be used for frequency modulation at rates not in excess of the bandwidth capabilities of the search oscillator and accompanying circuits.

4. Automatic Programming of Frequency This is provided in most modern synthesizers, in response to digital-control inputs to each of the decades to be programmed. In some synthesizers 10-line control is used, which means 10 control wires for each decade. In others, binary-coded decimal circuitry is included, to reduce the control lines for each decade from 10 to 4 (and consequently the number of line filters which must be supplied to reduce radio-frequency interference).

Amplitude-program capability is often also provided, sometimes combined with an amplitude-modulation feature. Continuous amplitude control through a 10- to 20-dB range (by the circuits of the usual leveling loop) may be supplemented by a programmable attenuator providing 10-dB steps.

Internal-sweep-generation circuits are included in some synthesizers having a search feature. These also are usually capable of being programmed.

5. Electrical Performance In synthesizers the electrical performance is unparalleled in resolution, repeatability, long-term stability, and accuracy. In exchange for these features certain defects in signal quality must be tolerated. These defects are common to all synthesizers but vary widely in importance among models. Let us consider some of them:

Spurs. Spurious outputs, or "spurs," are here defined as any frequencies not harmonically related to the synthesized frequency which appear (usually at very low level) in the output. From the general category of spurs some manufacturers separate out a subclass known as "sidebands," with "hum sidebands" at power-line frequencies as a still further subdivision. These signals are those spurious frequencies which maintain a constant spacing from the carrier. "Hum" sidebands are spaced at power-line frequency (or some low multiple of this frequency) from the carrier. Such spurs *maintain their spacing* no matter where the carrier may be set. Hum-sideband spurs are not unique to synthesizers, of course. They occur in greater or lesser degree in any frequency source operated from the power mains.

In synthesizers there are usually a few base frequencies (like 100 kHz, 1 MHz, 10 MHz) which are used repetitively in the synthesis process and have an unfortunate talent for modulating themselves onto other frequencies involved. Since subsequent frequency translations, multiplications, or divisions of such modulated frequencies can change only the sideband amplitudes, but not their spacings from their carriers, a number of sidebands symmetrically disposed about the output frequency at these several base frequencies may be expected. "Sidebands" are, of course, objectionable, but the view is sometimes taken (and employed by specification writers) that since their relative locations are easily predicted they are not as objectionable as spurs at unexpected frequencies.

Mixer-generated spurs are those spurs, usually the result of the heterodyning of relatively high harmonics of the mixer input frequencies, which do *not* maintain a constant spacing from the output frequency and may, on occasion, be *coincident* with it. Coincident spurs are often the most troublesome of any. Since their frequencies may pass right through the carrier frequency, they are not in general amenable to reduction by filtering of the output frequency. They must be kept low in the process of synthesis, and achieving this requires added complexity (and cost) in the instrument.

Mixer spurs can readily be predicted, if the input frequencies to the mixer are known. A simple method of making such predictions is given in Sec. 7.

Long-term Stability—Phase-windup Effects. Any frequency-coherent synthesizer has (over a long enough averaging time) a long-term fractional stability of its output frequency equal to that of its basic driving source. High-grade crystal oscillators, with close temperature control, usually display aging rates ranging from 2×10^{-9} per day to 1×10^{-10} per day or better. Atomic-frequency standards (to which most synthesizers can be phase-locked) may be two or three orders of magnitude more stable. One might assume that since the source frequency is so accurately known at any given time, the synthesizer output will be equally accurate. However, the usual synthesizer operating in even a slightly inconstant temperature environment may exhibit "medium-term" frequency error which is not negligible in demanding applications, particularly when used to generate a comparatively low frequency.

To understand this, remember that a synthesizer is likely to contain many sharply selective circuits. If such a circuit is not perfectly temperature-compensated, it will shift the *phase* of a completely stable frequency passing through it if the ambient temperature varies.

Recall, also, that if a frequency is multiplied by a factor n, any phase shift before multiplication will be n times as great after multiplication. Many frequencies controlling the synthesizer output undergo large multiplications in the synthesizing process, and the multiplied phase shifts often appear directly in the output. Now, since frequency is defined as $f = (1/2\pi)(d\varphi/dt)$, we calculate that if in the output we observe a phase drift $\Delta\varphi/\Delta t$ of only 1° per minute (say), the resulting frequency error is 46×10^{-6} Hz. Thus, at an output frequency of 100 kHz (say) the *steady-state fractional frequency error* occurring during whatever period of time the output frequency is drifting in phase at 1°/min will be $\Delta f/f = 46 \times 10^{-6}/10^5 = 4.6 \times 10^{-10}$. Since in most synthesizers the phase drift of the output, due to thermal effects, is nearly independent of the output frequency, we see that at $f_0 = 10$ kHz,

$$\frac{\Delta f}{f} = 4.6 \times 10^{-9}$$

Thus a synthesizer disciplined by a *known* frequency source may at any given time have an output *frequency* error of not negligible amount, because of thermal effects in the synthesizer itself. Such effects are not commonly defined by manufacturers, but information can generally be obtained in response to query.

Of course, over a long enough period of time these frequency errors, some positive and some negative, will average to zero.

Short-term Stability. This quality in precision frequency sources has been the subject of much analysis, yet the many ways in which such characteristics are defined are confusing to many nonspecialists. We have space here to take only a perhaps oversimplified look at the basic effect, which may provide a starting point for further study if desired.

The concept of instability is of course elementary. A mathematically *perfect* frequency source would have an output:

$$e = a \sin (\omega t + \varphi)$$

with ω and φ invariant constants. In this imperfect world the expression degenerates to

$$e = a \sin [\omega t + \varphi(t)]$$

which merely says that the phase of the signal, relative to a mathematically perfect signal, varies as a function of time. We may still consider ω constant.

We have seen that relatively long-term phase variations are caused by thermal drifts, and have calculated the effect of such *slow phase drifts* on instantaneous *frequency;* so in spite of constant ω our frequency is no longer completely constant. or stable.

There are corresponding *rapid* fluctuations in φ, caused, broadly speaking, by electrical noise voltages interacting with the frequency-generating process.

If the noise-produced phase variation is occurring fast, but with reasonably small peak amplitude, our calculations of its effect on frequency will depend upon how long we wait between observations of phase error, or upon "averaging time."

As an example, let us assume that the phase is being perturbed $\pm 10^{-3}$ rad at a single frequency rate of 10^3 Hz. Let us make a number of observations of phase error, and from our results calculate frequency error.

If the time interval between successive measurements is relatively long compared with the 1-ms period of the disturbance, we shall measure many values of phase deviations lying between -10^{-3} and $+10^{-3}$ rad, *but nothing greater,* and in this simplified example we calculate an rms phase jitter of about 7×10^{-4} rad.

Now what do we say has been happening to *frequency?*

If our averaging time "between measurements" has been relatively long (say 1 s), we say that the rms frequency instability has been

$$\Delta f = \frac{1}{2\pi}\frac{\Delta\varphi}{\Delta t} = \frac{1}{2\pi}\frac{(7 \times 10^{-4}) \text{ rad}}{1 \text{ s}} = 1.1 \times 10^{-4}$$

If the signal frequency was 1 MHz (say), then

$$\frac{\Delta f}{f} = \frac{1.1 \times 10^{-4}}{10^6} = 1.1 \times 10^{-10}$$

Now observe:

1. If we had measured at 0.1-s intervals instead of 1 s, we would still have observed 7×10^{-4} rad phase deviation (since the rate of the disturbance was 1,000/s, allowing plenty of time for all possible values of phase error to occur), but from this same phase jitter we would calculate, as above,

$$\frac{\Delta f}{f} = 1.1 \times 10^{-9}$$

2. If the signal frequency had been 10 MHz instead of 1 MHz and we had averaged for a second,

$$\frac{\Delta f}{f} = 1.1 \times 10^{-11}$$

It is common practice to specify short-term stability of oscillators (and synthesizers) in terms of fractional frequency deviations $\Delta f/f$ with averaging time specified. The usual measurement method (a period measurement of a low-frequency beat note between the test signal and a reference) effectively measures $\Delta\varphi$ as created by *all* noise disturbances within the cutoff of any filters used in the measurement. This direct measurement is then translated, by the above equation, to a $\Delta f/f$ figure to be included in tabulations of performance.

It should be observed from the above relationships that, for *constant-phase jitter,* the fractional-frequency deviation is inversely proportional to the signal frequency.

In synthesizers in which the output frequency is the beat between two much higher frequencies (the common type of synthesizer) the phase jitter is nearly independent of the output frequency (since it is essentially the uncorrelated jitter of the beating signals). Consequently, any synthesizer is apt to be characterized by $\Delta f/f$ figures which decrease as the output frequency increases.

As a final note, observe that if a frequency is *multiplied* in a noise-free multiplier, both the phase jitter and the signal frequency increase in the same proportions; so $\Delta f/f$ is unchanged.

As we shall see next, this is not true of *sideband-phase noise,* which increases proportionately with the multiplying factor.

Figure 3 is representative of short-term stability data.

Phase-noise and phase-noise-density data express the phase-jitter effects just discussed in a different way. Phase jitter of an otherwise stable signal produces FM sidebands. A frequency-modulated or phase-modulated signal is described (for single-frequency modulation) by

$$e = a \sin (\omega t + \beta \sin at)$$

where
$$\beta = \frac{\Delta f}{F} = \frac{\text{deviation}}{\text{modulating frequency}}$$

β is called the modulation index and is expressed in radians of phase displacement.

When β is small (as is usually the case for unavoidable phase jitter), only the first pair of modulation sidebands (instead of the many usually present when frequency modulation is deliberately impressed) are of importance. The amplitude of each of these sidebands relative to the carrier is equal to $\beta/2$, and the power carried by each sideband, again relative to carrier power, is of course $\beta^2/4$.

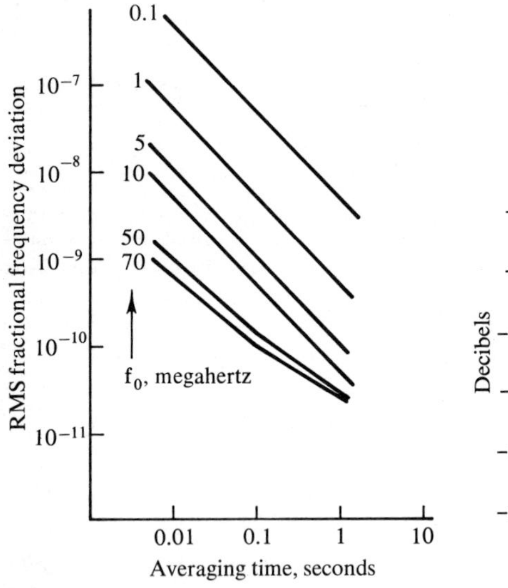

Fig. 3. Short-term stability of a typical 70-MHz synthesizer.

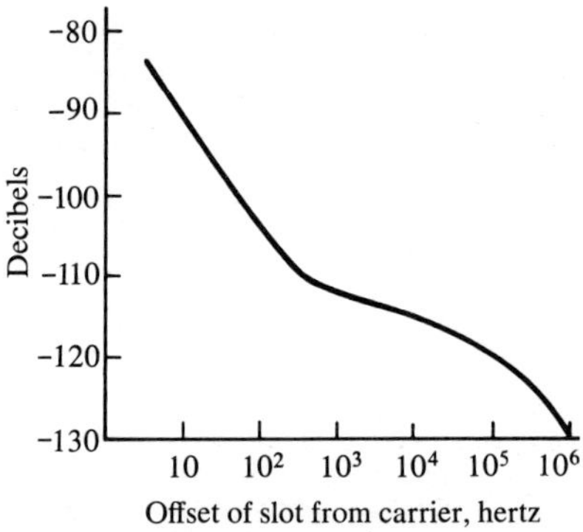

Fig. 4. Sideband-phase noise in 1-Hz-wide slot, relative to carrier, for high-performance 50-MHz synthesizer.

When phase jitter is the result of noise, there are many sideband pairs spaced from the carrier by each noise frequency; so the main signal is surrounded by an essentially continuous series of noise sidebands. The total sideband power in the continuum, out to some chosen frequency above and below the carrier, can be measured, and is often expressed as phase noise in a 30-kHz band centered on the carrier and excluding noise in a 1-Hz band centered on the carrier. (This exclusion is made because noise close in to the carrier is hard to include in the passband of a sensitive rms voltmeter used for the measurement, and if included would require extremely long-term averaging, since the frequencies involved have periods ranging from 1 s upward to infinity.)

Or, more elegantly, the power in the noise spectrum surrounding the carrier can be measured in narrow frequency slots, and the results plotted as phase-noise *density* as a function of frequency separation from the carrier.

Figure 4 is a typical plot of phase-noise density for a synthesizer, density being expressed as noise power in a 1-Hz-wide band, relative to carrier power.

Available measurement techniques make it relatively easy to distinguish between phase noise and amplitude-modulation noise. In most synthesizers the level of phase noise is 10 to 20 dB greater than amplitude noise; so the latter can generally be disregarded.

It is worthy of note that the data on phase noise or phase-noise density for the usual beat-frequency type of synthesizer are *nearly independent of the output frequency.* This is because phase noise is a measure of the effective modulation index of the noise sidebands; and as noted in the discussion of short-term stability, the phase jitter is nearly independent of output frequency.

Conversely, unlike short-term stability, in which performance figures are unaffected by multiplying the output frequency to some higher value, frequency multiplication increases the phase-noise figures in direct proportion to the multiplying factor. If a frequency of 50 MHz is multiplied (say) to 500 MHz, the noise sidebands (and also discrete spurs, of course) on the 50-MHz carrier will be 20 dB greater, relative to carrier, at the 500-MHz level.

Since in most applications the undesired sideband levels are ultimately the limiting factor, it would seem that phase-noise data are more informative and useful than short-term stability data, although the two are merely different ways of looking at the same phenomenon—phase jitter.

Switching Speed. This is of considerable importance in programmed synthesizers in some applications, such as secure communication systems. Of the several types of synthesizers (described in Sec. 6) the fastest are those which generate all necessary ancillary frequencies continuously, and utilize these frequencies as needed by using well-shielded diode switches to select them. Others, which employ phase-locked oscillators as switchable bandpass filters, are somewhat slower, since some settling time is needed after a frequency change. Synthesizers employing preset counters (scale of n) are generally the slowest, since to achieve even moderately fine-frequency resolution the reference frequency for comparison after the scale-of-n divider must be low. A considerable number of periods of this low reference frequency (10 to 100) must elapse before the output oscillator can be deemed to have achieved its new frequency.

Typical published specifications for switching speed range from 20 μs to several milliseconds. Definition of switching speed is often somewhat cloudy in the manufacturer's specification, in that the closeness to ultimate values in phase, level, spurious content, etc., achieved at the end of the specified switching interval is not precisely defined.

Radio Frequency Interference (RFI). The RFI generated by commercial synthesizers is often a question of interest and is rarely well defined in specifications. Many synthesizers exist in which shielding and other RFI-reducing measures are largely nonexistent. Others are built to signal-generator performance in this regard. Manufacturer's specifications should be subjected to detailed inquiry if these characteristics are important.

6. The Principles of Frequency Synthesis Many principles exist; several have withstood the test of time. The user of a synthesizer, of course, is more interested in what comes out of the output jack than in how the result is achieved. However, a knowledge of the inner workings is often useful, if only to understand the reasons for any lack of perfection in the generated signal, and to be able to comprehend, and make intelligent allowances, when unexpected results are observed in complicated measurement setups. A couple of the more important types of synthesizer techniques will now be discussed.

Most synthesizers which provide *fine-frequency resolution* depend on repetitive additions and divisions of frequency. Figure 5*a* shows a typical stage of such an add-and-divide synthesizer. (For convenience in understanding, frequency levels have been normalized.) Figure 5*b* is identical, except for the frequencies passing through it. The unit of Fig. 5*b* uses, for its input, the output of Fig. 5*a*. As Fig. 5 implies, a frequency can be processed through any number of identical iterative stages. In each stage digit information from preceding steps is reduced in rank by a decade (divided by 10) and new digit information chosen for that stage is added. Evidently this process can be carried on, in principle, to any degree of fineness of resolution. (Unfortunately, the instability of the source, and our ever-present enemy, noise, makes continuation of this process futile after a certain point.)

The example shows addition of a fixed frequency, 8, a digit signal ranging in 0.1 increments from 1.0 to 1.09, and an input signal at approximately that 1 level already carrying digit information from previous decades. The resulting sum of these three frequencies is then divided by 10, to return to approximately 1 again. The output of the final decade of such a series is usually heterodyned with another coherent stable frequency (either fixed, or adjustable in coarse steps) to achieve the desired output frequency.

The digit frequencies are sometimes generated continuously and selected, for insertion in the decades, by a series of crossbar switches. This technique produces

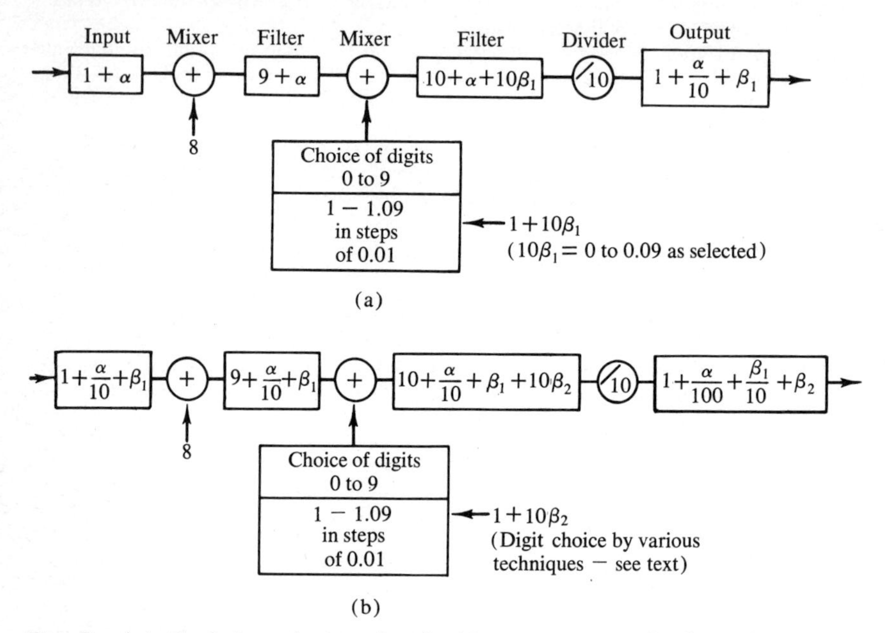

Fig. 5. (*a*) Typical synthesizer decade (frequencies normalized). (*b*) Typical following decade. It should be noted that in this normalized example the fixed parts 1 of the digit frequency add to 9. To minimize mixer spurs, some synthesizers use other frequencies totaling 9 (for instance, 8.4 and 0.6).

the most rapid switching. Other synthesizers use phase-locked oscillators to select desired digit frequencies.

A completely different synthesis technique, sometimes called *scale-of-n*, uses no mixers and no fixed dividers. It has the great advantage, for users not requiring fine resolution, of low cost and small size. This type of synthesizer has found frequent application in communication networks, where channels are preestablished at large frequency spacings (100 Hz to 100 kHz or more).

Figure 6 shows the basic element of such a synthesizer. The output frequency f_o of a voltage-controllable oscillator (VCO) is divided in a presettable digital counter, or scale-of-n divider. The output of the divider is thus f_o/n. This frequency is compared in a phase detector with a stable reference frequency f_x. The phase-detector output is connected to discipline the VCO to maintain $f_o/n = f_r$, or $f_o = nf_r$. The *divider* loop and VCO thus function as a frequency *multiplier*, with output frequency settable at will to an nth harmonic of f_r. By no other known simple process could a high harmonic of a reference frequency be selected unambiguously.

This appealingly simple scheme has, however, some drawbacks. First, any unavoidable phase jitter on f_r is multiplied by n, and (since n will in general be a large integer) the output frequency f_o will tend to be noisy.

Second, since the smallest step in the output frequency will be equal to f_r, it is generally necessary to use a low value of f_r. This means that since a substantial number of periods of f_r are required for the VCO to capture and stabilize, the switching speed is slow. It is made even slower by the necessity of using a relatively long time-constant filter in the phase-lock loop to reduce unwanted sidebands on f_o at f_r spacing.

Scale-of-n dividers are rather limited in top operating frequency (f_o at the divider

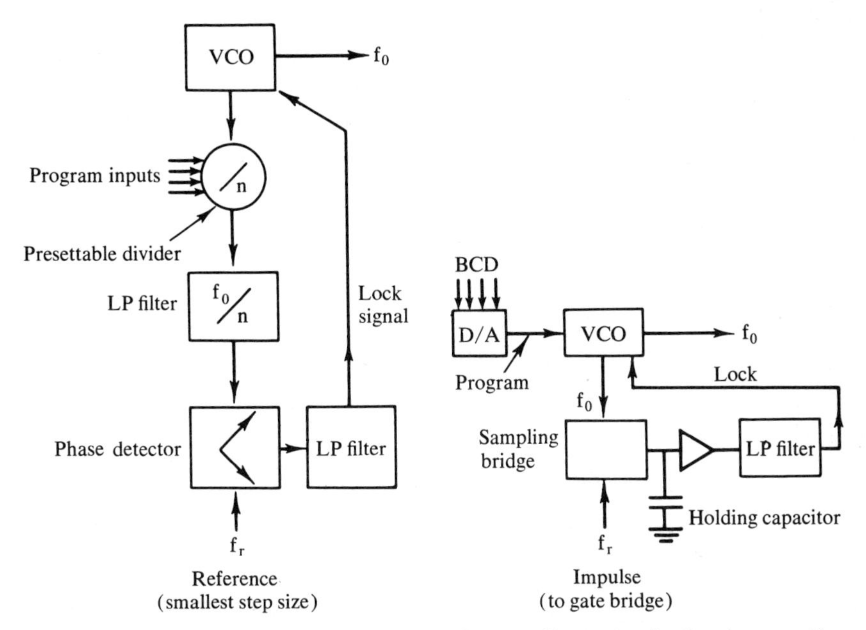

Fig. 6. Typical channel selector in scale-of-n synthesizer. (Note that $f_o = nf_r$.) f_o is commonly heterodyned to the desired frequency level.

Fig. 7. Channel selection by sampling phaselock. (Program rough-tunes VCO; minimum step size = f_r.)

input no higher than a few tens of megahertz) compared with simple frequency scalers; so this type of multiplier is at present limited to fairly low frequencies.

Another type of tunable multiplier for coarse steps, using sample-and-hold phase lock, is not so severely frequency-limited. It consists of a VCO phase-locked by a sampling detector driven by a very short pulse recurring at the reference frequency f_r, as shown in Fig. 7. $f_o = nf_r$, and n is selected by rough-tuning the VCO to within its capture range for the desired value of n.

Selectivity is attained in the relatively low-frequency sample-and-hold amplifier and loop filter (which is required to minimize f_r sidebands, since the balanced sampling bridge never achieves mathematical perfection of balance). As in earlier examples, the locked VCO frequency may be heterodyned to produce the desired output.

7. Other Synthesizer Building Blocks, and Their Influence on Signal-quality Output More conventional multipliers are also used as component circuits in many synthesizers. Among them are the iterative types in which frequency is increased by a series of relatively low multiplying factors like 2 or 3, or the large-jump types employing step-recovery diodes, where all the selectivity against unwanted adjacent harmonics (which create spurs) is provided in the filter at final frequency. Such multipliers, requiring rf selectivity in contrast to the low-pass filters used in the VCO schemes, are rarely used except for fixed frequencies, for economic reasons.

Frequency mixers are almost invariably part of any synthesizer. One of the most important of these (in beat-frequency-type synthesizers) is the *output* mixer in which a difference frequency between a fine-resolution component (scale-of-n, or iterative add-and-divide, for example) and a coarse-resolution frequency is produced and then amplified to form the final output.

Spurious frequencies originating in such an output mixer may well be the largest "spurs" generated in the instrument; so recognition by the user of the spurs to be expected from the final mix is often useful. Very simple principles can be used to pinpoint the frequencies of such spurs. The following equations and examples show how.

Consider a mixer (Fig. 8) to which are applied two signals f_h and f_l. The mixer may be an "adder" so that the output frequency is $f_h + f_l$ or a "subtractor" with $f_o = f_h - f_l$. Besides the desired output f_o there will generally be undesired output frequencies $f_{s1,2,3}$ . . . resulting from the heterodyning of harmonics of f_h and f_l.

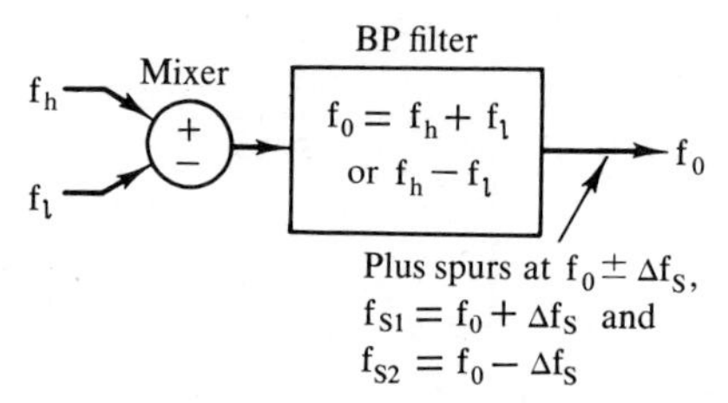

Fig. 8. Mixer and bandpass filter with associated outputs.

(These harmonics may be generated in the mixer itself or may have been supplied to the inputs because of sufficient prefiltering, or both.)

The following relations apply:

1. If $f_h/f_l = h/l$ where h and l are integers, a "coincident" pair of spurs will result. The "order" of such coincident spurs will be $h + l$ (for addition) or $h + l \pm 2$ (for subtraction). ("Coincident" spurs are spurs having exactly the same frequency as f_o; however, since they are formed by harmonics of f_h and f_l, they will rapidly depart from f_o and produce "birdies" if f_h or f_l vary slightly.)

2. If f_h/f_l is approximately but not exactly equal to h/l, noncoincident spurs will appear, *in pairs, spaced above and below f_o by an amount Δf_s.*

For either addition or subtraction:

$$\Delta f_s = hf_l - lf_h$$

If Δf_s is positive, f_{s1} is higher than f_o and f_2 is lower (see next paragraph.)

3. If we define the frequencies of the spur pair related to a particular h/l ratio by f_{s1} and f_{s2}, then

For an "adding" mixer:

$$(a) \qquad \begin{aligned} f_{s1} &= (h+1)f_l - (l-1)f_h \qquad &(\text{order} = h + l) \\ f_{s2} &= (l+1)f_h - (h-1)f \qquad &(\text{order} = h + l) \end{aligned}$$

For a "subtracting" mixer:

$$(b) \qquad \begin{aligned} f_{s1} &= (h-1)f_l - (l-1)f_h \qquad &(\text{order} = h + l - 2) \\ f_{s2} &= (l+1)f_h - (h+1)f_l \qquad &(\text{order} = h + l + 2) \end{aligned}$$

The term "order" is commonly used to denote the sum of the harmonic numbers of the two harmonics beating to produce the spur $[(h-1)+(l-1)$, or $(l+1)+(h+1)$ in the subtracting case].

Figure 9 is a chart showing the "order" of spurs as a function of f_h/f_l. This chart shows at a glance (if f_h and f_l are known and their ratio determined mentally or on a pocket slide rule) whether expected spurs will be important. The equations

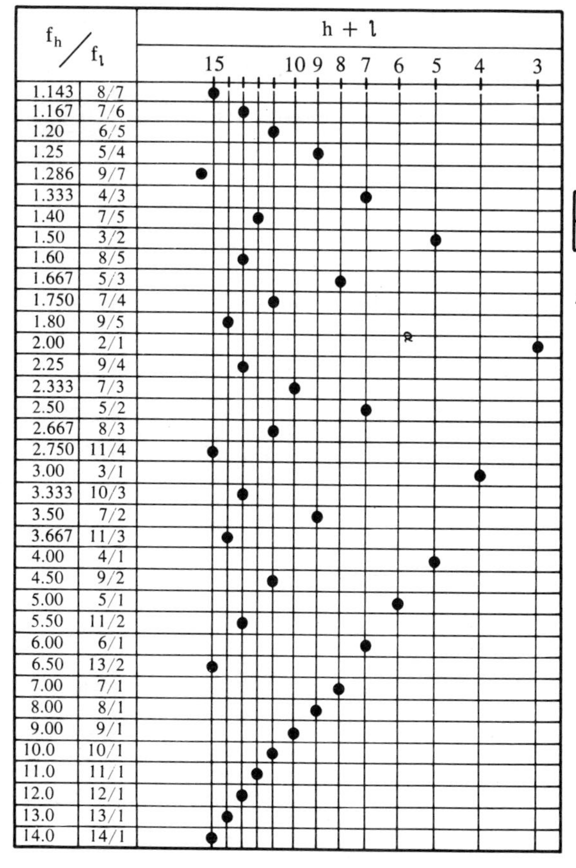

Coincidences through h + l = 15

	Order
Addition	h + l
Subtraction	h + l ± 2

$\Delta f_S = f_{S1} - f_0 = hf_l - lf_h$

Fig. 9. Mixer spurs.

in the above paragraphs permit exact determination of spur frequencies; so they can be predicted (and ignored by the user who knows where they are).

It should be noted that the simple expression for Δf_s (relation 2 above) permits easy estimate as to whether the spurs are filterable in any particular application.

Numerical Example:

Let $\quad f_h = 505 \text{ MHz} \qquad f_l = 400 \qquad f_0 = f_h - f_l = 105$

$$\frac{f_h}{f_l} = 1.26 \qquad \left(\text{close to } \frac{h}{l} = \frac{5}{4} = 1.25\right)$$

$$\Delta f_s = 5 \times 400 - 4 \times 505 = -20 \text{ MHz}$$

So, $\quad f_{s1} = 105 - 20 = 85 \text{ MHz} \qquad f_{s2} = 105 + 20 = 125 \text{ MHz}$

Directly (by relation 3*b*):

$$f_{s1} = 4 \times 400 - 3 \times 505 = 85 \text{ MHz} \qquad \text{(order 7)}$$
$$f_{s2} = 5 \times 505 - 6 \times 400 = 125 \text{ MHz} \qquad \text{(order 11)}$$

The output mixer is generally the creator of the most important "mixer" spurs. However, other mixers in the synthesis process may contribute.

In judging the likelihood of important spurs from other mixers, remember that just as multiplication of a contaminated frequency increases the contamination, division reduces it. So in general mixers which are followed by frequency dividers in the chain are less subject to suspicion than are those which contribute directly to the output.

8. Synthesizer Applications These are too numerous for detailed listing, but a few of the more common uses will be noted briefly.

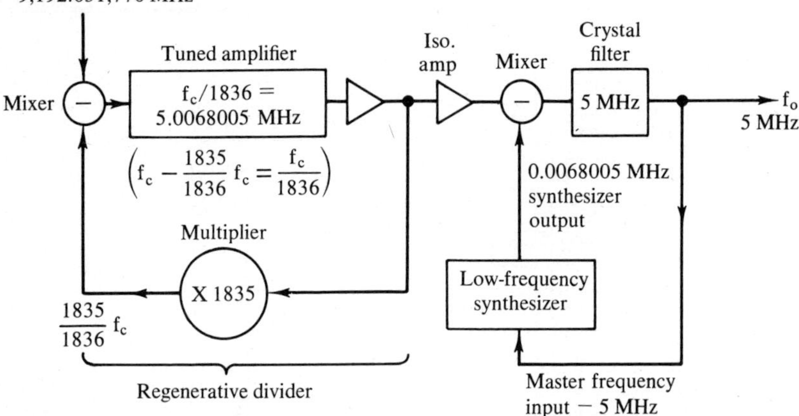

Fig. 10. One of many ways in which synthesizers have been used to help translate atomic-transition frequency to simple standard frequency.

1. In communications and telemetry, the availability of stable, agile sources has opened a whole new world of applications. Programmable models are, in general, most useful in these fields. In deep-space communications, bandwidths have been narrowed dramatically to improve signal-to-noise ratio. Computer-assisted Doppler-shift extractors are fundamental in some of these systems.

For "secure" communications, programming of frequencies to a prearranged schedule has become possible only with the advent of the synthesizer.

2. Even more obviously, in measurements of extremely high-Q resonators (including atomic resonators) full advantage is being taken of the extreme resolution and stability of synthesizers, often locked to primary frequency standards. The capability of sweeping over extremely narrow bands, with accurate frequency knowledge at all times, opens the door to measurements never before possible.

3. Another example (which requires resolution but no agility) is in the field of standard frequencies. Unfortunately the cesium atom, rubidium, and even simple hydrogen failed to recognize the universal urge of mankind for "simple" numbers; consequently, we often find it necessary to translate an 11- or 12-digit number to one having only perhaps one significant figure.

Synthesizers can help provide a bridge between 5.000 . . . MHz and 9, 192, 631, 770 Hz (for example), as shown in Fig. 10.

4. In fixed-channel communication—particularly airborne—the scale-of-*n* synthesizer has come into its own. Communication channels are traditionally widely spaced; so the disadvantages of scale-of-*n* are minimized, and the low-cost small-space advantages are controlling.

5. Since the discovery of alternating current, signal sources for generating such have been the starting point for all laboratory experiments. We have seen many types—*LC* oscillators, *RC* oscillators, klystrons, magnetrons, and others too numerous to list. However, until the advent of the synthesizer, all have been subject to uncertainty of the generated frequency, inconvenience in adjustment, and lack of

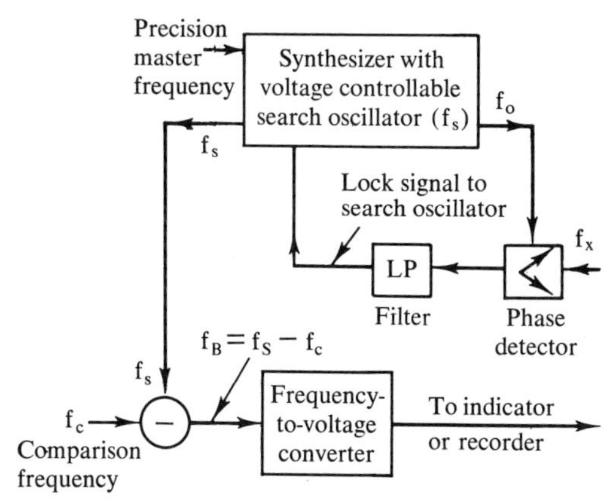

Fig. 11. Using precision master frequency and synthesizer to determine drift of less stable source f_x. With $f_o \equiv f_x$ (by phase lock), f_c is set slightly lower than search oscillator frequency f_s (to avoid ambiguity at zero beat). As f_o follows drifting f_x, much greater, but proportional, variations occur in f_s. Percentage change in f_B is greater than in f_s.

repeatability. As a general-purpose frequency source for laboratories, the synthesizer has no peer. Most laboratories find the high initial cost unimportant relative to the convenience and timesaving achieved.

6. Synthesizers with varactor-controlled search oscillators are useful devices for measuring aging or temperature drift of other frequency sources. The synthesizer can easily be phase-locked to the subject source (Fig. 11); so the drift of the unknown can be measured and recorded with as much precision as required by a measurement of the frequency variation of the "search" oscillator needed to keep the synthesizer and the unknown in frequency-coherent phase lock. Sensitivity of this measurement is selectable over many orders of magnitude. The "agility" of the synthesizer is very important here—any unknown can be matched and tracked.

Section Nine

Frequency- and Time-measurement Instruments

Time measurements or their corollary, frequency (number of events per unit time) are inherent in almost every instrument use whether the instrument measures or generates a signal. Time, as a quantity to be measured itself, is also an important instrument application.

Time can be measured to a very high degree of precision and accuracy. The most precise measurements are complex and require special instruments for use in well-controlled environments. Time and frequency measurements to a lower level of precision can be made at any place and time by pushing a button.

This section describes what time is and how it can be measured to any degree of precision necessary. The relationship of time to frequency ties all these chapters together. Liberal use of the index should be made to ensure that any problem the reader may be concerned with is completely covered.

Chapter 33

Electronic Counters

MARVIN J. WILLRODT

Hewlett-Packard Company, Santa Clara, California

APPLICATIONS OF ELECTRONIC COUNTERS TO FREQUENCY AND TIME MEASUREMENTS

Electronic counters are extensively used to measure the frequency, period, and time relationships of electrical signals. Nonelectrical phenomena can be measured with electronic counters by using transducers which convert the pertinent information from the system under test to electrical signals that can be measured by the electronic counter.

An electronic counter makes a measurement by actually counting each cycle of an electrical input signal for some precise interval of time. When measuring frequency, this precise interval of time is usually established by a quartz-crystal oscillator driving a series of 10 to 1 dividers; for instance, a 1-MHz crystal frequency divided by 1 million to 1 yields a 1-Hz output or can form pulses spaced exactly 1 s apart. The crystal oscillator and dividers plus some signal-shaping circuits make up what is known as the time base of the counter. In this example the counter would count the number of cycles of the input signal occurring in 1 s, which is by definition the frequency of the input signal in hertz. Instrument design and control settings determine if the answer is displayed as hertz, kilohertz, or some other engineering unit.

Electronic counters have become widely accepted for these measurements because of the high resolution and accuracy easily attainable in everyday measuring situations. The reading is presented to the user in digital format so the information will always be interpreted the same regardless of who makes the measurement.

The process used by the counter in making the measurement is such that the accuracy of the resulting measurement is easily traceable to the National Bureau of Standards. This factor becomes more important each day in our advancing technology. For some users, a production or procurement specification may require this traceability. For others it may be important that equipment built at a factory in one part of the country will work with equipment built at another factory in a different part of the country. A rather obvious example of this might be a two-way radio system where transmitters were built at one location and receivers at another; both must be tuned to the same frequency for optimum system performance. In addition a transmitter must satisfy the requirement by the Federal Communications Commission or other government regulatory body that it be on a specific frequency within certain tolerance limits. This requirement may be much more demanding than that the transmitter and receiver just work with each other and must be met regardless of whether it is necessary for proper system operation.

FREQUENCY MEASUREMENTS WITHOUT A COUNTER

The electronic counter is not the only way in which many of these measurements can be made—frequency can be measured by observing Lissajous patterns on an oscilloscope, by using beat frequency or heterodyne techniques, or with an absorption frequency meter, to name a few. However, compared with use of an electronic counter, all these other methods require more operator skill, are in general slower, are more prone to error, and may require a considerable amount of auxiliary equipment.

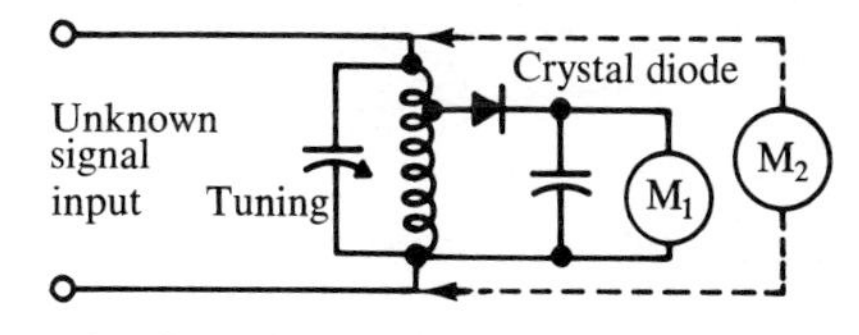

Fig. 1. Absorption frequency meter.

Absorption Frequency Meter. An absorption frequency meter functions by absorbing a portion of the input signal when tuned to the input-signal frequency. Referring to Fig. 1, correct tuning is indicated by an rf voltmeter (M_1) or by a lamp bulb which is a part of the frequency meter or by a change in the voltage across the line as measured by M_2. Once the absorption meter has been tuned, the unknown frequency is read from the tuning dial. The tuned circuit used in an absorption meter may be constructed using conventional coils and capacitors for low frequencies (below 100 MHz) or it may consist of resonant transmission lines or a resonant cavity if it is to work at higher frequencies or on up into the microwave region. A sensitive rf voltmeter is used as a tuning indicator when the input-signal level is low.

Lissajous Patterns. Lissajous patterns are oscilloscope displays generated when one frequency is connected to the vertical input and another frequency is connected to the horizontal input. The number of cross lines in the resulting pattern as well as the motion of the pattern or lack of motion can be interpreted in terms of the ratio and phase on one input frequency to the other. (See Fig. 2.)

Heterodyne Freqency-measuring Techniques. An unknown input signal F_x is combined with a known signal, as shown in Fig. 3, the local oscillator signal LO, in a mixer circuit. The difference frequency F_d, that is, the unknown input frequency minus LO frequency, is observed with headphones if within the audio range, with an oscilloscope if it has a large range, or with a "zero-beat" indicator such as a meter or tuning indicator tube.

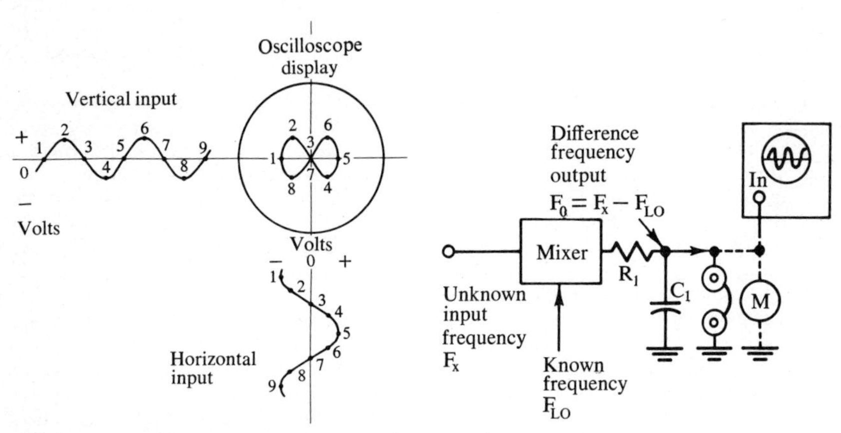

Fig. 2. Lissajous pattern when vertical-input frequency is exactly twice the horizontal-input frequency and phased as shown.

Fig. 3. Heterodyne frequency meter.

If the reference frequency can be adjusted to get a "zero beat," i.e., a zero difference frequency, with the unknown, the unknown equals the reference frequency or some integer N times the reference frequency. If the reference frequency cannot be adjusted for a zero beat, the unknown equals the reference frequency or N times the reference frequency plus or minus the difference frequency. The difference frequency is added if the reference frequency or its harmonic is below the unknown, subtracted if it is above.

The output of the mixer contains all modulation products (F_x, F_{LO}, $F_x + F_{LO}$, $F_x - F_{LO}$, . . .). A low-pass filter R_1C_1 removes all components except $F_x - F_{LO}$.

TYPES OF ELECTRONIC COUNTERS

Electronic counters are designed to make a number of different kinds of measurements on electrical signals.

1. Frequency Measurements The electronic counter counts the number of cycles of an electrical waveform for some precise time to determine frequency. Range can extend from a few hertz to beyond 100 MHz using direct counting techniques and can be extended on to several hundred megahertz using "prescaling" technique, or even extended on into the microwave region using heterodyne-conversion techniques, transfer-oscillator techniques, or automatic frequency dividers.

2. Time-interval Measurements The counter measures elapsed time between two electrical pulses with accuracy into the nanosecond (one billionth of a second) region or better and resolution to 0.1 ns.

Period Measurement. The electronic counter measures the time required for the input signal to go through one complete cycle. This measurement can be made with as little as 0.1 s resolution or as great as 1 ns for a single period of the unknown and with even greater resolution using period-averaging techniques.

Ratio Measurement. The electronic counter measures the ratio of one frequency input signal to a second input signal. Ratio averaging lets one achieve high resolution on this kind of measurement even when both signals are of nearly the same frequency, i.e., near a 1:1 ratio.

3. Universal Counters A function switching allows one electronic counter to make a variety of measurements such as frequency, period, time interval, frequency ratio, totalize and scale frequency, to name some of the more important ones.

4. Preset Counters These electronic counters fall into three general classes:

1. Those with the preset on the time base to perform normalizing functions. For example, pulses from a transducer on a fluid flowmeter can be mathematically manipulated so the electronic counter displays the result in terms of gallons per minute.

2. Those which have one or more presets on the visual-display register. The electronic counter can initiate some control action if the frequency or other function exceeds a previously preset number. For example, if pulses from a tachometer generator on an engine exceed a rate indicating a dangerous engine speed, an output from the preset circuits of the electronic counter could stop the engine.

3. Those which allow the decade-counting units to be reset to some predetermined count other than all zeros. This permits some starting number to be added to or subtracted from the final answer displayed by the counter. For example, a pressure transducer which operates by changing the tension in a vibrating string subject to pressure changes may have a frequency of 1,300 Hz when the gage pressure is 0 psi. The number 1,300 can be subtracted from the readout so at 0 psi the electronic counter will display 0000. As pressure is applied to the transducers, the increase in frequency is now a direct indication of psi gage pressure.

Control of these three parameters allows one to get a direct reading from any linear transducer.

5. Reciprocal Counters The reciprocal counter always makes a period or multiple-period average measurement on the input signal. A computer section in the counter then takes a reciprocal on this information and presents the answer on the visual display and binary-coded decimal (for printers) output as frequency. The more sophisticated versions of these counters automatically determine measurement time, decimal-point location, and measurement unit to give a visual readout with a predetermined number of digits resolution. Operation is completely automatic, except for perhaps setting the input-level controls. Accuracy for a given measurement time is always as good as or better than that of counters previously discussed for input frequencies lower than the internal clock frequency but is poorer when the input frequency is above the clock frequency.

6. Computing Counters A general-purpose version of the reciprocal counter, this type makes frequency, period, time interval, and other measurements. Since it has a small computer in its makeup, new measurement techniques are possible. A computing counter always makes a period or time-interval measurement and then does the necessary arithmetic manipulation on this information using its built-in computational capability to display the answer as a frequency, a period, or a time interval or in some normalized format called for by the operator. Measurement interval need no longer be decimally related to 1 s, as the computer divides by any integer as easily as it divides by 10. An auxiliary manual keyboard or prewired plug-in program board lets the operator manipulate the information so the visual display will be in the useful form for a particular measurement. Some keyboards have a built-in memory so a multistep program can be entered and then run automatically as often as desired. As an example, the counter may be actually making a delay measurement of the time required for an electrical pulse to travel through a section of RG/58U coaxial cable. By making the delay measurement in nanoseconds, then subtracting out the delay due to interconnecting cables of the measuring setup and dividing the result by the nanoseconds per foot electrical propagation constant of the cable, the visual readout on the counter can display in feet, inches, or other units the length of a section of cable connected between two designated terminals.

The more sophisticated of these counters also make use of interpolation systems which will increase measurement resolution in a given measurement time by 1,000 to 1 over a conventional counter and give resolution to 0.1 ns on time-interval measurements. As a basis of comparison, 0.1 ns is the time it takes light to travel approximately 1 in. Triggered measurement capability, similar to the triggered sweep on an oscilloscope, makes direct frequency measurement of pulsed rf signals a simple matter, as a measurement can be started by an external command signal and continued for any predetermined interval.

7. Microwave Counters An electronic counter is combined with an automatic transfer oscillator or automatic frequency divider in the same package. Gate length, decimal-point location, and measurement units are fixed so the visual display is direct-reading in the microwave frequency input. Operation of these counters is completely automatic; it is necessary only to connect a continuous-wave (cw) microwave signal which is within certain power levels to the input terminal to make the frequency measurement.

8. Reversible (or Up-Down) Counters These counters can count up, i.e., 0, +1, +2, +3, +4, as well as count down, +4, +3, +2, 0, −1, −2, −3, etc. Reversible counters have two inputs which can be used in one of four ways:

1. The signals may be added arithmetically, the visual display being the sum of the number of pulses (or cycles) appearing at each input during the time the signal gate is open. On the better counters pulse-coincident circuits keep track of all pulses so none are skipped even if they should occur simultaneously on both channels.
2. The signals may be subtracted.
3. One signal on the first input can be counted and displayed as with a conventional electronic counter. The second input can direct the decimal-counter assemblies to either add a count or subtract a count for each cycle of the signal on the first channel. Reversal can take place in 1 μs or less.
4. A transducer or other source may supply a two-phase signal to the two inputs of the counter. The signal on phase *A* goes to the decimal-counting assemblies and adds counts if it lags phase *B*. If it leads phase *B*, counts are subtracted from the decade-counter assemblies. This mode of operation is widely used for determining mechanical position accurately. A two-phase transducer with output signals 90° apart translates the mechanical motion into the two required electrical signals.

9. Special Counters These electronic counters are normally built to operate in special systems with specific transducers. The mode of operation, gate length, and other parameters are determined by permanent wiring so the visual display will be directly in gallons, gallons per minute, feet, or whatever unit satisfies the particular application. These counters are generally not suitable for any measurement except the one for which they were designed.

Counters have been built using ferroresonant counting devices, magnetron-beam switching tubes, and delay lines as part of the counting circuit; however, they have never enjoyed widespread use.

HOW THE ELECTRONIC COUNTER MAKES THE MEASUREMENT

Knowledge of the way in which the electronic counter makes the measurement may not be of much value to the user who is measuring the frequency of a high-amplitude noise-free sine-wave signal, since this involves only connecting the signal to the input of the counter and reading the resultant digital display. Many of today's measurements, however, will be with other than ideal signals; that is, the signal may have low amplitude, may be other than sinusoidal, or may be noisy or have other spurious information which makes a measurement more difficult to set up; but it will certainly not be impossible if the operator has knowledge of the method used internally by the electronic counter in making the measurement. A fairly detailed look at the signal-input circuits enables the operator to make the required measurements more easily and effectively and finally to evaluate the accuracy of the result.

Most electronic counters make a frequency measurement based on the definition of frequency:

$$f = \frac{\text{cycles of input}}{T}$$

where f = frequency
T = measurement time, s

The pulse-counting circuits of an electronic counter are first reset to zero, then count, without error, each electrical pulse presented to the signal input so long as the input-pulse rate of uniformly spaced pulses does not exceed the maximum counting rate of the counter. This maximum counting rate is determined by the design of the signal-input circuit and of the "units" (fastest) counting decade, which is located on the right end of the display. If the pulses are connected to the input of the decimal-counter units for precisely 1 s, the number displayed will be the number of electrical cycles in 1 s of time, or by definition this will be a measurement of the frequency of the incoming signal in hertz.

THE BASIC SECTIONS OF AN ELECTRONIC COUNTER

The input amplifier and trigger, the main gate, the decade counters, and the time base as shown in Fig. 4 can be interconnected in more than one way to make different measurements. A power supply is necessary, of course, but it is not shown, since this is incidental to the operation of the counter.

10. Input Amplifier and Trigger The input circuit must accept any electrical input signal such as sine wave, square wave, pulse, or complex signal of any amplitude of polarity or frequency (within the specified range of the counter) at its input and provide at its output one and only one electrical pulse per input cycle. This output pulse must be of constant amplitude and width, for any input signal, to drive the decade-counting circuits correctly. The input circuitry is generally an amplifier followed by a Schmitt-trigger circuit, which is discussed in detail in Sec. 46.

11. Main Gate The output of the trigger circuit connects to the decimal counter by way of a "gate," which in its simplest form might be nothing more than an off-on switch. When the switch is closed, the signal can pass from the signal-input connector on the front panel of the electronic counter through the gate to the input of the decimal counters; when the switch is open the signals cannot pass. A word of caution is in order when drawing circuits with or discussing gates as switches. The term "gate" is the garden-gate variety; i.e., the open gate lets the signals through and thus corresponds to the closed switch. The closed gate is, of course, the "open" switch. The two terms are 180° out of phase, so to speak. Since the term gate is used universally to describe the completion or disruption of the signal path, but line drawings of signal flow very often show switches, one must be careful when using these terms or confusion can result.

Decimal-counting Units (DCU or DCA). The electronic pulse-counting units are first reset to zero state (that is, so that the electronic-counter visual display reads 00000), then totalize pulses coming through the signal gate and display the answer digitally much the same as the mileage indicator of a car speedometer totalizes shaft revolutions to indicate the distance a car has traveled.

12. Time Base The time base, or clock, generates accurately spaced electrical pulses which tell the gate when to open and when to close so that the signal-input pulses will be connected to the counting decade for some precisely determined time, 1 s, for instance, as indicated in the earlier example.

The 1-s or other gate interval is generated by dividing a 100-kHz, 1-MHz, or 10-MHz crystal-oscillator frequency by the appropriate power of 10 using electronic decade (÷10) circuits or by dividing the 60-Hz power-line frequency by 6 and then by an appropriate power of 10.

Special measurements may dictate gate times of more than or less than 1 s; however, this does not affect the functional manner in which the frequency determination is made. Most general-purpose counters have gate lengths adjustable in decade steps from as short as 1 μs to as long as 10 s or more in decade steps. Thus the counted frequency can always be indicated by the simple expedient

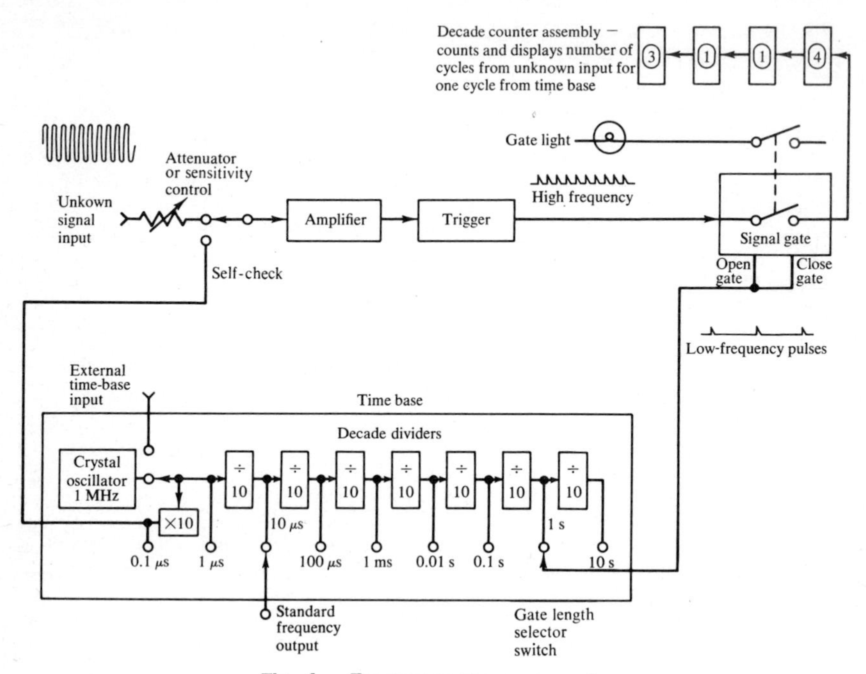

Fig. 4. Frequency measurement.

of properly placing a decimal point and choosing an appropriate measurement unit (Hz, kHz, MHz, GHz, etc.).

High-frequency Measurement. The direct-count range of electronic counters extends from dc to a few hundred megahertz. This covers only a small portion of the frequency spectrum in use today; so techniques other than direct counting are used to extend the capabilities of the electronic counter to above 40 GHz. This is usually accomplished by using plug-in units which fit into the electronic-counter main frame, although self-contained frequency dividers are available to divide a high-frequency signal by a factor which gets it within the counting rate of a low-frequency counter. Some of the techniques used, which are described in detail below, are as follows:

1. *Prescaling.* The high-frequency signal is divided by some numbers—2, 4, 8, etc.—using high-speed divider circuits to get it within the frequency range of the electronic counter.

2. *Heterodyne Converter.* The high-frequency signal is reduced in frequency, "down-converted," to one within the range of the electronic counter using heterodyne-conversion techniques.

3. *Transfer Oscillator.* A harmonic of a tunable low-frequency continuous wave oscillator is zero beat, with an unknown high-frequency signal. The low-frequency oscillator frequency is measured by the electronic counter, and this frequency is then multiplied by an integer, the harmonic number, to determine the unknown frequency.

4. *Automatic Divider.* The high-frequency signal is reduced by some factor such as 100:1 or 1,000:1 using automatically tuned circuits which generate an output frequency of one one-hundredth or one one-thousandth of the input frequency to get it within the range of the electronic counter.

NONFREQUENCY MEASUREMENTS

13. Period Measurement for Low Frequency Measurement accuracy becomes very poor for low frequencies (below 10 or 1 kHz) using the frequency mode

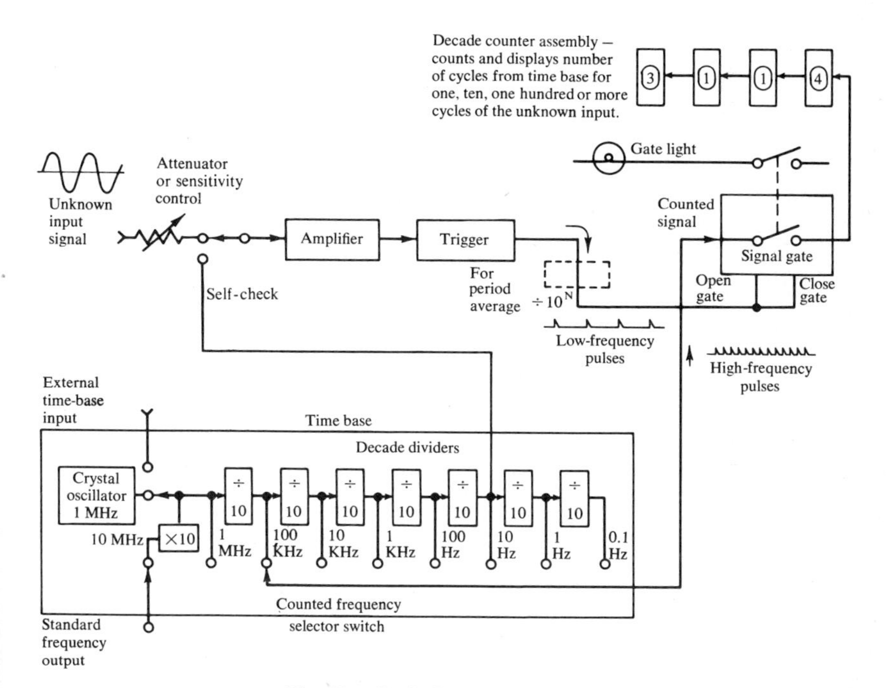

Fig. 5. Period measurement.

of operation. To get good accuracy at low frequencies, the electronic counter makes a period measurement. By definition:

$$P = \frac{1}{f} = \frac{T}{1 \text{ cycle of input}}$$

where P = period of input signal
f = frequency of input
T = time (some short time like 1 μs)

NOTE: This is the same as the definition of frequency except that it has been inverted, as period is the reciprocal of frequency by definition.

Electrically, a period measurement is made by interchanging the wires from the trigger circuit and the time base where they connect to the main gate as in Fig. 5.

The only drawback to using period measurements to get accuracy at low frequencies is that the operator must take a reciprocal of the answer displayed by the visual readout of the electronic counter if he wishes to know the input frequency.

For example, when measuring the period of the 60-Hz power line, the electronic counter might display 16.6673 ms.

$$\text{Frequency} = \frac{1}{P} = \frac{1}{16.6673 \text{ ms/cycle}} \times \frac{1{,}000 \text{ ms}}{\text{s}}$$
$$= 59.9977 \text{ Hz}$$

Higher accuracy can be had by making period-average measurements. This is done by connecting one or more of the decade-divider units (10:1 dividers) between

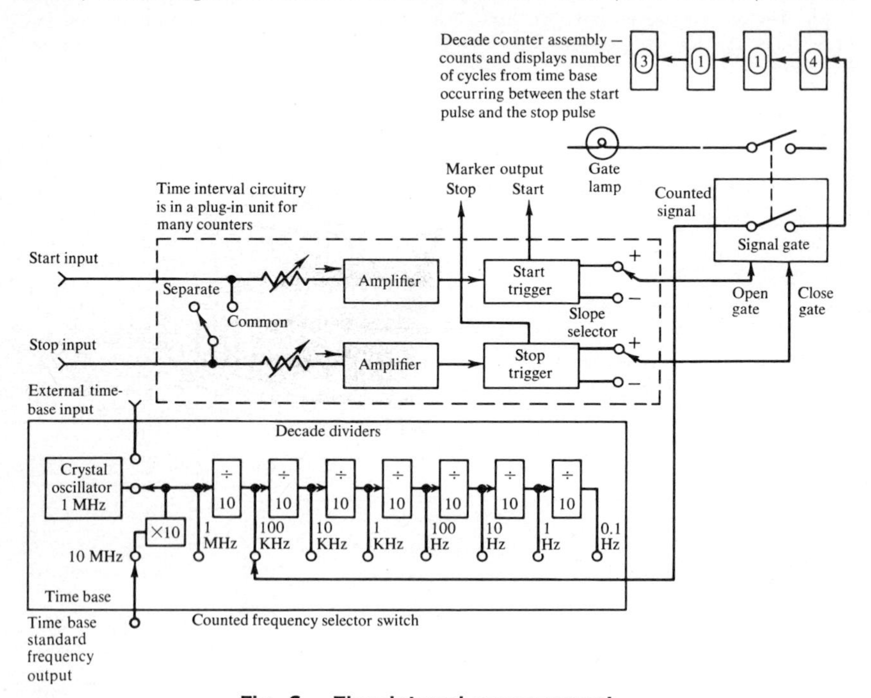

Fig. 6. Time-interval measurement.

the unknown signal input and open-close input to the signal gate. The gate is now held open for 10, 100, 1,000, or more cycles (periods) of the input signal, depending on the number of decade dividers used. The visual display on the electronic counter will show more digits of information; however, the decimal-point location and measurement unit are usually changed each time an additional decade divider is added, so that the display is always in terms of the period of 1 cycle of the input signal, even though the measurement may have lasted for 10 or 100 or more cycles.

14. Time-interval Measurement In this measurement, the counter performs the function of an electronic stopwatch, i.e., it measures elapsed time.

An electrical signal or some specific point on an electrical waveform opens the main gate to start a count.

The electronic counter then counts the crystal-oscillator frequency, some multiple or submultiple of this frequency, or an externally supplied frequency for so long as the gate is held open. The counted frequency is the "yardstick" with which the time measurement is made.

A second electrical signal or a second specific point on an electrical waveform closes the main gate to stop the count.

The visual display on the counter is the elapsed time from the start signal to the stop signal in microseconds, seconds, or whatever measuring unit was used. Figure 6 shows this mode of operation in block-diagram form.

15. Other Modes of Operation Other modes of operation are generally variations on the three modes just described. A ratio measurement, for instance, uses the same configuration as the period measurement, except that the higher of the two frequencies is now connected to the external time-base input. The decimal-counter assemblies total the number of electrical pulses (cycles) coming in here per cycle of the signal at the signal-input terminal. For higher resolution, the "EXT" time-base input frequency can be counted for 10, 100, 1,000, or more cycles of the lower frequency at the signal-input terminals by connecting one or more of the decade dividers between the trigger output and the main-gate open-close input just as for period averaging. This increases the resolution of the ratio measurement and is useful when making measurements near a 1:1 ratio.

Other Measurements. Besides measuring frequency, the electronic counter may also be used to measure time, voltage, and phase, and to normalize readings on any information which can be converted to electrical pulses.

Some counters have scaling capability; that is, they can divide any frequency up to the maximum accepted by the counter or plug-in units by powers of 10 (÷ 10, ÷ 100, etc.) to give a low-frequency output-pulse train which is coherent with a high-frequency input. Many counters also have a manual start-stop mode of operation so that they can be used as high-speed electrical-event totalizers.

COUNTER SPECIFICATIONS AND SIGNIFICANCE

Several basic specifications must be examined to see if the electronic counter is capable of measuring the unknown signal at the operator's location with required resolution and accuracy. These are as follows:

16. Functions Most counters will make one or more of the following measurements: frequency, period, time interval, ratio, scaling, and totalizing. One of these modes of operation must be suitable for making the measurement under consideration.

17. Maximum Count Rate This determines the highest continuous frequency at which a counter will count. It must be higher than the frequency of the signal to be measured.

18. Input-signal Requirements The unknown input signal must be capable of driving the counter; therefore, several aspects of the signal must be examined.

1. Amplitude must be greater than the minimum specified for the counter.
2. Source impedance of the signal must be low enough to develop the minimum required voltage across the input impedance of the counter as a load.
3. All counters have input sensitivity specified in terms of a minimum rms voltage of a sine wave. Additional requirements are imposed on the input signal when measuring pulses, square waves, or random signals or for any nonsymmetrical waveform. These requirements consist of specifications on polarity, the minimum peak-to-peak voltage, rise time, or the dc component, to name a few.
4. Ac or dc input coupling. This can make a big difference in the way a counter measures nonsymmetrical waveforms, random waveforms, or input signals which have a dc component.

19. Gate Time Long gates are necessary for high accuracy in frequency measurements. Short gates are used to characterize a signal which is changing.

20. Accuracy The summation of ±1 count error, ±trigger error, and ±time-base error determines the accuracy of the measurement and must meet the accuracy requirements imposed by the test.

21. Readout This should be easily readable and large enough for easy viewing from the operator's position. Remote readout may be desirable around engine test cells and for other industrial applications.

Overflow. A rear connector may provide an electrical indication that a count has gone higher than the capacity of the visual-display register; i.e., the most significant digit (farthest-left digit in the display) has gone beyond the count of 9 (that is, to 10 or above).

22. Sample Rate Setting of a sample-rate control is one of the factors which determines how long a counter waits after completing one measurement before it will start another one when in the automatic mode of operation. An INFINITE or HOLD position is usually included as a part of the sample-rate circuit to allow the counter to make just one reading. Each time the RESET pushbutton on the panel is operated or an electrical reset signal is applied to the counter, it will make one single reading which it will hold indefinitely unless another reset is supplied.

23. Display Storage Counters with display storage give a continuous visual and/or binary-coded decimal output of a previous reading while a new one is in progress. Upon completion of the new reading, the display is "updated" to the new reading. Counters with display storage can take readings much more rapidly and can be read with less chance of error than those which do not have this feature.

24. Reset A rear terminal permits remote reset of the counter with a voltage change or contact closure to ground on some counters. This may be desirable for systems applications.

25. Standard-frequency Outputs The crystal-oscillator frequency is usually 100 kHz, 1 MHz, 5 MHz, or 10 MHz and appears at a rear-panel connector. This output should be buffered, that is, isolated from the crystal oscillator with an amplifier or decoupling network so that connecting cables or other equipment to the output terminal do not change the crystal-oscillator frequency. For best oscillator stability some counters have a separate, regulated power supply which keeps the crystal oven hot and the oscillator operating whenever the power cord is energized. The crystal-frequency output on these counters can be used as an "in-house" frequency standard, since it is continuously available. Specifications on aging rate, temperature stability, variation with line voltage, and short-term stability must of course exceed the minimum requirement of the facility where used.

26. Binary-coded Decimal Output The binary-coded decimal (BCD) output is used to connect the counter to a digital printer, a digital-to-analog converter, a computer interface input, a card punch, or other data-acquisition equipment. The BCD output voltage and impedance levels and reference-voltage output of the counter must be examined to see if they will provide the correct drive to the device being used. The print-command output of the counter must be of correct polarity amplitude and rise time to drive the printer or other devices. Also, the inhibit or hold-off voltage and polarity must be right to keep the counter from starting a new reading before the data-acquisition device has had time to accept the previous information. Buffer storage of the BCD information by the counter helps here, as information from a previous count is stored until the new count is completed. BCD storage by the acquisition device is often an available option if the counter does not have this feature.

27. Auxiliary Outputs

Gate Output. A dc-level change when the main gate is open can be used as an external indication that a count is in process. It can also be used to intensify an oscilloscope trace of an input signal to show what portion of a signal is being processed by the counter.

Start-Stop Markers. Many counters which measure time interval generate marker pulses available for rear connectors. One marker coincides with the start of a measurement and the other with the ending of the measurement. These can be used as intensity markers on an oscilloscope displaying the input waveform or to trigger auxiliary equipment.

Power Requirement. The equipment may operate from batteries, from ac power 115 or 230 V, 50 to 60 Hz to 400 Hz or more. A suitable power source of adequate capacity must be available at the location where the measurement is to be made.

If these requirements are satisfied, some of the other considerations are as follows:

Remote Programming. This is often desirable on counters used in data-acquisition systems. Most of the functions selectable by front-panel switching can be programmed by contact closures, dc voltages, or multiline binary or BCD program inputs. Remote programming can be added to some counters but is available only as a factory-installed option on others.

FRONT-PANEL CONTROLS

Figures 7 and 8 show typical counter front panels. They are referred to for each front-panel term described. An electronic counter displays a reading representing

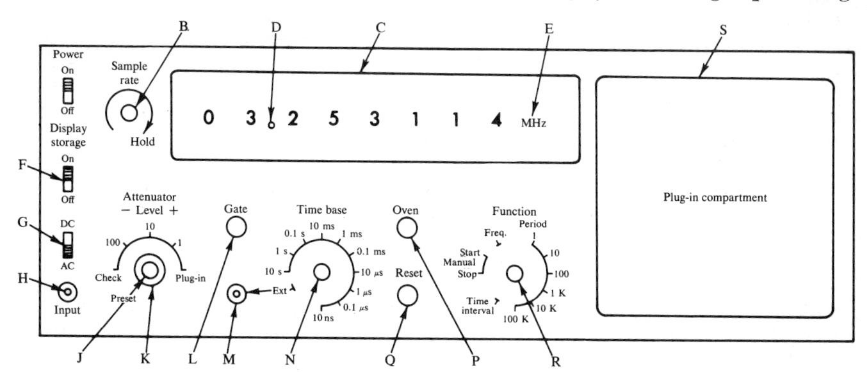

Fig. 7. High-frequency universal counter with provision for plug-in measurement extenders.

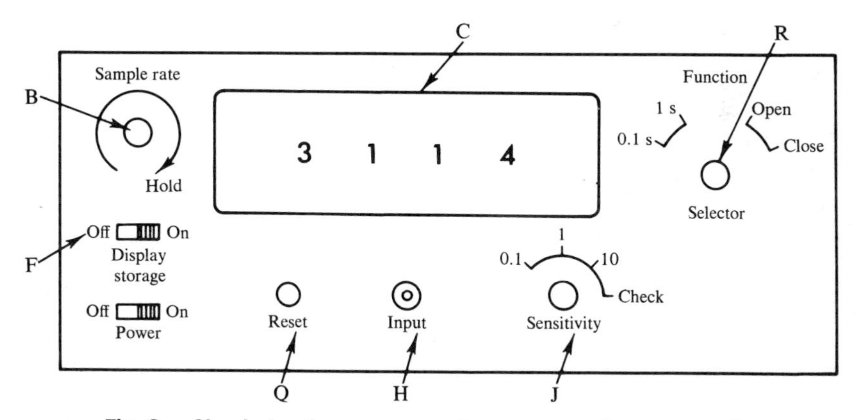

Fig. 8. Simple low-frequency counter measures frequency only.

the number of electrical pulses occurring in some known interval of time. These pulses might have been generated by a transducer which generates a pulse rate directly related to rpm, fluid flow, pressure, temperature, or other physical phenomena so that even though the readout might be in units other than frequency, basic operation of the instrument is always that of an electronic pulse counter. For this reason only those characteristics relating directly to electronic pulse counting will be discussed. Other aspects of transferring a physical phenomenon to an electrical signal are discussed in Chapter 6.

Input or Signal Input H. This is the main signal-input connector for the electronic counter when it is used for most measurements. Modern electronic counters have an input impedance of 1 MΩ shunted by 25 pF or less with an input sensitivity of 100 mV rms for frequencies to 100 MHz or so. Some counters also have a 50-Ω input as well for use when the counter must provide a good termination for a 50-Ω coaxial cable to prevent standing waves. This is particularly important for frequencies above 20 MHz. Some counters may have sensitivity to 10 mV rms or even 1 mV. Unless the measurement specifically requires high sensitivity, one can get into problems with electrical noise from power tools, ignition noise, neon signs, and stray pickup from radio, TV, or radar transmitters unless the whole experimental circuit is carefully shielded. Input sensitivity and impedance are generally not specified on the front panel of the electronic counter; therefore, the user must consult the operating manual or data sheet provided with the counter to get this information for his particular instrument. Electronic counters designed for time-interval measurements will have two identical dc-coupled inputs labeled 1 and 2, *X* and *Y*, *A* and *B*, or something similar. Electronic counters which make ratio measurements will also have two input connectors; however, electrical specifications for each may be quite different, since one would normally be connected to a much lower frequency than the other.

AC-DC Switch G. This switch connects a capacitor in series with the input connector so that the counter can measure ac signals which have a dc component.

Attenuator or Sensitivity J. Most electronic counters have a sensitivity control or attenuator between the signal-input connectors and the input amplifier. This attenuator decreases the input-signal amplitude so that levels as high as 100 V or more can be measured without overloading the input amplifier of the counter. Simple electronic counters may use a continuously variable control that functions in a manner similar to the volume control on a radio receiver. More sophisticated electronic counters use compensated step attenuators like those in the vertical-input channel of a wideband oscilloscope. The attenuation factor is usually 1:1 to 10:1 and 100:1. The input impedance, both resistance and capacitance, should remain constant at each attenuation step so that the electronic counter can be used with 10:1 voltage-divider probes to reduce the circuit loading of the circuit under test. On electronic counters designed to use plug-in units, it is desirable to have a position in the attenuator labeled PLUG-IN so that connections can be made to the plug-in compartment without using an external cable. It is also important to have the SELF-TEST or CHECK position of the electronic counter on the attenuator or on a switch other than FUNCTION and TIME BASE switches to permit self-check in all modes of operation and at all gate lengths.

Level K. A level control which is adjustable from − to + allows the operator to set the electronic counter to count negative or positive pulses. A "preset" position adjusts the input circuits for best sine-wave sensitivity. Electronic counters which do not have this control on the front panel can often be adjusted to count negative or positive pulses by adjusting an internal control in accordance with instructions in the operating manual. Some counters trigger on the leading edge of an unknown input signal; others trigger on the trailing edge. It makes little difference which one is used so long as the counter makes one and only one count per cycle of the input signal.

Function R. This switch selects the mode of operation of the electronic counter: frequency, period, multiple-period average, manual start-stop, time interval, ratio, or special modes of operation. The TEST position should not be on this switch, as this allows self-checking of the counter in only one mode of operation.

Gate Indicator L. This light comes on whenever the "gate" opens to start a count and goes off when the gate closes to end a count. On short gates, a "stretcher" circuit generates a pulse long enough to light this lamp, even though the actual gate may be shorter.

Reset Q. This pushbutton resets all internal counting and dividing circuits to zero and closes the "gate." The counter is now ready to commence a new measurement.

Sample Rate or Display Time or Recycle Rate B. This controls the time from the end of one measurement to the beginning of the next. Time between measurements is adjustable from 100 μs to several hundred milliseconds minimum to 5 or 10 s maximum, depending on the counter. A HOLD position at one end of this control puts the electronic counter in a "one-shot" mode of operation whereby it will take one reading and hold this reading indefinitely each time the reset button is depressed.

Time Base N. The time-base selector switch determines the length of time the gate remains open in frequency measurements or selects the counted frequency when making time-interval or period measurements. In ratio measurement, this switch may select the number of cycles, by powers of 10, of the lower-frequency input. For frequency measurements electronic counters generally have gate length from a minimum of 0.1 μs to 10 s for a universal counter. Gates of only 0.1, 1, and 10 s are common for counters which use the power line as a time base. Longer gate times are usually available as options when needed to get greater accuracy in frequency measurements. Gate lengths of 1 μs are seldom useful as the ±1 count error becomes very large.

External Connector M. This connector may be a standard-frequency output when the time-base switch is on one of the frequency positions but becomes an input connector when the time-base switch is in the external position. The operating manual for the counter must be consulted to find the specific function of the connector for various switch settings.

Display Storage or Latch F. Generally available only on transistorized and integrated-circuit counters, the display storage or latch mode of operation displays the visual information from one count while the electronic counter is making another measurement. At the end of the measurement, the stored visual display is "updated" to the new number. This feature makes reading an electronic counter faster and more accurate and is available on all modern counters. A switch disables this storage feature whenever the operator wishes to see the count accumulate. Along with this, some counters also offer "blanking" of insignificant zeros—that is, all zeros to the left of the first significant digit are turned off. Blanking enhances ease of reading the counter, particularly for nontechnical operators. On many counters, the binary-coded decimal information as well as the visual readout is stored.

Panel controls on plug-in prescaler, heterodyne converter, automatic dividers, transfer oscillators, digital voltmeters, time-interval units, and frequency multipliers will be discussed in detail in the section covering operation of these plug-in units.

The Visual Digital Display C. This is the most frequently used readout for an electronic counter. This readout may be: (1) columnar gas-tube readout (neon lamp or incandescent lamp); (2) an in-line gas-tube readout (Nixie* tube or edge-lighted plastic); (3) an electroluminescent display; (4) a light-emitting-diode readout; (5) a meter-movement type of readout; or (6) a projection display.

The in-line gas-tube readout is most popular because of ease of reading by both skilled and unskilled operators and because of long life. Disadvantages of this type of display included the high supply voltage required, which is not compatible with solid-state counter circuits, and the fact that the numeral size cannot conveniently be made very small. Light-emitting-diode readouts can be made smaller and thus more in keeping with new instrument requirements, but more important, supply-voltage requirements are the same as for the integrated circuits used in other parts of the counter.

High-frequency counters provide not only the digital information but also a positioned decimal point (*D*) and illuminated-measurement-units (*E*) annunciator for all combinations of switch settings. Where incompatible switch settings are possible, an asterisk or other indication on the annunciator warns the operator that readings may not be correct.

Low-frequency and single-function counters will generally display only the digital information; measurement units and decimal-point position are indicated by settings of the front-panel controls.

* Registered trade name, Burroughs Corp.

Oven Indicator P. The crystal-oven heater circuit may include either an indicator light, a meter, or a thermometer to indicate proper oven operation.

Plug-in Compartment S. This compartment accepts plug-in units which extend the measurement capability of the counter to higher or lower frequencies, permit voltage measurement, or give increased sensitivity.

Rear Panel. Front-panel space is at a premium on most solid-state and *IC* counters; so many of the auxiliary input and output connectors as well as secondary controls may be on the back of the instrument. When used as a bench instrument, the rear-mounted controls are readily accessible, but if the instrument is rack-mounted as part of a system, rear access may be difficult—so this factor must be considered in these applications of the counter. In many systems applications it is desirable to have all signal inputs on the rear to get away from front-panel cabling. Modified counters are usually available from manufacturers to meet these special requirements.

Connectors, controls, and features normally found on the rear panel are:

1. Power-input connector
2. BCD-output connector
3. Remote-programming connectors
4. Crystal-oscillator internal-external switch
5. Crystal-oscillator coarse-frequency adjust
6. Standard-frequency-output selectors and output terminals
7. Marker-pulse outputs for time-interval markers
8. 115/230 V changeover switch
9. Display-storage switch for some counters
10. Cooling fan and filter
11. Power-line and dc fuses on some counters
12. Auxiliary outputs such as gate output or scaler output

SIGNAL INPUT

28. Requires Electrical Signals The signal-input terminal of a counter will accept electrical signals which either get counted or trigger internal timing circuits. Most counters require a minimum input signal of from 10 to 100 mV rms into a 1-MΩ 25-pF input impedance. An input attenuator allows the counter to be operated from signals up to several hundred volts amplitude when set in the least sensitive position.

Solid-state input devices will not tolerate large voltage overloads without damage; so protective devices are used on these circuits. When a large overload is applied to the input, the impedance may drop to some very low value or go to some very high value in order to protect the input transistors. Recovery from a large overload or the change in input-signal waveshape due to the operation of these protective circuits may cause incorrect and misleading reading. Input protective circuits were seldom used on vacuum-tube counter inputs, as the tubes used could withstand overload without damage.

The Schmitt trigger is the circuit most commonly used at the input of an electronic counter to accept electrical waveforms to be measured. This input might be a pulse, a sine wave, or some complex waveform with variations in both amplitude and frequency. The output from this circuit is a pulse of constant polarity, width, and amplitude necessary to drive the electronic counting assembly correctly. This input circuit must generate one and only one output pulse for each cycle of the input waveform.

Sensitivity of the trigger circuit is usually in the order of 1 V rms (corresponds to 2.8 V, nominally 3 V, peak to peak). Trigger circuits can be made more sensitive; however, they are prone to give trouble due to drift, aging, and ambient-temperature and voltage changes, to name a few parameters, since the trigger is a dc-coupled circuit. To get better than 1 V rms input sensitivity and also to get a higher input impedance, an amplifier is often used between the signal-input terminal and the trigger circuit. Gain of this amplifier is about 10, which gives an input sensitivity of 100 mV rms, nominally 0.3 V peak to peak, although some amplifiers have a gain of 100 or more to get down to the 10 mV rms sensitivity range. The higher-gain amplifiers are subject to internally generated electrical noise and power-line noise and more prone to drift and so may actually be a disadvantage unless the high sensitivity is needed for a specific measurement.

Setting the input level to accept a higher-voltage input does not help in this case, as the level control is an attenuator between the signal-input terminal and the input-amplifier circuit. This control then merely reduces the signal input to a level acceptable to the input amplifier rather than decreasing the gain of the amplifier.

The signal to be counted might be the output signal from an electronic circuit, a signal generator, a transmitter, or the output of a transducer which translates mechanical phenomena to electrical signals.

A transducer converts mechanical, optical, and other nonelectrical phenomena to electrical signals which will operate the counter. To name a few possibilities, the transducer might be an ac tachometer generator which generates some specific number of pulses—60, for example—per revolution of its shaft. Each revolution of the tachometer may represent one revolution of the driving shaft of a motor, a specific number of gallons of fluid going through a flowmeter attached to the generator, or a certain number of inches of linear travel of the periphery of a wheel attached to the generator. It might be the output of a vibratory-string transducer where the string tension and consequently the frequency of vibration depend on pressure or tension on the device as a pressure transducer. It might be the output of a special quartz-crystal oscillator whose frequency changes linearly with temperature in a temperature transducer. It might be the dc change in a strain-gage bridge-load cell where the dc voltage is converted to a proportional frequency by a voltage-to-frequency converter, an example of which is a digital voltmeter; or it might be the output of an electro-optical device which generates electrical pulses in response to intensity changes of a light beam.

In each case, the electrical output signal of the transducer must meet the minimum amplitude, frequency, and rise-time requirements called for at the input of the electronic counter being used.

Spurious information must not be mixed in with the desired signal either through poor shielding of signal leads or through ground loops or other stray means, as this may get counted along with the desired input to give an incorrect reading.

29. Video Amplifier Video-amplifier plug-in units increase the sensitivity of an electronic counter to at least 1 mV rms on the most sensitive range, usually at 1 MΩ input resistance shunted by 20 or 30 pF. A meter indicates adequate signal level to drive the counter. Many units also have a 50-Ω auxiliary output terminal so that a high-frequency oscilloscope can be used to monitor the signal from the video amplifier to the counter while the measurement is being made. One word of caution—while these units are wideband amplifiers, they need only preserve the zero-axis crossing for a counter to make correct frequency measurements; consequently, they do not make good general-purpose video amplifiers since they are normally not phase-compensated.

Operation is straightforward except on the most sensitive ranges. When using the sensitive ranges, the operator must carefully shield the circuits to be checked, or erroneous counts will be added by rf pickup from broadcast stations, mobile radio stations, and other electrical interference. High sensitivity combined with the high resolution of a 50- or 100-MHz counter makes the measuring system so sensitive that even moving or bumping the shielded input cable or connector will cause the counter to count unless specially made "quiet wire" is used to connect the signal to the electronic counter. This shielded wire is constructed so it will not generate electrical noise when moved or flexed. Any stray pickup adds counts over and above those coming from the equipment under test and manifests itself as an incorrect reading on the counter, since the counter has no way of knowing which pulses come from the circuit under test and which are due to interference.

Input-cable termination therefore becomes very important at frequencies of 50 MHz or more; so all frequency-extender plug-ins, prescalers, heterodyne converters, transfer oscillators, and automatic dividers are designed with 50-Ω inputs so each will correctly terminate a 50-Ω transmission line without use of auxiliary loads or matching devices. If not properly terminated, a transmission line can alter an incoming waveshape because of reflections. The connected line may even look like an open or short circuit at the input end if it is an odd number of quarter wavelengths or half wavelengths long.

30. Prescaler A prescaler (Fig. 9), as the name implies, divides the input signal by some factor such as 2, 4, 8, or 10 before it reaches the input of the electronic counter. The counter can thus measure higher frequencies. The prescaler circuits must be capable of operating to the highest input frequency one wishes to measure. To get a direct indication of input frequency on the counter, the gate length is extended by the same factor that the input frequency is divided down, so that the system is direct-reading.

The disadvantage of using a prescaler over direct counting is that a longer time is required to make a measurement with a given resolution.

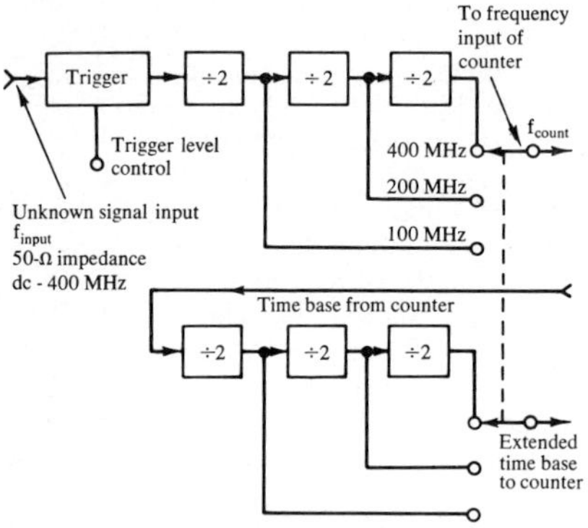

Fig. 9. Prescaler plug-in unit.

For example, if a prescaling factor of 10:1 is used, a 20-MHz counter can measure frequencies as high as 200 MHz; however, to get a resolution of 1 Hz would require a gate length of 10 s vs. the same resolution in 1 s for direct counting. Most prescalers have a 50-Ω input impedance and so will correctly terminate a 50-Ω cable. Dc coupling should be used if the prescaler is to count signals other than symmetrical waveforms to get away from problems of trigger-point shift.

While dc coupling is desirable to achieve a constant trigger point in aperiodic inputs, one must take care that a signal does not inadvertently have a dc level riding along with it, as the dc level may bias the trigger circuit to a nonoperating region. A trigger-level control permits triggering on positive or negative pulses when desired.

31. Heterodyne Converter Heterodyne converters are used to extend the frequency-measuring capability of an electronic counter above its direct count rate. Commercially available units work for frequencies as low as 10 MHz to as high as 18 GHz and make frequency measurements in this range as accurately and almost as easily as lower frequencies are measured directly. A heterodyne converter, as the name implies, is really a superheterodyne receiver with a video (wideband) amplifier, in place of the sharply tuned intermediate-frequency (if) amplifier, and a local oscillator tunable in steps of exactly 10, 50, 100, or 200 MHz instead of continuously variable. The local-oscillator frequency (LO) is generated by multiplying the crystal oscillator in a counter to one of the above-mentioned frequencies, 10 MHz for the example shown in Fig. 10, running it through a harmonic generator, and then choosing the appropriate harmonic with a tuned circuit. For harmonics above 50 MHz, the harmonic selector is invariably a tuned cavity. This local-oscillator frequency is mixed with the unknown signal to be measured, and the difference frequency is amplified in a video amplifier which has constant gain over some specified band (100 kHz to 12 MHz for the unit in Fig. 10). The counter measures the difference frequency out of the video amplifier. A tuning meter permits tuning the cavity precisely to one of the harmonics of the crystal oscillator in the counter, as indicated by a maximum meter indication. Precise tuning is not necessary for an accurate measurement; however, it does give optimum sensitivity. With the

LO peaked, the meter reading also indicates if the signal-output level of the video amplifier is high enough to drive the electronic counter correctly. The unknown frequency at the input is determined from this formula:

$$f_{\text{unknown}} = f_{\text{LO}} + f_{\text{video}}$$

where f_{video} is read on the electronic counter directly and f_{LO} is read from the dial or switch on the heterodyne converter.

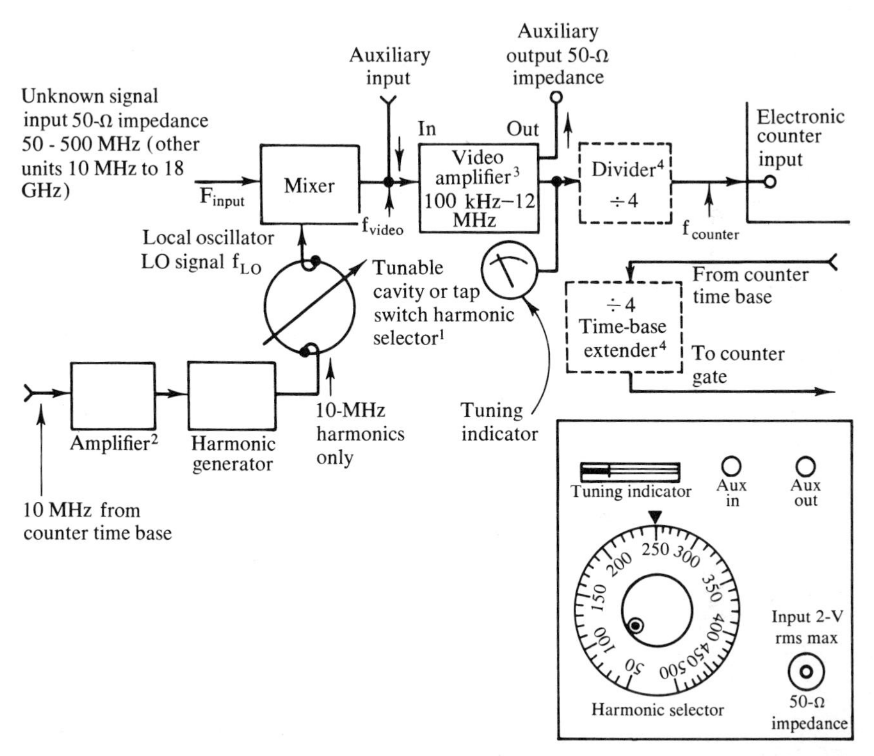

Fig. 10. Heterodyne frequency converter. Measures continuous-wave input with moderate AM, FM, or both. F is unknown. $F_{\text{unknown}} = f_{\text{LO}} + f_{\text{counter}}$. (1) Harmonic selector selects any 10-MHz harmonic in 10-MHz steps from 50 to 500 MHz. Steps may be 50, 100, or 200 MHz for high-frequency converters. (2) 5×, 10× or 20× multiplier for high-frequency converters. (3) Video amplifier has passband of 50, 100, or 200 MHz for high-frequency converters to match harmonic selector steps. (4) High-frequency converters may have these dividers.

The video-amplifier passband is such that the unknown input, the local-oscillator frequency, or the sum $f_{\text{unknown}} + f_{\text{LO}}$, which are also present at the output of the mixer, will not be amplified.

The correct procedure when using a heterodyne converter requires that one always start at the *low* end of the dial, tune up to the first harmonic that gives a high enough meter reading, tune for a maximum, then *add* the counter reading to the local-oscillator dial reading to get the unknown input frequency.

CAUTION: When doing this addition, be sure that the decimal point and measurement units from the display on the electronic counter are translated to the same units as on the heterodyne-converter tuning dial before adding.

NOTE: The LO frequency will always be below the signal-input frequency if this procedure is followed. As one continues tuning the dial to higher frequencies, another peak will be observed on the tuning meter, but this one must be subtracted from the dial reading to get the signal-input frequency, since the LO is now at a frequency above the input signal. The meter will always peak at two LO frequencies, as in the examples for 157 MHz, and in some cases at three LO frequencies, as indicated in the example for 151 MHz.

	Example 1	Example 2	Example 3	Example 4
Unknown input.......	157 MHz	157*	157 MHz	157 MHz
LO (dial reading) subtract this line from the one above.......	140 MHz	150	160 MHz	170
Difference............	17 MHz	7 MHz	3	13 MHz
Add LO and difference for unknown input..		157 MHz is unknown		
			160 −3 157 MHz is unknown	
	Beyond passband of video amplifier no reading on counter			Beyond passband of video amplifier no reading on counter
		Counter reads 7 MHz	Counter reading 3 MHz	

* This is the correct measurement.

In Example 2, the counter reads 7 MHz, adding dial reading 150 MHz to counter reading of 7 MHz = 157 MHz = unknown input. In example 3, the counter reads 3 MHz. Subtract counter reading of 3 MHz from dial reading of 160 MHz = 157 MHz = unknown input.

Resolution of the frequency measurement is determined by the gate length set on the electronic counter. Accuracy of the measurement is the same as for the basic counter measuring frequency since the heterodyne converter does not introduce additional errors. The ±1 count error in this case is 1 over the counter reading plus the dial reading. An example of this for a 10-MHz counter with heterodyne plug-in shows 7 MHz on the counter and 150 MHz on the dial of the heterodyne plug-in. If the counter were set for a 1-s gate and the time-base error was 1×10^{-8}, the counter would read 7,000,000 Hz.

$$\begin{aligned}
\pm\text{Count} &= \pm \frac{1\ \text{Hz}}{150\ \text{MHz} + 7{,}000{,}000\ \text{Hz}} = \frac{1}{157{,}000{,}000} \\
&= \pm 6.4 \times 10^{-9} \\
&= 0.00000064\ \text{percent} \\
\pm\text{Time-base error} &= 1 \times 10^{-8} \\
&= 0.000001\ \text{percent} \\
\text{Total error} &= \pm 0.64 \times 10^{-8} \\
&\quad \pm 1.0 \times 10^{-8} \\
&\quad \overline{\pm 1.64 \times 10^{-8}}
\end{aligned}$$

To get the error in hertz, multiply the frequency reading by the total error to get $157{,}000{,}000 \times 1.64 \times 10^{-8} = \pm 2.58$ Hz. Total error can also be read off the measurement-accuracy chart in Fig. 22 with sufficient accuracy for most work.

The video passband is wider than the steps on the dial; so for some input frequencies the meter will peak at three frequencies.

Unknown.......	151	151	151	151	151
LO............	130	140	150	160	170
Difference reading on counter	21	Add 11	Add 1	Subtract 9	19
	*	151 MHz	151 MHz	151 MHz	*

*Outside passband of video amplifier, so no indication on tuning meter

The mixer is designed to work over a wide frequency range and is completely untuned; so any frequencies or harmonics which can mix with the LO to give a sum or difference frequency within the passband of the video amplifier will be counted; therefore, an externally tuned filter may be necessary if a measurement is to be made on a signal source having several frequencies present simultaneously.

Some heterodyne converters have auxiliary connectors on the panel. The auxiliary output connector carries the same video information the counter input sees—that is, it is a down-converted replica of the input signal and as such will contain all the amplitude, modulation, and noise components present on the signal input plus noise introduced by the mixer and video amplifier of the converter. The converter is designed to keep internally generated noise to a minimum; so for most cases the spurious information appearing at the auxiliary output connector is also on the input signal. This, of course, can be examined with an oscilloscope or with other lower-frequency measuring equipment, since the video bandpass is not greater than 200 MHz for commercial heterodyne converters. One word of caution: When this auxiliary output is used, the video amplifier of a heterodyne converter is normally designed to have flat frequency response, since it has only to maintain the correct number of zero-axis crossings on information coming out of mixer to be correctly counted. The amplifier is *not* phase-compensated and so does not make a good general-purpose wideband amplifier for other than sine-wave signals.

The auxiliary input connector goes to the input of the video amplifier and takes advantage of the video gain to provide a high-sensitivity input to the electronic counter. When this auxiliary input is used, the operator must, of course, disconnect the regular signal input to the converter to get a correct measurement.

Video information must be continuous for the counter to read the difference frequency correctly; therefore, heterodyne converters work only with continuous-wave signals. If AM or FM modulation or both are present on the input signal, AM modulation cannot drop the input-signal amplitude below a point which gives a minimum acceptable video output signal to the counter. FM modulation cannot swing the down-converted video signal above or below the passband of the video amplifier, or the counter reading will be incorrect.

Pulsed radio frequency cannot be measured with a heterodyne converter without using a synchronized counter gate. This is available on some "computing" and reciprocal taking counters.* The tuning-meter level indication will generally not be correct when measuring pulsed radio frequency, since it is calibrated for continuous-wave signals. A peak-reading voltmeter or an oscilloscope connected to the AUX OUTPUT terminal serves as a satisfactory tuning indicator.

32. Transfer Oscillator A transfer oscillator permits frequency measurement of any rf signal—continuous-wave, AM-modulated, FM-modulated, pulse-modulated, or a combination of all—over a wide frequency range. Commercial units are available for measuring frequencies of 10 MHz or below, and others are available for frequencies to 40 GHz or above. The transfer oscillator, as the name implies,

* A New Technique for Pulsed RF Measurements, *Application Note* 120, Hewlett-Packard Company, Palo Alto, Calif.

is a transfer device for comparing an unknown frequency and a locally generated stable frequency which can be easily measured with high accuracy using an electronic counter. The transfer technique calls for establishing a "zero beat" between some harmonic of the stable variable-frequency oscillator (VFO) in the unit and the unknown input signal using a circuit configuration as in Fig. 11. Once zero beat is established by tuning the VFO while observing a zero-beat-indicating meter or by getting a zero-beat pattern on either an internal or an external oscilloscope, the VFO frequency is measured with an electronic counter. The counter in this case serves only as a precision dial on the VFO. The counter reading f_{VFO} is then multiplied by the harmonic number N, which relates the VFO frequency

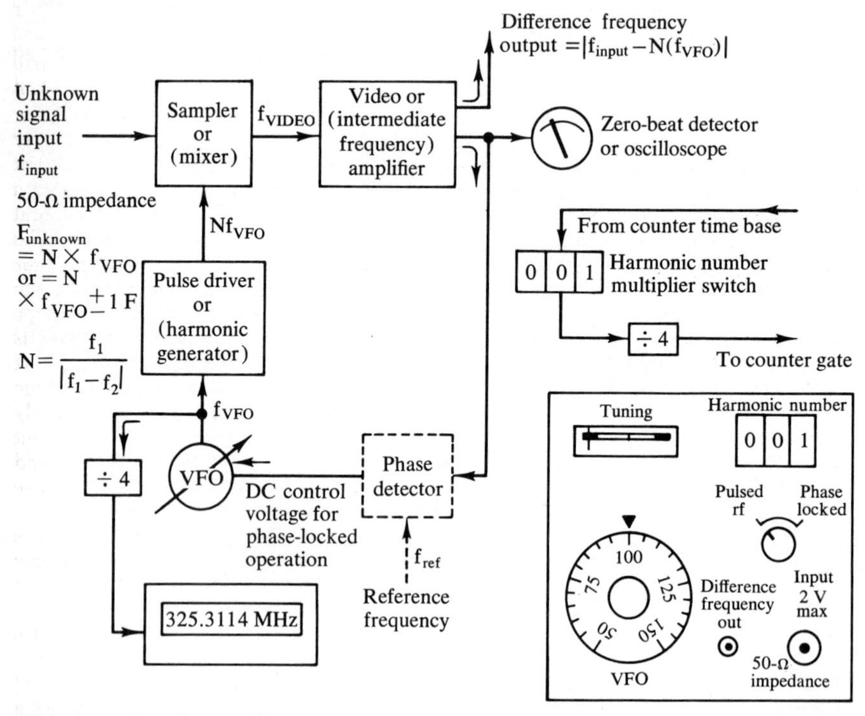

Fig. 11. Transfer oscillator. Phase detector is used only in transfer oscillators which use mixer for input and work with 20- or 30-MHz if amplifier.

and the unknown input frequency to establish the unknown. When using a separate transfer oscillator, the operator usually has to do the multiplication; however, most plug-in transfer oscillators have a built-in multiplier circuit so the operator merely has to set the appropriate harmonic number N on thumbwheel switches to have the counter multiply the VFO frequency by N and thus display unknown input frequency directly.

The following definitions of terms and equations show how the transfer oscillator works:

f_{input} = input frequency to be measured
f_{VFO} = variable-frequency oscillator frequency
f_{video} = video frequency
f_{if} = intermediate-frequency amplifier center frequency
N = harmonic number

Then

$$f_{\text{input}} \pm Nf_{\text{VFO}} = f_{\text{video}} \qquad \text{for } Nf_{\text{VFO}} < f_{\text{input}}$$

or

$$Nf_{\text{VFO}} \pm f_{\text{input}} = f_{\text{video}} \qquad \text{for } Nf_{\text{VFO}} > f_{\text{input}}$$

The restricted bandwidth of the video amplifier filters out the sum in each case; so only the difference frequency is present in actual operation.
Thus

$$f_{\text{input}} - Nf_{\text{VFO}} = f_{\text{video}}$$

Rearranging this,

$$f_{\text{input}} = Nf_{\text{VFO}} + f_{\text{video}}$$

The zero-beat tuning operation sets $f_{\text{video}} = 0$. Therefore, the unknown input frequency

$$f_{\text{input}} = Nf_{\text{VFO}}$$

where f_{VFO} = frequency of VFO counted by counter
N = harmonic number
Similar reasoning applies when Nf_{VFO} is greater than f_{input}.

The multiplication of f_{VFO} by the harmonic numbers is done quite simply by just extending the gate length of the counter. The counter always measures the frequency of the VFO and will display this frequency if the harmonic-number multiplier is set on 001 using whatever gate length has been set by the counter time-base switch. As an example, suppose the input frequency f_{input} is 1.1 GHz, i.e., 1,100,000,000 Hz. If the VFO is tuned to exactly 100 MHz, its eleventh harmonic will zero beat with f_{input}, and the counter will read f_{VFO} as 100.00 MHz on a 1-ms gate. The harmonic number N in this case is 11, and when set into the harmonic-number switch on the transfer oscillator, it extends the counter gate, 1 ms in this example, by a factor of 11 to 11 ms. The counter still counts at the f_{VFO} rate, 100 MHz, but since it counts for 11 times longer than it should to display f_{VFO}, the answer displayed will be Nf_{VFO} or 1,100.000 MHz (1.1 GHz), which is f_{input}.

The open-loop, or manual, mode of operation described above can be used to measure any kind of rf input signal (continuous-wave pulsed, modulated). The operator manually tunes the VFO to match one of its harmonics, the Nth harmonic, to f_{input}. From the equation $f_{\text{input}} = Nf_{\text{VFO}} + f_{\text{video}}$, it is apparent that the accuracy of the measurement depends on other things, on how accurately the operator can maintain zero beat, i.e., keep $f_{\text{video}} = 0$. If either f_{input} changes or f_{VFO} drifts, the operator must retune the VFO to again establish zero beat. Note particularly that in this mode of operation the counter reading will *not* change if the f_{input} frequency changes. However, the zero-beat indicator will show that the unit is no longer properly tuned. If the VFO drifts, the counter reading as well as the zero-beat indication will change. An operator can normally maintain zero beat to 1 part in 10^6 to 1 part in 10^7 on a continuous-wave signal after a bit of practice. On pulsed radio frequency a figure of 1/100 Hz off zero beat during the pulse interval is typical. This is 10 kHz for a 1-μs-wide rf pulse. These errors are in addition to the normal counter errors, namely, ± 1 count and $\pm$time-base error, as discussed in the sections on counter errors. Note also that since f_{VFO} and f_{input} are related by a harmonic number N, an error in measuring the frequency of f_{VFO} by 1 Hz represents an error of 11 Hz in measuring f_{input} in the previous example. Also, a given resolution in making the measurement takes N times as long as it would when either directly counting the frequency or measuring it with a heterodyne converter.

The phase-locked or APC, automatic-phase-control, mode of operation works only with continuous-wave (cw) signals. The output of the sampler (Fig. 11) is a dc control signal once the VFO has been tuned so that f_{input} and f_{VFO} are related by an integer N, that is, the VFO has been phase-locked to the input signal. This control signal is either a negative or a positive voltage if the input frequency tends to go low or high and is applied to a voltage-variable capacitor in the VCO to retune the VFO automatically so once again $f_{video} = 0$. The VCO frequency will thus track or follow a varying f_{input} frequency so the counter reading will now show the varying rf input frequency provided the lock range of the transfer oscillator is not exceeded. This lock circuit also corrects for any drift in the VFO so that the reading error now becomes the same as that of the counter itself, namely, ± 1 count and +time-base error, since exact zero beat is automatically maintained. Charts and graphs in the transfer oscillator's operating manual indicate the amount and rate of frequency or amplitude change the transfer oscillator will tolerate at various input frequencies without losing phase lock.

Instead of a sampler, a transfer oscillator may use a mixer driven by a harmonic generator. As shown by designations in parentheses in Fig. 11, f_{video} is not set to zero but rather to some reference frequency, usually 1, 10, 20, or 30 MHz. The stable reference is taken from the crystal oscillator in the counter and so contributes no additional error to the measurement.

Instead of a video amplifier, a bandpass amplifier or if amplifier is used to amplify the signal. The f_{if} frequency is compared with the f_{ref} in a phase detector to generate a dc control voltage for the VFO, as explained previously. Phase lock can be achieved with Nf_{VCO} either below or above f_{input} by a frequency f_{if}; so in determining the unknown frequency, f_{if} must be either added if Nf_{VFO} is below f_{input} or subtracted if Nf_{VFO} is above f_{input}. Some plug-in transfer oscillators are designed to phase-lock only when Nf_{VFO} is below f_{input}. The counter is reset to a number other than zero to add f_{if} to get the correct answer. The instruction manual for non-plug-in transfer oscillators should be consulted for the correct procedure to use in determining whether to add or subtract f_{if} when determining f_{input}. Some of the transfer oscillators which use an if amplifier for gain in the phase-lock mode of operation also have an FM discriminator driven from this same amplifier. This discriminator can be used to recover FM modulation, either intentional or spurious, on the down-converted signal ($f_{input} - Nf_{VFO}$) from the mixer. Some units also have AM detectors to recover AM modulation.

The transfer oscillator in conjunction with an oscilloscope connected to its "difference frequency" output terminal (Fig. 11) can be used to measure FM deviation on the unknown signal-input connector by tuning the VFO first to the highest frequency that will give a zero-beat indication and then to the lowest adjacent input frequency which will give a zero beat. Subtracting the two counter readings gives peak-to-peak frequency deviation, as indicated in Fig. 12. If deviation is greater than the bandwidth of the video amplifiers or oscilloscope, amplitude between points A and B of oscilloscope display 1 may fall to zero between the points, but this is of no great consequence. Maximum deviation cannot exceed the VFO frequency, or confusing patterns result.

The down-converted output could also be connected to an FM discriminator to recover modulations or noise information on the input signal.

33. Automatic Dividers Automatic frequency dividers which may be supplied either as plug-in units for an electronic counter or as self-contained instruments extend the precise frequency-measurement capability of an electronic counter up into the high gigahertz region. Two general methods are used to reduce the high frequency to the range of the counter. One system functions as an automatically tuned heterodyne converter. The local oscillator is automatically changed in steps electrically instead of manually as discussed earlier in this section. Provision is made to display the local-oscillator frequency automatically in addition to the difference frequency so the reading displayed can be the unknown frequency. This system retains the high resolution of the heterodynes techniques, namely, the capability of making a measurement to within 1 Hz in 1 s, and it also eliminates the manual tuning operation and the addition of two numbers to obtain the answer.

The second system functions as an automatically tuned transfer oscillator. The local oscillator is automatically tuned electrically to establish a zero beat between

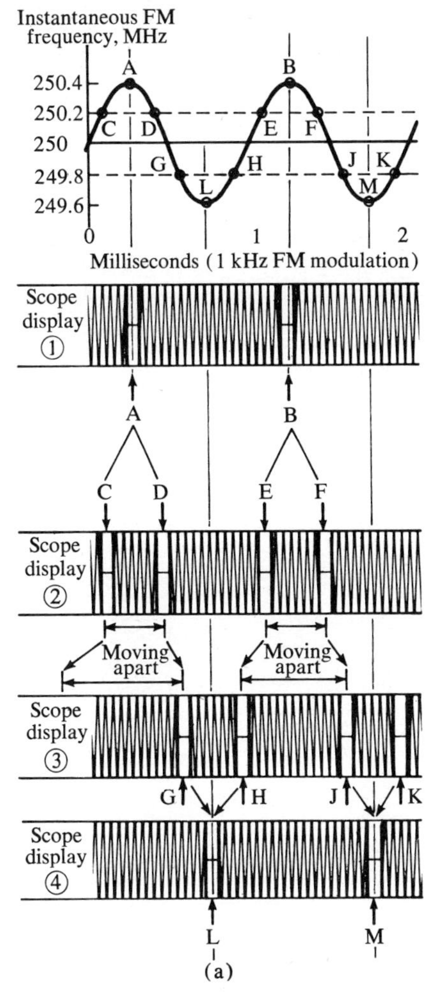

Fig. 12. FM-deviation measurement using transfer oscillator. Peak FM deviation is counter reading for oscilloscope display 1 minus oscilloscope display 4: 250.4 MHz − 249.6 MHz = 0.8 MHz. Oscilloscope pattern may show vertical amplitude decrease owing to rolloff of amplifiers in transfer oscillator. Ignore this and look for zero-beat indication. Sync oscilloscope from audio modulating frequency if possible. Phase shift in system can displace peak rf deviation from peak modulation excursion. *Oscilloscope display 1:* Transfer oscillator VFO dial tuned to 125.2 MHz, harmonic number 2, counter reads 250.4 MHz. The oscilloscope display shows zero beat at upper limit of deviation as shown at *A* and *B*. (Sync oscilloscope from 1-kHz modulation.) *Oscilloscope display 2:* Dial to 125.1 MHz, counter reads 250.2 MHz. Zero-beat patterns at *A* and *B* "split" to give zero-beat indication at *C*, *D*, *E*, and *F*. *Oscilloscope display 3:* Dial to 124.9 MHz, counter reads 249.8 MHz. Zero beat at *G*, *H*, *J*, and *K*. *Oscilloscope display 4:* Dial to 124.8 MHz, counter reads 249.6 MHz. Zero beats *G* and *H* merge at *L* and *J* and *K* merge at *M* for zero beat at lower limit of deviation.

one of its harmonics and the unknown input signal. Once zero beat is established, other circuits calculate the harmonic number N and extend the counter gate length so the displayed reading is the unknown microwave input frequency. As with the manual transfer oscillator, the measurement resolution will be less by the factor N than for a similar reading made with a heterodyne converter. Also, automatic dividers are limited to cw measurements only, whereas the manually tuned transfer oscillator can measure any type of rf input—modulated or not.

Both automatic measurement systems require some finite time to search for and lock on to an unknown input. Also, if the unknown cw input signal is not stable, the automatic system will "loose-lock" if the signal moves too far or too fast (either FM or drift). In general, the automatic devices do not work as well on noisy signals as the manually tuned devices as they must make all the decisions associated with a measurement, whereas the operator does part of this with manually tuned units. Speed, resolution, portability, operator skill, and susceptibility to error must all be considered when evaluating one of these measuring systems, as in many cases the same measurement could be made in several ways (see Table 1).

34. Frequency Multiplier Plug-in units are available to multiply the input frequency by 10, 100, or 1,000 using a phase-locked oscillator and digital dividers as in Fig. 13. These units are useful from a few hertz up to 100 kHz or so and are useful when high resolution on 60-Hz or 400-Hz power-line frequencies or other low-frequency inputs are required in a short measuring time. A 60-Hz power-line frequency can be measured as 60.000 Hz in 1 s, for

TABLE 1 Comparison Chart for High-frequency Measurement Techniques

	Frequency range	Signal	Sensitivity, mV	Ease of use	Auxiliary in	Auxiliary out	Notes
Prescaler . . .	Dc to 500 MHz	Any	100	Same as counter	. . . .	. . . .	Takes longer to get given resolution than direct-count or heterodyne converter
Heterodyne converter	10 MHz to 18 GHz	Cw—will tolerate considerable AM and FM	50–100	Requires tuning operation and addition of two numbers to determine unknown frequency	Can use video-amplifier section to get better sensitivity for basic counter within bandwidth of video amplifier	Down-converted rf signal available in bandwidth the same as dial steps	Highest resolution in shortest measuring time
Transfer oscillator	10 MHz to 40 GHz	Any—cw, AM, FM, pulsed rf	100	Requires tuning and harmonic-number calculations. Can be direct-reading	. . . .	Wideband receiver. Down-converts all noise and modulation in signal to range of low-frequency measuring instruments	Most versatile. Can measure any rf signal, modulated or not. Long measurement time for high resolution
Automatic divider	100 MHz to 18 GHz	Cw—will tolerate only moderate amount of FM and noise	10	Same as counter	. . . .	. . . .	Requires longest measuring time for given resolution

All high-frequency units have 50-Ω inputs, as it is not feasible to carry high-frequency signals on unterminated transmission lines. Good rf measuring practice is necessary to prevent damage to input circuits in high-frequency units, as the small physical size of high-frequency mixer diodes makes them subject to burnout on even short-duration overloads.

VSWR is always a tradeoff between standing-wave ratio and sensitivity. For example, a 6-dB pad between drive and input gives a worst possible VSWR of 1.6 :1. Sensitivities given are for complete environmental range. All units will usually show considerably better sensitivity under laboratory conditions (ambient temperature around 27°C, 115-V line, etc.).

example. Accuracy is the same as for the counter; however, these devices make use of phase-locked oscillators, and so there are limitations to how fast a frequency can be changing and still be multiplied correctly. An indicator tells the operator when the unit is not locked or for some units will even blank the counter readout if not locked.

35. Time Interval Measurements are made by using the counter as an electronic "stopwatch." One electrical signal opens the gate and a second electrical signal

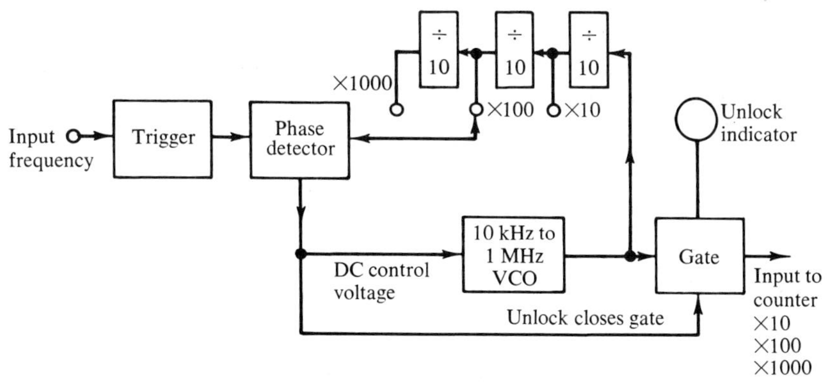

Fig. 13. Frequency multiplier.

closes the gate. While the gate is open, the counter counts one of the internally generated time units or counts an externally supplied timing signal as shown in Fig. 6. Operating in this mode, counters can measure time with resolution as great as 0.1 ns (the time it takes light to travel approximately 1 in.) and intervals of hours or days in length if necessary. The time-interval measuring feature may be built into the counter main frame or may be available as a plug-in unit.

Controls are shown in Fig. 14. The start and stop channels should have identical circuitry and controls to maintain equal time delays through these circuits, particularly for high-resolution units. Dc coupling is mandatory for slow-rise complex waveforms, or the trigger point will shift with waveform change and with change in repetition rate. Many units have an ac-dc switch so that ac coupling can be used when triggering from fast-rise pulses riding on a dc level. Attenuators drop signal levels of up to several hundred volts down to the 1 V or so required by the input circuit. These attenuators are frequency-compensated and should maintain a constant impedance at the input so as not to change the input waveform when switching from one step to another. Most input circuits include some protective devices to prevent damage to the input under heavy overload. As a result, input impedance may go either far above or far below specification under overload conditions. Most time-interval inputs have a sensitivity of 100 mV rms (300 mV peak-to-peak nominal). Dynamic range is in the order of 20 or 30 dB for solid-state devices; so for levels greater than this, input clipping usually takes place.

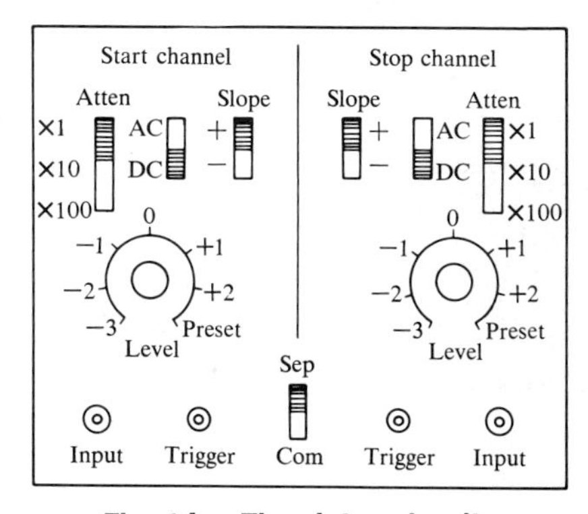

Fig. 14. Time-interval unit.

A slope switch allows the operators to select triggering on either the negative-slope (voltage falling) or positive-slope (voltage rising) portion of the input signal (Fig.

15*b*). This, together with a variable control which selects the dc level at which triggering occurs (Fig. 15*a*), gives the operator the capability of starting or stopping the counter at almost any place on an electrical waveform. Figure 16 shows some of the possible time measurements which can be made by changing the settings of the slope, amplitude, and polarity controls of the start and stop inputs.

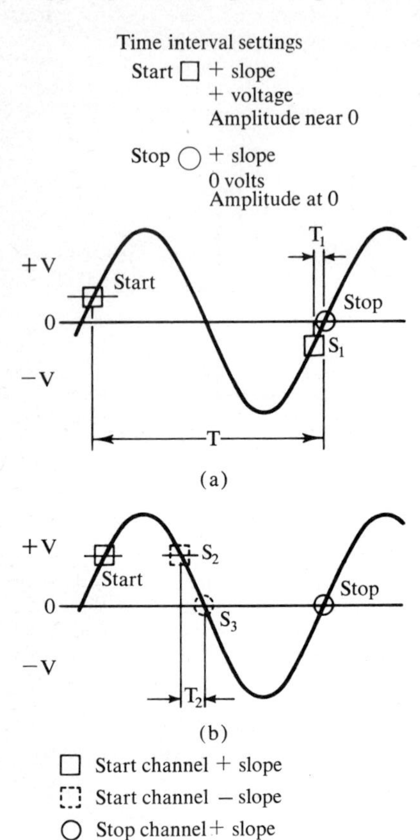

Fig. 15. Time-interval measurements. (*a*) Effect of trigger amplitude and polarity controls on time-interval reading. (*b*) Effect of trigger-slope setting on trigger points. (1) Time T increases as start channel voltage is brought closer to O V until it is the same as the period of the sine wave. (2) When the start channel is set to a negative voltage, the counter begins at S_1 and reads time T_1 (very short time). (3) Start and stop points can be positioned almost anywhere on the positive slope of this waveform with trigger amplitude and polarity controls. (4) Changing start slope switch to minus slope shifts the start point to S_2. Changing the stop slope switch to minus slope shifts the stop point to S_3. Counter reads time T_2 when both are set for minus slope.

To ensure continuous coverage of the input-voltage range from minimum to maximum requires an input attenuator with 1X, 10X, and 100X steps and variable level control with +3, 0, −3 V range. One other important consideration is the effect of the alternators on sensitivity. A time-interval unit may respond to a 300-mV pulse on its most sensitive range; however, if switched to the 10X range it requires a 3-V minimum pulse for triggering. Because of this, it may not be possible to measure some small pulse, 0.5 V, for example, on a large-amplitude (10-V) input signal

A separate common switch lets one tie the start and stop inputs in parallel internally to make measurements on a signal coming in on a single line such as in measuring rise time of a waveform. The "separate" mode isolates the two inputs and is used when the start and stop signals arrive on different cables, as in measuring the length of a delay line, for instance. The input to the line would also go to the start channel, and the output to the stop channel.

In making time-interval measurements on an unknown waveform, good practice calls for the use of an oscilloscope to observe the waveform, as it may be different from what the operator imagines. This is particularly important when measuring fast-rise-time signals, since they may cause ringing or distorting of the input signal if cables are not properly terminated.

High-resolution time-interval measurements (10 ns and above) require a carefully designed time-interval unit to ensure that the time delay through the unit is constant for all control settings, or accuracy is degraded. Also care must be used in setting up the measurement, as unequal cable lengths can contribute error. In some instances, the system can be set up without the delay device in place to make a measurement of all system delays, which can then be subtracted from the reading taken with the delay device in place. Cable length cannot be disregarded, since

0.1 ns represents the time it takes the signal to travel through about 1 in. of coaxial cable.

High-resolution time-interval measurements are possible in two ways: In one the counter interpolates by as much as 1,000:1 on what would normally be the ±1 count error displayed by the counter. This system is useful in making measurements on a phenomenon which occurs only once. The other system makes use of a time-interval-averaging technique; so it is useful only in measuring a stable delay which occurs over and over. The counter keeps track of the number of times the +1 count occurs in N measurements and then displays the average along with the balance of the measurement. Besides requiring a repetitive pulse, input-pulse repetition rate cannot be coherent with the counted frequency used in the time-interval mode, or the results are not valid. Also, the averaging time must be moderately short (a few seconds at most), or system drift due to voltage and temperature changes can invalidate the results.

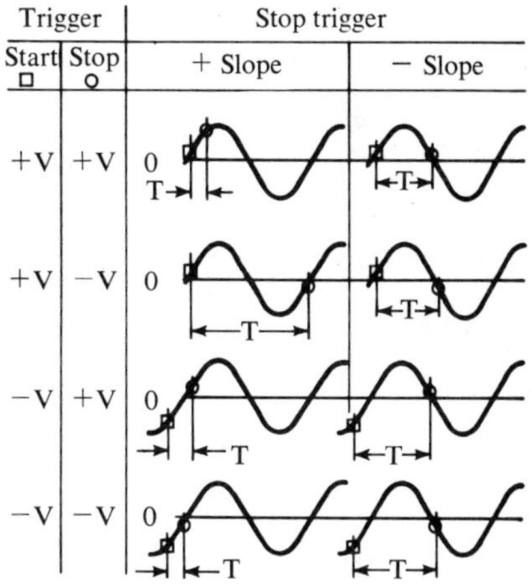

Sources of error in a time-interval measurement are similar to those in a period measurement. The start and stop channel which controls the gate can have an error similar to the 0.3 percent error of a period measurement if the input signal is a minimum-amplitude sine wave with noise 40 dB down. For fast-rise start and stop pulses voltage variations on the pulse rise introduce little or no trigger error and may be disregarded. Another error is the ± count in the final display. This can be reduced by using a counter which interpolates or by using time-interval averaging if the input signal permits. Finally, the crystal-oscillator (clock) error must be considered; however, for most time-interval measurements this will be insignificant compared with the other two error sources.

Fig. 16. Time interval T measured when slope, amplitude, and polarity controls of start and stop channels are set as indicated. Start-channel slope is always positive. A similar chart could be prepared for a negative start slope.

Some time-interval units provide "marker" pulses (narrow pulses coincident with triggering) which can be used to intensify the trace of an oscilloscope to show where a measurement begins; however, these pulses are useful only over a limited range of input rise time. If the rise time is very slow, the intensified portion of the oscilloscope trace becomes so narrow it is difficult to see. For fast-rise pulses, the marker becomes very wide; so it is difficult to determine the trigger point.

Some time-interval inputs include a trigger-voltage jack on the panel so the trigger point can be measured with a dc voltmeter.

36. Digital Voltmeter Digital voltmeters (DVMs) fall into two general categories: (1) separate instruments which can be used with any electronic counter and (2) instruments designed as plug-in units each for a specific make and model of electronic counter, or permanently built into the counter.

In the first category, the voltage-to-frequency converter (Fig. 17*a*) transforms any electronic counter into a dc voltmeter. These units convert a dc voltage into a proportional frequency putting out 0 frequency for 0 V dc at the input and a maximum frequency of from 10 to 100 kHz which can be measured with an electronic counter for maximum dc input, usually 1 V. An input range switch and a dc amplifier make this unit useful from a few hundred millivolts to 1,000 V or more.

The voltage-to-frequency converter and the counter function as an integrating digital voltmeter, since the counter counts the number of pulses from the voltage-to-frequency connector during its selected gate time. Noise is averaged out.

Most of these devices will operate properly with 200 to 300 percent overranging, i.e., 2 or 3 V input on the 1-V range, for instance, on all except the 1,000-V range.

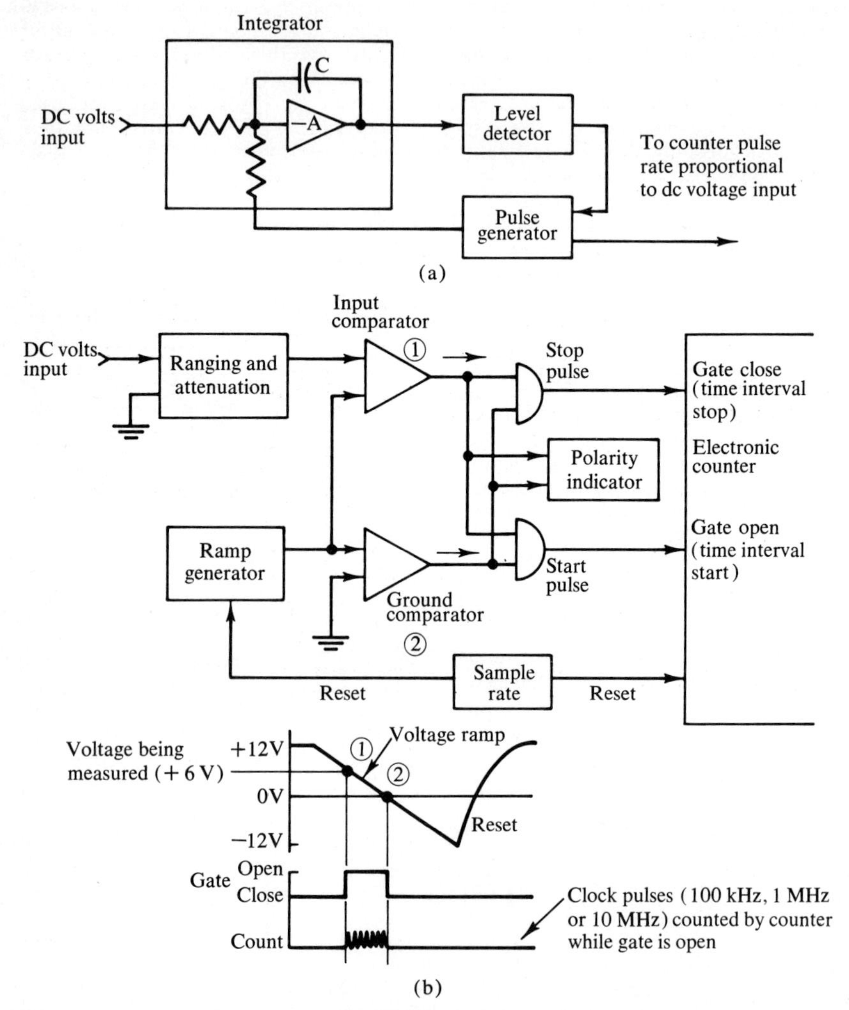

Fig. 17. Digital-voltmeter configurations. (*a*) Voltage-to-frequency converter (integrating DVM). (*b*) Voltage-to-time conversion (ramp-type DVM).

Signal output from the converter to the counter and other characteristics may vary widely from one unit to another; so the operating and technical manuals should be consulted before one of these devices is used with an electronic counter.

Plug-in DVMs may be either of the integrating type just described or of the ramp type (Fig. 17b), which makes a voltage-to-time transformation. This ramp type of DVM generates a time interval proportional to a dc voltage. The counter measures the time interval and displays the answer as the voltage at the input terminals of the DVM. Overranging for most ramp-type voltmeters is from 5 to 20 percent.

Considerable interconnection is required between the ramp-type voltmeter circuits and the counter; so these are supplied as either plug-in units for a specific model of counter or permanently built in.

Here again the instruction manual should be consulted to determine the capabilities and limitation of the DVM.

Plug-in DVMs for high-frequency counters often display many more digits than are consistent with the accuracy specification, since they make use of the available high-frequency clock signal in the counter. These extra digits, even though meaningless in terms of accuracy, can be useful in observing small voltage changes, as they are stable so long as the counter is operated in a reasonable constant environment as in a laboratory.

In general, plug-in voltmeters for an electronic counter are not as accurate as separate DVMs because of the greater amount of heat generated within the counter, which influences range resistors, etc., and because dc-voltage-supply lines have high-frequency switching noise from the counting circuits. Good filtering is difficult in the small space allotted to the plug-in unit.

General considerations in the use of digital-voltmeter plug-ins are the same as for general-purpose DVMs.

37. Preset Units Except for electronic counters which are specifically designed as preset counters, preset capability is available only on counters that accept plug-in units. This is because of the numerous interconnections required between the preset box and the electronic counter.

Preset capability lets the counter do a normalizing operation so the visual display will be in engineering or other units instead of pulses per second. For example, a flowmeter tachometer might put out 200 pulses per second for a fluid-flow rate of 40 gal/s. By using a preset gate length of $\frac{2}{100}$ s, 20 ms, the electronic counter will read flow directly in gallons per second, or by using a gate length of 1.2 s, the reading would be in gallons per minute.

These units will normally extend the gate length of a counter by a factor N (a five- or six-digit thumbwheel-switch presettable number) for a counter display of $N \times$ frequency and will extend multiple-period measurements by N for $N \times$ period. Some units can also do $N \times$ ratio as well as do preset counting, in which case the plug-in box will accept an input-pulse train and then give an output pulse for each N number of input pulses.

Some of these preset units are made so they can reset very rapidly—in less than 1 μs. These units can be used as f/N dividers, which will divide any input frequency below their maximum input rate by any number N set up on the N switches. Since reset takes place between pulses, none are lost; so this device now becomes a true digital divider with the same accuracy as the driving signal. This mode of operation is useful in counting down some high frequency, 90 kHz, for example, by the factor $N = 4{,}500$, to get a coherent low-frequency trigger pulse rate, 20 Hz, to drive an experimental circuit.

OUTPUT

Besides the direct crystal-output frequency, many counters also have the divided-down crystal frequency available to as low as 0.1 Hz in decade steps. The higher-frequency counters will also have 10 and 100 MHz available, as these are required for high-resolution period and time-interval measurements. These output frequencies may be selected either by the GATE LENGTH switch or, for greater flexibility, by a separate switch on the rear of the counter. Some have outputs from both available on separate connectors. A word of caution: Most counters reset the decade dividers after completion of a count in order to achieve minimum "dead" time between measurements; therefore, the standard-frequency output becomes meaningless whenever the gate is operating if it is taken from a decade divider that is reset. One must switch to MANUAL START, MANUAL STOP, or some other mode of operation which stops the gate if these lower frequencies (usually below 1 kHz) are to be used externally.

All output frequencies have the same accuracy as the crystal oscillator; however, short-term stability is usually not as good as the crystal-output frequency because of noise pickup from wires to the divider and multiplier circuits in the counter.

38. Binary-coded Decimal Output Besides the visual readout on the front panel, many electronic counters have an electrical readout available in a binary-coded decimal (BCD) form which is used when one wishes to couple the counter to a printer, a tape punch, a magnetic-tape system, a computer, a remote readout, or other data-acquisition devices. This information is available at a multiple-pin output connector on the rear of the instrument usually labeled BCD OUTPUT or PRINTER. The BCD output, usually an 8-4-2-1 code or 4-2-2-1 code, may have either the positive-state time or the negative-state time and may be presented in either a parallel or serial format. The parallel data format permits transferring all digits of information simultaneously but requires four wires per digit for data transfer (32 wires for 8 digits of information). The serial data format transfers only one digit of information at a time and requires only four wires to transfer any number of digits, but transfer is much slower.

Output code, voltage levels, reference voltages, and other pertinent information is not included on the rear of electronic counters; so one must consult the operating manual for detailed information.

The important factors to consider to see if a printer or similar device will function with a counter are as follows:

1. BCD output must be of the correct code to match the printers.
2. BCD swing between the 0 and 1 states must exceed the minimum required by the printer.
3. The counter must supply appropriate "reference" voltage to the printer, or these must be provided by an external supply.
4. The print command must be of the correct polarity, amplitude, and rise time to trigger the printer. This signal can be ac-coupled, as dc levels are not important so long as minimum amplitude is adequate.
5. An inhibit or hold-off from the printer must be able to keep the counter from starting a new reading until the printer has had time enough to accept and print the previous reading. The inhibit signal is dc-coupled; so the dc level as well as the amplitude must be correct for the system to function properly.

39. Digital-to-Analog Converter A graph of counter readings vs. time or some other parameter is frequently the most desirable readout. While this can be done by having an operator write down and plot each reading or plot the reading from a printed record, the process is at best slow and subject to error. Such a plot can be made automatically as fast as the counter takes readings by connecting the BCD output of a counter to a digital-to-analog converter which is connected to a strip-chart recorder or an *X-Y* plotter. The digital-to-analog converter is an instrument which can be switched to look at either the two least significant digits (two right-hand digits) of the display or any three successive digits displayed by the counter and then generate a dc voltage or current proportional to these two or three digits. The dc-voltage output is suitable for driving a potentiometer recorder or one axis of an *X-Y* plotter; the current output will drive a galvanometer-type strip chart recorder. When driving a strip-chart recorder, the plot shows the frequency measured by the counter as it varies with respect to time. A typical application might be to plot an oscillator frequency as the oscillator warms up, a frequency-stability measurement or a crystal oscillator, frequency stability of a transmitter throughout the day, or similar applications. The information from the counter could be on one axis of an *X-Y* plotter with temperature, line voltage, output load, or any second parameter on the other axis for a plot of frequency vs. temperature, etc. Measurement resolution can be very high; for instance, a frequency measurement on a 10-GHz source might be plotted to determine its stability. Using a heterodyne converter, a resolution of 1 Hz, or even 0.1 Hz, can easily be realized. Furthermore, the 1-Hz resolution is meaningful if the counter's time base is driven by a cesium or rubidium or other stable standard. For a 10-GHz frequency,

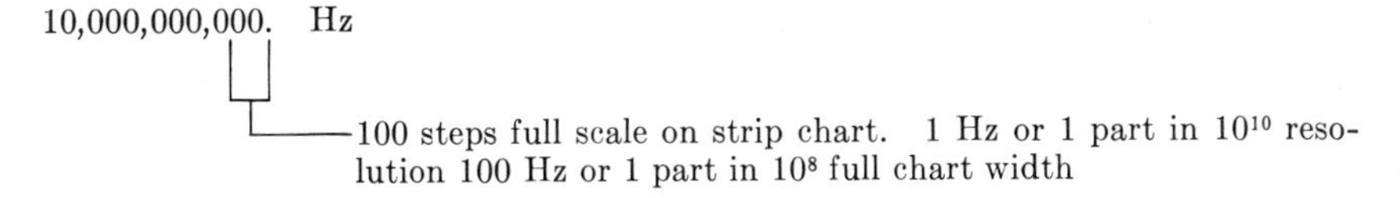

Plotting the two right-hand digits gives a plot of 100 steps with 00 at one edge of the chart and 99 at the other edge. Resolution is 1 Hz or 1 part in 10^{10} readable from the chart. One big advantage of this system over an analog frequency meter is that the record never goes off scale. An input frequency of 10,000,000,099 Hz, for example, would drive the recorder to full scale; however, if the input frequency increased by 1 Hz, the counter would read 10,000,000.100 Hz, the strip-chart recorder would merely go to 00 and start across the page again, and so no information is ever lost. Decreasing input frequencies would work just the opposite. The recorder would go to 00 and then instead of going off the bottom of the chart would go to 99 and start down again. When the input signal is not sufficiently stable to make the two least significant digits meaningful, the operator can select the three least significant digits for any three adjacent digits for a 1,000-step full-chart-width output:

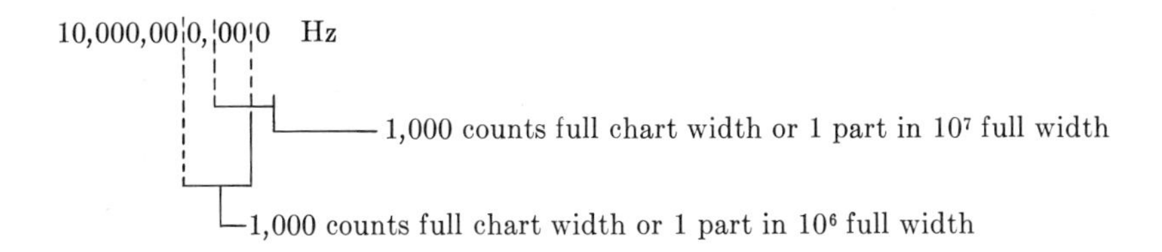

Figure 18 is an actual warm-up record of a high-stability quartz crystal in a proportional oven. A 200X multiplier increased the crystal frequency to 1 GHz (1,000,000,000 Hz), which was measured by a counter and heterodyne converter using a 1-s gate to get a resolution of 1 Hz in 1 s. A 1-Hz change in counter reading represents a 1 part in 10^9 change in crystal frequency.

The three least significant (right-hand) digits were plotted on the strip-chart recorder to give a full-chart-width resolution of 100 Hz (1 part in 10^6) in 1,000 steps. When the oscillator was turned on, the counter read 13,040 Hz (oscillator 1.3 parts in 10^5 high), decreased rapidly until it was exactly on frequency at the end of 2.8 min, went below the correct frequency by 3.8 parts in 10^7, then slowly recovered until it was 4 parts in 10^8 low after 9.2 min from turn-on. At this time the counter could have been set for a 10-s gate and the digital-to-analog converter switched to give a 100-step full-scale analog output from the two least significant digits of information to give a resolution of 1 part in 10^{10} or a full chart width of 1 part in 10^8.

A 2,000X multiplier could have been used instead of 200X to increase resolution to 1 part on 10^{11} in. for a full chart width of 10 Hz in 100 steps if the measurement justified that much resolution.

SOURCES OF ERROR INHERENT IN ELECTRONIC COUNTERS

As with many electrical measuring instruments, sources of error fall into two general classes: (1) those due to the instrument itself and (2) those due to misapplication of the instrument.

Errors due to the electronic counter itself fall into two groups, frequency and period, depending upon the type of measurement being made.

40. Making Frequency Measurements and Period Measurements These effects

Frequency Measurement (Best Accuracy at High Frequency)	*Period Measurement (Best Accuracy for Low-frequency Measurement)*
±1 Count	±1 Count
±Time-base inaccuracy	±Time-base inaccuracy
	±0.3 % per period (for 40-dB signal-to-noise ratio on input signal)

are added to give the greatest possible spread to define the maximum uncertainty in a given measurement.

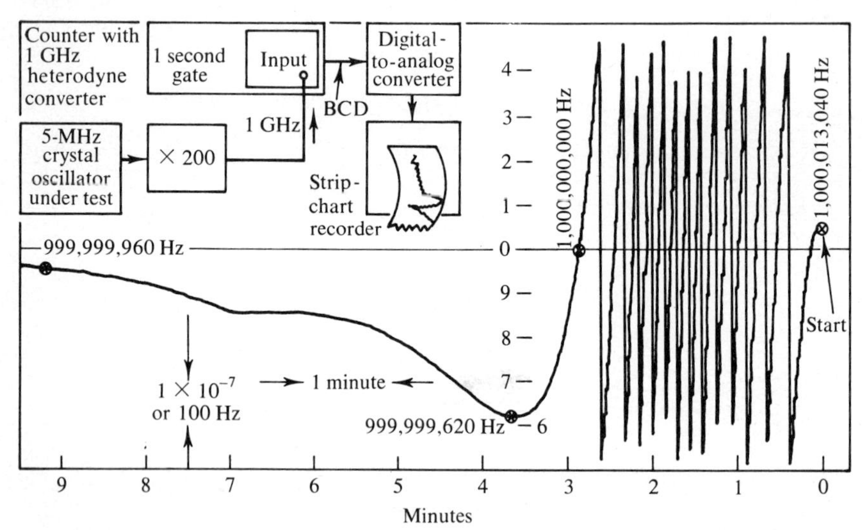

Fig. 18. Warm-up record of a 5-MHz proportional oven-type crystal oscillator from a cold start.

41. Other Measurements The two sources of error discussed above may apply to time interval, ratio, totalizing, or other measurements made by the counter. Looking at Figs. 4 to 6, the ±1 count error applies to the pulses which reach the decade-counter assembly whenever the signal gate is opened and closed while pulses are present at its input.

The 0.3 percent per period error applies any time a minimum-amplitude sine wave is used to generate the gate open-close signal so it applies to a period measurement and to the lower-frequency input when making a ratio measurement. This error does not apply to frequency measurements, since the gate is driven by high-amplitude fast-rise pulses from the time-base dividers. It may or may not apply to a time-interval measurement; it applies when the counter is triggering from a low-amplitude sine wave and is either minimized or does not apply when triggering from a fast-rise large-amplitude pulse. No error is introduced by the counter if it is used in a totalizing or scaling mode where the gate is opened before applying the input signal. The decade counters count, without error, each cycle of input so long as it satisfies the amplitude and repetition-rate requirements of the particular counter in use. The counter functions as a true digital counting and dividing device.

In any measurement situation, the ±1 count error can be minimized by using any technique which gives a large number of counts to the counting decades. The 0.3 percent per period error can be reduced either by using fast-rise-time gating signals or by extending the gate length as in making multiple-period averages.

Time-base accuracy of a particular counter is directly related to the quality of the crystal oscillator. Frequent calibration against an accepted standard can cut down on this error, or if necessary the time base can be driven by an external standard of higher quality.

Reciprocal taking counters or computing counters always make a measurement in the period mode of operation; that is, they count on internally generated "clock" intervals for some number N cycles of the input signal. The number N is determined by setting the measurement time with a panel switch. The counter then keeps its gate open until the period of N input cycles is the same as the allowable measurement time and closes on the following cycle.

Following gate closing, one counting register contains the number N, and a second register contains the number of clock pulses that occurred. The arithmetic portion of the counter divides clock pulses by N to get a single period and then takes a reciprocal on this to convert the information to frequency which is displayed. That is, frequency = N/counted pulses. Decimal-point position is calculated and displayed as is the correct measurement unit, i.e., Hz, kHz, MHz, etc. N need no longer be a power of 10 as for multiple-period averaging with a conventional counter, since the arithmetic portion of the reciprocal taking counter can divide by any integer just as easily as it can by 10.

Measurement errors are the same as for the period counter, namely, ±0.3 percent per period on the input signal, ±1 count on the clock pulses counted, and ± time-base error.

Even though the reciprocal taking counter may display six or seven digits for any frequency it measures, the display may not be meaningful beyond the two or three most significant digits when measuring a low-frequency sine wave. When measuring a high frequency, 10 MHz, for a 1-s measuring time, the number N will be 10^7. A 0.3 percent per period on this is only 3 parts in 10^{10}, which is insignificant compared with other errors. The arithmetic portion of the counter may also be used for interpolation; so some of these counters reduce the effect of ±1 count by as much as 1,000 to 1 using this technique. Considering all errors, accuracy of this type of counter is always as good as or better than a conventional counter for input frequencies below the clock frequency, but is poorer when the input frequency is higher than the clock frequency.

42. ±1 Count Error This error is not due to any counting error in the instrument but comes about because both the input information and time information have been digitized. The input signal has been run through a trigger circuit to generate one and only one trigger output pulse for each cycle of the input waveform regardless of input waveshape. These trigger output pulses are counted without error by the decimal-counting circuits in the electronic counter whenever the gate is open. Gate opening and closing is controlled by time-base circuits (an "electronic stopwatch") which consist of a quartz-crystal oscillator followed by a series of 10:1 electronic dividers. This time base determines the 1 s or other selected time for which the gate is held open. Since both the input information and time information have been digitized, there is no way for the electronic counter to interpolate between successive input pulses. This gives rise to the ±1 count error, since the decade-counting assemblies (DCAs) totalize only the pulses which come in while the gate was open but have no way of knowing that another pulse may have been just about to arrive when the gate closed. This is shown in Fig. 19.

The magnitude of the error in reading due to the ±1 count is 1 over the reading displayed on the counter—*disregarding* decimal-point position and measurement units.

For example, ±1 count error in a counter reading of 503.275 kHz is 1/503,275 or approximately 1 part in 500,000 or 2 parts per million.

The ±1 count error can be reduced by going to a longer gate time—for example, a 10-s gate might have given 503.2756 kHz for a ±1 count error of 1/5,032,756, or approximately 1 part in 5 million or 2 parts in 10,000,000, an improvement of 10:1 over the error with a 1-s gate. By the same token, shorter gates will give larger ±1 count errors.

43. ±Time-base Inaccuracy The error due to the time-base system will be that of the quartz-crystal oscillator used to drive the time-base dividers. For power-line

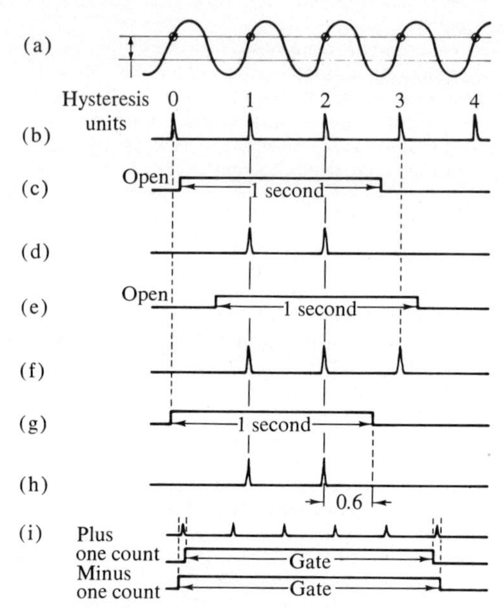

Fig. 19. ±1 count error with electronic counter. (*a*) Input signal 2.6 Hz. (*b*) Pulses from trigger circuit to units decade counter. (*c*) Gate can open at any time and closes 1 s later. (*d*) Two pulses get counted. (*e*) Gate could have opened at this time. (*f*) Three pulses get counted. (*g*) If gate had opened just after 0, pulse count would have been 2. (*h*) Correct number of cycles is 2.6. (*i*) Input pulses.

The gate could be any other selected interval such as 0.1 or 10 s.

1. The counter counts each cycle on the positive slope as shown at *a*.
2. The counter gate and the input signal are normally not synchronized; so the gate can open at any place on the input cycle in a random manner. The gate will close 1 s or other selected time after it opens as at *c*, *e*, or *g*.
3. The decimal-counter assembly counts without error each pulse it sees; however, it sees either two or three pulses in this example, dependent on when the gate opened to display 2 or 3 Hz as at *d*, *f*, or *h*.
4. The 1 count error is ½ or ⅓ for this example.
5. A 10 s gate would allow 26 or 27 pulses to come through. Display would be 2.6 Hz 2.7 Hz with 1 count error of $\frac{1}{26}$ or $\frac{1}{27}$.
6. At the extremes, the display could be one count short, −1, if the gate opened just after one pulse and closed just before some following pulse; it could be one count long, +1, if the gate opened just before one pulse and closed just after some following pulse, as shown at *i*.
7. With a stable input signal and a given gate length, the display should not change by more than one count.

time-base counters, the time-base error depends on the frequency stability of the power system.

A quartz crystal, regardless of how good it is, will have an aging rate; that is, its frequency will change with time as shown in Fig. 20. For a good crystal, this aging rate will always be in one direction, will not be erratic, and will decrease with time. Also, the better the crystal, the smaller the rate of change. The aging-rate specification is important, as it indicates the actual change with time and should thus always be given an outside or worst-possible specification if it is to be useful to the operator in computing maximum error in his measurement. A typical expression might be 2 parts in 10,000,000 (written as 2×10^{-7}) per month or 5 parts in 10,000,000,000 (written as 5×10^{-10}) per day. A crystal may age either up in frequency or down in frequency but should not change from aging up to aging down. It can never age at a rate greater than the number given in the data sheet without going out of manufacturer's specification; however, it can be and usually is considerably better than specified, particularly when the electronic counter is used under moderate environmental conditions as in a development laboratory. The maximum error in crystal frequency will not be greater than the aging-rate specification times the number of days or months since the last calibration, assuming that the crystal frequency was set exactly on frequency when calibrated. With the aging rate mentioned above, suppose the crystal had not been calibrated for 2 months. For the first example, maximum error would be not greater than

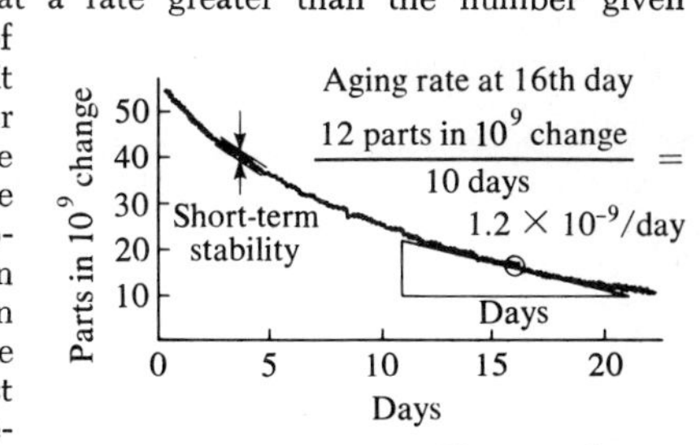

Fig. 20. Crystal-oscillator aging.

$$
\begin{aligned}
2 \times 10^{-7}/\text{month} \times 2 \text{ months} &= 4 \times 10^{-7} \\
&= 4 \text{ parts in } 10^{7} \\
&= \frac{4}{10{,}000{,}000} \\
&= 0.00004 \text{ percent}
\end{aligned}
$$

For the second example, maximum error would not be greater than

$$
\begin{aligned}
5 \times 10^{-10}/\text{day} \times 60 \text{ days} &= 300 \times 10^{-10} \\
&= 3 \text{ parts in } 10^{8} \\
&= \frac{3}{100{,}000{,}000} \\
&= 0.000003 \text{ percent}
\end{aligned}
$$

These two examples illustrate the time-base error that would be used in determining measurement accuracy.

High-stability quartz crystals mounted in proportional ovens (ovens that maintain an even temperature by continuously regulating the amount of energy used in the oven rather than turning all the way off like a thermostat) generally have the aging rate specified in change per day because they are sufficiently isolated from the environment (temperature change, line-voltage change, etc.) so that aging rate can be determined with a measurement lasting for a few hours to a day. While stability is high, oven crystals have the disadvantage that a warm-up time from 15 min to several hours or days may be required for the oscillator to come on to correct operating frequency after the electronic counter has been disconnected from ac power for a time. This disadvantage is overcome in most high-frequency counters by using a separate regulated power supply either to keep the crystal oven heated or to heat the oven and run the crystal oscillator whenever the ac cord is connected to power even if the power switch on the counter is turned off. When this is done, the electronic counter is ready to make accurate measurements as soon as it is switched on.

Nonoven room-temperature crystals usually have the aging rate specified in change per week or per month. One reason for this is that temperature changes of even a fraction of a degree can change the crystal frequency more than a day's aging. Therefore, the crystal frequency must be plotted for a week, a month, or more and the average frequency must be determined from the slope of the frequency vs. time plot. Room-temperature (nonoven) crystals can have very low aging rates and have the advantage of requiring no warm-up time to come on to correct frequency as do oven crystals. The disadvantage is, of course, that these crystals generally exhibit greater frequency changes with ambient-temperature change than temperature-controlled crystals.

Besides specifying the crystal-aging rate, all the better counters will also have the crystal-oscillator-frequency changes specified for:

Ambient-temperature changes... Specified as parts in 10^{10}/°C between some maximum and minimum temperature limit

Line volts.................... Parts in 10^{10} change for a ± 10 % change in line voltage

Load.......................... Parts in 10^{10} change for load changes from a short to an open circuit on the oscillator-frequency output connector

Short-term stability........... Changes in oscillator frequency due to random variations caused by oscillator circuit noise, supply-voltage variations, and other similar factors. For electronic counters, short-term stability is usually specified for a 1 s averaging time. Shorter averaging times are not specified, as the ± 1 count portion of the accuracy specification will always be more significant. Longer averaging times are not specified because they tend to make the oscillator look better but more important because most counters do not have gate lengths greater than 10 s so that a short-term specification over 1,000 s or 1 day averaging time is not compatible with measurements made by an electronic counter

For high-stability oscillators, each of these parameters is specified separately because some, such as the ambient temperature, line voltage, and load, can be controlled when highest possible stability is needed. The operator can determine how much improvement in performance he can achieve by controlling each parameter.

The magnitude of each of these effects can be found in the data sheet for a specific counter.

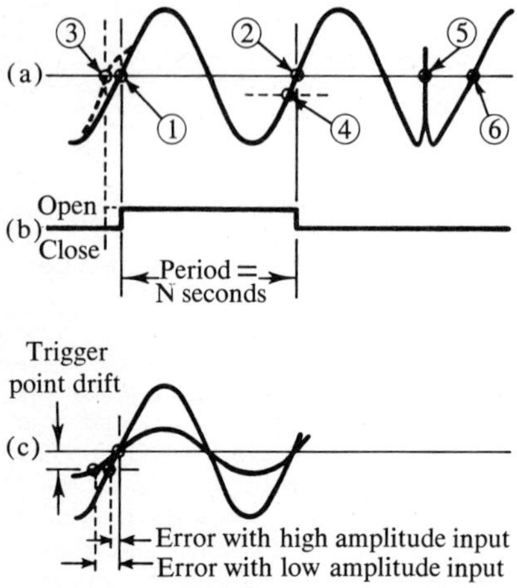

44. ±0.3 Percent per Period This error, associated with the input signal for the period mode of operation in Fig. 5, occurs when the gate is opened or closed too early or too late either because of noise coming into the counter along with the input signal or because of noise added to the signal by ground loops or by capacitive or magnetic coupling from other signals present within the counter. For most counters the internally introduced noise and drift is controlled to the extent that it contributes considerably less error than would be caused by a 40-dB signal-to-noise ratio (less than 1 percent noise) on the input signal for a sine-wave signal of minimum acceptable amplitude (usually 100 mV rms for most counters). Figure 21 illustrates the nature of this error.

Fig. 21. 0.3 percent per period error. (*a*) Input signal. (*b*) Counter gate. (*c*) Decreasing error.

For a period measurement the counter gate opens at a given voltage level on the input signal [as at zero volts shown by (1) of Fig. 21*a*] and will close at the corresponding voltage on the next cycle of input, as at (2)*a*, to give a counter gate length shown at *b*. Noise or distortion on one cycle of the input can alter its shape so triggering might occur at (3) instead of at (1) as it should. The result would be a gate that was too long. Also if the counter circuits were not well designed, drift from internally introduced noise might shift the trigger point either up or down from the time the count starts at (1) until it ends. A downward shift, for example, could cause the gate to close at (4) instead of at (2) to give a gate that was too short. A very narrow pulse (20 ns or less) riding on a low-frequency input signal could open the gate at (5) instead of at (6) as it should and cause a very large error in the measurement.

This 0.3 percent per period error can be reduced in two ways. One is by having more than the minimum-amplitude input signal required by the counter. The higher amplitude gives the signal a faster rate of rise as it goes through the trigger point; consequently, a given voltage error caused by noise or drift results in a much smaller time error. Furthermore, if triggering occurs exactly at zero volts, the trigger point does not change with changes in input-signal amplitude for symmetrical input waveforms. Voltage amplitude cannot be increased indefinitely, as most solid-state counters have protection devices which come into operation on a signal 20 or 30 dB above the minimum required at any particular input-sensitivity setting to protect the input circuit from damage from large overload conditions. Operation of these circuits changes the input impedance of the counter and so will distort the input signal. This error can occur when the gate opens, when the gate closes, or both.

A second way to reduce this error is to go to multiple-period average. Since the gate is opened only once and closed only once for any measurement, this error will be reduced in direct proportion to gate length, which can be increased to 10, 100, 1,000, or more periods of the input signal to reduce this error by a factor of 1/10, 1/100, 1/1,000 to 0.03, 0.003, and 0.0003 percent, respectively, as determined by the operator. The tradeoff for increased accuracy is increased measuring time.

This 0.3 percent per period applies to the signal that opens and closes the gate for any measurement the counter makes. In particular, it also applies to the lower of the two figures for ratio measurements and to the start and stop inputs for time-interval measurement. For signals of other than a minimum-amplitude sine wave, this error can be expressed as a gate-time error in terms of the rise time of the input signal and is

$$\frac{0.0025}{\text{Signal slope, V}/\mu\text{s}} \quad \mu\text{s}$$

Measurement error from this factor is determined by dividing this time error in microseconds by the gate length in microseconds.

The 0.3 percent per period error does not apply to gate length when making frequency measurements, as the gate is driven by high-amplitude fast-rise-time pulses from the time-base dividers. Rise time is fast enough so the error expression reduces to zero for all practical purposes.

45. Error Chart Figure 22 is a plot of the error equation for both the frequency mode of operation and the period mode of operation of an electronic counter and gives sufficient accuracy for most situations. The user locates the frequency of the input signal along the bottom line and follows it up to an intersection with the selected gate length or number of periods averaged and then to the left to read maximum error in the measurement, as might be achieved by calibrating an oscillator having an aging rate of approximately 5×10^{-10}/day every 20 days. The 1×10^{-8} line represents the total time-base error so that measurement accuracy could never be better than this. If higher accuracy is required, the time base could be driven by an external cesium-beam-tube frequency standard, in which case all the frequency-measurement accuracy lines would extend on down to 1 part in 10^{11} or better. For counters using the power line as a time base, the accuracy lines would all end at somewhere between 0.1 and 0.05 percent, this being a typical number for frequency accuracy of United States power companies. Accuracy charts will differ somewhat for each model of counter—on period measurement the ±1 count error will depend upon the maximum counted frequency available internally. For any measurement maximum possible accuracy cannot be any better than the time-base accuracy.

SOURCES OF ERROR DUE TO MISAPPLICATION

46. Incorrect Triggering The most commonly encountered problem in using an electronic counter comes about because the counter does not trigger as the operator expects on the input signal supplied. Trouble is most prevalent when measuring a nonsymmetrical waveform, particularly when electrical noise is also present. A rather careful look at trigger-circuit operation will show just what the counter

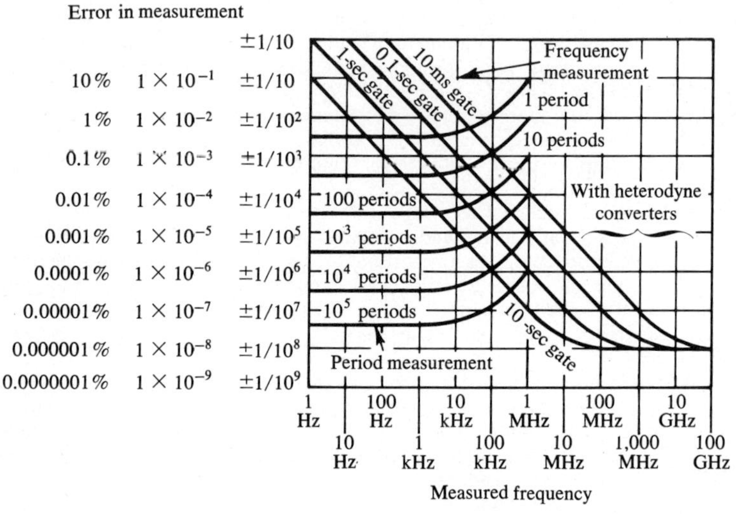

Fig. 22. Measurement error for conventional counter. Frequency measurement: ±1 count, ±time-base accuracy assumed to be ±1 part in 10^8 for this example. Period measurement: ±1 count, ±time-base accuracy, ±trigger error = 0.3 percent per period; counted frequency is 10 MHz.

does count but more important will point the way to getting around some of these problems.

Most counters have an input circuit consisting of an input amplifier, either ac- or dc-coupled, connected to a trigger circuit, usually a Schmitt trigger, which generates the pulse necessary to drive the counting circuit.

The Schmitt trigger is a dc-coupled circuit which will generate an output pulse corresponding to some specific voltage level on the input waveform. Once the trigger has generated an output pulse, the input signal must drop down to some lower voltage to "reset" the trigger before it can once again generate another output pulse. The two voltage levels which determine the trigger point and the "reset" point define what is known as the hysteresis limits of the trigger. Depending on the circuit, these may or may not be actual voltage levels which can be measured with a dc voltmeter. Figure 23 shows the two hysteresis limits, the upper limit (1) and the lower limit (2), symmetrically located with respect to zero volts. An input signal (3) must be of sufficient amplitude to cross both limits if it is to be counted. The output pulse can occur on either the positive slope of the input signal (4) or the negative slope (5) by connecting the output to the appropriate part of the circuit. Figure 23*b* shows the trigger points on a complex waveform when triggering on the positive (rising-voltage) slope. Note that the input signal must always go through the lower hysteresis limit, then generates an output pulse (7) when it crosses the upper limit (6). Another output pulse (10) cannot be generated unless the input signal first goes to a voltage lower than the lower hysteresis limit (8), then goes up through the upper hysteresis limit (9). The input circuit will function with a minimum-amplitude sine wave or symmetrical signal when the hysteresis limits are positioned symmetrically with respect to zero volts as shown.

A trigger-level control on some counters (see Fig. 14 for a panel drawing showing controls associated with a Schmitt trigger) allows the operator to position this

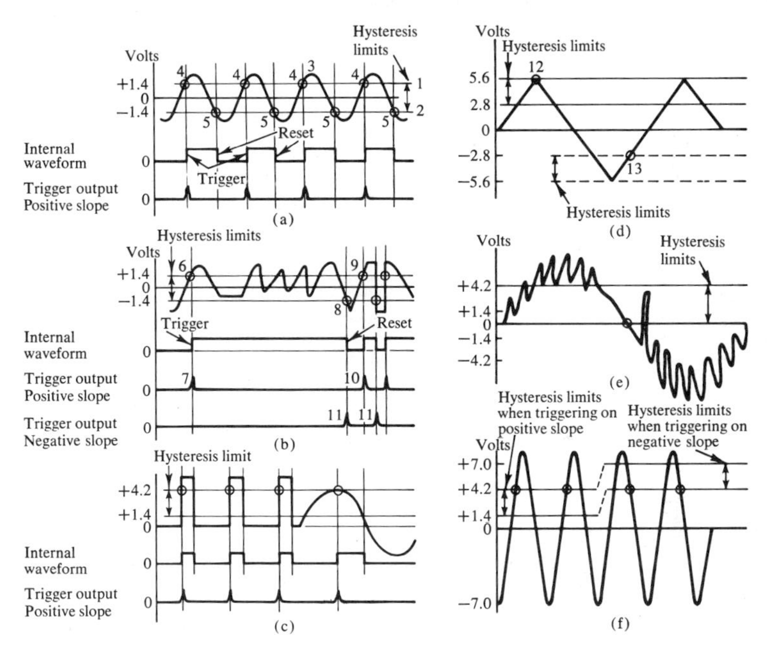

Fig. 23. Schmitt-trigger operation. (*a*) Sine-wave input signal. (*b*) Complex input waveform. (*c*) Input signal. (*d*) Range of trigger-level control. (*e*) Triggering at a positive-voltage negative slope on a noisy signal. (*f*) Action of hysteresis-compensation circuit.

trigger point above or below zero volts by moving the hysteresis limits up or down without changing the spacing between them. With the hysteresis limits set as in Fig. 23*a*, a string of clean positive pulses (no overshoot) will not drive the trigger since they do not cross both limits. The same holds true for a string of negative pulses. To count positive pulses at (12), the hysteresis limits are moved up so both limits are above zero volts as in Fig. 23*c*. The counter will still accept a sine-wave input, but the amplitude must be much greater than before or the positive peak of the sine wave will not cross by the upper hysteresis limit.

Triggering on the negative slope of an input signal is accomplished by using the internal signal corresponding to RESET to generate the output pulse.

For any of the cases discussed in the example the minimum signal which will get counted is 2.8 V peak to peak or 1 V rms.

The hysteresis limits can be moved up until the upper limit is at the positive peak of the input wave to trigger at (12) in Fig. 23*d*, or they can be moved down to get triggers at a negative-voltage positive slope as at (13); however, triggering is not possible below (13) since the lower hysteresis limit would go below the minimum input level so that the trigger would no longer get RESET. There are certain places on any waveform where triggering cannot take place without going to more elaborate circuitry.

These conditions are reversed when triggering on the negative (falling-voltage) slope of the input signal.

Counting a Noisy Signal. The trigger controls of a counter could be set to measure correctly the frequency or period of a very noisy signal in Fig. 23*e* by choosing a negative-voltage negative slope positioned as shown. Many counters have triggers that put out a pulse coincident with triggering which can be used to intensify the trigger point on an oscilloscope display of the input signals. Others have provision for measuring the dc-voltage level of the trigger point with either a built-in or an external voltmeter. Referring to Fig. 23*a*, triggering would occur at +1.4 V when triggering in a positive slope but would change to −1.4 V if the slope switch were changed to negative. Some counters have compensating circuits to keep the trigger point at the same place when slope is changed. This is done by introducing a dc voltage to move the hysteresis limits (see Fig. 23*f*) by an appropriate amount when the slope switch is changed. In some cases, the counter may quit counting when this is done, as one or the other of the hysteresis limits may be moved beyond the input-signal-voltage excursion. This feature makes a counter easier to use on time-interval measurements, as the trigger-voltage point stays the same when changing from positive to negative slope.

Input Amplifier. The hysteresis limits of a trigger cannot be spaced too close to achieve high sensitivity or the trigger becomes unstable with aging, line-voltage changes, temperature changes, or component aging. Therefore, higher sensitivity is achieved by using an amplifier between the input terminal and the trigger circuit. The amplifier must be a wideband amplifier with fairly constant gain across the counting range under all environmental conditions the counters must withstand. Amplifier noise is kept low, as this could lead to errors, particularly when making period measurements, because noise introduced by the amplifier has the same effect on the measurement noise coming in with the signal. Hysteresis limits are usually 2 to 3 V apart so an amplifier gain of 10 is required to get 100 mV rms (0.288 V peak-to-peak) sensitivity and a gain of 100 to get 10 mV rms sensitivity. Dc-coupled inputs are mandatory for versatile time-interval counters and desirable in most cases when measuring nonsymmetrical input signals, as ac coupling alters the shape of low-frequency inputs or moves the zero point with variable duty cycle of the signal because of the interstage *RC* time constants. A dc-coupled amplifier must be stable, as any variation in the amplifier operating point will shift the trigger point, which is dc-coupled to the trigger. Careful design is therefore necessary, and gain is usually limited to 10 or 20. Ac amplifiers, however, do not have this limitation, as they are ac-coupled to the trigger. Gains of 100 or more are practical; however, care must be taken to prevent noise pickup.

Figure 24*a* shows the positive-slope trigger points on a complex waveform when using a dc-coupled input. Figure 24*b* shows the trigger points for the same waveform with an ac-coupled input. The exact location of the trigger point is determined by the *RC* time constants of the input circuit.

The cycles in a waveform on a pedestal can be counted without error using a dc-coupled input; however, with an ac-coupled amplifier, the initial step from zero volts to the first cycle can charge up the capacitors in the coupling circuits and block the trigger until they discharge, so that the first few cycles of input are lost. In some cases, waveforms can be measured by putting a differentiating network between the signal and the counter. The differentiating network must have a time constant less than the narrowest segment of the signal. Dc-coupled inputs are a necessity when looking at pulses where both amplitude and spacing can be random as in pulses from a nuclear detector.

Many counters are designed with dc-coupled inputs and then have a capacitor between the input terminal and the amplifier when ac coupling is needed, as when measuring a signal riding on a high dc-voltage level. The only disadvantage of a dc-coupled amplifier and trigger is that any dc instability of the amplifier makes the trigger point "wander around." Careful design using balanced amplifiers and other techniques is necessary to build a dc-coupled input that is stable with time, temperature, line voltage, etc. A gain of 10 or so is a practical limit for dc-coupled systems, whereas ac-coupled inputs use higher-gain amplifiers since the dc instability of the amplifier is isolated from the trigger. Counters with ac-coupled inputs will have an input-frequency range specified as from 0.5, 2, or 10 Hz or as up to

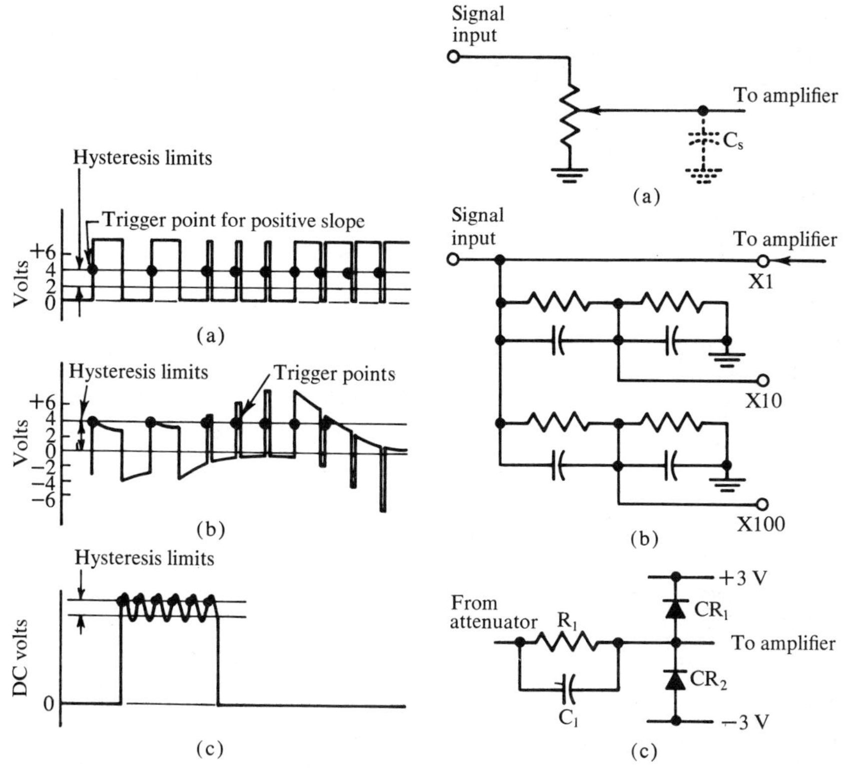

Fig. 24. Trigger points on complex input signals. (*a*) Dc-coupled trigger. (*b*) Ac-coupled trigger. (*c*) Ac signal with dc offset voltage.

Fig. 25. Input attenuator and overload-protection circuits. (*a*) Continuously variable attenuator. (*b*) Step attenuator. (*c*) Overload-protection circuit.

some maximum, whereas those with dc-coupled inputs will be specified as 0 or dc to some maximum frequency.

Attenuators and Overload. An input signal may be large, up to several hundred volts; so a variable attenuator may be used to decrease it to a level which will not overload or damage the input amplifiers. The attenuators may be a variable-control or a step type as in Fig. 25. The variable control is cheap but has the disadvantage that it tends to roll off high-frequency inputs because of the stray capacitance C across the output. The step attenuator maintains frequency response at any setting and also has a constant input impedance, which is desirable if the counter is to be used with a 10:1 divide probe at the input, as is the case if it is to be used for phase measurements. A continuously variable control together with the step attenuator allows the operator to place the trigger point almost anywhere on the input signal. For continuous coverage a counter of 100 mV rms sensitivity must either use a 1X, 10X, 100X attenuator and have a variable range of −3 to 0 to +3 V or use a 1X, 3X, 10X, 30X, 100X attenuator with a −1 to 0 to +1 V variable range. A greater range on the variable control in either case gives more overlap.

One other very important point to consider when using an attenuator between the input connector and the amplifier is this: The attenuator reduces the amplitude of the input signal to match the input circuits of the counter; or, looking at it from the amplifier, it expands the input capability of the amplifier to fit the input signal. In so doing, it also expands the space between the hysteresis limits, which might be 0.288 V (0.1 V rms) on the most sensitive range to 2.88 V on the 10X range and 28.8 V on the 100 X range. This is important to the operator, as it is now apparent that the counter cannot be triggered on a 10-V signal riding along on a 100-V signal, for instance, when using the 100X attenuator position, because the minimum signal which will cross both hysteresis limits in this case is 28.8 V.

Solid-state devices will not withstand large overloads without burnout; so most input circuits have some kind of overload protection as in Fig. 25*c*. At low frequencies an input signal of 100 V or more can be applied without damaging the circuit. The diodes clamp the signal level to ±3 V; so the voltage drop appears across *R*1 and thus protects the counter for large low-frequency signals (60 to 1,000 Hz) that might be introduced accidentally by ground loops, open ground leads, and such during normal use of the equipment. The input is *not* protected against high-amplitude signals at high frequencies, as the reactance of *C*1 is low, so that it looks like a short circuit. Therefore, the operator must exercise care when measuring transmitters or other high-power high-frequency equipment, or the counter can be damaged.

47. Digital Devices—All or Nothing Digital devices count electrical pulses, accumulating one count for each input pulse. If the input does not have quite enough amplitude or is deficient in some other way, the count either goes to zero or becomes extremely erratic. Internal-circuit malfunction, even though slight, can cause the same thing. This is in sharp contrast to analog devices such as a "nonelectronic" pointer-type voltmeter where small changes in input signal or minor instrument malfunctions show up only as a small error in reading rather than the all-or-nothing performance of digital devices.

48. RFI, EMI, and Susceptibility Counters can emit radio-frequency interference (RFI) or electromagnetic interference (EMI). The counting circuits use pulse waveforms which may have rise times in the nanosecond region with amplitude of several volts for fast counters. These pulses are rich in harmonics which may be radiated through openings in the instrument cabinet, through the window for the visual readout, through meters, or through other cabinet openings. This interference may also be conducted out of the instrument by the power cord. RFI can be troublesome, particularly when counters are used in screen rooms or other noise-free environments. Modified versions of counters which have added shielding and filtering are generally available from the manufacturer. Special parts are required to do this; so it is not feasible to try to change an existing standard counter to one which has low RFI and EMI. Counters may also be susceptible to RFI and EMI; that is, they may count incorrectly or erratically when in spurious electrical or magnetic fields. Most general-purpose counters have enough shielding and filtering so they are not affected by these environmental factors; however, some exceptions are worth noting: High-frequency counters used in the presence of high-amplitude fast-rise pulses, such as might come from the ignition systems of an engine on a test stand or pulses from relays or coils used in industrial control systems, may produce pulses which bother the counter. Because these pulses generally enter the counter via the signal-input channel, this type of interference can be cleared up by modifying the input circuit of the counter to limit its bandwidth.

Electromagnetic interferences may degrade the short-term stability of the crystal oscillator of a high-stability counter because of the magnetic field being picked up by coils in the crystal-oscillator circuit. Use of a magnetically shielded case on the counter helps reduce this. Also, fans, transformers, and other magnetic devices operating near the counter should be designed for low magnetic leakage and if necessary be provided with magnetic shields. Magnetic fields fall off quickly with distance; so it is sometimes possible to relocate the counter physically to reduce these effects.

49. Shock and Vibration Well-designed solid-state counters are not particularly bothered by shock and vibration unless the intensity becomes so severe as to damage physically the quartz crystal used in the oscillator, since it is perhaps the most delicate component, or even physically damage the counter itself. Vacuum-tube counters are more sensitive to shock and vibration, as it can cause the tubes to change characteristics as parts are momentarily moved internally. Shock mounting is about the only solution if this problem exists.

50. Expected Failure Rates Vacuum-tube counters will run about 2,000 h, after which time weak tubes may cause the instrument to malfunction. Other components normally have a longer life. Since most vacuum-tube counters, however, require from 150 to 600 W of power, elevated internal temperatures can cause component deterioration if air filters are not cleaned periodically.

A well-designed solid-state counter using either transistors or integrated circuits, or both, can run from one to several years without giving trouble as the solid-state active devices do not wear out as do vacuum tubes. Because power consumption is generally much less, internal temperatures are lower, and this also favors long component life. Some of the newer counters are miniaturized to such an extent that heat may be of consequence even though input power is low. With these counters also, the air filter when used must be kept clean to allow proper airflow.

High-stability quartz crystals may eventually age to the extent that they can no longer be set on frequency with the adjustments provided in the counter. When this happens, the crystal and oven assembly must be replaced. This does not happen often for lower-stability oscillators, as the adjustment range is greater.

CALIBRATION REQUIREMENTS

51. Self-check Each Time TEST or CHECK each time before using an electronic counter. The operator should always try the CHECK or TEST mode of operation. In this mode of operation a 100-kHz, 1- or 10-MHz, or 100-MHz signal derived from the crystal oscillator is connected to the signal input. The gate is opened for some interval, 1 s, for example, derived by dividing the same crystal-oscillator frequency by a series of 10:1 dividers. Since both the counted signal and the gate are derived from the same crystal, the electronic counter should always read 1 followed by an appropriate number of zeros—as 10000000 for an eight-digit counter counting 10 MHz for a 1-s gate. This is true whether the crystal oscillator is on frequency or off frequency, since this self-check mode of operation merely checks all the multiplying, counting, and dividing circuits in the instrument but does *not* check the crystal-oscillator frequency. This self-check may have a ± 1 ambiguity depending on the phasing of the counted pulses with respect to gate opening and closing, although most counters are designed so this will not show up in self-check.

The TEST or CHECK operation should be on either a switch by itself or one of the settings of the input attenuator so that the electronic counter can be checked in all modes of operation and for all gate lengths. The check position should not be one of the settings of the function switch, as a trigger circuit may be called upon to drive one of several counting circuits depending on the particular function. If marginal, the trigger circuit may drive some but not all of the circuits, and may thus malfunction only in certain modes of operation.

52. Crystal-oscillator Frequency Check Periodically the operator should check the frequency of the quartz-crystal oscillator in the counter, as the accuracy of all frequency, period, and time-interval measurements relates directly to the accuracy of the time base controlled by this oscillator.

This accuracy check is most easily made by comparing the time-base oscillator of the counter (usually a quartz crystal) to a better stability standard which is periodically corrected to agree with the U.S. Bureau of Standards standard-frequency-transmission broadcast on 60 kHz by station WWVB in Boulder, Colo. A special low-frequency receiver setup is used to make a continuous-phase comparison between the WWVB signal and the frequency standard on the quartz oscillator, as discussed in Chapter 35. Accuracy of most in-house frequency standards is adequate for checking the time-base oscillator of a low-frequency counter, since it will use either a room-temperature crystal or a simple oven crystal which has an aging rate of parts in 10^6 or 10^7 per week. Oscillators of this class can also be checked by comparison with the WWV high-frequency transmission for the following frequencies: 2.5, 5, 10, 15, 20, or 25 MHz or with WWVH on 2.5, 5, 10, and 15 MHz using a high-frequency communication receiver as shown in

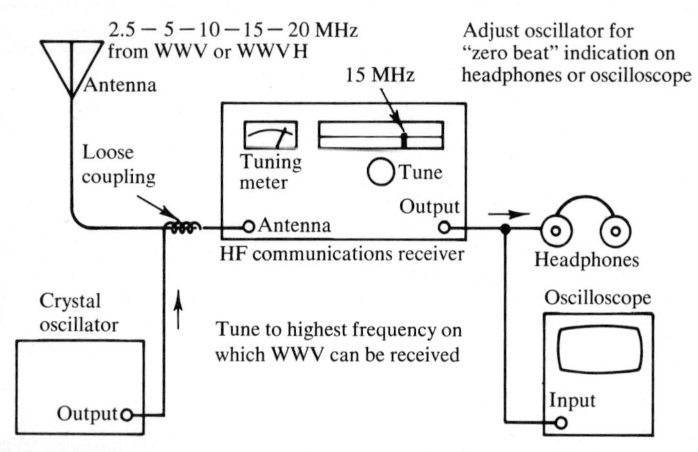

Fig. 26. Calibration of crystal oscillator against WWV or WWVH high-frequency transmission. This procedure is good only for calibrating an oscillator to 1 part in a million or so. This corresponds to an error of only 1 Hz in determining true zero beat.

Fig. 26. The comparison is made by tuning in the highest-frequency transmission of station WWV which can be received on the receiver. The oscillator under test is then loose-coupled to the antenna input by wrapping a few turns of wire around the antenna lead, increasing coupling until a beat note is heard on the headphones or speaker. The ear is not sensitive to frequencies much below 20 Hz; therefore, the tuning meter on the receiver or an oscilloscope should be used as a zero-beat indicator. The FREQ ADJ control on the oscillator is then used to get a zero beat between the oscillator under test and the WWV transmission. This high-frequency comparison technique is useful *only* with moderate-stability oscillators since Doppler shift in the WWV transmission will be several parts in 10^8 for much of the United States. Doppler shift occurs because most high-frequency communications are by reflected waves and the height of the reflecting surface is different in the daytime from what it is at night.

This shift is not predictable; so it is difficult to get an absolute oscillator accuracy of much better than 1 part in 10^6 to a part in 10^7 with these high-frequency comparisons.

Most modern transistorized or integrated-circuit universal counters, for operation at 50 MHz or above, use a high stability quartz crystal in a proportionally controlled oven as the time-base reference. Since aging rates on these oscillators range from a few parts in 10^9 per day to a few parts in 10^{10} per day, it becomes apparent that the Doppler error in the WWV high-frequency transmission could be as great as 100 to 1,000 days' aging of the crystal in the counter; therefore, these oscillators should be compared either with the U.S. Bureau of Standards transmissions by station WWVB on 60 kHz, or with a cesium-beam primary-frequency standard, or with a periodically checked rubidium secondary-frequency standard.

A cesium-beam frequency standard* as a primary standard does not have to be set on frequency by comparison with any other standard. It has an absolute accuracy of 1×10^{-11} or better whenever it is operating. Rubidium frequency standards have stability of 2×10^{-11} per month or so, but they must be compared with some primary standard for calibration, as they do "age." The best quartz oscillators have an aging rate of a few parts in 10^{11} per day and require periodic calibration the same as rubidium frequency standards.

One other important point must be considered when making very high accuracy measurements with an electronic counter, and that is the definition of time for the time-base reference frequency itself. Two references are in common usage. One is an atomic reference which is invariant with time; the other is a reference related to the rotation of the earth on its axis related to the sun.

The A1, or atomic time, is a reference to a hyperfine energy transition of the cesium 133 atom at 9,192.631770 MHz, which is now the international standard of frequency and time. This frequency is an invariant with aging and is therefore useful in scientific work. WWVB transmissions on 60 kHz use the A1 reference.

The UT, or universal time, reference related to the rotation of the earth was convenient when using the counter for real-time work such as timekeeping, navigational-system measurements, or investigating phenomena which relate to the rotation of the earth on its axis. For several years this reference had been offset by -300 parts in 10^{10} or -3 parts in 10^8 with respect to the WWVB A1 transmission. The WWV and WWVH transmissions were referenced to UT, as were all United States AM, FM, and TV broadcast stations. Universal time is not constant, and so it has been checked and a new offset determined once a year to keep the time scale in agreement with the earth's rotation. On January 1, 1972 this offset was changed to zero† by international agreement so WWV, WWVB, and WWVH transmissions are all the same frequency.‡

Comparison of a high-stability oscillator with WWVB is most easily made by using a low-frequency receiver and a linear-phase comparator (see Chapter 35).

FRONT-PANEL TROUBLESHOOTING

53. Check or Test In this mode of operation, the output of the crystal oscillator (Fig. 4) is internally connected to the input amplifier. The counter then measures the frequency of the time-base oscillator. The answer should always come out as 1 followed by an appropriate number of zeros (1000000 for a counter which counts a 1-MHz crystal for a 1-s gate). A +1 count, 1000001, or a −1 count, 999 999, may show up occasionally; however, for a particular model of counter at any one gate length, the reading should not vary between +1 and −1 (2 count variation). The highest internally available frequency is generally counted in CHECK, as this gives the decade-counter assemblies a better test. If the CHECK mode is on the input attenuator or input switch, SELF-CHECK can be made in all modes of operation with all gate lengths and for different multiperiod averages to check the instrument more completely. If the SELF-CHECK does not read 1000000 but reads 1250000, for example, this could indicate that the units-counting

* Comparison and calibration of high-stability oscillators are discussed in detail in Chapter 35.

† U.S. Naval Observatory, Time Service Announcement, series 14, no. 7, October 23, 1970.

‡ UTC Time Scale to Change in 1972, *Hewlett-Packard Journal,* p. 16, October, 1971.

decade was dividing by 8 instead of dividing by 10 as it should. Similarly, a reading of 833300 might indicate that the third decade from the right, the thousands decade, was dividing by 12 instead of by 10 as it should. A reading of 800000 might indicate one of the decade-divider assemblies in the time base was dividing by 8 instead of 10. Analyzing an incorrect self-check number can give a clue as to the location of the trouble. Trouble in both the decade-counting assembly and decade-divider assembly would give a reading which is the mathematical result of the two errors, but because it is usually difficult to interpret, other tests must be made to determine if the problem is in the time-base section or counting section.

The CHECK or TEST mode of a counter checks the divider and multiplier circuits in a counter but gives *no* indication at all of crystal-oscillator accuracy. The reason, of course, is that both the counted signal and the timing signal are derived from the same oscillator. If the crystal oscillator were high in frequency, for example, it would put out more cycles than it should in 1 s. The same crystal frequency is divided down to obtain the 1-s gate; so, with a crystal frequency that is too high, the gate length becomes proportionally short. The net result is that the self-check is still 1000000.

54. Gate Indicator The gate indicator (Fig. 1) can be a useful troubleshooting aid if the visual readout is erratic or is a result of more than one malfunction in the counter. The indicator—usually a neon or incandescent lamp—comes on when the gate opens and goes off when the gate closes. If the counter is in the frequency mode and set for a 10-s gate, the gate indicator should stay on for 10 s. This can be timed with reasonable accuracy using the sweep second hand of a watch or clock. If this time is approximately right, it could not be the cause of a self-check reading that was too large or too small by a factor of 2:1, for instance. Also, if the display is completely erratic but the gate rate seems uniform, trouble is very likely in the input or count circuits but not in the time-base circuits.

If the gate light does not go on and off as expected, switching to successively shorter gates eliminates the decade dividers one by one as the source of trouble, and this may indicate that the crystal oscillator is not operating.

If the crystal oscillator is not operating, correct gate operation can still be checked by going to a period measurement, as in Fig. 5. Connect a signal of appropriate frequency and amplitude to the INPUT terminal. The gate indicator should indicate the correct gate operation by flashing on and off if the input frequency is low enough for the eye to follow. If not, a multiple-period average setting increases the gate length until it can be seen. Here again, correct gate operation can be estimated as a 1-Hz input in a single period, or a 100,000-Hz input with 10^5 period average should keep the gate indicator on for 1 s.

55. Manual Gate Open The MANUAL GATE OPEN mode of operation can be very helpful in troubleshooting a counter. One of the internal time-base signals is connected to the input either by switching to CHECK or for some counters by connecting a cable from the external standard-frequency output on the rear panel to the input on the front panel. The MANUAL GATE OPEN function opens the gate regardless of any other control signals; so each input pulse should register in the visual display as it enters the input. A 1-Hz frequency input should smoothly step the units decade—on the right of the display—one digit each second. Likewise, a 100,000-Hz input should step the fifth column from the right at a one digit per second rate. Starting with 1 Hz and then using appropriate higher input frequencies, each decade can be stepped through all 10 positions while each is examined in turn for uniform counting rate, correct sequence of digits, and finally to see if each digit is formed correctly. Malfunctions in the counting section can be localized using this technique.

56. Reset Pushbutton In all except the MANUAL GATE OPEN mode, pushing the reset button closes the gate and resets the counting decades as well as other internal circuits. The display should go to all zeros, and the gate indicator should indicate gate closed. Any other behavior is an indication of trouble in the gate circuits.

57. Display-storage Switch The visual display on counters with display storage changes only when the gate closes and issues a transfer command. The nonstorage mode is very useful when troubleshooting, as each input pulse is registered in the display as soon as it enters the input of the counter. With a stable input frequency, the display should be examined to see if the stepping rate is uniform and for evidence of skipping numbers, if the counter is not working correctly. The sample-rate control should vary the time between completion of one count and reset to zero before a new count begins from a small fraction of a second out to several seconds. In the HOLD or ∞ position of the control, the counter should make one reading each time the reset button is depressed.

58. Input Trigger Indicators Some counters have indicator lamps which come on whenever the trigger circuit is operating, that is, when the input-signal amplitude, rise time, slope, and polarity satisfy the requirements to generate an output pulse. Even though the counter may not be working properly, these indicators show that the input circuit is functioning.

59. Oven Indicator Some electronic counters, with temperature-controlled ovens for the quartz-crystal oscillator, use a lamp, a meter, or a thermometer to help verify correct oven operation. The operator should look for a stable indication after some specified warm-up time. Failure of the indicator to stabilize is an indication of incorrect oven operation.

DEFINITION OF COMMON TERMS

ACCURACY: The degree to which a measurement approaches the actual measurement as defined by an approved reference or by a standards laboratory.

AGING RATE: Average rate of change of a quartz crystal measured over an interval of a day, a week, or a month depending on the type of crystal. Usually expressed in parts per million over some designated time.

AMPLITUDE: Absolute magnitude of signal.

BCD OUTPUT: Binary-coded decimal electrical output representing the numbers displayed by the visual readout. With parallel BCD output, BCD information from the counting decades is available from all digits of the display simultaneously. This requires four output lines or wires per digit. Information transfer can be very fast. With serial BCD output, the counting decade is available sequentially for the digits displayed. This requires only four lines or wires to transfer all the digital information to another device. Transfer is slower than for parallel output.

BUFFER STORAGE: A circuit configuration whereby one reading can be electrically stored while the counting decades are reset to be ready for a new count. Either visual-readout, BCD output or both may be stored.

CODE: The pattern of on and off voltage levels of the counting circuits in a decade which uniquely defines each decimal digit.

COMPLEMENTARY OUTPUT: An output inverted in state from a reference output.

COMPUTING COUNTER: An electronic counter with built-in capability to perform arithmetic manipulations such as add, subtract, multiply, divide, and take square roots on input information so that the visual display and BCD output can be in terms of engineering units, can be an rms reading, average reading, peak indication, a peak-to-peak indication, or other form as desired by the operator.

DECADE- OR DECIMAL-COUNTING ASSEMBLY: Circuit which counts electrical pulses and indicates the total number of means of a visual display or electrical readout or both. Abbreviated DCA or DCU.

DECADE OR DECIMAL DIVIDER ASSEMBLY: Circuit which counts electrical pulses and puts out one pulse for each 10 pulses in. Has no visual readout. Abbreviated DDA.

DIRECT COUNT: An electronic counter designed to count pulses at whatever rate they occur at the signal input. The gate is between the input circuits and the decade-counting assemblies as in Fig. 4.

DISPLAY STORAGE (OR LATCH): Counters with display storage give a continuous visual and/or BCD output of a previous reading while a new one is in progress. Upon completion of the new reading the display is "updated" to the new reading. Counters with display storage can take readings much more rapidly and can be read with less chance of error than those which do not have this feature.

DISPLAY TIME: A term used primarily with vacuum counters. This control determines how long the visual display is held before the decade resets and a new count begins. On nonstorage counters, the visual display is readable only during display time.

ELECTRONIC COUNTER: This refers to the whole instrument.

FREQUENCY COUNTER: This measures only the frequency of the incoming signal.

GATE: An on-off switch in a signal path. Like a "garden gate," an open gate lets signals pass through and thus behaves the same as a closed switch.

GATE INDICATOR: This is usually an incandescent or neon lamp which comes on whenever the signal gate is opened and goes off when it closes. Short gates, 1 μs, for instance, would not keep the gate indicator turned on long enough for the operator to see it; so most counters have a "stretcher" circuit which keeps the gate indicator on for 50 to 100 μs—long enough so it can be seen—on short gate settings (below 100 ms).

HOLD OR ∞: A position on the sample-rate switch which allows the counter to take one reading, which it will then hold indefinitely unless commanded to take another.

HOLD-OFF—ALSO INHIBIT: A control-line input which can be energized to keep a counter from resetting and thus destroying the BCD information. It is generally used to allow time for a printer or computer to read the BCD information.

IF: Intermediate frequency.

INHIBIT: See Hold-off.

KEYBOARD: Switch panel, similar to one on an electronic calculator, to enter numbers as well as commands into a computing counter.

LATCH: See Display Storage.

LO: Local oscillator.

MANUAL GATE: A gate operated by tuning a switch or by internal or external contact closure.

OVEN INDICATOR: Electronic counters with temperature-controlled ovens for the quartz-crystal oscillator may have a lamp, meter, or thermometer to help verify correct oven operation. Generally speaking, one would like to see a stable indication after the specified warm-up period. Some of the more stable oscillators may not have indicators because of the difficulty of sampling oven performance without adversely affecting stability.

OVERFLOW: Number of pulses passing through the gate exceeds the capacity of the counting register.

PERIOD COUNTER: Measures period only of the incoming signal.

POLARITY: Plus or minus signal voltage with respect to zero volts.

PRESCALING: A high-speed counting technique whereby the input signal is divided by some number N before going through the main gate of the counter. Gate lengths can be adjusted so the counter will be direct-reading; however, for a given resolution, the measurement will always take longer than with direct-counting techniques.

PRESET: An arbitrary number which can be set up on switches or into decades prior to the operation of the counter. It may determine a division ratio or a reset number or a high or low limit.

PRINT COMMAND: This is an electrical signal from the counter indicating that a reading has been completed so a printer or computer can interrogate the BCD output.

PROPORTIONAL OVEN: A quartz-crystal oven which continuously changes the rate of heat input to match the rate of heat loss to the surroundings. Control is stepless.

READOUT: The information output from a counter which indicates the number of pulses that have been counted. May be a visual panel display or electrical levels on output lines (BCD output).

RECYCLE TIME: Time between successive samples, i.e., gate length plus dead time between samples.

REGISTER: A place where electrical information can be stored.

RESOLUTION: The smallest change the electronic counter can recognize in any given measurement. This will be one count in the least significant digit (right-hand or units digit) of the visual display.

SAMPLE RATE: Setting of a sample-rate control is one of the factors which determines how long a counter waits after completing one measurement before it will start another one when in the automatic mode of operation. An ∞ or "hold" position is usually included as a part of the sample-rate circuit to allow the counter to make just one reading. Each time the "reset" pushbutton on the panel is operated or an electrical reset signal is supplied to the counter, it will make one single reading which it will hold indefinitely unless another reset is supplied.

SCALING: Dividing down a frequency or pulse-repetition rate by some factor N in decade steps or binary steps.

SELF-CHECK: A test position to check internal dividing, counting, and multiplying circuits but *not* time-base accuracy.

SLOPE: Defines the direction an electrical signal must be moving (plus or minus) to generate a trigger pulse.

TIME BASE: An electronic "stopwatch" which generates accurately spaced electrical pulses. These pulses are generally derived from a quartz-crystal oscillator driving an electronic divider chain. Inexpensive counters may use the power-line frequency to drive the divider chain.

TURNOVER TEMPERATURE: The minimum point on a frequency vs. temperature plot of an oven-controlled quartz crystal and thus the temperature at which a crystal exhibits minimum frequency change with temperature change.

UNIVERSAL COUNTER: This type of electronic counter can be switched so as to make frequency, period, and time-interval measurements plus other measurements depending on the make and model.

Chapter **34**

Frequency Analyzers

HARLEY L. HALVERSON

Hewlett-Packard Company, Palo Alto, California

The frequency analyzer is an instrument which divides a signal into its frequency components and analyzes them. It measures the signal energy which is present at a specific frequency.

Many types of analyzers are available. The more basic ones will be discussed in this chapter. Designs are changing rapidly, with the objective of making them more accurate and easier to operate. In spite of this, most analyzers are too complicated to use for making measurements without some knowledge of the design limitations and the precautions necessary to overcome them.

FREQUENCY-DOMAIN ANALYSIS

In 1822, Fourier showed that any periodic complex waveform can be represented by summing simple, harmonically related sine and cosine waves of varying amplitude and specified phase. For example, a trumpet playing the note A has the characteristic trumpet sound because of the harmonics that are added to the 440-Hz fundamental note by the instrument. Were it not for these harmonics, the trumpet would sound like a whistle or "pure" tone.

To prove that Fourier was right requires considerable mathematics. An indication that he might be right can be had by showing how a series of sine waves can be added to produce a square wave. To accomplish this, Fourier showed that only the odd harmonics are needed. The peak amplitude of each odd harmonic is given by the series 1, $\frac{1}{3}$, $\frac{1}{5}$, $\frac{1}{7}$, . . . , $1/n$ . . . . Figure 1 shows the results of adding the first three odd harmonics.

With this knowledge, suppose that a designer of electronic organs wishes to reproduce the sound of the trumpet, note A. He knows that he needs to add together a series of harmonically related oscillators each producing a pure tone or sine wave. But how much of each harmonic should he add? If he could express the trumpet note as a mathematical equation, he could perform a Fourier analysis of the equation, as was done for the square wave. Unfortunately, the designer has no idea what the equation of the trumpet note is. His only reasonable alternative is to measure the harmonic content of the trumpet. To do this, the designer makes a tape recording of the A note being played on the trumpet. He cuts out the tape on which the note is recorded and splices the ends together to form a loop. The loop can now be played back on the recorder as a continuous A note ready for analysis. The electrical output of the recorder is now fed through a tunable selective filter which allows the frequency to which the filter is tuned to pass through and rejects all other frequencies (see Fig. 2). An ac voltmeter is connected to the output of the filter to measure the magnitude of the harmonics. The filter is tuned to 440 Hz, and the fundamental component of the note is measured. Then the filter is tuned successively to each of the harmonics, and their magnitude relative to the fundamental is measured. The designer now knows exactly how much of each harmonic is needed to duplicate the trumpet tonal quality in the organ.

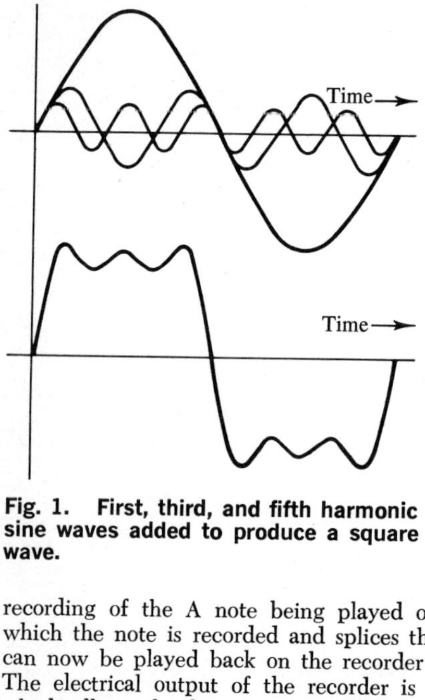

Fig. 1. First, third, and fifth harmonic sine waves added to produce a square wave.

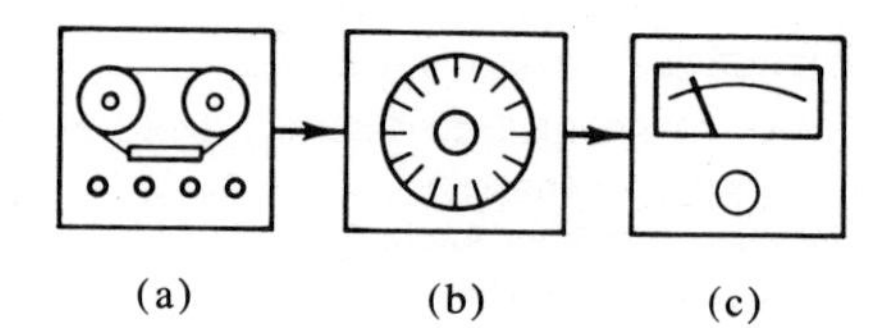

Fig. 2. A frequency-domain analyzer system. (*a*) Tape recorder. (*b*) Tunable filter. (*c*) Ac voltmeter.

The instrument consisting of a tunable filter and an ac voltmeter which was used to measure the fundamental and harmonics of the trumpet is the simplest form of wave or frequency analyzer. It is one type of a larger class of instruments known as frequency-domain analyzers. The class also includes such instruments as the frequency-selective voltmeter and the spectrum analyzer. The frequency-domain analyzer is the mathematical dual of the time-domain analyzer, the most common example of which is the oscilloscope. The time-domain analyzer plots a graph of voltage amplitude vs. time. The frequency-domain analyzer plots a graph of voltage amplitude vs. frequency. Figure 3 shows an oscilloscope plot and a spectrum-analyzer plot of the 440-Hz trumpet note. Both types of measurement present specific information about the waveform. The oscilloscope shows information such as peak voltage, rise time, and period. The frequency-domain analyzer gives information relating to frequency, harmonics, distortion, frequency stability, spectral purity, spurious signals, etc. These are only a few of the measurements made with these two classes of instruments. Both find broad use as basic electronic measuring tools.

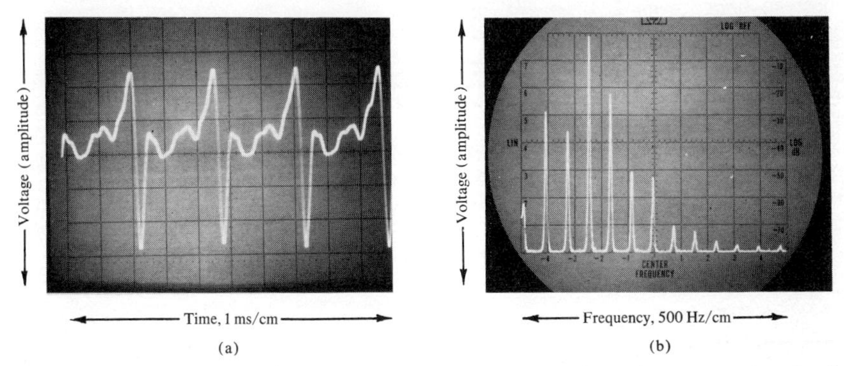

Fig. 3. Time-domain and frequency-domain presentation of a trumpet note A (440 Hz). (*a*) As viewed on an oscilloscope. (*b*) As viewed on a spectrum analyzer.

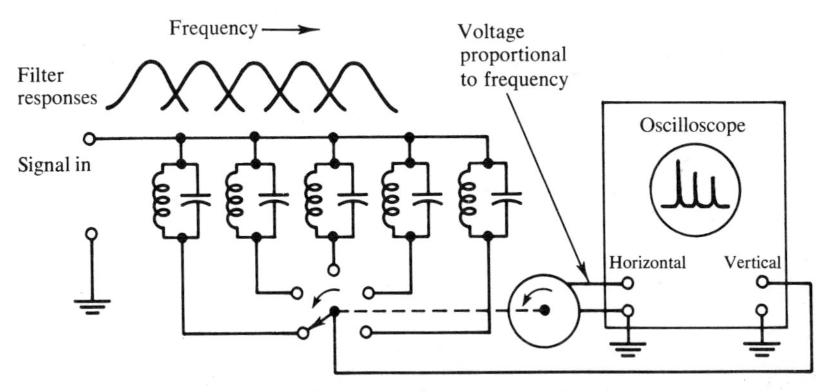

Fig. 4. Real-time frequency analyzer.

TYPES OF FREQUENCY-DOMAIN ANALYZERS

1. Real-time Analyzer The most ideal type of frequency-domain analyzer is made by presenting the input wave to a bank of parallel-resonant filters, each tuned to a slightly different frequency. This type of analyzer is called a *real-time analyzer* because it is looking at all frequencies in the band of interest at all times. Figure 4 shows how these filters might overlap to give continuous frequency coverage. The output of the filters could be fed to a bank of ac voltmeters, one for each filter, although this is not too practical. A more common technique is to sample the output of each filter sequentially at a high rate and plot the amplitude of the output voltage of each filter on the vertical axis of an oscilloscope.

A voltage proportional to the frequency of the filter being sampled is fed to the horizontal axis.

Real-time spectrum analyzers are a natural physical phenomenon. Both the eye and the ear are capable of real-time frequency analysis. The eye looks at a scene and identifies colors (frequency) and light intensity (amplitude). The ear also recognizes both the frequency and intensity of sounds it hears. The accuracy to which a specific frequency may be identified is called the *frequency-calibration accuracy* of the measuring device. For the eye this accuracy is fairly good. We know when a color is blue, red, green, etc. For the ear, accuracy is not always as good. Only a few people with perfect pitch can identify sound frequency accurately. The ability to differentiate between two closely spaced frequencies is called the *resolution* of the measuring device. The ear has very good resolution. It can resolve two notes that are only fractions of a hertz apart. The eye cannot do this.

The ability to work with intensities which range from very small to very large is called the *dynamic range* of the measuring device. Both the eye and the ear are outstanding in this respect. This is because their intensity (amplitude) response is logarithmic rather than linear. For example, the ratio of power in a sound which is just perceptible to one which can damage the ear is over 120 dB. In logarithmic terms, the power ratio in decibels is $10 \times \log P_1P_2$, where P_1 and P_2

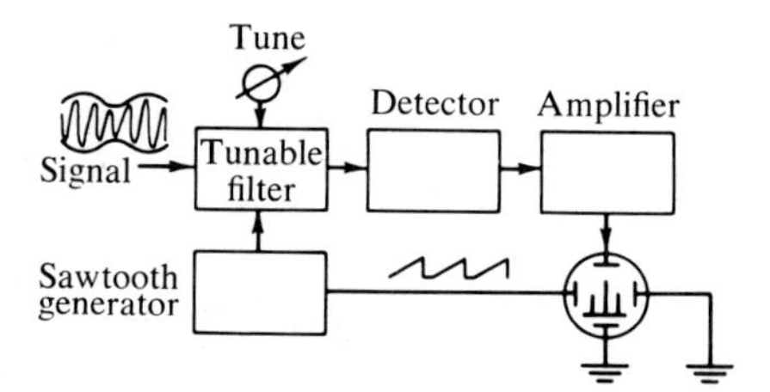

Fig. 5. Scanning-filter frequency analyzer.

are the two powers. This is a ratio of 1,000,000,000,000 to 1 in linear terms. Few manmade analyzers can approach this dynamic range.

The band of frequencies over which the measuring device responds is called the *frequency range*. Here is a serious design problem with the parallel-filter real-time frequency analyzer. If the resolution of the analyzer is to be good, the filters must have narrow bandwidths. As the bandwidth narrows, the number of filters necessary to cover a specified frequency range increases and soon grows out of reason. For this reason, parallel-filter analyzers are limited in usefulness to applications which require only a narrow frequency range.

2. Scanning-filter Analyzer To overcome the design problem of needing so many filters, another approach is often used. This is the approach which was used to analyze the trumpet note. Rather than use a large number of filters, each tuned to a slightly different frequency, one filter is used which can be tuned over the frequency range of interest. An instrument which uses this approach is called a *scanning-filter analyzer*. The *wave analyzer* and the *scanning-spectrum analyzer* are two important examples. These two instruments differ principally in how the voltage output of the filter is presented and how the filter is tuned. The wave analyzer reads the amplitude of the voltage on a meter, and the filter is generally tuned manually. The spectrum analyzer presents the amplitude of the voltage on the vertical axis of an oscilloscope. The frequency of the filter is tuned electrically across its frequency range, and a voltage proportional to the frequency of the filter is used to deflect the oscilloscope trace in the horizontal direction.

Since the spectrum analyzer and the wave analyzer are very similar in design, the description which follows will be limited to the scanning-spectrum analyzer. Figure 5 shows the simplest form of this instrument. The sawtooth generator produces a sawtooth-shaped voltage which tunes the filter and deflects the oscilloscope trace in the horizontal direction. The electrical signal which passes through the filter is detected and amplified and is connected to the vertical-deflection terminal of the oscilloscope. A typical signal which might be analyzed is shown at the input. It is a time-domain presentation of an AM radio station. The oscilloscope shows the frequency-domain presentation of this same signal.

3. Superheterodyne Analyzer Although this scheme would work well, good electrically tuned filters are very difficult to build. Fortunately, there is another

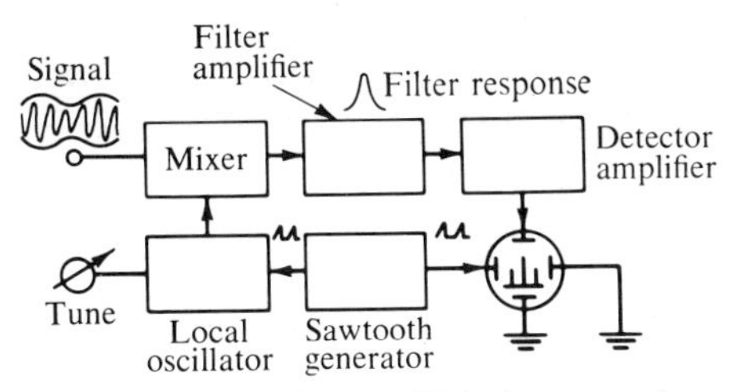

Fig. 6. Heterodyne frequency analyzer which tunes and scans with one local oscillator.

design which makes this type of filter unnecessary. It is called the superheterodyne analyzer. It works exactly like the common household AM radio except that it tunes electrically and presents its output to an oscilloscope rather than a loudspeaker. Notice this analyzer in Fig. 6 is expanded from the scanning-filter type by adding a mixer and a local oscillator. The output of the mixer is the signal frequency minus the local-oscillator frequency. The filter is tuned to this frequency difference and fixed. Since the filter is fixed in frequency, it can be designed to have variable bandwidth and steep skirts. The bandwidth is adjusted by the user to obtain

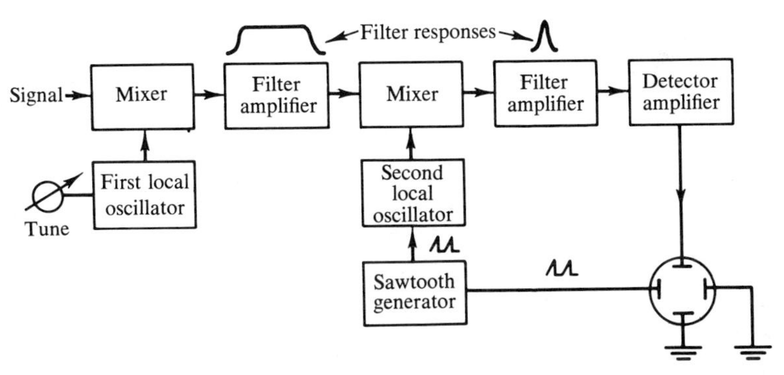

Fig. 7. Heterodyne frequency analyzer which tunes with the first local oscillator and scans with the second local oscillator.

the desired resolution. Scanning is accomplished by tuning the local oscillator with the sawtooth-voltage generator. The magnitude of the scan is set by adjusting this voltage. The center frequency around which the analyzer scans is set with a manual tuning control which adds a dc tuning voltage to the sawtooth voltage.

A popular type of superheterodyne analyzer is shown in Fig. 7. In this design a second mixer and local oscillator are added. Although this looks like a complication, it actually simplifies the design. The first local oscillator is used to tune the analyzer. The second local oscillator does the scanning and is tuned electrically by the sawtooth generator. By splitting these functions, the voltage-tuned oscillator design is made much easier than in the first case where one local oscillator performs both tuning and scanning. The disadvantage of this design is that the band of frequencies over which the instrument can scan is limited by the bandwidth of the first filter.

When it is desired to scan bandwidths as wide as the analyzer can tune, the first approach must be used. When only narrow scanning is desired, the second approach may be used and may be less expensive.

Both these designs have one significant limitation when compared with the real-time analyzer. The real-time analyzer looks at all frequencies within its frequency range at all times. If the spectrum being analyzed is changing rapidly, it may miss transients which occur at some frequency within its band when it is tuned to another. One possible solution for overcoming this limitation would be to scan so rapidly across the band that only very fast transients would be missed. Unfortunately, as we shall see later, there is a maximum rate at which the analyzer can scan with a given filter bandwidth. The faster the scan rate, the broader the filter bandwidth necessary. Thus, to scan rapidly, the analyzer will have poor resolution.

4. Dispersive-filter Analyzer To help overcome this limitation, a third type of analyzer is sometimes used. It is called a *dispersive-filter analyzer.* It can take the form of either of the types shown in Figs. 6 and 7. It is different basically in that the narrow filter is replaced by a broadband dispersive filter. A dispersive filter is one which delays signals at different frequencies by different times. Thus a band of signals separated in frequency which are presented at the input of the filter at the same time come out of the filter separated in time. By proper design, this analyzer scans at a very rapid rate because of its broadband filter, and because of its dispersive characteristic it still resolves closely spaced signals as if its bandwidth were much narrower. It can thus approximate a real-time analyzer in looking at rapidly changing spectrums. Good dispersive filters are very hard to build; so this type of analyzer is quite specialized.

FRONT-PANEL TERMS

Since an analyzer is an instrument which measures signal amplitude vs. frequency, it is important to keep in mind the units of these measurements. Analyzers could be built which measure electrical, acoustical, and mechanical vibrations, light, and probably other signals as well. The analyzer which measures electrical signals is the most common. This is especially so since many of the other types of signals are measured by transforming them first into electrical signals. For these reasons only those characteristics which relate to electrical signal analyzers will be discussed.

Signal Amplitude. The basic unit of electrical amplitude is the *volt.* The calibration may be in volts, millivolts (10^{-3} V), or microvolts (10^{-6} V). Another useful unit is power into a specified load resistance. The unit of power is the *watt,* milliwatt, or microwatt. The power is related to the voltage by watts = volts²/ohms of the load. The ratio of two different voltages or powers may be expressed in *decibels.* If V_1 and V_2 are the two voltages, dB = 20 $\log_{10}(V_1/V_2)$. If P_1 and P_2 are the two powers, dB = 10 $\log_{10}(P_1/P_2)$. Doubling the voltage is a +6-dB change. Halving the voltage is a −6-dB change. Ten times the voltage is a +20-dB change. Doubling or halving the power is a +3-dB or −3-dB change. Ten times the power is a +10-dB change.

A common measure of power is the decibel relative to 1 mW into a specified resistance (dBm). A 1-mW signal is a level of 0 dBm. A ⅒-mW signal is at −10 dBm. A 1-W signal is at +30 dBm. The signal level may be referenced to 1 W, in which case the symbol is dBW. Another common measure is the decibel relative to 1 μV(dBμV). A 1-V signal is at a level of +120 dBμV.

With so many different sets of units, the user is easily confused, and he often finds himself converting back and forth to the set he knows best. The ability to move from one set to another is important.

Frequency. The units of frequency are the *hertz* (Hz), *kilohertz* (kHz = 10^3 Hz), *megahertz* (MHz = 10^6 Hz), and *gigahertz* (GHz = 10^9 Hz). The hertz is equivalent to the old unit "cycle per second."

BASIC INSTRUMENT SPECIFICATIONS

The instrument specifications form a concise method for informing the prospective user what measurements can be made with the instrument and to what accuracy. Unfortunately, not all manufacturers specify their analyzers in the same way. When more than one name for the specification can be used, the alternatives are listed also. Since the most common type of analyzer is the scanning-filter type, the specifications which follow apply particularly to this type. Specifications for other types will be similar.

Center-frequency range. The range of signal frequencies which can be analyzed by the instrument. The tuning range of the instrument. This range may be covered by one or more bands.

Frequency Accuracy. The accuracy to which the tuning dial reads the frequency to which the analyzer is tuned.

Scan Width, Dispersion, or Spectrum Width. The band of frequencies over which the analyzer can be tuned electrically with the sawtooth-voltage generator. The horizontal scale on the cathode-ray tube. Scan width is usually adjustable from zero to some maximum.

Resolution, Filter Bandwidth, or IF Bandwidth. The frequency bandwidth (3 dB down from the peak) of the narrowest filter in the signal path of the analyzer. This number is approximately one-half the minimum frequency by which *equal*-amplitude signals must be separated to be analyzed. The bandwidth of the filter 60 dB down from the peak is always wider than the 3-dB bandwidth. The ratio of the 60-dB to the 3-dB bandwidth is call the *skirt factor* or *selectivity factor* and varies with the filter design. Two signals whose amplitude differs by 60 dB will need to be separated by more than one-half the 60-dB bandwidth to be resolved by the analyzer. The resolution of the narrower filters is useful for analysis only if the short-term frequency stability of the analyzer (residual FM) results in frequency variations less than the 3-dB bandwidth.

Frequency Response. The variation in amplitude which a constant-amplitude signal will appear to have as it is tuned through the frequency range of the analyzer. This is equivalent to the gain variation of the analyzer as its center frequency is varied.

Vertical-display Calibration. The *absolute vertical calibration* is the accuracy to which the absolute magnitude of the signal at the input may be measured. The *relative vertical calibration* is the accuracy to which a change in the magnitude of the input signal may be measured. The relative accuracy is always better than the absolute accuracy. The signal magnitude may be measured in volts, watts, or decibels relative to some reference voltage or power (see Front-Panel Terms).

Sensitivity. A measure of the minimum signal which can be detected by the analyzer. Sensitivity is specified in several ways. If the magnitude of the *minimum discernible* signal is specified, the filter bandwidth at which the measurement is made must be specified. Analyzer sensitivities so specified must be compared at the same bandwidth. If the sensitivity is specified in terms of *signal equal to noise* at the input (signal + noise = 3 dB above noise), the bandwidth must also be specified. This specification can be equated to that given at other bandwidths by multiplying the sensitivity in volts by ~3 or by adding 10 dB to the power for each 10X increase in filter bandwidth. Sensitivity is reduced as filter bandwidth is increased because a wider bandwidth allows more noise power to pass through the filter. This noise power is always present at the input to the analyzer. It is 114 dB below 1 mW for a 1-MHz filter bandwidth ($KTB = -114\ \text{dBm})|_{\text{MHz}}$. The noise power decreases by 10 dB each time the filter bandwidth is reduced by a factor of 10. Thus it is $-124\ \text{dBm}|_{100\text{kHz}}$, $-134\ \text{dBm}|_{10\text{kHz}}$, etc. A third method for specifying sensitivity is in terms of *noise figure*. This measure is independent of bandwidth. Noise figure tells how many decibels worse than a perfect analyzer the instrument is. A perfect analyzer is one which adds no additional noise to the always present thermal noise power at the input. By adding the noise figure to the thermal-noise-power level given above, the signal equal to noise sensitivity for that bandwidth is derived.

Maximum Input Level. This is the maximum signal power or voltage which may be applied at the input mixer or amplifier without causing more than a specific amount of distortion of signal compression (see Sources of Error).

Dynamic Range. Display dynamic range is the ratio in decibels of the signal which causes full-scale deflection to the one which causes deflection to the first major calibration point on the display. It tells the maximum amplitude difference between two signal levels which may be measured on the display at the same time.

Distortion dynamic range is the ratio in decibels of a signal equal to the noise power to one which is large enough for the nonlinear gain of the amplifier or mixer in the analyzer to distort. This number limits the distortion measurements which can be made on signals presented to the input of the analyzer. Smaller values of distortion cannot be made because of the distortion caused by the analyzer.

Often the ratio of the minimum detectable signal to the maximum input level is listed as a dynamic range. This is useful for knowing how far below the maximum input level measurements can be made.

Frequency Stability. The *long-term stability* of the analyzer is the magnitude and the rate at which the center frequency of the analyzer drifts with time and temperature. The *short-term stability* is the measure of residual frequency modulation and frequency noise which causes the center frequency of the analyzer to vary. In the heterodyne analyzer, both these stabilities are usually limited by the stability of the first local oscillator.

Spurious/Residual Response. A *spurious response* is a response on the analyzer resulting from a signal at the input but occurring when the analyzer is tuned to a frequency other than the frequency of the signal. These responses may result from limitations in the design, or they may be caused by distortion in the analyzer due to overdriving the input.

Residual responses are responses which occur when no signal is present at the input. These always result from limitations in the design.

FRONT-PANEL CONTROLS

The controls described here are those found on the scanning-filter spectrum analyzer with a cathode-ray-tube display. Other analyzer types will have similar controls. The information presented here should be sufficient to allow operation of most frequency-domain analyzers. The operating manual supplied with the instrument should be consulted for special controls and instructions.

Center-frequency Tuning. This is the main frequency-tuning control of the analyzer. It sets the center frequency of the band to be analyzed.

Centering (Frequency). This control is present only in heterodyne analyzers which scan with the second local oscillator. This control centers the scan with respect to the first filter (see Fig. 7). It may be used as a fine-tune control.

Frequency Range. On a multiband analyzer, this switch sets the frequency band of operation.

Scan Width, Dispersion, or Spectrum Width. This control adjusts the width of the frequency band to be scanned.

Resolution, Filter Bandwidth, or IF Bandwidth. This control adjusts the bandwidth of the narrowest filter through which the signal passes. There is an optimum setting for this control for the combination of scan width and scan rate which is set (see Electrical Problems and Sources of Error in Use).

RF Attenuation. This control sets the level of the signal reaching the first mixer or amplifier. It is used to prevent overloading the input and thus causing distortion. Ten decibels or more of rf attenuation usually improves the input impedance's match and should be used if sensitivity is not needed. Rf attenuation also reduces local-oscillator radiation out of the input.

IF Attenuation. This attenuator adjusts the level of the signal at some point after the scanning mixer/local oscillator. It is used to produce accurate shifts in the level of the signal displayed.

Presentation—Linear/Log/Square. This control adjusts the presentation so that the amplitude of the signal displayed is proportional to the voltage at the signal input (linear volts), the $\log_{10}$ of the voltage at the input (log, dB), or the power at the input (volts squared).

Video Gain. Adjusts the gain of the amplifier between the detector and the display. Used to set level only.

Video Bandwidth. This control is used in conjunction with the if bandwidth to filter noise in the display.

Scan Rate, Sweep. A control which sets the number of scans per second.

Stabilization. This is a system for reducing the drift and residual FM present in the analyzer. It is used for very narrow scan widths.

Trigger Mode. A switch which allows the sawtooth generator to free-run, be triggered by the power-line frequency, or single-sweep by pushing a button.

Scope Functions—Horizontal Positions, Vertical Position, Intensity, Focus, Storage Functions. These controls are identical to those found on an oscilloscope.

Intensifier or Base-line Clipper. This control allows the bottom of the cathode-ray tube to be blanked so that only signals above a set level will be displayed. It is used frequently when taking pictures of the display.

SOURCES OF ERROR

This first group of errors are those uniquely associated with the design. Care in using the analyzer will not prevent their occurrence or reduce their effect. As long as the user knows they exist, he can disregard them or calibrate them out as appropriate.

Multiple Responses. A superheterodyne analyzer of the type shown in Figs. 6 and 7 will respond to any signal whose frequency satisfies the following equation:

$$mf_s = nf_{\mathrm{LO}} \pm f_{\mathrm{filter}}$$

where m and n = integers starting at 1′
f_s = signal frequency
f_{LO} = local-oscillator frequency
f_{filter} = filter frequency (intermediate frequency)

This means that the analyzer is not tuned to one unique frequency but rather to a whole series of frequencies. The sensitivity of the analyzer at these various frequencies will vary greatly, but theoretically the analyzer will respond to any of them. If the input-signal level is low (less than −20 dBm), values of m other than 1 need not be considered (see the discussion of distortion below). Values of n other than 1 as well as both the $f_{\mathrm{LO}}+$ and $f_{\mathrm{LO}}-$ images are frequently used to extend the frequency range of the analyzer. These analyzers frequently include some method for identifying which value of n and which image is being used to receive a signal.

Analyzers which are designed to receive only a single band of frequencies will often use filters before the first mixer to filter out unwanted frequencies. These filters are called preselection filters. A preselection filter which tunes electrically along with the analyzer is sometimes available with multiband analyzers. This is a fine accessory to have when multiple responses would tend to confuse the user.

Amplitude Errors. The frequency-domain analyzer is used to measure signal amplitude vs. frequency. It is therefore somewhat suprising to discover that not all analyzers which measure below 10 MHz, and very few which measure above 10 MHz, have absolute amplitude calibration. Most analyzers are used to make relative measurements between signals rather than the absolute amplitude of the signal. To make accurate relative measurements, all that is needed is sufficient dynamic range and a good if attenuator. The attenuator can be used to calibrate the display, and as long as gain does not change during the measurement, good results can be obtained. To make accurate amplitude measurements, all the amplifiers and mixers must be gain-stable with time and temperature. In addition the mixers must have flat responses with frequency. Such instruments are difficult to build and are thus relatively expensive.

Any analyzer, calibrated or not, can be used to measure absolute amplitude by the substitution method. This is done by using the analyzer to measure the relative amplitude of the signal in question against the output of a calibrated signal generator at the same frequency. A high-quality signal generator can also be used to verify the vertical calibration and display accuracy of those analyzers which do have absolute vertical calibration.

Frequency Accuracy. The center-frequency accuracy of the analyzer and the accuracy of the scan-width control (if it is calibrated) should be checked periodically. A high-quality signal generator may be used if the frequency accuracy is known to exceed that of the analyzer. Reading the frequency of the generator with an electronic counter will assure this accuracy.

Another useful tool for checking the frequency accuracy of an analyzer is the comb generator. This instrument produces a very narrow pulse at a repetition rate which is derived from a highly accurate crystal oscillator. The Fourier transform of this pulse is a comb of signals nearly equal in amplitude up to a frequency of $\frac{2}{3} \times 1/\text{pulse width}$, and spaced in frequency equal to the repetition rate of the pulse. Such an instrument is much less expensive than the signal generator and counter combination and is equally accurate. The frequency comb has the added advantage of easily checking the scan-width accuracy and linearity as well as the center-frequency accuracy.

Spectral Purity. One of the important characteristics of an oscillator is spectral purity. A perfect oscillator would be one which had energy at a single frequency. No such oscillator ever exists. The output power of an oscillator is always distributed over a band of frequencies. Spectral purity refers to any quantity which describes the deviation of the oscillator from a perfect one.

The analyzer can be used to measure the spectral purity or the *power spectral density* of an oscillator. This is a plot of the oscillator's energy distribution as a function of frequency. Even if a scanning-type analyzer is used to measure the power spectral density of a near-perfect oscillator, the energy will not appear to be concentrated at a single frequency. This is so for two reasons. First, the analyzer always plots the response shape of its own filter as it tunes through a signal. Since the bandwidth of the filter is always finite and the skirts of the filter are never vertical, the oscillator signal will never appear narrower than this bandwidth.

The second limitation in measuring power spectral density is the stability of the analyzer itself. For a superheterodyne type, this is usually the stability of the first local oscillator. No oscillator being measured will ever appear more stable or spectrally more pure than the analyzer's oscillator. When the spectral purity of high-quality oscillators is being measured, the frequency analyzer cannot be used directly.

ELECTRICAL PROBLEMS AND SOURCES OF ERROR IN USE

Scanning-type frequency analyzers, unlike most other measuring instruments, can produce large errors if they are not used correctly. These errors can occur with no visual warning. They can, however, be detected by making some simple tests with the controls of the instrument. These errors and the tests for their detection will be described here.

Filter Rise-time Limitations. The narrow-bandwidth filter used in a frequency analyzer responds to a voltage applied as if the filter had electrical inertia. That is, the voltage in the filter builds up slowly when it is applied and decays slowly when it is removed. The rate of buildup and decay decreases as the bandwidth decreases. Thus, if a signal is applied to the filter for too short a duration, the voltage in the filter will not have time to reach a steady-state value. As a result, the indication of amplitude on the display will not be the true amplitude of the signal. This is an amplitude distortion caused by the limited rise time of the filters. This rise-time distortion occurs when the analyzer is scanning too fast for the filter bandwidth being used. The fast scan causes the signal to tune past the filter so quickly that the voltage buildup in the filter does not reach its peak. In extreme cases the response seems to broaden out as the scan rate is increased. This is caused by the slow decay of the voltage in the filter.

The test for rise-time distortion is to reduce either the scan rate or the scan width and note whether the response increases in amplitude. This should be continued until no further change in amplitude is noted. When this occurs, the analyzer is operating without rise-time distortion.

Rise-time distortion also occurs when the analyzer is being used to study the spectrum of narrow pulses. In this case the distortion cannot be eliminated by changing scan width or scan rate. It is an inherent part of the measurement if the pulse is to be analyzed. Thus, the amplitude display cannot be used to measure the height of the pulse directly. The magnitude of the amplitude distortion must be calculated and added to the display amplitude to determine the true pulse amplitude. Fortunately this measurement is seldom made. The relative amplitude of the various spectral components of the pulse will still be correct, and this is the information normally sought.

Harmonic and Intermodulation Distortion. If a low-level signal with no harmonic content other than the fundamental component (no harmonic distortion) is applied to the input of the analyzer, only one response at the fundamental frequency will be displayed (excluding spurious responses). As the level of the signal is increased, a point will be reached where the second harmonic of the signal begins to appear on the display. For each decibel increase in the level of the signal, the second-harmonic response will increase 2 dB. This is *harmonic distortion* caused by the nonlinearity of the amplifiers and mixers in the analyzer. If the signal level is increased still further, the third, fourth, fifth, etc., harmonics will appear. Each of these distortion responses will appear to increase in level faster than the fundamental signal.

The test to determine if a response on the analyzer is caused by distortion in the analyzer itself is to change the level of the input signal by a known amount. This is most conveniently done with the input or rf attenuator. If the change in the level of the response is different from the input-signal-level change, the response is caused in part by distortion in the analyzer. The input-signal level should be decreased until the change in signal level and the change in response level are the same. When this level is reached, the response is a true response and is not caused by distortion in the analyzer. This test should be made whenever the analyzer is being used to measure the harmonic content of a signal.

A second type of distortion occurs when the analyzer is being overdriven by two signals. In this case the distortion responses result from the mixing of the two signals in the nonlinear amplifiers or mixers. This is called *intermodulation distortion.* Two examples of this are shown in Fig. 8. The test for intermodulation distortion is the same as the test for harmonic distortion.

Mismatch Losses. One of the important sources of error in measuring the level of a signal is impedance mismatch between the signal source and the analyzer input. This is especially important above a few megahertz where the input to the analyzer is designed to be a low impedance. For low-frequency analyzers with high input impedances, mismatch is not as important as input-impedance changes with frequency.

Suppose that the signal-level variation of a tunable oscillator is being measured with a low-input-impedance analyzer. In order for the measurement to be accurate, all the signal power available from the source must be delivered to the input of the analyzer. If this is to happen, the input impedance of the analyzer must be the conjugate of the source, or alternatively, the mismatch must not change as the frequency is varied.

There is no simple test for mismatch error which can be made using the analyzer controls. The safest policy is to "pad" the input with a resistive attenuator to assure a constant input impedance as a function of frequency. A 10- to 20-dB pad is sufficient. The input or rf attenuator may be used for this purpose.

Radio-frequency Interference. Frequency analyzers can be both a source and a receiver of radio-frequency interference (RFI). In many analyzer designs the first local oscillator which controls the first mixer may present a fairly high level

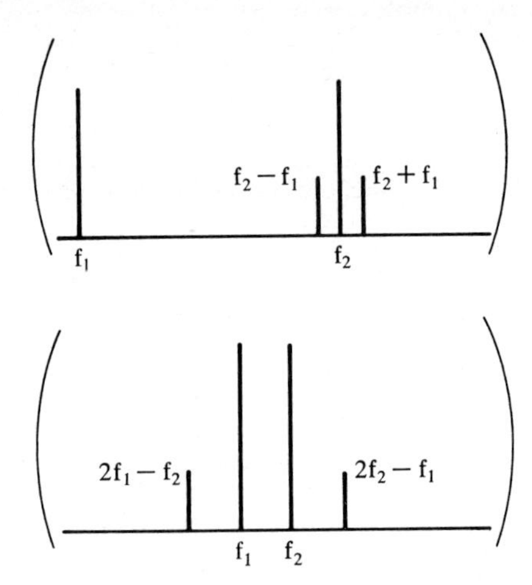

Fig. 8. Spurious distortion signals caused by mixing of signals at f_1 and f_2.

voltage at the input to the analyzer. If a broadband antenna is connected to the input, it may radiate this local-oscillator signal. A filter at the input which passes the desired signal into the analyzer but rejects the local-oscillator signal coming out of the analyzer will help to reduce the radiation. Attenuation at the input will also help.

If the analyzer is not well shielded and it is placed in a high electromagnetic field, it may receive signals even though nothing is connected to the input. Close radio or television stations may be received in this manner. Even with a well-shielded analyzer the device under test may act as an antenna to these strong signals and present them to the input of the analyzer. A test for this is to turn off the equipment under test but leave it connected to the analyzer. Tuning the analyzer across its range at maximum sensitivity will reveal these signals. Often measurements must be made in a shielded screen room to prevent this type of interference. Using good shielded rf cables to connect the analyzer to the device under test and watching ground loops through the power cables will help to reduce RFI in normal environments.

Chapter 35

Frequency-standard and Timekeeping Instruments

MARVIN J. WILLRODT

Hewlett-Packard Company, Santa Clara, California

EARLY REQUIREMENTS

Early man had little use for frequency standards as such but rather was interested in time to keep track of events which affected his life. The rotation of the earth gave him an easily recognizable unit one day long. As he felt need for more resolution in time measurement, he invented devices which registered time in terms of a burning rate as with a candle, material flow rate such as water or sand through an hourglass-like device, or oscillation of a mechanical device such as a pendulum.

The pendulum has a natural frequency of oscillation, each cycle of which requires a specific interval of time. These cycles could be counted to measure time, or one pendulum could be compared with another to see if they had the same frequency. As man's needs became more exacting, various other kinds of mechanical oscillators were built. Finally, with the coming of the age of electronics, oscillations were generated first by an electric arc, then with the vacuum tube, and now using solid-state devices, with appropriate circuitry. Stability of mechanical vibrations reaches the ultimate in a mechanically vibrating quartz crystal coupled to electronic circuitry to sustain continuous oscillation; however, the best of these oscillators exhibit a change of a few parts in 10^{12} per day even when carefully controlled (see Fig. 1). Good as these devices are, they are not primary frequency standards, as they do exhibit an aging rate, that is, a change in frequency with time, and the frequency can be influenced by outside factors such as temperature, vibration, or variation in the electronic driving circuitry. As a result the quartz oscillator must be compared with some other reference to establish its frequency and aging rate.

The space age has ushered in new requirements for accurate frequency and time control, as time errors which may seem small here on earth become disastrously large when multiplied by the enormous distances involved.

Since the reciprocal of frequency is a time interval, the first requirement of a time "standard" is an ultrastable oscillator.

Time, one of the three quantities basic to the meter-kilogram-second (mks) system of physical measurement, can be kept with unprecedented accuracy by driving a clock mechanism with electrical pulses generated by one of these extremely stable electronic oscillators. Frequency standards having an absolute accuracy of a few parts in 10^{12} and a stability of parts in 10^{13} achieve this performance through use of atomic-resonance control by utilizing quantum-mechanical effects in the energy states of matter, particular transitions between energy states corresponding to specific microwave frequencies.

FREQUENCY STANDARDS

1. Primary Standards Primary frequency standards are those which require no other reference for calibration. If a primary standard can be put into operation, as indicated by a correct reading on a built-in meter, the output frequency of the device will be within its specified accuracy. Two primary standards which have reached a high state of development are the cesium-beam standard and the hydrogen maser.

In 1964, the Twelfth General Conference of Weights and Measures adopted as the standard of frequency an atomic transition, specifically a hyperfine transition of an atom of cesium 133, and assigned the value 9,192,631,770 Hz to this transition.

The cesium-beam tube is utilized as a passive resonator; that is, the frequency of 9,192,631,770 is synthesized from a quartz oscillator whose frequency is continuously adjusted via feedback control circuits to keep the synthesized frequency in

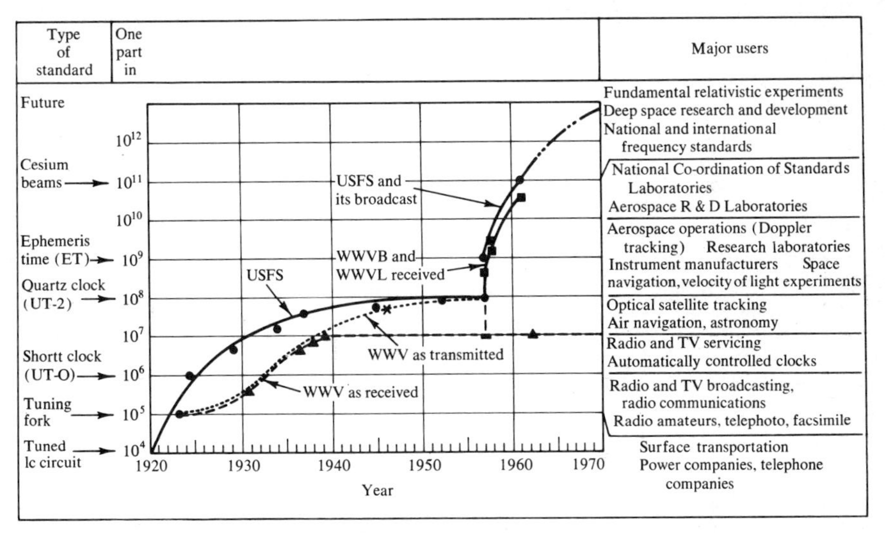

Fig. 1. Improvements in the precision of the U.S. frequency standards (USFS) and its dissemination. *(From Precision of the U.S. Frequency Standard, NBS Tech. News Bull., vol. 48, no. 2, p. 31, February, 1964.)*

exact agreement with the atomic-transition frequency of the cesium-beam tube.* The crystal-oscillator frequency, normally 1, 2, or 5 MHz, then has the same absolute accuracy as the cesium transition.

A time interval of great uniformity based on this transition has been defined as the "atomic second." This second is in as close agreement as is experimentally possible with an earlier definition based on the motion of the earth about the sun, ephemeris time (ET), established by the International Committee of Weights and Measures in October, 1956.

Cesium-beam-tube frequency standards have come into widespread use, as they provide a moderate-sized, rugged, portable primary standard with an absolute accuracy of 1 part in 10^{11} or better.

The hydrogen maser is an active primary frequency standard. In operation, this device generates a frequency of 1,420,405,751.778 Hz with an absolute accuracy in the order of parts in $10.^{13}$ Because hydrogen masers are much larger and more expensive than cesium standards and not as reliable, they have not come into general use.

2. Secondary Standards The rubidium-vapor frequency standard is a passive standard based on a hyperfine transition in Rb^{87}. A frequency of 6,835 MHz synthesized from a quartz oscillator is compared with the Rb^{87} resonance using

* Cesium Beam Frequency Standard, *Hewlett-Packard Company Publication* 02177-2.

an optical-pumping technique. A feedback control circuit continuously adjusts the quartz-crystal frequency to keep the synthesized 6,835 MHz exactly matched to the rubidium transition frequency.

The rubidium-vapor standard is a secondary standard because it is not self-calibrating. Once constructed, it must be compared with a cesium or some other primary standard to determine its exact frequency. Also, the rubidium standard has an aging rate of 1 or 2 parts in 10^{11} per month and so must be checked periodically to determine its frequency and aging rate. Since a well-designed rubidium standard has very good short-term stability, it is a good choice if the output is to be multiplied up into the microwave region. Cost of a rubidium frequency standard is about half that of a cesium-beam frequency standard, and so it offers a good tradeoff between cost and performance which is adequate for many calibration facilities.

3. Quartz-crystal Oscillators Crystalline quartz has great mechanical and chemical stability. It also has a small elastic hysteresis, which means that just a small amount of energy is required to sustain oscillation; hence the frequency of mechanical vibration is only very slightly affected by variable external conditions. The electrical and mechanical properties are linked by the piezoelectric effect; that is, when a quartz crystal is stressed mechanically, an electric potential is induced in nearby conductors; conversely, when such a crystal is placed in an electric field, it is deformed by a small amount proportional to the field strength and polarity. This piezoelectric effect makes it easy to use one of these quartz crystals in an electronic oscillator circuit.

Since the crystal is vibrating mechanically, the physical size determines its frequency; the larger the crystal, the lower its frequency. When very stable operation is necessary, the crystal is enclosed by a temperature-controlled oven. With constant temperature, the physical dimensions of the crystal stay constant, as does its vibrating frequency. The angle at which the crystal was cut from the piece of raw quartz also influences its behavior with temperature change. Careful orientation of the cut yields a crystal which has very small frequency change with temperature.

Quartz-crystal oscillators are available for frequencies below 50 kHz up to several hundred megahertz. Stability can vary 1 part in 10^4 up to 1 part in 10^{12} per day, depending on the type of crystal, its mounting, and the electronic circuitry used with it.

CALIBRATION

All secondary frequency standards require periodic calibration, first to establish the correct frequency and second to keep check on the frequency change with time, to establish an aging rate for the standard. Published specifications on a frequency standard show what the worst limits of performance will be; however, many standards do far better than this minimum performance, particularly when permanently mounted in a location free of shock and vibration, of constant temperature, and with constant line voltage such as one might find in a typical laboratory installation.

The actual aging rate of a standard is the number to use in all calibration work provided continuous records are maintained using reasonable procedures showing traceability to a recognized primary standard.

Even with primary standards, it is desirable to maintain a continuous record of performance of the standard with respect to the U.S. frequency standard to ensure the operator that there is no malfunction in his standard.

REFERENCES FOR FREQUENCY COMPARISON*

4. WWV and WWVH WWV, the U.S. Bureau of Standards station at Ft. Collins, Colo., and WWVH, at Maui, Hawaii, broadcast standard frequencies in the high-

* NBS Frequency and Time Broadcast Services—Radio Stations WWV, WWVH, WWVB and WWVL, U.S. Department of Commerce, National Bureau of Standards, *Spec. Publ.* 236.

frequency bands. See Fig. 2 for an example of the calibration system. These frequencies are offset from atomic time* to correspond to the universal time (UT) time scale. Although accurate to 2 parts in 10^{11} or better as transmitted, these frequencies will usually not be as accurate at the receiver location because of Doppler shift. The error may approach 1 part in 10^7 under worst conditions. Doppler shift occurs when the transmission path is by way of a reflecting layer, as in Figs. 3 and 4. The reflecting layers are not stationary—being influenced by sunspots and transition from day to night, among other things. This motion gives

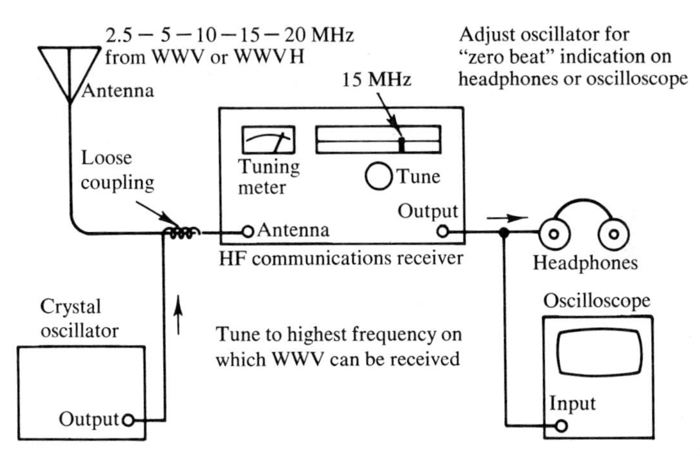

Fig. 2. Calibration of crystal oscillator against WWV or WWVH high-frequency transmission. This procedure is good only for calibrating an oscillator to 1 part in a million or so. This corresponds to an error of only 1 Hz in determining true zero beat.

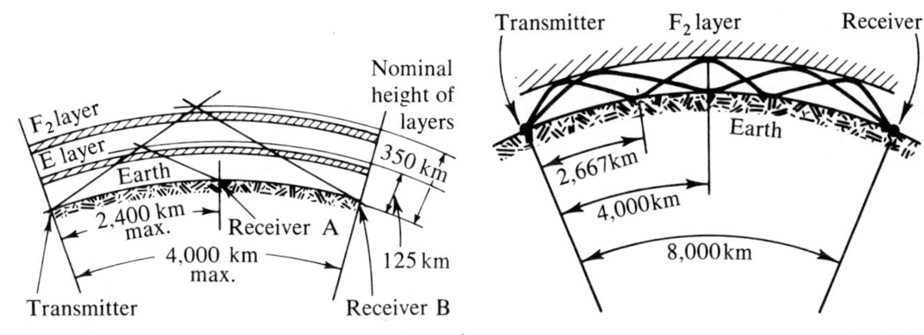

Fig. 3. Single-hop sky-wave paths for high-frequency transmission. *E* layer exists only in daytime; F_2 layer is for long-distance high-frequency transmissions.

Fig. 4. Multiple-hop transmission paths for high-frequency transmission.

rise to Doppler shift, a change in the received frequency with respect to the transmitted frequency whenever the reflecting layer is moving, the received frequency being higher than transmitted when the reflecting layer is moving down because the cycles of the rf signals are "squeezed together." Likewise, when the layer is moving up, the received frequency is too low.

The Doppler error can approach 1 part in 10^7 under worst conditions; so these transmissions are not satisfactory for setting the frequency of a high-accuracy standard. Since these transmissions are readily available using a communications receiver, they are useful for setting moderate-stability standards to 1 part in 10^6

* Prior to January 1, 1972.

or 10^7 at any time. Better accuracy can be achieved, but only with a carefully planned comparison program which may take days or weeks. WWVL or WWVH can also be used to check a high-stability frequency standard for gross failure as indicated by disagreement of greater than 1 part in 10^7; however, if the local standard is within 1 part in 10^7 or better of the high-frequency transmission, it should not be corrected, as the difference could be due to Doppler shift. All the better frequency standards, and many present-day electronic counters, have quartz oscillators with aging rates between a few parts in 10^9 and parts in 10^{11} per day. An oscillator with an aging rate of 1 part in 10^{10} per day could operate for 500 to 1,000 days before it would accumulate as much error as is caused by the Doppler shift when conditions are bad.

5. WWVB, the U.S. Frequency Standard (USFS) This standard is maintained by the National Bureau of Standards (NBS) and is broadcast from Ft. Collins, Colo., on 60 kHz referenced to atomic time. A 60-kHz receiver with a strip-chart recorder which continuously plots the phase of the local standard compared with WWVB is the easiest way to establish frequency precisely. WWVL on 20 kHz can also be used. However, the broadcast format is changed from time to time; so a current schedule should be consulted before this station is used. An accuracy of 1 part in 10^9 can be established in less than 1 h; 1 part in 10^{10} during daylight working hours, and 2 or 3 parts in 10^{11} in 24 h using WWVB transmission with normal signal conditions in the continental United States.

6. U.S. Naval Observatory The observatory maintains a master clock which is compared with observations for universal time made on each clear night using special photographic equipment. Frequencies based on UT are broadcast by several navy stations located around the world.

7. Any Frequency of Known Accuracy A second frequency of known accuracy can also be used as a reference for comparison or calibration purposes.

WAYS OF MAKING PRECISION FREQUENCY COMPARISONS

8. Phase Comparison A phase comparison between the WWVB 60-kHz signal, the U.S. frequency standard (USFS), and a 60-kHz signal generated by the local standard is the most generally used method of establishing accurate traceability to NBS. Phase comparison is used because, with good oscillators, the discrepancies will be in terms of a small fraction of a cycle rather than in terms of cycles. Figure 5 shows a typical very-low-frequency (vlf) phase-comparator system. The receiver is a high-gain narrowband tuned radio-frequency unit using a loop antenna to cut out electrostatic interference and also for its directional characteristics. A 60-kHz output synthesized from the local frequency standard is compared with the 60 kHz from WWVB using a linear-phase comparator circuit with the phase difference on a strip-chart recorder. A strip-chart recorder is essential when making an over-the-air comparison like this, as the transmissions are subject to different delays between day and night, may have seasonal variations, and may be bothered by electrical interference even at this low frequency. A continuous record shows all the variations occurring throughout each 24-h interval so the operator can visually scan the record for the time of most consistent reception to make the comparison. In general, the high-accuracy comparison should be made at the same time each day, as the transmission path will be essentially the same. Temperature, line voltage, and other environmental factors which can affect the local standard are also more apt to be the same than if done at different hours of the day.

A vlf comparator of the type shown in Fig. 5 can be used for comparing two frequency standards as well as for making comparisons with WWVB. Without the variations introduced by the radio link, high-accuracy comparisons can be made in a much shorter time. Some units have two scales and so can be used to compare very stable standards as well as those which are not quite so good. A comparator with 50 μs full scale and 1 in./h chart speed is useful for checking oscillators which deviate by not more than 1 part in 10^7, while comparators with

$16\frac{2}{3}$ μs full scale can be used for oscillators which deviate by not more than 1 part in 10^8. For oscillators with greater deviation, the slope of the trace on the strip chart becomes too steep to interpret. The 100-kHz output is useful for checking poorer oscillators using either Lissajous patterns or a triggered sweep-comparison technique.

Interpretation of the phase-comparison chart requires determining the phase change between the oscillator under test and the reference standard and relating this to

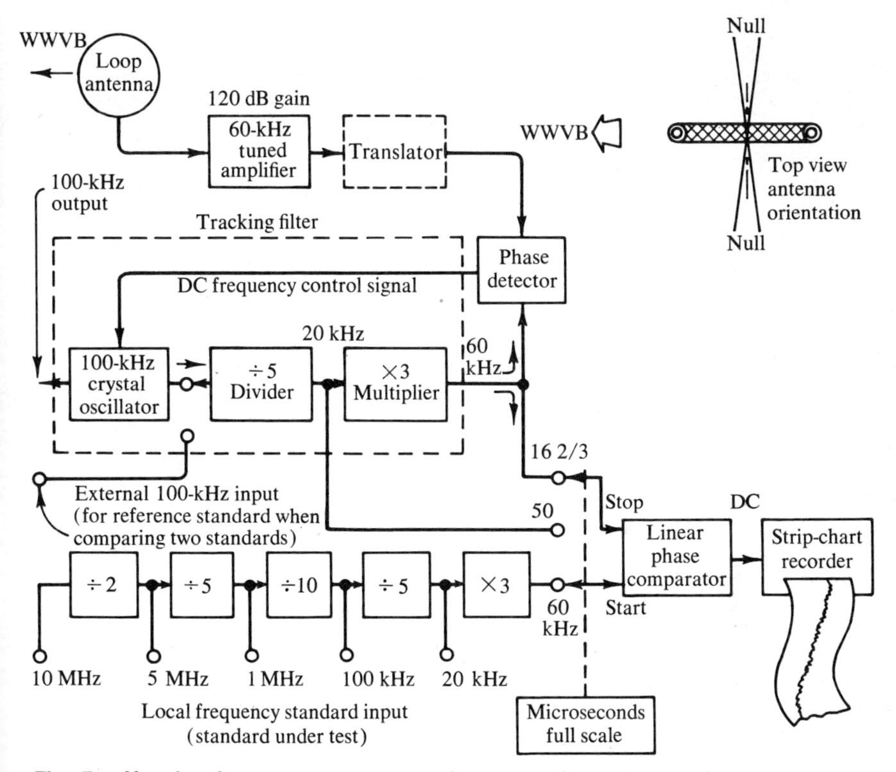

Fig. 5. Very-low-frequency comparator for comparison of local frequency standard with U.S. frequency standard on 60 kHz. Use translator if local frequency standard is to be offset from WWVB transmission.

the time it took for the change (see Fig. 6). Some useful numbers for making this comparison are

$$\begin{aligned} 1 \text{ day} &= 8.64 \times 10^{10}\ \mu\text{s} \approx 1 \times 10^{11}\ \mu\text{s} \\ 3 \text{ h} &= 1.08 \times 10^{10}\ \mu\text{s} \approx 1 \times 10^{10}\ \mu\text{s} \\ 1 \text{ h} &= 3.6 \times 10^{9}\ \mu\text{s} \\ 15 \text{ min} &= 9.0 \times 10^{8}\ \mu\text{s} \approx 1 \times 10^{9}\ \mu\text{s} \\ 1 \text{ min} &= 6.0 \times 10^{7}\ \mu\text{s} \end{aligned}$$

The period of one cycle of

$$\begin{aligned} 20 \text{ kHz} &= 50\ \mu\text{s} \\ 60 \text{ kHz} &= 16\tfrac{2}{3}\ \mu\text{s} \\ 100 \text{ kHz} &= 10\ \mu\text{s} \\ 1 \text{ MHz} &= 1\ \mu\text{s} \\ 5 \text{ MHz} &= 0.2\ \mu\text{s} \end{aligned}$$

Deviation is calculated by dividing the change in phase by the time required for the change to occur. For example, if a 1-MHz oscillator exhibited a phase change of 18 μs in 15 min when compared with a reference frequency, the deviation from the reference frequency would be

$$\frac{18\ \mu\text{s phase change}}{9.0 \times 10^8\ \mu\text{s in 15 min}} = \frac{2}{10^8} = 2 \times 10^{-8} \text{ or } = 2 \text{ parts in } 10^8$$

Similarly, a 1-μs change in 24 h represents a deviation of approximately 1 part in 10^{11} between standards, and a change of 1 μs in 15 min represents approximately 1 part in 10^9.

Aging of very stable standards can be determined by reading the offset with respect to the reference standard for the same 15-min interval on successive days and then subtracting the results to get the change in 24 h.

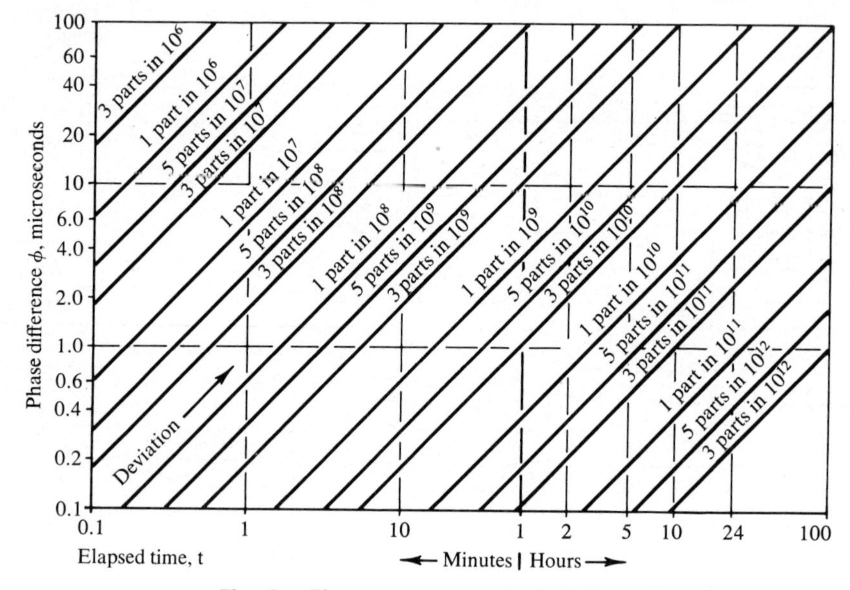

Fig. 6. Phase-measurement resolution.

Some vlf comparators come with a transparent template which can be placed over the strip chart to read offset directly without going through any calculations. For very low aging rates—below 3 parts in 10^{10} per day or so—one still has to go through the calculations, as the slope of the aging curve becomes so small that it cannot be easily read with a template.

Figure 7 shows a typical plot of a frequency standard compared with WWVB, and Fig. 8 has additional information on interpreting phase recordings. Some precautions are in order when using a vlf comparator system, as shown in Fig. 5.

1. The receiver portion of the system has sensitivity to 1 μV or so; therefore, it can lock on to a 60-kHz harmonic of 5, 10, 15, 20, or 30 kHz generated by other equipment. The antenna should be well removed from other equipment or signal lines to prevent this. Also, the loop antenna exhibits a sharp null; so it can be rotated to null an undesired signal without appreciably affecting the WWVB signal, since a 45° misalignment drops the signal by only 3 dB.

2. The WWVH signal can be recognized on the phase plot, as its phase is advanced 45° for 5 min once per hour at 10 min after the hour as in Fig. 7.

3. Abnormalities sometimes occur in standard-frequency broadcasts. These are

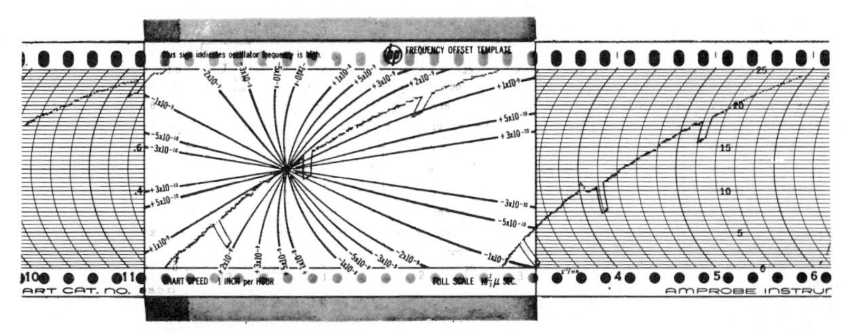

Fig. 7. Phase comparison between a local crystal frequency standard and WWVB. Offset at 1 P.M. is approximately +1.3 parts in 10^9, also written as $+1.3 \times 10^{-9}$.

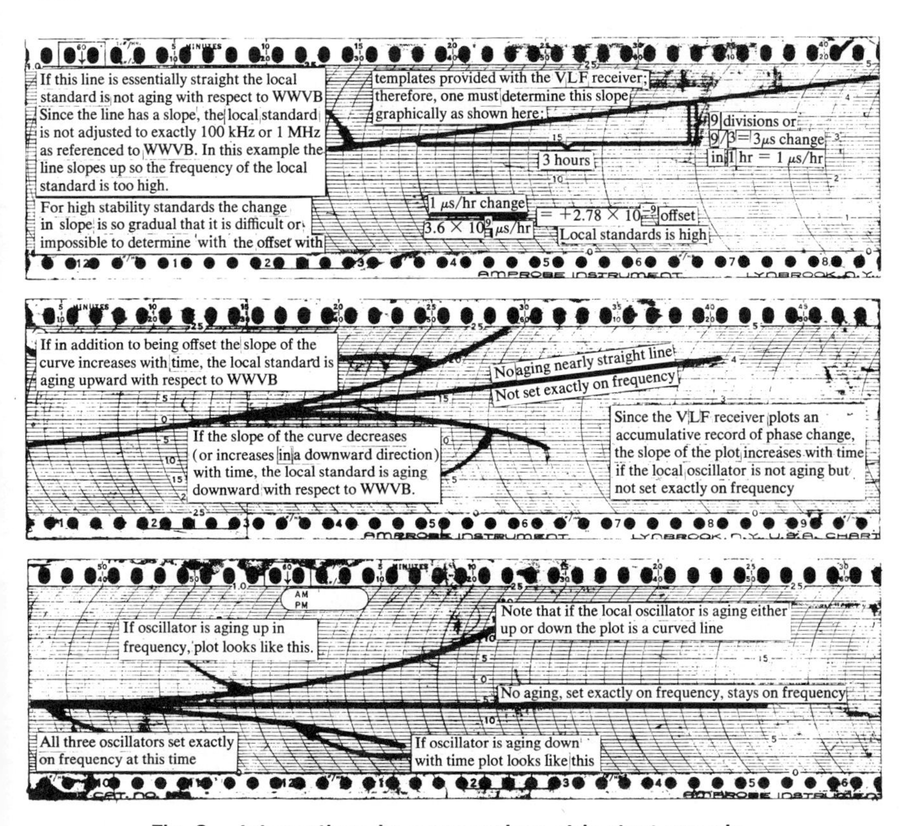

Fig. 8. Interpreting phase-comparison strip-chart records.

noted in a bulletin* put out by NBS. Anyone making measurements on high-stability high-precision frequency standards should subscribe to this bulletin. The U.S. Naval Observatory also puts out a time and frequency bulletin.†

* *NBS Time and Frequency Services Bulletin.* Subscription information can be obtained by writing to the Chief, Time and Frequency Division, National Bureau of Standards, Boulder, Colo. 80302.

† *Time and Frequency Bulletin,* Naval Observatory, Washington, D.C. 20390.

4. When a frequency-offset template is used, the center of the template must be at the center of the chart when records are read from recorders which draw an arc rather than a straight line to span the chart, or results will be in error.

9. Linear-phase Detector Operation of a linear-phase detector is very similar to that of the vlf receiver-comparator just described except that the unit has no radio-frequency amplifier and detector or filter section. The filter section is not necessary as it was in the receiver to reduce the noise introduced by the radio link. A linear-phase detector is shown in Fig. 9.

The two frequencies to be compared must be the same; the system will not work with a 100-kHz reference input and a 1-MHz local input, for example. The signals are amplified, shaped, and used to drive Schmitt triggers; a pulse from the local input channel then turns the flip-flop on, which drives the strip chart or phase-indicating meter to full scale. A pulse from the reference input channel turns the flip-flop off, which drives the meter to zero. The rectangular output waveform of the flip-flop in Fig. 9*b* is averaged by the strip-chart recorder or meter. A pulse which stays on for half of the 10-μs interval (10 μs is the period of 100 kHz and is equal to 360° of phase shift) would cause the strip-chart recorder to read half scale or 180° shift. Similarly if the on and off occur very close together as at *e*, the chart recorder will be near zero and the two signals will be nearly in phase. When on and off occur very far apart as at *f*, the chart recorder will be near full scale, representing almost 360° of phase shift. Note the chart recorder never goes off scale. As soon as it reaches 360° (full scale), further drift in the unknown takes it beyond 360°, which is near 0° on the next cycle; so the recorder merely goes to the opposite edge of the paper and starts over again. On and off inputs are assigned so that a higher meter reading indicates that the local input frequency is above the reference-input frequency. To get total phase change, one has to count up the number of times the recorder crosses the chart for total full-cycle change, as well as the partial-cycle change between start and finish.

If the local frequency is exactly the same as the reference, the pulse width *d* will remain constant. If the local frequency is low with respect to the reference, pulse width will decrease as at *e*, or if the local frequency is high with respect to the reference, the pulse width will increase as at *f*.

This linear-phase detector can be used to compare standards at any other frequency by down-converting the input frequencies of the 100 kHz required by a comparator using a heterodyne down converter consisting of a mixer in each channel driven by the same local oscillator. Mixers rather than frequency dividers are used in each channel, as they down-convert the input frequencies to 100 kHz without decreasing the phase change proportionally, as would a frequency divider. A common local oscillator is mandatory to cancel out the effects of local-oscillator drift. For 1-MHz inputs, the local-oscillator frequency is 900 kHz, and full scale on the chart becomes 1.0 μs; for 5-MHz input, the local-oscillator frequency is 4,900 kHz, and full scale on the chart becomes 0.2 μs full scale. A 1-μs change, five times across the chart, in 24 h equals approximately 1 part in 10^{11} deviation between the two input frequencies; so the system is capable of high resolution in a short time, particularly when comparing high-frequency inputs.

10. Vector Voltmeter A vector voltmeter is a phasemeter and as such is a convenient instrument for comparing frequency standards.* A 1° phase change in 1 s = $1°/360° \times 1$ Hz = 2.77×10^{-3} Hz change. At 5.0 MHz this becomes 2.77×10^{-3} Hz/5.0×10^{6} Hz = $0.55 \times 10^{-9} = 5.5 \times 10^{-10}$ or 5.5 parts in 10^{10} for a 1° change in phasemeter reading in 1 s. A change of 0.1° in 1 s is 5.5 parts in 10^{11}, in 10 s is 5.5 parts in 10^{12}, and in 100 s is 5.5 parts in 10^{13}; so a phasemeter makes an excellent instrument for making a high-resolution comparison of frequencies very rapidly. This system is easily checked by feeding the same signal to both inputs. Any change in the phasemeter reading is drift in the measuring system

* *Precision Frequency Comparison Application Note* 77-2, Hewlett-Packard Co., Palo Alto, Calif.

itself. Many phasemeters have a dc output proportional to phase difference which can be used to drive a strip-chart recorder, as discussed earlier. Chart interpretation is the same as for the vlf comparator discussed earlier.

11. Triggered Sweep Oscilloscope A triggered sweep oscilloscope can also be used to make a comparison between an oscillator and a reference frequency as

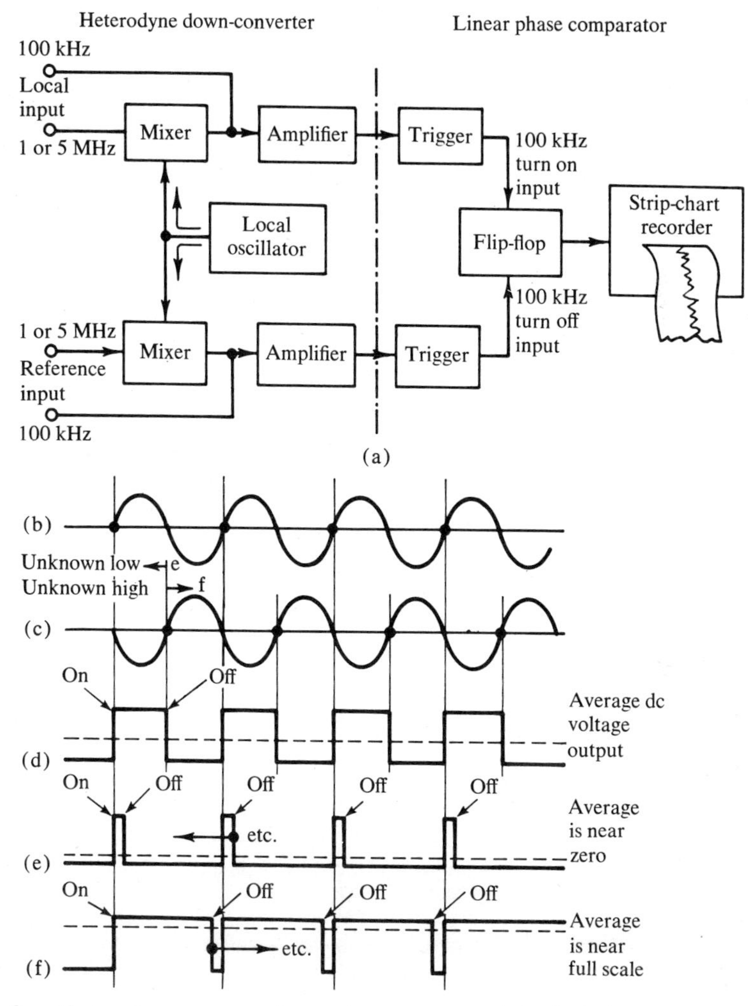

Fig. 9. Linear-phase comparator and waveforms. (*a*) Block diagram, full scale: 100 kHz = 10 μs, 1.0 MHz = 1 μs, 5.0 MHz = 0.2 μs. (*b*) Local input (turn on). (*c*) Reference input (turn off). (*d*) Output of flip-flop. (*e*) Output of flip-flop if phase decreases. (*f*) Output of flip-flop if phase increases.

in Fig. 10. This technique is useful because it gives the operator an analog indication of both magnitude of deviation and indicates if the oscillator under test is higher or lower in frequency than the reference. Comparisons to a part in 10^9 or 10^{10} can be established in a few minutes. Any error in oscilloscope sweep speed is a "second-order error"; that is, it is not added directly to the unknown frequency but may be decreased by a million to one or more depending on the frequency of the unknown oscillator. Also, when the unknown frequency is in agreement with the reference frequency, the pattern is stationary so that this error no longer enters in. Also an error in timing the movement of the pattern is a second-order error. Jitter and instability in the oscilloscope sweep are easily checked by connecting the Y (vertical) input of the oscilloscope to the reference standard. The pattern should remain stationary. If not, any movement or jitter is in the oscilloscope itself. This is the easiest way for most calibration and test facilities to set an unknown oscillator to a reference. About the only disadvantage of this system is that it is not feasible to drive a strip-chart recorder from it; so there is no easy way to get a permanent record of the calibration process.

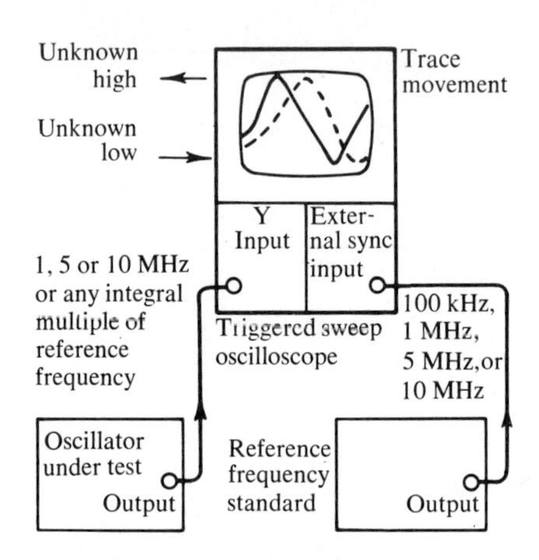

Calibration

Movement	Sweep speed			Notes
	1 μs/cm	0.1 μs/cm	0.01 μs/cm	
1 cm/s	1×10^{-6}	1×10^{-7}	1×10^{-8}	Time scope trace movement with second hand of watch or clock
1 cm/10 s	1×10^{-7}	1×10^{-8}	1×10^{-9}	
1 cm/100 s	1×10^{-8}	1×10^{-9}	1×10^{-10}	

Fig. 10. Precision frequency comparison between unknown oscillator and reference standard using triggered sweep oscilloscope.

12. Lissajous Patterns These can also be used as discussed in Chapter 33. However, pattern motion is so slow if the input signals are close in frequency that the time required for a comparison becomes impractically long.

13. Frequency Multiplication Even though an electronic counter makes frequency measurement very easy even when used by an unskilled operator, it is not useful for comparing or setting frequency standards without the use of auxiliary equipment because of the possible ±1 count error inherent in all frequency measurements. When measuring a 1.0-MHz oscillator, for example, on a 1-s gate, the ±1 count error is 1/1,000,000, or 1×10^{-6}. For a 10-s gate this becomes 1/10,000,000, or 1×10^{-7}. It becomes apparent that one could need a 100-s 1.6-min or a 1,000-s 16.6-min gate to achieve 1×10^{8} or 1×10^{9} accuracy in the measurement. Counters can be built with long gates; however, the long measurement time required for each reading makes it very difficult to set an oscillator on frequency. The operator really needs an analog output so the results of each change in the "fine" adjustment are immediately apparent and he knows if he is going in the correct direction. With a long gate time, the reading will inevitably overflow the counter readout capacity (1.0 MHz in a 100-s gate would give a count of 1,000,000.000 Hz, for example), but this is not a drawback, since only the digits to the right of the decimal point will be changing if the oscillator is stable.

The measurement can be speeded up by using a frequency multiplier of the type shown in Fig. 11 between the local-standard oscillator under test and the counter. The reference oscillator is used to drive the counter time base. For a 1.0-MHz oscillator, each cycle is multiplied by 100, 1,000, or 10,000. The multiplied output at 100 MHz can be read with a high-frequency counter, above that with a counter and heterodyne converter. A phase-locked transfer oscillator or an automatic divider is not suitable for this measurement, as either process makes a tradeoff between resolution and measurement time. Only the heterodyne counter gives the necessary high-frequency measuring capability without losing resolution. If the 1.0 MHz is multiplied to 1.0 GHz and read with a heterodyne counter, the result will be 950 MHz from the dial setting on the converter plus 50.000 000 MHz read on the counter or 1000.000 000 MHz. The ± 1 count error for this input is 1/1,000,000,000, or 1×10^{-9}, in a 1-s measuring time and would be 1×10^{-10}

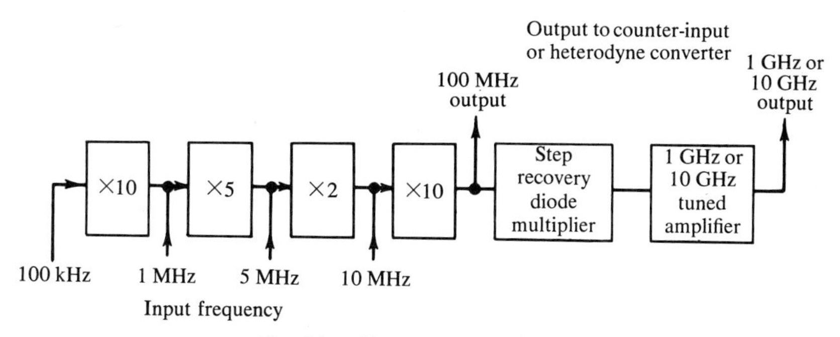

Fig. 11. Frequency multiplier.

for a 10-s measuring time. For a 10.0-GHz frequency each of these measurements would give 10 times more resolution.

This technique is an easy one to understand, since it in effect merely adds more digits to the right of the decimal point of the unknown frequency. Thus it is necessary only to subtract the frequency read by the counter from the frequency desired to determine both the magnitude and direction of the deviation.

The only requirement on the multiplier circuits is that they multiply the number of zero-axis crossings of the input waveform by the numbers indicated without introducing any spurious crossings and the output voltage adequate to drive the counter input. Output impedance should be 50 Ω to match the interconnecting cable.

An electronic counter which can interpolate by as far as 1,000:1 on the ± 1 count error of a conventional counter is useful in checking the comparing frequency standards, as it can resolve 1 part in 10^9 in 1 s.* This is adequate for all except the most exacting requirements. Results are easy to interpret, as the operator merely compares the counter reading with the input frequency he wants. A simple subtraction tells him how far he is off. Counters supplied with a keyboard can be programmed to subtract out the desired frequency, in which case the counter indicates directly the deviation and direction the operator is from the frequency he wants.

* Precision Frequency Measurements, *Application Note* 116, Hewlett-Packard Co., Palo Alto, Calif.

Many of the better electronic counters have quartz oscillators with parts in 10^9 or parts in 10^{10} per day stability and so can be used as the reference standard for calibrating oscillators which are not specified as close as that. A vlf comparator receiver should be used to maintain a comparison either periodically or continuously between the oscillator in the counter and the U.S. frequency standard, WWVB.

14. Offset Standard The offset-standard technique diagramed in Fig. 12 offers a convenient way of evaluating and adjusting high-stability oscillators, particularly in production testing of instruments or in calibration centers, since a given change in the reading of the electronic counter or a strip-chart record of its readings represents directly the deviation between two frequencies so that no calculations are necessary when interpreting the results even when an oscillator is checked to parts in 10^8, 10^9, or 10^{10}. This technique does, however, require a stable reference standard which can be set off frequency by some known amount, for example, +1 Hz at 1 MHz (1.000001 MHz). Initial offset is established at any desired

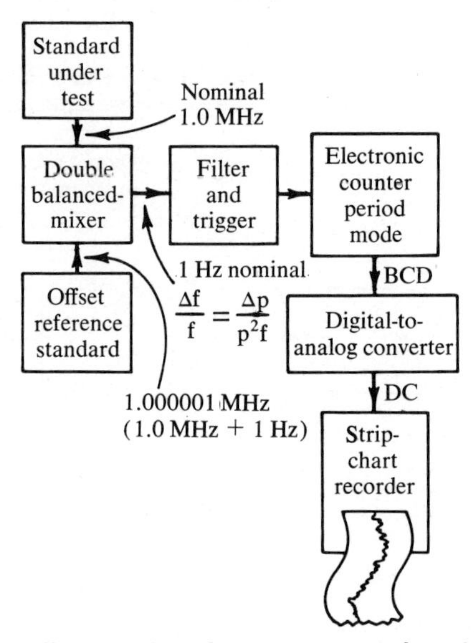

Fig. 12. Offset-standard frequency-comparison technique.

frequency by comparing the offset standard with a reference standard set exactly on frequency.

The example below shows the scale-factor calculation when a 1.0-MHz oscillator is compared with a reference standard offset by approximately +1 Hz. The reference is offset to the high side; so the counter reading will be high if the frequency of the standard under test is high.

1. An offset having a period of 1.01666 s rather than 1.000 s is used to make the system coherent with 60-Hz noise and ground loops. Since this will also mask 60-Hz noise on the standard under test, it must be checked in some other manner if it is important.
2. The counter is set for period average and counting a 1- or 10-MHz internal frequency.
3. A larger offset is used for shorter averaging times; i.e., a 10-Hz offset will give a 0.1-s averaging time.
4. A double-balanced mixer is used to keep undesired modulation products as well as the coupling from one standard to the other to a minimum.
5. A battery-operated transistorized Schmitt trigger and filter help keep down ground loop and noise problems.

6. A slow strip-chart speed, 1 in./h, gives a convenient record for determining frequency offset or aging rate or both. A fast strip-chart speed, 1 in./min, shows fine detail and is useful for evaluating short-term stability.

Calculation of scale factor:

$$f = \frac{1}{P}$$

$$\Delta f = \frac{1}{P^2}\Delta P$$

$$\frac{\Delta f}{f} = \frac{\Delta P}{P^2 f_0}$$

where ΔP = resolution of period measurement, usually 0.1 μg
P = period read on counter, 1.0 s for 1-Hz offset
f_0 = frequency being checked, 1×10^6 Hz, for example

$$\frac{\Delta f}{f} = \frac{1 \times 10^{-7}}{(1.0\text{ s})^2(1 \times 10^6\ N/\text{s})} = \frac{1 \times 10^{-7}}{1 \times 10^6\ N}$$

$= 1 \times 10^{-13}$ change per digit change in reading of counter
$= 1 \times 10^{-12}$ change per microsecond change in reading

1.0 1 6 6 6 6 6 → seconds period of offset

- last 6 → 1×10^{-13} per digit change
- 6 → 1×10^{-12} }*
- 6 → 1×10^{-11} }*
- 6 → 1×10^{-10} }*
- 6 → 1×10^{-9}

Another useful example is the calculation of the scale factor when comparing 1.00273790924 MHz, which corresponds to sidereal† time, with a 1.0-MHz standard In this case, the two frequencies are already different; so that difference can be used as the offset.

The counter reads the period of the difference of the two frequencies, or

1.002737.90924 Hz
1.000000.00000 Hz
Difference = 2737.90924 Hz

Period = 1/2737. . . . Hz
= 0.0003624223 s
= 3.65×10^{-4} s = 3.65×10^{-4} s
f_0 = 1.0 MHz

Then

$$\frac{\Delta f}{f_0} = \frac{1 \times 10^{-6}}{(3.65 \times 10^{-4})^2 \times (1 \times 10^6)} = \frac{1 \times 10^{-12}}{.133 \times 10^{-6}} = 7.5 \times 10^{-6}$$

$= 7.5 \times 10^{-6}$ parts per microsecond change in the reading on the counter

For a 10^4 period-average counter counting 10 MHz,

365.24223 μsec

- last digit → 7.5×10^{-11} parts per unit change here
- first digit → 7.5×10^{-6} parts per unit change here as calculated above

Averaging time is 3.6 s.

* These three columns give 1×10^{-9} full scale (1×10^{-10} per division) when a digital-to-analog connector is used to drive a strip-chart recorder.

† Sidereal time is described in detail in Sec. 20.

15. Difference-frequency Multiplier A difference-frequency multiplier (Fig. 13) takes a locally generated frequency $f + \Delta f$, multiplies it by 10, and then mixes it with a reference frequency which has been multiplied by 9. The difference frequency from the mixer is the same as the local input frequency, but the Δf portion has been multiplied by 10. Repeating this through several similar stages increases the ΔF by as much as 10,000 times. If two frequency standards differed by only 1 Hz, the output from the difference-frequency multiplier could be 10 kHz, which can be easily measured with an electronic counter. Some of these instruments also have built-in phase and offset meters so they can be used to compare or calibrate frequency standards. This system can be easily checked by

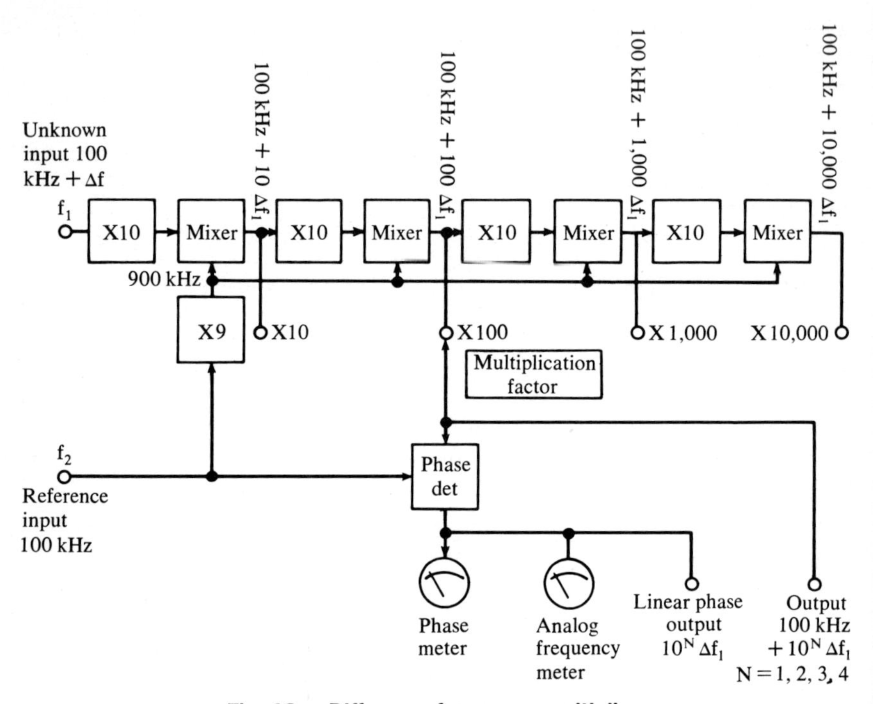

Fig. 13. Difference-frequency multiplier.

feeding the same signal to both inputs. Any output from the $f + \Delta f$ connector under these circumstances is due to noise in the instrument.

16. Time Comparison Frequencies can be compared by making time comparisons. The output of a standard being checked is divided down low enough to drive an electric-clock mechanism. If this clock and a clock driven from a reference standard are set to coincident time and then checked periodically, one can determine if the oscillator under test is high or low in frequency with respect to the reference by seeing if the clock driven by the oscillator under test is fast or slow with respect to the reference clock. This method was used extensively in the past to make frequency comparisons using station WWV's high-frequency time-signal broadcasts. The long time involved in such comparisons helped average out Doppler shifts, as discussed previously. This system is not useful for comparing modern high-accuracy standards, because it is generally not feasible to transfer time information by high-frequency radio links with sufficient accuracy, since the transmission's path is not known precisely.

TIMEKEEPING

An obvious reason for timekeeping is to keep track of our coming and going as it relates to other people and to the world around us. Accurate time is also the basis of navigation and is important in observation of the solar system and in tracking objects in space.

Because the solar system is in continuous motion, observations of the position of a body in space by two or more observers at different locations is meaningful only if the observers can record precise time for each of their observations.

In the past, mechanical clocks were used to keep precise time, and their accuracy was checked and, if necessary, periodically corrected by making observations of the sun, the moon, or the stars. Later, quartz oscillators or atomic-frequency standards were used to get higher accuracy—the frequency of a quartz crystal of 1, 2.5, or 5 MHz was divided down to 1,000, 60, or 50 Hz using electronic dividers. The divided frequency was used to drive a synchronous electric motor coupled to a clock mechanism. Today, highest accuracy is achieved by using an atomic transition as the reference for the frequency, which is divided down to drive the clock mechanism.

Keeping accurate time is much more difficult than maintaining an accurate frequency standard, since:

Correcting the frequency of a frequency standard consists only of resetting it to agree with an approved reference; however, if this same standard is driving a clock, correcting the frequency does not correct time.

If the oscillator frequency were too high, for instance, the clock would run fast. Correcting the oscillator frequency would once again run the clock at its correct rate but would *not* correct for the time it had gained while the oscillator frequency was high. Correcting time would require resetting the crystal oscillator low by the amount it had been high and leaving it at this low setting for the same amount of time it had been at the high setting. Since quartz oscillators age, that is, slowly change frequency with time, establishing a frequency-correction program which will also maintain correct time becomes quite involved. From this it is easy to see that the more stable the frequency standard is, the easier it is to maintain clock time, because the correction will be smaller and less frequent, consistent with a given timekeeping accuracy.

EPOCH AND INTERVAL

Timekeeping has two distinct aspects, epoch and interval. Epoch has to do with when an event occurs and is therefore referenced to a specific starting point. For example, the sighting of a satellite might be referred to the hour of the day when the sighting was made, and this relates to clock time. Interval, a time unit, is independent of the starting point. An example might be the measurement of the duration of an electrical pulse or of the time it takes a ball to fall 3 ft. This is useful in scientific and other work where duration of the event is important, but it does not have to be time-related to other events occurring at isolated locations.

TIME SCALES

Eight or more time scales have been used at one time or another. They are as follows:

17. Apparent Solar Time This is based on a theoretical uniform rotation of the earth on its axis with respect to the sun.

18. Mean Solar Time This is simply apparent solar time averaged to eliminate the variations due to orbital eccentricity and the tilt of the earth's axis. As a fundamental unit of time, the mean solar second is inadequate because it is tied to the earth's rotation, which is now known to be nonuniform.

19. Universal Time (UT) As with mean solar time, universal time (UT) is based on the rotation of the earth about its axis; the units of UT were chosen so that on the average, local noon would occur when the sun was on the local meridian. UT, thus defined, made the assumption that the rotation of the earth was constant and that it would therefore be a uniform time scale. It is now known that the rotation of the earth is subject to periodic, secular, and irregular variations, and universal time is naturally subject to these same variations.

The UT_2 time scale recognizes that the earth is subject to polar motion and also makes an additional correction for seasonal variations in the rotation of the earth. These variations are apparently caused by seasonal displacement of matter over the earth's surface, such as changes in the amount of ice in the polar regions as the sun moves from the Southern Hemisphere to the Northern and back again through the year. This cyclic redistribution of mass acts on the earth's rotation, since it amounts to seasonal changes in its moment of inertia. UT_2 represents the mean angular motion of the earth, freed of periodic variations but still affected by irregular variation and secular variation.

UT_2 or a linear approximation UTC are the two time scales in widest use today. The frequency determining the UT_2 time scale had an offset with respect to atomic time (discussed later) as the earth is slowing down. Each year the Bureau International de l'Heure examined records of the rotational behavior to establish, if necessary, a new offset on Jan. 31 of each year. The offset was made in accordance with an international agreement whereby time signals from cooperating stations are kept within about 100 ms of UT_2.

Since UT_2 time is not uniform, a time scale called universal time coordinated (UTC) has come into use. This is a uniform approximation of UT_2 which maintains the announced yearly slope of the UT_2 time offset but may be stepwise-corrected during the year if the deviation from UT_2 becomes greater than 100 ms. This was the time scale broadcast by stations WWV and WWVH but not by WWVB.*

20. Sidereal Time or Star Time Astronomers use a time scale that takes as its reference the relative position of the stars with respect to the rotation of the earth. Time defined in this manner is called sidereal time.

A sidereal day is strictly defined as the interval between two successive transits of the first point of Aries (a northern constellation) over the upper meridian of any place. In other words, it is the period of rotation of the earth obtained by observation of the stars and with reference to the stars. Sidereal time is not influenced by the orbital motion of the earth, since the stars that are observed are so very distant that their apparent positions do not vary as the earth moves about the sun.

A sidereal day contains 24 sidereal hours, each having 60 sidereal minutes of 60 sidereal seconds. In mean solar time, a sidereal day is about 23 hours, 56 minutes, and 4.09 seconds. The time difference in the two days is due to the earth's motion about the sun and the influence of this motion on the apparent position of the sun among the stars. What happens is that during the course of a day, orbital motion causes the sun to appear to move a little to the east among the stars. Even if the earth did not rotate, the sun would appear to move eastward completely around the earth during one period of the earth's orbit. The effect of this apparent motion is that the day referenced to the sun is about 4 minutes longer than the day referenced to the stars. Since sidereal time is based on the true rotation of the earth referenced to the stars, it provides a straightforward unit by which to fix the position of stars for astronomical observations. A clock keeping time in sidereal units must, in the course of a tropical year, indicate the passage of one day more than it would indicate in mean solar units. A clock designed to run from a 1-MHz frequency standard will keep sidereal time if the driving oscillator frequency is adjusted to 1,002,737.90924 Hz.

21. Mean Sidereal Time Mean sidereal time differs from apparent sidereal time because of the nodding, or nutation, of the earth's axis. This difference has a maximum value of only about a second or so. Because the difference between

* On January 1, 1972 this offset was made equal to zero by international agreement. Time changes of less than 1 s are made once or twice a year as needed to maintain a clock driven by an atomic reference oscillator within 1 s of UTC.

mean and apparent sidereal time is so small, sidereal time is the scale generally used by astronomers.

22. Ephemeris Time (ET) As mentioned earlier with regard to solar time, the rotation of the earth on its axis does not take place at a constant rate, and as a result, time units derived from it do not provide an invariable standard. Even when all possible corrections have been made, an insurmountable uncertainty still remains, since the rate of rotation of the earth fluctuates unpredictably. These irregular changes are thought to be due to readjustments in the interior of the globe that produce small changes in diameter. Furthermore, the earth is known to be slowing in its angular rate in a secular manner because of tidal friction. This change amounts to about 1 ms per century, and since it is secular, it does not lend itself to correction in uniform time units.

The search for a uniform time unit has led astronomers to define an additional kind of time called ephemeris time (ET). Ephemeris time is astronomical time based on the motion of the earth about the sun; however, it is obtained in practice from observations of the motion of the moon about the earth. In October, 1956, the International Committee of Weights and Measures defined the second of ET as the fraction 1/31,556,925.9747 of the tropical year for January 0, 1900, at 12 hours ephemeris time. The tropical year for the moment of 12 hours, January 0, 1900, is the length the tropical year would be if the sun continued at its apparent instantaneous rate, corrected for orbital eccentricity and nutation of the earth's axis.

The second of ET, thus defined, appears to fulfill the requirements for an invariable unit of time. ET is obtained in practice by observing the motion of the moon about the earth. Lunar-position tables that have been constructed in conformity with the internationally adopted solar ephemeris permit the determination of ET directly from the observation of the moon.

Because of the difficulty of making precise measurements of the position of the moon, except by observations made for a fairly long time, the delay in the determination of ET to any useful degree of accuracy is on the order of several years.

23. Atomic Time Effective Jan. 1, 1965, NBS low-frequency station WWVB began to broadcast the international unit of time based upon the atomic standard.

The atomic definition of the second was authorized in October, 1964, by the Twelfth General Conference of Weights and Measures, meeting in Paris. The conference action based the definition on a translation in the cesium atom for the present, in anticipation that an even more exact definition may be possible in the future.

The international second has been redefined before, always with the realization of increased exactness. In 1956, the second called the ephemeris second was defined as a certain fraction of the time taken by the earth to orbit the sun during the tropical year 1900. Earlier than 1956, the second was defined as a fraction of the time required for an average rotation of the earth on its axis with respect to the sun.

The atomic definition realizes an accuracy much greater than that achieved by astronomical observations. It results in a time base more uniform and much more convenient. Now determinations can be made in a few minutes to greater accuracy than was possible before in measurements that took many years.

The exact wording of the action of the Twelfth General Conference is as follows: "The standard to be employed is the transition between two hyperfine levels $F = 4$, $m_F = 0$ and $F = 3$, $m_F = 0$ of the fundamental state $^2S_{1/2}$ of the atom of Cesium-133, undisturbed by external fields and the value 9,192,631,770 hertz is assigned."

The new definition of the second is in as close agreement as is experimentally possible with the earlier (ephemeris) definition.

An atomic-clock operation at Boulder, Colo., is kept by the U.S. National Bureau of Standards. NBS maintains an atomic-time scale designated as NBS. The U.S. Naval Observatory maintains an atomic-time system designated USNO based upon a weighted average of cesium-beam standards.

The Observatory of Neuchâtel, Switzerland, also maintains an atomic-time scale.

Comparison between these time scales is reported periodically in the technical journals.

24. Standard Time This differs from UTC, which is maintained in terms of Greenwich mean time (GMT) by an integral number of hours. It is kept by the U.S. Naval Observatory's master clock, which consists of an atomic resonator, a quartz-crystal oscillator, and a clock movement.

The atomic resonator monitors a quartz oscillator, kept offset from the atomic frequency to yield UT_2. Oscillator output, divided down to 100,000 Hz, is fed to a clock consisting of a divider, clock movement, and seconds pulser. The 1,000-Hz output drives a synchronous motor geared to indicate hours, minutes, and seconds. The seconds pulser serve as the precise reference.

CLOCKS

Accurate electronic clocks consist of a clock mechanism driven by a synchronous electric motor. A synchronous motor is used because it makes a given fraction of a revolution for each cycle of the ac input and consequently moves the hands of the clock a known interval of time each cycle. The gear ratio between the motor and the clock hands determines how far the clock hands advance for each revolution of the clock motor.

The accuracy of such a clock depends only on the accuracy with which it was originally set to the correct time and on the frequency accuracy of the alternating current driving the motor. Conventional wall clocks are driven by the 60-Hz power-line frequency and so advance by 16.666 ms for each cycle of the input. Accuracy is that of the power-line frequency, which for United States commercial power lines is normally in the range of 0.01 to 0.1 percent. This might be expected to give time errors of 10 to 100 s a day if not corrected; however, the power company runs a comparison clock from its generated frequency. This clock will run slow if the line frequency is low, as it might be during the day when the demand for electrical energy by industrial users is great and during the evening when the demand for lighting is great. This clock is compared with a master clock kept in accurate agreement with the time maintained by the U.S. Naval Observatory. The generating station can then increase the line frequency at some time when the load is light, as during the middle of the night, so the electric clock will run fast and thus make up for the time it lost when the frequency was low.

Even though the clock may have been fast or slow at some time during the day, if the generator speed has been regulated so it generates exactly 5,184,000 cycles during the day, the clock will be in precise time agreement with the master clock at the end of the day. In the same way, an accurate frequency standard can be the basis of a very precise clock. For this service, the clock motor is generally designed to run on 1,000 Hz and has an appropriate gear train to drive the clock hands. The 1,000-Hz driving signal is obtained from a frequency standard with an electronic digital divider chain which contributes no error.

Time corrections can be made by setting the frequency standard high or low in frequency as in the previous discussion; however, this may be undesirable because it may affect the stability of the standard. A continuously variable phase shifter connected between the 1,000 Hz from the standard and the clock motor can either add or subtract cycles so that clock time can be advanced or retarded without changing the frequency of the standard.

Of the accurate electronic clocks, one driven by a quartz-crystal oscillator can maintain a time accuracy of 50 μs/day (5×10^{-10} per day aging rate) to 500 μs/day (5×10^{-9} per day aging rate) for moderately good oscillators. Next in order of stability come the best commercial quartz oscillators operated in a laboratory environment. Here a time accuracy of 1 μs/day (1×10^{-11} per day aging rate) to 5 μs/day (5×10^{-11} per day aging rate) can be achieved.

Rubidium-gas-cell frequency standards come next in order of improved performance. These are still secondary standards because they require initial calibration and have an aging rate, even though it may be small. A clock driven with one of these standards should not accumulate an error greater than a couple of microseconds a month (2×10^{-11} per month aging rate for the standard).

A cesium-beam-tube frequency standard driving a clock mechanism offers the ultimate in precision timekeeping. The cesium-beam tube is a primary frequency standard, as it is not necessary to compare its output with any other reference to establish frequency accuracy. It also has no aging rate, but it can have some fixed error of 1×10^{-11} or less. Even when driven by a cesium-beam standard, a clock must still be set against some reference to establish epoch.

ESTABLISHING EPOCH*

To establish a clock at some new locations, the timekeeping equipment must first be put in operation, and then the clock must be set to the correct time. Setting a clock to within a few milliseconds can be done by comparing clock "ticks" with radio station WWV time ticks using a high-frequency radio receiver and an oscilloscope. Available high-frequency broadcast time signals are not suitable for setting time much closer than 1 ms, as the transmission path and hence the time delay is not precisely known. Low-frequency signal paths are known, but the high Q of the transmitting-antenna system results in a narrow bandwidth and precludes transmitting a fast-rise-time pulse necessary to establish time accurately. Some stations, such as those used for Loran navigation systems, can transmit high-accuracy time information, but they operate in limited frequency bands and require special receivers to receive the time information.

Use of a "flying clock" is the easiest way to transfer precise time from one location to another. In practice a clock driven by a cesium frequency standard operating from a portable power supply is first set to correspond to epoch as maintained by the National Bureau of Standards or the Naval Observatory by physically transporting the portable clock to each location. Once set, the clock can be transported by land, sea, or air around the world if need be to make time comparisons with other clocks. After all necessary comparisons are completed, the flying clock is once again checked by comparing with NBS and the Naval Observatory to make sure that some malfunctions during the trip did not disturb the clock. If this time-closure error is small, time at each of the other stops during the trip can be considered to be accurate within these limits. Time closure of 1 to 3 or 4 μs can usually be achieved using commercially available equipment on the around-the-world trip of a month and a half duration.†

Once epoch has been established, a systematic correction procedure which takes into account the error and aging rate of the frequency standard must be instigated if time is to be maintained within acceptable limits. The frequency standard, frequency dividers, and clock should all be operated with a standby-battery power supply. Without this, even a momentary power interruption will destroy time accuracy.

* Frequency and Time Standard, *Application Note* 52, Hewlett-Packard Co., Palo Alto, Calif.

† L. N. Bodily, D. Hartke, and R. C. Hyatt, World Wide Time Synchronization, 1966, *Hewlett-Packard J.*, vol. 17, no. 12, August, 1966. L. N. Bodily, A Summary of Some Performance Characteristics of a Large Sample of Cesium Beam Frequency Standards. *Hewlett-Packard J.*, vol. 18, no. 2, October, 1966. L. N. Bodily and Ronald C. Hyatt, Flying Clock Comparisons Extended to East Europe, Africa and Australia, *Hewlett-Packard J.*, vol. 19, no. 4, December, 1967. Alan S. Bagley and Leonard S. Cutler, A New Performance of the "Flying Clock" Experiment, *Hewlett-Packard J.*, vol. 15, no. 11, July, 1964.

Section Ten

Recording Instruments

Very often a permanent record of the state of the phenomenon being investigated is required. It may be that the magnitude of a voltage or a current at a precise time in its existence is needed or the wave shape during the entire test time is wanted for study or reference. Three instruments are designed to perform these tasks: strip-chart recorders, *X-Y* recorders, and instrumentation line printers. These are described in this section. Devices primarily designed for other purposes can also be used to obtain permanent records, for example, an oscilloscope with a camera, but each of these cases is discussed separately in the chapter on that specific instrument elsewhere in the book. Therefore, the use of the Index and general Table of Contents is recommended when considering permanent records from a particular instrument. Also Chapter 8, Output Devices, should be reviewed as a general reference to the subject of recording devices.

Graphic recorders serve much the same function as oscilloscopes but for a more particular purpose: They provide a permanent record on paper. Since they contain many of the basic elements of voltage measurement instruments, Section Two, Fundamentals of Electronic Measurement Instruments should be consulted because it describes these elements as they pertain to recorders as well as to other measurement devices. Since the basic purpose of this instrument is to provide a permanent record and not to perform the measurement itself, however, it is most appropriate to have it emphasized separately along with line printers.

Chapter **36**

Graphic Recorders

FRANCIS L. MOSELEY

Servo Products Company, Altadena, California

INTRODUCTION

Graphic recorders generally are devices which display and store a pen-and-ink record of the history of some physical event. The event may be a varying voltage obtained from an electric circuit under observation, or perhaps a varying pressure which actuates a diaphragm and linkage to move a stylus in relation to a chart.

A recorder is of necessity a mechanical device; it may be electromechanical. Basic elements of a recorder include a chart for displaying and storing the recorded information, a stylus moving in a proper relationship to the paper, and suitable interconnection means to couple the stylus to the information source.

For the purposes of this book recorders will be considered in two categories, strip-chart and *X-Y* recorders.

Graphic recording devices and methods may be classified broadly: (1) one or more variables with respect to time, as strip-chart recorder, circular-chart recorder, oscillograph, or (2) one or more dependent variables with respect to an independent variable, such devices being known as *X-Y* recorders or function plotters.

As to recording methods and mediums, these include photographic, which may result in film to be darkroom-developed, or there may be immediate daylight processing. Other methods include pressure-sensitive paper and stylus, electrically conductive paper using electrode stylus, and heat-responsive paper with controlled-heat stylus.

Stylus-drive methods include a fixed light source and a small mirror moved angularly by a string galvanometer, the resulting moving light beam impinging upon a strip of photographic film or paper. Another basic method involves a moving coil in a fixed field, the coil driving the stylus directly or through a linkage to give a linear rather than arcuate motion to the system.

A broad class of recorders makes use of a closed-loop servosystem to position the stylus in response to the changing input information. Such servosystems may utilize a motor and gear as the final drive to the stylus or may employ a linear motor, similar to an elongated dynamic-speaker magnet system. In either case the position of the stylus will be measured continuously by a position transducer; voltage taken from the position transducer feeds back to a combining circuit in the servosystem to bring the system to a null or balance at a stylus position agreeing closely with the value of the input signal being recorded.

Recorders of the various types mentioned cover a wide range of frequencies to meet the needs of a variety of applications.

Recorders are often very slow in frequency response; examples would be a room-temperature recorder, a recording barometer, or a recorder for monitoring a massive industrial or chemical process. In these and similar applications slow response is a virtue; the recorders do not respond to meaningless transients such as might be due to noise on a signal line, and the rugged design made possible by the low speed requirement assures long life and reliability.

Other recorder applications require more rapid response, for example, an *X-Y* recorder used for plotting the characteristics of a transistor. Here the user would expect the full span of the paper to be traversed quite promptly, but very high speed would be meaningless and possibly an irritation. A full chart traverse of ½ s is usually suitable.

Higher-speed applications may involve multichannel photographic recording of geophysical-survey phenomena. Here a group of sensitive vibration detectors furnish signals up to several thousand cycles, and a broad frequency band should be recorded faithfully.

In order to cover the span of frequencies encountered by graphic recorders, the stylus drive must be intelligently chosen in each design situation. For maximum response, photographing of a cathode-ray-tube face would be the logical choice. For less stringent requirements, the galvanometer and mirror stylus, recording on photographic paper or film, would be used. At still lower frequencies, a moving-coil pen drive would be suitable. At lowest frequencies, say up to 5 or 10 cycles, a servosystem offers many virtues of linearity, stability, sensitivity, ample mechanical power to drive rugged pen systems, and ability to drive control elements, such as limit switches for power control, and retransmitting devices such as potentiometers, synchros, or mechanical digitizers.

1. Strip-chart Recorders Strip-chart recorders are instruments for the graphic recording and portrayal of phenomena varying with respect to time.

Such instruments generally comprise a stylus, moving horizontally in proportion to the magnitude of the phenomenon, and a chart, running vertically, driven at a suitable rate to achieve the desired record.

Figure 1 shows the basic elements of an electrical stylus-positioning system and paper drive. Some form of electrical system moves the stylus in a nearly exact replica or analog of the varying input signal.

The basic range of the instrument is chosen to suit the application; the range setting may comprise a factory-installed resistor divider network or in a general-purpose recorder may take the form of a very flexible calibrated stepped attenuator. As will be seen in more detailed diagrams, later in this text, refinements may include adjustable zero and a smoothly variable (as opposed to fixed-step) scale-range control.

Paper or chart drives exist in many forms, principal types being spring-wound with clockwork escapement for good timing control; electric motor (usually of the synchronous type); and external drive, wherein the chart is driven from some part of the process being monitored; an example is in oil-well survey work, where a cable, lowering a measuring device into the well, passes over a sheave which measures cable length. Rotation of the sheave drives the recorder chart through a synchro transmitter and motor link.

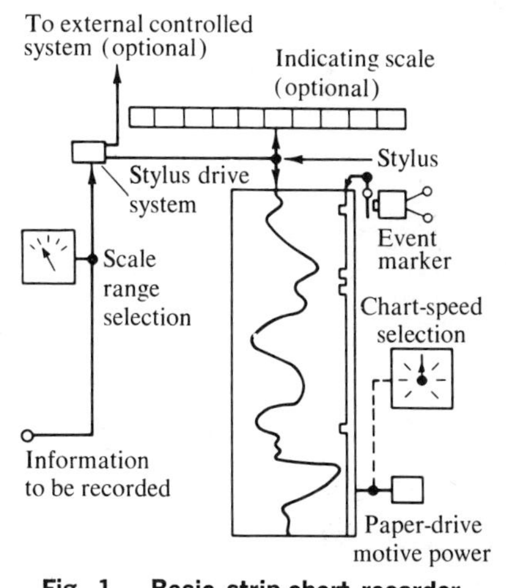

Fig. 1. Basic strip-chart recorder.

Figure 2 shows a laboratory strip-chart recorder of the two-pen type. Typical features and specifications of such a recorder are:

Two independent recording systems, individually identified by ink color, e.g., red and green.

Full-scale recording spans as low as 1 mV, and extending up to 500 V; choice of range or span is made by operation of a range switch on the front panel.

Customarily, zero is front-panel-adjustable and may be placed anywhere on the chart. In many instruments it may be displaced or suppressed by one full scale range or more. By this device, recordings may be made of signal values which start above zero; the recording will display the range of interest across the full span of the paper.

The inherent high sensitivity and stability of modern recorders enable the user to record directly low-level outputs from thermocouples, strain gages, and other transducers.

The recording chart is electrically driven, a wide variety of speeds being selectable from a front-panel control. Speeds may range from 1 in./h to a few inches per second, with greatly extended ranges available for particular applications. A feature available is a "jump-speed" control whereby a low paper speed is established for monitoring of a system (for example, a rocket-engine test stand) during setup and calibration and when firing begins, the jump-speed drive is activated by a remote contact closure, whereupon paper is fed for a brief time at a very high rate to take down every detail of the short-period event.

Other features generally available are remote electrical pen control and an event marker. These items allow the user to raise or lower the pen from a remote contact and to mark the edge of the chart to indicate the start or termination of some recording sequence.

A great variety of strip-chart recorders exists for fixed-installation industrial applications, for example, monitoring of chemical processes, heat-treat ovens, nuclear reactors, power stations, and steel mills.

In these applications, it is common to use the recorder for three purposes simultaneously:

1. As an immediate indicator of the value of the parameter under observation
2. As a means of making a permanent graphic record of the variations of value with respect to time
3. As a controller of the system being monitored

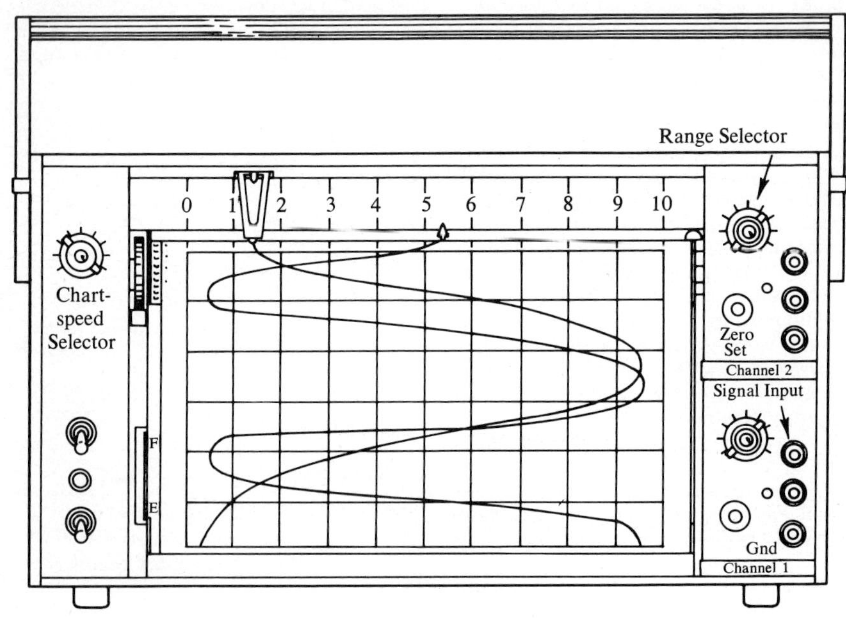

Fig. 2. Strip-chart recorder front panel and controls. (*Hewlett-Packard Co.*)

The control function of item 3 may take the simple form of high- and low-limit contacts actuated by the movement of the recorder-pen mechanism.

Other control methods are:

1. A retransmitting slidewire or potentiometer. This is a smooth, continuous voltage divider that is driven by the pen system and used to feed a voltage proportional to the pen position to some connected apparatus, for example, a servosystem controlling a process valve.
2. A digitizing disk or a linear digitizing strip which produces a finite value in digital-code form for each increment of pen position. Such encoders can be used to feed computing or control systems.
3. A synchro transmitter which feeds continuous angular information to suitable synchro receiving elements located elsewhere in the process system.

Instruments used in the situations mentioned are generally installed and wired in a fixed manner, with ranges, speeds, and features designed for the applications at hand; they are thus somewhat outside the scope of this text.

Specifications of strip-chart recorders are extremely varied to suit thousands of different applications in virtually every segment of science and industry. Generally, the following main points must be considered:

1. Type of chart record desired, i.e., paper or photographic film.
2. Type of writing to be employed, as pen and ink, electric discharge, heat-tipped stylus, pressure stylus.
3. Electrical-voltage range of phenomenon to be recorded.
4. Adjustable range, and adjustable zero if required by application.
5. Recording speed required expressed in seconds for full-scale or response, in cycles per second (hertz), as applicable.
6. Speed of chart drive, in inches per second, per minute, or per hour as applicable.
7. Accuracy required. Servo-balancing recorders are frequently accurate to a fraction of 1 percent, while galvanometer recorders of lower cost may have accuracies of 3 to 5 percent of full scale.
8. Sensitivity or dead band. This terms refers to the ability of the recorder to indicate reliably small parameter changes. Here again servo-balancing recorders excel, frequently having no observable dead band; i.e., the dead band is small compared with the width of the recording trace.
9. Service requirements of intended application, for example: (*a*) laboratory-bench use. (*b*) Panelboard for process monitoring. These applications imply the presence of an engineer or operator. Immediate or daily care of the recorder could be expected, and thus paper and ink would be resupplied as needed. (*c*) Remote, unattended, long-term use. In this situation slow chart speed and some self-maintaining writing system would be required, for example, electric writing or writing by contact stylus, leaving a legible imprint on a specially coated chart.
10. Control features desired, for example, high- and low-limit contacts, retransmitting potentiometer, digitizing means.
11. Input-circuit requirements: (*a*) Input impedance—may be low, i.e., a few hundred ohms if the recorder is intended for use with thermocouples; should be thousands of ohms up to 1 MΩ or more if the recorder is for general-purpose laboratory use. (*b*) Input-circuit isolation—the input should be free-floating, i.e., neither terminal grounded to permit the recorder to be connected to signal sources aboveground. For maximum utility and flexibility, the input should be provided with an internal guard shield and external guard terminal. The recorder should preferably have good common-mode rejection (CMR).

Specifications for CMR in a good present-day recorder (1972) are:

Recorder voltage range	CMR(dc), dB	CMR(ac), dB
1 mV/in	130	100
100 mV/in	90	60
10 V/in	50	20

2. *X-Y* **Recorders** An *X-Y* recorder is an instrument for the graphic recording of the relationship between two variables. It usually consists of a pair of servo-systems, driving a recording pen in two axes through a suitable sliding-pen and moving-arm arrangement, with reference to a fixed-paper chart.

Figure 3 is a block diagram of a typical *X-Y* recorder. In each channel, described in more detail later, a signal enters an input attenuator where it is adjusted to the inherent recorder full-scale range (often 0 to 5 mV). The signal then passes to a balance circuit where it is compared with an internal reference voltage. The difference resulting from this comparison is fed to a chopper or vibrator, which effects conversion of the signal to alternating current. The signal is then amplified for actuation of a servomotor which balances the system and holds it in balance as the value of the measured parameter changes.

The action just described takes place in both axes simultaneously, and thus a record is made of one variable with respect to another; i.e., a function is plotted on the graph paper.

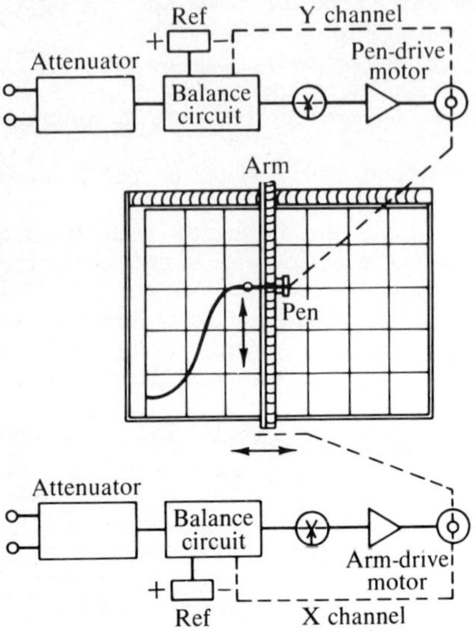

Fig. 3. Basic *X-Y* recorder.

The availability of an *X-Y* recorder in the laboratory greatly simplifies and expedites many measurements and tests, for example:

1. Speed/torque measurements of electric motors
2. Lift/drag wind-tunnel tests
3. Plotting of characteristic curves of vacuum tubes, transistors, rectifiers, zener diodes, etc.
4. Regulation curves of power supplies
5. Physical and mechanical measurements such as stress-strain
6. Electrical characteristics of materials such as resistance vs. temperature
7. Characteristics of governors, such as speed vs. load

Figure 4 represents a typical recorder showing the normal front panel controls.

Specifications of an acceptable *X-Y* recorder usually include the following features:

1. Ability to accept standard-page-size 8½- by 11-in. graph paper and, in larger instruments, 11- by 16½-in. or 30- by 30-in. charts
2. Multiple ranges on each axis, extending, on a full-scale basis, from a few millivolts to hundreds of volts
3. Low current drain, i.e., 200,000 Ω/V or better

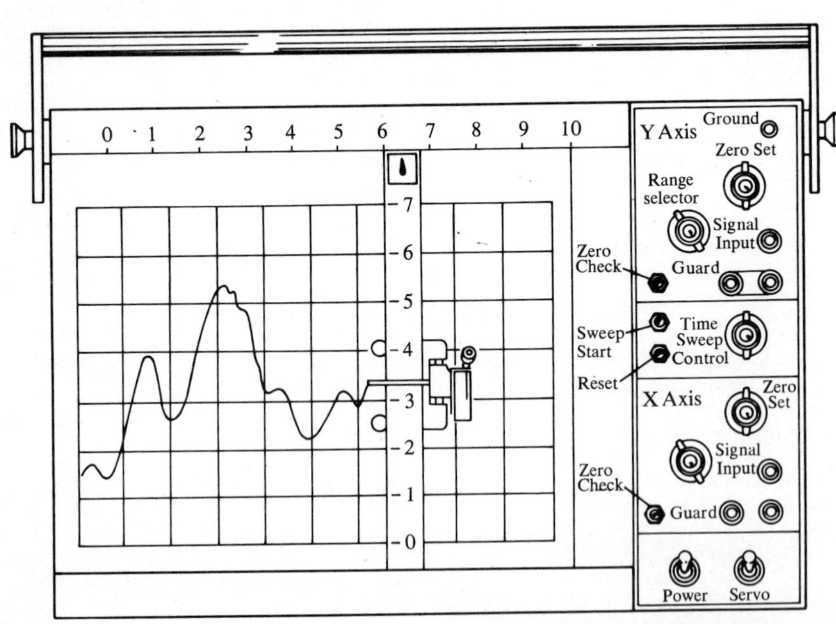

Fig. 4. *X-Y* recorder, showing controls. (*Hewlett-Packard Co.*)

4. Recording-pen speeds of 20 in./s or faster
5. Fractional-percent linearity and accuracy
6. Adjustable zero, and zero offset
7. Time base or sweep circuit, switch selectable on X axis
8. Internal reference voltages furnished from high-stability floating sources, i.e., mercury cells or line-powered zener.
9. Floating inputs, to permit connection of recorder to voltage-separated points in the system under test
10. Good common-mode rejection
11. Ac ranges—generally available as an optional feature
12. Two independent pens in Y and Y_1 axes—optional feature to permit dual trace recording.
13. Remote and local electrical control of pen lift

3. Recorder Pen-drive Systems The stylus or pen of a recorder may be driven directly from the information being recorded, for example, a simple recording thermometer or barometer, wherein the temperature- or pressure-sensing element is mechanically linked to the pen motion.

Alternately, an indirect drive may be employed, for example, a temperature recorder employing a remotely located sensing bulb, connected through small tubing to a pen-driving flexible bellows in the recorder. The entire system of bulb, tubing, and bellows contains a temperature-responsive fluid in liquid or vapor form.

Finally, there are the almost universal electrical pen-drive systems, which provide the ultimate in application flexibility. The electrical systems will of course connect directly to electrical apparatus being monitored, tested, or controlled. In addition, transducers are available which will detect and make accurate conversion of motion, both linear and rotary, temperature, pressure, shaft-revolution rate, chemical concentration, radioactivity, sound pressure, weight, and acceleration. The list is as long as the basic sciences are broad.

Electrical Pen-drive Systems. As strip-chart recorders are usually designed, the pen or stylus mechanism is in a fixed location, with the paper moving beneath the pen in linear fashion. In these circumstances, almost any conceivable means may be used to drive the stylus. The following are electrical systems in common use.

Galvanometer Drive, Direct. In general, the galvanometer types require a high level of signal power for recording. Where such levels are available (one or more milliamperes into a low-impedance coil), the galvanometer type is simple and easy to apply. The galvanometer coil may be thought of as a meter movement electrically isolated from ground and offering few problems in application.

Generally, direct galvanometer drive of the stylus does not permit fast response, as the energy available for pen drive is too low.

Fast response, up to hundreds of hertz, involves preamplification of the signal to be recorded. Both frequency response and accuracy may be improved by various feedback systems wherein the pen position is electrically measured and the resulting position signal is used to complete a servoloop.

Figure 5 shows a slowly varying dc input signal connected to the moving coil of the galvanometer, the pen being driven directly therefrom.

Galvanometer Drive with Preamplifier. Referring to Fig. 6, the utility of the galvanometer type may be considerably extended by the use of a preamplifier; it is apparent that the gain stability of the amplifier enters directly into the recording stability of the system.

In early designs, direct-coupled vacuum-tube amplifiers were often used for galvanometer recorder drive, but such amplifiers suffered from drift due to tube aging, temperature, and line-voltage variations. Refinements in such amplifiers were the chopper-input chopper-output amplifier and the chopper-stabilized amplifier.

A chopper amplifier, briefly, is one in which the dc input signal is converted to alternating current, amplified as alternating current, and then reconverted to direct current to drive the galvanometer.

The coupling of the amplifier to the galvanometer instrument makes it possible to provide a high-level drive to the moving coil, and this, in combination with a stiff return spring, allows the instrument to have greatly extended frequency response.

Galvanometer Drive, Servoloop. Figure 7 shows a moving-coil instrument engineered into a servoloop system. In the figure, a signal enters the system and finds its way into the amplifier, where its level is raised sufficiently to drive the

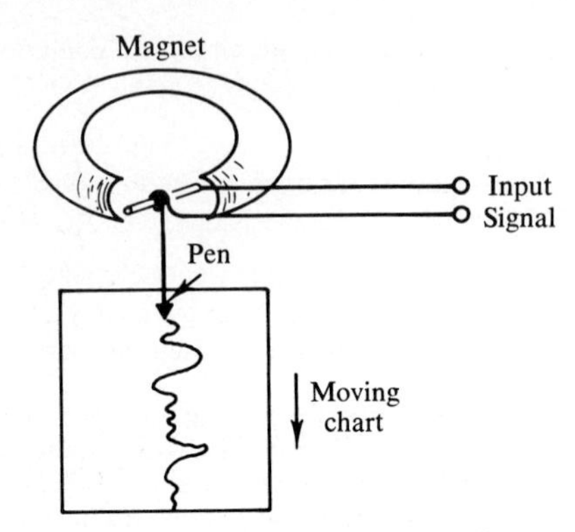

Fig. 5. Galvanometer recorder.

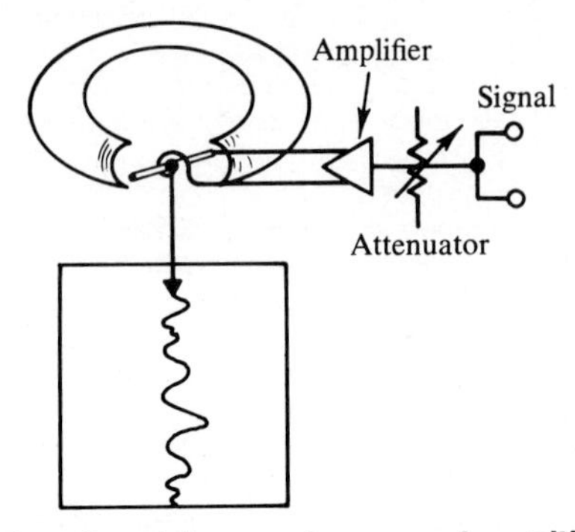

Fig. 6. Galvanometer recorder with preamplifier.

galvanometer coil. The coil-and-pen system carries a feedback or position-measuring element (here shown as a simple potentiometer) which moves until a voltage is derived which is equal and opposite to the input signal, whereupon the system comes to rest at the desired indicating and recording point.

The galvanometer movement no longer requires a restraining spring, as it seeks the correct position at all times. Any failure to reach the proper balance will leave a difference signal flowing into the amplifier with a consequent actuating current (plus or minus) flowing in the galvanometer coil.

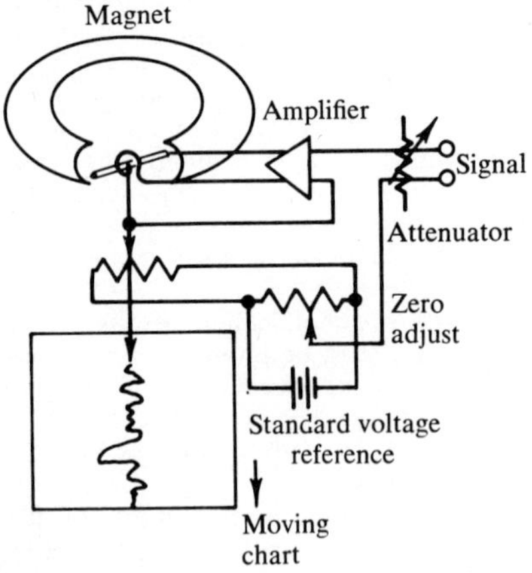

Ignoring servoloop problems, it can be seen intuitively that with sufficiently high amplifier gain, any desired degree of movement stiffness with respect to signal increment may be obtained.

In general, the moving-coil servorecorder (illustrated in Fig. 7) offers the highest performance of the various galvanometer types, but again, this performance is obtained at a certain cost in complexity.

Brief examination of the figure will show that the indicating stability of the instrument depends on a stable voltage-reference source but is not dependent on amplifier gain. Changes in amplifier gain affect system stiffness, or what is sometimes referred to as dead zone or dead band.

Fig. 7. Galvanometer recorder, self-balancing type.

4. Servomechanism Stylus Drive Classifying a recorder as a servomechanism type as distinct from a galvanometer which is fitted with a position-feedback device and a suitable amplifier is somewhat arbitrary.

For the purpose of this discussion, a servorecorder will be considered to be one in which an input signal is matched against a potentiometer-derived reference voltage, the resulting difference voltage being amplified to operate an electric motor. The motor, through suitable gearing, adjusts the potentiometer to balance, and thus positions the pen on the chart.

A simplified diagram of a servodriven strip-chart recorder is shown in Fig. 8. Referring to the figure, the user's dc signal (slowly varying) enters the system at *A* and passes through the attenuator *B*, finally appearing across resistor *C* at a level suitable for the particular instrument.

Balance voltage appears across terminals at *D*; the difference between the attenuated input voltage and the balance voltage is fed to amplifier *E*. The amplifier has high gain and power output in the range of 2 to 10 W. The amplifier output energy drives motor *M* through circuits which are reversible in nature; i.e., if the input signal is larger than the reference, the motor runs in a direction to drive the potentiometer slider and the recording pen upscale; if the reference signal

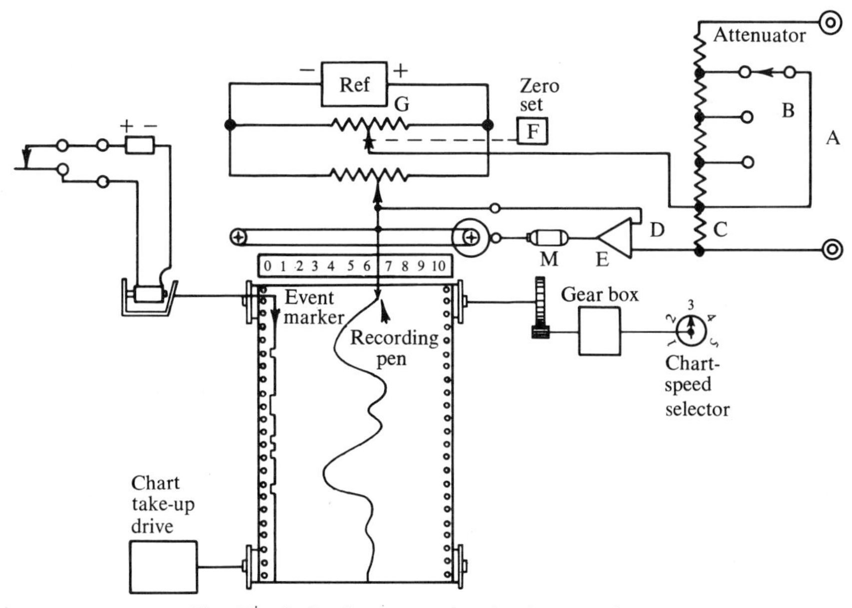

Fig. 8. Strip-chart recorder, basic servo type.

is larger than the input signal, the amplifier's output reverses and drives the motor, potentiometer slider, and pen downscale.

The balancing action described is smooth and continuous in a well-designed recorder. The pen tracks the varying input voltage closely, usually better than a pen width, so that for all practical purposes, errors due to null width or dead band are zero.

When graphic recorders were developed for laboratory use, a prime objective was to provide for the accurate measurement of signals displayed, and to this end, precision, stepped attenuators were included. Later, it was found desirable to add a variable adjustment which makes it possible to set the full scale of the instrument to agree with the full-scale value of any arbitrarily selected signal source. It may, for example, be desirable to record 100 lb of hydraulic pressure as a full-scale recorder signal, and thus the recorder may be adjusted to any transducer output level corresponding to the desired pressure value.

Many times, signals to be recorded start from below zero and do not reach a value of interest until well into the positive region. Such signals might, for example, be obtained when plotting the characteristics of solid-state rectifiers. When data of this kind are displayed, zero offset is a convenience, and for this purpose, circuits have been devised which allow the initial zero point to be pushed off the paper in varying amounts up to several scale lengths.

As a result of this arrangement, a user might wish to record, as full scale, voltages lying between 2 and 3 V, with the figure 2 appearing at the left-hand edge of the paper and the figure 3 at the right-hand edge. As far as recorder range was concerned, this would be 1 V full scale, but the zero would have been depressed by 2 V, the entire combination resulting in the display of voltages on the recorder in the range 2 to 3 V.

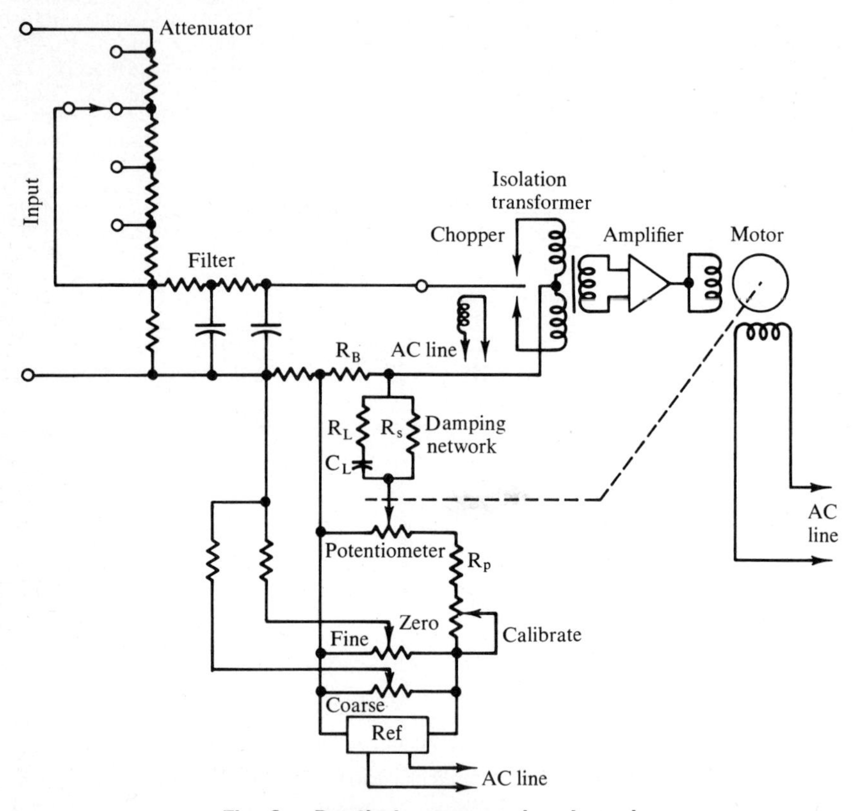

Fig. 9. Practical servorecorder channel.

5. Basic Servorecorder Circuits A practical servo-type recorder channel is shown in Fig. 9. Such a circuit may find use in a strip-chart recorder or in each axis of an *X-Y* recorder.

In the figure, the signal enters from the left; is set to the desired level by the attenuator, in either fixed, accurately calibrated steps or infinitely variable increments; is filtered to remove extraneous noise; and is balanced against zero and reference signals, modulated, amplified, and fed to a servomotor.

Referring in greater detail to the potentiometer-balancing system, the resistors surrounding the basic potentiometer perform a number of functions, supplying across R_B a balancing voltage in the millivolt region having the characteristics required by the servorecording system. At first glance, it might seem best to attenuate the reference-battery voltage down to a millivolt level and apply this voltage to the balancing potentiometer. Trouble is encountered in using this method, however, as the motion of a slider across a resistance gives rise to a friction-generated voltage known as "triboelectric emf." Rapid motion of the potentiometer arm across a wirewound element will generate "tribo" potentials of several millivolts, and with a full-scale recorder sensitivity of 5 mV or less, such voltages would constitute a tremendous disturbance. The use of a duplicate opposite-connected slider on a return element can be used to balance out "tribo emf," and such an arrangement is often employed. In the circuit shown, a different approach is taken wherein approximately 1 V of reference signal appears across a slidewire of several thousand ohms resistance. This voltage is attenuated approximately 200:1 by the combination of resistors R_S and R_B. The availability of a large drop across R_S makes it possible to use resistor capacitance network R_L, C_L as servodamping elements. These, in combination with feedback in the motor amplifier, provide the servostability needed for high static accuracy and good dynamic performance.

A further item contributing toward the linearity of the servobalancing system is the use of padding resistor R_P. The loading curve of a potentiometer supplied from a low-impedance source is a line rising to maximum error at about 0.7 of travel; the slope of error approximates a straight line to the point of maximum error. If a series resistor is used, such as R_P, to supply the potentiometer, the end of the basic potentiometer may be placed at the maximum error point; readjustment of operating levels then causes the potentiometer to be used over a nearly

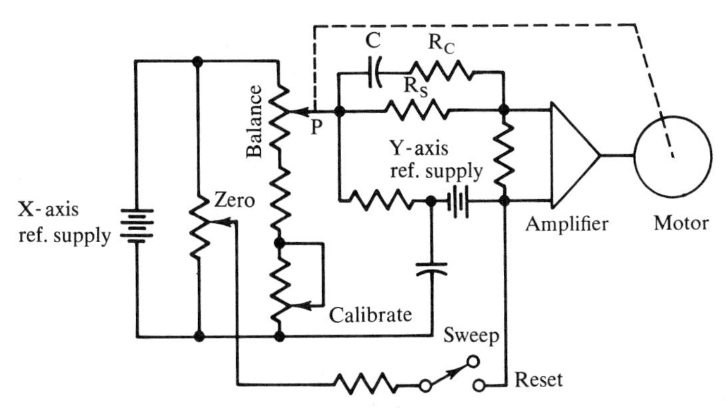

Fig. 10. Time-base circuit for *X-Y* recorder.

straight portion of its characteristic. Reduction of loading error of 5:1 or more may be achieved by this means.

The signal-voltage supply shown as "REF" is now generally supplied by a transformer, rectifier, and zener diode combination, the transformer being well shielded electrostatically so as to float free of the power line.

The schematic of Fig. 9 shows a zero-setting arrangement wherein slider *F* may be rotated to move a balancing slider across potentiometer *G*. Inspection of this circuit will show that the recorder, to remain at null, must seek a new zero position as knob *F* is rotated.

On any recorder having its indication spread over a wide expanse of paper, zero adjustment must be possible on a sort of micrometer basis. The figure shows a pair of balancing potentiometers connected in a voltage-addition circuit on a coarse and fine basis. In practice, two independently operating resistor elements are mounted on a common shaft to provide a combination of rapid setting and fine adjustment.

In the laboratory use of an *X-Y* recorder, it is often desirable to have the horizontal or *X* axis driven as a function of time. Operated in this way, an *X-Y* recorder may be thought of as a low-frequency direct-writing oscillograph. A circuit for time-base operation is illustrated in Fig. 10. A voltage taken from the basic recorder slidewire *P* feeds through condenser *C*, and any resulting charging current causes a drop across R_C. At rest, with the potentiometer and recording system at the left-hand edge of the scale, all voltages around the circuit are zero. Time-base action is initiated by closing switch S, which causes a small voltage to appear across R_S, this voltage being immediately communicated to the input of the servo-amplifier, thus causing the drive motor to rotate in a direction to move the slider along potentiometer P. Motion of the slidewire contact produces a rising voltage, which in turn sends a charging current through capacitor C, which appears as a drop across R_C, this drop being of proper polarity and magnitude to nearly cancel the initiating emf across R_S. In operation, a tight servoloop action causes the slider of potentiometer P and the pen connected to it to move across the paper at a uniform rate, thus providing a time base or sweep for the X axis. Various rates of sweep may be selected by variation of the initial drop across R_S, and variations in the size of capacitor C and resistor R_C. Full-scale sweep times are provided by the capacitor shown, varying from 5 s for full sweep down to as slow as 500 or more seconds. Linearity or accuracy of sweep provided are nominal but usually are better than 3 percent.

Both linearity and accuracy may be improved by the addition of active circuit elements.

RECORDER APPLICATIONS

6. AC Recording A self-balancing potentiometer instrument is inherently a dc-signal device. When ac signals are to be measured, it is expedient to rectify the alternating current, converting it to direct current, and thence employ the

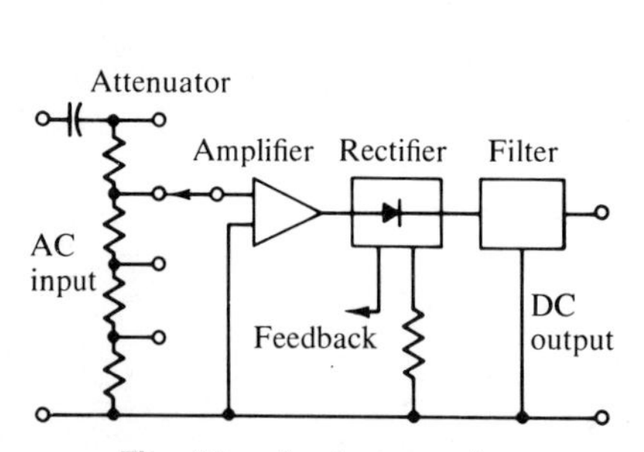

Fig. 11. Ac-dc converter.

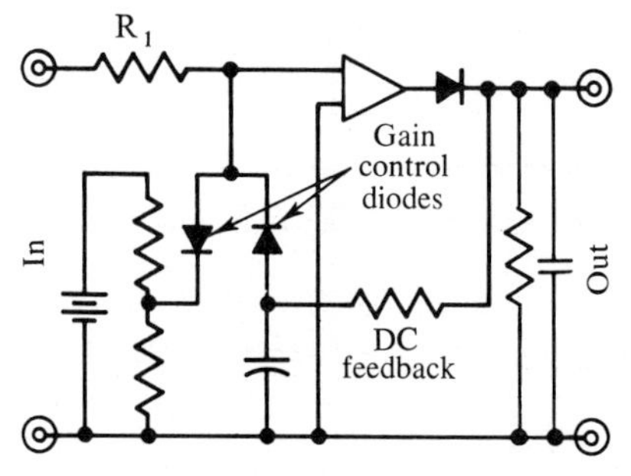

Fig. 12. Logarithmic converter.

self-balancing circuits inherent in the recorder. Figure 11 shows a simplified ac-dc converter schematic wherein the signal is picked up in a high-impedance frequency-compensated attenuator, fed to an amplifier, rectified, and presented to the recorder. The rectifier is both stabilized and linearized by feedback means. Typical specifications permit the recording of voltages to 20 kHz with fractional-percentage accuracy and up to 100 or 200 kHz with accuracies of 1 or 2 percent.

7. Logarithmic Recording A convenient method of accomplishing logarithmic recording is to use an electric circuit, which converts from volts to decibels; the output of such a circuit may be coupled to a linear, unmodified recorder. A device for effecting such a conversion is illustrated in Fig. 12.

Referring to the figure, a signal enters the unit, where it is applied to the grid of an amplifier tube through R_1. After suitable amplification, rectification takes place, and a dc signal for application to the recorder appears at the output terminals.

In order to effect logarithmic conversion, a portion of the output signal is fed back to a nonlinear control element at the input. As the output signal tends to rise, the gain of the system is progressively reduced in just the amount required to give a true logarithmic relationship between input and output.

The nonlinear control element comprises a pair of diodes initially set at the proper bias point and thereafter progressively biased toward a conducting direction by increasing values of signal fed back from the output rectifier. A device now available covers a 60-dB (1,000:1) voltage range, has an input impedance of 2 MΩ, covers a frequency range of 20 Hz to 20 kHz, and is linear in its conversion to within considerably better than ½ dB over the combined frequency and level ranges just mentioned.

The diode converting elements are mounted in a small crystal oven where they are maintained at uniform temperature. A thermistor element is included in the oven and connected in the bias circuit so as to shift the bias as required to overcome any deficiencies in the oven regulation. The result of these two actions imparts a high degree of temperature stability to the system. Suitable line-voltage regulation eliminates the remaining major cause of instability, and the result is an instrument which makes a dependable conversion without operator adjustment over a long period of time.

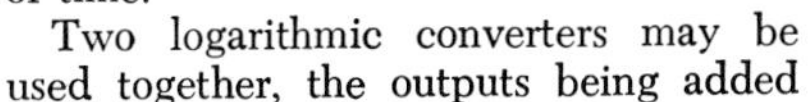

Fig. 13. Thermocouple reference junction.

Two logarithmic converters may be used together, the outputs being added for multiplication or subtracted for division. The resulting signal is then the logarithm of the ratio (in the case of divison) of two signals, and such a result is often wanted.

8. Temperature Recording: Thermocouple Methods Commercially available thermocouples serve well as temperature-sensing elements and are ideally adapted for use with servo-type graphic recorders. Four common thermocouple types, together with approximate characteristics, are listed below.

Thermocouple Characteristics

	Thermoelectric power	Max temp range, °F
Iron/constantan	30–32 μV/°F (32–1400°F)	−300 to 1800
Copper/constantan	23–24 μV/°F (32–212°F)	−423 to 1100
Chromel-P/Alumel	22–23 μV/°F (32–2200°F)	−300 to 2200
Platinum + 10 % rhodium/platinum	2.8–6.6 μV/°F (32–2900°F)	32 to 3100

The voltage developed by the thermocouple is measured basically as shown in Fig. 13.

In practical applications, the maintenance of the cold junction at 32°F is a nuisance, and it is avoided by introduction of an artificial cold-junction emf by one of several means, two of which are shown in Figs. 14 and 15.

Referring to Fig. 14, a standard source of emf supplies current to a temperature-sensitive resistor R, which is mounted in close proximity to the terminal which receives the negative lead from the thermocouple, i.e., the "cold junction." Since this junction is made up of constantan and a copper-bearing alloy (brass), a potential is developed in proportion to temperature. This voltage is canceled out by the IR drop occasioned by flow of reference current in the nickel resistor R_1 (temperature-dependent) and bucking resistor R_2 (fixed). As the ambient temperature changes, the drop in R_1 varies so as to produce the voltage which would have been produced by an ice-bath thermocouple.

Figure 15 shows another form of cold-junction compensation, wherein a reference thermocouple TC_2 is maintained at a fixed temperature, say 65°C, in a small oven. The voltage produced by TC_2 is constant and is balanced out by the fixed IR drop in R_1. The regulated dc source shown is, of course, the normal recorder internal reference supply.

9. Temperature Recording: Resistance Methods A servo-operated recorder, intended specifically for resistance/temperature measurement, may have a simple input circuit, as shown in Fig. 16.

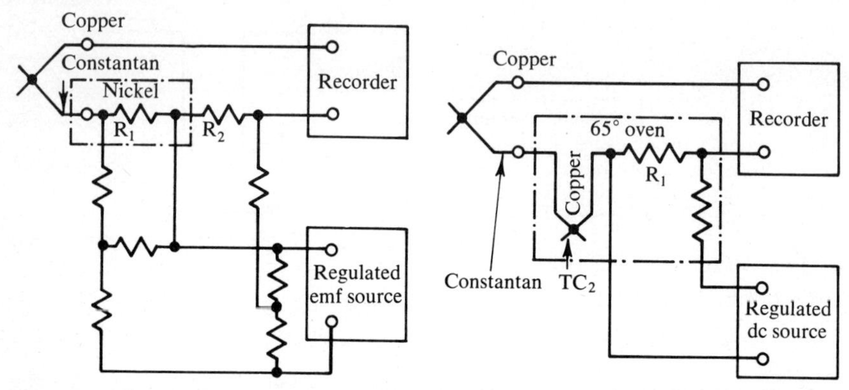

Fig. 14. Cold-junction compensation circuit.

Fig. 15. Cold-junction compensation circuit.

Resistance R_T, responsive to temperature, provides a varying voltage drop, which is measured by the null-balance system shown.

Bridge resistors R_1 and R_2 should be large compared with R_T and R_B. In function, R_1 supplies a constant current to R_T, which in turn provides an IR drop linear with its resistance change; R_2, being large, does not unduly load measuring potentiometer P.

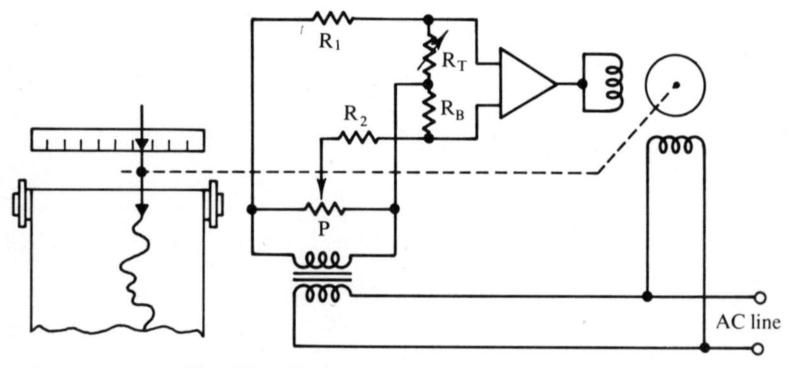

Fig. 16. Resistance-thermometry circuit.

Using a general-purpose high-sensitivity dc laboratory recorder, a temperature-measurement circuit may be as shown in Fig. 17. On a rule-of-thumb basis, R_1 and R_2 should be at least ten times the value of R_F, which in turn should be about equal to the mid-temperature value of R_T.

10. Strain-gage Recording The inherent stability of modern servo-type recorders allows their immediate use for strain-gage readout. The gages may be arranged in bridge form, as dictated by good practice, with a low, regulated dc potential applied to the bridge. The recorder, connected across opposite bridge corners, will have plenty of sensitivity for most applications.

For permanent strain-gage recording systems, the strain gage, its power supply, and the recorder rebalancing slidewire are generally wired into a unified circuit.

Figures 18 and 19 illustrate strain-gage recorder methods in a general way. In Fig. 18, *A* may be an active gage, subject to elongation and compression by the mechanical situation being monitored. For temperature compensation, *B* rides along as a dummy gage, subject to the same temperature changes as the active gage *A* but not disturbed mechanically.

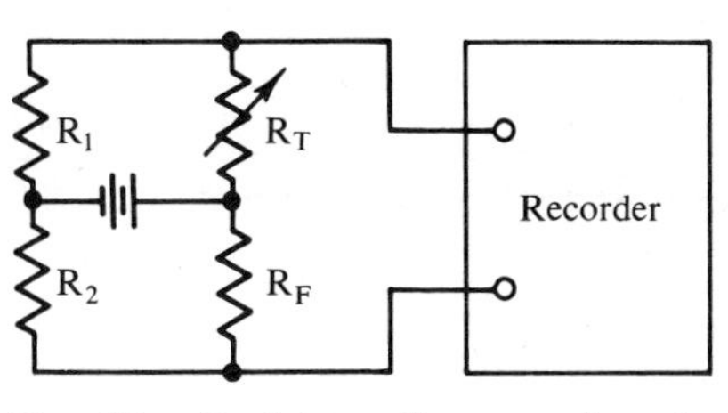

Fig. 17. Resistance-thermometry circuit.

11. Potentiometer Readout Methods Measurement of linear and rotational or angular motion is often a requirement in an electromechanical instrumentation setup. A potentiometer circuit for such service is shown in Fig. 20.

Potentiometer *N* should have very fine steps, to produce smooth data. A practical value would be 2,000 to 5,000 Ω. A series resistor feeds the potentiometer; this padding resistor linearizes the potentiometer output vs. the slider position.

Series resistor 10*N* is large enough to minimize current drawn from the potentiometer, and this also contributes to system linearity.

12. Solid-state Devices, Characteristic Plotting An *X-Y* recorder makes it easy to plot the characteristics of solid-state devices. As an example, Fig. 21 shows a circuit for plotting the characteristic of a zener diode. This circuit clearly demonstrates the flexibility and versatility of an *X-Y* recorder.

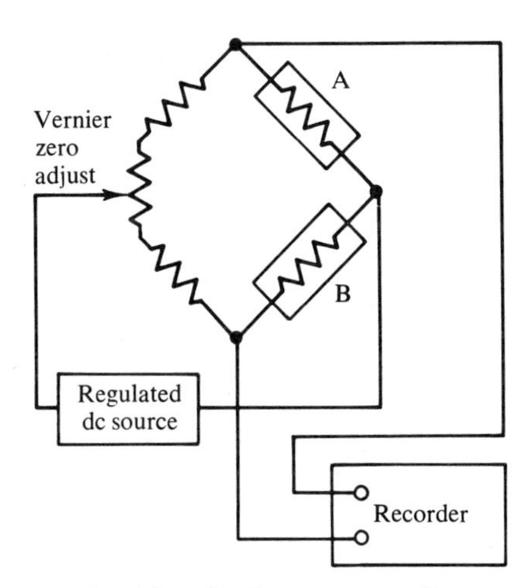

Fig. 18. Strain-gage recording.

Referring to the figure, the current through the zener diode is taken by measuring the drop across R_1, shown as 1 Ω. The *Y* axis of the recorder is set to record full-scale values of a few millivolts, so that a few milliamperes flowing in R_1 will produce the desired record.

The voltage across the zener is applied to the *X* axis. Zero on each axis is placed so as to display the data clearly on the recording chart. As potentiometer P_1 is rotated, the complete zener characteristic will be drawn.

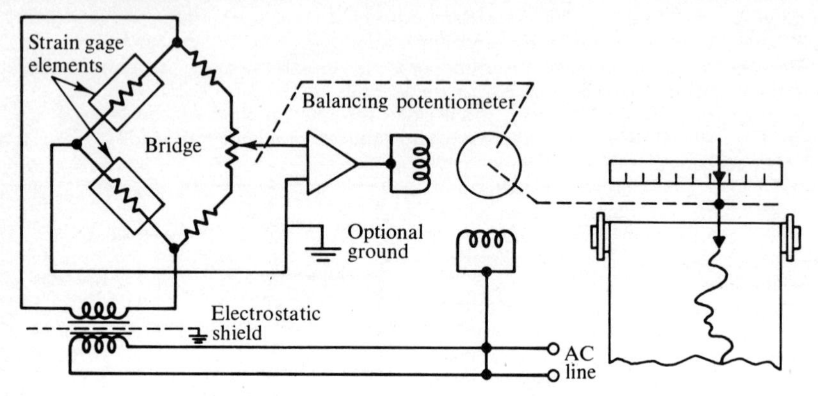

Fig. 19. Strain-gage recording.

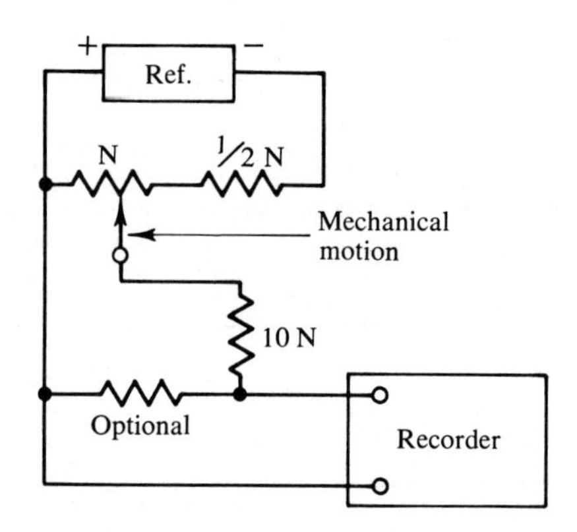

Fig. 20. Mechanical motion or potentiometer follower.

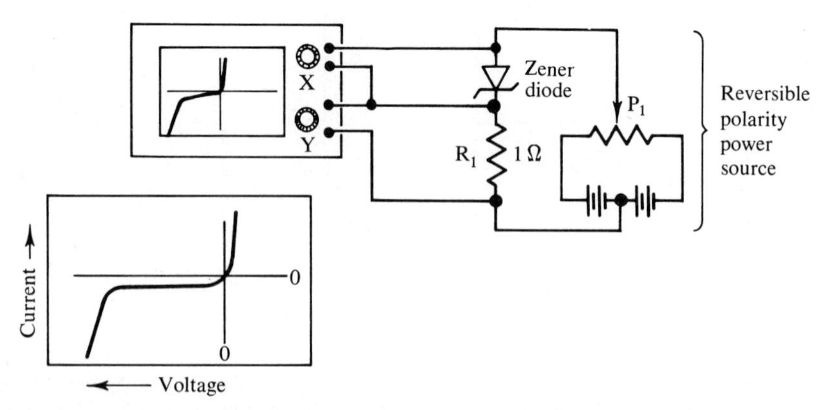

Fig. 21. Solid-state recording; zener-diode characteristic.

Similar circuits will suggest themselves for the plotting of characteristics of transistors, rectifiers, and thyristors, in fact, the entire spectrum of solid-state circuit elements.

13. Use of Recorders: Troubles In general use of recorders, the most common difficulties will be due to circuit noise, arising from ac components in the signals to be recorded and from above-ground conditions. These troubles are common in both strip-chart and *X-Y* recorders.

Figure 22 shows a particularly difficult situation wherein an unfiltered half-wave-rectified signal is furnished to the recorder. The signal contains the wanted dc information, plus a very strong line-frequency component; unless the recorder has an excellent internal filter, the ac component will overload and probably block the recorder amplifier. Further, there will be stray coupling to the power line through the interwinding capacitance of the rectifier transformer, and thus the entire rectifier circuit will be floating at some indeterminate ac level above ground. If the recorder is to cope with this unfavorable situation, it will need to have excellent common-mode rejection as an inherent feature of its design.

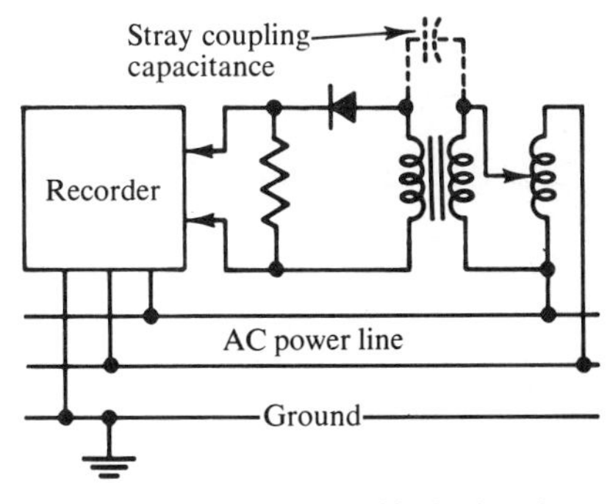

Fig. 22. Half-wave-rectified signal recording—troubles.

The term "common-mode" may be explained by reference to Fig. 23. Here, a very pure, completely floating signal is introduced by a photocell. Such a signal would be most acceptable to a recorder, but the circuit could be rendered inoperative by introducing a common-mode interference as shown. The term "common-mode" refers to unwanted input voltages flowing to the recorder along both input leads in parallel.

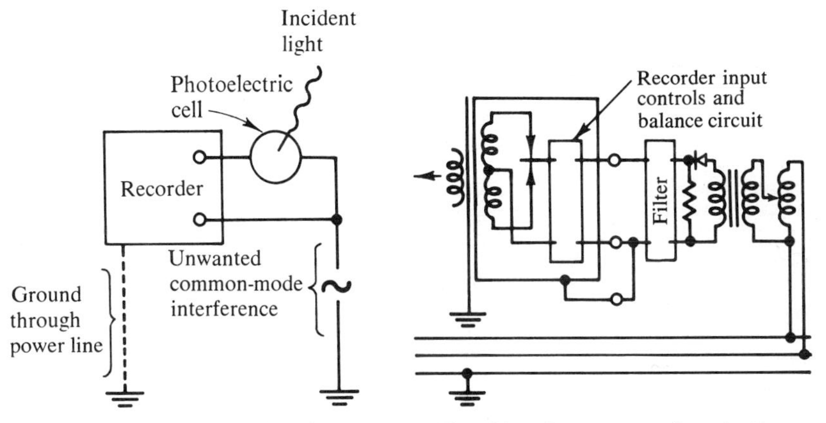

Fig. 23. Common-mode interference. **Fig. 24. Common-mode rejection.**

Figure 24 shows in a general way the configuration required for good common-mode rejection. The input circuits are electrostatically shielded, with the shield terminal brought out of the recorder along with the input terminals. The user may connect this shield-ground or guard terminal to a suitable point in his signal circuit; unwanted ac common-mode signals then carry the guard along with them, and hence currents do not flow to ground. The alternating current between the floating shield and the input-transformer secondary is passed to ground through a second electrostatic shield.

The figure includes a filter to remove the unwanted ac component of the input signal. Some commercially available recorders include filtering systems as part of their input circuits.

When using *X-Y* recorders in situations requiring signal filtering, it is important to have equal filtering delay in the two axes; if this point is overlooked, the record will be looped open between trace and retrace. A typical curve showing this defect appears in Fig. 25.

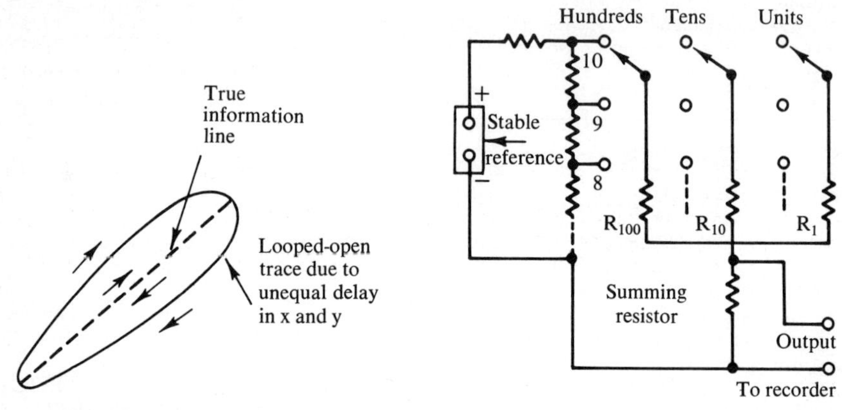

Fig. 25. Retrace diagram.

Fig. 26. Keyboard circuit diagram.

14. Use of Recorders in Digital Systems Data originating from digital sources may be plotted and displayed on an *X-Y* recorder. Data sources include the following:

Keyboard
Paper tape
Punched cards
Magnetic tape
Teletype receiving terminals
Computer readout

Recorders may be coupled to digital systems in two broad ways:

1. The recorder may be analog-type, responding to voltage levels on each axis. Voltages for actuation of *X* and *Y* motions are derived from the output of digital-to-analog converters, the input to these converters being furnished by the digital systems involved.

2. The recorder is designed solely for digital-systems use and is fitted with step-by-step drive systems; data enter the recorder at a bit rate suitable for the stepping speed of the digital drive systems.

15. Systems Using Analog Recorders Figure 26 shows an outline of a circuit used to produce analog-recorder signals from digital inputs. The controls shown would be closed by keyboard keys or, in the case of tape or card reader, by relays, either mechanical or solid-state.

Figure 27 blocks out the main elements of digital systems feeding an *X-Y* recorder. In each case the digital information must be "massaged" to put it into analog-voltage form. Since each system is unique to the individual manufacturer as well as to the particular equipment situation, it is not possible to fit circuit details into this text.

16. Systems Using Digital Recorders Figure 28 shows the general organization of systems employing digital recorders. The computer is programmed to produce output information broken down into *X*- and *Y*-coordinate form and is operated at a digital rate which the recorder will accept.

The recorder axes are driven by powerful and positive stepping motors, giving an incremental movement to the recording system for each small step of data entered.

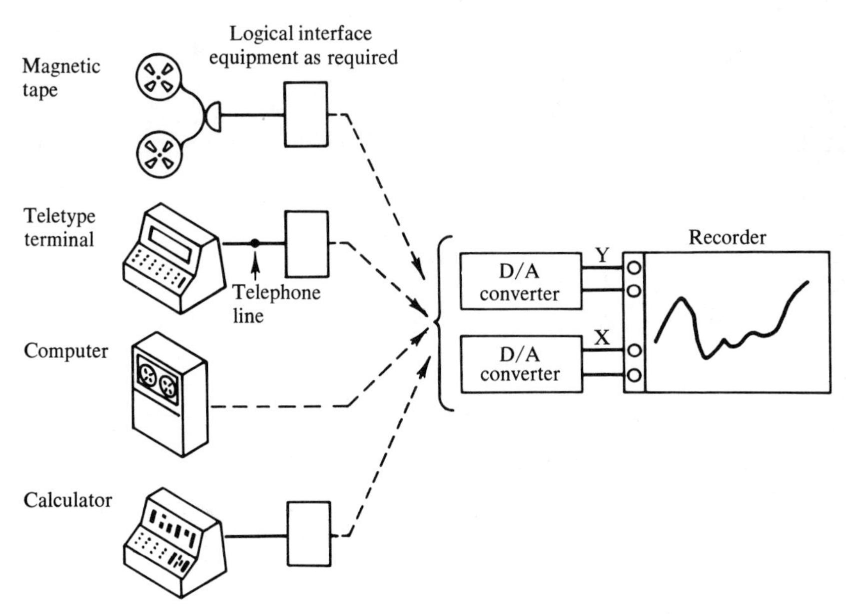

Fig. 27. Digital recording using analog recorder.

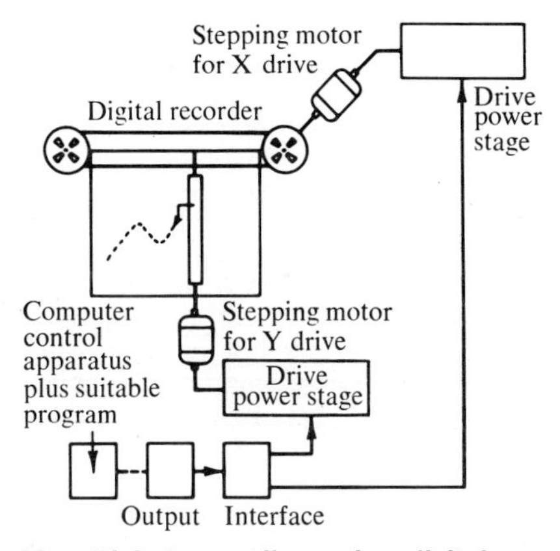

Fig. 28. Digital recording using digital recorder.

Successful application of these digital systems requires a thorough understanding of computer technology and programming, which as stated in the case of the digital-to-analog systems, lies outside the scope of this text.

17. Maintenance and Calibration Recorders are generally electromechanical devices. The subsystems on which they depend, and some remarks on troubles and maintenance, are as follows:

Electrical. The usual recorder requires a high-gain input amplifier which must be maintained as a piece of electronic equipment. If it is of vacuum-tube type, the tubes should be checked and replaced; if of the solid-state type, preventive maintenance should be performed in accordance with the manufacturer's handbook instructions.

Mechanical. The pen-drive system may include a drive motor, gear reduction, an overload slip clutch, pulleys, and drive cable. All these elements should receive periodic examination as to lubrication and adjustment. The slip clutch may be checked by running the recorder to the upper and lower limits of travel; and upon application of a slight additional signal, the drive motor should begin to run, thus slipping the clutch. If this action does not take place, the clutch should be disassembled and cleaned, reassembled, and again checked.

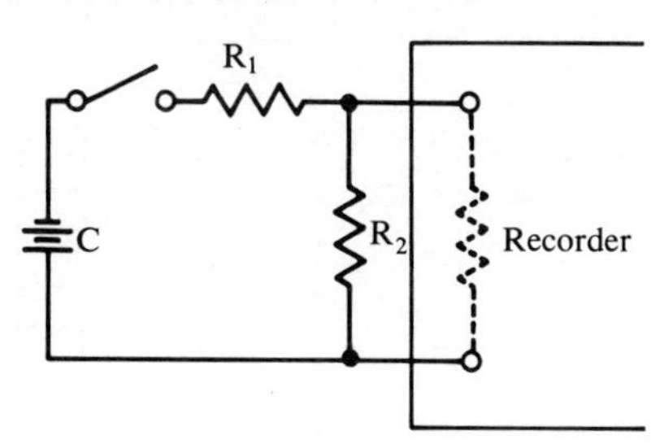

C = Mallory cell (fresh) voltage on light load = 1.35 V
R_1 = 1,000 Ω (or symbol)
R_2 = 100 Ω (or symbol)
R_C = recorder loading; determine from recorder specifications, and make allowance for this loading on final voltage available across R_2.

Fig. 29. Recorder calibration.

Paper-drive systems are varied in design; instructions of the manufacturer will usually be adequate as a guide. The general principles of cleanliness, free running of parts, tightness of all screws, etc., should be observed.

Pens exist in liquid-ink, absorbed-ink (wick systems), and crayon or pencil types. Pens of liquid-ink type should be cleaned with water or alcohol, and fine passages should be cleaned out with a fine-wire probe.

Calibration. As a general statement, recorders may be calibrated by applying a known voltage to the input terminals and observing the recorder reading. At the outset, the instrument, with no input signal, should be adjusted to read exactly zero. Upon application of the known voltage, internal adjustment (usually provided) may be used to bring the instrument reading into agreement with the applied standard voltage. A simple source of medium-accuracy voltage, together with suggested circuit, is the Mallory-cell arrangement shown in Fig. 29.

Chapter 37

Instrumentation Printers

DEXTER C. HARTKE

Hewlett-Packard Company, Santa Clara, California

INTRODUCTION

After all the tests have been completed and the data generated, it becomes necessary to record the numbers and in some cases reduce the data to a more meaningful form. A digital printer can be specified to interface with electronic instrumentation in order to perform this task, thereby providing high-quality hard copy for records and minimizing the drudgery required of the staff.

The laboratory digital printer is a true peripheral whose sole function is to provide data-logging capability with limited symbology for units and other identification. It prints from 1 to 32 columns on varying-width paper at rates from 1 to 100 lines per second with a choice of character sets from arabic numerals only to full alphanumerics in a subset of the ASCII* code. Fully alphanumeric

* For a definition and discussion of the ASCII code, see Chap. 8, Sec. 19.

printers of less than full-page width may be considered extensions of the data-logging printer and are finding increasing applications in instrumentation systems as they become more sophisticated and computer-oriented.

There are no generally observed standards in the field of instrumentation printers, and each manufacturer's designs are unique; hence it is helpful to have a well-researched table of specifications on hand when selecting a laboratory printer. Such tables are compiled from time to time and published in the literature; three are given in the Bibliography.

PRINTER CATEGORIES

Laboratory printers can be categorized as shown in Table 1; each category will be described.

TABLE 1

1. Impact
   a. Font bar or print wheel, "tab"
   b. Rotating drum, "on the fly"
2. Nonimpact
   a. Electrostatic
   b. Electrosensitive
   c. Thermal
   d. Optical
   e. Ink jet
   f. Others

1. Impact Printers Impact printers have had many years of refinement and represent a high level of design maturity which is not likely to see any major breakthrough in the foreseeable future.

In the font-bar or print-wheel system, hereafter referred to as "tab," the entire character set is on a metal or plastic part which is positioned to print the selected character on a column-by-column basis. When all columns are positioned, the print can be made. Adding machines have been adapted to this function and are representative of this class. The print rate is low because the motion of the mechanism is intermittent.

In the rotating drum, or "on-the-fly," system, all the characters are on a continuously rotating drum assembly which has a shaft-position-location system built into it. The electrical system which accepts the input data also keeps track of the print-drum angular position on a column-by-column basis and fires individual column hammers when the desired characters are in print position. This system is capable of print speeds several times faster than those of "tab" printers.

2. Nonimpact Printers Although nonimpact print systems have great potential, only a few relatively expensive printers are deliverable at this writing. There is no metal font; printing is accomplished electrically, optically, or thermally; and mechanical movement can be reduced to a paper-advance mechanism. Special paper is frequently required and is likely to cost several times more than impact-printer paper.

3. Advantages and Disadvantages Compared The major advantages of the nonimpact system are extremely high speed and low noise level.

Table 2 can be helpful in making a determination of the type of mechanism required. Note, however, that there is a fairly large overlap in the impact printers where a choice can be influenced by other considerations such as those in Table 3. Note also that the major if not the sole justification for a choice of the nonimpact printer has to be the need for a print rate greater than 40 lines per second.

PRINTERS IN SYSTEMS

Once a printer type is selected, many other considerations must be given attention, and a choice is dictated in general by the other instrumentation to which the printer is to be mated in a system.

TABLE 2

Printing technique	Character set	Lines/s print speed	No. of columns	Approx price range	Marking medium	Comments
Tab.	10–16 numeric, some alphabetic	1–5	1–24	$100–$2,500	Ink ribbon, pressure-sensitive paper	Noisy
Flying.	16/64 numeric/alphabetic	3–40	10–32	$1,000–$15,000	Ink ribbon, ink roller, pressure-sensitive	Most are very noisy
Nonimpact. .	64+	100+	32+	$5,000+	Frequently* special paper	Low noise

* Some use ink-spray techniques which will work on any paper, and some work has been done on xerographic printers which use ordinary paper.

TABLE 3 Other Considerations in Choosing between Impact and Nonimpact Printers

1. Environment—MIL requirements
2. Radio-frequency interference
3. Paper costs—ink costs
4. Maintenance costs
5. Serial or parallel entry
6. Buffer storage
7. Reliability of instrument operation in general and consistent reproduction of input information

4. System Considerations

Marking Method. There are three marking methods other than nonimpact. They are ink ribbon, ink roller, and pressure-sensitive paper. Ink freezes at low temperatures and is runny at high. Pressure-sensitive paper is expensive but more temperature-tolerant.

Entry Mode. Data may be introduced to the printer in serial, parallel, or some combination of these. For example, one may have a four-line parallel, character serial entry system, which, though not a standard, is gaining acceptance by usage.

Input Codes. There is no standard here, but subsets of ASCII are gaining acceptance. For numeric-only printers, 1248 seems to have near-universal acceptance.

Connectors and Cables. These are the tangible interface between printer and data source and must be meticulously specified right down to the last pin.

Electrical Interface Logic Levels. Here again no absolute standard exists, but TTL* has emerged as the high-usage logic interface for short-haul interconnects up to 10 ft or so in a mild electrical environment where 0.8- to 2.0-V switching levels will not receive a high level of interference.

Maintenance. All printers will need some attention, preferably preventive maintenance, where reliable performance is required. Most electronic repair departments do not have personnel with the particular mechanical repair skill necessary for a particular printer. Therefore, a comprehensive service policy should be considered.

Electromagnetic Compatibility. Are there any rf interference specifications to

* TTL is the abbreviation for transistor-transistor logic, a form of integrated-circuit design for gates and flip-flops, with 0.0 V for the on level and 2.5 V for the complements.

be met? Some printers emit pulse radiation, and this should be clarified with the vendor before making any commitments.

Operational Codes. Who is in command, the printer or the data source? Will asynchronous operation be necessary? That is, will the buffer storage of input data be necessary? These vital operational requirements must be specified.

Special Options. Will any special options ever be needed such as time-of-day clock, motor control, multiple data sources to be printed on one machine, rack mounting, code mixing, roll or fanfold paper, paper receiver, acoustic noise suppression, or character or insignificant zero suppression?

The usual result of a market search for a printer is to find one that does not quite fill the bill, in which case the data sources are modified or the printer vendor is requested to modify his product, which he must do in about 50 percent of his shipments.

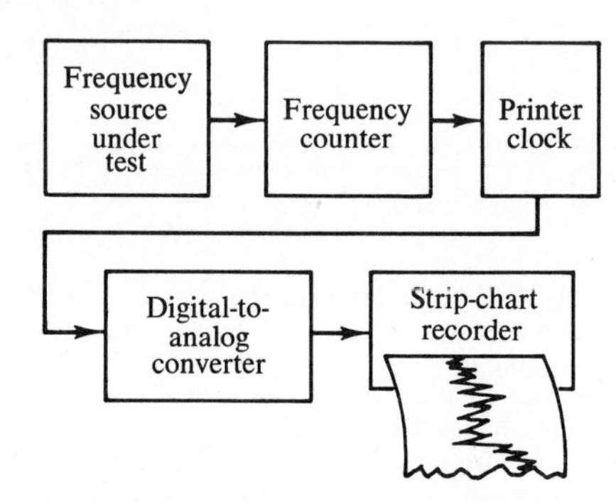

Fig. 1. System for simultaneous printing of digital and analog information.

5. Digital-to-Analog Conversion It is occasionally desirable to add a digital-to-analog converter and a strip-chart recorder to an instrumentation configuration, which can then reduce the tabulated data to a continuous strip-chart record as a function of time. A representative example of such a system is shown in Fig. 1.

The net result of such a system is

1. Digital-data output from the printer at time intervals predetermined by the integral clock
2. Any three columns of data selected for plotting on a continuous basis

The final record can easily be interpreted by inspection to perceive the behavior of the source under test, and any periods of interest can be more precisely examined by referring to the printed digital data.

BIBLIOGRAPHY

Data Logging Printers, *Computer Design,* part I, January, 1966, p. 24; part II, February, 1966, p. 48.

Lab Digital Printers, *EEE,* April, 1970, p. 60.

Miller, R.: Digital Printers—Survey, *Electromechanical Components and Systems Design,* vol. 10, no. 10, pp. 30–32, 34–35, October, 1966.

Section Eleven

Special-function Instruments

Some instruments neither measure a quantity nor generate a signal but are used in conjunction with others that do. This category of devices includes a great variety of instruments; however, we have chosen to isolate only two: amplifiers and power supplies. Some other instruments that might have been included in this section, such as digital-to-analog converters, analog-to-digital converters, and graphic recorders, have been included in various other chapters where their special features are important to the operation of another instrument or where they can be considered along with another class of instruments. (For example, recorders are treated in this handbook as measurement instruments rather than as output devices.) These decisions are arbitrary; therefore, it is strongly suggested that the index be used to help locate discussions of instrument functions.

Amplifiers in this section are described in very general terms. Their use as separate instruments is discussed as well as their use as portions of larger instruments.

Since any circuit needs power to operate, the source of the power plays an important role in the proper functioning of the circuit. The power supply itself becomes a vital device in the instrument or system although it is probably the least understood and most taken for granted part. It is useful to understand the operation and limitations of the surprisingly large number of power supplies available before blindly connecting one to a circuit.

Chapter 38

Amplifiers

CHARLES HOUSE

Hewlett-Packard Company, Colorado Springs, Colorado

Amplifiers are encountered in virtually every electronic system. Their purpose is to amplify, or increase, the magnitude of an electronic signal. Since signals vary greatly in different situations, amplifiers are found in many specialized forms to accommodate these needs.

CATEGORIES

Amplifiers may be categorized in several ways. Table 1 lists several common types by *function* and *application*.

TABLE 1 Amplifier Categories

Function	*Application*
Linear amplifier	Television video amplifier
Logarithmic amplifier	Stereo preamplifier
Operational amplifier	Stereo power amplifier
Wideband amplifier	Radar-pulse amplifier
Tuned amplifier	If amplifier
Differential amplifier	Impedance converter

1. Function Amplifiers categorized by function are distinguished usually by their characteristic gain function. The gain function is a mathematical expression of the ratio of the output signal to the input signal. For example, a *linear* amplifier has an output signal E_o equal to some constant K times the input signal E_{in}. This results in a linear gain characteristic (Fig. 1*a*). By contrast, a *logarithmic* amplifier will have an output signal proportional to the logarithm of the input signal (Fig. 1*b*). An *operational* amplifier performs some mathematical operation, such as time integration, much as the mathematics of integral calculus would do (Fig. 1*c*).

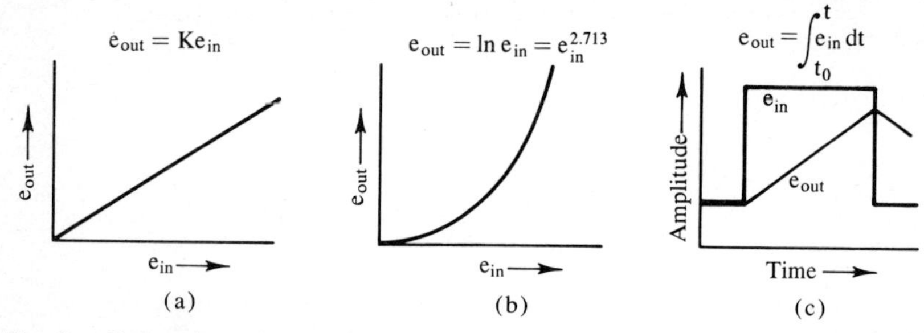

Fig. 1. Categories of amplifiers by function. (*a*) Linear amplifier. (*b*) Logarithmic amplifier. (*c*) Operational amplifier.

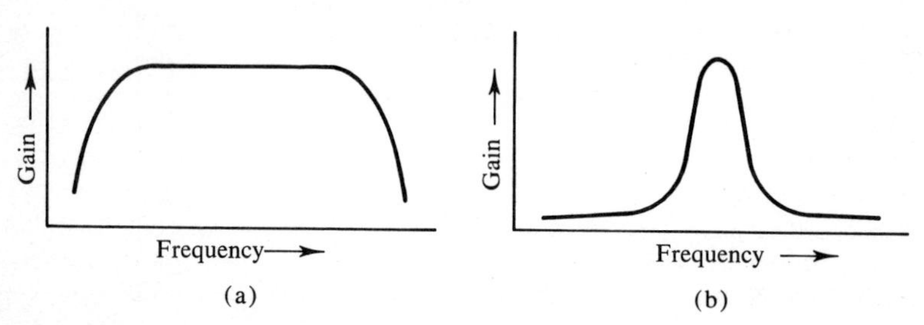

Fig. 2. Categories of amplifiers by frequency response. (*a*) Wideband amplifier. (*b*) Tuned or narrowband amplifier.

The frequency spectrum of an amplifier is another functional classification. A *wideband* amplifier has a gain that is essentially constant over a wide frequency range, whereas a *tuned* amplifier is characterized by high gain in a small frequency band (the tuned frequency) and low gain at other frequencies (Fig. 2).

Still other function categories exist. One that is often encountered is a *differential* amplifier. This amplifier, unique in many respects, is primarily distinguished by having two inputs and two outputs rather than one. The function that it performs is amplification of difference signals between the two inputs and rejection or nonamplification of common signals (Fig. 3). This is of great value in applications where small signals exist in the presence of large noise or hum signals (as from 60-Hz power lines).

Note that an amplifier may be categorized by more than one function. For instance, a description of "a wideband, linear, differential amplifier" would not be uncommon.

2. Application Application categories are more frequently employed than function categories, since one term may be substituted for several functional names. Many amplifiers are designed to do a specific task, and it is thus natural that they should be named accordingly. A television *video* amplifier, for example, is the amplifier which produces the "video" or intensity pattern of the television picture. Such an amplifier has a very detailed list of functional requirements and performance specifications which are not easy to describe, but the amplifier is readily classified by simply calling it a TV video amplifier. Similarly, *stereo* amplifiers have very special gain-frequency compensation curves which are different for tape recorder, phonograph records, or radio-tuner music sources—none of this is mentioned except in the detailed specifications, but it is implied whenever an amplifier is called a complete stereo amplifier.

Further subdivision may be found—a *stereo preamplifier* contains all the gain-curve compensation for the various music sources, while the *stereo power amplifier* is a linear amplifier which multiplies the output of the preamplifier to drive the loudspeakers. It is important to note that a stereo power amplifier could be used for power amplification in some other application, where it might even get a new name—the title "stereo power amplifier" simply describes what it was originally designed to do.

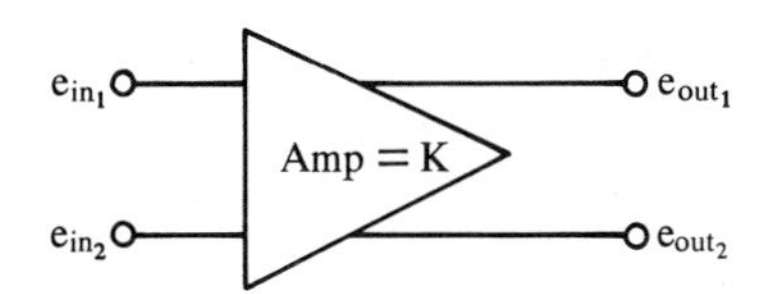

Fig. 3. Differential amplifier. Two cases may be distinguished: (1) $e_{in_1} = e_{in_2}$. This is *common-mode* signal. Then $e_{out} = |e_{out_1} - e_{out_2}|$ = zero. It is hoped that e_{out_1} and e_{out_2} are each equal to zero (which is total rejection of the common-mode signal). (2) $e_{in_1} = -e_{in_2}$. The input signals are equal in magnitude and opposite in phase, constituting a different signal $e_{in} = |2e_{in_1}|$. Then $e_{out} = |2Ke_{in_1}|$.

Application categories may be either specialized or broad-usage. *Radar-pulse amplifiers* are units designed for short bursts of high-power pulses, a rather specialized design and application requirement, while *if* (intermediate frequency) amplifiers are probably among the most common amplifiers found. Intermediate frequency amplification is used in all communications receivers, whether it be AM or FM radio, TV sound, telephone repeaters, or space broadcasts. The frequency band may be quite different for different applications (e.g., 455 kHz in AM radio, 10.7 MHz in FM), but in essence if amplifiers are a special application class of the tuned function described earlier.

Impedance converters represent a broad application class in voltage-amplification requirements. Voltage signals are especially susceptible to distortion (or "loading"), where the input impedance of the amplifier is so low that it modifies the original signal enough that the amplifier's value is reduced considerably. In general, the higher the input impedance of the amplifier, the less the loading on the original signal. Thus, since the wideband amplifier to be used may have a fixed (and relatively low) input impedance, an impedance converter may be used between the signal to be amplified and the amplifier (Fig. 4). Consequently, the primary function of an impedance converter is to present a high input impedance and a low output impedance with a gain of approximately 1. Actually the impedance converter is a special form of the general class of power amplifier. It serves as a good example of assigning an application name to distinguish a particular amplifier from the general class.

3. Miscellaneous There are other categories, of course, which may be distinguished on a data sheet. The terms "solid-state" or "integrated" are often used to denote the use of transistors or integrated circuits for the amplifier-circuit design. From a user standpoint, these claims are of secondary interest; the pertinent parameters are cost, performance, and reliability of the entire amplifier. Reliability is seldom specified, and while information about the circuit components may give an indication of the quality of the unit, it is at best an imperfect index.

Commonly, in amplifier design, the terms Class A, Class AB, Class B, and Class C design are used to describe circuit biasing and operation. For the nondesigner, these terms are of little interest or utility; the same is true for design terms such

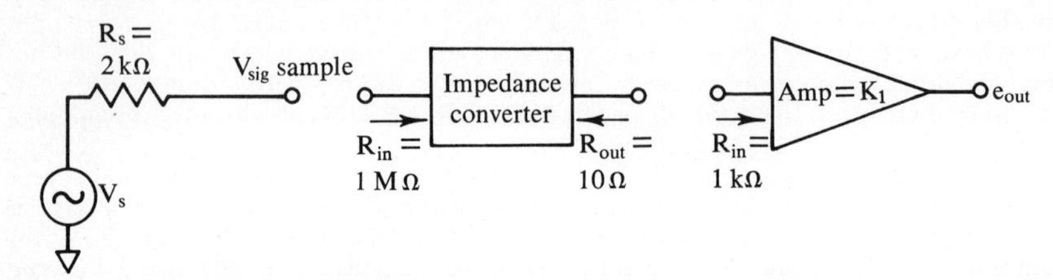

Fig. 4. Impedance-conversion amplifier. Connecting input of amplifier to signal point will "load" the signal by 3×, since R_{in} of the amplifier makes a voltage divider with R_s. Inserting the impedance converter, we find $V_{sig\ sample}$ is not affected greatly

$$\left(\frac{1\ M\Omega}{1\ M\Omega + 2\ k\Omega} = 0.2 \text{ percent reduction}\right)$$

and the 1 K Ω R_{in} of the amplifier loads the output of the impedance converter by only 1 percent. Thus we find $e_{out} \approx 0.33 K_1 V_{sig}$ without an impedance converter and $e_{out} \approx 0.99 K_1 V_{sig}$ with the impedance converter.

as "cascade," "cascode," "Darlington," or other amplifier descriptions. On the other hand, *feedback* amplifiers and *chopper-stabilized* amplifiers are functional classes occasionally of concern to the user.

PERFORMANCE SPECIFICATIONS

Amplifiers all have *performance specifications* to describe in detail how well they do a given function and the conditions under which they work properly. Specifications may be divided into *primary* and *secondary* categories, depending upon their degree of commonality to all amplifier types (Table 2). For instance, *gain* is a primary specification since it is meaningful for all amplifiers. However, common-mode-rejection for a differential amplifier is a secondary specification, since it is important to only one specific amplifier type.

4. Primary *Gain* and *frequency response* (or *bandwidth*) are the two specifications most important to all amplifiers. Because they are related to each other, the gain curve as a function of frequency is often used to specify them (Fig. 5). Alternatively, for the gain-frequency curve shown, the specifications may be written as gain = 20 dB ± 1 dB, bandwidth = 100 kHz to 100 MHz. This form indicates the gain level inside the bandwidth frequencies, but it says nothing about gain outside those frequencies (the usual assumption is that the gain is lower outside the bandwidth points).

TABLE 2 Performance Specification

Primary	*Secondary*
Gain	Attenuation
Frequency response (bandwidth)	Common-mode rejection
Input impedance	Distortion
Output impedance	Drift
Dynamic range	Noise
	Repeatability
	Rise time
	Sensitivity

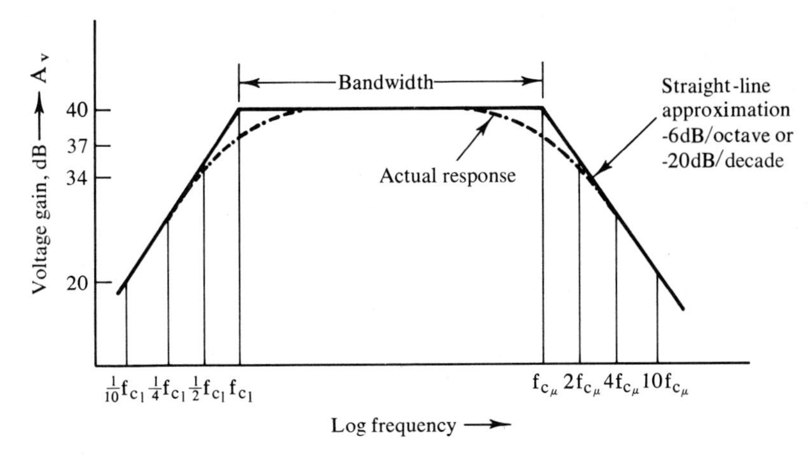

Fig. 5. Definition of bandwidth.

Gain may be written in a variety of ways. It may be stated in terms of a ratio, such as output voltage/input voltage = 100:1, or a voltage gain of 100. More commonly, this ratio is converted into decibels, a logarithmic term which allows easier graphing of the gain-bandwidth curve. Simply stated, the decibel power gain A_p is equal to ten times the common logarithm of the ratio of output power to input power.

$$A_p = 10 \log \frac{P_{\text{out}}}{P_{\text{in}}} \tag{1}$$

The decibel voltage gain A_v is twenty times the logarithm of the voltage ratio.

$$A_v = 20 \log \frac{V_{\text{out}}}{V_{\text{in}}} \tag{2}$$

A conversion chart to convert easily from decibels to gain ratios for both power and voltage is found in Table 3.

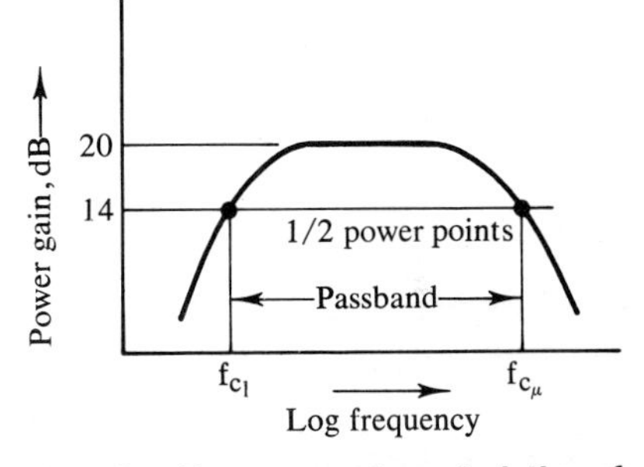

Fig. 6. Response characteristic of bandpass amplifier.

The frequency response or bandwidth of an amplifier is usually defined as the total frequency band where the power gain is equal to or greater than 50 percent of its midband specification (Fig. 6). The 50 percent points, —6 db from the maximum gain, are termed the *upper-* and *lower-frequency cutoff* points. The bandwidth is then

$$\text{BW} = f_{c_u} - f_{c_L} \tag{3}$$

For voltage-gain specifications, the —3-dB points are the cutoff frequencies.

Amplifiers may be *broadband, dc-coupled* ($f_{c_L} = 0$), *low-pass, high-pass,* or *bandpass* (Fig. 7). Shaped rolloff functions may be designed such as gaussian or Chebyshev curves, or adjustable *hf-cutoff* or *lf-cutoff* filters may be provided to eliminate noise or drift.

Input and output impedances are of primary importance in using the amplifier because they indicate the loading effect which the amplifier will impose upon the system (Fig. 4). Impedance is a frequency-dependent term due to various *R, L,* and *C* components. It is usually specified as a shunt input resistance in ohms perhaps in parallel with a shunt capacitance in picofarads (10^{-12} F), and an output series resistance in ohms, with perhaps a series inductance in microhenrys

TABLE 3

Power ratio	Voltage ratio	Decibels
1.0233	1.0116	0.1
1.1220	1.0593	0.5
1.2589	1.1220	1.0
1.5849	1.2589	2.0
1.9953	1.4125	3.0
2.5119	1.5849	4.0
3.1623	1.7783	5.0
3.9811	1.9953	6.0
10.000	3.1623	10.0
15.849	3.9811	12.0
25.119	5.0119	14.0
100.00	10.000	20.0
10^4	100.00	40.0
10^6	1,000	60.0
10^8	10^4	80.0
10^{10}	10^5	100.0

(10^{-6} H) and a shunt capacitance in picofarads. Ordinarily, at low frequencies (<1 MHz), the only factor to be concerned about is the resistance, but at higher frequencies, strict attention to cabling and the total impedance is required for optimum amplifier performance. Many 50-Ω input- and output-impedance amplifiers

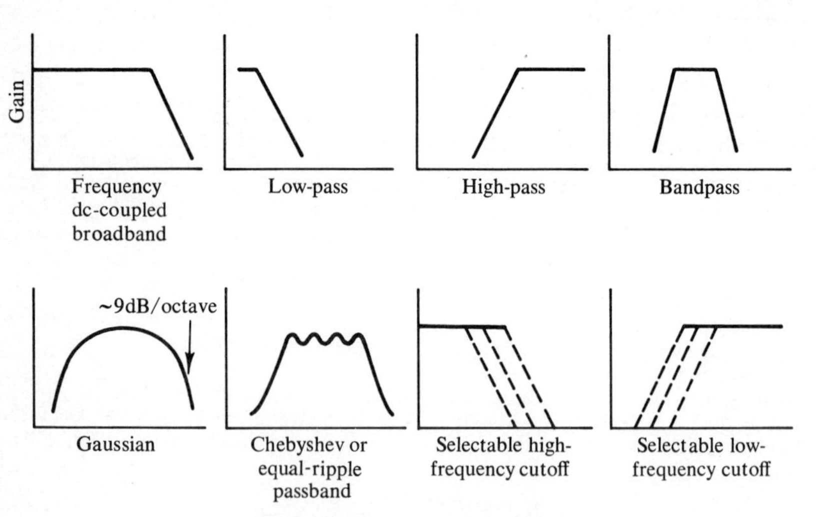

Fig. 7. Gain-frequency plots of amplifier types.

exist, and there are standard 50-Ω cables for connection of such amplifiers. With these systems, frequencies well beyond 100 MHz may be used without concern for the effects of input or output capacitance or inductance.

Dynamic range, the last of the primary specifications, is stated in a variety of ways on amplifier-specification sheets. Perhaps the most common listing is the *maximum output level,* which, for example, might be >10 W into 50 Ω (the input impedance of the next stage, or the "load" seen by the amplifier output), or in another system, >2 V rms into 50 Ω. Another frequent listing is the input dynamic range, which may be stated as 1 V peak-to-peak.

5. Secondary

Attenuation. Since amplifiers commonly are used in a variety of situations, it is usually desirable to have a way to modify the gain to fit a particular requirement.

Attenuators serve the purpose of reducing, or attenuating, the maximum gain. Such attenuation may be continuously variable, as on a volume control for a public-address or stereo amplifier. Alternatively, it may have discrete steps, such as a 20-, 40-, or 60-dB step choice of gain. Many units will include both a calibrated step attenuator and a vernier which allows continuous adjustment between the calibrated steps.

Sensitivity and Deflection Factor. Many amplifiers are designed for use with specific output devices, such as loudspeakers, strip-chart recorders, or television cathode-ray tubes. In such cases, it usually is more meaningful to define the amplifier's gain in terms of its output response to a given input signal. Two terms, one the reciprocal of the other, are encountered.

Sensitivity is the output-signal deflection for a given input signal, such as 8 cm/mV or 10 dB (sound)/volt. *Deflection factor* is the amount of input signal required for a given output deflection, for example, 10 mV/in. In equation form,

$$\text{Sensitivity} = \frac{1}{\text{deflection factor}} \tag{4}$$

In certain cases, the ratio is not explicitly stated. While this occurs most frequently in amplifiers built for the consumer rather than the industrial market, it is not unknown in high-grade equipment. If a specification such as sensitivity = 0.0001 V is encountered, the amplifier name will usually reveal an application category which has a known or constant output characteristic, say 1 V. Thus, "sensitivity" used as listed is really a deflection-factor specification where both the input and output signals are in volts. Gain, of course, may be figured for such an amplifier if desired.

Often a dynamic-range specification is written in terms of sensitivity (e.g., 50 in. when the sensitivity is 5 in./mV) or deflection factor. Calculation will show how much input signal (10 mV in this example) could be accommodated before distortion occurs within the amplifier.

Distortion. Although the largest distortion errors in amplifiers occur when signals exceed the amplifier dynamic range, this is clearly not a valid operating mode. Thus the distortion which concerns us here is what happens to the fidelity or quality of a proper-size input signal as it is amplified.

Several types of distortion specifications are found on amplifier data sheets. Audio (public-address, radio, stereo, and general-purpose) amplifiers are usually concerned with *harmonic distortion,* which is a measure of how much a pure frequency signal (e.g., 1 kHz) gets converted into other frequencies by the amplifier. High-quality amplifiers often have less than 1 percent harmonic distortion for all frequencies within their passband. Linear amplifiers, on the other hand, specify *linearity,* as one would expect. A typical specification might be ± 0.01 percent of full scale (dynamic range), referred to a straight line drawn through zero and the full-scale output. An amplifier may also be specified for its time-domain *pulse distortion,* although this is the least common of the three ways. Such specifications will list rise time in preference to bandwidth, and *overshoot* (e.g., ≤ 2 percent of step) instead of harmonic distortion. Ringing pulse perturbations or other terms are occasionally encountered.

Repeatability and Settling Time. Amplifiers used for display deflection or *X-Y* recorder plotting often mention two specifications nearly unique to those requirements. *Repeatability* is a measure of the ability to hit the same spot again from any point on screen, and may be thought of as repeatable accuracy to a given *X-Y* coordinate. A typical specification might read "less than 0.15 percent error for readdressing a point from any direction."

Settling time is considered to be the total time required for deflecting the beam from one position to another within a stated accuracy. It is written as "less than 200 ns to within 0.25 percent of final value."

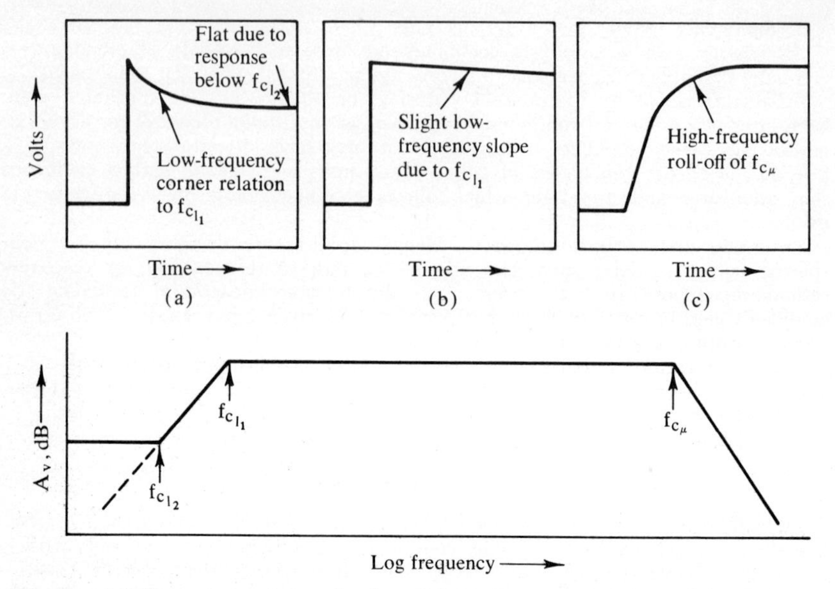

Fig. 8. (*a*) Long-time picture (ms). (*b*) Medium-time picture (μs). (*c*) Fast-time picture (ns).

Terminology changes with different manufacturers on these parameters. Other names for repeatability include plotting accuracy, line-relocation accuracy, and random-access accuracy. Settling time is also referred to as step-function response, random-positioning time, beam-deflection time, and jump-scan time.

Rise Time and Delay Time. Time-domain amplifiers, such as those found in oscilloscopes, radar-pulse amplifier systems, and general-purpose areas, are often specified by *rise time* instead of or in addition to bandwidth. There is a correlation between frequency response and step response. Since a perfect step function contains all harmonics of a sine wave, theoretically a step-function response displays all frequency imperfections simultaneously. Figure 8 shows the interpretation of the resulting waveform (as seen on a time response of an oscilloscope) in terms of the classical gain-frequency curve.

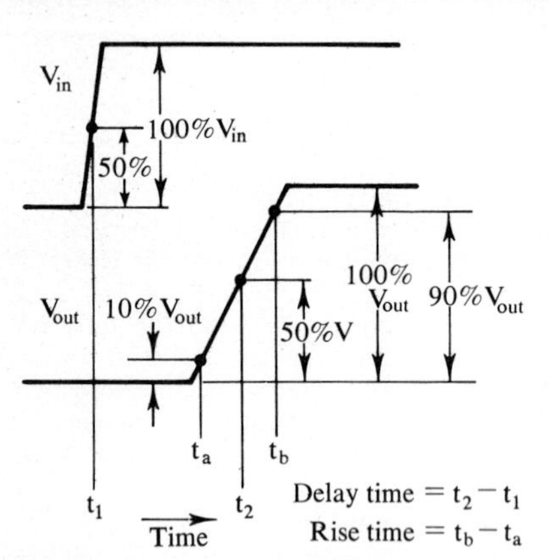

Fig. 9. Time-domain picture illustrates delay-time and rise-time comparison.

The time-domain picture of Fig. 9 illustrates both *rise-time* and *delay-time* specifications. Rise time is the time of transition between the 10 and 90 percent points of the total step amplitude. It is related to the amplifier bandwidth by the equation

$$t_R = \frac{0.35}{\mathrm{BW}} \tag{5}$$

Thus, if $t_R = 10$ ns, the bandwidth is 35 MHz. The delay time is a measure of the time between application of the step to the amplifier input and the rise of the output to 50 percent of the final step value. This specification is far less common than rise time, but it is useful if either time-delay or phase-correlation data are needed.

Special Gain Functions. Open-loop gain A_o is analogous to the intrinsic gain of an unconnected amplifier box while closed-loop or feedback gain A_f is the useful output gain with a feedback gain β in the loop (Fig. 10). A transfer-function specification, frequently termed a scale factor K, may appear as K_1 A/V or K_2 V^2/V in two of the many types of operational amplifiers (Fig. 11). See also sensitivity and deflection factor.

Noise. Amplifier *noise* generation can be a serious problem in situations where low-level signals such as physiological phenomena are to be amplified. There are several components of noise that contribute to an overall specification; three of the most common types are *thermal noise* in the input resistance, vacuum-tube *shot noise,* and *transistor noise.* Noise is usually a frequency-oriented problem as well, with *white noise* being broadband in contrast to some low-frequency-dominant transistor noise.

Noise specifications may be referred to the input (rti) or referred to the output (rto), which are not necessarily related to each other by the amount of gain in the amplifier because of the different components which affect noise. Additionally, noise levels may be described as *peak-to-peak* (p-p), *root-mean-square* (rms), or *tangential,* depending upon whether the measurement is based upon peak excursions, sinusoidal mean, or pulse average.

Examples of noise specifications might be as follows: (1) For an amplifier with a gain of 1,000 (voltage ratio), 0 to 10 Hz, 1 μV p-p rti and 10 μV p-p rto; to 50 kHz, 5 μV rms rti and 500 μV rms rto. (2) For an amplifier with a bandwidth of 20 MHz with either 50-Ω or 1-MΩ inputs, 300 μV p-p rti (50-Ω input), 30 pV/Hz rms rti for 1-MΩ input.

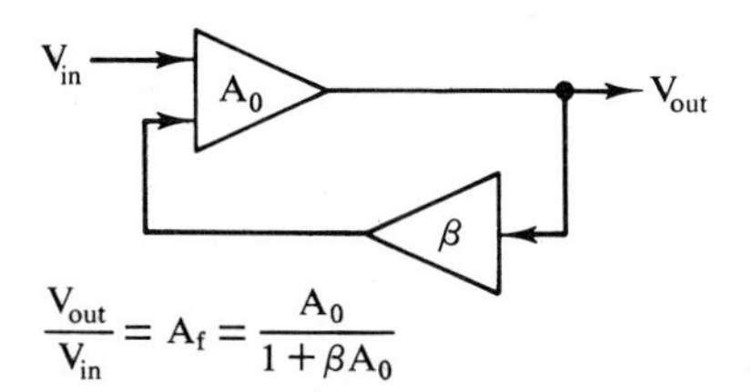

Fig. 10. Useful output gain of amplifier with feedback gain.

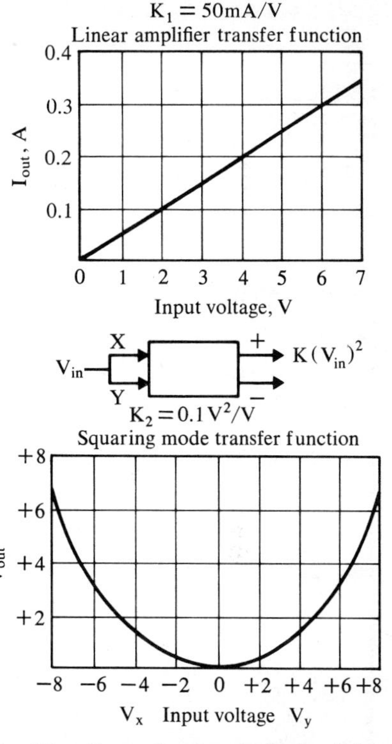

Fig. 11. Example of scale factor *K* for amplifier transfer function.

Drift. A drift specification may refer to either a gain or a position drift with time in an amplifier. The more common meaning is a position drift, which would show up on any deflection display as a changing (i.e., drifting) dc level of the amplifier output voltage.

As with noise, a drift specification is usually referred to the input (rti) or to the output (rto). It is listed for both short-term (minutes usually or days) and long-term (days or months) effects. Environmental changes, especially temperature, affect drift significantly enough that a temperature coefficient of drift is often included on a specification sheet.

A typical drift specification might read as follows: Zero drift (offset) per day: ±5 μV rti, ±200 μV rto; per month: ±25 μV rti, ±500 μV rto; temperature coefficient ±1 μV rti, ±40 μV rto per °C.

Common-mode Rejection Ratio. Differential amplifiers encounter either common-mode or difference signals or a combination (Fig. 3). It is desirable that common-mode signals be rejected, but as a practical matter, since the two sides of the amplifier circuit are never precisely balanced in all respects, some conversion of the common-mode signal occurs. The common-mode-rejection ratio (CMRR) is a measure of the amplifier's ability to avoid this conversion.

If a signal of $+X$ V is applied to both inputs of a differential amplifier, and some conversion to differential signal occurs, Y V of differential output signal will result ($X > Y$). By contrast, if $+X$ V is put into one side of the amplifier and $-X$ V into the other side, the differential gain gives Z V of differential output ($Z > X$).

$$\text{CMRR} = \frac{Z}{Y} = \frac{\text{differential signal gain}}{\text{differential conversion gain}} \tag{6}$$

CMRR is usually given in decibels, a 100-dB level indicating that a differential signal of 100 μV is displayed equally as well as a common-mode signal of 10 V. Such ratios are especially important when measurements of low-level signals (such as strain-gage or medical-transducer signals) are made in the presence of large electromagnetic fields (such as 60-Hz power transformers). CMRR is usually degraded by inclusion of attenuators and other front-panel controls such as ac coupling, as well as high frequencies.

FRONT PANEL

The front panel of an amplifier is usually very simple to understand. Figure 12 illustrates a standard amplifier panel configuration, from which we may note its operation. The power switch is self-explanatory along with the light to indicate whether the power is on or not. An input connector is provided, this instance being a BNC connector, to accept a common type of connecting cable. The input impedance, here 1 MΩ with 20-pF shunt capacitance, is listed near the connector. The output connector and impedance are handled similarly except that the capacitance and inductance are considered negligible with 50 Ω. A brief description of the amplifier's function is usually found with the model number; in this case, the bandwidth is simply said to be "wideband." Since no other qualifier is mentioned, we may assume that the gain is linear. The gain itself is variable two ways, first with the calibrated "gain" attenuator control which provides steps of 20-dB gain from 0 to 60 dB, and second with the "vernier" which allows setting any gain between the calibrated steps. The "uncal" light is lighted whenever the "vernier" is being used to indicate that, for example, the gain is really less than the 40 dB that the "gain" knob indicates in the picture. The panel does not say anything about whether the gain is voltage or power, but we may conclude that it is voltage gain since the gain attenuator works in 20-dB steps. A power amplifier would typically be calibrated in 10-dB steps.

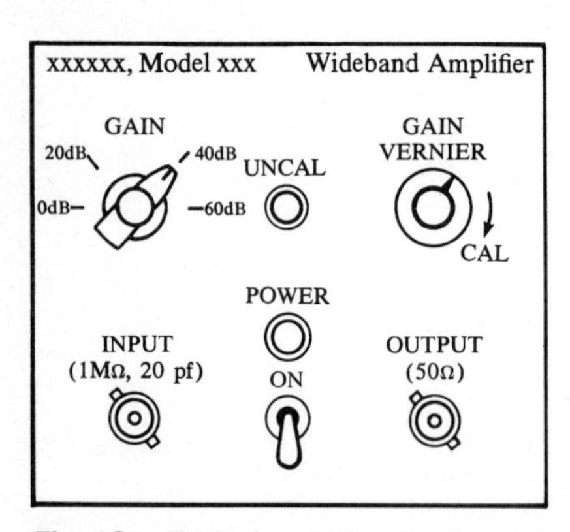

Fig. 12. Typical amplifier front panel.

Figure 13 shows a much more complex amplifier front panel, which represents a specialized type of time-multiplexed differential amplifier intended for use as a "plug-in" oscilloscope amplifier. Observe first that two separate sets of controls exist, one for channel A and the other for channel B. The input connectors are differential, with the plus (+) and minus (−) inputs clearly marked. A ground lug is also provided, so that either side of the input may be grounded if only a single-ended signal is to be amplified. The input impedance is marked as before. Note, however, that no output connector is seen. The output is on the back panel, mating with the connector to the oscilloscope cathode-ray tube (CRT), when the amplifier is "plugged in." Power for the amplifier is also provided from the oscilloscope through this connector so that no power switch is found on the front panel.

The gain is marked in "deflection factor" rather than decibels, since a given input-voltage signal will cause a given deflection on the CRT. The most sensitive range (maximum gain) is the 1 mV/div range, and the attenuator has ranges in a 1, 2, 5, 10 division ratio up to 500:1. The "vernier," concentric with the "gain" knob, works just as before, but no "uncal" light is included.

The frequency bandwidth is stated to be between dc (zero frequency) and 1 MHz, but both the low-frequency cutoff and the high-frequency cutoff points

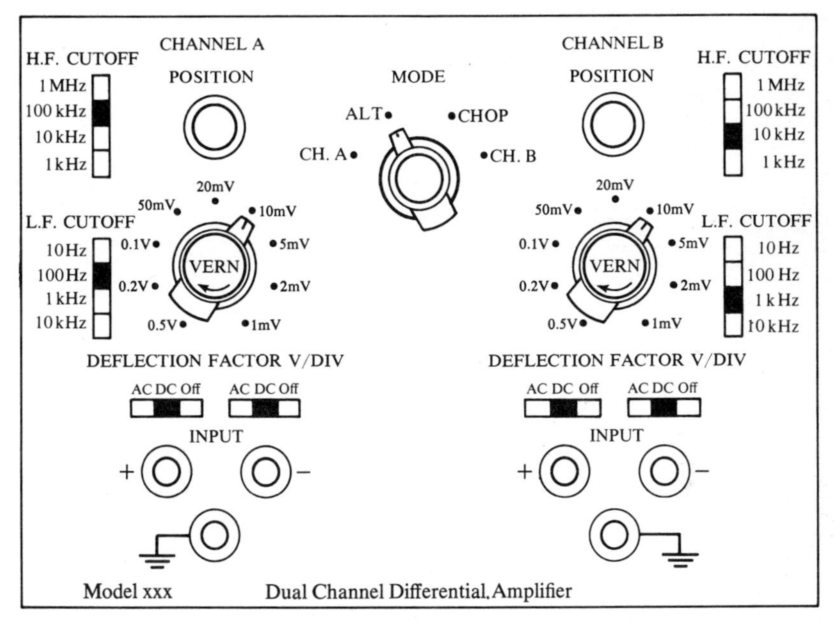

Fig. 13. Complex amplifier front panel.

are adjustable. This permits using the amplifier as either a wideband amplifier or a selectable narrowband amplifier for special measurements.

Lastly, a "function" knob is noted. This controls the time-multiplexing of the two channels. The display modes available are channel A only, channel B only, or both channels displayed "simultaneously" in either an "alternate" or "chop mode." This presentation takes advantage of the CRT display and human-eye characteristics. For high-speed sweeps, the multiplexer may alternate between channels, and the eye will see two nonflickering traces for the same reason that the eye does not discern the alternating current in electric light bulbs. At lower sweep speeds, the beam is chopped between the two channels with rapid electronic switching, and provided enough segments occur (>500), the segments merge to appear continuous to the eye.

SOURCES OF ERROR

6. Gain Specifications Gain is defined in a variety of ways, and it is therefore important in checking specifications to determine which definition is being used.

Figure 14*a* depicts an amplifier as a two-port black box with an input impedance Z_i, an output impedance Z_o, and an intrinsic voltage generator of gain μ.

Insertion of the amplifier between a source and load as shown in Fig. 14*b* permits several gain definitions. The *actual gain* is most often specified. This is simply $A_v = V_2/V_1$ for voltage gain and $A_p = P_2/P_1$ for power gain. The *insertion power gain* $A_{i_p} = P_2/P_d$ is a measurement of the gain difference resulting from insertion of the amplifier. *Transducer gain* is defined as P_2/P_s and is of primary importance when maximum power amplification is sought.

Power gain in decibels, mentioned earlier as a logarithmic expression, is fully written as follows:

$$A_p = 10 \log \frac{P_2}{P_1} = 10 \log \frac{V_2^2 Z_1}{V_1^2 Z_L} = 20 \log \frac{V_2}{V_1} + 10 \log \frac{Z_i}{Z_L} \tag{7}$$

Voltage gain in decibels is the first term of the right side of the above equation; note that it is equal to the power gain only with $Z_i = Z_L$. Power or voltage

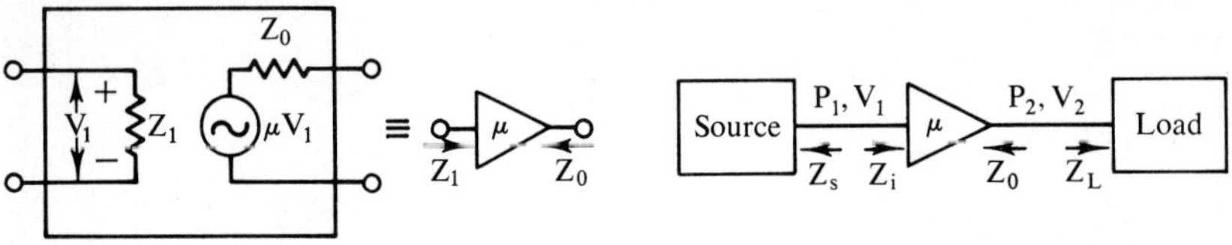

(a) (b)

Fig. 14. Examples of amplifier gains.

$$\text{Actual voltage gain} = \frac{V_2}{V_1} = A_v = \frac{\mu Z_L}{Z_o + Z_L}$$

$$\text{Actual power gain} = \frac{P_2}{P_1} = A_p = \frac{V_2^2 Z_i}{V_1^2 Z_L} = \frac{\mu^2 Z_i Z_L}{(Z_o + Z_L)^2}$$

$$\text{Insertion power gain} = \frac{P_2}{P_D} = A_{i_p} = \frac{V_2^2 (Z_s + Z_L)^2}{Z_L^2 V_s^2} = \frac{\mu^2 Z_i^2 (Z_s + Z_L)^2}{(Z_o + Z_L)^2 (Z_s + Z_i)^2}$$

$$\text{Transducer power gain} = \frac{P_2}{P_s} = \frac{4\mu^2 R_s^2 Z_L Z_i^2}{(Z_o + Z_L)^2 (Z_s + Z_i)^2 Z_s}$$

Note: At low frequencies, resistances R may be substituted for impedances Z.

gain expressed in decibel form is especially useful for two reasons. First, the decibel gains of cascaded amplifier stages may simply be added to find the total gain; second, a plot of decibel gain against logarithmic frequency (Fig. 5) results in approximately linear curve plotting.

7. Bandwidth and Rise Time Since step-response testing is an easy method to determine amplifier frequency response, it is important to note that while many amplifier responses approximately follow Eq. (5), some do not. A range of values for the constant from 0.30 to 0.50 accommodates virtually all amplifier types. It is safe to assume 0.35 is accurate only if the step response reveals no more than 2 percent *overshoot* or *hook* at the top of the step.

Unlike gain expressed in decibels, rise times are not simply additive for cascaded stages. Rather, a composite rise time (and hence bandwidth) may be calculated within about 10 percent with the following equation:

$$t_{R_{comp}} = \sqrt{(t_{R_1})^2 + (t_{R_2})^2 + \cdots + (t_{R_n})^2} \tag{8}$$

This equation is valid for $n \leq 6$; overshoot of each stage ≤ 2 percent.

8. Cable Connections The errors due to cable connections are often troublesome for the user. The most obvious consideration is the effect of cables with the input and output impedance.

If the amplifier has a 50-Ω output, it will perform best with a 50-Ω termination at the far end of a 50-Ω cable. Otherwise, the inductance and capacitance of the cable will cause high-frequency mismatch. If unshielded cable is used, radiation of the output signal may be expected. This could conceivably couple back to the input and cause distortion, oscillation, or unstable operation.

Differential amplifiers often suffer CMRR distortion from mismatch of input cables, such as a 50-Ω cable on the positive side and a 600-Ω cable on the negative side. While at dc conditions, such a situation will work adequately, but at high frequencies the common-mode distortion from the cables alone is usually far in excess of the amplifier's specification.

Chapter **39**

Regulated DC Power Supplies

ARTHUR DARBIE

Hewlett-Packard Company, Berkeley Heights, New Jersey

INTRODUCTION

Virtually all electronic devices and circuits require one or more sources of direct current for their operation. According to the requirement, this dc source may be referred to as "B+," the "bias supply," the "collector source," or simply the "power supply."

Most electronic measuring instruments contain their own internal power supplies, but separately packaged power supplies are required in many electronic systems applications and for use as basic bench instruments. Dc power supplies are also required in a wide variety of applications unrelated to electronic circuitry—e.g., powering lasers, electromagnets, and special-purpose gas lamps; charging batteries; and energizing electrochemical solutions.

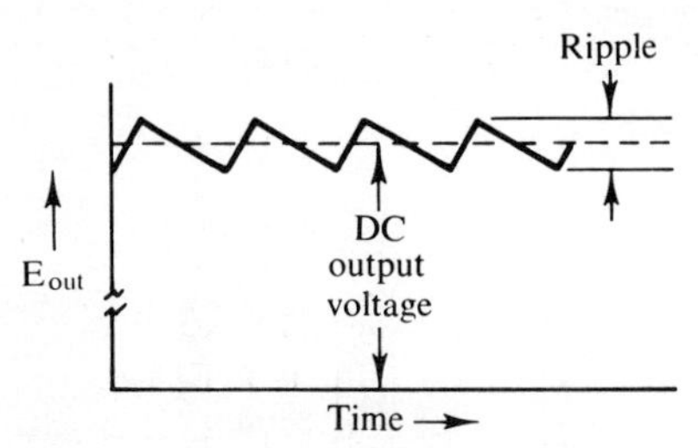

Fig. 1. Typical power-supply output-voltage waveform.

The basic function of a dc power supply—converting readily available alternating current into direct current—can be accomplished using any basic rectifier circuit. However, the resulting direct current will still have a sizable ac component (called "ripple"—see Fig. 1), and even the dc level will vary significantly with normal changes in input ac voltage ("line regulation"), output load resistance ("load regulation"), temperature ("temperature coefficient"), and time ("stability").

The dc output imperfections of a simple rectifier circuit are of small importance in less critical applications; however, as technology in all fields becomes more sophisticated, the need for a more constant dc output level becomes imperative if the performance of the device, circuit, or system fed by the power supply is not to be impaired. Consequently, *regulated* dc power supplies are considered *basic* bench instruments in the same class with oscilloscopes, VTVMs, counters, etc.

The circuit of a regulated power supply differs from its unregulated cousin because of the addition of a control element in parallel with, or in series between, the rectifier and the load device. Since a parallel (or "shunt") regulator must withstand the full output voltage under normal operating conditions and is less efficient for most applications, it is less often used than the series regulator.

Figure 2 is a simplified schematic of a power supply employing a series regulator, or series control element, which acts as a variable resistance connected in series with the load resistor. Internal circuitry automatically and continuously varies the resistance of the control element in such a way as to keep the power-supply output

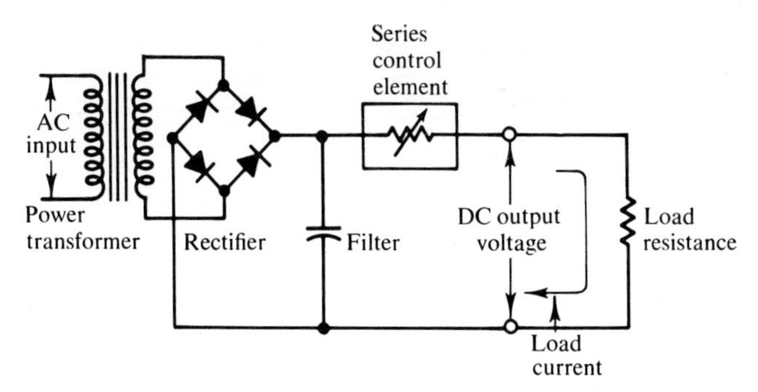

Fig. 2. The basic series-regulator circuit.

more nearly constant in spite of ac-input-line disturbances, load changes, temperature changes, etc.

THE ADJUSTABLE CONSTANT-VOLTAGE POWER SUPPLY

Although the voltage setting of a power supply may be intentionally altered by the operator, at any given setting the output voltage of an *ideal* constant-voltage power supply will not change in response to the passage of time or variations of ac line voltage, load resistance, or ambient temperature (the temperature of the air surrounding the power supply). Figure 3 shows the independence of the output voltage with respect to output-current load demands. Since the ratio of $\Delta E_{out}/\Delta I_{out}$ is zero, the *ideal* constant-voltage source has a zero-ohm output resistance. *Practical* constant-voltage power supplies come remarkably close to the ideal, with output resistances of less than 1 mΩ being common. At this value, the output resistance of a constant-voltage (CV) power supply is usually less than the resistance of the leads used to connect it to its load.

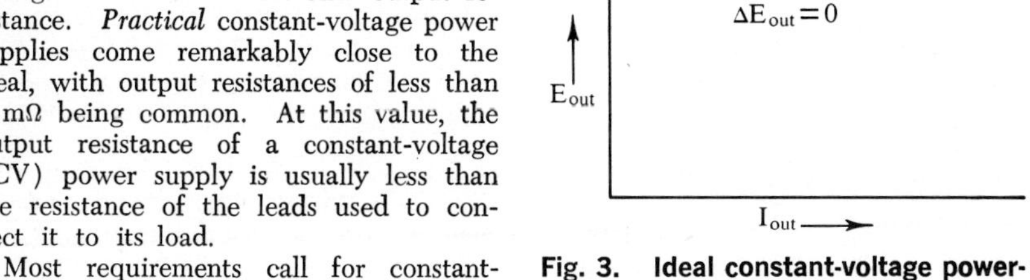

Fig. 3. Ideal constant-voltage power-supply output characteristic.

Most requirements call for constant-voltage power supplies (rather than constant-current supplies). For example, amplifier design is normally based on a constant-voltage dc supply as its primary energy source, and the main power supply feeding a multiple-stage amplifier or counter-logic circuitry will in virtually all cases be a CV power supply.

Thus, unless otherwise indicated, the name "power supply" generally implies a *constant-voltage* dc power supply.

A constant-voltage power supply can be one of three types:

1. Fixed output voltage
2. Output adjustable over a narrow voltage span, or "slot," typically ±5 or ±10 percent of nominal

3. Output adjustable over a wide voltage span, usually from zero to maximum rating

Type 3 is most common for general-purpose bench use, although type 2 is also frequently employed, for example, when powering operational-amplifier or digital-logic circuitry; type 1 is most commonly found as a "built-in" power supply.

Although exact circuit techniques depend upon the manufacturer, the output capability, and whether the supply has a fixed, slot, or wide-range variable output—the general concept of a CV power supply can be discussed in terms of Fig. 4, which shows the basic feedback-circuit principle used in most low- and medium-voltage power supplies of small to moderate power capability.* The principle is the same whether it is called a bridge regulator, an operational-amplifier regulator, or simply a power-supply regulator.

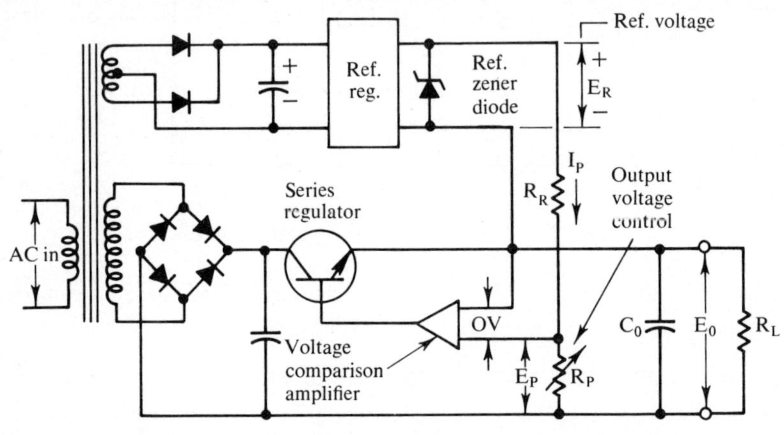

Fig. 4. Constant-voltage regulated dc power supply.

The ac input, after passing through a power transformer, is rectified and filtered. The series regulator, by feedback action, alters its voltage drop so as to keep the regulated dc output voltage constant in spite of changes in the load, unregulated rectifier output, or other disturbances. The comparison amplifier continuously monitors the difference between the voltage E_P across the front-panel voltage control R_P and the output voltage E_o. If these voltages are not equal, the differential comparison amplifier produces an amplified error signal. This error signal is of such a magnitude and polarity as to change the conduction of the series regulator, thereby changing the current through the load resistor until the difference between E_o and E_P reduces to zero volts.

Keeping the net difference between the two voltage inputs to the comparison amplifier at zero by feedback action also results in the voltage across the resistor R_R being held equal to the stable reference voltage E_R. Thus the programming current I_P flowing through R_R is constant and equal to E_R/R_R. The input impedance of the comparison amplifier is very high, and essentially all the current I_P flowing through R_R also flows through R_P. Because this programming current I_P is constant, E_P (and hence the output voltage) is variable and directly proportional to R_P. Thus the output voltage becomes zero if R_P is reduced to zero ohms.

* For clarity and consistency, it is assumed throughout this chapter that *npn* power transistors are employed as series-regulating elements, and that the reference circuit and comparison amplifier have the positive output bus as a common terminal. The use of *pnp* series power transistors would have the effect of reversing all terminal and diode polarities (including the polarity of the reference circuit), without in any other way altering the diagrams and concepts.

The quality of performance of a power supply depends upon many factors, including immunity of the reference zener diode, the output-control resistors (R_R and R_P) and the comparison-amplifier input stages from changes due to noise and temperature; the gain and bandwidth of the comparison amplifier and the series regulator; and adequate separation of heat-producing components from heat-sensitive elements, electric-field-producing components from field-sensitive components, etc. Typical general-purpose laboratory supplies have load and line regulation of 0.01 to 0.05 percent, and ripple and noise of 200 μV to 2 mV rms, while more expensive high-performance supplies improve these figures by factors of 10 or more.

Most power supplies include a large output capacitor C_o, but not primarily in order to reduce ripple, as at first might seem likely—the high-gain amplifier and series regulator actively cancel the rectifier ripple. The power-supply regulator is actually a multistage feedback amplifier, and the large capacitor C_o is included to prevent this amplifier from oscillating regardless of whether the load is essentially resistive or has added capacitance or inductance.

THE ADJUSTABLE CONSTANT-CURRENT POWER SUPPLY

For some applications, it is desired to set the output *current* (rather than the voltage) to a desired value. The ideal constant-current power supply retains the set value of output current in spite of any change in ac line voltage, load resistance, and ambient temperature. Just as the constant-voltage supply changes its output *current* whenever the load resistance changes, so the constant-current supply alters its output *voltage* in response to load-resistance changes. Figure 5 shows this independence of output current with respect to output-voltage demands. Since the ratio E_{out}/I_{out} is infinitely large, the ideal constant-current source is described as having an infinite output resistance.

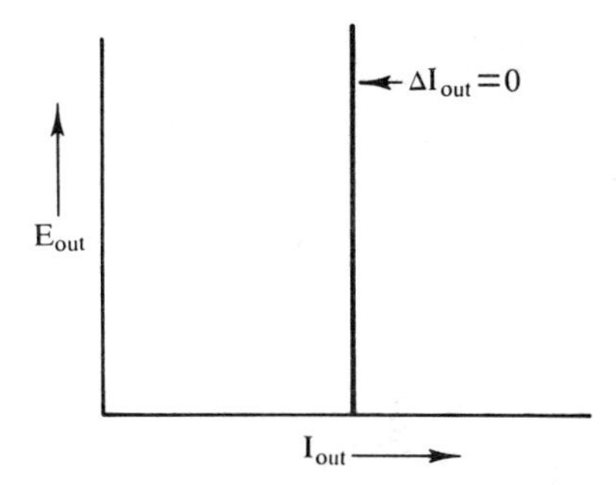

Fig. 5. Ideal constant-current power-supply output characteristic.

Practical constant-current power supplies achieve output resistances in excess of a megohm—large enough that placing an ordinary voltmeter in parallel with the output can degrade regulation performance.

Constant-current (CC) power supplies find many applications in semiconductor circuitry and component testing, and are also used to feed the coils of electromagnets—the magnetic field is proportional to the current through the coil, not the voltage across it, and a constant-current power supply correctly compensates for the inevitable coil resistance changes due to self-heating and external temperature deviations. CC supplies are also employed in precision electroplating, in many electrochemical applications (e.g., coulometry), and for powering lasers and other special-purpose gas-discharge lamps.

Just as multiple loads for constant-voltage power supplies are always connected in parallel (never in series), multiple loads for constant-current power supplies must be connected in series (never in parallel).

As in the case of CV power supplies, various circuit techniques exist to achieve CC regulation, but most commonly the circuit concept of Fig. 6 is employed. Notice that many of the elements of this CC supply are identical with the basic elements of the CV supply of Fig. 4. Just as in the case of the CV circuit, the feedback loop acts continuously to keep the two inputs to the comparison amplifier equal; one of these inputs is the voltage drop across the front-panel current control R_Q, while the other is the IR drop developed by the load current I_o flowing through the current-monitoring resistor R_M. If these two inputs to the comparison amplifier are momentarily unequal, then the comparison-amplifier output changes the conduction of the series regulator, thereby changing the load current and the voltage drop across R_M until the error voltage at the comparison-amplifier input is reduced to zero.

The performance achieved using the circuit concept of Fig. 6 depends on the factors given previously for the CV circuit, and upon the stability, temperature coefficient, and ohmic value of R_M. Regulation of the order of 0.01 percent for load or line changes, and ripple and noise of 100 μA to 1 mA are typical of general-purpose constant-current power supplies, while more sophisticated units improve upon these figures by factors of 10 or more.

Notice that Fig. 6 includes an output capacitor C_o. Some amount of output capacitance is present in most general-purpose power supplies as a practical deterrent against feedback oscillation. However, the ideal constant-current supply must be able to change its output voltage rapidly in response to sudden load-resistance

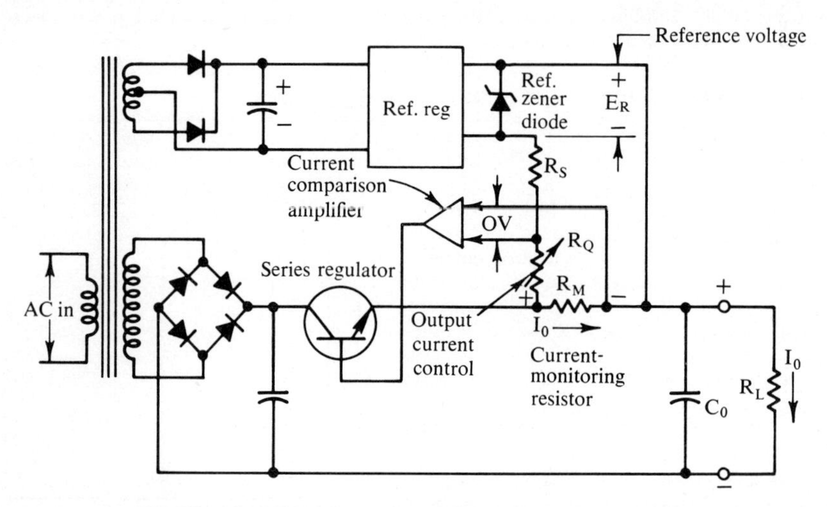

Fig. 6. Constant-current regulated dc power supply.

changes, and C_o seriously reduces the speed with which output-voltage changes can be accomplished. More sophisticated CC supplies therefore reduce or eliminate C_o.

CONSTANT-VOLTAGE CONSTANT-CURRENT (CV/CC) POWER SUPPLIES

The fact that so many elements are common to the block diagram of the constant-voltage power supply (Fig. 4) and the diagram of the constant-current power supply (Fig. 6) suggests the possibility of combining these two circuit principles in one supply as illustrated in Fig. 7. Fortunately, most of the expensive, heavy power elements are common to both the constant-voltage and constant-current circuit configurations, and only low-level circuitry need be added to a constant-voltage power supply so that it can also be used as a constant-current source. Because of its unusual versatility and its fully adjustable output-protection features, many general-purpose laboratory supplies employ this CV/CC circuit technique.

Two comparison amplifiers are included in a CV/CC supply, one for controlling output voltage, the other for controlling output current, but they do not operate simultaneously. For any given value of load resistance, the power supply must act *either* as a constant-voltage source *or* as a constant-current source—it cannot be both; transfer between these two modes is accomplished (automatically by

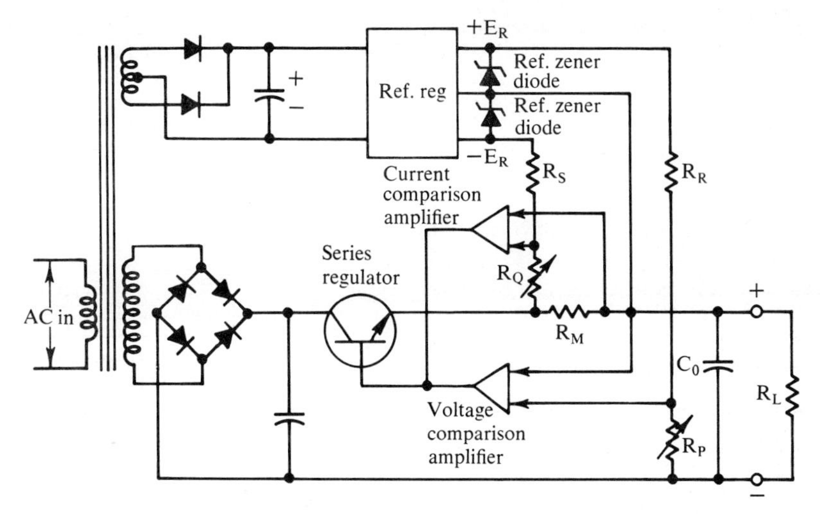

Fig. 7. Constant-voltage constant-current (CV/CC) power supply.

suitable decoupling circuitry) at a value of load resistance equal to the ratio of the output-voltage control setting to the output-current control setting.

Figure 8 shows the output characteristics of a CV/CC power supply. With no load attached ($R_L = \infty$), $I_{out} = 0$ and $E_{out} = E_S$, the front-panel voltage-control setting. When a load resistance is applied to the output terminals of the power supply, the output current increases, while the output voltage remains virtually constant; point D thus represents a typical constant-voltage operating point. Further decreases in load resistance are accompanied by further increases in I_{out} with no substantial change in the output voltage until the output current reaches I_S, a value equal to the front-panel current-control setting. At this point the supply automatically changes its mode of operation and becomes a constant-current source; still further decreases in the value of load resistance are accompanied by a drop in the supply output voltage with no accompanying change in the output-current value. Thus, point B represents a typical constant-current operating point. Finally, with a short circuit across the output load terminals, $I_{out} = I_S$ and $E_{out} = 0$.

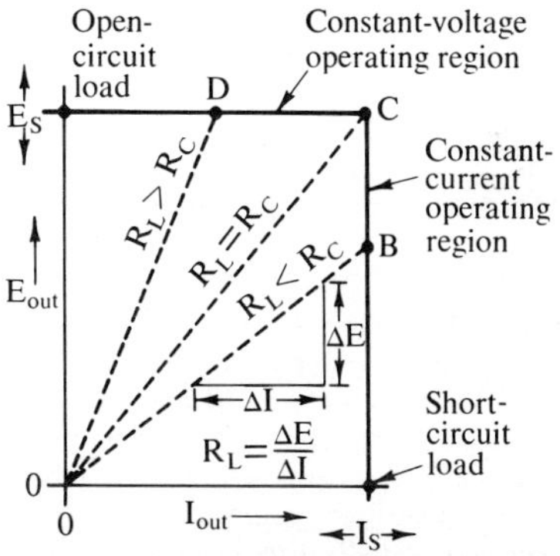

Fig. 8. Operating locus of a constant-voltage constant-current power supply. E_S = front-panel voltage-control setting, I_S = front-panel current-control setting, $R_C = E_S/I_S$ = "critical" or "crossover" value of load resistor.

By gradually changing the load resistance from a short circuit to an open circuit, the operating locus of Fig. 8 will be traversed in the opposite direction. Full protection against any overload condition is inherent in the constant-voltage constant-current design principle, since no load condition can cause an output which lies off the operating locus of Fig. 8.

Whether one is primarily concerned with constant-voltage or constant-current operation, the proper setting of E_S and I_S ensures optimum protection for the load device as well as full protection for the power supply itself. In CV operation, a CV/CC supply has continuously adjustable current-limit protection; in CC operation, it has continuously adjustable voltage limiting.

The line connecting the origin with any operating point on the locus of Fig. 8 has a slope which is proportional to the value of load resistance connected to the supply-output terminals. Thus there exists a "critical" or "crossover" value of load resistance $R_C = E_S/I_S$; adjustment of the front-panel voltage and current controls permits this "crossover" resistance R_C to be set to any desired value from 0 to ∞. If R_L is greater than R_C, the supply is in constant-voltage operation, while if R_L is less than R_C, the supply is in constant-current operation.

CONSTANT-VOLTAGE CURRENT-LIMITING (CV/CL) POWER SUPPLIES

The difference between a CV/CC power supply and a CV/CL power supply is one of degree rather than kind. Because a current-limiting supply uses less sophisticated circuitry in the current-regulating loop, regulation in the current-limiting region is not as tight as in the case of constant-current operation. Thus the current-limiting portion of the locus of Fig. 9 does not come as close to being a vertical line as the current-operating region of a CV/CC power supply (Fig. 8).

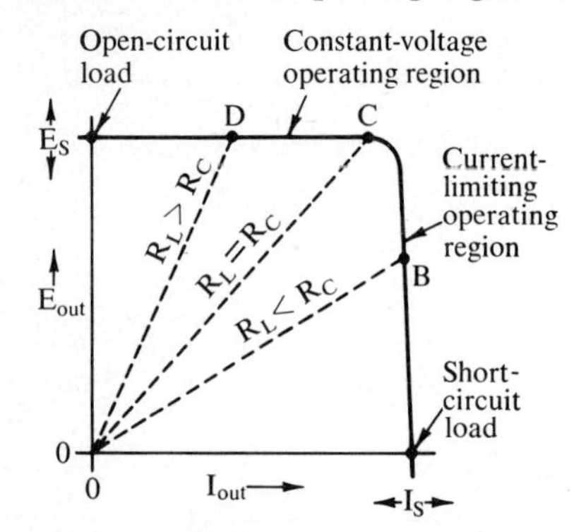

Fig. 9. Operating locus of a constant-voltage current-limiting power supply.

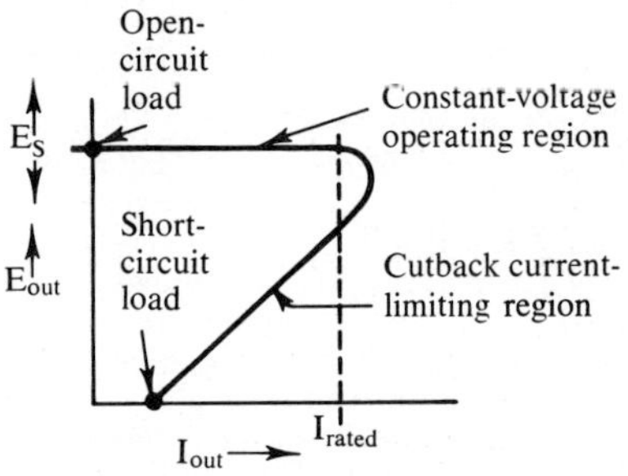

Fig. 10. Operating locus of a constant-voltage supply with cutback current limiting.

CV/CL supplies may employ either a fixed current limit or a continuously variable limit. In either case the change in the output current of the supply from the point where current-limiting action is first incurred to the value at short circuit is of the order of 2 to 20 percent of the current rating of the power supply.

Constant-voltage cutback-current limiting (Fig. 10) is a variant of fixed current limiting which provides for a reduction of *both* output voltage and output current in the overload region. This reduces series regulator power dissipation during overload, usually the worst-case condition.

TYPICAL OPERATING FEATURES

1. Remote Error Sensing Normally, a power supply achieves its optimum load and line regulation, its lowest output impedance, drift, ripple, and noise, and its fastest transient recovery performance at the power-supply output terminals. If the load is separated from the output terminals by any lead length, most of these performance characteristics will be degraded at the load terminal by an amount proportional to the impedance of the load leads compared with the output impedance of the power supply.

Some idea of how easily even the shortest leads can degrade the performance of a power supply can be obtained by comparing the output impedance of any bench power supply (typically of the order of 1 mΩ or less at dc and low frequencies) with the wire resistance shown in Table 1.

TABLE 1 Resistance of Typical Load Leads

AWG (B & S) wire size	Annealed copper resistance at 20°C, mΩ/ft	Nominal current rating, A*
22	16.1	5
20	10.2	7
18	6.39	10
16	4.02	13
14	2.53	20
12	1.59	25
10	0.999	40
8	0.628	55
6	0.395	80
4	0.249	105
2	0.156	140
0	0.0993	195
00	0.0779	260

* Single conductor in free air at 30°C with rubber or thermoplastic insulation.

For example, a 1-A power supply capable of 1 mV load regulation, connected to two No. 12 load leads, each 5 ft long, results in 17-mV load regulation at the load terminals!

With remote sensing, however, the 16-mV "excess" regulation due to the lead resistance can be eliminated. Two extra leads are connected from two power-supply "sensing" terminals, as shown in Fig. 11*b*.

There is a limit, however, to the amount of *IR* drop for which remote sensing can compensate. Excessive *IR* drop in the load leads can result in improper biases being established within the power-supply feedback amplifier. For this reason, most power-supply manufacturers stipulate that the *IR* drop in each current-carrying

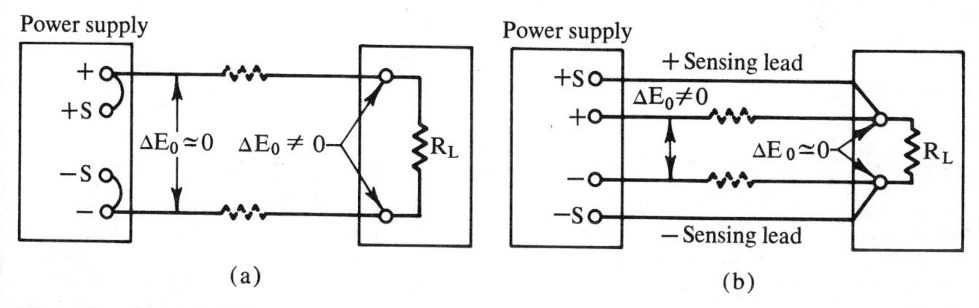

Fig. 11. Regulated dc power supply with sensing connected to (*a*) the output terminals and (*b*) the load.

lead must be limited to 1 or 2 V. Even following this precaution, the load-transient performance will be inferior to that obtained with normal sensing and short load leads.

In extreme remote-sensing applications (e.g., loads located 50 or more feet from the power supply), additional problems can be caused by the equivalent inductance and time delay of the load and sensing leads, and the resulting phase shift inside the power-supply feedback loop can cause the power supply to oscillate. In many cases such oscillations can be eliminated by readjusting feedback-equalizing components within the power-supply loop, and/or removing the power-supply output capacitor and connecting it directly across the load terminals. In extreme cases, the manufacturer should be consulted for specific recommendations and possible design changes.

Remote sensing may also be accompanied by a significant reduction in the power-supply voltage available at the load. For example, a supply rated for 0 to 10 V output can only be depended upon to deliver up to 6 V at the load if the load leads each have a 2-V drop—remote sensing in no way alters the maximum dc output voltage available at the *power-supply* terminals!

The power-supply user should also remember that remote sensing can be accomplished only with respect to a single terminal pair. If the power supply is being used to feed a large number of load terminals in parallel, or even a pair of load busbars, remote sensing can at best provide optimum performance only at a single pair of load terminals, or at one pair of points on the busbar.

In spite of these limitations, remote sensing does make it possible for greatly improved power-supply performance to be achieved at a remote load.

2. Remote Programming Remote programming, a feature included on most well-regulated bench and rack power supplies, permits control of the regulated output by means of a remotely varied resistance or voltage.* There are four common types of remote programming:

1. Controlling the constant-voltage output using a remote resistance
2. Controlling the constant-voltage output using a remote voltage
3. Controlling the constant-current output using a remote resistance
4. Controlling the constant-current output using a remote voltage

Connection of the remote resistance or voltage is usually simple, involving the changing of straps on special terminals in accordance with diagrams in the instruction manual.

Remote programming is commonly used not only to permit remote control of the power-supply output but also to facilitate rapid switching to preset output values. In addition, remote programming with a voltage input converts a regulated power supply into a single-ended dc-coupled power amplifier with low noise, low distortion, and bandwidth from dc to between 1 Hz and 20 kHz, depending on the power-supply design, load impedance, etc.

Constant-voltage Remote Programming with Resistance Control. Using an external resistor and/or rheostat, the output voltage can be set to some fixed value, or made continuously variable over the entire output range, or made variable over some narrow span above and below a nominal value.

The manufacturer normally specifies a "programming coefficient," a constant which defines the output voltage in terms of the externally connected programming resistor. For example, programming a power supply with a 200 Ω/V programming coefficient to an output level of 30 V requires a programming resistor of 6 kΩ.

The power consumed in the programming resistor can be readily determined by remembering that the programming current is the inverse of the programming coefficient. Using the same example, a 200 Ω/V programming coefficient corresponds to a 5-mA programming current, and for 30 V output (and thus 30 V across the programming resistor), 150 mW will be dissipated in the programming resistor. A stable programming resistor must be used, since a percentage change in its value results in the same percentage change in the output voltage of the power supply being controlled.

In order to avoid possible damage from surges and short-term temperature-dependent shifts in the resistance value (and hence the power-supply output voltage), the programming resistor used should be wirewound and have a temperature coefficient of 20 ppm/°C or less, and a wattage rating in excess of ten times the actual dissipation. Thus, in the previous example, the programming resistor should have a minimum power rating of 1.5 W.

The leads connecting the programming resistor to the power supply should be kept as short as practical and away from stray electric fields. Any ripple which

* It is also possible (and easy) to employ a remote current source to control the regulated output, but this is less common.

is picked up on the programming leads becomes part of the command voltage for the power-supply regulator and is therefore reproduced on the output terminals; to avoid this, the programming leads should be twisted, or preferably, shielded two-wire cable should be used, with the shield being connected at the power-supply end to the ground terminal—*the other end of the shield being left unconnected.*

Using remote programming, several different values of fixed output voltage can be set up with a switch and resistors, so that the output voltage of the supply can be switched to any preestablished value with a high degree of reproducibility. Figure 12 illustrates switching schemes which can be used to resistance-program a power supply. Suppose it is desired to program a supply having a programming coefficient K_p of 200 Ω/V; the circuit of Fig. 12*a* is a typical configuration. However, if a break-before-make switch is used in this configuration, there will occur for a short interval during switching a very high resistance between the two programming terminals, and the power supply will momentarily raise its output voltage in response to this high resistance input.

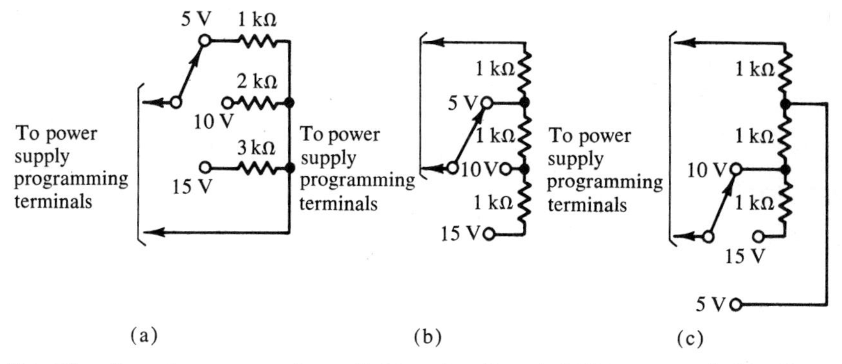

Fig. 12. Remote-programming switching circuits. (*a*) Unrecommended configuration. (*b*) Recommended in-sequence programming circuit uses make-before-break switch. (*c*) Recommended out-of-sequence programming circuit uses make-before-break switch.

To eliminate this output overshoot, a make-before-break switch can be employed. However, this solution has the disadvantage that during the short interval when the swinger of the switch is contacting two switch terminals, two programming resistors will momentarily be paralleled across the power-supply programming terminals, and the supply will for this short interval seek an output voltage which is *lower* than either the initial or the final value being programmed. This output undershoot increases the time required for the supply to settle to its new value.

The switching circuit of Fig. 12*b*, using a make-before-break switch, eliminates both the overshoot and the undershoot problems associated with Fig. 12*a*, since when rotated clockwise the resistance value between the two programming terminals will go directly from 1,000 to 2,000 Ω, and then from 2,000 to 3,000 Ω.

Constant-voltage Remote Programming with Voltage Control. Instead of controlling a power supply by means of a programming resistance, it is possible to control the output of most remotely programmable supplies with an input voltage. Thus, the power supply becomes a low-frequency dc power amplifier—and can in fact be analyzed and applied in terms of its operational-amplifier equivalent circuit. However, this discussion makes use of the same equivalent power-supply circuits already developed in this chapter.

Two distinct methods can be employed to voltage-program most dc power supplies. The simpler method, shown in Fig. 13, requires that the external voltage be exactly equal to the desired output voltage.

The current required from the external voltage source E_P is at most several milliamperes. Of course, this voltage source must be free of drift, ripple, and noise, and any other undesired imperfections, since within the regulator bandwidth the power supply will attempt to reproduce on its output terminals the programming-voltage input on a one-for-one basis.

Figure 14 illustrates the method by which a power supply can be programmed using an external voltage with a voltage gain dependent upon the ratio of R_P to R_R. Note that this method is no different from the circuit normally used for constant-voltage control of the output except that an external reference (the programming-voltage source) has been substituted for the internal reference.

External terminals are usually provided so that the connections shown in either Fig. 13 or 14 can be accomplished without any internal wiring changes.

Constant-current Remote Programming. Most of the general principles given for programming constant-voltage supplies are equally applicable to the remote programming of constant-current supplies. In addition, one must be certain that no open-circuit programming condition can exist for even the shortest interval,

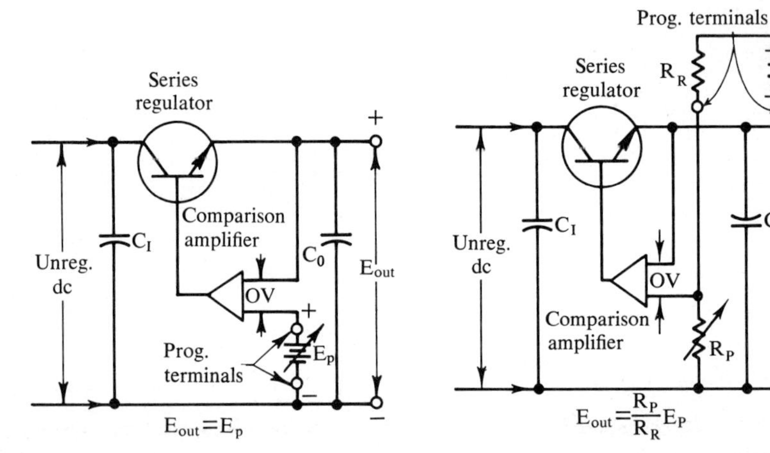

Fig. 13. Voltage programming with unity voltage gain.

Fig. 14. Voltage programming with variable voltage gain.

since such a condition will cause the power supply to deliver an output current in excess of its rating, with almost certain destruction of power-supply series-regulator components, and possible damage to the load and other components in the power supply.

A good safety precaution, which can be followed only if nonlinear programming of the output current can be tolerated, is to place directly across the constant-current programming terminals a control resistance corresponding to the maximum output current. The remotely located programming resistor(s) can then be used to shunt this "safety" resistor to the degree necessary to obtain any desired lower values of output current.

Remote-programming Accuracy. Figure 15 shows the relationship between programming resistance and output voltage for an ideal power supply with perfect remote programming. Ideally, zero ohms across the programming terminals would result in exactly zero volts out, and all other values of programming resistance would yield the output voltage predicted by the programming coefficient (K_P, in ohms per volt).

As Fig. 16 suggests, all power supplies deviate somewhat from this ideal. The application of a short circuit across the programming terminals results in an output voltage which is slightly different from zero, typically by tens of millivolts. While the linearity of the programming characteristic is nearly perfect, the actual slope may differ from the value predicted by the programming coefficient by from 1 to 5 percent. The fact that this slope is extremely linear can be utilized in improving the absolute accuracy in programming a supply; for if we can pinpoint two points on this straight-line segment, all other points are thereby determined. The two points which are the easiest (and best) to fix are the points corresponding to zero output voltage and the maximum output voltage. Both the slope and the zero crossing points can be adjusted on most programmable power supplies, by means of either screwdriver adjustments or some other alignment procedure described in the instruction manual. However, once a power supply has its programming characteristic aligned "perfectly" in accordance with the characteristic shown in Fig. 15, this alignment will retain an absolute accuracy only within a tolerance found by adding that power supply's specifications for:

1. Load regulation
2. Line regulation
3. (Temperature coefficient) × (ambient-temperature variation)
4. Stability

Any change in the load resistance, input line voltage, ambient temperature, or warm-up time can be expected to cause slight variations in the output voltage of the supply even though the value of the programming resistance has not been

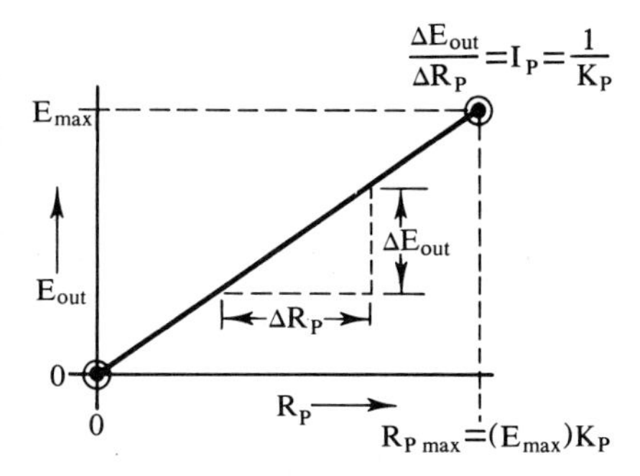

Fig. 15. "Ideal" remote-programming characteristic.

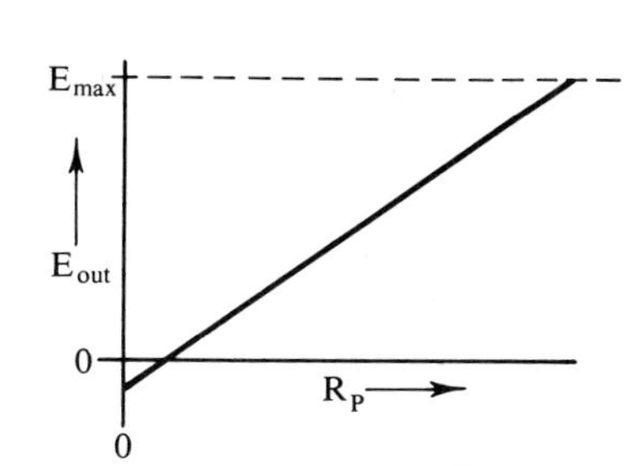

Fig. 16. Practical remote-programming characteristic.

altered. The *capability* for remote-programming *accuracy* therefore increases with improvements in the four specifications mentioned, and high-stability power supplies are capable of greater long-term programming accuracy than standard supplies.

Remote-programming Speed. A constant-voltage regulated power supply is normally called upon to change its output *current* rapidly, in response to load-resistance changes. In some cases, however, notably in high-speed remote-programming applications and constant-current applications involving a rapidly changing load resistance, a power supply must change its output *voltage* rapidly. If the power supply does not employ a preregulator,* the most important factor limiting the speed of output-voltage change is usually the output capacitor and load resistor.

The equivalent circuit and the nature of the output-voltage waveform when a typical supply is being programmed upward are shown in Fig. 17. When the new output is programmed, the power-supply regulator circuit senses that the output is less than desired and turns on the series regulator to its maximum value I_L, the current-limit or constant-current setting. This constant current I_L charges the output capacitor C_o and load resistor R_L in parallel. The output therefore rises exponentially with a time constant R_LC_o toward a voltage level I_LR_L, a value higher than the new output voltage being programmed. When this exponential rise reaches the newly

* An internal supply that minimizes the series-regulator dissipation of larger power supplies by automatically adjusting the rectifier dc output. The preregulator correcting action is generally much slower than the series-regulator reaction time. See below, under Higher-output DC Power Supplies.

programmed voltage level, the constant-voltage amplifier resumes its normal regulating action and holds the output constant. Thus the rise time can be determined using a universal-time-constant chart or the formula shown in Fig. 17.

If no load resistor is attached to the power-supply output terminals, the output voltage will rise linearly at a rate of C_o/I_L volts/second when programmed upward, and $T_R = [C_o(E_2 - E_1)]/I_L$, the shortest possible up-programming time.

Figure 18 shows that when the power supply is programmed down, the regulator senses that the output voltage is higher than desired and turns off the series transistors entirely. Since the control circuit can in no way cause the series-regulator transistors to conduct backward, the output capacitor can only discharge through the load resistor. The output voltage decays exponentially with a time constant R_LC_o and stops falling when it reaches the new output voltage which has been demanded.

If no load resistor is attached to the power-supply output terminals, the output voltage will fall slowly, the output capacitor being discharged only by bleed resistors and currents within the power supply.

Whether the supply is required to increase or decrease its output voltage, the output capacitor tends to slow the change. Many regulated power supplies therefore make it possible to remove a major portion of the output capacitance simply by removing a terminal-connection strap. After this has been accomplished, the output

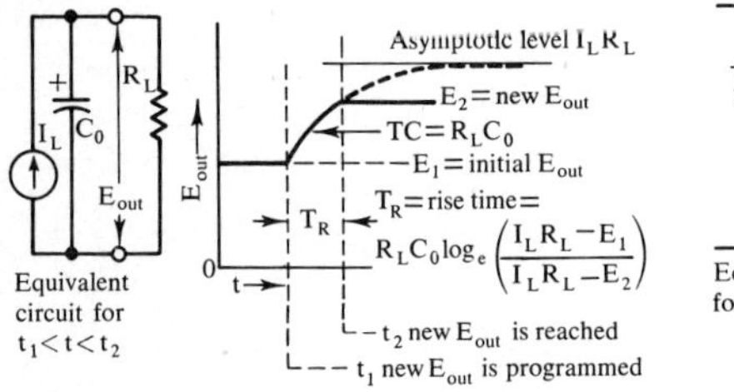

Fig. 17. Speed of response—programming up.

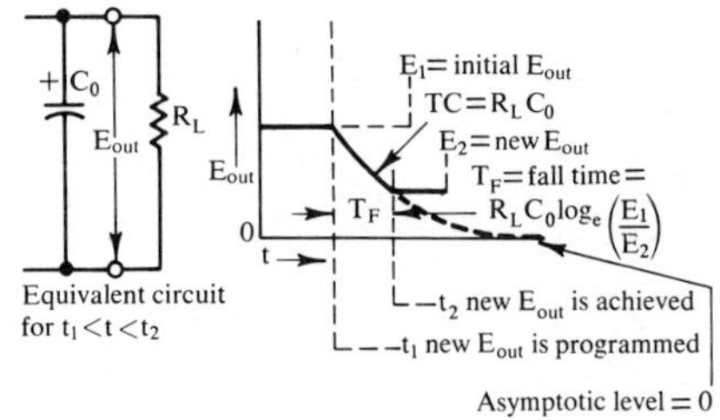

Fig. 18. Speed of response—programming down.

voltage of some bench supplies may typically be programmed to new output-voltage settings in 1 to 10 ms, instead of roughly 0.1 to 1 s with the normal output capacitor in place. But reducing the output capacitor may tend to cause the power supply to oscillate under certain load conditions, and to increase output ripple.

Besides, beyond a certain point, further reduction in the size of the output capacitor C_o will not result in greater speed of programming, since other power-supply circuit elements will eventually limit the maximum rate of change of the output voltage.

Some manufacturers offer "bipolar power supplies" or "power supply/amplifiers" (power supplies whose outputs can go through zero in either direction, as compared with normal power supplies, whose output terminals cannot reverse polarity) with programming speeds at least an order of magnitude faster than standard power-supply designs with reduced output capacitance. These instruments, which are continuously adjustable from a maximum rated positive output through zero volts to an equal negative output rating, are useful either as dc power supplies or as "push-pull" power amplifiers with bandwidth from dc to about 20 kHz.

POWER-SUPPLY PROTECTION CIRCUITS

3. Crossover Limiting—the Basic Protection Solid-state devices can be quickly damaged or destroyed as the result of overvoltage or overcurrent; fuses and circuit breakers typically do not react fast enough to protect semiconductor components from current and voltage excesses. Hence special protection circuits are incorporated into modern regulated power supplies. Some of these circuits protect the power supply, some the load, and some protect both.

As described in the sections on constant-voltage constant-current/constant-voltage current/limiting power supplies, overloaded constant-voltage supplies cross over into either constant-current operation, variable or fixed current limiting, or cutback current limiting when the load resistance becomes too low; conversely, constant-current supplies are usually designed to cross over into constant-voltage operation or variable or fixed voltage limiting whenever the load resistance becomes too high. Fixed and cutback circuits protect the power supply, while variable limit controls (including those inherent in CV/CC supplies) permit the user to protect the load as well.

However, crossover limiting does not provide all the protection which may be required. There can occur external influences (such as sudden load, line, or programming changes) which are not inherently or fully protected against by crossover

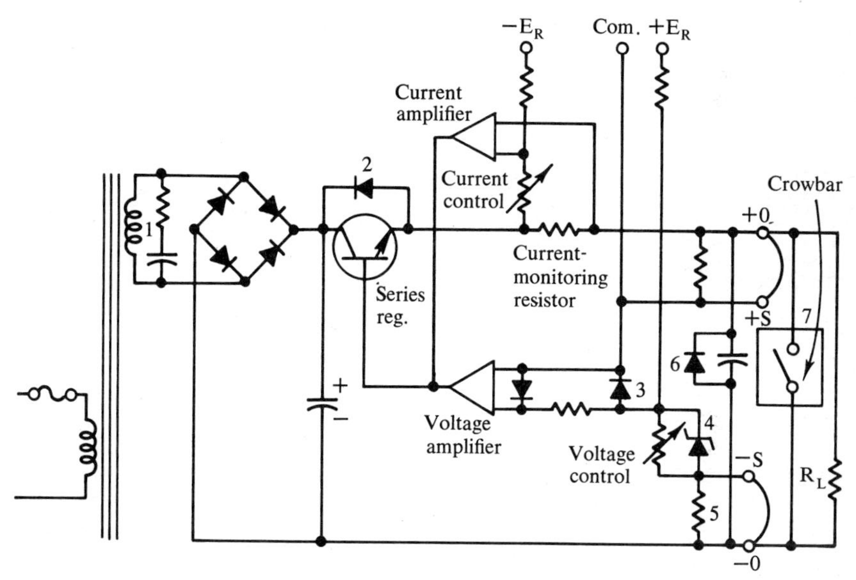

Fig. 19. Typical power-supply-protection elements.

operation. Moreover, an internal failure or malfunction of the series regulator, the voltage-comparison amplifier, or the current-comparison amplifier can invalidate crossover-limiting protection and bring about a load-damaging high output.

4. Additional Protection for the Power Supply and the Load A power supply should continue to operate normally in spite of unwanted line-voltage transients. Usually the transformer and rectifier components are rated to withstand higher than normal current during the period required for the main fuse or circuit breaker to react. But ac line-voltage "spikes" can still cause damage to semiconductor components unless additional protection circuits are provided. In some cases, an *RC* network or Thyrector diode* is strung across the power-transformer secondary to suppress the high-frequency component of such transients (No. 1 of Fig. 19). In addition, line-bypass capacitors, rf chokes, and power-transformer shielding may be added to reduce the effect of ac line transients.

Thermostats are sometimes included inside supplies, frequently on the heat sink, to shut off the regulator circuit or the input alternating current in the event the

* Trademark of General Electric Company.

sink becomes overheated from internal power-supply dissipation and/or excessive temperature of the air surrounding the supply.

Figure 19 shows some of the more frequently encountered power-supply-protection elements; depending on the application, the user may choose to add some of these elements even if they have not been included by the manufacturer.

1. *Rectifier Damping Network.* Protects power-supply elements against short-duration input-line transients
2. *Series-regulator Diode.* Protects series regulator against reverse voltage from external source (active load or parallel power supply)
3. *Amplifier Input-clamp Diodes.* Protects voltage amplifier by limiting its input to less than 1 V during sudden large changes in the output or the voltage-control setting
4. *Voltage-limit Zener.* Protects load against possibility of power-supply output voltage greater than zener voltage, even if voltage control or remote-programming circuit opens, or if voltage control is accidentally turned too high
5. *Remote-sensing-protection Resistors.* Protects load from receiving full rectifier voltage if remote-sensing leads or straps are accidentally open-circuited (silicon diodes are sometimes used here instead of resistors)
6. *Output Diode.* Protects the power supply against reverse output voltage from external source (active load or series power supply)
7. *Crowbar Circuit.* Protects load independently of any other power-supply malfunction by providing fast clampdown of undesired overvoltage

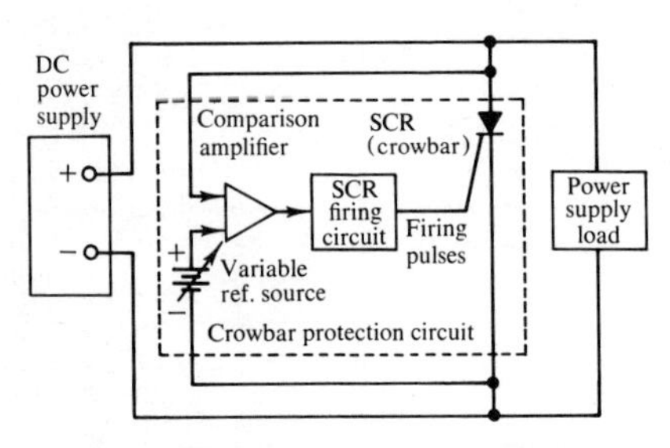

Fig. 20. Typical crowbar overvoltage-protection circuit.

There are many ways control over the power-supply output can be accidentally lost. Components can fail and cause load destruction—the most common power-supply failure is a shorted series-regulator transistor, which inevitably causes the output voltage to climb rapidly to the rectifier limit, with no current-limiting action.

The best way to provide protection to expensive, fragile loads (some of which can perish in less than a millisecond) is the "crowbar," an independent circuit which monitors the power-supply output and can initiate output-voltage shutdown in microseconds. These crowbar circuits are frequently included as an integral part of the power supply and are sometimes available as an added option.

As shown in Fig. 20, a typical crowbar includes a silicon controlled rectifier (SCR) connected across the output of the power supply. When the output voltage exceeds a preset limit (usually adjustable), the crowbar SCR is triggered into conduction (typically within 10 μs), effectively shorting the power-supply output and removing the voltage from the load. The SCR remains in the conducting stage until the output of the power supply is removed.

HIGHER-OUTPUT DC POWER SUPPLIES

Up to this point we have shown the power supply as including a single series-regulator transistor. The principle of operation is the same if a vacuum tube is substituted—this is done in some designs for higher-voltage supplies (300 V and up). Somewhat increased current and voltage output can be achieved using multiple power transistors or tubes, but economy, efficiency, and reliability place an upper limit on the maximum output power rating of supplies using this approach. Supplies having output ratings over 200 W commonly employ the preregulator technique shown in Fig. 21.

These preregulators minimize the dissipation across the series regulator by controlling the rectifier output voltage so that it is always just enough higher than the output voltage to keep the series regulator conducting properly—the rectifier

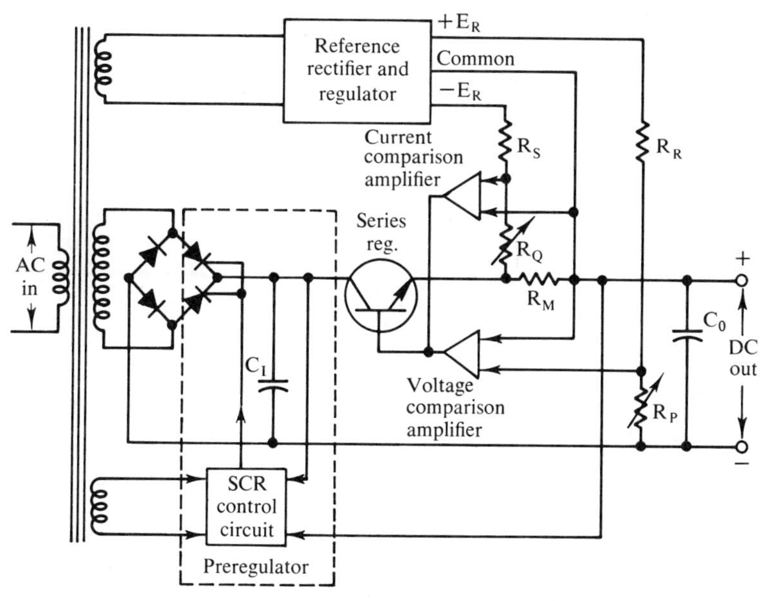

Fig. 21. Constant-voltage constant-current power supply with preregulator.

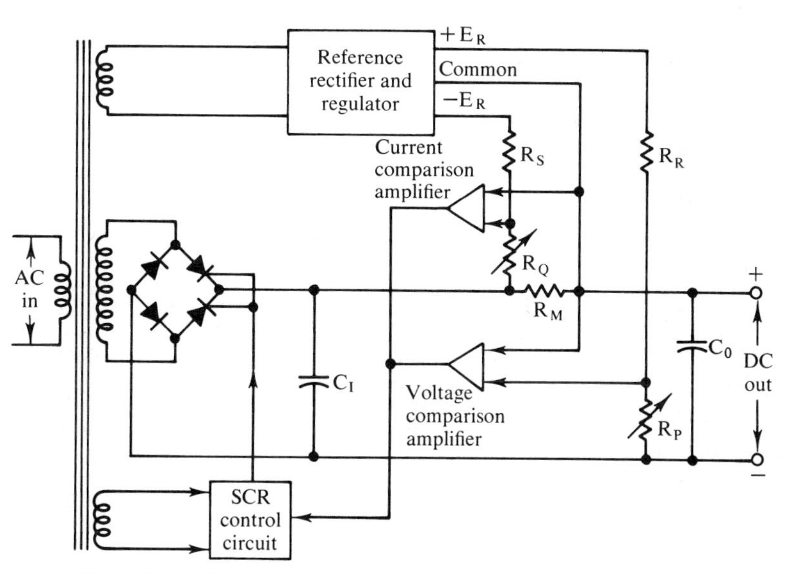

Fig. 22. Silicon controlled rectifier regulated power supply.

voltage automatically increases and decreases with any changes in the output voltage. Most commonly, such preregulators employ phase-controlled silicon controlled rectifiers (SCRs) or triacs, but saturable transformers and other magnetic techniques are also used.

These same power-handling techniques can be employed without the benefit of a series regulator, thus resulting in a simpler and more economical power supply suitable for applications requiring less regulation. Figure 22 is a block diagram of an SCR supply which contains no series-transistor regulator—note the similarity to Fig. 7. Alternatively, the SCRs may be located on the primary side of the power transformer. Power supplies with output ratings over 2 kW extend these techniques to controlled rectification of three-phase input alternating current.

POWER-SUPPLY RATINGS AND SPECIFICATIONS

5. AC Input Ratings Most dc-regulated power supplies are rated to operate continuously over a span of permissible input ac line voltage of approximately ±10 percent about a nominal value. Not stated, but implied for nearly all power supplies, is the requirement that the line-voltage waveshape be reasonably sinusoidal and that the line-source impedance have a "normal" low value.

A square or clipped line-input waveshape will not have sufficient peak-voltage content to enable most regulated power supplies to deliver full output voltage and current simultaneously at the low line-voltage limit. In higher-output supplies employing preregulators, the presence of unusual perturbations in the line waveshape can cause malfunctioning of the preregulator circuit, with consequent loss of regulation.

The input circuitry of a power supply is both inductive and nonlinear; thus the input current not only lags the voltage but also occurs in pulses lasting less than one-half cycle. Ac power cords of insufficient wire size can limit the conduction of these input current pulses and adversely affect power-supply performance. This impeding of the natural flow of input current can also result from an input-variable autotransformer or a line regulator of inadequate rating; an autotransformer used with a power supply should be rated to handle the *peak* (not just the rms) current of the power supply.

The user should not attempt to improve the short-term stability or line regulation of a power supply by interposing a line regulator between the ac line and the power supply. Generally, such regulators do not improve the performance of the supply to any significant degree; in fact, they are more likely to degrade the performance. Most line regulators control the regulated ac voltage by changing its waveshape as well as its amplitude. These waveshape changes, while tending to preserve a constant rms voltage, can result in rectified voltage changes within the power supply that are at least as large as would be caused by the original line amplitude changes. Furthermore, the impedance looking back into a line regulator is generally higher than the impedance presented by the original ac line, and typically is characterized by a resonant peak. When feeding a power supply having an internal preregulator, this resonant characteristic becomes a part of the feedback loop of that preregulator, which can lead to feedback instability and cause some preregulators to oscillate (or "motorboat") at a low frequency.

6. DC Output Ratings The output voltage and current rating spans indicate the limits of output operation within which the other specifications will be met. For example, a 0- to 40-V, 0- to 5-A constant-voltage supply will feed any dc load requiring 5 A or less at any voltage setting of 40 V or less, while meeting all its other published specifications.

In the case of constant-current supplies, the term "compliance voltage" frequently occurs. This term refers to the voltage span over which the supply output can vary in order to accommodate load-resistance changes at any output-current setting within the rating. According to intent, the term may refer to static or dynamic compliance, or both.

What meaning should be inferred with respect to zero-volt operation of a supply rated, for example, "0 to 40 V at 0 to 5 A"? It is obvious that the supply cannot deliver *any* current at *exactly* zero volts output. Instead, such a rating means that for any voltage setting arbitrarily close to zero (e.g., 0.1, 0.01, or 0.001 V) the supply will deliver up to 5 A, depending upon the load (virtually a short circuit), and meet all its other published specifications. In practice, the usefulness of a power supply at near-zero output will be limited by its output control resolution, short-term drift, load and line regulation, and ripple. For example, operation at 1 mV is meaningless for a supply with 5-mV ripple, 10-mV line regulation, and 10-mV short-term drift.

For some applications, the peak-load current and average-load current differ markedly, and it must be recognized that virtually all regulated power supplies are rated on a peak, not an average, output basis. Almost every laboratory power supply contains a fast-acting current-limiting circuit, the action of which prevents the series regulator from exceeding the output-current rating or the output-current setting, whichever is smaller. Thus, a 10-V 1-A power supply cannot be used to feed a load that continuously varies between 20 and 5 Ω, even though the *average* current requirement may be less than 1 A. As shown in Fig. 23, any attempt to use a well-regulated power supply with such a load results in an output-voltage "droop" during and following the interval when the load resistance requires more than the rated output current.

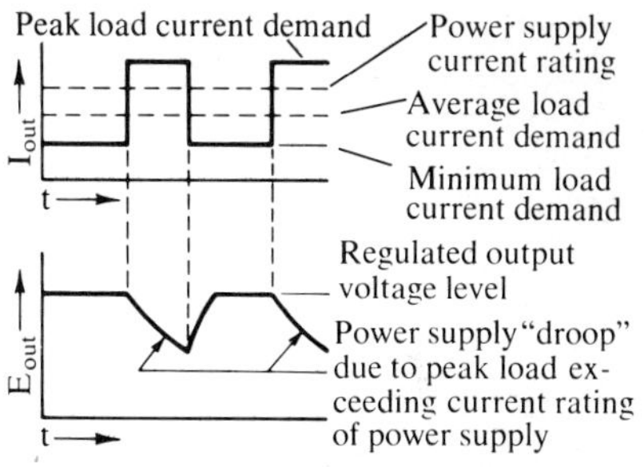

Fig. 23. Power-supply output sag resulting from load peaks in excess of supply rating.

7. Load Regulation Load regulation refers to the dc output change which occurs as a result of a load-resistance change. For a constant-voltage supply, this is the change in the output voltage accompanying a specified change in the output current—usually no load to full load (or vice versa).

For a CV supply any adjustable current-limit or constant-current control must be set somewhat above the peak current which the load will require if load regulation is not to be impaired. A similar allowance must be made with any voltage-limit or constant-voltage setting of constant-current supplies.

The load regulation specification of a CV supply relates only to the measured performance *at the power-supply output terminals*—the resistance of load leads in series with the load causes some amount of deterioration, regardless of how large or short these leads may be.

Just as CV supplies require multiple loads to be connected in parallel, so CC supplies require multiple loads to be connected in series. Even the shunt loading of a voltmeter may significantly alter the constant current through a load connected to a high-performance CC supply.

8. Line Regulation Line regulation is the change in dc output (voltage or current) resulting from a change in ac line voltage over a specified span—usually from the low limit to the high limit (or vice versa) of the input ac line rating.

For some supplies, line regulation is stated as a percentage preceded by a "±" symbol. Depending upon the manufacturer, this symbol may have two meanings—"plus *and* minus" or "plus *or* minus." For example, a line-regulation specification of "±0.01 percent for 115 V ±10 percent" could mean either:

1. "If the line voltage is changed from 103.5 to 126.5 V, the output voltage will change less than 0.01 percent; this output change may be either positive-going or negative-going."

2. "If the line voltage is changed from 115 to 103.5 V, the output may increase or decrease 0.01 percent. In addition, if the output is changed from 115 to 126.5 V, the output may again change either up or down 0.01 percent."

In the first case a maximum change of 0.01 percent is permitted, while in the second, an overall output variation of 0.02 percent is allowed!

9. Ripple and Noise Ripple is the periodic portion of the residual ac component of the dc power-supply output, and is harmonically related to the ac input-line frequency (or to internally generated switching rates). Not all ac output components are periodic—the ones that are not are called noise. Because these two ac output components occupy overlapping frequency spectra and are difficult to measure separately, they are usually lumped together for specification purposes.

It is usually understood that either the positive or negative power-supply output terminal must be grounded for this specification to be applicable—some degradation can be expected if the power supply is "floated."

Most laboratory power supplies have their output ripple and noise specified in terms of an rms value. A drawback of the rms ripple specification is that a power supply with high output ripple spikes of short duration can have the same rms specification as a competitive unit with lower peak-to-peak ripple (see Fig. 24). Yet the ripple "spikes" may be of serious consequence in some applications—causing, for example, false triggering of low-level digital *IC* logic circuitry.

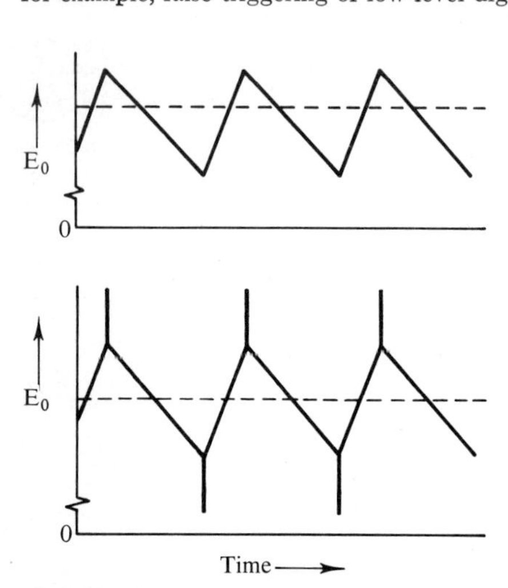

Fig. 24. Two ripple waveshapes with essentially identical rms value, except that spikes in the lower waveshape give it double the peak-to-peak value of the upper waveshape.

Since significant (and costly) design changes are often required to reduce peak-to-peak ripple spikes, many power supplies include a peak-to-peak, as well as an rms, ripple specification. Such a peak-to-peak specification preferably includes an indication of the bandwidth of the measurement. A 500-kHz oscilloscope measurement of peak-to-peak ripple is usually inadequate to preserve waveform peaks, since most of the energy content of ripple spikes lies at frequencies above 1 MHz. The measuring technique should have a bandwidth of 20 MHz or more.

In fact, the ripple and noise specification should, strictly speaking, include both an upper and *lower* frequency limit—the latter is necessary in order to distinguish between low-frequency noise and drift. Although this lower frequency limit may not be explicitly stated, it is usually implied by the manufacturer's recommended measuring technique for ripple and noise, which typically cuts off somewhere below 10 or 20 Hz.

The ripple performance of which a power supply is capable may not be achieved when remote sensing and remote programming are used, unless the user takes adequate precautions to shield the sensing and programming leads from stray pickup. It is equally important that such shields not be used as current-carrying conductors, deliberately or inadvertently; instead, the sheath should be connected to a "quiet" potential (i.e., a terminal free of noise or signal voltages, such as a ground terminal) at *one end only*.

10. Temperature Coefficient and Stability After a power supply has warmed up so it has reached thermal equilibrium, both internally and with respect to its surroundings, it will be found that under conditions of constant output setting, load resistance, and line voltage, a change in the temperature of the surrounding air (the ambient temperature) will be accompanied by a change in the output. The ratio of this output change (voltage or current) to the ambient-temperature change causing it is the "temperature coefficient" of the power supply.

Similarly, "stability" defines any dc output change (after a specified warm-up interval) with *all* other parameters—line, load, and ambient temperature—held constant; time is the only variable.

"Drift" is sometimes used in place of "stability" as defined above; in other cases "drift" has been used to refer collectively to output changes resulting from temperature coefficient and stability effects combined. In the case of well-regulated power supplies, both temperature coefficient and stability specifications are in some cases difficult to measure without placing the supply in a temperature-controlled oven.

11. Load Transient Recovery Time Transient recovery time is more frequently specified for CV operation than for CC, although the concept is readily applicable to either case; this discussion is given in terms of the operation of a CV supply.

When the load connected to a power supply is varied slowly, the output voltage varies within the limits described by the load-regulation specification. But when the load resistance is altered in a step-change fashion, the bandwidth limitation of the power-supply regulator does not permit the output current to change instantaneously, and an output transient ensues until regulator equilibrium is reestablished. The time required for the output voltage of the power supply to return to and remain within a specified level approximating the normal dc output is the load transient recovery time—sometimes referred to more simply as the recovery time, the transient response time, or the response time.

Load transient recovery time for small transistor-regulated laboratory supplies is normally specified for a full-load change—a typical specification is 50 μs. Such a specification is incomplete, however, unless one also specifies the *degree* of recovery during the specified time interval. A meaningful transient recovery specification is expressed in terms of the recovery time interval and a recovery voltage band (see Fig. 25) usually of the order of tens of millivolts —i.e., of the same order of magnitude as the load-regulation specification.

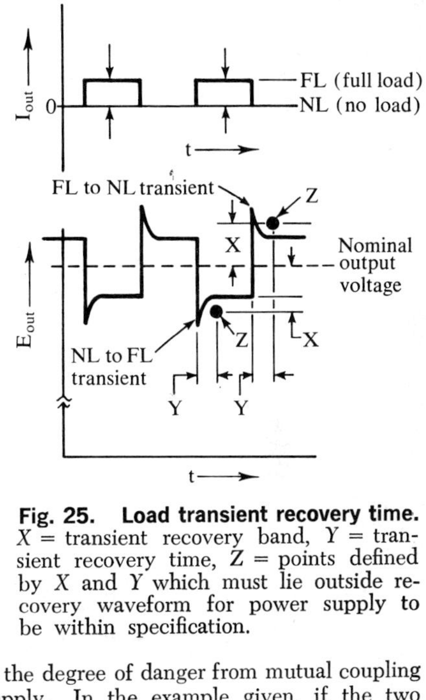

Fig. 25. Load transient recovery time. X = transient recovery band, Y = transient recovery time, Z = points defined by X and Y which must lie outside recovery waveform for power supply to be within specification.

12. Output Impedance Assume that two amplifiers are being fed by a small constant-voltage power supply, rated for 2 A. The first load is drawing a current which varies periodically between 0.5 and 1.0 A, while the second draws a relatively steady current of 0.7 A. Because the power supply does not exhibit the zero-ohm source impedance of the ideal CV source, its output voltage shifts periodically in response to the varying demand of the first load; this small voltage change is transmitted to the second load along the dc lines and may cause some added noise output or malfunctioning of the second load.

Thus the output-impedance specification not only defines the output degradation due to load changes but also describes the degree of danger from mutual coupling between loads using the same power supply. In the example given, if the two loads were actually the output and input stages of the same amplifier, the mutual coupling via the power-supply impedance could cause amplifier oscillation, or "motorboating." In digital circuitry, the spurious coupling of pulses between logic blocks using the same power supply can result in false triggering of logic circuitry.

The output impedance of a power supply depends on frequency, and a statement of maximum or nominal output impedance is incomplete without a specification of the frequency associated with it.

Figure 26 shows a typical output-impedance characteristic (and the equivalent circuit) for a high-quality constant-voltage power supply.

Output impedance is defined at any frequency as E_{ac}/I_{ac}, where I_{ac} is a sine-wave load disturbance, and E_{ac} is the resulting power-supply output-voltage disturbance.

Thus, the low output impedance of Fig. 26 is achievable only within the bandwidth of the power-supply regulator. At high frequencies, the output impedance increases and becomes equivalent to the series combination of three inductances—the equivalent inductance of the output terminals, the output capacitor, and the leads interconnecting this capacitor with the output terminals.

13. Consistency and Concurrency of Power-supply Specifications For most well-regulated dc power supplies all the important power-supply specifications are valid simultaneously over their entire range. Thus most power supplies are intended to meet their ripple and noise specification at any output-voltage setting within the rating, combined with any rated input line voltage, load current, and ambient temperature. However, the power-supply used should check the specification sheet for modified output-rating limits at different line voltages, or output-current limitations which are dependent on output voltage or ambient temperature.

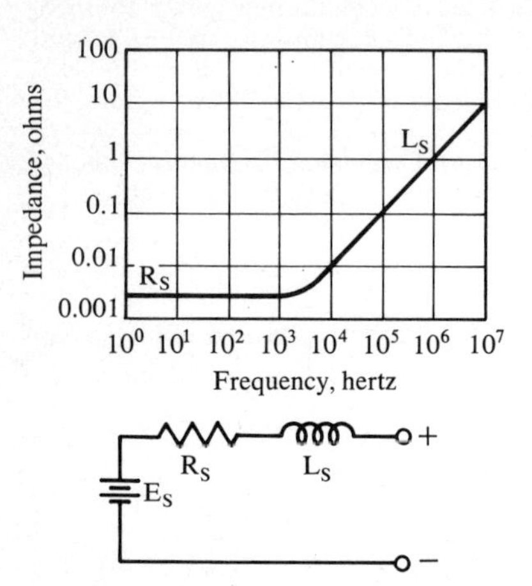

Fig. 26. Typical output impedance of a constant-voltage power supply.

Any power-supply design technique results in interrelated limitations on the degree of perfection which can be achieved with respect to regulation, ripple, transient response, etc. Unwittingly, the potential user often searches for a unit with inconsistent performance specifications, or he may be puzzled when he relaxes the requirement of one specification and does not thereby reduce the probable cost of the power supply. The fact is that if a transistor regulator is called for in order to achieve a desired low ripple, that same regulator invariably results in excellent load and line regulation, etc.

Generally speaking, a regulated dc power supply employs one of two basic circuit techniques—(1) a transistor regulator* or (2) an SCR regulator. Nearly all low-power-output power supplies use circuit technique 1, since this results in both lower cost and better performance. Either circuit technique 1 or 2 may be utilized in a supply of moderate output-power capability. Power supplies of very high output power employ circuit technique 2.

These two circuit techniques result in distinctly different performance characteristics (Table 2)—particularly with regard to regulation, ripple, and transient response.

TABLE 2 Typical Power-supply Performance

Specification	Transistor regulated	SCR regulated
Load regulation.	0.001–0.05 %	0.1–1 %
Line regulation.	0.001–0.05 %	0.1–1 %
Ripple and noise.	50 μV to 1 mV	0.1–1 %
Load transient response.	Less than 50 μs	Less than 50–200 ms

PRECAUTIONS AND LIMITATIONS

The preceding sections have already included some mention of precautions necessary when using power supplies—e.g., the limitations of autotransformers and line regulators on the power-supply input, the necessity of limiting remote-sensing *IR* drops, the switching and shielding safeguards necessary with remote sensing and remote programming, etc. But there are other, perhaps more fundamental, precautions

* In the case of moderate output ratings (roughly 200 to 2,000 W output), the transistor regulator may be preceded by an SCR *pre*regulator.

which are frequently overlooked—considering the number of regulated power supplies in use and the assumed expertise with which most operators approach them, power supplies are probably the most commonly misapplied electronic instruments.

14. Making Connections Casual clip-lead connections to power-supply output terminals will inevitably lead to power-supply performance degradation. Remember that the contact resistance of a clip lead connected to a binding-post or barrier-strip screwhead is typically more than 100 times the output resistance of the power supply. Whether connecting one load or many to a power supply, use wires with spade lugs which can be slipped under the barrier-strip screw or binding-post nut, and make sure the lugs are clamped down *tightly*.

15. DC Power Distribution and Multiple Loading Figure 27*a* illustrates the most common error in using dc regulated power supplies. The effective source impedance feeding each of the three loads is the output impedance of the power supply

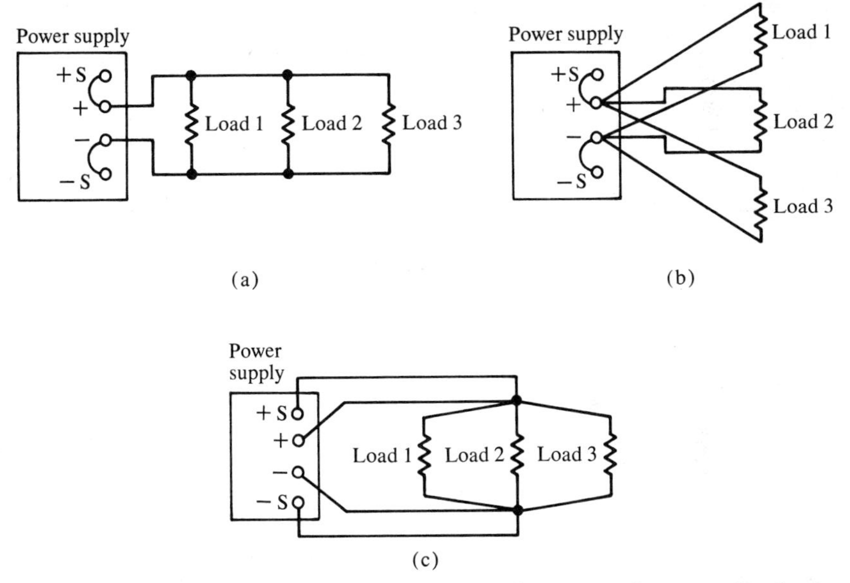

Fig. 27. (*a*) Incorrect dc power distribution. (*b*) Correct dc power distribution using local (normal) sensing. (*c*) Correct dc power distribution using remote sensing.

plus the effect of any lead resistance and inductance which separates each load from the power-supply terminals. Since nearly all loads draw from a constant-voltage power supply a current which varies with time, there will be a variation of the voltage drop in the leads connecting the loads of Fig. 27*a* to the power supply. The output impedance of a well-regulated power supply is extremely low, frequently less than 1 mΩ, and any load wire common to two or more loads seriously increases the mutual coupling. This mutual-coupling effect can be particularly serious in logic circuitry, where improper wiring may result in large spikes being developed across the impedance of the load leads, leading to false triggering of other logic circuits fed from the same power-supply leads.

To achieve proper dc power distribution without mutual-coupling effects, one must first decide where the distribution terminals of the power system will be located. If the output terminals of the power supply are to be used as the distribution points, then each of the several load devices being fed by the power supply must have separate pairs of leads connected directly from the load to the power-supply terminals as shown in Fig. 27*b*.

If the distribution terminals are to be separate from the power-supply output terminals, then a separate pair of remote-sensing leads should be connected between the power-supply output and the remote distribution terminals (Fig. 27*c*). It will be desirable in most cases to add a large electrolytic capacitor across the remote distribution terminals to further minimize mutual-coupling effects at high frequencies. The precautions already described in Sec. 1 should also be observed.

Another common source of performance degradation relates to ground connections of the power supply and its load. It seems to be a basic law of nature that no two ground points are at exactly the same potential—the voltage difference may be small, but when connected through the low resistance of ground and load leads, a sizable current (often of the order of 1 A) can result, with consequent deterioration of the effective power-supply ripple and noise performance at the load terminals.

Figure 28 illustrates such a ground-loop path, with the ground-loop current I_G circulating through the negative power-supply load lead and the power supply and load cabinets. The ground current I_G produces an *IR* drop in the negative load lead (mostly at line frequency and harmonies thereof) which, as far as the

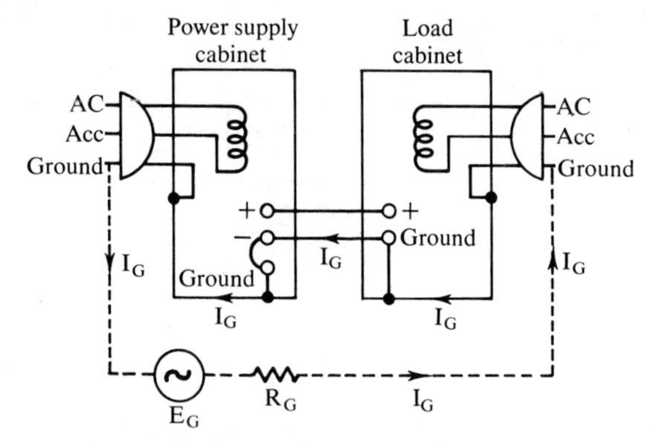

Fig. 28. Ground-loop path involving power supply and load.

load is concerned, is added directly to the power supply's normal ripple and noise output. The situation can degenerate further when multiple loads are involved, since each load may have its own separate ground.

The problem illustrated by Fig. 28 is no different if a measuring instrument (e.g., a single-ended input oscilloscope or VTVM) is substituted for the load. Notice that even if the load has no third-wire safety ground on its ac plug, a problem may still exist because the load cabinet is grounded by being screwed into a relay rack.

In some cases, the only way to eliminate this ground loop is to open-circuit the third-wire ground lead at the power supply, or to remove the link between the power-supply output terminal and the ground terminal. The former is undesirable from the standpoint of safety, while the latter may tend to increase the ripple and noise output of the power supply.

In large systems the solution to ground-loop problems of this type involves designing all load devices "floating" (not using the metal chassis as a circuit return or power-supply ground). In any case, it is best to make sure that the system consisting of power supply and loads has only one ground point, with each element in the system connected to this central ground point via one—*and only one*—ground path.

16. How Not to Get Two Outputs from One Supply Often it is required to use both a positive and negative dc power source having roughly the same voltage and current capability. It might seem reasonable to meet such requirements using a single regulated dc power supply with a resistive voltage divider center-tapped to ground. Figure 29 shows, however, that such an arrangement results in a drastic increase in the effective dc source impedance feeding each load; assuming that the power supply has a zero output impedance, each load looks back into a source impedance consisting of the two arms of the voltage divider in parallel with each other and the *other* load resistance.

Thus, a change in the current requirement of either load results in not only a change in its *own* dc voltage, but also a change in the dc voltage feeding the *other* load, and extreme conditions and unbalance can develop. In nearly all cases, a simultaneous need for positive and negative dc voltages necessitates the use of two separate regulated power supplies.

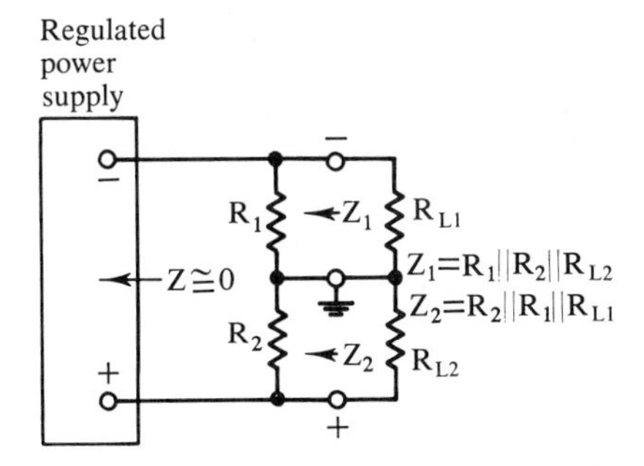

Fig. 29. Center-tapped power-supply output.

17. Combined Operation of Two or More Supplies It is sometimes necessary to achieve a voltage or current which is higher than that available from a single supply—the possibility of series or parallel connections of two or more supplies immediately suggests itself. Such combinations, while more expensive than a single supply of adequate rating, often furnish a useful expedient for laboratory purposes.

Most laboratory power supplies can be connected in series or parallel with similar supplies, but the behavior of such combinations depends on the circuit techniques used. Moreover, not all laboratory power supplies include the added protection components which such combinations require—see Sec. 4.

Parallel Operation. The operation of two constant-voltage power supplies in parallel is normally not feasible because of the large circulating current which results from the small but inevitable voltage difference between two low-resistance sources. However, if the two power supplies have CV/CC or CV/CL crossover operation, parallel operation is feasible; as shown in Fig. 30, the supply with the higher output-voltage setting will deliver its constant-current or current-limited output and drop its output voltage until it equals the output of the second supply, which will remain in constant-voltage operation and deliver only that fraction of its rated output current which is necessary to fulfill the total load demand. For example, if two CV/CC power supplies each rated for 10 A are connected in parallel across a 15-A load with one of the supplies set for 30.0 V and the other supply set for 30.1 V, the latter supply will deliver 10 A as a constant-current source, while automatically dropping its output voltage to 30.0 V. The second supply will continue to act as a constant-voltage source, delivering 5 A at the 30.0-V level.

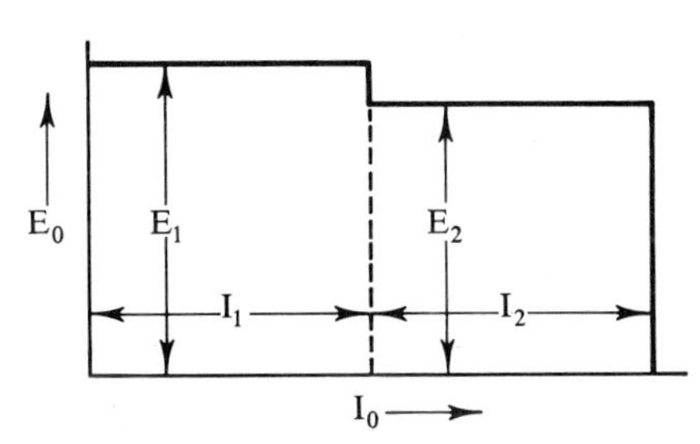

Fig. 30. Parallel output characteristic of two constant-voltage constant-current supplies. E_1 and I_1 are the output voltage and current settings of the higher-voltage supply. E_2 and I_2 are the output voltage and current settings of the other supply.

To eliminate unequal current sharing and the voltage step which occurs when the second supply starts (or stops) conducting, some supplies provide for automatic current sharing in a "master-slave" configuration. Added wiring connections between special terminals result in one-knob control and assure that multiple supplies will automatically contribute essentially equal output currents to the load, under all load conditions.

Series Operation. Series operation of two or more supplies can be accomplished up to the limit of the rating of each supply for "off-ground" or floating operation. Such series-connected supplies can be operated with one load across the entire voltage span or with separate loads connected to each supply. However, the user would do well to check whether the supplies include the output-protection diodes described in Sec. 4; if such diodes are not included, one should be added across the output of each supply in the series strung.

18. Grounded and Floating Operation Most power supplies are floating—that is, a power transformer isolates the dc output from the ac input, and neither the positive nor the negative output terminal (nor any point within the regulator circuit) is connected to chassis or ground. Thus, the power supply may be used as either a positive or negative dc source by grounding the negative or positive output terminal, respectively.

In some applications, however, it is desirable to "float" the power-supply output off ground (ground neither output terminal). Most regulated low-voltage supplies will operate up to at least 300 V off ground; special factory modifications in many

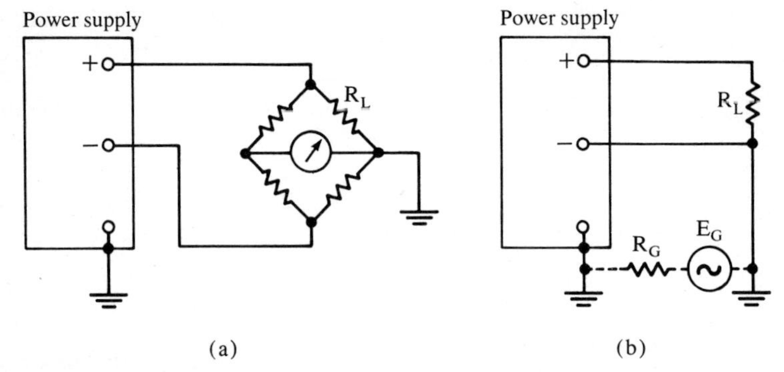

Fig. 31. Power supply feeding two types of grounded loads.

cases will permit operation to still higher values. One limiting factor is the mica washers which on most units separate the power transistors from the heat sink.

Since the output ripple of most power supplies will increase somewhat when operated floating (neither output terminal shorted to ground), it is sometimes desirable to place a 1-μF capacitor (with short leads) between one output terminal and ground so that the low-output-ripple performance of the supply may be restored.

Sometimes floating operation is necessary, not to elevate the output potential of the power supply, but to eliminate or reduce the effects of ground problems. Figure 31 illustrates two situations in which it is not practical to connect a power-supply output terminal to ground with either a direct short or a bypass capacitor.

In Fig. 31*a*, a power supply is shown feeding a bridge circuit, one end of which must be grounded at a point other than the power-supply case. This configuration arises frequently in strain-gage applications. Grounding either output terminal of the supply with either a short or a capacitor would have the effect of shorting out one arm of the measurement bridge at dc and/or signal frequencies.

Figure 31*b* shows a power supply feeding a remote load which must be grounded at a point removed from the power-supply case. Because of unavoidable ground potentials, connecting either output terminal of the supply of Fig. 31*b* to ground through a short or bypass capacitor will result in a circulating ground current which will develop an *IR* drop in the lead between the load and the grounded power-supply terminal. This *IR* drop, usually having the power-line frequency as its fundamental component, is added in series with the power-supply output to the load, thus adding ripple and noise to the power-supply voltage delivered to the load.

19. Operating as Sink Instead of Source In some applications it is necessary for a power supply to retain its normal regulated output voltage in the presence of reverse current flow during part of the operating cycle of an active load device. Such situations can arise, for example, in pulse and digital circuitry and in the case of bias supplies for class C amplifiers.

Figure 32*a* illustrates the nature of this problem. It is assumed that the active load device normally draws a current of 5 A, but that during part of its operating cycle it *delivers* a current of 3 A. Since the series transistor cannot conduct current in the reverse direction, the reverse current originating from the load device would charge the output capacitor of the power supply, causing an increase in the output voltage, with loss of regulation and possible damage to the output capacitor and other components within the power supply.

To correct these deficiencies and permit the normal operation of a regulated power supply with loads of this type, it is only necessary to add a shunt or dummy-load resistor R_D (Fig. 32*b*), thus shifting the zero-bias level of the power-supply output so that it is required only to *deliver* (not absorb) current.

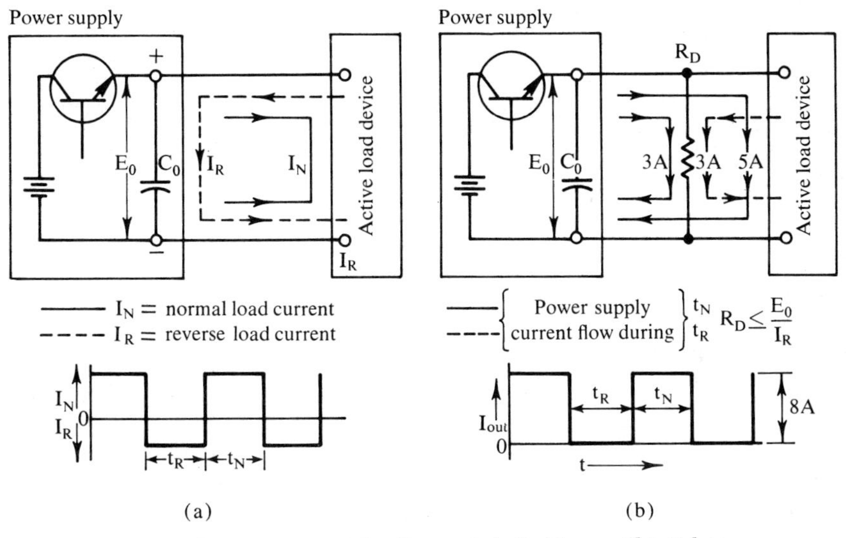

Fig. 32. Reverse-current loading. (*a*) Problem. (*b*) Solution.

In terms of the numerical example shown in Fig. 32, it is necessary to add a resistor R_D which will draw 3 (or more) A at the operating voltage of the power supply. With this resistor added, the power-supply output current varies between 0 and 8 A rather than between −3 and +5 A. During the interval when the load device is absorbing current, current flow follows the paths indicated by the solid lines of Fig. 32*b*; when the load device delivers current, current flow follows the path indicated by the broken line. Since the power supply is operating normally under both conditions, the voltage across the active load device is maintained continuously at the regulated level.

20. Ambient-temperature Limitations Most power supplies have a maximum-temperature rating which is well above the average room temperature in an open laboratory or factory environment. However, when power supplies are placed in relay racks or small system cabinets along with other heat-producing instruments, the ambient temperature which the power supply experiences is not the room temperature but the temperature inside the rack or cabinet. An unventilated rack full of equipment may surround a power supply with an effective ambient of 60°C or more even though the room temperature is kept at or below 40°C. In such cases, ventilation (fans, extra rack-panel spacing) must be added to ensure that the temperature immediately surrounding the power supply does not exceed the rating.

An exact measurement of the temperature of the air separating two adjacent instruments mounted in a rack can be difficult if not impossible. However, instruments are available which permit easy measurement of the temperature of a power supply while it and adjacent pieces of equipment are operating in the rack, and the power-supply manufacturer can usually furnish on request an indication of the maximum heat sink and internal temperatures which should be allowed; sufficient ventilation can then be added until these temperatures are safely below the specified limits.

The watts of heat which the power supply itself is adding inside the cabinet or rack can be found by measuring the ac power input with a wattmeter. and then subtracting the product of the dc output voltage and current.

TYPICAL FAILURE MODES AND FRONT-PANEL TROUBLESHOOTING

21. Introduction Because a regulated dc power supply is a complex feedback system, it is not easy to troubleshoot. Yet, in spite of the wide variety of circuit-design techniques employed in power supplies, there exists a basic procedure for localizing failure modes which is applicable to nearly all designs.

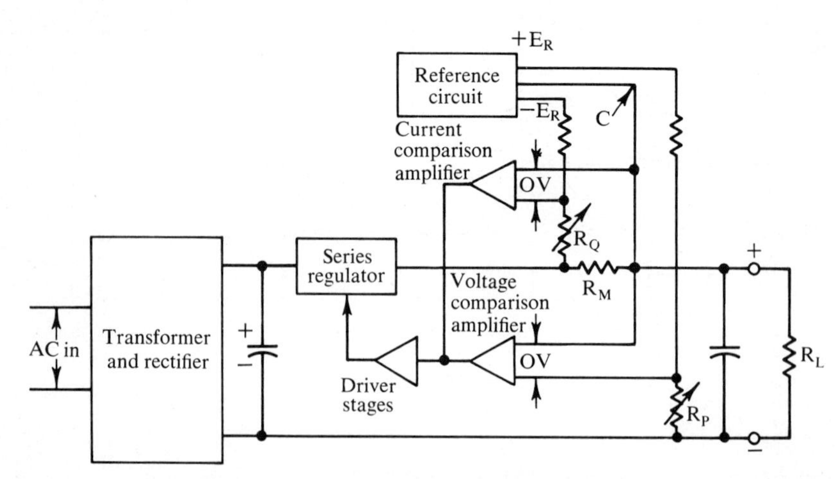

Fig. 33. Block diagram of a regulated dc power supply. R_L = load resistor, R_M = current-monitoring resistor, R_P = output-voltage control, R_Q = output-current control, C = power-supply circuit common.

This common approach is based on the fact that most supplies conform more or less to Fig. 33. There are variations, of course, but these tend to modify this block diagram rather than to destroy its validity. In constant-voltage supplies, for example, a fixed current-limit circuit is a degenerate form of the adjustable constant-current circuit shown; in higher-power and higher-voltage supplies, the "transformer and rectifier" box includes some form of preregulator; with SCR regulated supplies, the series regulator is omitted (replaced by a short circuit), and the output of the "driver stages" is connected to the "transformer and rectifier" box, etc.

Thus, the troubleshooting concepts described here are all based on the block diagram of Fig. 33; however, while these methods are generally applicable, they do not supersede specific and more detailed procedures recommended in the instruction manual for a particular power supply; in case of discrepancy, the instruction-manual information should govern.

22. Pre-plug-in Checks

1. Check all fuses for condition and correct value.
2. Visually inspect the unit for obvious defects.
3. Be sure terminal strapping pattern is identical to that defined as "normal" in the instruction manual.
4. Tighten *all* terminal strip screws.
5. Check power supply for proper input-line voltage-transformer connections.
6. Where practical, lift power supply, and shake and rotate while listening for loose screws, wire clippings, etc.

23. Pre-turn-on Setup

1. Disconnect all power-supply load, sensing, and programming leads.
2. Check that power switch is off; then connect ac input power.
3. Set coarse and fine current controls full counterclockwise.
4. If supply has only one meter, switch to voltmeter position. If supply has no voltmeter, attach external voltmeter.
5. Set coarse voltage control to midvalue.

NOTE: Until something is known of the nature and probable cause of power-supply failure, *never* turn the voltage control to zero, since this will be likely to cause the failure of the voltage control.

24. Localizing Probable Causes of Common Failure Symptoms Turn on ac power switch.

1. If voltmeter pegs full scale, turn off immediately.

Probable cause—a shorted series regulator, and/or an open output-voltage control.

Area of other possible causes—anywhere along the chain which includes "voltage-comparison amplifier," "driver stages," and "series regulator," including their auxiliary bias supply feeds. Also, check for loose or open-circuited remote-sensing and remote-programming terminal connections. Check for shorted protective diode in parallel with the series regulator.

2. If voltmeter stays at zero, turn the current control up slowly—voltmeter should rise abruptly to a midscale value. If voltmeter still stays at zero:

Probable cause—no rectifier output, open series regulator, or short across output (check output capacitor and protective diode).

Area of other possible causes—"transformer and rectifier," "series regulator," "driver stages," "voltage-comparison amplifier." Remember, some large supplies have dc output relays or a heat-sink thermostat to disconnect the series regulator or preregulator control circuit in event of overtemperature.

3. If voltmeter goes to a midscale value after step 1 or 2 above, "series regulator," "driver stages," and "voltage-comparison amplifier" are probably OK, but "current-comparison amplifier" may still be defective. With output voltage still at midvalue, attach a load resistance and verify that current limiting occurs.

4. With the same load attached, verify that adjusting both voltage- and current-output controls results in the expected output changes.

25. Two Other Common Failure Symptoms and Their Causes

1. *Symptom*—output ripple *slightly* high. Fundamental component observed on an oscilloscope is 60 Hz (or 50 Hz), not 120 Hz (or 100 Hz). *Probable cause*—incorrect measurement setup—pickup and ground-loop problems.

2. *Symptom*—load regulation *slightly* high, line regulation OK. *Probable cause*—incorrect measurement procedure. If the power-supply regulator loop has failed, load regulation normally will be out of specification by a factor of 100, 1,000, or more. If the power supply is out of its load-regulation specification by only a factor of 2 to 10, chances are excellent that the measuring instrument is not connected by two *separate* leads *directly* to the power-supply output terminals.

26. When Is the Reference Circuit Suspect? It can be readily demonstrated that a power supply is actually a power operational amplifier with the following equivalences:

Amplifier	*Constant-voltage Power Supply*
Input signal	Dc reference
Output signal	Regulated direct current
Amplifier	Regulator
Output stage	Series regulator transistor
B+ source	Rectifier
Gain control	Output-voltage control

Remembering that the reference voltage is the dc input signal to the dc amplifier (power-supply regulator), we can determine whether the reference circuit is causing any output difficulty merely by comparing the output imperfections and the reference imperfections *on a percentage basis.* For example, if the line regulation of the power supply is out of specification and is measured to be 1 percent (instead of a normal 0.01 percent), the reference circuit is the cause of trouble *only if the line regulation of the reference voltage is 1 percent.* Thus, if a 10-V reference circuit has a line regulation of 0.1 V, it will cause a 1-V variation on the output of a 100-V supply. Similarly, high ripple on the output of a power supply is due to the reference circuit only if the output ripple and the reference ripple are roughly equal on a percentage basis. *A percentage defect at the output of the reference circuit will result in the same percentage defect on the power-supply output.*

27. Opening the Regulator Feedback Loop If the preceding steps have been followed, we have already eliminated the most likely causes of failure and have found that the reference-circuit output is normal. This means that any remaining trouble must be in the main-regulator path. Unfortunately, if any component in a feedback loop is defective, measurements made *anywhere* in the loop may appear abnormal. Under these conditions, it is next to impossible to separate cause from effect with the loop closed. *At this juncture a point-by-point cause-and-effect troubleshooting procedure of the power-supply regulator is virtually impossible unless one opens the main-regulator loop.*

Proper methods of opening the feedback loop depend upon the manufacturer and the particular instrument design—the instruction book should be consulted.

28. Troubleshooting Supplies with Preregulators Interaction between the main series regulator or loop and an internal preregulator loop can make logical troubleshooting difficult, and if the supply has simultaneous component failure in both loops, localizing the trouble may be impossible unless the actions of the two feedback loops are temporarily separated.

Fortunately, there is a very simple way to separate the action of the regulator and preregulator loops so that troubleshooting can proceed on either loop separately, regardless of the possible malfunction of the other loop; this method should be followed whenever troubleshooting a preregulator supply gets beyond the "quick and easy" stage or whenever loop interaction is suspected.

1. Disconnect the preregulator drive signal (e.g., the gate leads to the SCRs). Turn the power supply on; there should be no preregulator output—no voltage across the rectifier capacitor. If rectifier output does exist, check for shorted rectifier elements. Checking whether the rectifier-capacitor ripple frequency is 60 (50) or 120 (100) Hz and noting unusual half-cycle imbalance will help determine whether one or both sides of the rectifier path are defective.

2. Connect the output of a small laboratory-type power supply across the rectifier capacitor of the power supply being serviced, observing polarity. Using a small laboratory supply for this purpose (or a larger power supply with a low output-current-limit setting) will reduce the possibility of further damage to the power supply being serviced.

After setting the output of the small supply so that the rectifier voltage of the supply being serviced is the same as the voltage drop normally required across the series regulator (obtain this information from the instruction manual), first verify proper operation of the entire reference-circuit and series-regulator loop using the methods already described; then check the various waveshapes in the preregulator control circuit, and determine at which point these waveforms first deviate from normal. Notice that this method permits troubleshooting of the preregulator loop without risking damage to other supply components.

Turning down the voltage impressed across the rectifier capacitor should cause the preregulator control signal to increase proportionately; on the other hand, increasing the externally supplied rectifier-capacitor voltage should decrease the preregulator drive.

Remember that with the SCR gate leads removed and an external supply connected to "pump up" the rectifier capacitor, we can proceed with troubleshooting separately *either* the SCR preregulator loop *or* the series-regulator loop in accordance with the methods already outlined. After proper operation of both loops is obtained separately, the external supply should be removed and the preregulator drive leads reconnected; satisfactory operation of the entire circuit should result.

BIBLIOGRAPHY

Birman, Paul: "Power Supply Handbook," Kepco, Inc., Flushing, N.Y., 1967.

Darbie, Arthur M.: Avoid the Pitfalls of Power-supply Connections, *Electron. Design,* vol. 18, no. 4, p. D10, Feb. 15, 1970.

Darbie, Arthur M.: EID Surveys the Scope of Laboratory Power Supplies, *Electron. Instr. Dig.,* vol. 3, no. 1, p. 49, January, 1967.

Darbie, Arthur M.: Interpreting and Verifying the Specifications of Laboratory Power Supplies, *Electron. Instr. Dig.,* vol. 3, no. 6, p. 7, June, 1967.

Darbie, Arthur M.: Protection Circuits for Solid-state Power Supplies, *Electron. World,* vol. 79, no. 4, p. 49, April, 1968.

Darbie, Arthur M.: What Is It—Power Supply or Amplifier?, *Electron. Prod.,* vol. 10, no. 6, p. 64, November, 1967.

DC Detective for HP Power Supplies, *Hewlett-Packard Service Note* M-38, Berkeley Heights, N.J., November, 1967.

DC Power Supply Handbook, *Hewlett-Packard/Harrison Division Application Note* 90, Berkeley Heights, N.J., 1967.

Power Supply/Amplifier Concepts and Modes of Operation, *Hewlett-Packard/Harrison Division Application Note* 82, Berkeley Heights, N.J., September, 1966.

Section Twelve

Microwave Passive Devices

As the frequency of an electronic signal increases, the problems associated with controlling it become much different from those at lower frequencies. Wire is no longer capable of confining the signal, and the small distributed parameters of inductance and capacitance have more of an effect because they are multiplied by the larger number representing frequency.

This section defines the various devices available for control of electronic signals at frequencies high enough to require waveguide. The problems associated with signals at these frequencies are discussed, and the individual waveguide devices that solve those particular problems are described. None of these devices has any active element. Those microwave instruments that either generate or measure signals at these frequencies are discussed in the sections devoted to that type of instrument.

Although waveguide is emphasized here, many of the concepts can be translated into use with coaxial cable, so neither a separate discussion nor a chapter has been included for that subject.

Chapter 40

Waveguide and Waveguide Devices

G. J. WHEELER

Consultant in Microwave Electronics, Los Altos, California

INTRODUCTION

Waveguides and devices utilizing waveguides are not measuring instruments in themselves, but at microwave frequencies waveguide devices are frequently used in conjunction with many measuring instruments. For example, a waveguide directional coupler is used to sample power in a transmission line, and a variable phase shifter is used when measuring phase shift in a network. These and other waveguide devices are examined in this chapter.

1. Waveguides Although any transmission line effectively guides electromagnetic energy, the term *waveguide* usually refers to hollow pipes used as transmission lines. The most commonly used waveguide has a rectangular cross section, as shown in Fig. 1*a*, but square and round guides are also frequently used (Fig. 1*b* and *c*). For special applications irregular shapes may be used, such as the ridged guide shown in Fig. 1*d*.

Waveguides are made of metal, and since the electromagnetic energy travels inside the pipe, they are shielded transmission lines. There is very little penetration into the surface of the metal because of the *skin effect*. (This is the tendency of rf currents to flow nearer the surface of a conductor as the frequency is increased.) The current density is greatest near the surface and decreases exponentially with depth into the metal. The *skin depth* is the depth of penetration at which the current density is $1/e$ of its value at the surface. The skin depth is proportional to the square root of the conductivity of the material and inversely proportional to the square root of the frequency. With an excellent conductor such as copper or silver the skin depth at 10 MHz is less than a thousandth of an inch, and at microwave frequencies it is negligible. Thus the wall thickness of a waveguide is determined by mechanical factors rather than electrical problems. Losses in the waveguide are a function of the conductivity of the surface metal, and therefore, the surface metal should be a good conductor. For considerations of economy, ease of fabrication, or light weight, aluminum and brass are commonly used metals for waveguides. These materials are then plated inside the tube with a few thousandths of an inch of silver or rhodium to increase the conductivity.

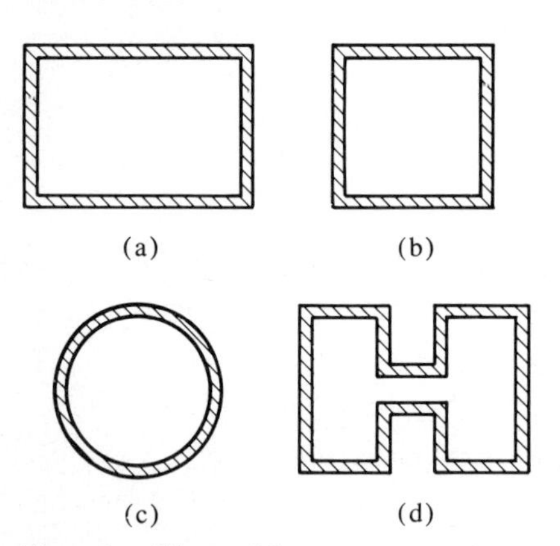

Fig. 1. Waveguide cross sections. (*a*) Rectangular. (*b*) Square. (*c*) Round. (*d*) Ridged.

2. Modes in Waveguides The electromagnetic wave in a waveguide consists of a voltage vector and a magnetic vector which are perpendicular to each other. There are many different possible patterns or arrangements of these vectors, and these patterns are called *modes.* In general, there are two kinds of modes. In one set of modes, called *transverse electric,* or *TE* modes, the electric vector is *always* transverse or perpendicular to the direction of propagation. In the second set, *transverse magnetic,* or *TM* modes, the magnetic vector is *always* transverse to the direction of propagation. In all modes, the electric field must always be perpendicular to the waveguide wall at the surface, and the magnetic field at the wall surface is always parallel to the wall.

The modes in rectangular waveguides are designated further by two subscripts. The first subscript indicates the number of half-wave variations of the *electric* field (in both TE and TM modes) across the wide dimension of the waveguide, and the second indicates the number of half-wave variations of the electric field across the narrow dimension. Some typical voltage patterns are shown in Fig. 2.

In each case, the magnetic field is perpendicular to the voltage field. The length of the arrow indicates the relative amplitude of the voltage at that point.

In round waveguides, two subscripts are also used to designate mode, but the subscripts have more complicated meanings. It is simpler to remember what the patterns look like. The three most common modes in round guide are shown in Fig. 3.

In square guide, there is, of course, no wide dimension. The first subscript designates the number of half-wave variations of the voltage field across the horizontal dimension, and the second across the vertical. Strictly speaking, the same rule applies to rectangular guides, but they are usually depicted with the wide dimension horizontal. Two modes in square guide are shown in Fig. 4.

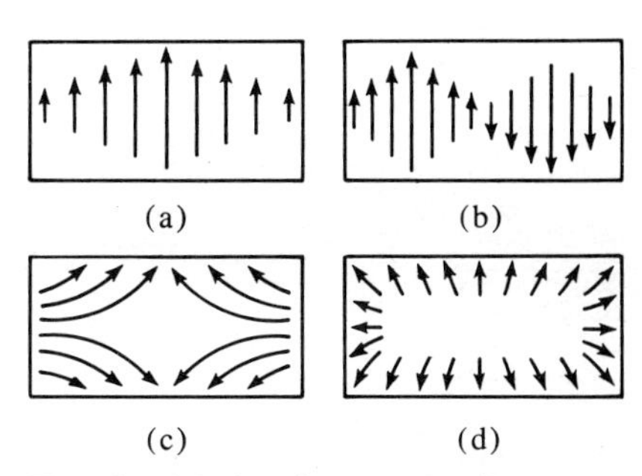

Fig. 2. Modes in rectangular waveguide. (*a*) $TE_{1,0}$. (*b*) $TE_{2,0}$. (*c*) $TE_{1,1}$. (*d*) $TM_{1,1}$.

3. Cutoff Wavelength There is a lower limit to the frequency which can be transmitted through a fixed size and shape of waveguide. The *cutoff wavelength* is the largest wavelength, corresponding to the lowest frequency, that can be propagated. For rectangular guide, the cutoff wavelength *c* is given by

$$\lambda_c = \frac{2}{\sqrt{(m/a)^2 + (n/b)^2}} \tag{1}$$

where m and n = subscripts, as $TE_{m,n}$ or $TM_{m,n}$
a = wide dimension of the guide
b = narrower dimension

Thus, for the $TE_{1,0}$ mode in rectangular guide the cutoff wavelength is $2a$, or twice the wide dimension. For the $TE_{0,1}$ in square or rectangular guide, $\lambda_c = 2b$.

From Eq. (1) it is evident that the $TE_{1,0}$ mode has the highest cutoff wavelength. Therefore, for a given frequency it is possible to select waveguide dimensions so that only the $TE_{1,0}$ mode will propagate, and for all other modes that frequency will be *below cutoff*. The $TE_{1,0}$ mode is consequently called the *dominant mode,* and all other modes are *higher modes.*

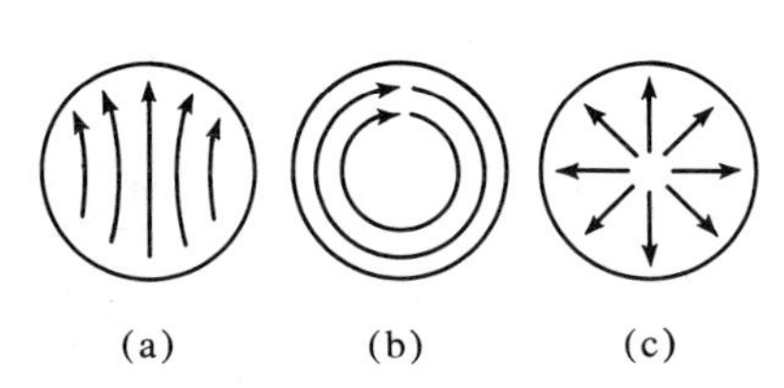

Fig. 3. Modes in round waveguide. (*a*) $TE_{1,1}$. (*b*) $TE_{0,1}$. (*c*) $TM_{0,1}$.

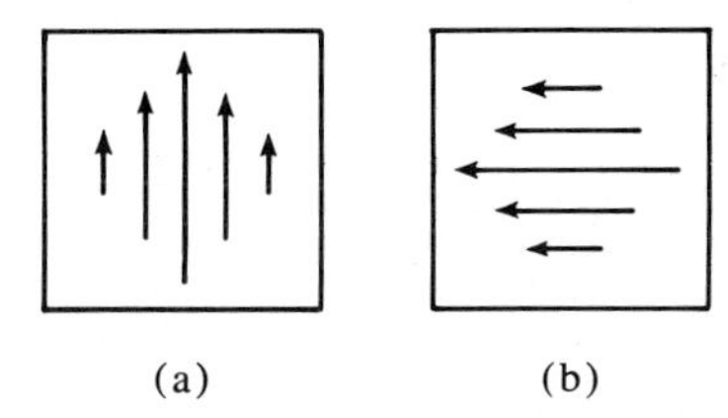

Fig. 4. Modes in square waveguide. (*a*) $TE_{0,1}$. (*b*) $TE_{0,1}$.

Frequencies below cutoff are attenuated very highly in a waveguide, and to all intents and purposes they do not propagate. A discontinuity in a guide may excite higher modes, but they die out quickly if they are below cutoff. If two or more modes were *above* cutoff and propagated together, they could interact in an undesirable manner. For this reason, waveguide sizes are chosen to cover specific frequency bands so that only the dominant mode can propagate at these frequencies.

For the three modes shown in Fig. 3 for round waveguide, there are also cutoff wavelengths. These are

For the $TE_{1,1}$ mode	$\lambda_c = 1.706d$
For the $TE_{0,1}$ mode	$\lambda_c = 0.820d$
For the $TM_{0,1}$ mode	$\lambda_c = 1.306d$

where d is the inside diameter of the round guide.

Since the $TE_{1,1}$ mode has the largest cutoff wavelength, it is the dominant mode in circular waveguides, and with proper choice of diameter, it is the only mode which will propagate. However, if the waveguide is bent, this mode could propagate in the wrong polarization, that is, with the voltage vector rotated from the vertical. The other two modes shown in Fig. 3 are symmetrical and are not affected by rotation of the axis. In fact, the $TM_{0,1}$ mode is used in rotary joints where symmetry is important. The $TE_{0,1}$ mode has the lowest attenuation of all modes in round waveguide and is thus useful in long waveguide runs.

4. Guide Wavelength The wavelength of a signal propagating in a waveguide is greater than the wavelength of the same signal in free space. It is a function of the cutoff wavelength, which in turn depends on the dimensions of the guide. The exact relationship is

$$\frac{1}{\lambda_g^2} = \frac{1}{\lambda_o^2} - \frac{1}{\lambda_c^2} \tag{2}$$

where λ_g = wavelength in the guide
λ_o = wavelength in free space
λ_c = cutoff wavelength

Equation (2) applies to all modes in all cross sections of waveguide.

It should be noted that if $\lambda_o = \lambda_c$ in Eq. (2), then the right-hand side is zero, and λ_g must be infinite. If $\lambda_o > \lambda_c$, the right-hand side is negative, and λ_g must be imaginary. This would indicate that there can be no propagation in the guide when the free-space wavelength exceeds the cutoff wavelength.

5. Velocity of Propagation The velocity of propagation of a signal in free space is equal to the speed of light, designated c. Since the velocity of propagation equals the product of wavelength and frequency,

$$c = \lambda_o f \tag{3}$$

In a wavelength, the velocity of propagation v_p is also equal to the product of wavelength and frequency. That is,

$$v_p = \lambda_g f \tag{4}$$

Since λ_g is greater than λ_o, it must follow that the velocity of propagation in a waveguide exceeds the speed of light, which is contrary to physical principles. However, the guide wavelength is the length of one cycle in the guide, and the velocity v_p is the velocity of the phase of the signal. No intelligence or modulation travels at this velocity. Therefore, v_p is called the *phase velocity*.

If the signal is modulated, the modulation will travel at a slower rate in the guide. That is, the modulation keeps slipping backward compared with the phase of the carrier. The velocity of the modulation envelope is called the *group velocity* and is designated g. The group velocity is reduced from the speed of light by the same ratio that the phase velocity exceeds the speed of light. Therefore,

$$v_p v_g = c^2 \tag{5}$$

6. Waveguide Losses Waveguides have lower attenuation than coaxial lines, but they do have measurable loss. Attenuation in an empty (or air-filled) guide is copper loss as a result of currents in the waveguide walls. If the waveguide contains a dielectric material, the dielectric loss will be added to the copper loss.

The waveguide attenuation depends on the resistivity of the metal, as might be expected, but more important, the resistance of the walls increases as the frequency is increased. This is caused by the skin effect, since at higher frequencies the thickness of metal carrying the current is decreased. In addition, the larger the guide, for a specific frequency, the lower will be the attenuation. This means that the attenuation is greatly increased at higher frequencies since smaller waveguides are used, and the skin effect increases the resistance. Typically, at 3,000 MHz, the attenuation in standard waveguide for that frequency is about 0.6 dB/100 ft; at 10,000 MHz, it is about 5 dB/100 ft; and at 25,000 MHz, it is about 15 dB/100 ft in brass guide and 10 dB/100 ft in silver guide. Thus, attenuation is usually negligible at frequencies below 3,000 MHz, and it may be neglected in short runs at frequencies up to 10,000 MHz. However, at higher frequencies it is an important consideration.

The $TE_{0,1}$ mode in round waveguide is exceptional in that its attenuation decreases as frequency is increased. Thus at frequencies above 25,000 MHz for long, straight runs, this mode is sometimes used, but care must be taken to prevent lower modes such as the $TE_{1,1}$ from being excited.

7. Characteristic Impedance In a conventional open-wire line or a coaxial line the characteristic impedance is determined by the physical dimensions of the line and is independent of frequency. This is not true of waveguides. An expression for the characteristic impedance of a waveguide carrying any TE mode is

$$Z_o = 377 \frac{b}{a} \frac{\lambda_g}{\lambda_o} \tag{6}$$

For TM modes, the characteristic impedance is

$$Z_o = 377 \frac{b}{a} \frac{\lambda_o}{\lambda_g} \tag{7}$$

The wide and narrow dimensions of the waveguide are a and b, respectively. For square or round guides, $a = b$.

It should be noted that since λ_g is greater than λ_o, the characteristic impedance for a TE mode is greater than that for a TM mode. The ratio λ_g/λ_o is not constant with frequency, and therefore, Z_o must vary with frequency.

From Eqs. (1) and (2), it is evident that for the $TE_{1,0}$ mode in rectangular waveguide, the guide wavelength λ_g is independent of b, the narrow dimension of the guide. Therefore, from Eq. (6), the characteristic impedance for the $TE_{1,0}$ mode is directly proportional to the dimension b. This is an important consideration in impedance matching.

8. Dielectric In some applications, the waveguide is filled with a dielectric material in order to reduce the size or increase the power-handling capability of the system. Since all materials exhibit some loss at microwaves, the dielectric loss must be added to the copper loss. This dielectric loss is appreciable, and for this reason, dielectrics are used only in short lengths of waveguide.

Lossy material is sometimes used deliberately to make waveguide *pads* or attenuators. A short piece of guide is wholly or partially filled with a dielectric material which has the desired loss characteristics to achieve a desired fixed attenuation through the section.

If free space were filled with a dielectric material, the "free-space" wavelength (that is, the wavelength in the dielectric) would be reduced by the square root of the dielectric constant. When a waveguide is filled with a dielectric, the cutoff wavelength is unchanged and is still given by Eq. (1), but in determining λ_g from Eq. (2), the value of λ_o must be this reduced value of the free-space wavelength. Also, in determining whether a waveguide is below cutoff for a specified frequency, the dielectric free-space wavelength must be used. For example, a standard-size waveguide has a wide dimension of 0.622 in. Thus, from Eq. (1) the cutoff wavelength for the $TE_{1,0}$ mode is 1.244 in., which corresponds to a frequency of about 9,460 MHz. If empty, this guide would pass 9,500 MHz but would not propagate 9,400 MHz. If the guide is now filled with a material which has a dielectric constant of 2.25, the "free-space" wavelength of a signal will be reduced by $\sqrt{2.25} = 1.5$. Thus, a signal at 6,500 MHz has a free-space wavelength of 1.84 in., which is greater than the cutoff of 1.244 in. That is, 6,500 MHz cannot propagate in the empty guide.

However, with the 2.25 dielectric in the waveguide, the dielectric free-space wavelength for 6,500 MHz is 1.84/1.5 = 1.22 in., which is less than the cutoff wavelength, and therefore, 6,500 MHz will propagate.

The dielectric constant ϵ can be included in Eqs. (2), (6), and (7). Equation (2) becomes

$$\frac{1}{\lambda_g^2} = \frac{\epsilon}{\lambda_o^2} - \frac{1}{\lambda_c^2} \tag{8}$$

For TE modes, the characteristic impedance becomes

$$Z_0 = \frac{377}{\sqrt{\epsilon}} \frac{b}{a} \frac{\lambda_g}{\lambda_o} \tag{9}$$

For TM modes, it is

$$Z_0 = \frac{377}{\sqrt{\epsilon}} \frac{b}{a} \frac{\lambda_o}{\lambda_g} \tag{10}$$

It should be noted that if $\epsilon = 1$, as for an empty waveguide, Eqs. (8), (9) and (10) reduce to Eqs. (2), (6), and (7).

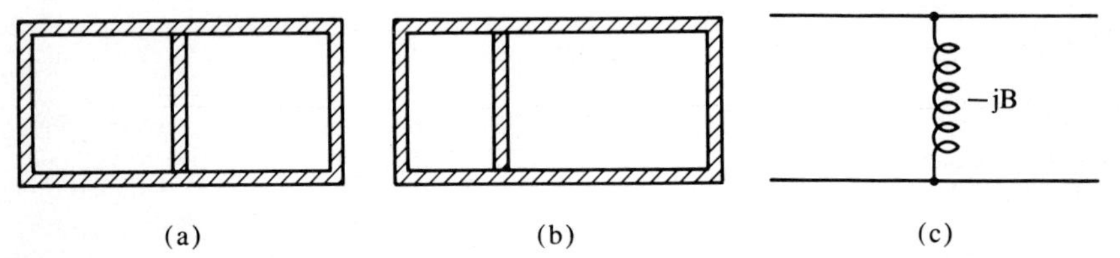

Fig. 5. Inductive post. (*a*) Centered. (*b*) Off center. (*c*) Equivalent circuit.

9. Discontinuities At lower frequencies in conventional transmission lines, coupling networks made up of capacitors and inductors are used to match transmission lines to the source or load. Since these networks are purely reactive, there is no additional loss in the matching process. At microwaves, as at lower frequencies, mismatches cause some power to be reflected back toward the source. Matching is accomplished by introducing a discontinuity in the waveguide which creates a reflection which is equal in amplitude to the reflection caused by the mismatch but is of opposite phase. Thus, the two reflected waves cancel, and the waveguide transmission line is matched. In order to avoid adding additional loss to the circuit, the introduced discontinuities must be purely reactive.

A thin vane or post extending across the waveguide parallel to the voltage field is a shunt inductance. This is shown in Fig. 5. Since the electric field is strongest at the center, the centered post shown in Fig. 5*a* will cause a larger reflection than the asymmetrical post in Fig. 5*b*. In either case, the post acts as a shunt inductive susceptance, as shown by the equivalent circuit in Fig. 5*c*. If the post extended across the wide dimension of the guide instead of the narrow, it would have a negligible effect and cause very little reflection, because it would be perpendicular to the electric field.

Another type of inductive susceptance is the inductive iris shown in Fig. 6. This consists of a thin vane or vanes narrowing the wide dimension of the guide as indicated. The equivalent circuit, as shown in Fig. 6*c*, is the same as that for the inductive post.

In practice, posts are preferred to irises, since it is easier to drill a hole and insert a wire than to cut a slot and insert a vane. However, larger reflections are attainable with irises.

Shunt capacitive susceptances are achieved by having the irises narrowing the narrow dimension of the guide as shown in Fig. 7. As with inductive irises, capacitive irises may be arranged symmetrically or asymmetrically.

The tuning screw shown in Fig. 8 is an adjustable discontinuity, similar to a trimmer capacitor in a lumped-constant network. When the screw is first inserted,

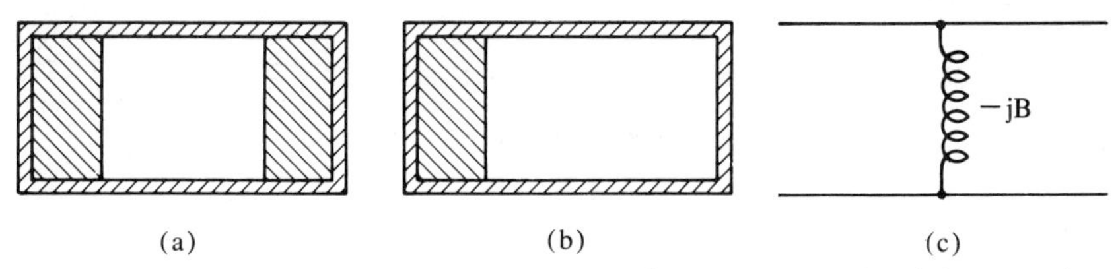

Fig. 6. Inductive iris. (*a*) Symmetrical. (*b*) Asymmetrical. (*c*) Equivalent circuit, $y = -jB$; admittance is pure inductive susceptance.

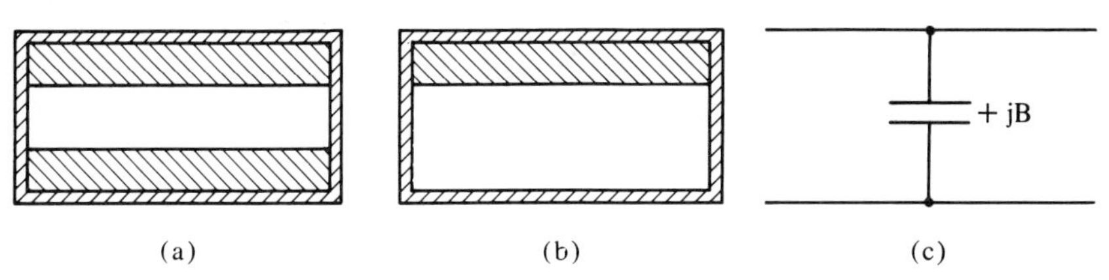

Fig. 7. Capacitive iris. (*a*) Symmetrical. (*b*) Asymmetrical. (*b*) Equivalent circuit.

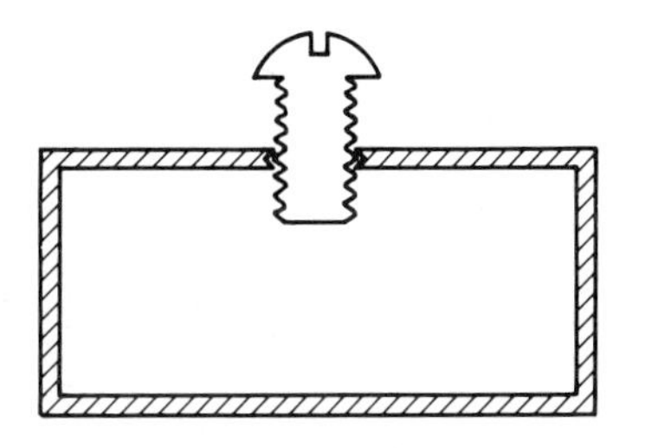

Fig. 8. Tuning screw.

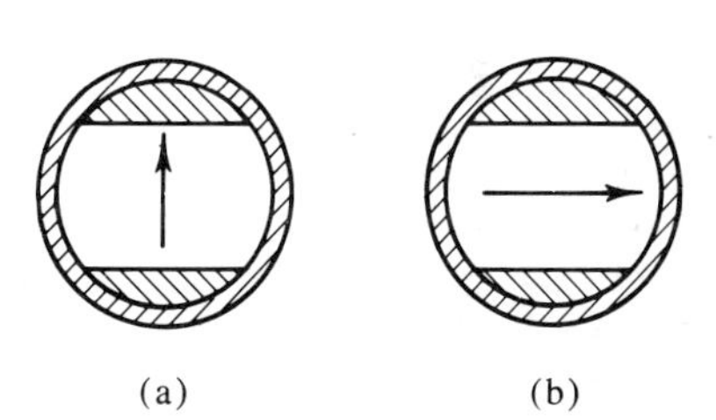

Fig. 9. Irises in round waveguide (electric field indicated by arrow). (*a*) Capacitive iris. (*b*) Inductive iris.

it acts as a shunt capacitance similar to a capacitive iris. However, if it extended all the way across the guide, it would be an inductive post as shown in Fig. 5. The transition point from capacitive susceptance to inductive susceptance varies with frequency and position but is approximately five-eighths of the way across the guide. At this point, the screw acts like a resonant circuit with infinite susceptance. Again, since the voltage field is greatest at the center, a screw which is centered will have a greater effect than one placed asymmetrically.

In round waveguide there are no narrow and wide dimensions. If a screw is inserted parallel to the electric field, it starts as a capacitive susceptance, just as in rectangular guide. A post across the guide, parallel to the electric field, is an inductive susceptance. When the edges of irises are perpendicular to the electric field, as shown in Fig. 9*a*, the irises are capacitive. When the edges are parallel to the field, as shown in Fig. 9*b*, the irises are inductive. The same criteria apply to irises in square guide.

Deformations. Deformations in waveguides also cause reflections. In general, deformations are reactive. For example, a dent or dimple in the broad wall of a guide is similar to a screw inserted a short distance and is therefore a shunt capacitive susceptance. If the waveguide is squashed so that the broad walls are brought closer together, this causes a reduction in characteristic impedance, indicated by Eq. (6). If the narrow walls bulge outward or are forced inward, there is a change in λ_c, which in turn causes a change in λ_g and a change in Z_0.

Waveguide Bends (Turns). Waveguides may be bent or twisted without causing reflection or introducing loss, as long as the cross-section of the guide is kept uniform. When the waveguide is bent, the bend is designated an *E-plane* bend, if the direction of the *E* field is changed. Otherwise it is an *H-plane* bend, since then the magnetic lines or *H* field must be bent. Waveguide bends are shown in Fig. 10. These are 90° bends, but bends may be made with the arms at any angle to each other as long as the bend is made uniformly and smoothly.

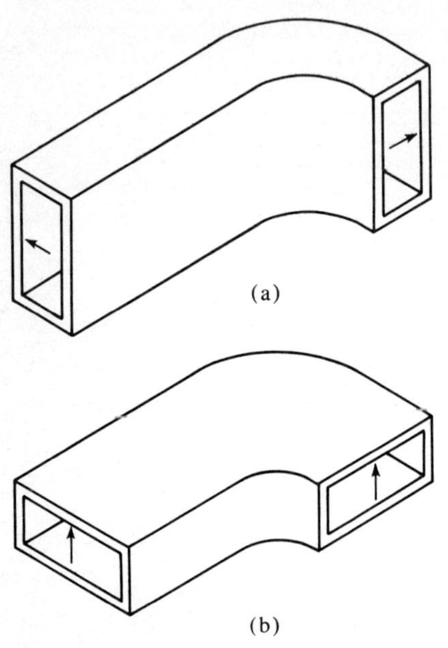

Fig. 10. Waveguide bends. (*a*) *E*-plane bend. (*b*) *H*-plane bend.

SIGNAL-CONDITIONING DEVICES

10. Power Dividers The simplest power divider is a three-port junction called a waveguide tee. There are two types, as shown in Fig. 11. The designations *E plane* and *H plane* are determined in the same manner as they were for the bends in Fig. 10. In both tees, the input arm is the leg of the tee which is perpendicular to the other two legs. (It is also common to refer to them as *arms.*) The other two are called *side* legs or arms.

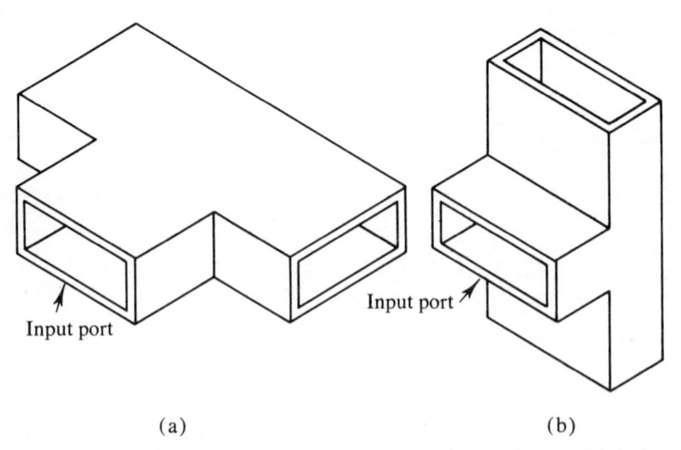

Fig. 11. Waveguide tees. (*a*) *H*-plane tee. (*b*) *E*-plane tee.

The H-plane tee in Fig. 11*a* is also called a *shunt* tee, because the two outputs are in shunt with one another across the input. Thus, the input sees an impedance only half that of the main line. In addition, there are fringing fields caused by the abrupt junction which add a reactive element to the impedance. The input arm can be matched to this impedance, however, by a post or an iris. When this arm is matched, power entering splits equally and *in phase* in the other two arms.

Since it is impossible to match all three parts of a three-part junction, the sidearms are not matched. If power enters a sidearm, a large part of it will be reflected back toward the source. However, if two signals of equal power and phase are fed into both sidearms, they will add and the sum will appear at the input arm, with no reflections. That is, the reflection in a sidearm is equal to and out of phase with the signal coming from the other sidearm, so that the two cancel.

The E-plane tee of Fig. 11*b* is called a *series* tee, since the two outputs are in series across the input. Thus, the input sees twice the impedance plus the effect of fringing fields. Again, it may be matched with an iris or post. When the input arm is matched, power splits equally and *out of phase* in the other

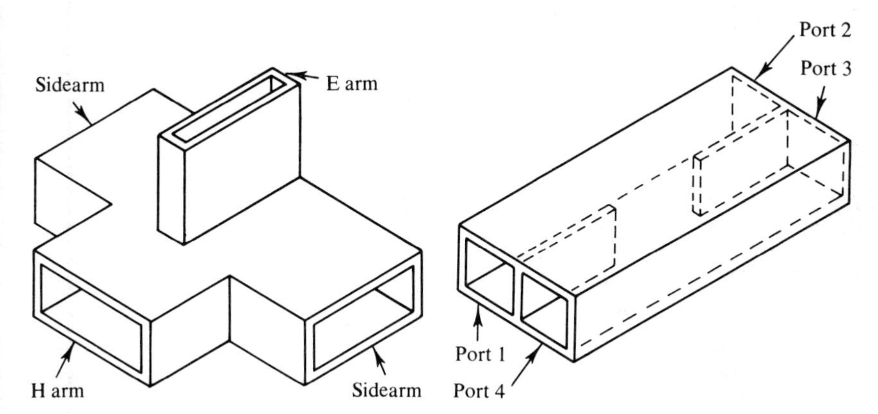

Fig. 12. Hybrid tee.

Fig. 13. Short-slot coupler.

two arms. By reciprocity, if two signals of equal amplitude but out of phase are fed into the sidearms, their sum appears at the input arm.

The *hybrid* tee in Fig. 12 is a four-port junction which is a combination of an E-plane tee and an H-plane tee. When the E arm and the H arm are matched, the other two arms are also matched automatically, and the tee exhibits unusual properties which have caused it to be called a *magic tee.* If power is fed into the H arm of a magic tee, it divides equally and in phase in the sidearms, just as in an H plane tee. There is no coupling to the E arm, since the E arm and H arm are cross-polarized. Also, if power is fed into the E arm, it divides equally and out of phase in the sidearms, as in an E-plane tee, with no coupling to the H arm. If power is fed into a sidearm, it divides equally in the E arm and H arm, with no coupling to the other sidearm. If signals are fed into both sidearms, even signals of different amplitude and phase, the algebraic sum of the signals appears in the H arm, and the algebraic difference appears in the E arm. Thus, the H arm is also called the *sum* arm, and the E arm the *difference* arm.

Any four-arm junction which exhibits the same characteristics as a magic tee is called a *hybrid* or *hybrid junction.* The important characteristic is division of an input signal between two ports and isolation of the remaining port.

Another form of hybrid is the *short-slot coupler,* shown in Fig. 13. This device is essentially two waveguides with one narrow wall in common and a short section of this narrow wall missing. Since the device is symmetrical, the ports or arms are usually referred to sequentially by numbers from 1 to 4 as shown. Assuming a signal is fed into port 1 as the input arm, it travels into the coupler until it reaches the slot. In each of the four arms, only the $TE_{1,0}$ mode can be propagated, but in the vicinity of the slot, the guide is twice as wide, and it will support the $TE_{2,0}$ mode also. Thus, when the input signal reaches the slot, the sudden discontinuity causes the $TE_{2,0}$ mode to be excited along with the $TE_{1,0}$ mode. Both modes travel toward all four arms, but because of their different guide wavelengths, they arrive at the ends of the slot and pass into the arms in different phases. By choosing the proper length of slot, the device can be made to act as a hybrid. The reflections from the slot of the two modes cancel each other in both arms 1 and 4. This means arm 1 is matched, and arm 4 is isolated from it, just as the E and H arms of a magic tee are isolated. The two modes add in such a way in arms 2 and 3 that half the power appears in each arm, but the two signals are 90° out of phase. For this reason, the short-slot hybrid is also called a *quadrature coupler*.

The four arms of the short-slot hybrid may be extended individually by sections of straight guide or E- or H-plane bends so that each arm can be connected separately to another part of the circuit without interference. Special connectors and adapters have been made to accomplish this.

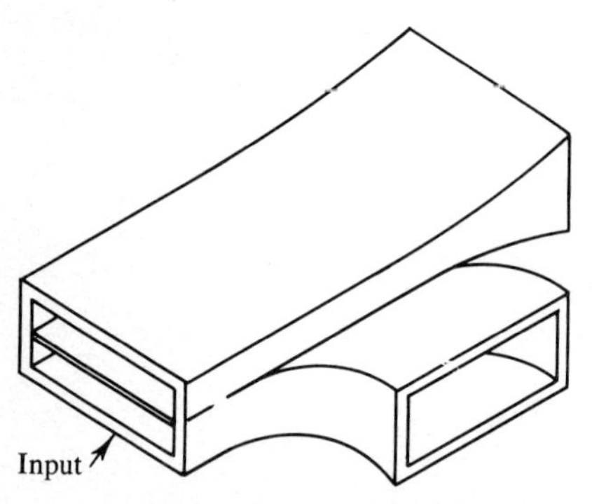

Fig. 14. Septum power divider.

The tees and hybrids divide the power into two equal parts. It is possible to divide the power unequally by placing a septum or partition in the waveguide parallel to the wide dimension. This is shown in Fig. 14. The input edge of the septum is very thin so that it presents a minimum discontinuity to the incoming signal. The power will be divided proportionately to the heights of the two resulting waveguides. For example, X-band waveguide has internal dimensions 0.900 by 0.400 in. If a septum is placed across the guide dividing the 0.400-in. dimension into 0.100 in. and 0.300 in., one-fourth of the power will enter the 0.100-in. section and three-fourths the 0.300 in. These two waveguides are now tapered back to 0.400 in. in order to have the same characteristic impedance as other parts of the system. The gradual taper is a simple impedance transformation without mismatch. In Fig. 14 the lower guide is tapered in an H-plane bend, while the upper guide is extended straight ahead. This is done to separate the two waveguides so that connections can be made without interference. The guides can be terminated in any combination of E- or H-plane bends or straight extensions.

In the septum power divider, the outputs are in series across the input, as in an E-plane tee. If more than one septum is used, dividing the waveguide into three or more guides, the power is split among all the guides in proportion to their input heights.

The output arms of a power divider must be matched to their loads, or reflections will upset the power division. For example, if the H-plane tee in Fig. 11*a* has one sidearm matched but a mismatch in the other, there will be a reflection from the mismatch which reënters the junction. Part of this reflected signal will cross to the other sidearm, where it will combine vectorially with the power there. Thus, the power in the match arm may be more or less than half the input power, depending on the phase of the reflected signal. In the mismatched arm, the power is always less than half the input, since some power is reflected back to the junction. The same thing holds true for the E-plane tee and the septum power divider. In the magic tee, a reflection in one sidearm will not affect the power in the other sidearm, since the two are isolated from one another. The same applies to arms 2 and

3 in the short-slot hybrid. In the hybrids, the mismatch in an arm affects only the power in that arm.

11. Directional Couplers A directional coupler is a four-port device which permits sampling the signal in a waveguide without having the sample affected by reflections in the guide. The four-port network consists of two waveguides which are coupled in such a way that the direction of the signal in the sampling guide depends on the direction of the signal in the main guide. The schematic symbol for a directional coupler is shown in Fig. 15. In this figure the four ports are numbered, but the numbers are not part of the symbol. The designation "30 dB" is usually included in the symbol to indicate the amount of coupling from the first guide to the second and is used here as an example.

The coupler indicated schematically in Fig. 15 could be connected in a circuit with arm 1 connected toward the signal source and arm 2 connected toward the load. Then the waveguide from arm 1 to arm 2 would be the *main* guide and the other would be the auxiliary guide. If the device were an ideal 30-dB coupler, a signal would appear at port 3 which is 30 dB below the power incident at port 1. Port 4 would be completely isolated. In a practical coupler, perfect isolation is impossible, and some signal appears at port 4, although it is much less than that appearing at port 3. A usable directional coupler might have 20 dB less power at arm 4 than at arm 3. Such a coupler is said to have a *coupling* of 30 dB and a *directivity* of 20 dB. It should be noted that the coupling in port 3 is compared with the *incident* power at port 1 and not with the power out of port

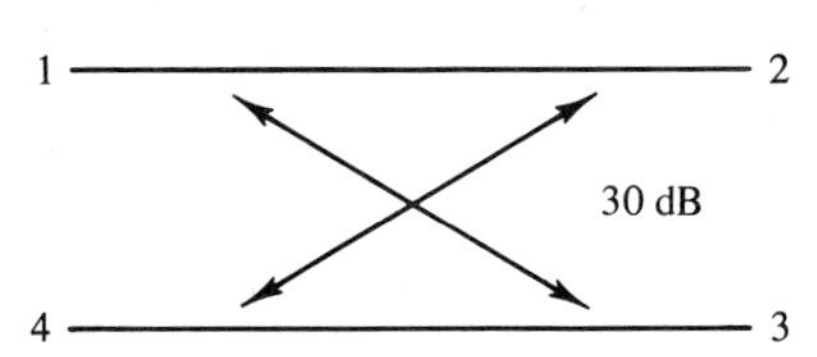

Fig. 15. Directional-coupler symbol.

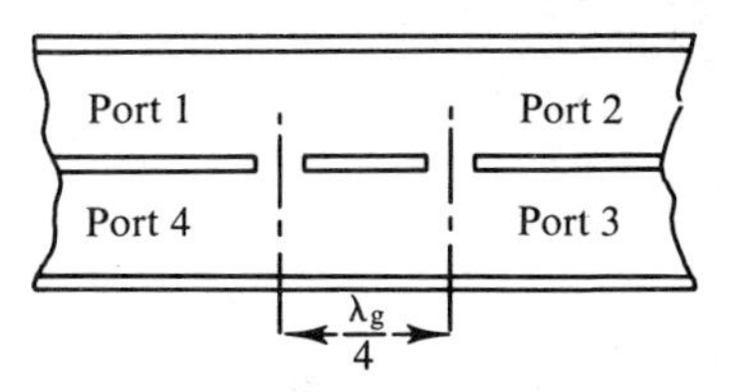

Fig. 16. Sidewall coupler.

2. In the case of a 30-dB coupler, there would be little difference, since the power tapped off is only 0.1 percent of the incident power, and 99.9 percent remains for arm 2. (It is assumed the power taken by arm 4 is negligible.) However, in a 10-dB coupler, 10 percent of the incident power appears at port 3 and thus only 90 percent at port 2.

If there is a reflection from a mismatched load connected to arm 2, part of this reflection is tapped off and appears at arm 4, but only a negligible part reaches arm 3, so that the original sample of power incident in arm 1 is essentially unchanged. It is important, however, to have the signal source matched. Otherwise, part of the reflection from arm 2 will travel back to the source and be re-reflected. Then, since it is traveling in the same direction as the incident signal, it will affect the signal at arm 3.

The short-slot coupler shown in Fig. 13 is a directional coupler with 3-dB coupling. That is, the power at port 3 is half of the incident power at port 1, or "3 dB down" [$10 \log_{10} 2 = 10(0.3) = 3$ dB]. The power remaining at port 2 is also half of the incident power. Port 4 is usually isolated at least 20 dB in a practical short-slot coupler.

In order to achieve directional coupling, there must be at least two coupling mechanisms between the two guides. The phases of the coupled signals must add in one direction of propagation and cancel in the other. The two coupling mechanisms in the short-slot coupler are the $TE_{1,0}$ and $TE_{2,0}$ modes, but in other couplers, coupling is achieved through two or more holes. An explanation of the operation is shown in Fig. 16 for a *sidewall* coupler. The two waveguides are joined so that they have one common sidewall. Two identical holes in this common wall are spaced a quarter of a guide wavelength apart. When a signal is incident at port 1, each hole couples some energy into the auxiliary guide, and the energy from *each* hole flows equally toward ports 3 and 4. The energy traveling from port 1 to port 3 travels the same distance through *either* hole, and thus the two coupled signals are in phase and add in this direction. However, in going from arm 1 to arm 4, one of the coupled signals must travel half a guide wavelength more than the other. Therefore, in the direction of arm 4 the two coupled signals cancel. It should also be noted that each hole is a discontinuity which sends a reflection back to arm 1. However, since one path from arm 1 to the hole and back is half a wavelength different from the other, the two reflections cancel, resulting in a good match.

In order to achieve tighter coupling, additional holes may be used. In general, the match, directivity, and bandwidth are all improved by increasing the number of holes.

The same type of coupling mechanism may be used on the top wall of the guide, resulting in a *top-wall* coupler, shown in Fig. 17. Again holes are placed a quarter of a guide wavelength apart. For maximum bandwidth, holes are not placed at the point of maximum coupling but about halfway between the sidewall and the centerline. Thus, to increase coupling an additional pair of holes may be placed symmetrically near the other sidewall, as shown in Fig. 17*b*.

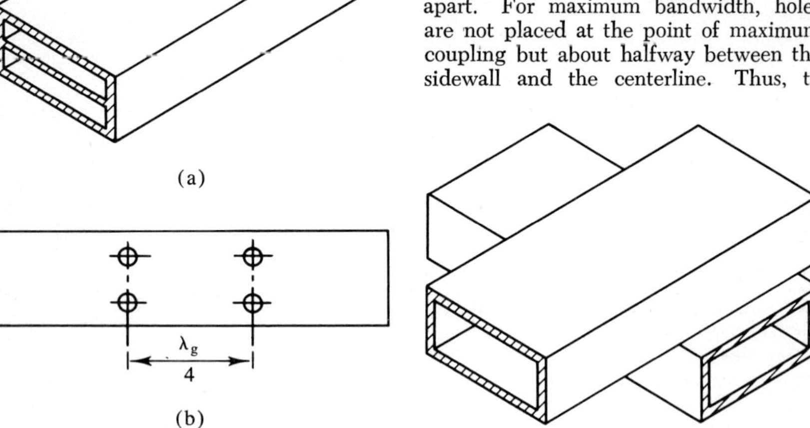

Fig. 17. Top-wall coupler. (*a*) Physical construction. (*b*) Common wall.

Fig. 18. Cross-guide coupler.

The *cross-guide* coupler shown in Fig. 18 is frequently used when space is at a premium. The coupling mechanisms are usually a pair of slots in the common wall, spaced a quarter of a guide wavelength in each guide.

In the top-wall and sidewall couplers, one or more of the arms may be brought out in an *E*-plane or *H*-plane tee so that connections may be made to it without interference. In the cross-guide coupler, all four arms are separate so that this is not necessary. If the coupler is used to sample power in only one direction in the main guide, it is not necessary to measure the power out of arm 4. In that case, arm 4 is usually terminated with a built-in matched load, and the other three arms have suitable flanges for connecting them to other parts of the circuits.

12. Matched Loads In many applications, including most measurement checks, it is necessary to have a matched load terminate a line or one or more arms of a network. The fourth arm of a directional coupler is a typical example. The matched load may be used to prevent unwanted radiation when checking a system or as a termination for a network under test. In measuring the impedance of a multiport network, all ports but the one being checked must be terminated in order to ensure that the measurement is of only the internal match and not the result of external reflections entering an unterminated port and reaching the input.

A simple form of matched load for laboratory use is shown in Fig. 19. A section of slotted waveguide is used, through which a piece of ordinary resistance card is set at an angle. Resistance card is simply thin plastic material coated with a lossy material such as carbon.

Two important principles are illustrated by the load of Fig. 19. First, if a thin slot is cut in the center of the broad wall of a waveguide, it will have a negligible effect on the signal in the guide. The sides of the slot are at equal voltages, and thus there is no radiation from the slot, and the slot itself is a minimum discontinuity. It should be noted that if the slot were *not* on the centerline, there would be radiation from the guide, and this radiation would increase the farther the slot is removed from the centerline. Secondly, if a dielectric or lossy material presents a taper to the signal, there is no short discontinuity and no mismatch. In the load of Fig. 19 the card is placed through slots in the

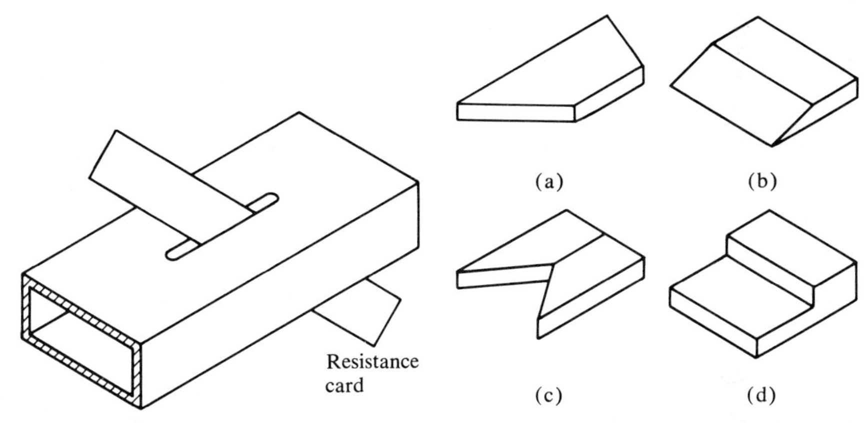

Fig. 19. Slotted-guide matched load.

Fig. 20. Solid matched loads. (*a*) Sidewall taper. (*b*) Broad-wall taper. (*c*) Double taper. (*d*) Step.

top and bottom of the guide at an angle so that it does present a gradual taper to the signal.

If the lossy material has 30 dB of attenuation, it would allow only one-thousandth of the power to go through. Any reflection, even total reflection from a short or open circuit, would cause at most one-thousandth of the incident power to start toward the input. But, since the reflected power would also be attenuated 30 dB, the power reflected from the load would be one-millionth of the incident power. This corresponds to a voltage standing-wave ratio (VSWR) of 1.002. Thirty decibels is readily achievable using ordinary off-the-shelf resistance card.

When a more permanent or more compact load is desired, it is usually made of a solid lossy material completely filling the waveguide except for a tapered section facing the incident wave. Frequently used shapes are shown in Fig. 20. In Fig. 20*a*, the taper begins at a sidewall where the power is minimum, and the starting edge of the taper is at a point of zero voltage so that it is a negligible discontinuity. In Fig. 20*b*, the starting edge of the taper is perpendicular to the voltage vector and again presents a negligible discontinuity. The double-tapered load in Fig. 20*c* has a shorter length than the single tapers but is more difficult to machine. It may be made of two pieces cemented together as shown. Where space is at a premium, the short step load may be used. Essentially, this block has two discontinuities which are spaced so that the two reflections cancel each other. At X band, 30 dB can be achieved in a step load in less than 1 in. of length with a VSWR under 1.02 over a 10 percent frequency band.

Each of the loads shown in Fig. 20 is usually mounted in a short piece of waveguide with the step or taper toward the front and a shorting plate across the back. A flange on the front of the guide permits connecting the load to whatever network or circuit is being tested. In a permanent installation, such as the fourth arm of a directional coupler, the load is simply cemented in place in the proper location without using a flange.

13. Attenuators The card load shown in Fig. 19 is simply a waveguide *attenuator* in that it reduces or attenuates the signal. When used as a load, the card should introduce at least 30 dB of attenuation, so that the reflection from *any* discontinuity at the output is decreased 60 dB. As was indicated in the preceding section, even a short circuit will look like a good match if it is attenuated 60 dB.

In many applications it is necessary to use an attenuator to keep a source from seeing a mismatch which might cause the source to be unstable. For example, suppose a source is designed for a maximum VSWR of 1.2:1, but the antenna that it feeds has a VSWR of 2:1. About 12 dB of attenuation is necessary to reduce the reflection from a 2:1 mismatch so that it appears as a 1.2:1 VSWR. Thus, it is necessary to use a card with only 6 dB of attenuation in the configuration of Fig. 19 to achieve the 12-dB loss (6 dB in each direction). Such an attenuator would be called a *6-dB pad.* By choosing the appropriate width of card, any size attenuator may be created.

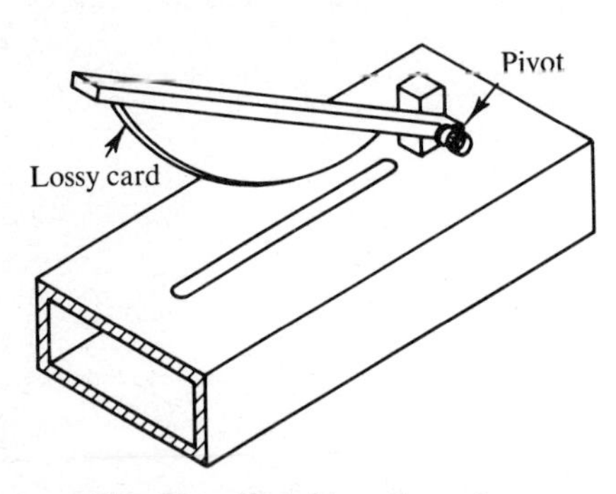

Fig. 21. Variable attenuator.

In an attenuator, the output should be tapered or matched, just as the input is, to prevent multiple reflections between the output discontinuity and the end of the attenuator. Since the configuration of Fig. 19 is symmetrical, it will have the same taper and match at both ends. Attenuators using solid lossy material, as shown in Fig. 20, may be built as long as the output side is matched just as the input is. This means either a taper or a step on the output side.

The attenuators formed by putting a fixed amount of lossy material in the waveguide are called *fixed attenuators.* In some applications the amount of attenuation required is not known or may change if an oscillator or a detector is changed. Then it is necessary to use a *variable attenuator* so that the amount of loss can be adjusted for the particular application. One form of variable attenuator is shown in Fig. 21. A lossy card is fixed to a metal bar which is pivoted at one end in such a way that the card can be inserted into the waveguide through a slot centered in the broad wall. There is sufficient friction in the pivot to maintain the card in any position. Thus it can be inserted until the proper attenuation is achieved. The card is shaped so that it presents a matched taper at any insertion.

Another form of variable attenuator makes use of the fact that the voltage in a waveguide (for the dominant mode) is maximum at the center and zero at the walls. A piece of lossy material tapered at both ends is placed inside a waveguide and is controlled by thin horizontal metal rods. Since these rods are perpendicular to the electric field, they have a negligible effect on the match. The lossy material may be resistance card or glass coated with a thin film of metal or carbon. When it is against a sidewall of the waveguide where the voltage is minimum, it causes little attenuation. As it is moved from the sidewall to the center, the attenuation increases. The movement may be controlled by a calibrated knob on the outside of the waveguide, so that the amount of attenuation for each position may be read directly on the scale.

All the attenuators discussed thus far are frequency-sensitive in two respects. First, the attenuation or loss in a fixed length of lossy material is a function of frequency. Second, the phase shift through the material is also a function of frequency. A frequency-insensitive variable atenuator can be built in round waveguide as shown in Fig. 22. The attenuator contains three cards of lossy material. The input and output cards are fixed with their planes perpendicular to the voltage field in the guide. The guide is designed to support only the $TE_{1,1}$ mode or dominant mode in round waveguide. The center card can be rotated about the axis of the round guide. Each of the three cards is long enough to attenuate a signal to a negligible value when the plane of the card is parallel to the voltage field. In this variable attenuator, the loss depends only on the angle of rotation of the center card and is independent of frequency.

One disadvantage in using an attenuator as a pad between a source and a device under test is that the full power of the source is not available. If, for example, 20 dB of attenuation is needed to reduce the reflection to a satisfactory level, a 10-dB pad must be used. This means that only 10 percent of the power out of the source reaches the device under test. What is needed is a one-way attenuator, which will have negligible attenuation in the forward direction and 20 dB in the reverse direction. Such a device can be built using a piece of magnetized ferrite material in the waveguide. This nonreciprocal attenuator is called a *ferrite isolator*.

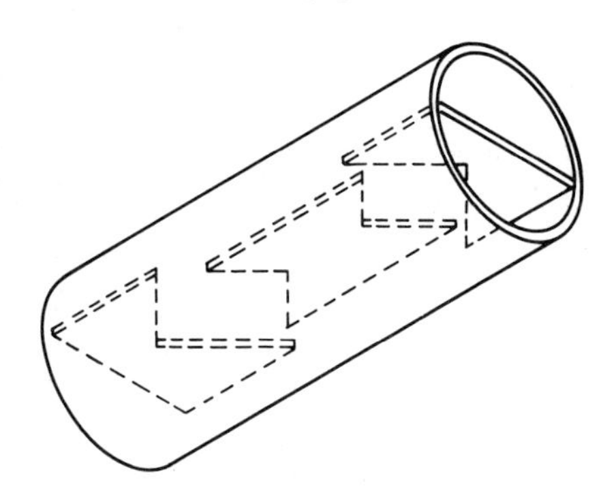

Fig. 22. Frequency-insensitive attenuator.

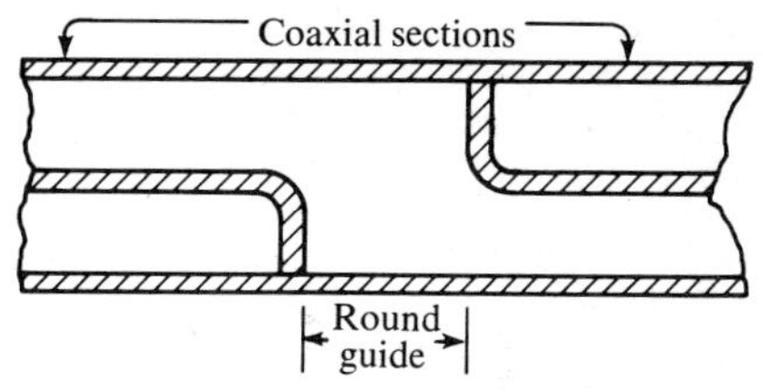

Fig. 23. Cutoff attenuator in coaxial line.

The forward attenuation, which is usually only a few tenths of a decibel, is called the *insertion loss*, and the reverse attenuation is called *reverse loss*.

14. Cutoff Attenuator A special form of attenuator which contains no lossy material can be built around a section of waveguide which is below cutoff. Such a device is called a cutoff attenuator.

Earlier it was pointed out that a signal cannot be propagated in a waveguide if the wavelength of the signal is less than the cutoff wavelength of the guide. In fact, if a signal below cutoff is fed into a waveguide, *most* of it will be reflected as if the waveguide were an open circuit. Some of the signal will enter the guide and be rapidly attenuated. If the wavelength of the signal is much greater than the cutoff wavelength, the attenuation is

$$\alpha = \frac{2\pi}{\lambda_c} \tag{11}$$

where α = attenuation, nepers per unit length
λ_c = cutoff wavelength

Equation (11) shows that the attenuation is only a function of the length of the cutoff section and is independent of frequency.

A practical cutoff attenuator consists of a section of round guide placed in a coaxial line, as shown in Fig. 23. The coaxial inner conductor is stopped at the section of round guide and is bent and attached to the outer conductor to form a coupling loop which will excite the $TE_{1,1}$ mode. However, with the guide below cutoff, the $TE_{1,1}$ mode is attenuated. Some signal reaches the far end of the cutoff section where another loop couples the $TE_{1,1}$ mode back to a coaxial mode. From Eq. (11), the attenuation is proportional to the spacing between the two coupling loops. In variable form, the spacing can be varied by turning a calibrated knob.

15. Variable Phase Shifter When a waveguide is filled with a low-loss dielectric material, the guide wavelength is reduced, as is indicated by Eq. (8). Thus a given length of guide will contain more wavelengths when filled with dielectric. In effect, then, the phase shift through the guide has been increased. When a thin slab of dielectric is placed in the guide, it also increases the phase shift, but not as much as filling the guide completely. As with a variable attenuator, the effect of the dielectric slab is greatest near the center of the waveguide and minimal near the sidewall. Therefore, a variable phase shifter can be constructed in the same manner as a variable attenuator, by replacing the lossy material with a low-loss dielectric. In Fig. 21, for example, if the lossy resistance card is replaced by a piece of polystyrene or other low-loss dielectric material, the result is a variable phase shifter. Similarly, the attenuator using a metallized glass slab moving inside the waveguide becomes a variable phase shifter if the metal coating is left off the glass. The dial controlling the movement of the slab could be calibrated in degrees rather than decibels.

16. Resonant Cavities If a short circuit is placed across a waveguide, an incident signal will be completely reflected. If now a short circuit is placed a half-guide-wavelength back toward the source, the reflected signal will be reflected again and travel in the original direction. Most important, the second reflection will cause the signal to be *in phase* with the incident signal, assuming there is some way to keep the incident signal coming into the closed section of guide. This section will then support a signal which bounces back and forth between the two shorting plates. The closed section is called a *resonant cavity,* or simply a cavity, and is analogous to a resonant "tank" circuit at lower frequencies. Basically, a resonant cavity consists of a section of transmission line and two large discontinuities which are so spaced that reflections from them are in phase with the incident signal. Any kind of transmission line, including coaxial lines as well as waveguides, can be used. There must also be some means of coupling an incident wave to the cavity, that is, some means of getting the signal inside. It should be noted that the discontinuities or shorting plates can be spaced any number of half wavelengths apart.

Just as several modes exist in a waveguide, so too are there several cavity modes. Cavity modes are designated by a third subscript which indicates the length of the cavity in half wavelengths in the guide. Thus a rectangular cavity mode designated $TE_{1,0,1}$ would mean a $TE_{1,0}$ mode in the rectangular guide, and the shorts spaced one half wavelength apart. The $TM_{1,1,2}$ mode would indicate a $TM_{1,1}$ mode in the waveguide, and the cavity length two half wavelengths long. In round guide, the $TE_{1,1,1}$ mode indicates the dominant $TE_{1,1}$ waveguide mode in a cavity half a guide wavelength long. In cavities in round guide, there is also another set of TM modes in which the electric field is always parallel to the axis of the cylinder. The third digit is always zero for one of these special TM modes.

17. Coupling As has been noted, there must be some opening in the cavity to get the signal in and out. When there is only one coupling mechanism, used only to get the signal into the cavity, the cavity is called the *absorption* cavity. When an output coupling is also used, the cavity is a *transmission* cavity.

In a rectangular cavity, formed by placing suitably spaced plates across a waveguide, coupling can be accomplished by small openings in the shorting plates, as shown in Fig. 24. The round hole in Fig. 24*a*, if small enough, permits some power to enter and still has little effect on the operation of the cavity. As the hole size is increased, the resonant frequency of the cavity decreases and the Q decreases. As with a resonant-tank circuit at lower frequencies, at resonance the transmitted signal passes through the cavity with little loss, since the two discontinuities produce reflections which cancel each other.

Instead of holes in the plates, reactive discontinuities may be used. Inductive apertures are shown in Fig. 24*b*. As with the holes, when the openings in the inductive apertures are increased, both resonant frequency and Q are decreased. If capacitive irises are used, increasing the opening increases the resonant frequency, but still decreases the Q. Instead of inductive irises, posts may be used for low-Q cavities.

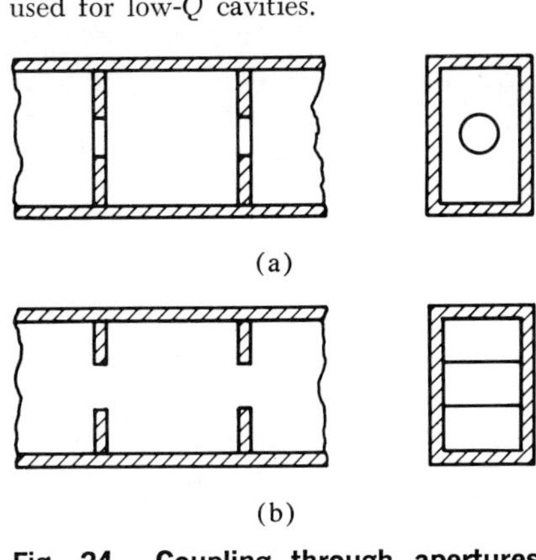

Fig. 24. Coupling through apertures in rectangular cavities. (*a*) Hole. (*b*) Inductive aperture.

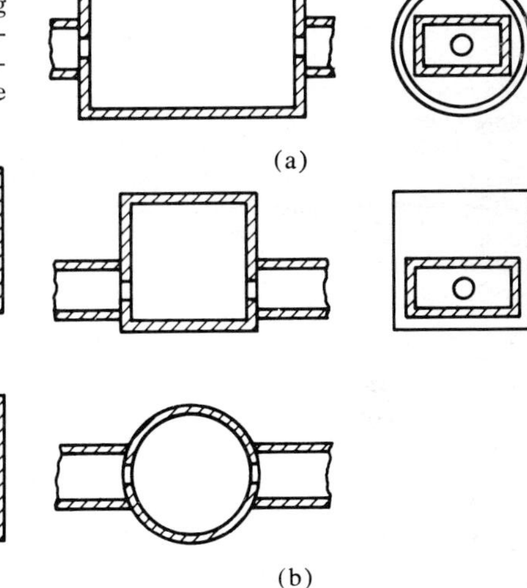

Fig. 25. Aperture coupling in round cavities. (*a*) End-wall coupling. (*b*) Round-wall coupling.

Coupling into a cylindrical cavity in a round-waveguide transmission line can be accomplished simply by using a round hole in the shorting plate, as with rectangular guides. In general, a cylindrical cavity can be built with a high Q than is achievable with rectangular guide; so it is frequently desirable to use a cylindrical cavity in conjunction with rectangular guide. Again a round hole may be used, and two possible configurations are shown in Fig. 25.

A cavity is sometimes used in conjunction with coaxial lines, and it becomes necessary to couple from the coaxial line to the cavity. Two methods of coupling a cylindrical cavity to coaxial line are shown in Fig. 26. In Fig. 26*a*, the inner conductor of the coaxial line is simply extended into the cavity to form a coupling probe. In Fig. 26*b*, the inner conductor is looped around and fastened to the inside wall of the cavity. Both methods may also be used to couple coaxial lines to rectangular cavities.

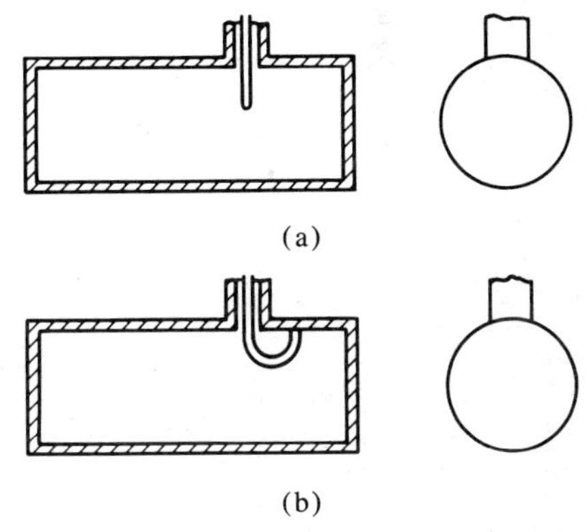

Fig. 26. Coupling from coaxial line to cavity. (*a*) Probe or voltage coupling. (*b*) Loop or current coupling.

18. Cavity Q As is true with a resonant-tank circuit, the Q of a cavity is

$$Q = 2\pi f \frac{\text{max energy stored}}{\text{power loss}} \tag{12}$$

In a resonant cavity the power loss is copper loss in the walls and is proportional to the skin depth δ. The energy stored depends on the ratio of volume to surface area. Thus, a good approximation for the Q of a cavity is

$$Q = \frac{V}{A\delta} \tag{13}$$

where V = volume
A = surface area
δ = skin depth

For a rectangular cavity, maximum Q occurs when all three dimensions are equal. For a round cavity, maximum Q occurs when the diameter and length are equal. The Q can be increased by polishing the inside of the cavity and plating it with a highly conductive material such as silver or copper.

The resonance curve of a cavity is identical to the resonance curve of an *LC* tank. The distance between the half-power frequencies is termed the *3-dB bandwidth* of the cavity and is designated Δf. The Q of a loaded cavity is given by

$$Q = \frac{f_0}{\Delta f} \tag{14}$$

where f_0 is the resonant frequency. The loaded Q includes the effect of the coupling mechanisms on the intrinsic Q of the cavity.

19. Filters A waveguide is by itself a high-pass filter, inasmuch as there is a cutoff frequency below which the waveguide will not propagate a signal. Also, any transmission cavity is essentially a bandpass filter, since it will pass only a small band of frequencies centered about the resonant frequency of the cavity. Combinations of cavities can be used to build high-pass as well as low-pass filters and bandstop as well as bandpass filters.

In general, any type of filter which can be built at lower frequencies using *LC* circuits can be synthesized at microwaves using cavities. Cavities may be used in series with the main line for bandpassing or in shunt to shunt out a band of frequencies. By coupling several low-Q cavities to each other in series, bandpass filters having almost any required passband and any required out-of-band rejection can be constructed.

20. Transitions Most systems are not restricted to one type of transmission line but may consist of a combination of different sizes or shapes of waveguides as well as sections of coaxial line. It is necessary then to provide transitions, or "transducers," which couple signals from one type of line to another without loss due to mismatch or lossy elements.

A common type of transition between two different sizes of waveguide is a linear taper from one to the other. The two guides may differ only in their narrow dimensions, in which case the taper is in that dimension only. This is simply a gradual change between two impedances, since the impedance of a guide is proportional to its height. If the taper is four or more wavelengths long, the VSWR will be under 1.05, indicating a good impedance transformation. If it is desired to make the transition in a shorter distance, a quarter-wave transformer can be used, just as at lower frequencies, although it is more easily done with waveguides. This is simply a section of guide which is one-quarter of a guide wavelength long and which has a characteristic impedance which is the square root of the product of the other two characteristic impedances. That is,

$$Z_0 = \sqrt{Z_1 Z_2} \tag{15}$$

where Z_0 = characteristic impedance of quarter-wave matching section
Z_1 = characteristic impedance of input line
Z_2 = characteristic impedance of output line

If the two lines to be matched have the same width, their characteristic impedances are proportional to their heights. Thus, if the quarter-wave transformer is made the same width, the height is given by

$$b_0 = \sqrt{b_1 b_2} \tag{16}$$

where b indicates the height, or narrow guide dimension, and the subscripts are the same as in Eq. (15). A typical quarter-wave transition is shown in Fig. 27. This will be a good match only over a narrow frequency band, since the transition is exactly a quarter wavelength at only one frequency. Somewhat broader bandwidth can be achieved by using two or more quarter-wave sections, in each case matching to some intermediate impedance.

Tapers may also be used between rectangular and round guides, but in general they present an extremely difficult fabrication problem. Instead, the rectangular guide may be butted end to end with the round guide, and the resultant mismatch can be corrected by using reactive discontinuities such as posts or irises near the junction. This type of transition is shown at the left-hand end of the round guide in Fig. 28. It is also possible to have the rectangular guide meet the round guide perpendicular to the axis of the round guide, as shown at the top of the cylinder in Fig. 28. In this case, the distance between the rectangular guide and a shorting plate in the round guide is adjusted for match and bandwidth. Further improvement in match is made by using reactive discontinuities.

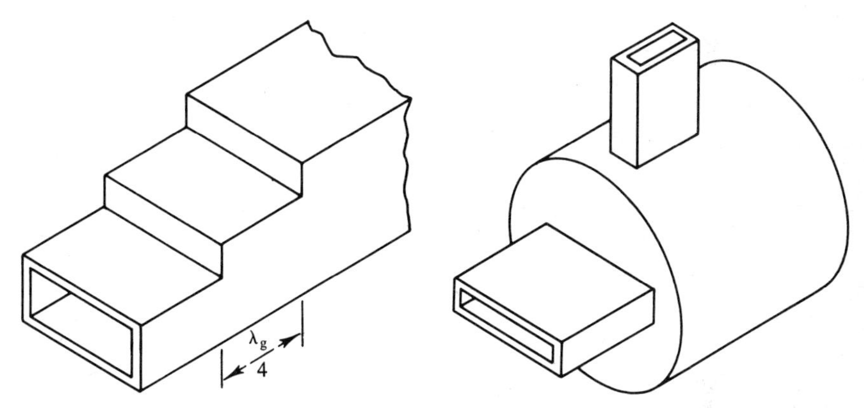

Fig. 27. Quarter-wave transformer. **Fig. 28. Rectangular-to-round transitions.**

It should be noted that a shorting plate is required so that energy entering the rectangular guide travels only in one direction in the round guide. In Fig. 28, there is a shorting plate, but it has another rectangular waveguide attached to it. This waveguide is perpendicular to the exciting waveguide and is therefore cross-polarized to it. In effect, the voltage vector of the $TE_{1,1}$ mode in the round guide sees the width of the opening as the narrow dimension of the rectangular guide at the end, and this would have a cutoff wavelength much shorter than signal wavelength. In effect, then, this opening does not exist for a signal entering from the rectangular guide at top. Thus, although a simple rectangular-to-round transition would consist of a round guide and *either* of the two rectangular guides, it is also possible to have a dual transition with both. In the dual transition, two different signals with voltage vectors perpendicular to each other can travel in the round guide, and one will be coupled to the end guide and the other to the top. These two signals may travel in the same or opposite directions without coupling between them, and they may be at the same or different frequencies.

Transitions between coaxial lines and waveguides are similar to the couplings between coaxial lines and cavities shown in Fig. 26. The probe coupling is simply a probe formed by extending the inner conductor of the coaxial line, as shown in Fig. 29*a*. The loop coupling may take many forms, but in all of them, the inner conductor is attached to the waveguide wall. Two common examples of loop coupling are shown in Fig. 29*b* and *c*. In all three of the transitions in

Fig. 29, the length of the shorted section of guide beyond the coaxial line is adjusted for best bandwidth. Matching is accomplished by irises in the waveguide.

21. Slotted Line When a transmission line is terminated in a load which has an impedance different from the characteristic impedance of the line, there will be a reflection from the load. The amplitude and phase of the reflected wave are dependent on the impedance of the load relative to the line's characteristic impedance. The reflected wave and incident wave are in phase and thus add together at some points in the line, and at others they will be out of phase. The result is a voltage standing wave on line.

The standing wave can be detected and measured by means of a slotted line. This consists of a long section of waveguide with a slot in the center of one wide wall. A carriage containing a probe is moved along the slot, and the probe protruding into the slot detects the voltage maximums, where the two waves are in phase,

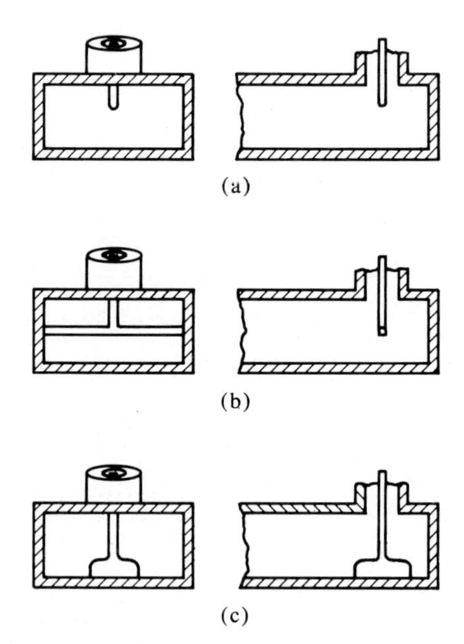

Fig. 29. Coaxial-to-waveguide transitions. (*a*) Probe. (*b*) Crossbar. (*c*) Doorknob.

and voltage minimums, where they are out of phase. The VSWR is the ratio of the voltage maximum to the voltage minimum, and is a measure of the quality of match between the line and the load. The position of the voltage maximum from the end of the line is also a function of the load impedance. Thus, by noting the VSWR and the position of the maximum (or minimum), it is possible to calculate the load impedances exactly at one frequency, that of the incident wave, by changing the frequency of the signal generator supplying the incident wave. By changing the frequency of the signal generator supplying the incident signal, it is possible to make a set of measurements covering the desired frequency band.

In most laboratories and all production setups, the slotted line has been replaced by automatic test equipment. Signal generators sweep over the required frequency range electronically, and the reflection from the load is detected and compared with the input signal, and a continuous plot of impedance as a function of frequency is displayed on the face of an oscilloscope or plotted on suitable graph paper.

Index